AIDS

GRAPHIC
ARTS
MANUAL

GRAPHIC ARTS MANUAL

Senior Editor
JANET N. FIELD

Consulting Editors
MICHAEL H. BRUNO
PAUL D. DOEBLER
GLADYS S. FIELD
EDWARD M. GOTTSCHALL
ROBERT LOEKLE

Executive Editor
IRVING E. FIELD

ARNO PRESS
MUSARTS PUBLISHING CORP.
NEW YORK, NEW YORK

Manufactured in the United States of America.

Library of Congress Cataloging in Publication Data
Main entry under title:

Graphic arts manual.

   Includes index.
   1. Printing, Practical—Handbooks, manuals,
etc. 2. Graphic arts—Handbooks, manuals, etc.
3. Photography—Handbooks, manuals, etc.
I. Field, Janet N.
Z244.G83   686.2'24   79-6549
ISBN 0-405-12941-6

BOOK DESIGN
Nancy Dale Muldoon

**COVER DESIGN/
TITLE AND SECTION PAGES**
Jack Rothman

EDITING AND PRODUCTION
Susan Reisler
Marion Jill Sendor
James Green
Francesca Lyman
Nancy Field
Tim Brooks
Terry Nasta

CONTRIBUTORS

Charles Aaron
Howard Aber
Andrew J. Alagna
G. H. Anthony
Samuel N. Antupit
Edmund C. Arnold
John R. Battiloro, Jr.
Joseph V. Bellanca
Ralph F. Box, Jr.
Alfred Brooks
Michael H. Bruno
Steve Byers
Clive A. Cameron
Thomas J. Cavallaro
Frank E. Church
Jim Cokeley
Thomas L. Cordier
Michael P. Corey
Thomas B. Cosden
James F. Cosgrove
Daniel M. Costigan
Robert S. Crandall
Peter de Florez
Paul D. Doebler
Warren R. Erickson
Eugene M. Ettenberg
Philip C. Evanoff
Murray A. Falick
Bernard Fein
Stanley J. Fenvessy
Irving E. Field
William Field
William B. Freedman
Ronald C. Gibson
Wayne M. Gilgore
Jack Golden
Edward M. Gottschall
Ellen Greene
Mark Harberman
Abraham Hardis
O. Willis Hawrylkiw
Walter L. Hecht
Ralph S. Heilman
Lawrence Herbert
Thomas E. Hess
Richard S. Hunter
Kenneth W. James

John Klein
Fred Klinger
Hans Kung
Harvey Langlois
Kenneth B. Latimer
Alexander S. Lawson
Leo Lehrer
Joel A. Levirne
Stanley E. Loeb
Robert Loekle
Jon Lopez
Kenneth D. Love
Theodore Lustig
William B. McCain
C. S. McCamy
Timothy B. McSweeney
Charles Mertz
Max Michalski
Ralph W. Mirkin
Richard D. Murray
Edward R. Novota
Ann Novotny
Frank Preucil
Archibald D. Provan
Bently Raak
Steve J. Reiter
William A. Rocap, Jr.
Frank J. Romano
Bob Salpeter
Bernard T. Sendor
Harold Sigler
Matt Sloves
George Sohn
Dan X. Solo
Victor Spindler
Liz Stalcup
J. James Stone
Robert R. Strack
Walter L. Strong
William R. Thompson
Fred G. von Zuben
James Wageman
Dave A. Ware
William A. Whitescarver
Jay Wieder
Gary G. Winters
Ernest Wuchner

FOREWORD

The scope of the *Graphic Arts Manual* points up the interrelationship between the technological aspects of graphic arts and what are usually considered the creative aspects. The interrelationship might be traced back to the first person who endeavored to convey his thoughts to his contemporaries using ashes from a fire to draw pictures on the walls of a cave. In modern terms, you might say that he was the first free-lance illustrator, having the tribe as his client and acting as his own production man.

From that first production job to the complicated graphic arts procedures of today, man has found ways to communicate information, true and false, and ideas, good and bad, to his fellows. We can thank some excellent "production people" along the way for the Rosetta Stone, the illuminated manuscripts of the Middle Ages, the Gutenberg Bible, the quartos of Shakespeare, the graceful designs of Caslon, and the first color TV image. On the other hand, we have reason to wonder about the vulgarizations and misleading claims that surround us today, brought to us through otherwise commendable graphic techniques. Marshall McLuhan demonstrated the extent to which the means of communicating a message can change its meaning. Applied to the graphic arts, this idea can be reduced to a matter of sound craftsmanship—making certain that the right medium and the right techniques are being used to deliver the message effectively, attractively, and without distortion.

□

The graphic arts industry is above all a collection of varied crafts, skills, and techniques linking the worlds of art, esthetics, technology, and mass communication. This manual is an ambitious and comprehensive assemblage of the ABC's, as well as virtually everything from A to Z, in these diverse yet complementary fields. A look at the table of contents reveals an awesome collection of expertise and detail.

So comprehensive a manual as this serves varied needs. It will be a "how to" book for some readers, telling them how to do a paste-up, how to copyfit a manuscript, or how to choose a typeface or a typesetting method for a job. To other readers, it will be a primer of graphic arts technologies and processes, answering their questions, "Why?" and "How does it work?" Here the reader will find explanations of the theory of color reproduction, the esthetics of type families, and the functioning of electronic color scanners. As a "what's new?" survey, the *Graphic Arts Manual* will take readers to the technological frontiers of the industry, with information on the latest electronic composition techniques, advances in laser platemaking, and new ink technologies. A newsletter publisher can find out about available art materials, new office copying equipment, and low-cost binding machines. Advertising and magazine people can compare various color proofing techniques, check on quality control methods, pinpoint common printing faults, and evaluate new ink matching systems. Designers and production people in all fields can buttress their general knowledge, particularly for the odd job that comes along outside of the regular line of work.

The graphic arts can be seen as a fraternity of skilled and creative people who do an amazing number of different things for a living. The designer, the trade-book publisher, the job-shop typesetter, the author, the science illustrator, and the copy editor are all involved with some area of the graphic arts. Most of these people are bound by a common denominator: the question, posed at the end of their day's work, "How does it look?" The threads of concern for production efficiency and visual quality are common to all; all must cope with problems such as impractical deadlines and treacherous production pitfalls. This manual, with its detailed technical information, is bound to be useful to anyone in the field and can help enhance communication among people in various areas of the graphic arts.

The *Graphic Arts Manual* presents a view of the graphic arts as an industry—a very large one that touches and services virtually every other business enterprise of any size. The manual offers insights into the financial problems that can result from ill-planned or hasty investment in expensive and sophisticated computer technology. Such technology is changing so rapidly that any equipment may quickly be outdated. Publishers, printers, and manufacturers of presses, "hardware," and "software" must consider the hard figures of capital outlay and relate them to the less precise but real demands of competitive marketing, product improvement, and more efficient operation. Medium-size newspapers, for example, with mechanical photocomposition systems, often look longingly at electronically generated typesetting equipment capable of producing 500 lines a minute. Purchasing this equipment would be expensive and would entail scrapping a functioning system. To add to the complexity of such a decision is the fact that newer electronic equipment, even more sophisticated, more efficient, and faster, is being perfected, at an even higher price. It is financially out of reach of all but the largest newspapers. In printing, in platemaking, in book manufacturing, the story of technological revolution is the same. So apart from the "how to" aspects of graphic arts, this manual is a fascinating view of exquisitely refined arts and skills as a varied and highly capitalized business.

□

Two major movements amounting to revolutions in their totally separate fields, yet riding in tandem, form an interesting background to the publication of this manual at this time. The first is the revolution against modernist dogma in the arts. The second is the revolution in computer-allied technologies.

Not more than a generation ago, a firm touchstone existed for most of us in the arts: Mies van der Rohe's dictum, "Less is more." Equally influential was Louis Sullivan's earlier dictum, "Form follows function."

Nurtured by the Bauhaus, the early constructivists, and the abstractionists, a principle of economy of means came to pervade the arts. In design, the results were simplicity, white space, disciplined use of type, the advent of the grid structure, and other recognizable mannerisms. In drawing, the spare lines of Steinberg and Bemelmans seemed to convey a great deal with a minimum of detail. In typography, stark new sans serifs were developed, and even capital letters were considered needlessly complicated for a time. Modernists seemed to be hardening into classical forms that belied their own revolutionary beginnings.

In recent years, however, we have been experiencing a wild escalation in our visual expectations and a rebellion against the imposed order of doctrinaire modernism. Robert Venturi, in the book *Learning From Las Vegas*, published in 1972, signaled a new freedom (some would call it looseness) in architecture, which is still producing a mixed and confused bag of results. In the graphic arts, many artists seemed to be saying that "more is more" is better than "less is more." A mood of extravagance fostered startling new graphic approaches. Some were exciting and innovative—the graphic techniques in the Beatles' first color movie, "Help," in 1965, comes to mind. Others ran a fantastic gamut that included decorated T-shirts, supergraphics, neon sculptures, and the revival of hand lettering on the sides of luggage. Anticipating high-tech design, the Museum of Modern Art produced a book with covers made of ⅛-inch plexiglass and binding secured with industrial bolts. More recently, paperbacks have been embossed and made shelf-attractive with metallic and patent-leather finishes. In illustration, pop, camp, and nostalgia for the twenties, thirties, and forties became grist for the graphic mill. Complication took the place of simplicity, placing unprecedented demands on virtuosity in reproduction techniques. Even in modest commercial work, color became the norm. Irving Penn's polarized portraits (again the Beatles!) were representative of the many visual sleights of hand that became commonplace in the graphic arts.

Paralleling this revolution in perception is the technological revolution. What is happening at *The New York Times* is probably typical of changes in other areas of the graphic arts industry. Virtually overnight, Linotype machines and related hot-metal machinery have disappeared, replaced by electronic typesetting equipment that can set a thousand lines a minute. Reporters and editors generate their stories on video display terminals, which feed directly into the typesetters. Platemaking no longer requires the "mats" that were used to make the curved stereotypes for rotary presses. Instead, paste-ups go into a laser scanning machine, and in two minutes a flexible plastic plate emerges. A satellite plant in New Jersey, where the country's largest newspaper offset printing facilities are located, is tied to the home office by electronic relay. In some departments, computerized word processors make a direct line possible from typist to typesetting. For the near future, artists and editors, as well as production people, are looking toward computer-aided chart and map production. Well within sight is the technology for page makeup, already a reality in producing advertisements and magazine pages. A complicated broadsheet newspaper page will be designed and assembled on a video screen and sent in one unit to the press.

In other areas of the graphic arts, the story of technical revolution is much the same. The changes are everywhere. They affect how we work, with whom we work, and, in some cases, whether there is any job left at all.

□

I recall a simple little booklet produced recently—self-cover, black and white, no frills. It was a commemorative booklet with one halftone used as the frontispiece. During platemaking, the halftone was poorly etched. It reproduced gray and washed out. What could have been an elegant job became a mediocre job, best forgotten except as an example from which something is to be learned (or, in reality, relearned, because most of us in the graphic arts know it): not until the ultimate consumer sees the finished job, be it a reproduction of Cezanne's apples, a full-color catalog, or an ad in a national magazine, can one judge its success. No single element—not the layout or the pasteup or the words or the printing—can guarantee a successful job. All along the line, there are many who share the responsibility for success or failure. A complex production process means a necessary and almost frightening dependence on other people. When the process works, it's exhilarating; there are congratulatory lunches. When it fails, there is a placing of blame and a feeling of uneasy self-doubt: "Why didn't I foresee that?" Fortunately, among professionals, it almost always works. Not the least interesting aspect of the entire graphic arts business is how artists, writers, production people, and business people communicate and work together toward the common goal of making the job look good.

Louis Silverstein
Assistant Managing Editor
The New York Times

PREFACE

The purpose of this book is to provide a comprehensive guide to creating, producing, and purchasing printed materials. Designed to be a practical, wide-ranging, and up-to-date reference book for the graphic arts industry, it contains detailed information on graphic arts technology and processes. The material is presented in the form of individual articles, carefully coordinated and organized to form an overall picture of printing production.

The book is arranged in 16 sections. Section 1, *Overview of the Graphic Arts*, gives basic information on the industry and its technology and, in addition, presents an outline of printing production. This outline, represented in chart form at the beginning of each section, serves as the organizational basis of the book. Although it is difficult to categorize all of the complex operations that make up the graphic arts, we expect that the system we have developed will be useful to readers both in and outside the industry.

Sections 2 through 16 are made up of articles written by industry authorities with experience in various areas of the graphic arts. After a discussion of color theory (Section 2, *Color*), the sections are organized to follow the production of printed materials from conception (Section 3, *Design*) to dissemination (Section 15, *Fulfillment*). Each of these sections deals with a major step or element of printing production. The book concludes with information on trade practices and legal matters in Section 16.

The *Graphic Arts Manual* includes introductory material—such as the principles of design, typography, and color reproduction—as well as current technical information on all areas of production, from composition methods to printing and binding systems. The first article in each section usually is the most basic, providing an introduction for the novice, but with enough detail and thoroughness to give the experienced reader a useful overview. The other articles in the section cover various aspects of the subject; the articles have been arranged logically within each section.

The design and the editorial organization of the *Manual* work together to make it an easy-to-use reference book. Headings and subheadings, printed in blue, indicate subdivisions of the articles and provide a means of pinpointing specific information. Over 450 illustrations—including flow charts, diagrams, and photographs—clarify and expand on the text. Tables and lists are used to present material concisely and to introduce, emphasize, or summarize important points. Technical terms are italicized when they are introduced. Cross-references throughout the text suggest sources of supplementary information, and the detailed index enables the reader to locate discussions of any subject.

The *Graphic Arts Manual* is intended for a wide audience, including those already knowledgeable about the graphic arts and those seeking to learn the basics of the industry. It will prove an invaluable reference source in advertising agencies, publishing houses, corporations, printing plants, technical schools, colleges, and libraries. Both occasional and seasoned purchasers of printed materials will find the information they need in the *Manual*. The book will be useful to art directors, production managers, editors, technical and promotional writers, designers, graphic artists, and students. We believe that it will be of interest and value to anyone involved in, or curious about, the complicated and challenging world of the graphic arts.

This book would not have been possible without the cooperation of countless individuals, business firms, and organizations. The consulting editors and the contributing authors have given generously of their time and knowledge through the stages of planning, writing, and revising. Graphic arts associations have furnished information and advice; numerous companies have supplied technical details about their products. Experts throughout the industry have been ready with answers to the innumerable questions that have arisen. We are indebted to them for their assistance and acknowledge with thanks their courtesy and support.

Janet N. Field

CONTENTS

ILLUSTRATIONS

OVERVIEW OF THE GRAPHICS ARTS

1

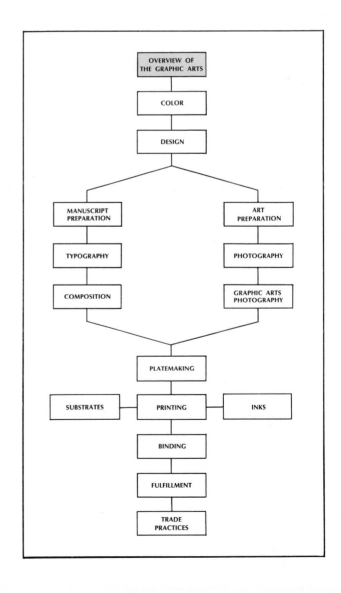

THE term *graphic arts,* as used in this book, refers to the creation, duplication, and transmission of words and illustrations in the form of printed images for the purpose of mass communication. The *graphic arts industry* consists of printing and related fields of activity, such as typesetting and binding, involved in the production of the printed image. This "Overview of the Graphic Arts" first analyzes the industry in terms of areas of activity and economic structure; then describes the basic graphic arts technologies and processes; and finally outlines the overall flow of operations as it will be followed throughout the book.

THE GRAPHIC ARTS INDUSTRY

The graphic arts industry is a vast field of diversified cultural and economic activity. It is actually a widespread community of industries, based on printing and associated technology, delicately interlaced and highly coordinated to produce an incredible array of modern communications media.

Scope of the graphic arts

The immense size of the graphic arts industry in the United States can be gauged in part by examining data on the commercial publishing and printing industries collected by the Bureau of the Census and published in the Census of Manufactures. In 1977, the most recent year in which the Census of Manufactures was taken, the commercial publishing and printing industries (Standard Industrial Classification 27) totalled $50.3 billion in the value of products it produced and shipped to customers. Publishing activity accounted for $25.0 billion of this total, and printing activity for $25.2 billion. These industries are expected to grow to a combined volume of $84.3 billion by 1983.

These figures reflect only a part of the graphic arts activity in this country. The packaging industry, for example, uses a great deal of printing in the production of boxes, cans, bottles, and other containers. Most of this printing is classified outside of SIC 27. Such packaging activities are estimated to have produced shipments worth about $38.0 billion in 1977. This figure is expected to grow to about $67.0 billion by 1983.

These industry groups—commercial publishing, commercial printing, and packaging—form one of the largest industrial complexes in the United States. Together they rank first among all industry groups in number of plants, second in average hourly wages paid to employees, seventh in total payroll, eighth in value of shipments, and tenth in dollars reinvested in capital expenditures.

We still have not accounted for all of the graphic arts activity in the United States economy. A large and rapidly growing volume of printing is done in plants owned and operated by companies in other industries. These *captive* or *in-plant* printing establishments usually work solely for their parent firms, and most of their production is not measured by any available statistics.

In addition, nonprofit organizations such as foundations, professional societies, trade associations, and governments operate captive printing plants, often sizable ones. Although there is no precise way to measure this hidden printing activity, one major supplier of graphic arts equipment estimates its worth at half the value of commercial printing—that is, all printing in SIC 27 except for newspapers—or roughly $12.6 billion in 1977.

Moreover, various industries use the *stencil* or *screen process* to make printed circuit boards for electronics or to decorate ceramics, textiles, and other materials. This specialized printing accounts for perhaps another $2.5 billion in dollar volume, according to industry trade association estimates.

Finally, a vast amount of publishing activity also lies outside SIC 27. Corporations, governments, foundations, societies, and associations publish in parallel to commercial publishing companies. Again, the volume of work cannot be measured directly, but based on typical ratios of product value to printing cost, this publishing activity may have been worth $11.1 billion in 1977.

In summary, in 1977 the graphic arts industries in the United States earned roughly $36.1 billion in commercial and hidden publishing, $25.2 billion in commercial printing, $38.0 billion in packaging, $12.6 billion in captive-shop production, and $2.5 billion in specialized screen printing—a total of $114.4 billion, or about 6.1 percent of the gross national product.

Products of the graphic arts

A breakdown of the statistics for SIC 27 in the Census of Manufactures provides a good idea of the kinds of printed products manufactured by the graphic arts industry. Table 1.1 presents the value of products shipped by various product and service groups for five census years, as well as the size of the gross national product in those years.* The column at the far right shows the percentage of growth in various industry segments between 1958 and 1977.

A major distinction must be made here between printing and publishing. While the Census Bureau lumps publishing with printing as a "manufacturing" industry, publishing is, in fact, not a manufacturing activity but a creative, entrepreneurial undertaking, closer to research and development work. Printing, on the other hand, is a "conversion" activity—a form of manufacturing in which basic materials supplied by other industries such as the paper and ink industries are converted into finished products.

Publishing traditionally has been classified with printing because at one time printers were also publishers. But over printing's 500-year history, these functions

---

* The Census of Manufactures does not present its product statistics in exactly this format. Some of these groupings were developed from census data by a trade magazine, *Book Production Industry,* which first published the groupings and the formula by which they were derived in June, 1968. The statistics for 1967, 1972, and 1977 were compiled by the same method for this article.

TABLE 1.1: VALUE OF PRODUCTS SHIPPED (1958–1977)

| Product categories | Value in millions of dollars | | | | | Growth in % |
	1958	1963	1967	1972	1977	(1958–1977)
Gross national product	441,700.0	583,900.0	789,700.0	1,171,100.0	1,889,600.0	328
All printing and publishing–SIC 27*	**12,082.6**	**15,836.1**	**21,200.3**	**29,609.1**	**50,254.8**	**316**
Commercial publishing	**6,238.0**	**8,391.5**	**11,206.6**	**15,341.4**	**25,011.7**	**301**
Daily and Sunday newspapers	3,125.3	3,792.0	4,961.6	6,960.6	10,692.9	242
Weekly and other newspapers	333.0	462.8	588.2	947.8	1,778.3	434
Periodicals	1,578.4	2,037.3	2,668.2	3,197.7	5,528.6	250
Books*	888.3	1,686.0	2,380.0	3,177.0	5,127.8	477
Catalogs and directories	93.6	133.0	184.6	244.1	437.4	367
Business service publications	72.9	101.6	123.0	241.9	409.8	462
Other miscellaneous	139.9	178.8	301.0	572.3	1,036.9	641
Commercial printing	**5,844.6**	**7,444.6**	**9,993.7**	**14,267.7**	**25,243.1**	**332**
Periodicals	730.7	859.3	936.2	1,251.6	1,940.4	166
Books and pamphlets	613.9	850.3	1,237.8	1,419.1	2,307.8	276
Integrated book manufacturing	422.9	607.0	900.3	1,049.9	1,823.7	331
Trade binding services	191.0	243.3	337.5	369.2	484.1	153
Catalogs and directories	252.4	364.7	527.9	758.4	1,823.7	623
Blankbooks and looseleaf binders	213.6	252.0	362.3	566.2	1,037.4	386
Advertising materials	932.7	1,010.8	1,381.5	1,976.9	2,890.4	317
General job printing	1,203.5	1,645.2	2,310.9	3,548.5	6,259.6	420
Financial and legal	126.9	223.1	290.6	461.2	682.9	438
Labels and wrappers	478.6	529.5	615.3	1,053.2	1,578.4	230
Business forms	374.0	598.4	895.8	1,381.9	2,721.2	628
Greeting cards	276.6	310.2	441.4	583.5	762.5	176
Engraving and plate printing	79.5	96.3	131.4	185.8	231.0	191
Preparatory trade services	562.3	704.8	862.6	1,081.4	1,737.3	209
Typesetting	175.5	249.6	362.1	508.7	773.8	341
Lithographic platemaking	68.0	129.5	151.2	263.0	631.5	829
Electrotyping and stereotyping	81.5	71.9	61.4	35.5	15.0	–82
Rubber and plastic platemaking	14.2	21.4	19.9	19.2	33.3	135
Photoengraving	208.5	214.7	237.1	221.3	227.7	9
Gravure platemaking	14.6	17.6	30.9	33.7	56.0	284

* All data in this table except for book publishing was derived from the U.S. Census of Manufactures. Book publishing data was derived from annual statistical reports compiled by industry trade associations.

have grown apart until today they are performed by fully developed separate industries. Except for newspapers, the vast majority of publishers today do not own or operate their own printing facilities; they contract their printing needs out to commercial printers. The publishers represented in table 1.1, therefore, are the customers of printers represented under commercial printing, and part of the dollar volume of commercial printing products is actually a cost paid out of the dollar volume of commercial publishing products. Newspaper publishers continue to operate their own printing facilities because newspapers must be printed locally for fast distribution and because installing the large and costly equipment required is beyond the resources of most local commercial printers.

Except for packaging, which produces a distinct group of products apart from those shown in the table, the major unmeasured segments of the graphic arts industry—institutional publishing and in-plant printing—produce the same types of products as the commercial publishing and printing industries. Their emphasis may be different (a corporate publishing unit may produce technical manuals, while a commercial publisher dealing with the same field of knowledge may produce text-

books), but the physical shape of the products and the steps through which they are developed and manufactured are similar.

The graphic arts industry, as represented in SIC 27, has grown at almost the same rate as the national economy, closely following trends in the gross national product. Individual products however, often vary significantly from this overall trend, as the growth percentage column in table 1.1 shows. The table also indicates that in recent years the publishing growth rate has lagged significantly behind the GNP; in the 10 years between 1967 and 1977, the GNP increased 139 percent, while publishing grew only 123 percent. This lag represents a slowdown in the exceptionally rapid expansion of book publishing, coupled with a continuing deceleration in periodical publishing growth. The printing segment of SIC 27 led GNP at 153 percent. Total growth in printed products possibly is higher than shown in SIC 27 statistics because in-plant printing has expanded substantially in recent years.

The graphic arts as a marketplace

The graphic arts industries form a unique kind of marketplace—the world's largest bazaar, in which customers can choose or have made to order just the kind of printed product they desire. While printing and its allied trades make up one of the ten largest industrial complexes in the United States, most of their products are individually custom-crafted to exact specifications of thousands of customers; relatively few printed products are manufactured to standard designs developed and marketed by printers through standard retail, wholesale, or catalog sales outlets. Most of the nation's 30,000-odd commercial printers and trade service firms are relatively small, obtaining individual jobs by competitive bidding. Even the largest commercial printer—who accounts for less than 4 percent of SIC 27's $25.2 billion in commercial printing—bids competitively for individual jobs or long-term manufacturing contracts to produce products designed by customers.

Almost any type of organization or individual is likely to be a customer for a commercial printer at some time. Often special types of service firms, such as advertising or sales promotion agencies, public relations companies, and art studios, are engaged to aid in the design of printed material; these companies are especially important customers. The jobs that customers award printers range all the way from a few dollars for a handful of business cards or form letters up to multimillion-dollar contracts for national publications or catalogs.

Printing establishments are found in virtually every community of any size across the nation. The major cities in which publishers, advertising agencies, and other communications organizations are located are also the country's major printing centers, containing more and larger printing establishments than other localities. However, as costs of operation in these cities have risen in the past several decades, more and more printing has migrated from city plants to facilities located in suburban areas and even across the country from the purchaser's office. Larger printing organizations now typically operate plants outside the main marketplace cities such as New York and Chicago, maintaining sales offices in these cities.

While customers formerly were limited to purchases in their own localities, the increasing ease of dealing with printers located across the country has in effect created a national market for many printed products. At the same time, the more forward-looking printers have tended to specialize in one area of printing. Thus there is a growing trend toward specialized national markets dominated by large companies. Periodicals, books, directories, blankbooks, looseleaf binders, financial and legal printing, labels and wrappers, business forms, greeting cards, and engraved printing (a large number of the product categories listed in table 1.1) are all produced primarily by specialized printers. The general job-shop printers—who are still in the majority in the industry—have steadily been squeezed into handling the overflow from these specialized areas as well as a great deal of advertising and general job work. While the large specialized printers tend to deal in broader markets, with customers across the country or at least throughout a region, the small job shop is essentially a local operation, often simply a neighborhood service printer. About one-third of the printers produce more than 90 percent of all commercial print-

ing, and in the highly specialized markets the top 50 printers typically control from 50 to 90 percent of their markets.

The time-honored method of purchasing printing is the *estimated-bid system.* The customer initiates the transaction by describing the job to be produced, often calling in several printers to compete for the order. Each printer takes the customer's specifications back to the estimating department, which prepares a plan for manufacturing the job and works out a set of estimated costs. An appropriate profit margin is added to arrive at a final price, which is submitted to the customer. The customer awards the job to the company which he believes offers the best combination of price, quality, and service.

Over the years, certain kinds of contract arrangements have grown up in some product areas, particularly for large and continuing jobs. Periodical publishers, for example, require printing of similar issues month after month, and it is highly advantageous to contract this production to a printer for a long period of time—one or more years—in order to obtain a lower price and better service. So, too, major corporations often write long-term contracts with printers for stationery, business forms, and other standard items. Other types of products, such as advertising pieces or books that are printed only once, have tended to remain under the individual job-bidding arrangement. There is, however, a gradual trend to greater use of contracts and increasing standardization of products such as books and catalogs, to give more stability to printing operations and to make it possible for printers to arrange financing of the most modern and costly automated facilities.

The long-range effect of the new trends in the structure of the graphic arts marketplace has been to change the face of the commercial printing industry. From a sprawling aggregate of small firms—most of them similarly equipped and producing a little of every kind of printed product—commercial printing has slowly evolved into a series of vertical industries closely aligned with the product categories in table 1.1, each increasingly dominated by its larger specialist firms. The dominant printers in these product-oriented industries have developed special technology for manufacturing their products, special procedures for expediting work at lower cost, and special understanding of customer requirements, enabling them to provide extra service that the general printer is not equipped to offer. This trend toward increasingly specialized product-oriented printing shows no sign of abating for many years to come.

GRAPHIC ARTS TECHNOLOGY

The graphic arts industries achieve their common purpose—the reproduction of graphic images in large quantities—by selecting from shared techniques of preparation, printing, and assembly. The printing processes are at the core of this technology.

Printing processes

All printing processes reproduce images by applying ink selectively to the *image* areas of the final printed piece and preventing its application to *non-image* areas. The conventional printing processes use intermediate *image carriers*, usually plates or stencils, which have two distinct kinds of areas, ink-bearing image areas and ink-blocking non-image areas. Some radical new printing technologies instead turn ink flow to the printed pieces on and off electronically. The essential differences among printing processes lie in the means by which they separate the image areas from the non-image areas.

Four major printing processes are in use today—*letterpress, gravure, lithography,* and *screen printing.* In addition, several specialty processes are used for special types of work. A number of unconventional new imaging technologies threaten to displace some of today's processes, although not in the immediate future. Some of these new methods are already in use in other industries such as the computer industry.

Letterpress is the oldest of the major processes. For hundreds of years, letterpress printing consisted of printing from metal type which was set by hand. Later, letterpress plates were developed on the same principle—printing from a raised or *relief* surface. The image area is raised above the rest of the type body or printing plate; when an ink-coated roller is passed over the type or plate, the ink adheres only to the top surface, the image area. The inked type or plate is then pressed against the paper or other substrate to transfer the ink to it.

Gravure printing, based on the *intaglio* principle, works in just the reverse manner. Rather than raised image areas, gravure plates have image areas made up of tiny cups or ink wells recessed in the plate surface. During printing, ink is spread liberally over the plate, and a steel blade is drawn across the surface to scrape the excess ink away, leaving the cups filled with ink. As the plate then rolls against the substrate, the ink is drawn out of the cups and onto the substrate.

Lithography is a relatively recent technique, developed in the early 1800's. This process uses *planographic* plates, with the image and non-image areas essentially on the same level or surface. These areas are differentiated in a lithographic plate by means of chemistry, using the principle that water-based fluids and greasy substances such as inks tend not to mix. Image areas of the plate are made receptive to inks, and non-image areas are made receptive to water-based solutions. Both substances are applied to the plate during printing, but each adheres only to its own area. This printing process is often called *offset lithography* or simply *offset.* The term *offset* refers to the primary design principle of most lithographic presses today—the use of three main cylinders to get the ink image onto the paper or other substrate. The first cylinder holds the printing plate; the second holds a rubber blanket which rolls against the inked plate, picking up the image; the third holds the substrate and rolls it against the rubber blanket to pick up the ink from it. The image is said to be "offset" from the plate to the blanket to the paper, rather than being printed directly from plate to paper.

Screen printing uses the *stencil* principle. A fine mesh screen of fabric carries the image. In image areas, the holes between the fibers or threads are left open so that ink can pass through; in non-image areas, these spaces are filled in so nothing can pass through. During printing, the screen is laid over the substrate; ink is pushed across the screen and down into the open spaces, coating the substrate only in the image areas.

Other printing processes include *collotype, steel-die engraving, thermography, flexography, mimeographing,* and *electrostatic printing. Typewriting,* too, might be considered a reproduction process when equipment is set up to produce duplicate copies automatically. All of these processes are used in limited special situations, and all employ the same basic imaging principles as the four major processes. Collotype uses a planographic photogelatin plate which accepts ink in proportion to the sensitivity imparted to it in different areas of the plate. Steel-die engraving is an intaglio process like gravure, often used for stationery and invitations. Thermography and flexography are basically letterpress processes. Thermography involves application of a powder over a printed image, which is then heated and fused to take on the appearance of the more expensive steel-die engraving. Flexography uses flexible rubber plates and special inks for high-speed letterpress printing. Mimeographing uses an inexpensive stencil cut on a typewriter to produce small quantities of simple typed documents in offices. Electrostatic printing involves placing an electrically charged image area on the sheet, which subsequently attracts ink particles; the process is used in a variety of forms, but the best-known application is in photocopying systems. Typewriting, of course, imprints a relief image by striking a raised metal type character against an inked ribbon, which in turn strikes the paper.

The four major processes account for most printing. About 28 percent of all graphic arts printing is done by letterpress, much of it for newspapers and long-run magazines. Another 12 percent is flexographic printing, used mainly for packaging, labels, and books. Lithography accounts for roughly 40 percent of all printing but is far more dominant in the commercial printing industries, accounting in many product segments for 75 to 90 percent of production. Another 15 percent is done by gravure, primarily long-run magazines, catalogs, newspaper supplements, packaging, and specialty products such as wallpaper and floor tiles. The balance of printing is divided among screen printing and the minor processes.

Preparatory operations

A variety of supporting technologies is required both before and after printing. The major operations leading up to printing are often called *preparatory* or *prepress* operations.

Typesetting and *composition* are the processes of assembling type characters into pages. Various methods are used, including metal processes, which require casting and assembly of pieces of metal type; photographic processes, in which type characters are exposed in position on photographic film or paper; and strike-on, which involves imprinting of type characters on paper by striking of an inked ribbon. Composition technology is one of the most volatile areas of the graphic arts today, changing rapidly with the development of computers, video display terminals, optical character recognition, and other electronic systems to control the typesetting process.

Graphic arts photography involves photographic processes especially engineered to convert original art or photographs to printable images. Among these processes are line and halftone photography, and color separation and correction. In halftone photography, the gradations of tone in an illustration such as a photograph are translated into discrete light and dark areas on photographic film. Later, ink will print solidly or not at all in each of these tiny areas, creating the impression of the original tonal gradations. Line photography is used when it is not necessary to reproduce a subject using the halftone principle. In color-separation photography, colors are broken up into basic components on separate pieces of film. Later, the inks of the component colors are printed in register to recreate the original image. Because the inks do not precisely match the original colors, however, color correction is usually necessary.

The remaining preparatory processes are *image assembly*, the process of making up master assemblies from individual film components for use in platemaking, and the *platemaking* processes themselves—photoengraving, stereotyping, electrotyping, rubber and plastic plate molding (all for letterpress), lithographic platemaking, gravure cylinder making, and so on—the methods by which master film assemblies are converted into the final image carriers that will be used to print from on press.

In the early days of letterpress printing from metal type, most preparatory processes did not exist; all but composition are modern-day phenomena and even composition has been revolutionized by the new technology that has given rise to most of the other preparatory functions. This technology is photographic chemistry, the use of light-sensitive materials to record, manipulate, and transfer images. The rise of photography since the turn of the century has been a major factor in the expansion of the graphic arts. It made possible the widespread use of all the printing processes that compete with letterpress because their plates are made *photomechanically*—that is, using light-sensitive coatings which receive the image. Even letterpress, with its photoengravings and new photopolymer plates, now relies largely upon photography. Photographic technology also vastly increased the use of illustration in printing; in addition to contributing the photograph itself, it made possible for the first time the reproduction of most other kinds of illustration.

Assembly processes

The processes that follow printing have not changed with the rapidity of the preparatory processes, but they too are undergoing profound alterations today.

The major activity following printing is the fastening of printed pages, a group of operations generally called *binding*. Bookbinding is as old as hand lettering and illuminating of original manuscripts. From a handcraft, binding has grown to include a variety of automated processes for the assembly of many kinds of printed products. Binding operations include taking printed materials from the press and folding, cutting, gathering, gluing, covering, and otherwise assembling them into finished products.

Four major binding processes are used today: sewing, wire stitching, adhesive, and mechanical (including looseleaf). Books sewn with thread and periodicals

held together with staple-like wire stitches are the older binding form. Mechanical bindings, consisting of formed wire or plastic devices used to hold pages together, have been steadily growing in variety over the years. Looseleaf binders have been used for years in special situations. The newest and fastest growing method is adhesive binding, a process in which the back edges of a book are coated with a thin layer of glue to fasten the pages together and hold them to the book cover. Adhesive binding lends itself easily to automation and to use on continuous binding lines, which are increasingly dominating the binding field.

Besides binding, assembly includes a variety of secondary fastening and decorating techniques known loosely as *finishing operations*. These specialty processes include stringing, tagging, easeling, die stamping, and flocking. In addition, several methods of decorating and construction are used in making covers for different types of books and other bound products.

Growth of technology

If a major theme runs through graphic arts technology today, it is the transformation of graphic arts processes from their time-honored craft basis to a modern scientific basis. What was done for generations by craftsmen who learned at the bench and passed their knowledge down to their heirs is now being scientifically analyzed, documented, quantified, and made predictable before production ever begins. Even the new technological processes are changing under the weight of science. Mechanical means of assembling, transferring, and fastening are giving way to the use of chemistry and physics to accomplish the same tasks. The materials used in the graphic arts, from the films and plates to the papers and glues, have become ever more complex in their composition, as well as more capable in their performance. To control these complex materials and processes, the computer has been brought into the graphic arts. From a rather backward industry a few decades ago, the graphic arts industry has become one of the nation's more technologically sophisticated fields.

GRAPHIC ARTS PRODUCTION FLOW

The various areas of graphic arts technology fit together into a tightly interlocked network through which all printed jobs must move. The specific paths that jobs take are quite diverse, but there is a fundamental production flow pattern that all of them follow.

The production flow is represented in figure 1.1. As already discussed, the process of producing a printed job begins well before it reaches the printing plant. The complete graphic arts flow can be divided into four major phases, as indicated by the horizontal bands in figure 1.1. The first is the *creative* stage, in which the project is conceived, the specifications are made up, and the text and illustration copy are prepared. The remaining three stages are manufacturing stages, during which the basic specifications and creative work are turned into printed pieces. *Preparatory operations* convert original words and illustrations into a form ready for printing. *Reproduction* involves the combination of ink and paper (or other substrate) into printed images. In the *assembly and dissemination* phase, the various

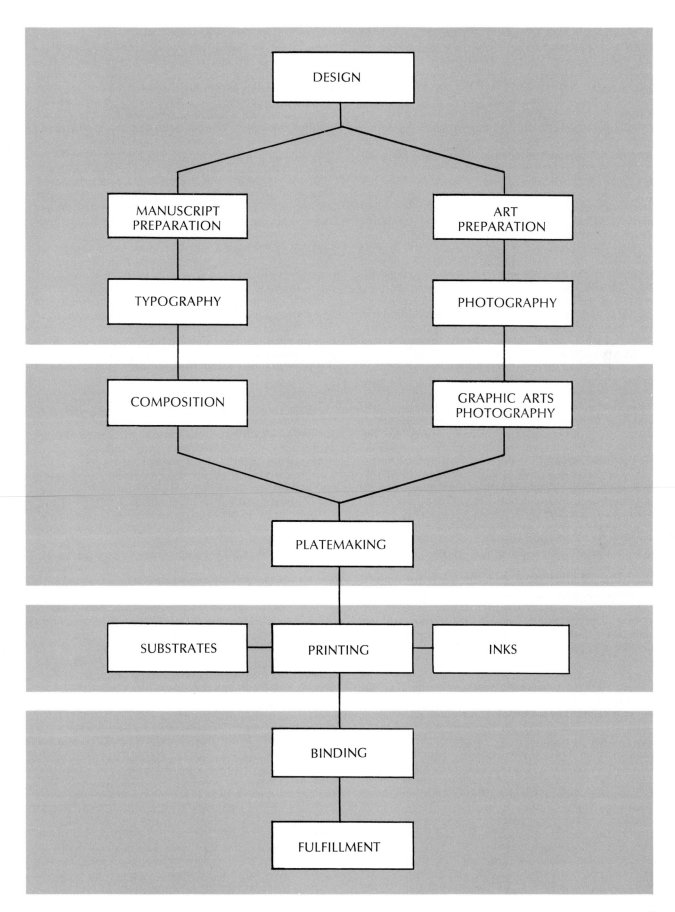

Figure 1.1: Graphic arts production flow chart.

printed elements are brought together into assembled products, are packed appropriately, and are shipped to their users. Each individual box in figure 1.1 represents a major production area or processing step within this basic format.

Design

Although projects usually begin when someone writes or organizes thoughts, data, or some other form of information into text, tables, diagrams, or rough sketches for illustrations, the first step in the actual production of a printed piece is *design*—the work of creating an organized visual presentation. Given the raw materials, the graphic designer conceives and proposes visual alternatives for presenting the information. The possibilities are discussed with the author or client, the presentations are revised, and one is finally chosen. The specifications for producing the job are assembled: typefaces and type sizes are chosen for text, page formats are designed, illustrations are selected or commissioned to be created by artists or photographers, materials such as paper are designated, and processes for the various production steps are decided upon. The result is essentially a blueprint that will be followed throughout production.

At one time, printers carried a great deal of responsibility for creating graphic designs for the jobs they printed. Over the years, however, the design function has moved from the printing plant into offices of customers or into independent agencies and studios that specialize in design work exclusively. Today, for the most part, jobs proceed through the design step without the involvement of a printer. The information required in the competitive bidding process is available upon completion of the design, and the job is usually submitted to printers for bids at that time.

However, the job is not sent to the selected printer for production until several other creative processes are complete. As indicated in the chart, these processes may be thought of as forming two parallel paths leading from design to the printer: one for text, tables, and other material to be set in type; the other for illustrative materials, including photographs and artwork. The preparation of such materials once was done in the printing plant, but for the most part, like design, it has been taken over by the customer or a special independent agency.

Manuscript preparation

In the *manuscript preparation* stage, material is put into a form that the typesetter can use easily. Most of this work falls under the heading of *editing*.

The work is done by someone in the customer's office or an agency. In some organizations such as magazines, editing may be done by a writer or the person responsible for the content of the finished product, such as the managing editor. Often, especially in commercial publishing houses, the editing function is divided between a *project editor* in charge of the overall preparation and flow of the manuscript and a *copy editor* who is responsible for more specific aspects of language and content.

Copy editing includes a wide range of activities, depending upon the kind of material and the practices of the organization preparing it. It may involve only correcting the mechanics of language—spelling, grammar, punctuation—or it may include actually rewriting material to achieve greater clarity or more readable style. Editors may question authors about vague or seemingly conflicting statements in their work.

In some organizations, editors handle copy and also are responsible for coordinating various areas of production, including design, composition, and printing —sometimes working with a production manager. They may be involved, along with art department personnel, in finding illustrations or in laying out pages.

One of the more mechanical aspects of editing essential to proper production of text matter is typographic *mark-up*, the process of writing out complete instructions for the typesetter. Usually the instructions are put on the manuscript itself, but sometimes a separate specification sheet is used. With the movement of creative design and editing from the printing plant into editorial and art departments, typographic mark-up has increasingly become the province of the printer's customer. However, compositors working in typesetting departments still do a significant amount of this work when customers are content to leave the minute details of type specification to someone else or when new composition technologies require special sets of instruction codes that are not widely known.

Typography

Typographic mark-up should not be confused with *typography*, which is universally understood to be the aesthetic use of type to achieve good graphic design. Typography, as opposed to typographic mark-up, is firmly in the hands of the design community. Typographic mark-up is simply the mechanics of preparing instructions which will enable compositors to produce the typography called for by designers.

Typography is based on a number of principles of good type design and type use. Typefaces are usually designed and judged on the basis of readability as well as aesthetic appeal. How type is used also affects readability: variables include type size, line length, leading, and so on. Type is an important design element. Such factors as the shape of the letterforms, the placement of the type on the page, and the appropriateness of the typeface to the subject of the text have an impact on the presentation of the material.

Composition

Next the manuscript enters the printing plant or a special trade composition plant for typesetting. After the marked-up copy has been set, printed copies of the type, called *proofs*, are made and read to find the errors which typesetters inevitably make in transcribing and converting original material into type. The corrected proofs are returned to the typesetters, who reset the incorrect lines and insert them into the type. This cycle may be repeated several times before all the errors are corrected. Then new proofs are made and sent to the customer, who again checks the type and also may make new changes in the text. The typesetter incorporates the new corrections and then makes up the type into pages. Proofs of the pages then are put through similar rounds of reading, checking, and correction before final approval is given to send the pages on for platemaking and printing.

Depending upon the kind of typesetting and the printing process to be used, the job now moves either to a lock-up operation in the composition department or to the camera department.

If the job has been set in metal type from which printing is to be done directly, the type, made up into pages, is locked into a steel frame for mounting directly on the press; from lock-up, the pages and the frame are taken directly to the pressroom. If a letterpress plate is to be used in printing, the locked-up type is sent to a platemaking department.

If the job is being printed in any other way, the final pages must be photographed to convert them into film, which is needed for platemaking. Pages which have been pasted up from reproduction proofs and pages composed of type set photographically can be sent to the camera department without further processing. Metal type composed into pages may be used to produce reproduction proofs which can be photographed. In these cases, composition actually meets graphic arts photography, represented on the chart as the parallel box in the illustration path on the right. While many of the techniques involved in graphic arts photography (such as halftone photography and color separation) deal specifically with the reproduction of illustrations, similar photographic techniques are needed for text material so that plates can be made from type matter.

Art preparation and photography

Meanwhile, the preparation of illustrations proceeds separately, as indicated by the boxes on the right of figure 1.1. There are two major types of illustration: photographic, including both opaque prints (black-and-white and color) and film transparencies; and non-photographic, including all forms of artwork from simple drawings to oil paintings. Photographs are *continuous-tone* illustrations; that is, they are made up of a wide range of tonal values. They require special halftone work to convert them to printable form. Artwork may be *line art*—that is, have only two discrete tones—or continuous-tone art.

Typically, the creation of photographs or artwork is handled by photographers and artists who either are employees of the customer or work on a free-lance basis. In some cases, the customer will seek out a specialist in a certain style of art or photography.

Another procedure, *picture research*, is used to locate already existing materials—both photographic and non-photographic—which may be used in the new job. Beyond the complicated research work needed to find the materials, picture research usually involves obtaining permission from the owners and arranging any payment that may be required for use.

A kind of art preparation that must be considered as a special area of its own is the creation of *mechanical* art. *Mechanicals*, as these pieces are often called, are finished pages or panels with various graphic elements pasted into position. They contain only type and line art; elements such as photographs are added later. In effect, a mechanical is a substitute for the composed page which would otherwise have been produced by the composition department or firm.

Prior to the development of photomechanical platemaking, printing had to be done from raised metal type,

a product that only composition departments could produce; therefore all page makeup was performed in composing rooms. However, the introduction of photography to convert images on film or paper into printing plates permitted customers to substitute mechanical art techniques for part of the composing room work traditionally done in printing plants at substantially higher costs.

For many years, mechanicals have been pasted up by special artists, using high-quality *reproduction proofs* supplied by the typesetter. The artist cuts out printed blocks of type and pastes them into position on a board, along with line illustrations if desired. The finished paste-up is sent to the printer for processing in the graphic arts photography stage.

However, radical changes in composition technology, such as the use of photographically composed type, have brought paste-up techniques back into many composition departments to replace metal type makeup. The artist is no longer the exclusive user of paste makeup and mechanical art techniques.

At the same time, the newer photographic composition systems have become economical and simple enough for office workers to use, and many new typesetting machines are being installed by customers in their own offices. Thus, typesetting is no longer the exclusive province of printers' composition departments and trade composition companies. This merging of functions of art and composition departments will continue at a rapid pace in the next few years, with a great deal of composition work being absorbed by customer art departments.

In the flow diagram shown in figure 1.1, these changes might be represented by a new box at the point where the parallel text and illustration paths meet. Such a new box, perhaps labeled "page assembly," would refer to functions traditionally classified under either composition or art preparation. Because of the movement of these activities into the customer's offices, this new box, as well as other composition functions, will probably move up above the line separating creative activity from the job's entry into the manufacturing plant.

Graphic arts photography

The position of graphic arts photography in this new alignment will become clear only after a period of gradual evolution. Graphic arts photography, as shown in the chart, is the first preparatory stage through which illustration materials pass before being used to make printing plates. As such, it is roughly comparable to the composition stage in the processing of text. It is the stage at which original illustrations are converted into a form that can be used on the printing press.

As mentioned earlier, however, graphic arts photography is not limited to the processing of illustrations. It is also used to convert composed pages of type into film when the job is to be printed from photomechanical plates. Like line artwork, pages assembled by paste-up in a composition department or mechanical art department are photographed in the printing plant's camera department. If the pages are assembled from type set on film rather than on photographic paper, they may be converted to photographic negatives by *contact printing* rather than by camera photography.

Graphic arts photography is highly technical, requiring very specialized and expensive equipment as well as sophisticated knowledge and skills. Such facilities are best set up in special manufacturing plants rather than in a variety of general locations such as offices. This requirement militates strongly against an otherwise logical movement of these functions above the line separating customer from printing plant.

Film images of pages and converted illustration films meet at the final operation of graphic arts photography just prior to platemaking. This operation, called *image assembly* or *stripping*, involves the positioning and fastening of page and illustration films onto large sheets of paper or plastic the size of the printing plate. These *flats* are then sent to the platemaking department.

Platemaking

In the *photomechanical* platemaking process, the flats are laid over the plates, which have been coated with photosensitive solutions, and the plates are exposed to light. The light passes through the clear areas of the film, altering the photosensitive coating. After exposure, the plates are processed with chemicals which differentiate printing areas from non-printing areas so that only the printing areas will pick up and transfer ink during printing.

This procedure is used today for the vast majority of printed jobs. When a job is to be printed directly from metal type, however, relief plates of the individual illustrations, called *engravings*, must be made and sent to the composition department. There they are inserted into the pages along with the type and locked into steel frames for mounting on the press.

The finished plates move from the preparatory stage of production to the reproduction stage, in which they are mounted on presses for printing. Before actual printing, the customer is often given proofs of the final pages for approval. These may be *prepress proofs*, made by various means before the job is placed on the production press, or *press proofs*, pulled on the production press itself.

Printing

Starting with the printing step, production becomes relatively straightforward compared to the complex interlacing of operations characteristic of the creative and preparatory stages. On the other hand, the reproduction and assembly stages involve the processing of large amounts of heavy and costly materials. Mistakes made or discovered in these stages may require the rerunning of a job, which entails great expense in terms of lost time and materials. Therefore, every effort is made to make sure that jobs are correct before they reach the printing and binding operations.

The presses used for printing may be classified into two types: *sheet-fed* presses, which handle cut sheets of paper, and *web-fed* presses, which process paper from rolls in a continuous stream. There are many different kinds of presses, from small office duplicating machines that handle 8½" x 11" sheets to huge rotary newspaper and publication presses that print continuous webs of paper 65" or more in width. Press speeds range from a few thousand small sheets per hour to one or two thousand linear feet per minute on large web presses.

In addition to printing, web presses usually perform subsequent operations. Either they fold and cut the webs of paper into groups of pages called *signatures*, or they cut the webs into flat sheets and stack the sheets automatically in piles. Occasionally web presses are equipped to reroll the printed paper in preparation for mounting on binding equipment that accepts rolls.

Typically, the press operation uses the most costly equipment in the graphic arts, so printers plan their operations to keep the presses as busy as possible.

Inks and substrates

As represented in figure 1.1, the two basic materials needed for printing—ink and paper (or other substrate material)—come together at the printing press. Both inks and papers are available in many colors and with a wide range of characteristics for various applications. Inks are often mixed to order for specific jobs; paper can be made to order for large jobs, but more often a standard paper is used.

Inks almost universally are purchased by the printer for use on the customer's job, but paper may be purchased by either customer or printer. Mixed inks are often obtained from an ink supplier, but many large printers maintain their own ink mixing facilities, purchasing raw materials rather than mixed inks. The usual practice in general commercial printing is for the printer to purchase and supply the paper. In the publishing industries and in the case of certain large industrial corporations which use very large amounts of paper, paper mills usually sell directly to the printer's customer, delivering the stock to the printing plant specified by the customer.

Binding

After printing, the final printed materials go to the bindery for assembly into finished products. For books, magazines, pamphlets, and other bound pieces, one of the various binding methods is used to fasten the pages together.

Regardless of the fastening method, the binding process follows a basic sequence. Traditionally, the first step has been folding large printed sheets into signatures or cutting them into page-size sheets. (With the coming of web presses, folded signatures are often produced automatically as the last step on the press, eliminating this step from the bindery.) The folded signatures or individual page-size sheets are then gathered or collated into proper sequence. Next the pages are fastened together, and a cover is attached. Sometimes the cover is assembled with the body before fastening; sometimes it is attached after the body is fastened together. At some point, the assembled product is trimmed so that the edges of all pages are even; trimming, too, may be done either before or after the cover is applied, depending on whether or not the cover overhangs (extends out beyond) the edges of the pages. Finally, the bound products are stacked and packed into cartons or packaged in some other manner for shipping.

The binding processes have been characterized by a great deal of handwork and materials handling between each operation. In recent years, however, in-line binding systems gradually have been developed that permit the rapid assembly of products from start to finish at high speeds. Moreover, current trends are to match bindery operating speeds and conditions to those of presses so that the two stages of production can be linked in a continuous production system from raw paper to complete product. Although now limited to only a few areas, the use of such systems promises to become a major trend in many areas of printing and binding over the next few decades.

Some printed products, such as labels, tags, posters, and easel-like displays, are not bound but require their own specialized finishing operations. Some operations —foil stamping and blind embossing, for example— may be used for decorating both bound and other products.

Fulfillment

Fulfillment is the process of preparing the packed products for shipment to their ultimate destinations through various distribution channels. In the case of jobs to be delivered to the customer directly, the problem is relatively simple: the packaged products are simply shipped in bulk to the customer's warehouse or another delivery point. Many customers, such as magazine publishers and mail advertisers, ask the printer to perform additional distribution functions required to deliver the products directly to the consumer.

Fulfillment involves a number of operations: labels must be prepared and attached; packages must be sorted and grouped according to delivery point; lists of recipients must be kept current. Often in publication or direct mail plants, such fulfillment operations as labeling and packing are performed on automatic equipment at the ends of binding lines. There are also many specialty firms called mailing or fulfillment houses which will accept printed and bound products and perform the fulfillment operations.

USING THE FLOW CHART

The articles which follow explore all the technologies, processes, and methods that make up the graphic arts. They are carefully arranged and organized into sections which follow the production flow described in this overview. Each stage of production that is represented by a box in figure 1.1 corresponds to one of the major sections of this book. As an aid to the reader, this flow chart is repeated at the beginning of each section, identifying the stage under discussion and clarifying its position in the total picture.

It should be noted that two sections of the book have not yet been discussed. Section 2, *Color*, deals with the theory and measurement of color, subjects that apply to many phases of production. Section 16, *Trade Practices*, discusses business procedures and practices in the industry, trade customs, metrication, and copyrights and patents. Because these sections are not actually part of the production flow, they are not included in figure 1.1; however, they are represented in the chart that appears throughout the book by boxes before and after the first and last stages of production.

Paul D. Doebler

COLOR

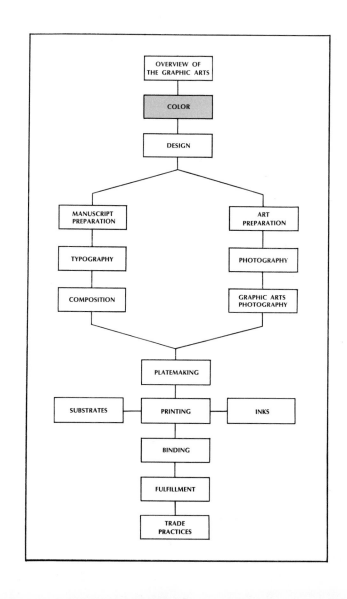

2

COLOR AND LIGHT
Michael H. Bruno, GRAPHIC ARTS CONSULTANT

Color and light are so closely related that it is impossible to have one without the other. The third part of the system, of course, is the observer. Since light is the primary requisite to seeing color, it is appropriate to discuss it first.

LIGHT

Light is a form of radiant energy. It occupies a very narrow band in what is known as the electromagnetic spectrum (fig. 2.1), which includes the whole range of radiant energy, from the very short-wavelength cosmic rays, gamma rays, and X rays, to ultraviolet rays, visible light, infrared rays, and radio waves. All radiant energy consists of tiny bursts of electromagnetic waves. The bursts behave as particles, called *quanta* or *photons*. The waves are transverse waves similar to those produced when a stone is thrown into water. The best known light sources are the sun and electric lights, of which there are many types (see "Lights for Photography and Platemaking," page 338).

violet for the shortest wavelengths and, as wavelength is increased, appears blue, green, yellow, orange, and finally red, for the longest wavelengths. The violet end of the visible spectrum is bordered by the invisible ultraviolet region, and the long red wavelength end is bordered by the invisible infrared region. Wavelengths from about 4 nm to 380 nm are in the ultraviolet region of the spectrum. The waves in the range from 210 nm to 300 nm are useful in the absorption of Vitamin D by the body and can cause sunburn. The range from 300 nm to 400 nm is useful in exposing photographic and platemaking emulsions. Radiant energy having wavelengths in the range below 210 nm is very dangerous, as it can cause serious eye damage and, in large doses, skin cancer. Fortunately for mankind, most of these rays are filtered from sunlight by the ozone in the earth's outer atmosphere.

Radiant energy having wavelengths from 700 nm to about 10 *micrometers* (μm) is known as infrared energy. (A micrometer, formerly known as a *micron*, is equal to one millionth of a meter, or 1000 nm.)

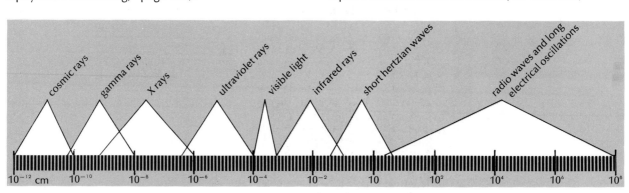

Figure 2.1: The electromagnetic spectrum.

The various types of electromagnetic energy vary in *wavelength* (the distance from the crest of one wave to the crest of the next) and *frequency* (the number of waves that pass a point in a given period of time), but they all travel at the same speed in a vacuum—30 billion centimeters (cm) per second (there are 2.54 centimeters to the inch) or 186,284 miles per second. As the wavelength increases, the frequency decreases, and vice versa. Wavelengths range from less than one trillionth of a centimeter for cosmic rays to over 500 million centimeters or 3100 miles for the waves coming from a 60-hertz electric motor. The wavelength range from 380 to 775 *nanometers* (nm) is the visible portion of the electromagnetic spectrum (1 nm = 0.0000001 cm). The angstrom unit (Å) is another unit of wavelength, equal to 0.1 nm.

Light in a very narrow wavelength band appears

In graphic arts we are concerned with the range of electromagnetic wavelengths from about 310 nm to about 3.4 μm. The ultraviolet energy is used in exposing printing plates and photographic emulsions and in curing inks. Some new ink-drying systems use electron beams. Their use requires lead shielding to absorb stray electrons and any X rays that are produced when electrons strike metal surfaces. The visible range from about 400 nm to 700 nm is important in photography and color reproduction. The infrared rays having wavelengths up to 3.4 μm are used to dry inks.

Properties of light

Light has a number of important properties that are very useful in graphic arts. It can be transmitted, reflected, absorbed, and polarized—all properties which are important to the appearance of objects and to

14

photography. The glass elements in lenses and the glass or plastic used for making light filters for photography transmit and absorb light. Shiny or colored surfaces reflect light.

Special thin coatings, often of metallic fluorides, having a thickness of about half a wavelength of light, are coated on the glass elements of lenses to minimize the reflection by such surfaces. This type of coating reduces the interreflections between lens elements, which produce lens flare. The bluish or gold color of the surface of a glass lens element is an indication that the element is coated.

As light passes from one medium into another its speed is changed; in going from air into glass, for example, the speed is reduced almost one-third. The ratio of the speed of light in a medium to that in a vacuum (or oftentimes air) is known as the *index of refraction* of the medium. In lens making, the glasses for the various elements are specially selected with different indices of refraction to correct for aberrations (errors) in the image-producing properties of the lenses.

Light from a frosted incandescent lamp is made up of electromagnetic waves showing no particular preference for direction of vibration. If one could visualize the electric field of a ray coming to the eye from such a source, he would see the field randomly oscillating, sometimes vertically, sometimes horizontally, and at other times, all of the various angles in between. When such a beam is reflected from a shiny surface, such as glass, the reflection process removes some of the modes of oscillation, leaving a beam tending to oscillate more in one plane than another. A beam showing such preferred direction is said to be *polarized*. Some natural crystals and some man-made sheet materials can cause an unpolarized beam to become polarized. Such a device is called a *polarizer*, or *polarizing filter*. Such a filter can be used to eliminate unwanted reflections from the edges of a camera copyboard. The specularly reflected ray from the side of the copyboard is polarized. The diffusely reflected light from the artwork on the copyboard is unpolarized. A polarizing filter may be placed on the camera lens or on the sources of illumination. If the camera filter is properly oriented, it will admit a large part of the light from the artwork, but will stop the rays that were specularly reflected. If filters are on the light sources, the filters must be oriented so that the specular reflection process virtually eliminates all of the light that might have been reflected if it were not initially polarized. The diffuse reflection from the artwork is unaffected by the initial polarization.

Light intensity

For photography and graphic arts applications, one of the most important properties of a light source is its intensity. A 100-watt bulb has more intensity than a 40-watt bulb of the same kind. The amount of light per unit area on an illuminated surface is called the *illumination*, which depends on the intensity of the source and its distance. Illumination is very important in photography because photography is a recording on a light-sensitive film of the spatial pattern of variations of light reflected from or transmitted through a subject.

The higher the level of illumination, the shorter is the exposure time needed to produce a developable image. A light meter can be used to measure incident or reflected light. When electric light sources are used, a change in voltage can alter the intensity of the source. In such cases, a light integrating meter is needed to control the exposure (see "Exposure Controls," page 331).

Color temperature

If anyone has had the experience of watching iron being heated in a forge, he knows that as the iron increases in temperature its color changes. It goes from *red hot* to *yellow hot* to *white hot*, at which point it is very soft and malleable. A substance like iron, when heated, gives off all the wavelengths of visible light, which is known as a continuous spectrum. The temperature of the source is expressed in *kelvins*. (The *degree Kelvin* no longer exists. The internationally ac-

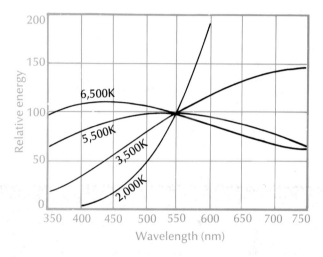

Figure 2.2: Spectral power distributions of light sources emitting continuous spectra at various color temperatures.

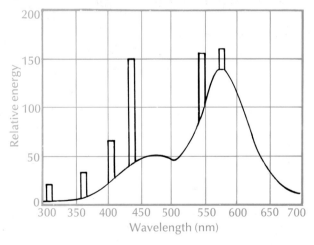

Figure 2.3: Spectral power distribution of a fluorescent lamp. Narrow peaks superimposed on continuous curves of phosphor radiation represent the contribution of mercury line emission.

15

cepted unit is the *kelvin*.) The kelvin temperature is equivalent to the absolute temperature of the source (°C + 273.1° C). A color temperature of about 5,500 kelvins shows an approximately equal distribution of all wavelengths of light and looks nearly white. Light having a color temperature slightly lower than this is richer in yellow light and poorer in blue so it looks yellower. Light of a higher color temperature is richer in blue and poorer in red and looks bluer. This is demonstrated in figure 2.2. Mean noon sunlight in a temperate zone about mid-June has a color temperature of about 5,600K, which means that it has nearly equal amounts of radiant power in equal wavelength intervals over the visible spectrum. A tungsten light bulb gives off light with a color temperature of about 2,800K, so it appears yellowish in comparison with daylight. North sky light is usually about 7,500K, appearing bluish in comparison with direct sunlight, and the blue sky can have a color temperature of 20,000K or more.

The method of light production in fluorescent lamps is a combination of glow discharge and fluorescence. Neither of these produces a spectrum identical to the spectrum of a glowing body (see figure 2.3). For this reason, fluorescent lamps cannot be adequately characterized by a simple statement of color temperature.

When incandescent electric lamps are used, not only does the intensity of the light source vary when the voltage changes but also its color temperature. The higher the voltage, the higher the color temperature and intensity, and vice versa. An example of this is the photoflood lamp, which has a filament like an ordinary tungsten lamp designed to operate at about 70 volts. When the lamp is operated at 110 to 120 volts, the tungsten is overheated, so the intensity is increased and the color temperature rises from 2,800K to about 3,400K. The life of the bulb, of course, is shortened because of the overload on the tungsten filament. This variation in color temperature is a serious problem in photography because films are color sensitive and their exposures depend on constant illumination, color temperature of light source, and color transmission of the filters used. This makes the need for light integrators doubly important for color photography.

Metamerism

One of the most accurate ways to specify a color of any object is to measure it in a *spectrophotometer*, which produces a *spectrophotometric curve* for the color. If two objects have the same spectrophotometric curves, they always have the same color regardless of the light source or viewing conditions used to examine them. Two objects without identical spectrophotometric curves can have the same color under one set of viewing conditions. This is known as *metamerism*. Such a match is known as a *metameric* match.

Lasers

Certain elements and compounds, when energized or excited in a specially designed device, emit radiant energy in a single wavelength band. These substances include argon, helium, neon, carbon dioxide, carbon monoxide, gallium, arsenic, and some organic dyes, either alone or used as mixtures. The device in which they emit in this way is called a laser. *Laser* is the acronym for *light amplification by stimulated emission of radiation*. Because of their unusual property of emitting light in a single direction, lasers are beginning to find a number of important applications in graphic arts, from producing hologram images to facsimile transmission, image scanning, and platemaking.

COLOR

Color is a combination of the physical sensation of light and the psychological interpretation of it. Physically, visible light is radiant energy having wavelengths in the range from about 400 nm to 700 nm. The equal combination of all wavelengths of visible light produces the sensation of white light. When the radiation is divided into individual wavelengths—as when it is passed through a prism (fig. 2.4) or in a rainbow—each wavelength causes a different color sensation. The shorter wavelengths in the blue end of the spectrum are bent more in passing through a prism than the longer wavelengths in the yellow, orange, and red end of the spectrum.

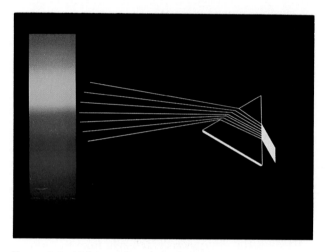

Figure 2.4: Light passing through a prism and being dispersed into a spectrum.

The eye divides the visible spectrum into three broad bands of color—blue, green, and red (fig. 2.5). The eye has receptors on the surface of the retina, which are sensitive to light and color. The eye is sensitive to very great differences in intensities of light, ranging from the light of the bright sun to a dim moonlit night (a range of some one million to one in intensity). The *rods* in the retina are sensitive to very dim light but do not sense color. The *cones* are sensitive not only to light but also to color. It is generally believed that

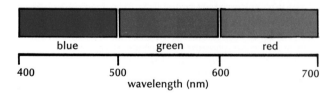

Figure 2.5: The visible spectrum divided into the three wavelength bands perceived by the human eye.

some cones are sensitive to red light, others to green light, and a third kind to blue light. When the eye views a scene, the red light from the scene affects the cones sensitive to red light, and the cones send impulses to the brain. The green light affects the green-sensitive cones, and these transmit their impulses to the brain. The same happens to the blue light. The brain then recreates the scene based on the signals the various cones have sent to it. What the brain sees is the result of the experience of the viewer and the condition of the cones on his retina. If some are diseased, his interpretation of some colors will be affected, and color blindness might result.

Additive primaries

The colors *blue, green,* and *red* are called *additive primaries,* because when lights of these colors are combined together they form *white light.* This can be easily proved by taking three projectors and covering the lens of one with a *blue* filter, the second with a *green* filter, and the third with a *red* filter. Shining all three projectors onto a screen would show white light where the three colors overlap. Where blue and green overlap, a third color forms which is a combination of blue and green and which is called *cyan.* Where blue and red overlap, another new color forms which is a combination of blue and red, and this is called *magenta.* Where red and green overlap, the new color formed is called *yellow.* This principle of *additive mixture* is illustrated in figure 2.6.

The mixture of red and green light to form yellow is the most difficult concept for most people learning the theory of color to understand, because most peoples' experience with color has been with paints or crayons and not with light. Red and green pigments can never make yellow, but red and green light actually produce yellow light.

Subtractive primaries

These new colors—yellow, magenta, and cyan—are called *subtractive primaries.* They are the colors that we deal with when we print color. When we subtract an additive primary color like red from white light, the color we have left is cyan, which is the additive mixture of blue and green light. Cyan, therefore, is the color that is left when red light is subtracted from white light; and when we print with a cyan ink, blue and green light are reflected to the eye wherever the cyan ink is printed.

When we subtract green light from white light, the spectral components left are red and blue, and the additive mixture of these we call *magenta.* Magenta, therefore, is the color that is left when green is subtracted from white light; and whenever we print with magenta ink, red and blue are reflected to the eye.

When we subtract blue light from white light, the spectral components left are red and green, and this mixture we call *yellow.* Yellow, therefore, is the color that is left when blue is subtracted from white light; and whenever yellow is printed, red and green light are reflected back to the eye.

Red, blue, and green are the colors of the filters used in color-separation photography. Cyan, magenta, and yellow are the colors of the printing inks with which we print color reproductions. Each printing or subtractive color represents two of the additive primaries of light that remain after one of the additive primaries is subtracted or absorbed.

Process-color printing

Most printing inks are *transparent;* that is, they allow light to pass through them to the paper. As the light passes through the ink, it is modified according to the characteristics of the ink. The paper then acts as a reflecting surface which reflects the light back through

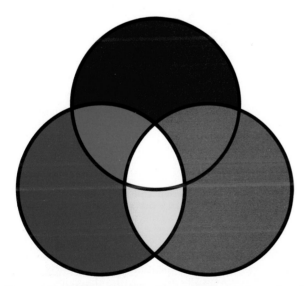

Figure 2.6: Additive mixture. The additive mixture of red, green, and blue lights, two at a time, in various proportions, produces all gradations of orange and yellow, purples such as magenta, and blue-greens such as cyan. A mixture of all three in the right proportions produces white light.

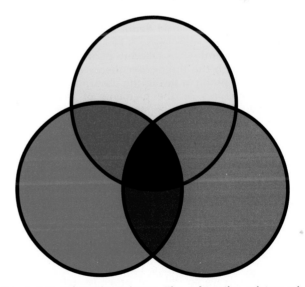

Figure 2.7: Subtractive mixture. The subtractive mixture of yellow, magenta, and cyan colorants, two at a time, in various proportions, produces all gradations of orange and reds, purples and blues, and greens. A mixture of all three in the right proportions produces black.

the ink to the eye. Each process-color ink *absorbs* one of the components of the light passing through and *transmits* the other two components to the paper so that they may be reflected back to the eye.

Inks that are not transparent—that is, *opaque inks*—do not have this property. They reflect light to the eye independently of the substrate. When two opaque inks are overlapped, only the top layer reflects light to the eye.

With transparent inks, however, light can go through both layers and produce a new color. If cyan and yellow are overlapped, for example, both the red and blue components are absorbed, leaving only green to be reflected back to the eye. The combination of all three process-color inks can absorb all three components of white light and produce black. This is known as *subtractive mixture*, which is illustrated in figure 2.7. (Combinations of colors may also be produced by tiny halftone dots of two colors placed adjacent to each other. This is an additive rather than a subtractive mixture.)

(Some of the above information on additive and subtractive color theory has been oversimplified in order to provide an introduction to the subject. "The Measurement and Specification of Color," page 21, presents this information more scientifically for use by the more serious student or practitioner.)

Three-color theory

The three-color theory of light described above is known as the Young-Helmholtz theory. It would work very well if ink pigments matched the theoretical subtractive primaries. If printing inks were ideal, they would produce colors as shown in figure 2.8. Because inks are not ideal—that is, they do not reflect and transmit the colors they should—the colors they produce are not pure, and considerable manipulation or correction must be done in color reproduction to create the appearance that printing inks reproduce the colors in the original copy.

The inadequacy of printing inks to reproduce the proper colors is shown in figure 2.9. As demonstrated in the illustration, the yellow inks are quite good, but the magentas and cyans are very poor. There is nothing wrong with the three-color theory of color reproduction; the problem lies in the absorption and transmission of colors by the pigments of the inks that are used. Fluorescent pigments are better in their spectral properties than conventional pigments, but they are not quite good enough, so they still require corrections. (Color reproduction and color correction are discussed in Section 9, *Graphic Arts Photography*.)

ANALYZING COLOR FOR COLOR REPRODUCTION

In studying inks for reproduction, it is common practice to utilize diagrams on which densitometric data is plotted. The Graphic Arts Technical Foundation has developed three simple diagrams—the Color Circle, Color Triangle, and Color Hexagon—for plotting data relative to color in order to determine the suitability of inks for color reproduction. These diagrams have applications only where inks and color reproduction are concerned; they are not to be confused with the color order systems discussed in "The

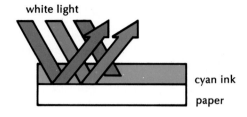

white light

cyan ink

paper

white light

magenta ink

paper

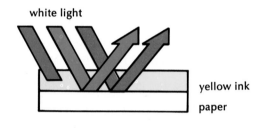

white light

yellow ink

paper

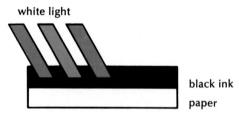

white light

black ink

paper

Figure 2.8: Ideal printing inks. In theory, cyan ink absorbs the red part of white light and transmits the blue and green parts to the paper so that they are reflected back to the eye, combining to produce the sensation of cyan. Magenta ink absorbs the green part of white light but transmits the red and blue parts to the paper so that they are reflected back to the eye, producing the sensation of magenta. Yellow ink absorbs the blue part of white light and transmits the red and green parts to the paper, and they are reflected to the eye, producing yellow. Black ink absorbs all three parts of white light, so that none are reflected to the eye.

Measurement and Specification of Color" (page 21). While not theoretically accurate, the diagrams are useful for analyzing the suitability of inks for printing.

The GATF Color Circle and the GATF Color Triangle are used to plot the same information—hue and grayness. An advantage of the triangle is that the mixture

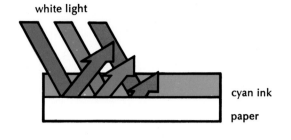

white light

cyan ink

paper

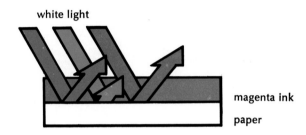

white light

magenta ink

paper

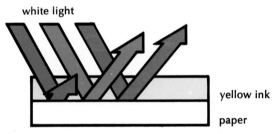

white light

yellow ink

paper

Figure 2.9: Actual printing inks. Because printing inks are not ideal, they do not behave exactly as described in figure 2.8. Represented here are the actual proportions of each part of white light reflected from white paper on which each of the process inks is printed. Cyan ink absorbs most but not all of the red part of white light, some of the green, and a bit of the blue. Magenta ink absorbs most of the green part of white light, some of the blue, and a little of the red. Yellow ink is closer to ideal but absorbs a little of the green part of white light.

of two colors falls on a straight line joining the two colors, whereas on the circle the lines are curved. The triangle has also been modified so that masking percentages for photography (see "Manual and Photographic Color Correction," page 353) can be read directly from the triangle. Masking percentages can also be derived from the circle, but a specific template must be used.

The Color Hexagon is used to plot hue and color strength. The description and use of all three diagrams is contained in the GATF Research Progress Bulletins Nos. 38, 53, and 81. These bulletins are available from the Graphic Arts Technical Foundation, 4615 Forbes Avenue, Pittsburgh, Pennsylvania 15213. (Additional

discussion of the diagrams will also be found in "The Measurement and Specification of Color.")

As an example of how the Color Circle can be used to analyze color reproduction, consider the following color matrix, which shows the optical density of each of the colors in a typical set of process inks. For each ink color, the matrix shows the amount of absorption of each of the three colors of light that make up white light. (The numbers in parentheses after the color of the filters correspond to the Wratten numbers of the filters used in the densitometer that is used to make the readings. Further discussion of this color matrix will be found in "Color Reproduction," page 346.)

Printed inks	Red filter (25)	Green filter (58)	Blue filter (47)
Yellow	0.01	0.06	0.95
Magenta	0.10	1.15	0.46
Cyan	1.20	0.50	0.20

To plot these colors on the Color Circle, the following formulas must be used:

$$\text{Hue error} = \frac{M - L}{H - L}$$

$$\text{Grayness} = \frac{L}{H}$$

where

H = high density reading
M = medium density reading
L = low density reading

for each color.

For the yellow ink, the lowest reading is 0.01, the middle reading is 0.06, and the highest is 0.95. The formulas would therefore read as follows:

$$\text{Hue error (yellow)} = \frac{0.06 - 0.01}{0.95 - 0.01} = \frac{0.05}{0.94} = .05 = 5\%$$

$$\text{Grayness (yellow)} = \frac{0.01}{0.95} = .01 = 1\%$$

The hue error is plotted on the circle opposite the color corresponding to the highest reading (blue) and toward the color with the lowest reading (red). Grayness is plotted as the distance in from the outer perimeter of the circle.

The same procedure is used for plotting all colors. The figures for the magenta and cyan in the sample color matrix would be as follows:

$$\text{Hue error (magenta)} = \frac{0.46 - 0.10}{1.15 - 0.10} = \frac{0.36}{1.05} = .34 = 34\%$$

$$\text{Grayness (magenta)} = \frac{0.10}{1.15} = .09 = 9\%$$

$$\text{Hue error (cyan)} = \frac{0.50 - 0.20}{1.20 - 0.20} = \frac{0.30}{1.00} = .30 = 30\%$$

$$\text{Grayness (cyan)} = \frac{0.20}{1.20} = .17 = 17\%$$

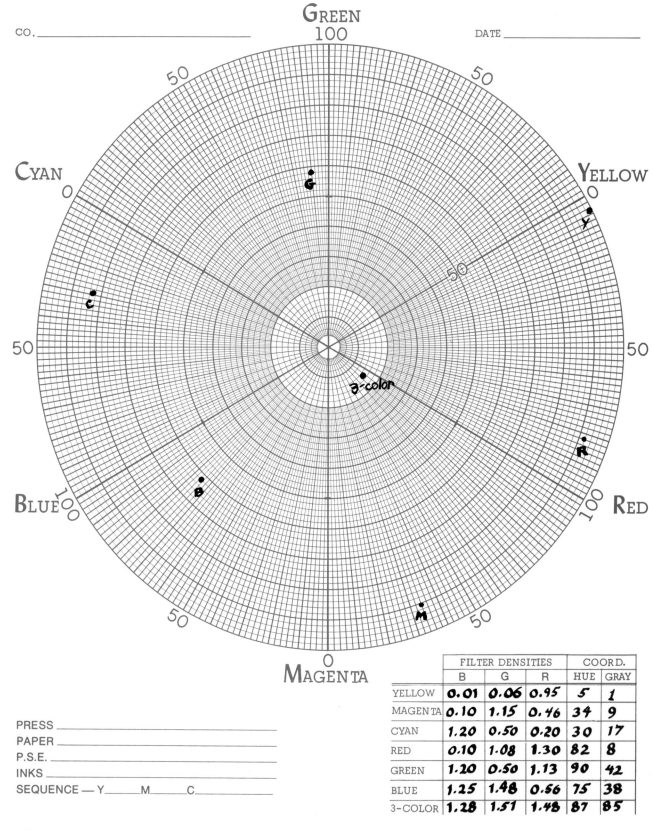

GATF COLOR CIRCLE
INK HUE AND PURITY CHART

CO. _____

DATE _____

GREEN
100

50   50

CYAN   YELLOW
0   0

G

Y

50

C

50   50

3-color

R

BLUE   RED
100   100

50   50

B

M

0
MAGENTA

| | FILTER DENSITIES | | | COORD. | |
	B	G	R	HUE	GRAY
YELLOW	0.01	0.06	0.95	5	1
MAGENTA	0.10	1.15	0.46	34	9
CYAN	1.20	0.50	0.20	30	17
RED	0.10	1.08	1.30	82	8
GREEN	1.20	0.50	1.13	90	42
BLUE	1.25	1.48	0.56	75	38
3-COLOR	1.28	1.51	1.48	87	85

PRESS _____

PAPER _____

P.S.E. _____

INKS _____

SEQUENCE — Y_____ M_____ C_____

20

Figure 2.10: Color Circle. Percent hue error of a yellow, magenta, or cyan ink is plotted on this circular chart as an angular displacement from the direction marked Y, M, or C, found by plotting opposite the color of the highest filter density reading and toward the color with the lowest. Hue error for the overprint colors red, green, and blue, and the three-color combination, may be plotted in the same manner. Percent grayness is plotted as the distance from the outer circle (0%) toward the center (100%). The two coordinates for hue error and grayness describe a single point representing each ink color. *Courtesy of Graphic Arts Technical Foundation.*

These three colors are plotted on the Color Circle in figure 2.10.

In color reproduction, the overprint colors are as important as, if not more important than, the actual printing colors, as most of the picture consists of mixtures of colors rather than pure colors. The rest of the color matrix, which includes the overprint colors, is as follows:

Printed inks	Red filter (25)	Green filter (58)	Blue filter (47)
Red	0.10	1.08	1.30
Green	1.20	0.50	1.13
Blue	1.25	1.48	0.56
3-color	1.28	1.51	1.48

For these values, the formulas would become:

$$\text{Hue error (red)} = \frac{0.98}{1.20} = 82\%$$

$$\text{Grayness (red)} = \frac{0.10}{1.30} = 8\%$$

$$\text{Hue error (green)} = \frac{0.63}{0.70} = 90\%$$

$$\text{Grayness (green)} = \frac{0.50}{1.20} = 42\%$$

$$\text{Hue error (blue)} = \frac{0.69}{0.92} = 75\%$$

$$\text{Grayness (blue)} = \frac{0.56}{1.48} = 38\%$$

$$\text{Hue error (3-color)} = \frac{0.20}{0.23} = 87\%$$

$$\text{Grayness (3-color)} = \frac{1.28}{1.51} = 85\%$$

A plot of these colors on the circle shows what is considered to be almost ideal reproduction with this set of inks. Regardless of what inks are used, the position of the overprints can be controlled by the pressman because he can control the amount of ink he runs and thus the hue of the overprint color. The stronger a cyan that is printed over a yellow, the closer the printed green will be toward cyan on the Color Circle, and vice versa.

For optimum color reproduction in printing, the strength of the yellow is determined by the blueness of the magenta. The bluer the magenta, the stronger the yellow should be run. Once the strength of the yellow has been set, the pressman runs the cyan so that the overprint, green, plots about 10% to the left of the green line on the circle. The magenta is then printed so that the red overprint is almost exactly opposite the cyan on the Color Circle. The blue overprint then plots about 25% to the right of the blue line. The actual printing inks determine the grayness of the overprint colors, but the pressman determines their hues by the strengths of the inks that he runs. As long as the overprints are correct and the grays are neutral, the reproduction will look good even if the printing colors are not ideal. Neutral grays can be achieved through the use of the black printer and a gray-balance chart available either from the Graphic Arts Technical Foundation or from Rochester Institute of Technology.

SPECIFYING COLORS

In addition to the properties of light and color described in this article, there are many other characteristics of color that need to be considered when specifying certain colors to produce a special color match or to make sure that a new lot of paper or ink matches the previous ones. These characteristics are described in the article that follows.

THE MEASUREMENT AND SPECIFICATION OF COLOR

C. S. McCamy, MACBETH DIVISION, KOLLMORGEN CORPORATION

A bibliography appears at the end of this article. Superscript numbers in the body of the text refer to the publications in this reference list.

Color vision evolved because it was useful in the struggle for survival, but civilized man has also become very discriminating in the use of color merely to satisfy his aesthetic sense. The demand for color, for any reason, has made color a valuable physical property. It is frequently as important as linear dimensions, area, volume, or mass. Just as these other physical properties are measured, we must measure color and express it in numbers. This permits accurate description and the ability to record color information and communicate it readily. The measurement of color is called *colorimetry*. This science involves both physics and psychology.[1, 2, 3]

COLOR SPACE

There are over ten million perceptibly different colors. Identifying and specifying colors in such a vast assortment is made possible by the fact that we perceive or can generate orderly relationships among colors. The normal human observer finds that surface colors may be light or dark, that some pairs of colors may be considered equally light, and that those that differ in lightness can be arranged in order from darkest to lightest. Furthermore, we can select a series from the darkest to the lightest, in which each appears to differ from its predecessor by an equal amount. One may interpolate real or imaginary samples until successive differences are as small as the eye can detect. By numbering the elements of the uniform series, a numerical scale of *lightness* can be established, and lightness may be considered a dimension in a *color space*.

The normal observer finds that colors may be ordered in another way, according to whether they appear blue, green, yellow, orange, red, purple, or something in between. Such a series of colors differs in *hue*. As numerous samples are interpolated in this series, we find that the series naturally constitutes a ring, from blue to purple and back to blue. A numerical scale of hue may be established, and hue may be considered another dimension in a color space.

Some colors, called *neutral* colors, are named black, gray, or white. They may be arranged on the scale of lightness, but have no hue. We may find or imagine a series of colors, all of the same hue and same lightness, gradually ranging from gray to a color having a pronounced hue, such as vivid red. We say such a series differs in *saturation*, the color of pronounced hue being considered the more saturated. Saturation may be considered a third dimension in a color space.

Experience has shown that the colors of all surfaces can be ordered in a *three-dimensional* space having the dimensions of lightness, hue, and saturation. Experience has also shown that normal observers cannot order all colors on the basis of less than three attributes. When we order light sources or self-luminous surfaces, we use a scale of *brightness* instead of lightness. All colors lie in a bounded region of three-dimensional color space called the *color solid*. A color order system based on the three appearance attributes —lightness, hue, and saturation—is called a *color-appearance system*. Such a system can provide a uniform sampling of the color solid.

THE MUNSELL SYSTEM

In 1905, A. H. Munsell proposed the use of a color-appearance system, which has come into very widespread use and is known as the *Munsell system*. He used the term *value* instead of *lightness*, and the term *chroma* instead of *saturation*. In the Munsell system, the hue circuit is divided into 10 hue segments of 10 steps each, giving 100 equal parts. The hues are designated red, yellow-red, yellow, green-yellow, green, blue-green, blue, purple-blue, purple, and red-purple. The hue symbols are R, YR, Y, GY, G, BG, B, PB, P, RP. The fifth or center step of each hue segment is often merely designated by the letter symbol, such as GY, but it may be designated 5GY. The other steps are given symbols from 1 to 10, for example 1GY to 10GY, for the GY segment. The value scale is divided into 10 visually equal parts ranging from 0 for black to 10 for white. The chroma scale is divided into equal parts, ranging from 0 for neutral colors to an upper limit that is not fixed but depends on lightness, hue, and the nature of the source. Standard color samples have been made with a chroma as high as 16.8.

Munsell also founded the Munsell Color Company to provide physical standards in the form of painted-paper "chips." This operation, now a part of the Macbeth Division of Kollmorgen Corporation, is to this day the principal supplier of such standards to colorists in business, science, and industry. Each standard is identified by a *Munsell notation* made up of three symbols indicating Munsell hue, Munsell value, and Munsell chroma. For a standard having a hue designated 5R, a value designated 4/, and a chroma designated 6, the Munsell notation is: 5R 4/6. Charts and displays of standards are generally arranged in a cylindrical coordinate system with the neutral series in a vertical line (black at the bottom and white at the top), colors of increasing chroma arranged from the neutral axis outward, and the various hues lying at various angles about the neutral axis. A physical embodiment of the system, called a *color tree*, is pictured in figure 2.11.

Samples of unknown color can be specified in the Munsell system by visual comparison to the Munsell chips, using visual interpolation, if necessary. Color tolerance sets provide samples of the extreme permis-

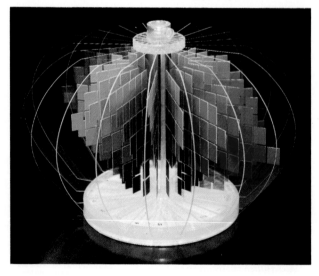

Figure 2.11: Munsell Color Tree. The Color Tree is a sampling of color space. The various hues radiate at different angles from the center. Colors increase in value (lightness) from bottom to top, and in chroma (saturation) from the center outward. *Courtesy of Munsell Color, Macbeth Division of Kollmorgen Corporation.*

sible deviation from a desired color for some particular application.

For such visual comparisons, the illumination must be standardized. Usually artificial daylight is used, because it is consistent all day, from day to day, and from one place to another. Viewing booths with such illumination are commercially available. The interior of the booth is neutral gray to standardize the visual field in which comparisons are made. Judgments are often made in simulated daylight and by incandescent lamplight to assure that the colors in question match under both illuminants.

Visual judgments are commonly used in industry because they are fast, cheap, and generally very sensitive to small differences. They are, however, subject to the kinds of errors and uncertainties usually associated with human judgments. There are individual differences in color vision, the angular conditions of viewing are often poorly controlled, and inspectors become fatigued. The inevitable small errors in making the color standards contribute to the overall error. For all these reasons, the need for completely objective methods of colorimetry was recognized over fifty years ago, and such methods were developed.

COLORIMETRY

To understand colorimetry, we need to review a few basic facts of physics and visual science. You may recall that white light is dispersed by a prism or grating, to display a spectrum. The various parts of the spectrum are made up of light of different wavelengths, ranging from about 380 nanometers at the violet end to about 760 nanometers at the red end (25.4 million nanometers equal 1 inch, and the symbol for the nanometer is *nm*). The general physical principle accounting for the colors of surfaces is that the surfaces selectively reflect light incident on them. Things that reflect light of longer wavelengths and absorb light of shorter ones look yellow, orange, or red, depending on the exact nature of the reflection. Two surfaces that have the same spectral reflectance characteristics have the same color. We might ask, "How different can the two spectral reflectances be and yet produce the same color appearance?" More precisely, if we were to break the spectrum up into a number of intervals and merely made the average reflectance of the two samples equal in each interval, the question would be, "What is the minimum number of intervals we could use?" Surprisingly, experience shows that only three such intervals are needed. The human visual system analyzes spectra in terms of three broad bands, without regard for finer detail. This is evidenced by the fact that red, green, and blue light can be mixed in various proportions to produce light of all hues, white, and a continuous range of saturation. This is known as the production of color by *additive mixture*. The lights are added to one another.

In 1853, Grassman published the facts he observed when lights are mixed. He found that lights of the same color produce identical effects in mixtures, regardless of their spectral composition. Two lights of the same color added to two other lights of the same color produce two lights the same color. Likewise, re-

moving two the same color from two the same color leaves two the same color. Increasing or decreasing the amount of light from two matched beams, by equal ratios, while holding the spectral distribution constant, does not alter the match. The luminance of a mixture is the sum of the individual luminances.

These laws of additive color mixture suggest that a color can be measured by finding the amounts of three given lights that must be added to match the color. A device designed to do this is called a *tristimulus colorimeter*, and we call the lights that are mixed *primaries*. If we had two colorimeters, having different primaries, Grassman's Laws tell us that if we know the tristimulus values on one colorimeter, for a given sample, we can compute the tristimulus values for the other colorimeter by simple linear transformation.

There is no set of primaries that can produce matches of all pure spectral colors. To match such highly saturated colors, we must add some of one of the primaries to the pure spectral light. When this is done, we say we have added a negative amount of that primary to the mixture of primaries.

The CIE system

To establish a basis for objective color measurement, the International Commission on Illumination (abbreviated CIE for Commission Internationale de l'Eclairage) adopted a series of recommendations in 1931.[4] Based on much experimental work on human observers viewing colored patches subtending 2° at the eye of the observer, red, green, and blue primaries or *color mixture functions* were adopted, and these were transformed to the set of spectral power distributions shown in figure 2.12. This transformation eliminated the need for adding negative amounts of primaries, permitting the whole spectrum to be matched with positive amounts. The transformation also made one of the functions, $\bar{y}$, match the relative spectral sensitivity of the average normal human eye adapted for daytime vision. Two samples requiring the same amount of this primary in the mixture would have the same lightness; thus, the amount of this primary would be a direct measure of lightness. The CIE selected two standard geometric arrangements of illumination and "viewing" for objective measurements: (1) normal illumination and collection of light reflected at all angles, and (2) illumination at 45° and normal collection. In addition, the CIE selected standard illuminants, Illuminant A representing light from a tungsten incandescent lamp, Illuminant B representing direct sunlight, and Illuminant C representing daylight, including the light from the sky. The method of producing such illumination was standardized, using an incandescent lamp and liquid filters.

On the basis of these conventions, it became possible to construct colorimeters, using sources and filters to produce the spectral power distribution of the standard illuminant and detectors with filters to produce the standard color mixture functions. Many such instruments have been made, but it has always been difficult to make filters having exactly the required spectral transmittances. As a result, these instruments have not been as accurate as we might like for many applications.

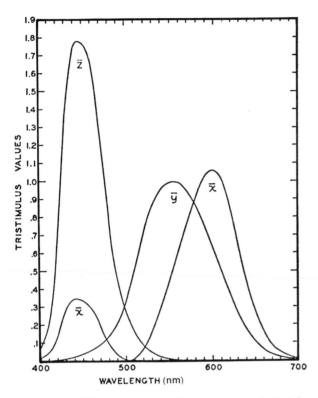

Figure 2.12: Tristimulus values. These values, adopted by the International Commission on Illumination, define a standard observer.

However, the existence of these international agreements permitted another approach that did not suffer from this inaccuracy. A spectrophotometer can be used to measure the percent of incident light reflected from the sample at each of many narrow wavelength bands in the spectrum. Now we can compute the tristimulus values X, Y, and Z that would have been obtained with an ideal filter colorimeter, based on the CIE system:

$$X = k\Sigma\ RS\bar{x}\ \Delta\lambda$$
$$Y = k\Sigma\ RS\bar{y}\ \Delta\lambda$$
$$Z = k\Sigma\ RS\bar{z}\ \Delta\lambda$$
$$k = 100/\Sigma\ S\bar{y}\ \Delta\lambda$$

where X, Y, and Z are the tristimulus values; R is the reflectance factor of the sample surface as a function of wavelength; $\bar{x}$, $\bar{y}$, and $\bar{z}$ are the standard CIE spectral tristimulus values (color mixture functions); $\Delta\lambda$ is the wavelength interval; and S is the spectral power distribution of the illuminant. Because of the way $\bar{y}$ was defined, Y is a measure of lightness. Having the tristimulus values X, Y, and Z, we can compute the relative amounts of these in the total:

$$x = \frac{X}{X + Y + Z}$$

$$y = \frac{Y}{X + Y + Z}$$

$$z = \frac{Z}{X + Y + Z}$$

This gives us x, y, and z, which we know as *chromaticity coordinates*. Since x + y + z = 1, we need state only x and y to identify the chromaticity. When x and y are plotted, we obtain what is known as the *chromaticity diagram*, shown in figure 2.13. In this figure, the arched curve is the plot of the chromaticity coordinates of the pure spectrum, usually called the *spectrum locus*. The wavelengths, ranging from 400 nm to 700 nm, are shown on the plot. Point C represents the chromaticity of Illuminant C. It also represents the chromaticity of light from the illuminant reflected in turn by a nonselective reflector or transmitted by a nonselective transmitting body. Since such nonselective objects would not alter the spectral quality of light incident on them, they would be perceived as white, gray, or black, depending on the percent of incident light they propagate. Point G is the chromaticity of a green sample. There may be many colors of this same chromaticity but of various lightnesses.

On this diagram, the chromaticities of light resulting from the mixture of lights represented by any two points will lie on the straight line joining the two points. The chromaticities of all possible mixtures of light from the extreme ends of the spectrum (400 nm and 700 nm) must lie along the straight line joining the ends. All possible chromaticities must lie in the region bounded by this line and the spectrum locus. The light represented by Point G could be produced by a mixture of white light (Illuminant C) and pure spectral light of wavelength 550 nm, found by extending a line through C and G to the spectrum locus. The wavelength found in this way is called the *dominant wavelength* of a color having a chromaticity plotting at G. If we take the ratio of the distance from C to G to the

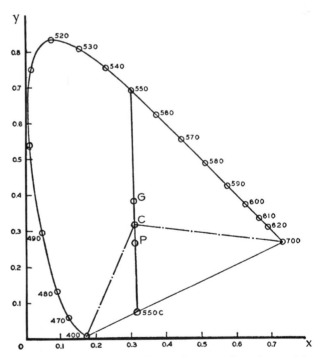

Figure 2.13: CIE Chromaticity Diagram. The Chromaticity Diagram provides a means of plotting the attributes of color other than lightness.

24

distance from C to the spectrum locus at 550 nm, we obtain the *colorimetric purity* of the color having the chromaticity G. Chromaticities may be specified by dominant wavelength and purity. Since there is no spectrum beyond the point P, representing a purple sample, we specify the *complementary wavelength*, 550C nm, in place of the dominant wavelength and indicate that it is complementary by adding the letter C. The complementary wavelength is the wavelength of spectral light we would add to the purple light P to obtain white light C. The purple colors in the triangular region at the bottom of the diagram are called *non-spectral colors*, because they cannot be produced by the mixture of white light and spectral light of any one wavelength.

Munsell Renotation

The three quantities, luminous reflectance, dominant wavelength, and purity, correspond roughly to the visual attributes of value, hue, and chroma, used in the Munsell system. When the standards in the original *Munsell Book of Color* were measured spectrophotometrically and the CIE tristimulus values were computed and plotted, some irregularities were observed. In 1937, the Optical Society of America formed the Subcommittee on the Spacing of the Munsell Colors, a subcommittee of the Colorimetry Committee. In the course of the study, three million color judgments were made. In the report, issued in 1943, the subcommittee recommended modifications of the Munsell color solid to achieve equispacing of the separate hue, value, and chroma scales and precise applicability. The new solid was defined in terms of the CIE system, using Illuminant C. Subsequent editions of the *Munsell Book of Color* were made to conform to this "renotation." Color specifications may be converted from the CIE system to the Munsell renotation system, or vice versa, using the charts in Wyszecki and Stiles.[2] The Munsell value Scale V is related to luminous reflectance Y by the equation:

$$Y = 1.2219V - 0.23111V^2 + 0.23951V^3 - 0.021009V^4 + 0.0008404V^5.$$

Color Names and the NBS Dictionary

The evolution of color names began out of necessity, flowered in literary embroidery, and exploded in the ethereal atmosphere of fashion. There is no end to it. There have been numerous dictionaries of color names, with little more than general agreement. The Inter-Society Color Council and the National Bureau of Standards, however, have provided a series of easily understood color names referring to subdivisions of the Munsell color solid. This system is known as "the ISCC–NBS method of designating colors." NBS has published correlations of 7,500 color names listed in the major color dictionaries with the ISCC–NBS names in their circular entitled *Color, Universal Language and Dictionary of Names*.[5] A supplement to this dictionary displays colored chips representing the centroid of the ISCC–NBS subdivisions of the Munsell solid, for which such chips are available. With the dictionary and the supplement, you can interrelate color names, Munsell notations, and actual physical samples approximating given colors. Widespread use of the dictionary could greatly reduce the general confusion attending color names.

COLOR IN PHOTOGRAPHY AND PRINTING

The colors of most things we make, as well as many naturally occurring things, are attributable to dyes and pigments, which are chemicals that selectively absorb light. In color photography and printing, it is desirable to produce the widest gamut of colors with the smallest number of colorants. It has been known since the time of the ancient Greeks that all hues can be produced from three suitably chosen colorants. The fact that a satisfactory gamut can be achieved with only three colorants is demonstrated in the color photographs that are so much a part of our way of life. The colors of the three colorants are called *primary colors*. Good colors can be obtained by printing with three colored inks, but dark colors are much improved by the additional use of a black ink.

Photography and printing utilize essentially the same three primary colors. Photographers in general and scientists who deal in the theory of printing call these colors *yellow*, *magenta*, and *cyan*. Magenta is a purplish-red color named for a dye of that color. The dye was so called because it was first synthesized about the time of a decisive battle at the town of Magenta, in Italy. *Cyan* is an ancient Greek name for bluish-green.

A century ago, it was generally believed that a painter could obtain the greatest gamut of colors by the use of yellow, red, and blue. These were the colors used for the first three-color printing, but, around 1900, as printers gained experience and the theory was explored, the red was shifted toward blue and the blue was shifted toward green. However, to this day, printers commonly call the primary colors "yellow," "red," and "blue," sometimes indicating their knowledge that "red" and "blue" are not really right by the use of the modifier *process*, as in "process blue" and "process red." Unfortunately, few art teachers have any experience with or knowledge of the technicalities of photography and printing, so they go on parroting the long-abandoned theory of yellow, red, and blue primaries. That misinformation has to be "unlearned" before the theory of color printing can be understood.

The human visual system detects the relative amounts of light in three ranges of wavelengths, each covering about a third of the light spectrum. The light of short wavelengths is blue, that of middle wavelengths is green, and that of long wavelengths is red. Light of these three colors can be added in various proportions to produce a wide gamut of colors; thus red, green, and blue are called *additive primaries*. Red and green light combine to produce the range of hues from red through orange, yellow, yellowish-green, and green, depending on the proportions in the mixture. Blue and green light combine to produce the various bluish-green hues, while red and blue produce the purples. All three, in the right proportions, produce the sensation of white and, of course, the absence of all three produces the sensation of black. Additive mixtures may be thought of as starting with no light (black) and adding various proportions of red, green, and blue light to produce all available brightnesses, saturations, and hues. The principle of additive mixture of red, green, and blue light is illustrated in "Color and Light," figure 2.6, page 17.

Photographic and ink-printing systems are called *subtractive* processes because they start with white paper and subtract light, by the use of absorbing dyes or inks in various proportions. A large amount of all of the primaries produces black. The principle of subtractive mixture of yellow, magenta, and cyan is illustrated in "Color and Light," figure 2.7, page 17. (Full printings of all three primary inks usually do not produce a satisfactory deep black, and black ink is cheaper than the primary inks, so black ink is usually used on dark colors.) The three subtractive primaries are related to the three additive primaries in a very simple way: yellow ink absorbs blue light, magenta ink absorbs green light, and cyan ink absorbs red light. Subtractive systems control the light in three bands of the spectrum just as additive systems do.

Color measurement in photography and printing

A given photographic or printing process employs a particular set of three colorants. For this reason, the measurement of color can be much simpler than it is in general colorimetry, where any kind of spectral absorption might be encountered. The aim of the measurement is merely to find the amounts of the three colorants used. This is done by measuring the amount of red, green, and blue light reflected from a printed area, relative to the amount reflected by a white surface.

The instrumentation differs from colorimeters for general-purpose measurements in several regards. First, it is desirable to establish a scale of values that increases with the amount of colorant and evaluates the amount as the eye would. These demands are met by the use of instruments that indicate *optical density* instead of reflectance. Optical density, or simply *density*, is the common logarithm of the ratio of the amount of light reflected by a white surface to the amount reflected by the printed area in question ($D = \log_{10} R_w / R_p$). The darker the ink deposit, the higher the density; and a series of steps of equal increases in density appears fairly uniform to the eye. Instruments that measure density are called *densitometers*. A second way in which densitometers differ from colorimeters is that densitometers are designed to measure anywhere on large sheets. The measuring probe is made movable, so it can be placed on the sample rather than having to place the sample on the instrument, as is usual in colorimetry. Thirdly, the printer is interested in color reproduction on specific areas of pictures and other designs, so the sampling area is usually quite small, one-fourth inch in diameter or less.

The densitometer has a light source to illuminate the sample and a photoelectric receiver to measure reflected light. It is made to measure in the red, green, or blue region of the spectrum by the use of colored filters, usually placed in the receiver. Each of three filters is designed to have its maximum transmission in that part of the spectrum where the particular colored dye or ink has its maximum absorption. Thus, the red filter is used to measure the cyan deposit, the green filter the magenta, and the blue filter the yellow.

The values measured depend on the geometric arrangement of the illuminator and receiver with respect to the sample. This geometry is standardized by the American National Standards Institute. The light is usually directed normally to (straight at) the sample surface, and the receiver usually collects the light reflected at 45° to the sample. The measured values depend on the sensitivity of the receiver in various parts of the spectrum. This sensitivity depends on the photodetector and the kinds of filters used. These spectral factors have not been nationally standardized, but instrument manufacturers follow fairly uniform practice. Measured values also depend on the calibration standards employed. The American National Standards Committee on Densitometry considers barium sulfate to be the best basic standard, but recommends the use of more permanent materials as routine working standards. The working standards are calibrated with respect to pressed barium sulfate.

Graphic representation of color in printing

If points representing colors can be plotted on a graph of some kind, relationships and changes can often be more readily evaluated and a complicated mass of numerical data can be presented or stored in simplified form. Some of the corrections required to achieve good color reproduction can be computed, by graphic methods, from plots of measured values.

For a given set of three primary inks, there is some ratio of densities that produces a neutral color, which may be white when all three densities are near zero, gray for intermediate densities, and near black for high densities. The neutral appearance is associated with nearly, but not necessarily exactly, equal densities as a result of the interaction between the spectral nature of the inks, the filters used in the densitometer, the spectral nature of the rest of the densitometer, the illumination for viewing, and the human visual process.

If red, green, and blue densities of a solid printing of cyan ink are measured, we find a high red density, as we might expect, since cyan ink is chosen to absorb red light. However, because the ink does not satisfy the "printer's dream," it will have some "unwanted absorption" in the green and blue regions of the spectrum. (This is discussed in greater detail in "Color Reproduction," page 346.) The red, green, and blue densities might be 1.20, 0.40, and 0.20. Since approximately equal red, green, and blue densities represent gray, we may say that this ink has an amount of gray represented by densities of 0.20, 0.20, and 0.20. We may say that the grayness g is represented by the ratio

Figure 2.14: Color Triangle. Percent hue error and percent grayness of a yellow, magenta, or cyan ink are plotted on this triangular chart in much the same way as they are on the circular chart, shown in figure 2.10. Hue error is plotted opposite the color representing the highest filter density reading and toward the lowest; grayness is plotted from the outer perimeter toward the center. This chart generally indicates the characteristics of the masks required for color correction. *Courtesy of Graphic Arts Technical Foundation.*

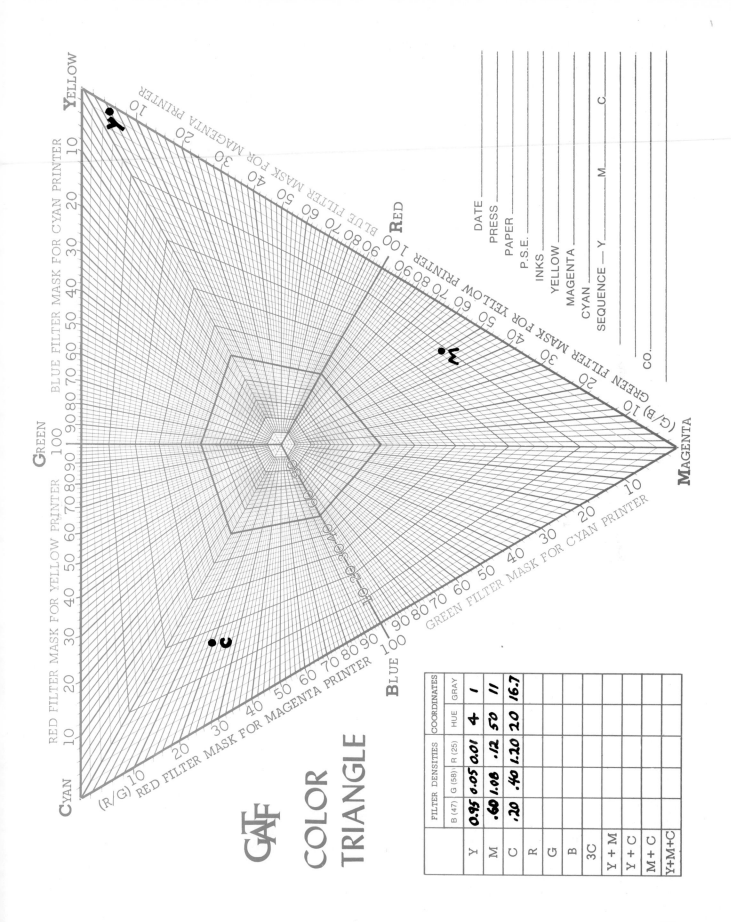

GAF
COLOR
TRIANGLE

	FILTER DENSITIES			COORDINATES	
	B (47)	G (58)	R (25)	HUE	GRAY
Y	0.95	0.05	0.01	4	1
M	.60	1.08	.12	50	11
C	.20	.40	1.20	20	16.7
R					
G					
B					
3C					
Y + M					
Y + C					
M + C					
Y+M+C					

DATE
PRESS
PAPER
P.S.E.
INKS
YELLOW
MAGENTA
CYAN
SEQUENCE — Y ___ M ___ C ___
CO.

GATF COLOR HEXAGON
INK HUE AND SATURATION CHART

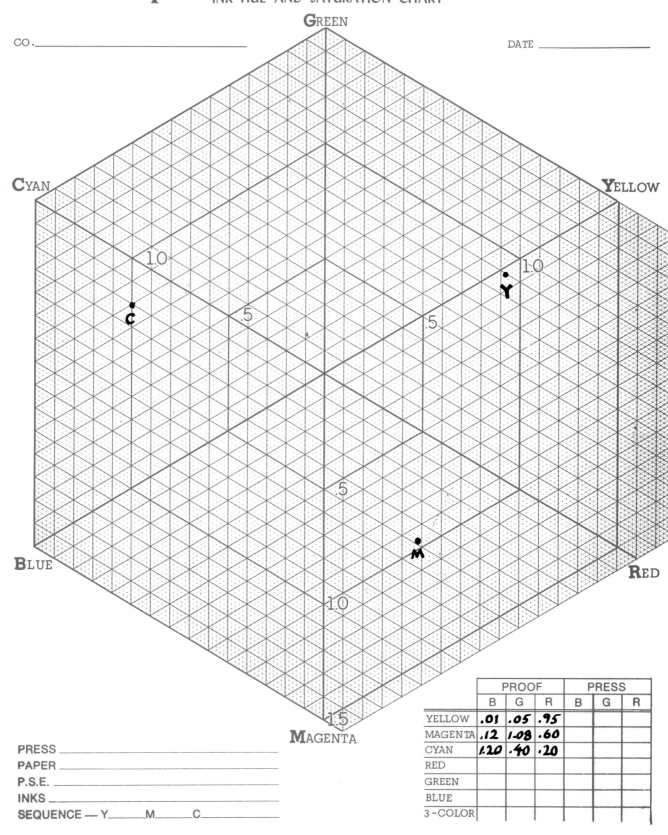

GREEN

CO. _____

DATE _____

CYAN

YELLOW

1.0

1.0

.5

.5

.5

BLUE

RED

10

MAGENTA

15

PRESS _____

PAPER _____

P.S.E. _____

INKS _____

SEQUENCE — Y_____ M_____ C_____

	PROOF			PRESS		
	B	G	R	B	G	R
YELLOW	.01	.05	.95			
MAGENTA	.12	1.08	.60			
CYAN	1.20	.40	.20			
RED						
GREEN						
BLUE						
3-COLOR						

of this lowest density L to the highest density H. We convert this ratio to percent grayness P_g by multiplying by 100:

$$P_g = 100 \; (L/H).$$

Using the values cited in the example above, we find

$$P_g = 100 \; (0.20/1.20) = 16.7.$$

This figure represents a grayness of 16.7%.

If we subtract the lowest density L from each of the densities, we remove the neutral gray component. The lowest density then becomes zero. The remainder of the middle density implies a hue error, because it describes unwanted absorption in a region of the spectrum other than the principal region represented by the highest density. The hue error h is represented by the ratio of the remaining middle density to the remainder of the high density. We convert this ratio to a percent hue error P_h by multiplying by 100:

$$P_h = 100 \left(\frac{M - L}{H - L} \right).$$

For the example cited above,

$$P_h = 100 \left(\frac{0.40 - 0.20}{1.20 - 0.20} \right) = 20.$$

The ideal cyan ink would have zero densities for both the green and blue regions; this would mean complete reflection of light in those regions. The higher of these two amounts of reflection (lower density) is in the blue region, so the hue error is toward the blue. Cyan with a 20% hue error toward blue may be annotated as follows: C20%B.

Preucil proposed the use of percent hue error and percent grayness and plotted them on a circular diagram, as discussed in "Color and Light" and illustrated on page 20. It must always be kept in mind that this representation of values derived from measured densities is not a true representation of color. It is not necessarily correlated with visual observations. It is used because it provides guidance in the general nature of corrections needed for good color printing.

Preucil proposed another approach, resembling the CIE computation of chromaticity coordinates, but based on density measurements instead of reflectance factors. Given red, green, and blue densities, R, G, and B, he computed cyan and magenta parameters c and m:

$$c = \frac{R}{R + G + B}$$

$$m = \frac{G}{R + G + B}$$

These values may be plotted on a triangular graph. The triangular chart has also been adapted to plotting hue error and grayness. (See figure 2.14.) Blank charts of this kind may be obtained from the Graphic Arts Technical Foundation, in Pittsburgh.

Another type of plot is the hexagonal type, developed in the field of color photography. (See figure 2.15.) A color is plotted by starting at the center, moving an amount R in the cyan direction, G in the magenta direction, and then B in the yellow direction. The same point is plotted regardless of the order in which the moves are made. The same point can be reached by plotting the two amounts remaining when the lowest density is subtracted from each density. Preucil has recommended this chart for detecting changes in hue of two-color overprints. Blank charts may be obtained from GATF.

COLOR ORDER SYSTEMS

A color order system based on the three appearance attributes, lightness, hue, and saturation, is called a *color-appearance system.* A color order system may be established by considering the three CIE tristimulus values, or other quantities derived from them, as the dimensions of a color space, and varying the tristimulus values in a systematic way. Such a color order system is called a *color-mixture system,* because it is based on a systematic variation of the additive mixture of colored light.

The colors exhibited by colored photographs are produced by the presence in the image of various amounts of three dyes. Painters obtain a wide gamut of colors by mixing a few well chosen pigments. A color order system based on the systematic variation of the amounts of colorants in the mixture is called a *colorant-mixture system.*

In the usual ink-printing process, various colors are produced by overprinting yellow, magenta, cyan, and black inks on white paper, with halftone plates having varying percentages of dot area, depending on the colors to be printed. A selected microscopic area of such a printed sheet may be the unprinted white of the paper; or it may be printed with a single impression of yellow, magenta, cyan, or black ink; or it may be overprinted with any combination of these inks. Where the dots do not overlap, the colors that appear to the unaided eye depend on the relative areas of the various colored dots, and may be predicted on the basis of the rather simple laws of additive color mixture. White light and light of essentially three other colors are simply mixed in various proportions, the black areas being considered nonreflective. However, when the halftone dots overlap, the effect is that of inks combined in approximately equal proportions. That is, the combination behaves as a colorant mixture, obeying the laws of subtractive color mixture. Thus, a color order system based on a systematic variation of halftone dot percentage is not any of the types defined above. We may call this type of color order system a *halftone-mixture system.*

Color-appearance systems

In 1905, A. H. Munsell proposed the use of a color-appearance system which has come into very widespread use and is known as the Munsell system. This system was described earlier.

The DIN-Color System is the system adopted by the Deutsche Industrie Norm, the national standards institution of West Germany. The color solid is described in terms of hue, saturation, and relative degree of darkness, which is a logarithmic function of relative lightness (DIN-Farbton, DIN-Sättigung, and DIN-Dunkelstufe). Colors of the same DIN-Farbton have the same CIE dominant wavelength, the hue circuit being divided into 24 perceptually equal steps. DIN-Sättigung is correlated with CIE saturation or colorimetric purity, independently of DIN-Dunkelstufe. DIN-Dunkelstufe is a logarithmic function of luminous reflectance relative to the luminous reflectance of the optimal color having the same CIE chromaticity as the sample. Physical embodiments have been made in the form of painted chips, each identified by the DIN notation (F:S:D:), the CIE coordinates, dominant or complementary wavelength, colorimetric purity, Munsell notation, and Ostwald notation.

Color-mixture systems

The best known examples of color-mixture systems are *Color Standards and Color Nomenclature*, by Robert Ridgway (A. Hoen and Co., 1912), the Ostwald system, and the *Color Harmony Manual* (Color Standards Dept., Container Corporation of America).

Ridgway's book has long been out of print but is still available in a number of libraries. About 1,000 named samples are given. These names have been widely used to specify colors of rocks, soils, plants, flowers, insects, and birds.

The Ostwald system is represented by 30 triangular arrays of chips, one for each of 30 hues. The neutral series is arranged vertically, forming one side of a triangle, and a saturated color, the *full color,* lies at the opposite vertex. The graded series between the full color and white is called the *light clear series,* and the series between full color and black is the *dark clear series.* Other series are arrayed parallel to the light and dark clear series so that those that fall in a vertical line have the same saturation, but vary only in reflectance. Such a vertical series is called a *shadow series* and is said to lie along an *isochrome* of the space. Colors are described in terms of hue, white content, and black content. The system is widely used in Europe.

The *Color Harmony Manual* has 943 colored chips made of clear plastic painted on one side, so they are glossy on one side and matte on the other. The ⅞-inch hexagonal chips are displayed according to hue, as measured by dominant wavelength in the CIE System, and identified by Ostwald notation. The Ostwald notation specifies a color only in the sense that it identifies one of the samples in this particular collection. The scale of lightness (V) is based on Weber's law; that is, the steps are related to reflectance by a logarithmic function. The ends of the scale, $V = 0$ and $V = 10$, correspond not to ideal black and white, but to black and white that may be produced by good pigments. The light and dark clear series are not those that would be obtained by pure color mixture, but were adjusted to obtain more uniform appearance. (Thus, this system is not a pure example of the color-mixture type.) The *Color Harmony Manual* is, as its name indicates, designed primarily as an aid to the selection of

Figure 2.16: Munsell-Foss Color Order System. This four-color reproduction displaying the colors obtained in a printing process is produced from color separations provided by the Graphic Arts Technical Foundation. *Courtesy of GATF.*

harmonious color combinations. It serves this purpose very well.

Colorant-mixture systems

Among the best known colorant-mixture systems are the *Nu-Hue Custom Color System* and the *Nu-Hue Color Coordinator*, of the Martin-Senour Company. The Custom Color System is based on 6 chromatic paints, one near-black, and white. There are 54 hues and 9 levels of admixture of near-black, white, or combinations of them, to produce 1,000 different colors. For each color, the amounts of the 8 basic paints are known. This system was very influential in promoting the acceptance of prescription mixing of paint at the point of sale. The Color Coordinator employs 10 highly saturated toners, 5 moderately saturated toners, a grayish-brown one, and white, to make 497 chips. Equal parts of pairs of toners are mixed with various amounts of white. This system exhibits the way the toners behave in mixture and thereby facilitates accurate interpolation.

The *Plochere Color System*, of Gladys and Gustave Plochere, has 1,248 colors identified by name and serial number. For each of 26 hues, there are 5 *shades* made by adding graded amounts of base until a near-black is reached, while maintaining constant hue. Seven *tints* of each of these colors are made by adding graded amounts of white paint.

The *Colorizer*, of Colorizer Associates, uses 12 chromatic base paints and equal mixtures of them chosen in a systematic way, along with 4 less saturated colors, white, and gray to produce 1,322 chips. These systems are all useful to the interior decorator, architect, or homeowner who wants to choose from a wide gamut of readily available paints, and to the paint dealer who mixes the paints.

There are color systems which are in widespread use in the graphic arts, although they are not easily classified as color order systems. They most closely resemble colorant-mixture systems. These systems are typified by the Pantone Matching System of Pantone, Inc. (Moonachie, New Jersey). This company provides 564 colored samples, each of which bears a serial number. The color specified by that number can be obtained with proprietary inks, colored papers, colored overlay film, or marking pens. The artists' materials are generally used for preliminary work, and the inks are used for printing. An ink of prescribed color is obtained by mixing specified amounts of ten basic inks. Pantone licenses ink manufacturers to use its name on inks and monitors the colors produced. This company also provides physical standards for control of the printing of corporate and packaging colors, viewing booths for judging colored samples under controlled conditions, a four-color reflection densitometer designed for the measurement of solid colors produced by printing, and a compact proofing press. The *Pantone 4-Color Process Guide* is a chart of 15,000 colors created with combinations of screen-tint values of the four Pantone Balanced Process Colors on coated and uncoated paper. The Pantone Color Data System provides equipment and computer services for precise measurement of color at the printing plant, rapid transmission of color data, remote computation of the formula for an ink to match the color submitted, and direct transmission of the formula to the plant. A similar ink system, including numbered color catalog, ink formulary, and proprietary inks, is offered by Metricolor Ink Systems. (The Pantone and Metricolor systems are discussed more fully in "Color Matching," page 508.)

Halftone-mixture systems

Three-color halftone printing naturally suggests the production of color charts by selecting a series of dot-area percentages, covering the range from 0 to 100 percent, and printing all combinations of the three inks with all combinations of percentages of dot area.

The *Hickethier Color System* (Druckerei H. Osterwald, Hannover) is an illustration. A 10-step dot scale was adopted, resulting in 1,000 colors, which are displayed 100 to a page. The same 100 printings of combinations of magenta and cyan inks appear on each page, but succeeding pages have increasing amounts of yellow.

A Dictionary of Color, by A. Maerz and M. Rea Paul (McGraw-Hill Book Co.) has 7,056 colors printed from 8 chromatic pigments and 7 grays. Each chart has 6 or 12 rows and 6 or 12 columns, with a progression of hues from the upper-right corner to the lower-left corner. Samples along lines through the upper-left corner are of approximately constant hue. Succeeding charts are also printed with gray, with a different sheet for each of the 7 levels. The daylight luminous reflectances of the gray base inks printed on stock are .74, .67, .48, .38, .28, .20, and .10. An alphabetical list of about 4,000 color names is keyed to the charts, and the names are given on the charts. There are so many colors in this collection that it is often unnecessary to interpolate between them.

The *Villalobos Colour Atlas*, by C. Villalobos-Dominguez and Julio Villalobos, has even more samples—7,279, printed from 38 chromatic inks. The series from chromatic ink to white, chromatic ink to black, and black to white, are in two stages, the intermediate colors being obtained not by the halftone process but by mixing inks before they are used in the halftone process. The samples are displayed one hue to a sheet. Each color is identified by hue, "lightness value," and "degree of chromaticity." The large number of samples, excellent spacing, and careful quality control make the atlas an excellent reference. The principal drawback is the small size of the samples. They are 10 mm square, with a 4-mm hole cut out to facilitate comparison with an underlying surface.

The Munsell-Foss Color Order System is unlike other halftone-mixture systems. It is not a set of colored samples to be bought and used for comparison, but is a set of screened separation negatives or positives used to make plates to be printed with a given four-color process to produce samples characteristic of that process.[6] An illustration of the four-color reproduction is shown in figure 2.16. The charts are arranged to bring similar saturated colors together. The Hickethier charts, mentioned earlier, may be regarded as simple slices through the cubic color solid in a three-dimensional space, where the dimensions are content of yellow, magenta, and cyan. Such a cube would have corners of white, yellow, magenta, cyan, blue, green, red, and black. The Munsell-Foss charts may be thought of as groups of cubic elements taken from such a cubic color solid, one layer at a time. Each group is made up of half of one face of the cube and half of an adjoining face. One group, for example, may be mapped on the cube by straight lines passing from white to blue, to black, to cyan, and back to white. Those not accustomed to thinking in the geometry of color space might better regard the charts as systematic displays of the printing obtained with various amounts of yellow, magenta, and cyan inks. Nine tone levels are used. To accommodate the black printer, each chromatic square is divided into four parts by diagonal lines, corner to corner, and each part is overprinted by black. Since nine levels are used (0 to 8), two whole charts are required, Chart 1 covering the black range 0 to 3, and Chart 2 the range 4 to 7. An attendant gray scale includes the eighth black level, full black. Each area is identified by a four-digit number. The notation 4281, for example, means the fourth level of yellow, second of magenta, eighth of cyan, and first of black. The tone levels, in terms of dot percentage, are approximately 0, 5, 13, 22, 35, 51, 72, 85, and 100. These were selected to give approximately equal visual increments between the colors of adjacent samples. The GATF Gray Balance Chart and the GATF Color Reproduction Guide are included also. These include tone scales on 10% intervals of the three primaries, paired combinations, and three-color; a chart of various combinations of yellow and magenta, from 10% to 30%, all with 30% cyan; and a chart of various combinations of yellow and magenta, from 35% to 75%, all with 75% cyan. This color order system was designed by Carl E. Foss, who also designed the Nu-Hue systems mentioned above. The chart is the property of Koll-morgen Corporation, but the color-separation negatives and positives are distributed by the Graphic Arts Technical Foundation.

The color-appearance systems described were attempts to sample color space in such a way that successive steps on various scales appear uniform. Euclidean geometry provides a method of sampling a three-dimensional space very uniformly: when uniform spheres are closely packed, the centers are equidistant from the nearest other centers. For many years, colorists attempted to find color samples bearing the same visual relationships as the geometric relationships in such an array, but the human visual system simply would not conform. Visual space is non-Euclidean! However, through the efforts of a committee of the Optical Society of America, an approximation to such a color order system has been constructed.[7] It is fascinating to contemplate the many color charts resulting from slicing such an array in various planes.

VIEWING CONDITIONS

A color printing job passes or fails on the basis of visual judgments of the printed product. Such judgments are made by pressmen, artists, photographers, engravers, advertising agents, publishers, and those who purchase advertising space. Rarely, if ever, are all of these people in the same place at the same time. If they judge the product under different conditions, they may reach different conclusions. Costly and time-consuming conflicts can arise. These problems are avoided by the use of standardized viewing conditions for comparing the original art with the printed reproduction. Standard conditions are specified in "American National Standard Viewing Conditions for the Appraisal

Figure 2.17: Transparency viewer. The projection viewer permits the examination of small transparencies and comparison of transparencies with reproductions under proper viewing conditions. *Courtesy of Macbeth Division of Koll-morgen Corporation.*

of Color Quality and Color Uniformity in the Graphic Arts," ANSI Standard PH2.32–1972, and "American National Standard Projection Viewing Conditions for Comparing Small Transparencies with Reproductions," ANSI Standard PH2.45–1979 (both available from the American National Standards Institute, 1430 Broadway, New York, N.Y. 10018). The first standard deals with two separate kinds of problems: first, the appraisal of color quality and comparison of a photomechanical reproduction to the original art and, second, the appraisal of color uniformity by comparing press sheets with approved proofs. The transparencies covered by the first standard are limited to those from 4" x 5" to 11" x 14" in size. The second standard provides viewing conditions for small transparencies, such as the 2" x 2" slides resulting from 35mm photography.

For appraisal of color quality, reflection materials (art or reproduction) are illuminated with light having a color temperature of 5,000 kelvins and providing adequate amounts of power in all parts of the visible spectrum to provide good color rendition. The background area surrounding the samples to be viewed is painted a matte, neutral, gray with reflectance factor of about 60% (Munsell notation N8/). The specified light is not as blue as north sky light, nor as yellow as incandescent lamp light. It is a good representation of natural and artificial illumination normally used to view and appreciate colors.

Large transparencies are viewed on transparency illuminators, which provide light having a color temperature of 5,000 kelvins and adequate amounts of power throughout the spectrum to provide good color rendition. A neutral surround is specified.

Small transparencies are judged in special projection viewers (see figure 2.17), which present an enlarged view of the transparencies.

The appraisal of color uniformity of press sheets with respect to approved proofs poses a slightly different problem. It is important to detect small color shifts in the printing process before they become unacceptable. The use of illumination having a color temperature of 7,500 kelvins provides a higher proportion of light in the blue end of the spectrum, giving somewhat better visual discrimination of greens and warm colors such as yellow, orange, and red.

BIBLIOGRAPHY

1. Deane B. Judd and Gunter Wyszecki, *Color in Business, Science, and Industry*, John Wiley and Sons, New York. Second Ed. (1963).

2. Gunter Wyszecki and W. S. Stiles, *Color Science, Concepts and Methods, Quantitative Data and Formulas*, John Wiley and Sons, New York (1967).

3. Committee on Colorimetry, Optical Society of America, *The Science of Color*, Thomas Y. Crowell, New York (1953).

4. "Colorimetry, Official Recommendation of the International Commission on Illumination," Publication CIE No. 15 (E-1.3.1.) 1971, Bureau Central de la CIE, 4 Av. du Recteur Poincare, 75 Paris 16e, France.

5. *Color, Universal Language and Dictionary of Names*, U.S. Department of Commerce, National Bureau of Standards Special Publication 440 (1976). Obtainable from U.S. Government Printing Office, Washington, D.C.

6. GATF Research Progress Reports 67, 83, and 96, Graphic Arts Technical Foundation, Inc., 4615 Forbes Ave., Pittsburgh, Pa. 15213.

7. David L. MacAdam, "Uniform Color Scales," J. Opt. Soc. Am. *64*, 1691 (1974).

DESIGN   3

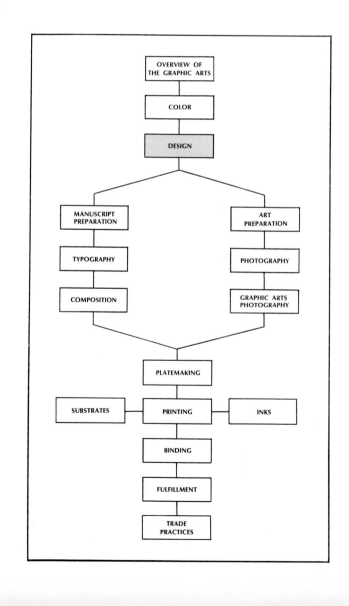

PRINCIPLES OF DESIGN

Jon Lopez, JON LOPEZ DESIGN, INC.

Design is the discipline of manipulating space, shape, color, and other graphic elements in their most abstract forms to achieve patterns in pure graphic terms. To these patterns, then, are added the elements of word and picture content to form the complete graphic presentation. While graphic designs will vary almost infinitely from one communication medium to another, from one kind of message to another, the basic principles and methods employed by the graphic designer to arrive at the final result remain fundamentally the same.

In the practice of graphic design there are four elements which are essential to the designer's execution of an assignment. The first is inspiration—in effect, priming the pump. Inspiration has many sources, not the least of which is the intellectual enjoyment derived from creating order out of chaos. But primarily it comes from the problem itself and the interest the subject can generate.

The second necessary element is a logical and clear statement of the problem: an intelligent assessment of what is to be said; a statement in brief terms about the content of the material and its intended audience.

The selection of form is third. This is a determination of the style and treatment of the content. How will the problem and its attendant solution be handled? Aesthetically and technically, what are the inherent and externally imposed restrictions of the job?

The last element is taste, the one upon which all of the others are dependent and the factor which determines how effectively they are applied. It reflects the emotion of the designer and his view of the world. It is a summation of his knowledge and experience.

ESTABLISHING AN ORDER

The design of any kind of printed product must be a reflection of a clear statement. It should be a distillate of the designer's thoughts, achieved by narrowing down the graphic alternatives so that the idea is expressed using the most essential means. Once a concept is established, there should be a unity between the idea and the execution of the idea. The design should be like a symbol: it should be easily recognizable and memorable in its simplicity.

What are some of the considerations that are an intrinsic part of the design process? A designer must establish and impose a fundamental geometry—an order —to the work. Initially, this is achieved by settling every major detail beforehand. This includes budget, size, number of colors, amount of text, number of paper folds and illustrations, the method of reproduction, and the concept to be represented. At the same time, the designer must maintain an overall view of the job and must not become immersed in one aspect of the design to the detriment of the entire piece.

The formal design process may begin with sketches and rough drawings, to be followed by a dummy if time permits. Once the formal design process has begun, the designer must keep in mind the relationship of all parts to the whole—to the total unit—constantly reconsidering the proportions and relationships of its parts. The selection of type, illustrations, stock, and inks should be made to reflect the tone and sensibility of the content.

FORMAL CONSIDERATIONS

Whether the designer selects a symmetrical or asymmetrical format, the elements must be organized with precise relationships and without ambiguity. Establishing a grid is the best way to insure continuity and uniformity throughout the piece (see "The Grid System," page 39). In this way, a system is imposed with regard to the text, captions, photographs, and all other elements. The correct placement of elements is as important as the concept to be presented. The application of a grid throughout a printed piece can be seen in figure 3.1, showing the cover and a spread from an annual report of the Museum of Modern Art. Note that the type block on the left-hand page and the photograph on the cover occupy areas of the same shape and size, leaving the same proportion of white space at the top and side of the page; this basic area is divided into two areas (columns) on text pages. The overall page area is defined by the full-page photograph on the right-hand page. The basic margins of the page, easily seen around this photograph, are maintained on the cover by the position of the title and on the text page by the folio and the caption at the left.

It is useful to consider the design and its elements as an abstract painting of tone, mass, and form. The designer should create order out of primary forms and simple contrasting elements—circle/square, big/little, thick/thin, light/dark—rather than thinking in terms of individual letters, words, and pictures. This approach is helpful in maintaining perspective. Consider again the double-page spread in figure 3.1. The dark photograph on the right should be thought of as a strong rectangle being offset or balanced on the left by two light rectangles and the white space above.

The relative position of elements to one another will create a rhythm because the surface upon which these elements are placed will be divided. Tensions will be formed by confrontations of parts with the page and with each other. There should be no alien elements.

As Jan Tschichold said, "Every shape exists only in relation to the space around it." The designer must consider the positive and negative areas formed by the elements. Shapes and letterforms can be positive or negative; a black letter can be seen either as a hole

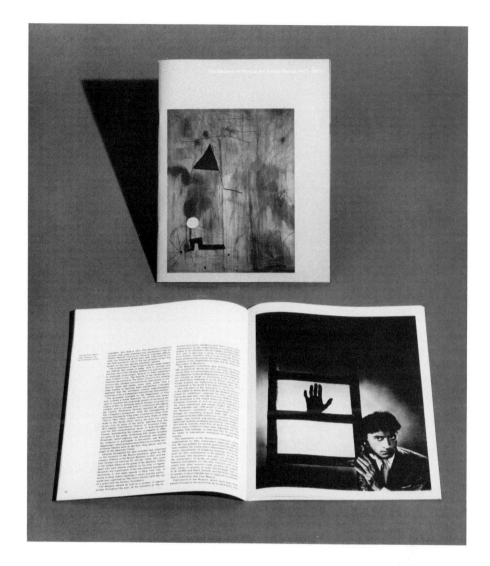

Figure 3.1: Application of a grid. Annual report cover and two-page spread illustrate the uniformity and harmony achieved in the report through use of a grid. Basic divisions of the page are established by the grid; these basic areas work as design units, balancing and contrasting with one another. *From* The Museum of Modern Art Annual Report 1972–1973, *New York, 1973.*

Figure 3.2 (below): Type "color." The "color," or over-all lightness or darkness, of a block of type depends upon such factors as the design of the type, the weight in which it is set (light, regular, bold), how much space there is between lines of type, and the size of the type area.

As Jan Tschichold said, "Every shape exists only in relation to the space around it." The designer must consider the positive and negative areas formed by the elements. Shapes and letterforms can be positive or negative; a black letter can be seen either as a hole in a page or as a solid sitting on the surface. Another consideration is the luminosity and radiating power of objects and how their power will enhance or subdue other

objects. Every block of type also has a "color" which interacts with other elements. Most text blocks form varying shades of gray; the color of the type is dependent on the typeface itself, the leading, and the column width. The designer must be aware of the overall color that all the elements produce and their relationship to the white space of the page.

in a page or as a solid sitting on the surface. Another consideration is the luminosity and radiating power of objects and how their power will enhance or subdue other objects. Every block of type also has a "color" which interacts with other elements. Most text blocks form varying shades of gray; the color of the type is dependent on the typeface itself, the leading, and the column width (see figure 3.2). The designer must be aware of the overall color that all the elements produce and their relationship to the white space of the page.

It is also important to consider the scale or relative size of the elements and their distances from each other. Imaginative scaling and positioning of elements will give interest and meaning to a group of elements and will avoid a static, boring layout (see figure 3.3). Static relationships among major elements can be avoided by significant contrasts in size, which can produce an illusion of three-dimensional space on a two-dimensional plane or can create a sense of movement.

Often, the least significant element will affect the structure of the entire design. An example of this is the length of captions placed in the margins of a book, as in figure 3.1. If these captions were longer, they would

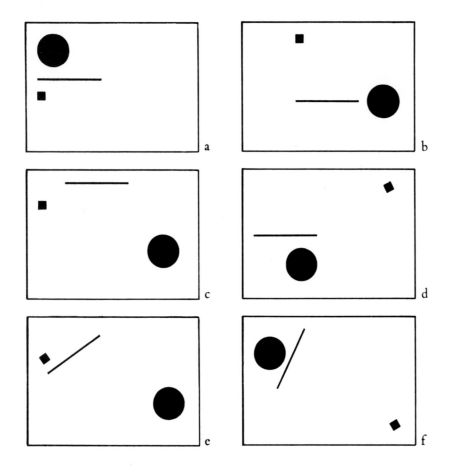

Figure 3.3: Scaling and positioning of elements on a page. The six abstract arrangements show that there are always several possibilities when there are several elements to arrange. The first (a) is a boring, visually meaningless arrangement, with all three elements lined up beneath one another. In the other examples, there is some tension between the elements. The second (b) shows a geometric horizontal-vertical arrangement. In the third (c), the line and the square follow the directions of the page outline, but their relationships to each other are not as geometrically fixed as in the second example. The line and circle in the fourth example (d) are more closely connected; the square is placed in opposition to the outline. In the fifth (e), square and line stand together in opposition to the outline; and in the last (f), they both strike out on different lines from each other and from the outline. The circle remains indifferent and peaceful. In none of the examples except the first is the placing accidental; each one shows a possible and significant arrangement. In every case, the placing of the elements, their relationship to one another, and their distances apart are intentional and not fortuitous. *From Asymmetric Typography, by Jan Tschichold, Van Nostrand Reinhold, New York, 1967.*

reduce the column width of the text, driving up the number of pages and possibly affecting the size and number of illustrations that could be used.

The key to successful design is harmony. All elements must be brought into agreement and must be considered in relation to each other and to the whole. Harmony is derived from coherence in design, from clarity of thought transferred by the designer to his work through a singleness of aim.

SYMBOLS: A POINT OF VIEW

In ancient Greece the swan was the symbol for the sun; in Great Britain it represents the royal family; in Australia it is the corporate symbol for a brewery. Every culture has its own vocabulary of symbols which is understood by the members of the culture. It is essential, then, in design, to communicate visually a selection of symbols that will be understood by the majority of one's audience.

Let us assume for the sake of discussion that a design problem is to portray a postage stamp. What are the representational alternatives? (Selection of a means of execution here is not of immediate concern—that is, whether it is to be a photograph or an illustration—but rather what is the most efficient way of saying "postage stamp" graphically to most people.) The stamp could be shown with its edge facing the viewer, but then it would look like a straight line. It could be viewed at

a three-quarter angle—meaningful, but not immediately recognizable. Viewed from the face front or the glue side, the perforations on all four sides are apparent, and the object's shape and what it represents are immediately evident.

Choosing the right point of view—the most symbolic point of view—for an object is essential if communication is to be successful. For many objects and forms, the profile is easiest to understand; for other forms, full-front or three-quarter or top view is the most appropriate. The silhouette or contour of the object, the mass of its form, and the negative space produced around it in its most characteristic pose will provide visual recognition.

ORIGINALITY

One of the most important elements in successful design is originality. The graphic designer must be able to form a bridge between heretofore unrelated objects which, when juxtaposed, form a new symbol to express a new idea. In advertising the motion picture "Jazz on a Summer's Day" (see figure 3.4), the problem was to transmit to the viewer the essence of the film's title. The use of the cornet bell as a cone for ice cream demonstrates the linking up of two disparate objects to communicate a message. Here again, the most recognizable point of view was used to represent each of these objects.

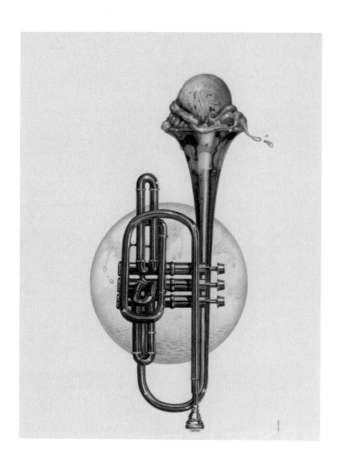

BIBLIOGRAPHY

Day, Kenneth, ed. *Book Typography, 1815–1965, in Europe and the United States of America.* Chicago: University of Chicago Press, 1966.

Hoffman, Arminn. *Graphic Design Manual.* New York: Van Nostrand Reinhold, 1965.

Müller-Brockman, Josef. *The Graphic Artist and His Design Problems.* New York: Hastings House, 1961.

————. *A History of Visual Communications.* New York: Hastings House, 1971.

Rand, Paul. *Thoughts on Design.* New York: Van Nostrand Reinhold, 1970.

Tschichold, Jan. *Asymmetric Typography.* New York, Van Nostrand Reinhold, 1967.

Figure 3.4: **Imaginative juxtaposition of elements. When combined in an unusual manner, the cornet and the ice cream take on a new meaning.** *Courtesy of New Yorker Films.*

THE GRID SYSTEM
Hans Kung, GRAPHIC DESIGNER

Layouts can be approached in numerous ways. The form does not always have to be based on a system; however, when the assignment becomes intricate and requires a uniform graphic appearance over many pages, the grid system can be a unique solution. A grid is set up which divides every page into the same standard units; all graphic elements, such as titles, body copy, captions, and illustrative material, are organized within the established format.

The grid system is not only a great help for the designer in arranging type and pictorial material, but it also facilitates the work of the typographer and printer. It can reduce errors and make production more economical when understood by all concerned.

The grid system has been widely acclaimed in the graphic design world. A great many magazines, newspapers, and other publications are based on a grid system. Some maintain the system rigidly, while others fall away from it because of limitations of the particular system. The success of the grid system depends upon proper preparation.

In developing a grid, it is essential to use the same unit of measurement throughout. Since type is a major element in most printed products and is measured in points, a grid should similarly be measured in points. When point and inch measurements are mixed, it is most likely that the grid will not work effectively. Once a grid has been developed, it should remain constant while the arrangement of the elements is varied.

The first step in the development of a grid is to think about its purpose. What elements have to be accommodated? How flexible should the grid be? How much copy and illustrative material will be used? What is the size of the text type, the headlines, the captions? How much of the surface will be occupied by the type area? How wide will the margins be?

When the basic questions have been answered, the page is broken up into vertical and horizontal divisions. Let us consider a page size of 8½″ x 11″ with a basic type size of 9 points with 1 point leading.

The vertical divisions, based on the type size, will be 10 points, measuring from base line to base line of the

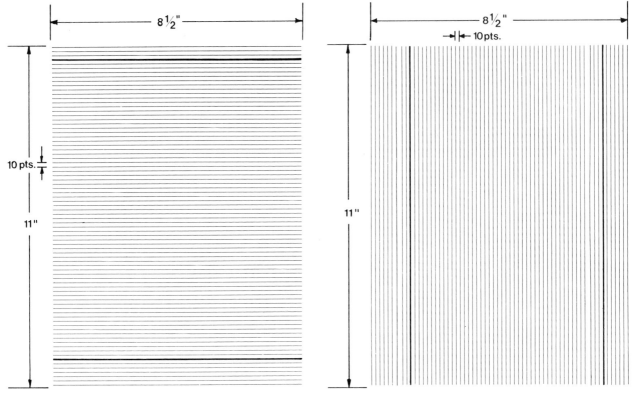

Figure 3.5: Vertical division of grid. Horizontal rules are spaced 10 points apart, giving 70 vertical units for the type page (indicated by heavy rules), with 3 units above and 6 units plus 2 extra points below for top and bottom margins.

Figure 3.6: Horizontal division of grid. Vertical rules divide page width into 46 units for type area, with 6 units at right and 9 units plus 2 points at left for margins.

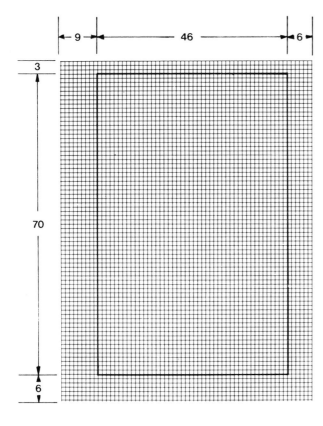

body copy. The surface is ruled with horizontal lines 10 points apart (see figure 3.5). The page depth is 11 inches, which equal 66 picas or 792 points, so it may be ruled with 79 lines separated by the basic unit of 10 points, with a remainder of 2 points. In the development of this grid, we have decided to leave 3 lines blank on top and 6 lines plus the remainder of 2 points on the bottom for margins, leaving 70 lines for the type area.

The horizontal divisions determine the width of the columns and the space between them. It is not necessary to use the same 10-point unit for the horizontal divisions: an 8-point or 12-point horizontal unit can be combined with a 10-point vertical unit, or any other combination, as long as the vertical division corresponds with the basic type size. Here, however, we will use the same 10-point unit. Since 8½ inches equal 51 picas or 612 points, we may rule 61 vertical lines, 10 points apart, with a remainder of 2 points (see figure 3.6). Blank space is allowed for the left and right side margins; in this case there are 6 lines left blank on the right and 9 lines plus the remainder of 2 points on the left side of the surface. This leaves 46 units of division for the type area. The entire type area is therefore 46 x 70 units (see figure 3.7).

Figure 3.7: Grid ruled horizontally and vertically. The type area, indicated by heavy rule, is 46 units by 70 units.

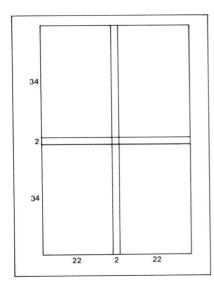

Figure 3.8: Two-column page division based on 46 x 70 grid. Page is divided into 2 columns of 22 units each and 2 major vertical divisions of 34 units each, with 2-unit spacing.

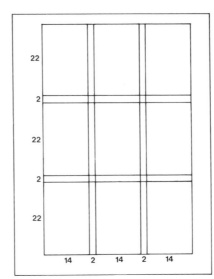

Figure 3.9: Three-column page division based on 46 x 70 grid. Page is divided into 3 columns of 14 units each and 3 vertical divisions of 22 units each, with 2-unit spacing.

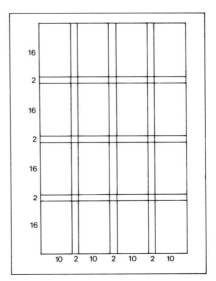

Figure 3.10: Four-column page division based on 46 x 70 grid. Page is divided into 4 columns of 10 units each and 4 vertical divisions of 16 units each, with 2-unit spacing.

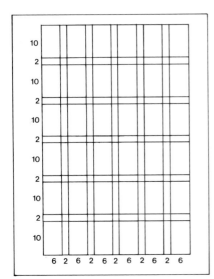

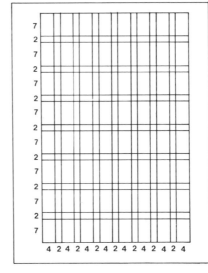

Figure 3.11 (far left): Six-column page division based on 46 x 70 grid. Page is divided into 6 columns of 6 units each and 6 vertical divisions of 10 units each, with 2-unit spacing.

Figure 3.12 (left): Eight-column page division based on 46 x 70 grid. Page is divided into 8 columns of 4 units each and 8 vertical divisions of 7 units each, with 2-unit spacing.

The 46-unit page width can now be divided into columns. With a constant 2 units for column spacing, there are several possibilities: 2 columns each 22 units wide, 3 columns each 14 units, 4 columns each 10 units, 6 columns each 6 units, and 8 columns each 4 units. Written as equations, these alternatives are easy to visualize:

$2 \times 22 + 2 = 46$
$3 \times 14 + 2 + 2 = 46$
$4 \times 10 + 2 + 2 + 2 = 46$
$6 \times 6 + 2 + 2 + 2 + 2 + 2 = 46$
$8 \times 4 + 2 + 2 + 2 + 2 + 2 + 2 + 2 = 46$

Based on the 70 vertical units of the page depth, the following large vertical divisions are possible: 2 divisions each 34 units, 3 divisions each 22 units, 4 divisions each 16 units, 6 divisions each 10 units, and 8 divisions each 7 units. The equations are:

$2 \times 34 + 2 = 70$
$3 \times 22 + 2 + 2 = 70$
$4 \times 16 + 2 + 2 + 2 = 70$
$6 \times 10 + 2 + 2 + 2 + 2 + 2 = 70$
$8 \times 7 + 2 + 2 + 2 + 2 + 2 + 2 + 2 = 70$

Possible combinations of these depth and width divisions are shown in figures 3.8 to 3.12. These illustrations show the flexibility of the grid.

Grids may be based on other such divisible numbers,

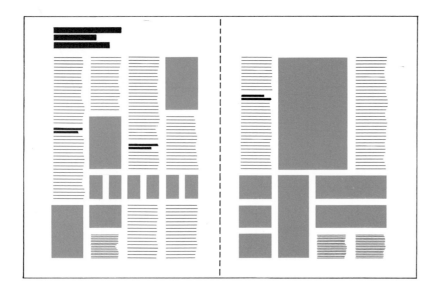

Figure 3.13: One of the many possible layout solutions. This layout, based on the grid in figure 3.12, shows a double-page spread with text, headlines and subheads, pictures, and captions.

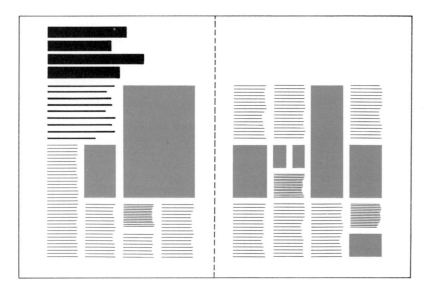

Figure 3.14: Another layout solution. Also based on the grid in figure 3.12, this layout uses a different size headline, two-column introduction, and wider margin on top.

such as 58 and 94, which work in the same way as 46 and 70 with 2-unit spaces between divisions. There are a great many other possibilities, if the constant spacing of 2 is changed to 1, 3, 4, or another number. For example, 59 and 71 are divisible numbers if just 1 unit of space is allowed between columns and vertical divisions. With 59, for example, the width may be divided into 2, 3, 4, or 6 columns, as follows:

$2 \times 29 + 1 = 59$
$3 \times 19 + 1 + 1 = 59$
$4 \times 14 + 1 + 1 + 1 = 59$
$6 \times 9 + 1 + 1 + 1 + 1 + 1 = 59$

Whatever grid is decided upon, it is up to the designer to use it effectively. Besides the overall type area, other elements must be considered. A 10-point unit measurement accommodates headlines of 20, 30, or 60 points, set solid, or other point sizes leaded to a total of 20, 30, 40, 50, or 60 points. Other typographic elements work within the same 10-point system. The type size for photo captions, for example, could be 5 points set solid. The designer must also determine if the type areas of a spread of several pages need to match or not. When they do match, the margins must be reversed on a double page: the left margin of the left-hand page matches the right margin of the right-hand page. The margins on top and bottom stay the same. Illustrations, of course, also are sized and positioned to fit into the grid. Figures 3.13 and 3.14 show two possible applications of the grid set up in figure 3.12.

The grid system always works well if it is used well. With some experience and study, the designer can use this system to bring order and uniformity to assignments, especially such materials as multi-page brochures, books, and catalogs. A highly satisfying and useful tool, the grid system has been widely and successfully used in many areas of graphic design. Some applications are discussed and illustrated in other articles in this section.

BOOK DESIGN
James Wageman, GRAPHIC DESIGNER

Anyone who has ever been faced with the question "What kind of work do you do?" and has had the misfortune to have to answer "I'm a book designer" is almost certainly familiar with the look of mild puzzlement that appears on the face of the questioner, followed by the nearly inevitable, "Oh, yes; you do the jackets, do you?" The designer then goes on to explain that, yes, he or she does design jackets (or perhaps not), but that the job involves much more than that—namely, the design of the book itself. This usually leads to more bewilderment, since a common reaction is to wonder what there can be about such an ordinary object as a book that needs to be designed. A rather charming observation of Paul Valéry's (in "The Physical Aspects of a Book") provides the beginnings of an answer:

Like a man, a book has its physical aspect, its visible and tangible exterior which can be as ordinary or individual, as ugly or pleasing, as insignificant or remarkable as that of any member of our species. As for its voice, which is heard the moment the book opens, does it not reside in the appearance of the page, the paper it is made of, the type face used, the spacing, and the quality of the make up?

This article does not attempt to be a comprehensive guide to the practice of book design. Entire books have been devoted to the subject, some of which are listed in the accompanying bibliography, and anyone wishing to pursue the matter in depth will certainly want to read one or more of them. The more thorough a designer's knowledge of production methods and processes, the more intelligently will he or she be able to go about the creation of a successful product. The book designer should know standard paper and press sizes, for example, in order to avoid a design that will result in waste and excessive cost in production. He should be able to make a manuscript fit into a given number of pages and into even printing forms when the situation so demands. He should know how to lay a book out so that, say, a second color will fall on one side only of the printed sheet (while appearing on several pages of the bound book). He should know the various typesetting and printing techniques and what to expect from them in terms of final product, quality, and cost.

Discussion of this whole area, vital though it is to the designer's job, is too vast and complex for the scope of this paper. In addition, much information that is touched on only superficially in this article—if not omitted altogether—is covered more thoroughly elsewhere in this volume. The intention here is to present a general overview of what is involved in the design of books, to suggest certain basic principles that the designer must consider, and to clarify the designer's function in the overall conception and production of a book.

DESIGN AS PROBLEM SOLVING

The book designer's role is not unlike that of the architect in his profession. Both must devise a basic plan that will determine the size and shape of the end product according to the needs of the particular job at hand, select the elements and materials that go into it, and, hopefully, put them all together into some sort of unified, pleasing whole. Just as a building can be built without an architect, a book can be manufactured without the assistance of anyone who calls himself a designer. But, with or without a designer so called, the same problems must be faced and decisions made that will affect the final appearance and cost of the book and the degree of its success in fulfilling its function.

Book design begins as problem solving. Marshall Lee has pointed out that the book designer has two basic tasks: to facilitate communication and to make a successful product. He has also noted that every book presents three kinds of problems: *mechanical, editorial,* and *commercial.* To extend Valéry's simile, one might say that, like people, no two books are precisely alike in their natures and purposes, and for this reason no one solution to the problems of book design can be expected to serve more than rather limited purposes. The successful solution is tailored to the specific needs and peculiarities of the individual manuscript.

There are times when the designer can best facilitate communication by keeping himself in the background, so to speak, by doing nothing that will draw undue attention to the typography, layout, or other graphic elements of the printed page and cause the reader to shift attention from the content of the book to its physical appearance. Most books, rightly or wrongly, are designed in this way, which probably explains the puzzlement on the part of the average person as to what constitutes book design. There are other times when the designer will be called on to create a stunning graphic presentation that will in itself provoke a response on the part of the reader, when the visual content is an important part of what is to be communicated. And there are, of course, many times when the designer's task will be to come up with a treatment that falls somewhere between these two extremes.

The book designer must begin by grasping the mechanical, editorial, and commercial problems of the manuscript he is working on and finding appropriate solutions to them. These three problem areas are interrelated. Mechanical problems include questions of the book's trim size (width and height), how many pages it will run to, how it will be printed and bound, what effect the manufacturing processes may have on its layout or physical makeup, and so on. The direction in which the designer moves in working out answers to these questions is determined by the editorial and commercial factors involved, which in turn raise more questions. What type of book is it: trade (intended for a broad readership and sold mainly through bookstores or book clubs), scholarly (usually intended for a limited audience within a given academic discipline), textbook, reference, technical manual, direct mail (available by mail only), limited edition, or what? What, specifically, is the book's subject? What, if any, new or unique contribution is it intended to make to its field? What is its intended audience and use? What kind of budget is available to produce it? How many copies do the publishers plan to manufacture, and at what price do they hope to sell the book? What is the expected life span of the book: is it topical—on a politician running for office, for instance, an issue that might well be dead in a matter of months—or is it, by contrast, a definitive study that is likely to remain of interest to readers in fifty or a hundred years? What are the projected marketing and sales approaches the publishers intend to use in its promotion? Answers to these and similar questions—if only tentative or general at first—must be known beforehand in order for the designer to proceed to shape the book in an intelligent manner.

A trade book may need to have a more sprightly look than a scholarly monograph. For a biography of, say, Samuel Johnson, an oldstyle typeface such as Caslon might create an appropriate feeling typographically, whereas the same face could become a visual nuisance in a technical manual, where the need would be for a more precisely cut, less mannered face such as Times Roman or Helvetica.

Sophisticated typesetting equipment would be used for a book striving for quality of presentation; another book's budget might allow only typewriter composition or another inexpensive strike-on method.

A low-grade binding material, such as an A-grade cloth ("A," curiously, being the lowest of book cloth *grades*; some inferior cloths are ungraded) or even paper over boards would be indicated for a hardbound book with a limited life span, whereas a C-grade (or higher, depending on the book's size, bulk, weight, etc.) might be necessary for a book that is expected to have some permanence. A pyroxylin-impregnated cloth would be the obvious choice over a starch-filled one for the binding of a cookbook, which one would expect to get soiled in use in a kitchen: the former could be wiped clean with a damp cloth; the latter might suffer permanent damage to the binding. A book that is being marketed by mail may need no jacket at all; if a jacket is desired in such a case, it could well maintain a quiet elegance that might not be possible if it had to serve as the point-of-purchase advertising in bookstores.

Illustrations will dictate the format in a book where they are of prime importance. Where they are of minimal importance, they may have to be worked in as gracefully as possible within a less than ideal format. An uncoated paper is generally most suitable and economical for an unillustrated book. But if the book is illustrated, an uncoated, pigmented, dull coated, or glossy coated sheet might be used, depending on the nature of the illustrations, the particular effect desired in their reproduction, how they are being printed, and so on. Original subjects that are themselves shiny, for example the stainless-steel sculptures of David Smith, would be sensibly reproduced on a glossy coated sheet, which would clearly be inappropriate for the reproduction of, say, the prints of Goya.

Of course within the different categories of paper there are various grades, weights, textures, and colors (including a variety of "whites," off-whites, and ivories), so that selection is further determined by appropriateness to the subject, by final weight of the book, by the bulk desired, by budget in relation to the number of copies being printed and the retail price, by intended audience and use, and so on. Weight is particularly important if mailing costs will be significant in marketing the book. A high-priced book intended for a discriminating buyer should deliver a higher level of quality than one intended for mass consumption. A book that may be read and referred to over many years should probably be printed on an acid-free sheet with high strength and durability.

These kinds of considerations should influence decisions and choices affecting virtually every aspect of the book's final physical makeup and appearance. A comment of Le Corbusier's (in *Towards a New Architecture*) is probably pertinent to all this: ". . . a problem well stated finds its solution."

At this point it might be said that the designer frequently finds that many of the important preliminary decisions have been made before a manuscript is released for design. Sometimes this is as it should be, for obvious reasons: the book may be part of a series; it may be planned to be printed on a given sheet (of a given size) that the publisher has bought in bulk for several titles as an economy measure; a printer may have been selected whose equipment handles a particular sheet (and trim) size most economically; a standard trim size will handle the average manuscript quite adequately and with the greatest economy; and so on. In many cases, however, the designer is not involved in the initial planning and conception of the book as a result of simple oversight or failure to understand the important role that he or she can play in helping to shape the project. A capable designer often is able to see possibilities for effective presentation or logical organization that might otherwise be missed. He may be able to suggest ways to effect economies in production; or, conversely, he may recommend a more expensive treatment that will enhance the sales potential and thus create a more successful product than originally envisioned. Time spent making decisions before the designer is consulted could be wasted; steps taken might have to be undone or redone. More seriously, if too many decisions have been made and implemented, it may be too late for changes, with the result that the book fails to meet its own potential and may even be very unsuccessfully developed and produced.

DESIGN PRINCIPLES

Book design is guided by the same basic principles that underlie all good design, among them *unity, harmony, balance, contrast,* and *variety.* These principles are essential to good typography and layout, but they are also central to the design of the book as a total object. The most successful design achieves a careful interplay among all of the parts, from jacket through binding and endpapers to the interior of the book. This interplay can be one of close harmony, in which colors, textures, typefaces, illustrations, etc., are in pleasing accord and evenly balanced, whether in restraint or in forcefulness. However, it can also be one of contrast—a rough, natural-finish cloth played off against a smooth, shiny text paper; a striking color juxtaposed against one that is more subdued; a bold display typeface contrasted with a restrained text face. The first approach will seem appropriate for some books, the second for others. Neither assures an easy success; success depends primarily on the sensitivity of the designer to his materials and their appropriateness to the nature and content of the manuscript.

Physical qualities of a book

Each of the physical attributes that go into the makeup of a book lends a quality that helps mold the overall character and feeling of the book as an object. *Size, shape, weight, color,* and *texture* are some of the elements that function in this way. Because our reactions to them are subjective, it is nearly impossible to generalize about specific effects that such elements create. But, to oversimplify, one might suggest, for example, that a smallish book will tend to have a more intimate feeling than a larger one, while a large book might be impressive by its scale alone. A square book can satisfy the eye by the geometric purity of its form, whereas an oblong book, even a smallish one, may derive a feeling of spaciousness (especially lying open) from its shape. The mere thickness of a book tends to affect our responses to it in subtle ways. A thick volume promises more extensive, although not necessarily better, treatment of its subject than a thin one. (Many publishers have long felt that the thick book suggests to the buyer that he is getting more for his money— somewhat as if knowledge were sold by quantity rather than quality—and so have used high-bulking papers to swell out what would otherwise have been slender volumes; of course even that basic deception can fail when the buyer picks up the book and is surprised by its cream-puff quality.) On the other hand, it is possible for a thin book to possess a certain grace and elegance that a thicker book may lack.

Organization of elements

In most books, various levels of importance are established editorially to organize the parts. In brief, these would include some or all of the following, in descending order of importance:
 • Jacket or cover
 • Title page (or spread)
 • Half-title page(s) and part title pages
 • Chapter headings
 • Subheads within the text (sometimes running to several levels)
Although some designers are able to establish the organizational pattern with minimum differentiation among these various elements and thus attain a high degree of unity throughout the book, more frequently the unity is maintained simply by uniformity of typeface used and position on the page (for the major elements at least), while a descending order of type *sizes*

serves to establish the relative importance of each of the parts.

This would all seem so obvious as to scarcely merit mention; however, it is, unfortunately, not uncommon to come upon books in which the designer has failed to establish a clear relationship among the parts of the book and has further failed to create a unified approach to them. Thus, for example, it is possible to find books in which the chapter headings are given greater importance than the type on the title page, or where the designer clearly establishes a symmetrical, centered approach at one point and then abandons it for an asymmetrical approach elsewhere. Occasionally this kind of inconsistency can be made to work successfully, but such success is extremely rare. Usually it seems clear either that the designer was unaware that a unified design requires some consistency or that he simply decided to take the easy way out—preferring, for instance, a flush-left treatment basically but abandoning it where it became difficult to work into a good-looking arrangement on a page without some real effort (and sensitivity) on his part. This kind of basic inconsistency and lack of unity is perhaps one of the most common shortcomings one can find in the design of books, and one for which there really is no excuse.

TYPOGRAPHY

A well-rounded book designer will probably have some knowledge of the historical backgrounds of type and typography and printing in general, and will want to have some familiarity with the work of the great figures of the past and present—from Aldus to Zapf (and beyond, in both directions), so to speak. It is of some importance to have an awareness of the traditional historical categories in the development of type design—oldstyle, transitional, modern, square serif, sans serif, and so on—and to know how and why typefaces are divided into these categories. One might conceivably set a book on Shakespeare in Bodoni, for instance, but it could be embarrassing to propose to do so without being aware that one was suggesting a nineteenth-century Italian design for a book on a sixteenth-century Englishman.

Type area in relation to space

How type is used, and particularly how it is positioned within the space around it, however, is of greater importance than the selection of an individual typeface. A statement that Jan Tschichold originally made in 1935, discussing typography, is a commonplace that is too frequently ignored: "Every shape exists only in relation to the space around it." Type size, measure, and leading should be judiciously selected for legibility and "color" (the gray tone and texture that a block of type creates), but the appearance of the page as a whole is greatly dependent upon the way the type area is organized within its space. What might be called a "traditional" layout places the type within the space in such a way that the margins serve as a frame, and the overall effect is usually somewhat static. Such a layout is shown in figure 3.15. The traditional page derived its form in part from the limitations of the predominant

D. JUNII

JUVENALIS

ET

AULI

PERSII FLACCI

SATYRAE.

BIRMINGHAMIAE:
Typis JOHANNIS BASKERVILLE.
MDCCLXI.

Figure 3.15: Title page from Baskerville's **Juvenal and Persius,** 1761. A splendid example of a traditional, formal page; the margins serve as a "frame" surrounding the type.

technologies of years past, movable metal type and letterpress printing, which required printing elements to be locked into rectangular frames. The development of photomechanical plates, paste-up composition techniques, and alternative printing processes more amenable to handling unusual spatial shapes combined to open the way for a new approach to page design. This more modern approach activates the entire page by placing the type in such a way that the space around it no longer remains a neutral "frame" but becomes a dynamic part of the composition. Figure 3.16 is an example of this type of layout.

The traditional and modern approaches to page layout to some extent parallel those approaches to art in general. Compare, for example, the two portraits of different periods in figures 3.17 and 3.18. Note the similar static quality of the early title page and portrait (figures 3.15 and 3.17) and the more dynamic effect of the modern ones (figures 3.16 and 3.18).

Paul Rand has written:

I believe the real difference [between a traditional and a modern approach] lies in the way space is interpreted: that is, the way in which an image is placed on a sheet of paper. Such incidental questions as the use of sans-serif type faces, lower case letters, ragged settings, primary colors, etc., are at best variables, which merely tend to sidetrack the real issue.

He goes on to explain that:

By carefully arranging type areas, spacing, size, and "color," the typographer is able to impart to the printed page a quality which helps to dramatize the contents. He is able to translate typematter into tactile patterns. By concentrating the type area and emphasizing the margin (white space), he can reinforce, by contrast, the textural quality of the type.

The Art Museum
Princeton University
Princeton, New Jersey

ROBERT MOTHERWELL
RECENT WORK

Figure 3.16: Modern approach to the layout of a title-page spread. Surfaces of pages are activated as integral parts of the composition through dynamic placement of the type

and, further, through contrast in color (black type on white at left, white on red at right). *From Robert Motherwell: Recent Work, The Art Museum, Princeton University, 1972.*

Figure 3.17: Seventeenth-century *Portrait of a Lady* by Cornelis de Vos. The subject is framed within a receding background, and the overall organization is similar to the Baskerville title page. *Courtesy of The Art Museum, Princeton University.*

This is not to suggest that to abandon a traditional approach is to do violence to the page and startle the reader. An untraditional page should have its own kind of balance and will frequently be a more inviting arrangement—especially if it has a more open look—than much traditional typography. Again, there are times when a traditional approach will seem most suitable. But designers (and editors and authors) would do well to consider the possibility of trying to bring a freshness to the page when there is no good reason not to. (An untraditional layout is illustrated in figure 3.19.)

Practical typeface categories

Typefaces have been categorized in various ways (one of which was mentioned above). It would seem, however, that a practical way for today's designer to approach type classification would be to consider what effect one desires type to create in a given context. The designer can then set up whatever categories seem of value (and call them by whatever names seem appropriate), but they might include some or all of the following: type as neutral, elegant, decorative, mannered, and allusive.

A *neutral* typography would be one that stressed simplicity and avoided drawing attention to itself, as in figure 3.20.

Elegant typography, on the other hand, would be

Figure 3.18: Twentieth-century portrait, an untitled drawing by Hans Hoffman. Here the "background" has been raised to the surface of the page to become a dynamic part of the composition. The artist has abandoned the illusion of three-dimensionality in favor of the tensions possible upon the "flattened" surface. *Courtesy of The Art Museum, Princeton University.*

that attempting to go beyond the merely functional, in which simplicity gives way to a desire to present the beauty of the typeface being used (see figure 3.21).

Decorative typography would use or arrange the type first for its graphic qualities, as decoration or design, with considerations of legibility definitely subordinate to that purpose (see figure 3.22).

Mannered typography would, like elegant typography, tend to call attention to itself, but not for the beauty inherent in the letterforms being used; on the contrary, the typeface would probably not be used for its beauty but to create a specific feeling—one of strength, for example, or humor or irony (see figure 3.23).

Allusive typography would be used if the desire were to suggest a reference to something—to an earlier historical period, for example, or, in a book about bridges as in figure 3.24, to the precise structural forms of the engineering.

It would be easy to put individual typefaces arbitrarily into such categories. One thinks, for example, of such faces as Times Roman, Caledonia, Helvetica, and perhaps Optima as being basically neutral in appearance (at least in text sizes); whereas Palatino, Bembo, and some versions of Baskerville are letterforms that might be considered elegant.

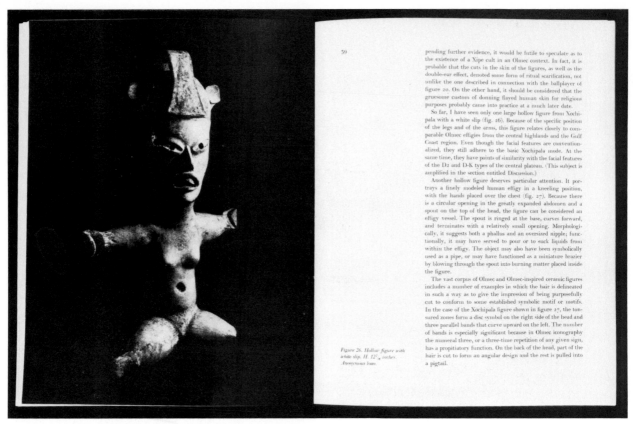

pending further evidence, it would be futile to speculate as to the existence of a Xipe cult in an Olmec context. In fact, it is probable that the cuts in the skin of the figures, as well as the double-ear effect, denoted some form of ritual scarification, not unlike the one described in connection with the ballplayer of figure 20. On the other hand, it should be considered that the gruesome custom of donning flayed human skin for religious purposes probably came into practice at a much later date.

So far, I have seen only one large hollow figure from Xochipala with a white slip (fig. 26). Because of the specific position of the legs and of the arms, this figure relates closely to comparable Olmec effigies from the central highlands and the Gulf Coast region. Even though the facial features are conventionalized, they still adhere to the basic Xochipala mode. At the same time, they have points of similarity with the facial features of the D2 and D-K types of the central plateau. (This subject is amplified in the section entitled Discussion.)

Another hollow figure deserves particular attention. It portrays a finely modeled human effigy in a kneeling position, with the hands placed over the chest (fig. 27). Because there is a circular opening in the greatly expanded abdomen and a spout on the top of the head, the figure can be considered an effigy vessel. The spout is ringed at the base, curves forward, and terminates with a relatively small opening. Morphologically, it suggests both a phallus and an oversized nipple; functionally, it may have served to pour or to suck liquids from within the effigy. The object may also have been symbolically used as a pipe, or may have functioned as a miniature brazier by blowing through the spout into burning matter placed inside the figure.

The vast corpus of Olmec and Olmec-inspired ceramic figures includes a number of examples in which the hair is delineated in such a way as to give the impression of being purposefully cut to conform to some established symbolic motif or motifs. In the case of the Xochipala figure shown in figure 27, the tonsured zones form a disc symbol on the right side of the head and three parallel bands that curve upward on the left. The number of bands is especially significant because in Olmec iconography the numeral three, or a three-time repetition of any given sign, has a propitiatory function. On the back of the head, part of the hair is cut to form an angular design and the rest is pulled into a pigtail.

Figure 26. Hollow figure with white slip. H. 12¹⁄₄ inches. Anonymous loan.

Figure 3.19 (above): Untraditional layout. This layout creates its own kind of balance and helps to "dramatize the contents." The wide inner margin emphasizes the contrast between the dark halftone and the facing white page, and enhances the textural quality of the type. *From* Xochipala, *by Carlo Gay, The Art Museum, Princeton University, 1972.*

Figure 3.20 (opposite bottom and above): Neutral typography. Optima, a twentieth-century sans-serif face designed by Hermann Zapf, used in a book on the arts and crafts movement in America. Optima creates a relatively neutral, unbusy type area that serves as a foil to the objects from an earlier era reproduced in the book. The contrast thus created—between historical objects and the more modern context (type and layout) in which they are placed—allows the objects to come alive with renewed freshness to a reader viewing them in the late twentieth century. *From* The Arts and Crafts Movement in America, *by Robert J. Clark, The Art Museum, Princeton University, 1972.*

RUBIN has often said that at first New York, with its forest of tall buildings and hurrying crowds, inspired in him a feeling of dread. He felt lost, bewildered, and of no account, and wondered how he had dared venture into such a metropolis. The first months were wretched. He had no connections at all with the New York art world, and the only people he knew were a brother of his father's who lived on the Lower East Side, and the director of the Rumanian bank to which his paintings had been consigned. He lost the urge to paint and spent most of his time walking about New York with Kolnik. By chance, he made the acquaintance of some Jewish writers, with whom he became friendly and with whom he rented at small cost an old shabby house in Far Rockaway, where he passed the summer months in pleasant company. With the approach of autumn he returned to New York, physically refreshed but low in spirits. He had been some six months in America and had not been able even to take the first steps toward arranging an exhibition. As he recalls it, "I was haunted by a feeling of time wasted and was afraid I would sink into a state of apathy, when I would not be able to grasp an opportunity even if it were offered to me." But shortly Rubin was to meet a man who would not only help establish him as a professional painter but would also confirm his belief in himself as an artist. This was Alfred Stieglitz, the noted photographer and art patron, who had a remarkable flair for recognizing new talent. Stieglitz found impressive qualities in Rubin's paintings, with the result that an exhibition was arranged for November in the then well-known Anderson Gallery.

The exhibition by two unknown painters from faraway Rumania aroused interest in the New York art world, which at the time was excited by the first big show of Impressionist and Post-Impressionist paintings, and the *New York World* wrote: "In view of the present controversy over the modernistic paintings shown at the Metropolitan Museum of Art, the offerings at the Anderson Gallery are doubly interesting,"[5] while the *New York American* stated: "Think of two such apocalyptic artists opening a show in materialistic New York with the idea of 'possibly selling some of their pictures.' It is preposterous and yet it is sublime. The very audacity of faith and despair may triumph at that."[6]

Of Rubin *The New York Times* wrote: "The self he expresses is ardent and very young. He knows his craft. In spite of the dreary subjects, the gallery vibrates with

Figure 3.21 (left): Elegant typography. Monotype Perpetua with Centaur initials to mark breaks in the text, in a book on the Israeli artist Reuven Rubin. The typefaces were chosen not for simplicity but for the beauty of their forms. *From* Reuven Rubin, *by Sarah Wilkinson, Harry N. Abrams, Inc., 1974.*

Figure 3.22 (below): Decorative typography. A chapter title in Monotype Garamond Bold italic with swash characters, used primarily for its decorative qualities. *From* Elizabeth's Admiral, *by Robert W. Kenny. Copyright © 1970 The Johns Hopkins University Press.*

VIII: *The English Armada*

Philip II did not give up hope of conquering England when his battered ships came trailing home. Knowledge of that fact underlay the anxiety and dread that Englishmen felt throughout the next decade. Reports of naval preparations and expeditionary schedules so flooded the country that the queen had to maintain a defensive posture, keeping forts in readiness, trained bands alerted, and the fleet close at hand. Periodically, when the coming of a new Armada seemed imminent, more elaborate preparations were taken in hand. At those times

INTRODUCTION

On May 6, 1937, twenty-two news photographers from New York area newspapers and wire services found their way to Lakehurst, N. J., to make ship arrival photographs on the occasion of the docking of the German dirigible *Hindenburg*. The event was of more than routine interest; transatlantic passenger flight was still new, and the ship itself was completing only its eleventh crossing. Those disembarking from it would automatically be celebrities in the reflected glamour of the craft they had ridden on.

None of the photographers got the pictures that he was sent to make. They did, however, accidentally produce the most spectacular collection of on-the-spot disaster pictures ever made. One of the most famous of these is reproduced here.

Along with a handful of other similarly fortuitous shots, the *Hindenburg* pictures have been cited for a generation as the apotheosis of the news photographer's craft. This view is in fact a serious distortion, which does an injustice to the photographers themselves. A news photographer too young to vote in 1937 would today be in his mid-fifties, and would in the intervening years have made one hundred thousand exposures, without once having had presented to him such good fortune (professionally speaking) as having a great work of engineering and commerce die sensationally in the sky before him, while his camera was focused and ready. The news photographer spends his life making pictures from much more modest materials, and it is to these pictures that we should look for an understanding of his contribution to our modern visual life.

There are doubtless those who would claim that the important news of any given day could be engraved on the face of a dime. Those holding such a view, even more than those of us with more liberal and forgiving

standards, should be impressed with the skill and inventiveness with which the journalist fills the one- or two-pound newspaper that arrives even on days when nothing whatsoever has happened that the historian will call important. It must be understood that with news photographs, as with news stories, the extent of coverage depends not so much on what has happened as it does on the number of pages and the number of journalists that technology, reader interest, and advertising inches have made possible. The point was made with exceptional clarity in Senator Survine's recent remark to Senator Gloss (as reported by R. Baker, Dec. 12, 1972) concerning the lot of journalists: "Their publishers... insist on grinding their noses to the presses whether there's any news or not."

A test case may be useful. Yesterday (as this is written), Dec. 13, 1972, was an ordinary day, even a slow day, in the news business. No wars were begun or ended, no new planets were landed on, no heads of government were unseated, or even seated, no epoch-making laws were signed or judicial decisions rendered, and no crucial football games were played. Nevertheless, New York's three major circulation papers (to use an example conveniently at hand) printed on that day a total of sixty-eight different news photographs, exclusive of portraits and other pictures which made no claim to describe events specific to a particular day. Considered iconographically, these pictures bear a striking similarity to those reproduced in this book, which were made over a period of half a century. Included in the Dec. 13 group are: two ribbon-cutting ceremonies, a fire, assorted winners and losers, a stray dog, a mountain of Christmas mail, handshakes, a beauty queen, and confrontations between the principals of a prizefight, a labor-management dispute, and a diplomatic negotiation.

Figure 3.23: Mannered typography. Century Schoolbook with Aurora Condensed display type, used to make a straightforward statement of typographic frankness, in the catalog for an exhibition of newspaper photographs. In its suggestion of newspaper typography, this also borders on the allusive. *From* From the Picture Press, *John Szarkowski, ed. Copyright © 1973 The Museum of Modern Art, New York. All rights reserved. Reprinted by permission.*

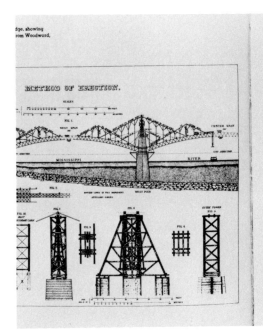

dge, showing
rom Woodward.

the scientific and visual in large-scale engineering. This objective guided our first such exhibition at the Princeton Art Museum in 1972, on the bridges of Robert Maillart, which began what we hope will be a continuing effort to make visible the potential for education sponsored jointly by humanists and civil engineers, in this case through art history and structural engineering.[12]

This scientific-visual connection, while implied in the present exhibition, has an explicit and general application to engineering education, for which the Eads Bridge provides a major illustration.

Imagine an education in the visual arts that begins with abstract principles of aesthetic theory and then proceeds to studies of how those principles apply to the design of art works, while never considering any completed works of art as objects for study. This has been the general trend for engineering education in the twentieth century, to such an extent that the post-World War II generation of civil engineers could graduate without ever hearing the name of Maillart or Eads. The leading textbooks had become so abstract that references to completed structures were confined largely to captions for a meager scattering of photographs. Imagine majoring in art history and never hearing of van Ruysdael or Turner!

Thus the principal consequence of exhibiting the works of one man, and in this case only one of his works, is to proclaim that the Eads Bridge has the

same type of centrality for American civil engineering education as Turner's *Rain, Steam, and Speed* has for English art-history education. An exhibition of Maillart bridges might be likened to a show devoted to the major landscapes of Jacop van Ruysdael. This centrality shows forth in ways related to scale, sequence, and setting.

For scale, the Eads Bridge had the largest spans of any previous arch. Most contemporaneous leaders in the civil engineering profession believed it an improper design, and thus Eads provided, probably for the first time in America, a detailed mathematical analysis that is as valid today as it was one hundred years ago. Therefore, the engineering educator has a complete and practical illustration for modern structural analysis available for students, who can practice either computer-oriented analyses or simplified manual analyses by using the Eads Bridge dimensions and loads. If one is to study the structure of a poem—rhyme, meter, form, etc.—there is no reason for the English professor to make up an example when Shakespeare and T. S. Eliot have left us theirs.[13]

If the implications of scale lead to scientific analysis, for which the Eads Bridge provides one connection to a visually significant work, then the implications of sequence lead to a constructional analysis connected also to a work of visual importance. Whereas the first disconnection of modern engineering education is between abstract theory of mathe-

25

Figure 3.24: Allusive typography. Memphis Medium, a square-serif face, used to allude to the structural forms of the engineering, as well as to the nineteenth-century origins, of the Eads Bridge in St. Louis, the subject of the book. *From* The Eads Bridge, *The Art Museum, Princeton University, 1974.*

But the point is that any given typeface can be used in a variety of ways; as Tschichold has said, "Good typography depends only secondarily on types, primarily on the way they are used." In a heavily illustrated book where one wants the illustrations to dominate, Optima or Helvetica would create a much more neutral and less "busy" type area to play off against the illustrations than would Caledonia. On the other hand, either Optima or Helvetica could certainly be handled in a way that would be elegant or decorative; and one could use, say, Helvetica Bold in a way that would be basically mannered. Furthermore, there is no need to limit the approach to a single category: typography can be both elegant and allusive at the same time, and so on. In addition, it is possible to pick a typeface for its allusiveness to an earlier historical period but to place it in a fresh, untraditional context and so create, through contrast between old and new, a richer visual experience than would conventionally be possible (see figure 3.25).

To look at typography in this way is, first, to clarify what specific effect(s) one wants type to achieve in a given context; but it is also to free one's thinking from narrow prejudices in favor of or against certain typefaces and, hopefully, to broaden one's appreciation of the variety of possibilities that typography can offer.

LAYOUT

The basic layout of a book, like the typography that is a part of it, should attempt to be in harmony with the editorial concept behind the book. This is an ambiguous area in which there often are no clear guidelines (and for that reason, it might be better to

state the proposition negatively: the layout should not do violence to the editorial concept), but one or two examples may help to clarify what is meant.

Harmony with nature of text

A book of one hundred photographs from the collection of The Museum of Modern Art was conceived as one that would present a single photograph per spread with an expository text on the facing page, as shown in figure 3.26. The idea was, first, to present the photographs themselves. As the author put it, "This is a picture book, and its first purpose is to provide the material for simple delectation." This, then, was clearly an instance in which the layout ought to place primary emphasis on the photographs, and in which the overall design should do nothing to distract from them as the chief focus of the book. Beyond that, the photographs were being presented as works of art, so that no thought could be given to cropping or bleeding (and thus losing part of the image). In addition, they were being presented, editorially, more or less as equals; there was no intention of featuring some as of greater significance or interest than others.

For these reasons, the obvious layout solution was to present all the photographs in the same manner: they were all placed on right-hand pages, and all were centered on the page. Other solutions were certainly possible, but this was perhaps the most suitable, since here was a situation in which the space around the photograph was best used simply as a "frame," and in which a formal, static layout best served the purpose of drawing attention to the photographs themselves and not to the layout of the book. Even the simple device of putting, say, half of the photographs on left-

Travels
in the
Old South

*Selected from
Periodicals of the Times*

Edited by Eugene L. Schwaab
with the collaboration of
Jacqueline Bull

Volume I

THE UNIVERSITY PRESS
OF KENTUCKY

Figure 3.25: Allusive typography in an untraditional context. Monotype Ehrhardt, printed in dark brown in the original, used to create an allusive period flavor in harmony with the many old engravings that were a part of this two-volume boxed set. The type was laid out on an untraditional page in which wide outer margins helped to create a feeling of sumptuousness and also served to carry the major display type (on title pages and part titles) as well as the folios and running heads. Engravings were blown up and bled to heighten their graphic qualities and to present them in a somewhat fresh and untraditional way. *From* Travels in the Old South, *Eugene L. Schwaab, ed. Copyright © 1973 The University Press of Kentucky. Used by permission of the publishers.*

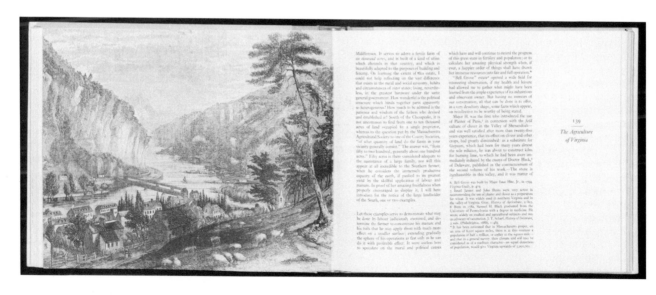

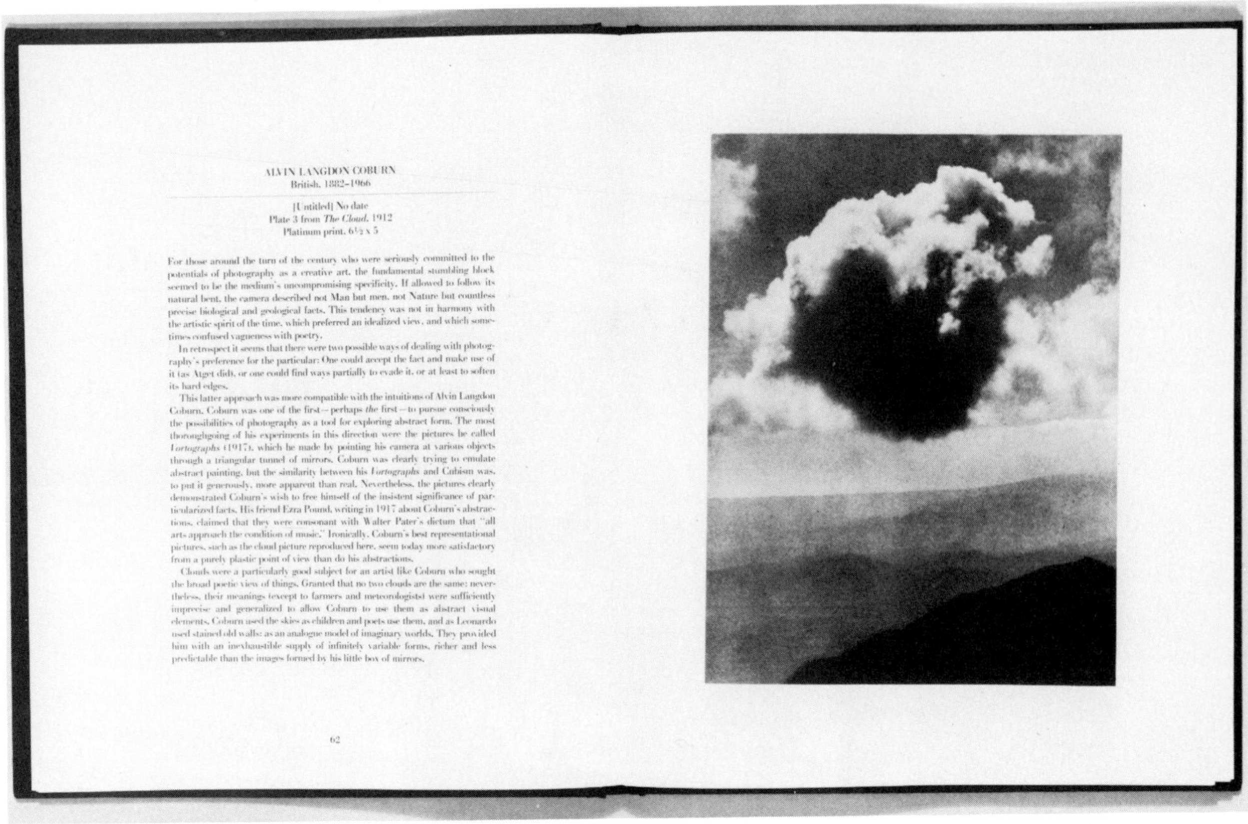
ALVIN LANGDON COBURN
British, 1882–1966

[Untitled] No date
Plate 3 from *The Cloud*, 1912
Platinum print, 6½ x 5

For those around the turn of the century who were seriously committed to the potentials of photography as a creative art, the fundamental stumbling block seemed to be the medium's uncompromising specificity. If allowed to follow its natural bent, the camera described not Man but men, not Nature but countless precise biological and geological facts. This tendency was not in harmony with the artistic spirit of the time, which preferred an idealized view, and which sometimes confused vagueness with poetry.

In retrospect it seems that there were two possible ways of dealing with photography's preference for the particular: One could accept the fact and make use of it (as Atget did), or one could find ways partially to evade it, or at least to soften its hard edges.

This latter approach was more compatible with the intuitions of Alvin Langdon Coburn. Coburn was one of the first—perhaps *the* first—to pursue consciously the possibilities of photography as a tool for exploring abstract form. The most thoroughgoing of his experiments in this direction were the pictures he called *Vortographs* (1917), which he made by pointing his camera at various objects through a triangular tunnel of mirrors. Coburn was clearly trying to emulate abstract painting, but the similarity between his *Vortographs* and Cubism was, to put it generously, more apparent than real. Nevertheless, the pictures clearly demonstrated Coburn's wish to free himself of the insistent significance of particularized facts. His friend Ezra Pound, writing in 1917 about Coburn's abstractions, claimed that they were consonant with Walter Pater's dictum that "all arts approach the condition of music." Ironically, Coburn's best representational pictures, such as the cloud picture reproduced here, seem today more satisfactory from a purely plastic point of view than do his abstractions.

Clouds were a particularly good subject for an artist like Coburn who sought the broad poetic view of things. Granted that no two clouds are the same; nevertheless, their meanings (except to farmers and meteorologists) were sufficiently imprecise and generalized to allow Coburn to use them as abstract visual elements. Coburn used the skies as children and poets use them, and as Leonardo used stained old walls: as an analogue model of imaginary worlds. They provided him with an inexhaustible supply of infinitely variable forms, richer and less predictable than the images formed by his little box of mirrors.

62

Figure 3.26: Layout in harmony with editorial intention. The photographs are emphasized in this book from The Museum of Modern Art, and they are placed formally on the page, with margins serving as a frame. The typography is restrained, and the overall effect is one of harmony among the various elements of the book. *From* Looking at Photographs/100 Pictures from the Collection of The Museum of Modern Art, *by John Szarkowski. Copyright © 1973 The Museum of Modern Art, New York. All rights reserved. Reprinted by permission.*

hand pages in order to create some minimal variety would have tended to throw the balance off slightly; right-hand pages somehow command greater attention in such a book than do left-hand pages, presumably because the right-hand page is seen first when turning to a new spread.

The text for each photograph was then centered on the facing left-hand page to maintain the overall formality of the layout. The typography was intentionally restrained, in order not to draw undue attention to it.

As an additional example, assume a book of some three or four hundred photographs with text, in which the intention is to present some of the diversity of experiences and colors to be found in the Southwestern United States, and which is to be published as a book of 224 pages. Assume further—as would normally be the case in such a book—that the photographs are of varying quality and interest and that they are being presented primarily for their content and not as works of art in themselves.

The most appropriate layout for such a book would almost certainly be one that rejected a static formality in favor of a dynamic approach that emphasized the strongest pictures and exploited contrasts in size and color in order to create a variety of visual experiences within the book. In such a book, too formal an approach to layout would probably tend to draw attention to the layout itself, just as, in the opposite way, a dynamic layout employing strong contrasts would have done in the Museum of Modern Art book.

These are fairly obvious examples of how layout can coincide with editorial intention. In many, if not most, books, however, the way in which layout can harmoniously reflect editorial intention is far less obvious. In such cases, the designer probably has the option of choosing from a variety of possible approaches to layout, as long as care is taken to assure that the layout is not working against the basic editorial concept.

To say that layout should strive for harmony in this way, however, is not the same as saying that the layout must attempt to reflect the *subject* of the book. A book on eighteenth-century England, for example, need not be laid out in a way that reflects the formalism typical of much of that period. If the concept in publishing such a book were similar to that behind the hypothetical volume on the Southwest, then a formal, static approach would again seem inappropriate. Furthermore, even if the book were an unillustrated scholarly monograph on the eighteenth century, there is no reason why the typography and layout could not be asymmetrical and informal, as long as the design did not begin to assert itself to the point of becoming a distraction to the reader. A book of modern scholarship about the eighteenth century, designed and produced

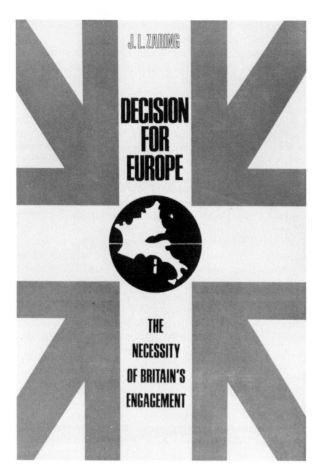

Part I: The Economic Community

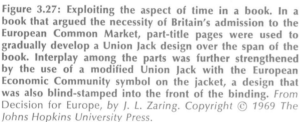

Figure 3.27: Exploiting the aspect of time in a book. In a book that argued the necessity of Britain's admission to the European Common Market, part-title pages were used to gradually develop a Union Jack design over the span of the book. Interplay among the parts was further strengthened by the use of a modified Union Jack with the European Economic Community symbol on the jacket, a design that was also blind-stamped into the front of the binding. *From Decision for Europe, by J. L. Zaring. Copyright © 1969 The Johns Hopkins University Press.*

today, might not unreasonably be expected to look like what, in fact, it is: a twentieth-century book.

Time and space

Unlike some other areas of graphic design, book design offers the opportunity to work not only in two-dimensional space but in time as well, in that a book unfolds gradually, spread by spread, over a period of time, and is not taken in virtually all at once in the way that, say, a poster is. It would be interesting to see this aspect of book design more thoroughly exploited than it has been. One technique, which is fairly obvious but is rarely seen, is to introduce a suitable graphic device that is developed and modified in some way—multiplied or allowed to disintegrate, for instance—at major points in the book, such as on part-title pages as in figure 3.27.

The aspect of time in book design is important in relation to layout, particularly in an illustrated book.

Part II The Political Community

Part III The Importance of Britain

Part IV The Preservation of Europe

There are instances when uniformity of presentation may be indicated for the illustrations, as suggested earlier, but when this is not the case, the designer should try to introduce variety into the layouts in order to avoid monotony. This means, first of all, varying the sizes of illustrations in order to introduce and to emphasize scale: a large picture will tend to look even larger when placed beside a small one. Especially if the designer is able to have some freedom in establishing the sequence of the pictures, further interest can be created through juxtaposition of contrasting colors (or tones in black-and-white illustrations—a dark, low-key photograph beside one that is high-key, for instance) or of textural patterns. Shapes and implied lines of motion within the illustrations can be exploited to create a feeling of movement across the page or spread. Further contrast can sometimes be established within a context of square (or rectangular) halftones by silhouetting an object or figure, as in figure 3.28. And of course cropping can often be greatly effective in heightening the dramatic impact of a photograph.

Each layout should be conceived in terms of spreads (not individual pages), since that is the way it will be viewed within the finished book. This is important even if the spread consists of nothing more than a single illustration facing a page of text: the illustration should be carefully scaled and positioned on the page to create whatever specific emphasis and interrelationship between type and illustration is appropriate in a given context (see figure 3.29).

Variety of pace is an aspect of layout that should be developed as individual spreads are brought together into a sequential whole. If all of the spreads are laid out in a similar way, there will be no such variety and the result may well be monotonous. To break such monotony, it is often desirable to modify the way in which illustrations are presented from one spread to the next, mixing spreads containing smallish pictures with those having full-bleed illustrations, and so on.

Throughout any such sequence, however (and in fact throughout the book as a whole), there must be a controlled rhythm, so that emphasis falls where it properly should and the overall organizational pattern remains clear. This is true regardless of whether the layout is of a static or a dynamic character. In fact, a successful "dynamic" layout is almost always carefully controlled; elements are not arbitrarily positioned but are placed on the page with a coherence from one spread to the next, so that the total effect is one of order and unity and not of visual chaos. There is a balance to the entire structure that is the result of carefully emphasizing the important parts and de-emphasizing the subordinate elements.

Variety within unity

Books presenting the most complex layout problems

Figure 3.28: Silhouetting for contrast. In an exhibition catalog of Robert Motherwell's work, most of the illustrations were done as square halftones. By way of contrast, silhouetting was used for such photographs as this one, bled at the bottom of the page to create a surface tension and implied feeling of movement in relation to the caption and block of type on the facing page. Contrasts of color and texture were brought into play by printing the halftones on a coated white stock and the text on an antique-finish gray sheet. *From* Robert Motherwell: Recent Work, *The Art Museum, Princeton University, 1972.*

56

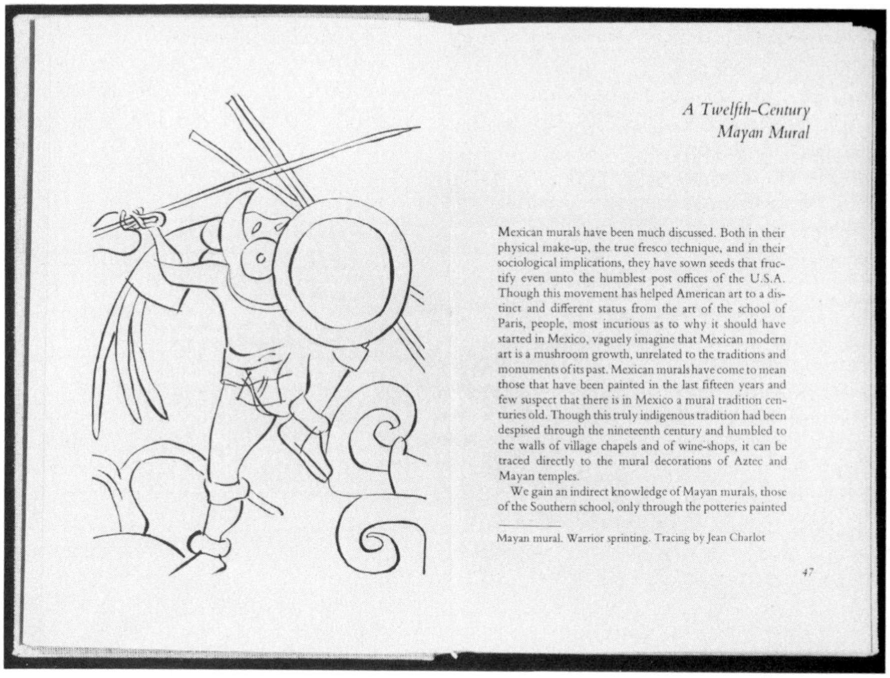

A Twelfth-Century
Mayan Mural

Mexican murals have been much discussed. Both in their physical make-up, the true fresco technique, and in their sociological implications, they have sown seeds that fructify even unto the humblest post offices of the U.S.A. Though this movement has helped American art to a distinct and different status from the art of the school of Paris, people, most incurious as to why it should have started in Mexico, vaguely imagine that Mexican modern art is a mushroom growth, unrelated to the traditions and monuments of its past. Mexican murals have come to mean those that have been painted in the last fifteen years and few suspect that there is in Mexico a mural tradition centuries old. Though this truly indigenous tradition had been despised through the nineteenth century and humbled to the walls of village chapels and of wine-shops, it can be traced directly to the mural decorations of Aztec and Mayan temples.

We gain an indirect knowledge of Mayan murals, those of the Southern school, only through the potteries painted

Mayan mural. Warrior sprinting. Tracing by Jean Charlot

47

Figure 3.29: Careful scaling and positioning of a single illustration facing a page of text. Chapter titles (and folios) were set into the outer margins in this book, and the dynamism implicit in that treatment was heightened on spreads like this, where the strong feeling of movement created by the illustration is carried across to, and picked up by, the chapter head. *From An Artist on Art, by Jean Charlot, The University Press of Hawaii, 1972.*

are most in need of organization to maintain an order and unity. One means of achieving an ordered structure and, at the same time, of creating variety within the overall unity is to develop a grid that will successfully handle the various elements that must go into a given book (see "The Grid System," page 39). To establish a grid, a designer must begin by studying the materials—the illustrations, their shapes and desired final sizes, and the positions where they should fall in relation to the text; the text, its length, organization, and subdivisions within it; and any other elements that will be a part of the book, including captions, footnotes, and running heads.

The designer then looks for ways to subdivide the page on which these elements will be laid out, and he considers what consequences such subdivision would have with regard to the materials going into the book. If, for example, the page is divided into two columns and the illustrations are then scaled to be either one or two columns wide, will they end up being the right size, or will many of them be too large or too small? If the text area is of a given size and in a certain position, will it be possible to insert illustrations at the appropriate places (and in the right sizes), or will they end up falling somewhere away from the references to them in the text? Will the subdivision of the page accommodate all the elements that must go into the layout, and will it allow enough flexibility to serve as an aid in the creation of a varied layout and not simply as a straitjacket?

After determining the answers to such questions and making any necessary adjustments in the way he has subdivided the page, the designer should be able to come up with a grid that will allow him to lay the book out with a good deal of freedom and, at the same time, control. Figure 3.30 suggests some varied ways to treat a basic grid.

A FINAL WORD

"There is one profession and one only . . . in which progress is not considered necessary, where laziness is enthroned, and in which the reference is always to yesterday." When Le Corbusier wrote these words (in *Towards a New Architecture*) in 1923, he had the profession of architecture in mind. But the same might be said of the state of much of today's book design. Films, television, and magazine design have had an impact on our sensibilities and the ways in which we perceive and process information, and book design can profit from a discriminating use of some of the methods and techniques that these other media have made familiar to vast audiences. The book designer inevitably builds on past knowledge and experience, but if his work is to remain vital he must continue to be open and receptive to new influences and to avoid complacency.

Even in studies of a historical nature, an area of book design where the temptation is perhaps greatest to recreate an atmosphere of the past, the designer would do well to consider how the contrast between older elements (typeface, illustration, or whatever) and newer (a twentieth-century typeface, layout, and so on) will allow the one to enhance the other so that the past is revivified within a fresh context. The designer who attempts simply to mimic earlier styles fails to take advantage of this opportunity to create meaningful new combinations with the materials at his disposal.

To go beyond a hackneyed approach to book design requires an understanding and sensitivity on the part of the designer in order to assure that his contribution to the finished book will be a truly positive one. Attempts to do so may encounter resistance at times on the part of those who are comfortable with the familiar, are quick to ascribe a low level of visual acuity to the average reader, and who prefer an easy

Figure 3.30: Grid and pages from a book on Hawaiian sculpture. The book consisted of an illustrated text followed by a catalog section that reproduced every known extant piece of Hawaiian sculpture of the human figure. The grid shifts from a two-column page for the main part of the book to a three-column page for the catalog. The wide text column was flanked on the outside by a marginal column that could be used for long, narrow halftones or captions. The grid proved flexible enough to accommodate a diversity of material presented with varying pace but with an overall cohesion and unity. Rhythm as an organizing element was established by such means as use of full-bleed halftones to mark chapter openings—halftones that were tightly cropped to emphasize the dramatic intensity inherent in many of the pieces. *From Hawaiian Sculpture, by J. Halley Cox with William H. Davenport, The University Press of Hawaii, 1974.*

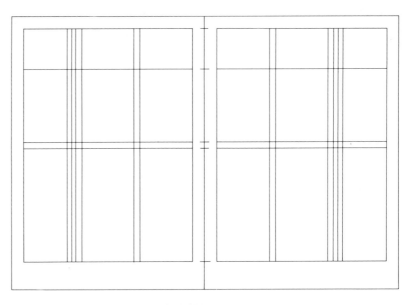

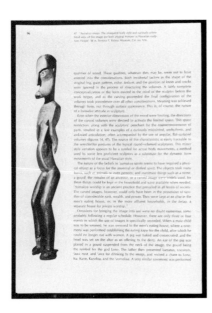

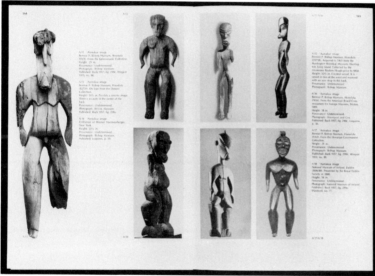

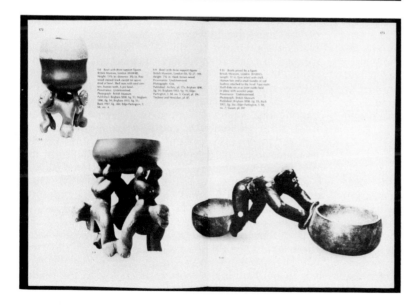

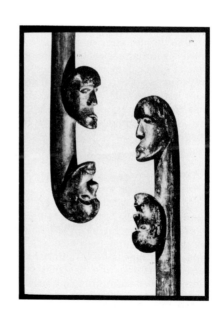

mediocrity to an attempt to bring new clarity and to raise the reader's level of aesthetic enjoyment and appreciation. But the effort is certainly worth making. What Tschichold wrote nearly half a century ago is still relevant today: "We will have books worthy of our times only when publishers and authors [and, one might add, designers] approach the problem with less caution."

SELECTED BIBLIOGRAPHY

Bain, Eric K. *Display Typography: The Theory and Practice of Typographic Design*. New York: Hastings House, 1970.

Dair, Carl. *Design with Type*. Toronto: University of Toronto Press, 1967.

Day, Kenneth, ed. *Book Typography, 1815–1965, in Europe and the United States of America*. Chicago: University of Chicago Press, 1966.

Gerstner, Karl. *Designing Programmes*. New York: Hastings House, 1968.

Le Corbusier. *Towards a New Architecture*. New York and Washington: Praeger, 1960. (Originally published in 1923 as *Vers Une Architecture*.)

Lee, Marshall. *Bookmaking: The Illustrated Guide to Design and Production*. New York: R. R. Bowker, 1965.

A Manual of Style. 12th ed., rev. Chicago: University of Chicago Press, 1969.

Morison, Stanley, and Kenneth Day. *The Typographic Book, 1450–1935*. Chicago: University of Chicago Press, 1963.

Müller-Brockman, Josef. *The Graphic Artist and his Design Problems*. 3rd ed. Teufen AR, Switzerland: Arthur Niggli, 1968.

Rand, Paul. *Thoughts on Design*. New York: Van Nostrand Reinhold, 1970. (Originally published in 1947.)

Ruder, Emil. *Typography: A Manual of Design*. New York: Hastings House, 1967.

Tschichold, Jan. *Asymmetric Typography*. New York: Van Nostrand Reinhold, 1967. (Originally published in 1935 as *Typographische Gestaltung*.)

Updike, Daniel Berkeley. *Printing Types*. 3rd ed. 2 vols. Cambridge, Mass.: Harvard University Press, 1951.

Valéry, Paul. "The Physical Aspects of a Book." In *Aesthetics*. Bollingen Series XLV, The Collected Works of Paul Valéry, vol. 13. Princeton, N.J.: Princeton University Press, 1964.

Williamson, Hugh. *Methods of Book Design*. Oxford: Oxford University Press, 1956.

Wilson, Adrian. *The Design of Books*. New York: Van Nostrand Reinhold, 1967.

MAGAZINE DESIGN
Samuel N. Antupit, PUBLICATION DESIGNER

Good magazine design is a matter of organizing every conceivable detail into a structure that is flexible enough to allow for occasional modification. The emphasis is on the structure; the modifications are for special effects and must be used sparingly. The aim of the structure is to establish, from page to page and from issue to issue, a look that is unmistakably that of a particular magazine. The secret, if there is one, is to use as few elements as possible but to use them with imagination.

TRIM SIZE

Trim size, the most crucial decision, is hardly ever in the hands of the designer. With the decreasing number of magazine printers and the increasing cost of producing magazines, the trim size decision is made for practical rather than aesthetic reasons most of the time. If the magazine is national and will (or hopes to) carry advertising, the designer will probably be presented with uncompromising arguments for a trim size of 8½" x 11" or slight variations thereof. Paper can be ordered most economically for this size, and the majority of magazine printers can accommodate it. Most of the pressure, however, is from advertisers: their plates are prepared for this size. Remember the large formats of *Look* and *Holiday*: they shrank to oblivion, while their sisters *McCall's*, *Fortune*, and *Esquire* merely shrank. It is a sad state of affairs but, in these times, hard to circumvent. If the magazine can live happily on a small circulation, the designer can bargain for a more original size; and if national advertising is not a concern, the options are limited only by the imagination of the designer and the capabilities of the printer and the bindery. Magazines have been designed with such dimensions as 6 x 9, 7 x 10, 10 x 10, 4½ x 10¼, 10 x 13, 9 x 12, and 12 x 17½ inches, in addition to the "standard" 8½ x 11. Some magazines of various sizes and proportions are shown in figure 3.31.

If design considerations can be purely aesthetic, these factors should be kept in mind:

• The larger the page, the more inventive the type has to be. Nothing is more intimidating to the reader than large sheets of plain gray type.

Figure 3.31: Magazines of different sizes and proportions. *Magazine covers reprinted with permission of the publishers.*

• The larger the page size, the greater will be the number of illustrations to be dealt with (assigned, designed, and paid for). Nothing looks sillier than a style consisting of small spots peppered through a mass of type. Artwork will have to be especially well conceived, executed, and presented because of the great attention it will get. The designer or art director must be up to the challenge.

• The smaller the page size, the less freewheeling the typography can be, but the more essential it becomes. The designer will have to strike a balance between design and the more practical problem of legibility.

• The smaller the page size, the longer the articles will run in terms of page number. While one smashing illustration can be interesting in a magazine with large pages, art and typography should be used in a magazine with small pages to keep the pages alive throughout an entire article.

• Most important to keep in mind is that page size and page number are functions of each other. The decision on size will ultimately have to resolve the question of choosing between a thick, small magazine or a thin, big magazine. This is additionally a function of the paper selected.

PAPER

Most of the problems in stock selection are similar to those involved in choosing trim size. Since national advertisers prefer to see their ads glisten on coated paper, coated stock is the most available. In addition,

cost considerations may limit paper selection. The increase in postal rates has been the largest single deterrent to good reproduction; it has produced a demand for lightweight papers, which, coupled with high-speed presses, have produced results which are seldom outstanding, often only passable, and sometimes dismal. Matte (dull) coated papers are available for large-run (web offset) publications; if four-color art is not being used to a great degree, these papers are worth investigating. They tend to make the four-color printing rich and dense; sometimes this effect is desirable if the art is not too detailed.

For a short-run magazine and where there is control over advertising, the standard 8½" x 11" format can be "customized" through the choice of paper with a variation in color, texture, and weight. The cover is generally of a heavier weight to protect the inside (increasingly important as the inside pages get lighter).

The whole feel of the magazine can be altered by the use of inserts of a different stock. The production manager, as well as the designer, will undoubtedly have a voice in this: the insert will have to be a multiple of 8 or 12 pages depending upon the equipment and paper available. Often, since the insert is run apart from the regular text, it is possible to print the whole section in a color other than black. If halftones are to be printed in the second color, the ink must be dark enough to hold the image clearly.

FORMAT

Once the practical decisions are out of the way, the real work begins. Establishing a format is the first step.

It is important for the designer to know for certain what the flavor or feel of the magazine is to be. The designer cannot decide this alone but should interview the editor to find out how he or she envisions the magazine. Note the word *envision*; it is the key. It does not mean *visualize*; that is the designer's job. The designer gets an overall impression (sincere, weird, scholarly, loose, classic, classy) of the editor's feelings, in words, and then interprets them. There are only three tools to work with: type, art and photography, and pacing.

Even before the typeface is selected, a grid should be drawn (see "The Grid System," page 39). Planning the margins (top, bottom, and sides) comes first. Margins should not be equal; there should be less space at the gutter so that the pages are held together as spreads rather than looking like separate units. The designer should play with these spaces even before determining column width and space between columns. Folios will have to be positioned somewhere; in whatever margin they are placed, the sense of space will be diminished, and the spacing must be planned accordingly. (A variety of possible formats is shown in figure 3.32.)

If the magazine has advertising, this is the time for it to be considered. The width of small space ads must be taken into account for the front and back of the magazine. Small ads should be kept out of the center section, the editorial "sandwich." As a matter of fact, all ads should be kept out of the "sandwich" to keep it purely editorial.

Any legible typeface should be considered for the

61

Figure 3.32: Variety of page formats. Represented on layouts are margins, text, headlines, and illustrations.

text. The designer should not settle on one face until he has seen a page of it set and has compared it with a page of his second choice. Before deciding upon column widths and column spacing, it is a good idea to set (or stat) a page of type, full from side to side and top to bottom. It is possible to get a feeling of how the page will look by trimming strips of white paper (for the timid) or masking tape (for the headstrong) to represent column spaces; arranging the vertical strips to see how the type looks in two-, three-, four-, or even five-column widths; and cutting jagged pieces to try out ragged-right columns. Once that has been settled, it is time to start thinking about titles.

The first decision is how much of the page to devote to titles. It can be the top of the page, a side of the page (killing a column or two), or a well between

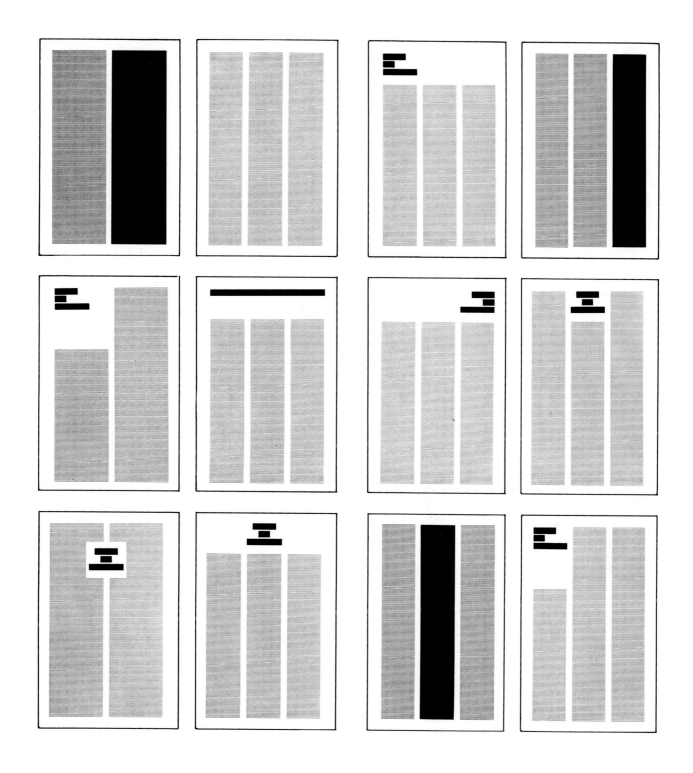

columns. Again, cutting pieces of white paper will help in finding a good ratio of text to white space. Strips of gray can represent titles. The type should not be chosen yet; the space should be resolved first. Then it is time to start experimenting with type. Again, any legible type will make a good title; the selection must be readable and must reflect the character of the magazine.

When text and title are resolved, the miscellaneous typographic components can be chosen. The choice, bearing in mind that "less is more," is to relate the miscellany to either the title or the text. The relationship should be established in terms of face (assuming the two are not the same), size, roman/italic, color (light, medium, bold), width (condensed, expanded).

The miscellany falls into three groups: (1) by-line,

subtitle (deck, kicker, etc.); (2) subhead (within text); (3) footnote, credit, folio.

Group 1 is generally larger than the text and smaller than the title. Two times the text is a good rule to be either followed or broken. Group 2 should be the same size as the text but set in either the italic or the bold, in upper- and lowercase; but not, please, in all caps. Group 3 can be in the same size as the text if handled adroitly or, more conventionally, two-thirds the size of the text either in upper and lower if the type is bold enough or in all caps if the face is light.

Initials can be useful but should be kept to one style, either stick-up or set-in. They work well when the same size as the title but, when well handled, can be gigantic.

The last step is to rule up a master layout or grid sheet. This will eventually have to contain all the graphic work and must allow for all the necessities: page number, date of issue, name of magazine. Page numbers can go on all pages, but the date should be on one side and the name on the other; it is too much to clutter one page with all the information.

This is the time to decide where art and photography credits will go. If they are to be placed on the page with the art or photograph (a generous gesture), space must be allowed for them now—preferably at the foot of the page, running horizontally, and positioned so as not to bang into the folios. When type is selected for the credits, their relation (or non-relation) to the other elements should be kept in mind.

ILLUSTRATION

Unless the magazine is a comic book, it would be better to use less art and make it perfect than to use a lot and have some of it deplorable—badly drawn or photographed, or badly conceived. Nearly as bad is using art which, although well drawn or photographed and well conceived, is exactly what every other magazine is publishing. Art should be appropriate to the particular magazine; if it can be seen in other magazines, then the designer has not thought hard enough —nor has the illustrator or photographer. Even when stock photos are used, they should be cropped or displayed in a unique way.

If more than one piece of art is used in a single article, all pieces should be treated in the same manner. This can be done by positioning them in the same part of the page or by sizing or proportioning them to match each other. If a photograph is silhouetted on the opening page, the silhouette technique should be used throughout the article. Perhaps all the art in a particular story could bleed out of the gutter, or it could all be run in a coarse screen. Similar art treatment unifies the article and helps distinguish it from the next one.

All art does not have to be full page, full color, full bleed! It is worthwhile to experiment carefully with odd sizes, shapes, and positions.

COVER

The cover is the single most crucial element. It is most critical for newsstand magazines. In all instances,

it functions as a poster. It must tell, with clarity and speed, what the magazine is all about.

Editors and publishers of newsstand magazines tend to feel that the logo is the most important display feature. This is not true. The first thing one sees is the *whole* cover. All the elements must be so organized that the casual passerby catches the feeling of the magazine and then sees the cover's information in the intended order. If illustration (art or photography) is used for the cover, it generally relates to the lead article. This can be a problem if the lead article has scant visual possibilities; the designer might be forced to create an "important" cover that would not necessarily be a strong visual one. This is a trap to be avoided. If the lead article must be featured and no superb visual image appears, it is better to do it typographically. The editor can write a terrific phrase which can be displayed for its impact.

It may be better not to illustrate the lead article but instead to use the strongest visual from another article. In that way, there is a better chance of attracting the reader; but the cover must be strong enough to hold the reader's attention long enough to deliver the remaining cover information.

Cover lines, announcing the magazine's contents, are generally placed at the left side so as to be legible

Figure 3.33: Newsstand magazines with cover lines.

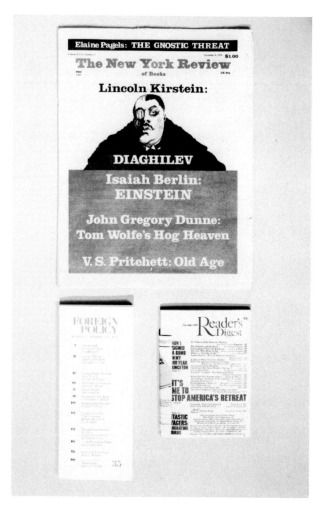

Figure 3.34: Magazines with table of contents covers. *Magazine covers reprinted with permission of the publishers.*

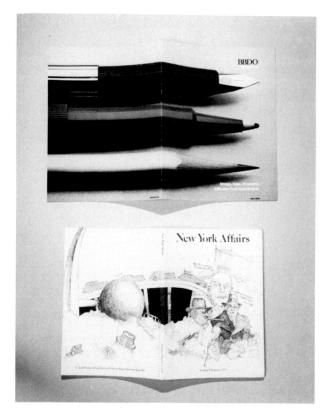

Figure 3.35: Magazines with art extending from front to back cover. *Magazine covers reprinted with permission of the publishers.*

when the magazine is lined up with its competition on the newsstand (see figure 3.33). Often a line is put above the logo. These elements must be used with care. The cover gets only a fleeting glance; all its elements must be arranged for the quickest, most meaningful, and most forceful impact.

Magazines without newsstand problems are more casual affairs. The cover must still function as a poster, but it does not have to sell as hard. It is closer to book jacket design; a newsstand cover relates more to advertising design. The cover lines, if any, can be positioned with much more freedom and do not require the impact of their newsstand counterparts. Some magazines use the cover to list the contents (see figure 3.34). Often, if the magazine has limited circulation, the designer will have the luxury of designing the back cover also. It should be used as an extension of the front cover, not as a billboard hawking the contents of the next issue (see figure 3.35).

PACING

A magazine, properly designed, is a kinetic experience. Good visual pacing is a necessity which is often overlooked; in its simplest terms it means that all the text articles, all the photographs, or all the illustrated pieces should not be grouped together unintentionally.

The placement of color is usually predetermined by production considerations, but its use is in the hands of the designer. Color should be used imaginatively: not every full-color page has to be a full bleed; a monochromatic effect, whether harsh or subtle, should not be overlooked.

Text pieces and visual articles should be alternated to establish a visual rhythm. The layouts of lesser articles can function to build in intensity, leading to the most important article. Then the reader should be given a slight rest before the next peak is built up to. The design can be thought of in terms of music: the calm or frantic qualities of a page can be used, bearing in mind the tone of the previous and the following articles.

The visual success of a magazine will be judged on two counts: How accurately does the form relate to the content of the magazine? How much impact has been achieved with how few elements?

NEWSPAPER DESIGN

Edmund C. Arnold, CONSULTANT, NEWSPAPER DESIGN

While the designer of fine books and alluring advertising gets gold medals at Type Directors Shows, the designer of newspapers is rarely acclaimed. For every person who sees a fine book and reads a slick magazine, thousands read newspapers—but the newspaper typographer remains anonymous. Yet his work is as vital, as important, and as challenging as that of the designer of more conspicuous visual messages. In many ways, the visual problems the newspaper designer must solve are more demanding and more critical to effective communication in society.

The newspaper designer must consider three problems simultaneously: the mechanics of reading, the psychology of reading, and the economics of reading.

Because the newspaper reaches the whole spectrum of American population, it must appeal to people with a wide range of reading ability. The typographer must assure maximum ease, convenience, and comfort in reading.

In addition, the typographer must convince the reader beforehand that the newspaper is worth the effort of reading. A visually attractive newspaper in which the elements are arranged in an easy-to-follow and easy-to-look-at manner will draw the reader into the articles themselves. Always the aim is: turn the looker into a reader.

And always the newspaper typographer battles a budget. A newspaper is a consumer product in a highly competitive market; there is a ceiling on its retail price. Because the typography of a newspaper is a major cost in itself and a major factor in most other costs, it is a major factor in the selling price. The budget of time is an even greater constraint. There comes a point in the production cycle where you can't buy time. Adding a dozen pressmen can't speed up the revolutions of the press one bit.

So the format of a newspaper must be one that can be "dummied," not "designed," and made up quickly and easily. An ad is "designed": every element in it is specified to its own dimensions; nothing is standardized; each element must be positioned by measurement. News columns, however, must be filled with standardized modules. Every element must be in increments of column widths and must be placed on axes of column rules (hairlines between columns)—or the "alleys" of white space that have replaced them. There can be modifications, of course; but basically pages must be built from prefabricated modules to allow speedy makeup without sacrificing quality.

FUNCTIONAL TYPOGRAPHY

The single stone that kills three birds (or at least whomps them satisfactorily) is *functional typography.* This is a philosophy that demands that every printed element do a useful, necessary job of communicating —for communication is the only reason a newspaper exists.

We test elements by asking the question, "Does this element do a useful, necessary job?" If the answer is yes, then we ask, "Can we do this job faster, better, easier, more profitably?" But if the answer is no, we say "Throw it out!" Nonfunctional elements waste materials and time of handling, and they waste the reader's time, too.

By applying these criteria, American newspapers

Figure 3.36: <u>The Kansas City Star</u> in 1880. This issue (Vol. 1, No. 1) used typography typical of its time. Headlines were small, all one-column, and illustrations were nil. Interestingly enough, it was in six columns—a format considered an innovation decades later and adopted by many newspapers. *Courtesy of* The Kansas City Star.

have rid themselves of second and third decks of heads, column rules, most cutoff rules, 30-dashes, and assorted ornamentation. (Some of these design changes can be seen in figures 3.36 through 3.39.)

Most nonfunctional elements are also malfunctional. Not only do they fail to do a good job; they have a bad effect on the reader. Elements that fail to attract a reader distract him; those that fail to communicate quickly will waste the very limited time the hurried reader is willing to spend with a newspaper. The reader allots the same amount of time to every issue, fat or comparatively lean. It is the typographer's job to make sure that maximum information is acquired during that fixed span.

PAGE LAYOUT

The reader must be lured first into picking up a newspaper. Because most American newspapers are still home-delivered, that must be done in the reader's

Figure 3.37: The Kansas City Star in 1969. The Star looked somewhat conservative for the era but not too different from typical Midwestern metropolitans. *Courtesy of* The Kansas City Star.

home. Because only half of the folded front page is visible—and because it could be the lower half as readily as the upper—the "basement" is an important sales appeal. It must have a minimum of one strong picture and two strong, multicolumn heads.

Then editors seek to create "reader traffic," luring readers all the way through a paper, and "reader exposure," stopping them on a page long enough to read something, perhaps advertising, usually editorial matter. A crucial moment when many a reader is lost is that between the head and the body type. The path between those two elements must be as short and direct as possible. So must the "wraps," when type reads from one column into another. For this, page layout is a decisive factor.

Just as a hammer, a wheel, an aerodynamic shape are designed to do a specific job, so newspapers are designed for—and by—their function. And because the reader is an active participant in the transfer of information, the way he functions will also influence the form.

The reading eye enters the page, or any printed area such as an ad, in the top left-hand corner, the *primary optical area* (POA). When it reaches the lower right corner, it has finished the page; this is the *terminal area* (TA). The strong pull on the reading eye downward and to the right is as strong, constant, and unalterable as the pull of gravity. Like gravity, the pull can be modified somewhat. "Optical magnets" are used to direct the eye, especially into the "fallow corners," top right and lower left.

Just as we do not like to fight gravity by climbing stairs or a steep hill, the reading eye, no matter where it is on the page, resists attempts to make it go "against gravity"—upward, to the left, or anywhere in the arc between. These reading functions are determined by the Latin alphabet which reads left to right and top to bottom. Semitic alphabets create a POA in the top right corner. Ideogrammatic writing effects different reading paths, too.

The layout editor places a strong "attention compeller" in the POA of each page. That is where the reader first enters a page, and that first glance is the best point at which to capture his attention.

Advertising is pyramided to the right on all pages. This leaves the POA open for strong editorial display. Also, because columns get shorter as the reader proceeds across the page and fatigue sets in, he is subtly encouraged to continue. Right- and left-hand pages are designed the same way. The old technique of designing two-page symmetry by building ads up to, or away from, the gutter has proven nonfunctional. A two-page spread is far too large for the reader even to see at the 14-inch range of ordinary reading. So what is opposite a page is as immaterial as what is on the back of it; both are invisible to the reader.

Each page requires a "dominant headline," the obviously heaviest one on the page. This acts as a nucleus for a good page design. Where several heads are of the same approximate optical weight, the page looks disorganized and unattractive, accumulated rather than designed.

When two or more pictures are used in combination, one picture must be dominant for the same reason. This requires an area at least 50 percent greater than any other picture.

Pictures are being treated, more and more, according to the rules of functional typography: crop ruthlessly; enlarge generously; explain adequately.

Color is used boldly but in no more than three areas on a page; it is never allowed to compete with itself. For the same reason, headlines are kept as widely isolated as possible from each other. "Jammed heads" (those running adjacent horizontally are "tombstones"; a narrow one immediately under a wider one is an "armpit") are avoided. Each headline is a salesman, attempting to sell its story to the reader. Any salesman works best when the competitor is distant.

In essence, the fundamental design structure of any newspaper must allow specific page designs to be compiled daily by editorial people who use an "editing" approach to building layouts. Editing—whether in the manipulation of words or of nonverbal elements—

Figure 3.39: The Kansas City Star in 1979. The Star has reduced its page width by an inch and has gone back to its original six-column format of a century ago. Column and cutoff rules are gone. Headlines and photographs work to organize the page. *Courtesy of* The Kansas City Star.

Figure 3.38: The Kansas City Star in 1970. A complete overnight restyling in 1970 incorporated the principles of functional typography which had become almost standard by that time. *Courtesy of* The Kansas City Star.

is simply choosing among alternatives. When the layout editor decides to handle a head, picture, wrap, or ad pyramid in one way rather than another, he is choosing what to show the reader, how much, and what emphasis to apply in relation to the other contents of the paper.

OPTIMUM FORMAT

In response to reader needs, *optimum format*—six columns for a broadsheet, four for a tabloid—was developed. "Op" format gets its name from *optimum line length*. This is the measure that can be read most easily and swiftly, with minimum fatigue and maximum comprehension. Using the only mathematical formula that typographers own, the optimum line length is determined by multiplying the lowercase alphabet length of a font by 1.5. For a typical news font, that makes an

Figure 3.40: **The National Observer.** This weekly, a pioneer in op format, began in 1962 with basic newspaper typography. Later it started using more and more magazine techniques on its front page. In this issue from 1975, for example, the word "Torture" is set in Caslon Antique for connotative value. The panel at the bottom, advertising inside-page stories, has become a much-imitated device. *Copyright* © *1975 The National Observer. Reprinted with permission.*

optimum measure of about 14.9 picas. This formula also establishes a *readability range*, from Op − 25% to Op + 50%. Ignoring either limit places a heavy burden on the reader that the contemporary American is reluctant to assume. If the optimum is 14.9, then the shortest line we can set and expect a reader to consume efficiently and pleasurably is 11.2 picas. Most eight-column newspapers were significantly under that minimum; the optimum measure of 14.9 picas is one sixth, not one eighth, of a broadsheet. So the slow, and later suddenly burgeoning, trend to op format began.

The Wall Street Journal had long been in six columns, but it was less than nerve-tingling in typographic appeal. When its sibling *National Observer* was founded, it was demonstrated that op format can be as bright and lively as a format providing two more columns for maneuvering (see figure 3.40). However, the *Observer* was a weekly, and daily editors were little impressed.

Even when the daily *Christian Science Monitor* adopted optimum line lengths—in this case a five-column format because its fat body type had a long lowercase alphabet length (lca)—it was written off as atypical of other metropolitans.

It was *The Courier-Journal* and the *Times* of Louisville, pioneers in the use of Linotype and respected as journalistic purists, that established beyond cavil that a big daily could advantageously adopt op format (see figure 3.41). Some others followed. Typically it was the smaller dailies and weeklies that went all-out; larger papers used op format only on "key pages," those without ads.

Besides readability, there are other advantages to the op format. Longer lines reduce hyphenation from one in 5 lines of 11 picas to only two in 19 lines of 14 picas. This gives 3 percent more words per square inch. More importantly, end-of-line functions, which take substantial time in any setting operation, are reduced

Figure 3.41: **The Courier-Journal** of Louisville. The first metropolitan daily to adopt op format, The Courier-Journal customarily plays its lead story in the POA and always has strong display in the "basement." Horizontal layout is stressed throughout. Heads are "downstyle"; only the first word and proper nouns are capped. *Copyright* © *1975, The Courier-Journal. Reprinted with permission.*

Figure 3.42: <u>The Toronto Star.</u> The Toronto Star used a nine-column format until September 1978, when it adopted a six-column format, keeping the same 63-inch web. In April 1980, the web size was reduced to 58 inches and the six columns were narrowed accordingly. *Courtesy of The Toronto Star.*

by a third. End-of-column functions (for justifying columns) are reduced by 25 percent.

Op format reduces composing room costs. One publisher, who zealously guards anonymity, estimates a 17 percent saving during his first year in complete op format.

PROBLEMS AND PREDICTIONS

Complicating the use of optimum format has been the trend toward a narrower paper web. Since the days of newsprint rationing in World War II, the web has been steadily whittled down. It has continued to the point where many paper mills are attempting to make a 55-inch roll the standard (see figure 3.42).

To accommodate the narrower web, some publishers are spending substantial sums in "modifying" their presses. This makes about as much sense as paying someone to cut three feet off the end of every delivery truck. A principle that goes back to 1450 is that profitability demands maximum productivity. Any machine must produce at its maximum capacity, including printing presses. It makes no sense to use a 12″ x 18″ press to print business cards; it makes no more sense to revolve, man, amortize, heat, light, and pay taxes on 62 inches of cylinder while using only 55 inches thereof.

Even publishers who don't know a pica from a page proof come to realize that an 82-pica page—minus margins and intercolumn spacing, of course—divided

World

Ship seized —only to be stuck in ice

LEROUX Anisette 150x3 It's a natural.

Offering to the Pope

Park's grip on Korea may be slipping

We make all our cordials and liqueurs with natural flavors and we always will.

Kissinger's charm sways Mrs. Sadat

GOLDBLATT 158x8

Greatest Innovation! Greatest Value Ever!

SALE! WALL-GLIDER RECLINER

It GLIDES on a track . . . it needs to be only 1½ inches from the wall!

SAVE $40

119⁸⁸

Regular 159.88

Save 28% to over 38% Stylish Recliners 49⁸⁸ to 99⁸⁸

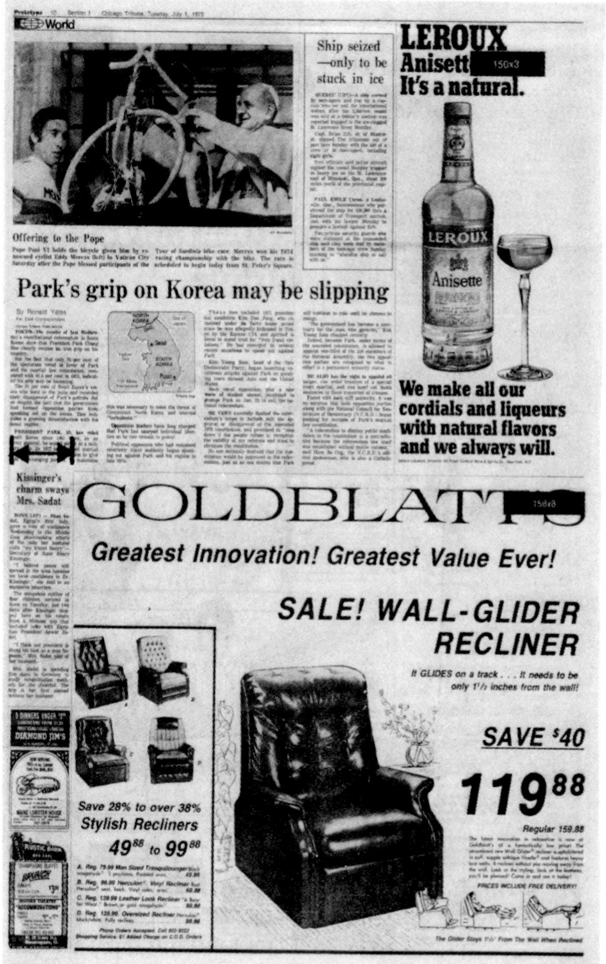

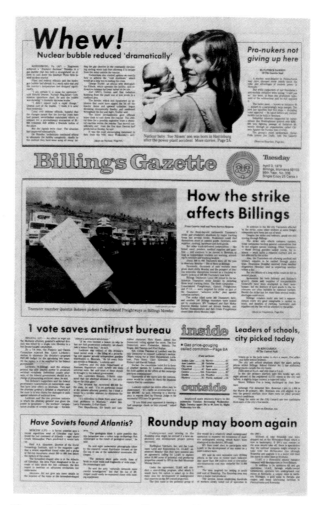

Figure 3.43: The Chicago Tribune. The Tribune replaced its former eight-column format with a combination format. Ad widths have been narrowed so that there are nine columns per page (one such column, marked with arrow, is in lower left corner); editorial matter is in six columns. The ad at top right is conventional three-column size and occupies two wide editorial columns. The ad at lower right is eight columns wide, formerly full-page width. Ad depths are measured in agate lines. *Courtesy of the* Chicago Tribune.

Whew!

Nuclear bubble reduced 'dramatically'

Pro-nukers not giving up here

Billings Gazette

Tuesday

How the strike affects Billings

1 vote saves antitrust bureau

inside

Leaders of schools, city picked today

outside

Have Soviets found Atlantis?

Roundup may boom again

Figure 3.44: The Billings Gazette. This paper uses conventional eight-column broadsheet format. However, most of the effect of optimum format is obtained by setting stories in two-column measure, as in the story to the right of the index; in column-and-a-half width, as in the lower right corner; and in bastard measure. On inside pages, one-column matter readily wraps around advertising set in conventional column units. *Courtesy of* The Billings *(Mont.)* Gazette.

into eight columns gives very slim line lengths. With self-congratulatory fanfare, they announce adoption of a six-column format. They fail to realize, however, that the magic is not in the six columns but in the approach to the optimum line length. On the narrow web, those six columns are barely past the readability minimum and significantly far from the optimum.

The *Chicago Tribune* solved the problem by retaining its web width, adopting a six-column format for editorial content but making up ads—and billing them —on the basis of a nine-column page (see figure 3.43).

For it has been the illogical measuring system of advertising that has complicated the entire situation.

Although a newspaper sells area, it bills in linear increments. Billing by the agate line instead of by square pica, square inch, or square anything is like selling land by the acre and pricing it by the furlong. But newspapers have traditionally used the agate system, and most ads are prepared according to this measure. The agate itself is an imprecise measurement, further complicating the situation. Newspapers that narrowed their columns in the past often stressed that they were maintaining old, economical line rates. But their advertisers knew that a price of *x* cents for an agate line 5½ points by 10 picas meant an increase over the rate of the same *x* cents for a line 5½ points by 11 picas.

Newspapers who think they are saving newsprint costs by adopting the narrow web are like the grocer who "saves" the cost of merchandise by selling only half as much. The only way a newspaper can save on newsprint is to raise rates, so that the smaller number of square inches of printing will return as much revenue as did the larger area of the wider roll. The real

saving would be to use the total width capacity of the press, print more square inches each time the cylinder revolves, but obtain more revenue from each of those square inches. That, of course, means raising rates, and publishers—quite properly—fear diminishing returns. There is the fear, usually expressed by advertising managers, that advertisers will interpret a change to op format as a hidden rate increase.

An answer seems to be adoption of an obvious pricing system—by square inch or, even more advantageously, by fractions of a page. The latter offers long-range benefits. If ads can be sold in modules specified by the newspaper, more advantageous use can be made of available space. Now a plethora of five-column ads, for instance, can force an increase of pages because, even though there are adequate column-inches still open, they are not in areas adequate to place such ads.

Some editors, looking far into the future, speculate that a century from now they may be publishing four or five newspapers. The customer could buy the news, sports, financial, family, and amusements sections separately or in combination—sort of a journalistic smorgasbord. Total newsprint consumption would be cut down. The packages would all be smaller, the reader would pay a larger share of the cost, advertising rates would be raised but could be justified by the extra exposure an ad would get with less competition.

Over the last two decades, the production and cost aspects of newspaper publishing have predominated in the thinking of the industry's executives, and with good reason. The computer is providing the means for totally automating the setting and makeup of pages, and new

Figure 3.45: The New York Daily News. The News, with the nation's largest circulation, maintains the tabloid format it invented nearly 65 years ago. *Courtesy of the* Daily News.

Figure 3.46: Newsday. This paper uses a tabloid-size page, but its front page has a strong magazine flavor. *Courtesy of* Newsday.

Figure 3.47: **The Providence Journal.** The *Journal* uses a six-column format. The illustrated summary-index, set in column-and-a-half width, always runs across the top of the page. Centered heads tend to create inconsistent indents that break reading rhythm. *Courtesy of* The Providence *(R.I.)* Journal.

Figure 3.48: **The St. Louis Post-Dispatch.** This famous Pulitzer prize winner epitomizes functional typography. It eliminates all extraneous elements: second decks, column and cutoff rules, 30-dashes, for instance. The page is "woven"; every alley is crossed by at least one multicolumn head. *Courtesy of the* St. Louis Post-Dispatch.

plate imaging systems, wire transmission facilities, and improved printing processes have greatly changed the ways in which newspapers are produced and the quality of their production. It is easier than ever to start a newspaper; the multimillion-dollar investments of the past have been scaled down to the production costs of a single issue and a good system for collecting ads for it.

But the big need is not for new hardware; it is for the realization that newspapers must first serve their subscribers, especially with the good typography that makes using the newspaper easy, convenient, pleasurable, and rewarding for the reader. The reader is the ultimate consumer; his needs must determine the form of the newspaper, for form always follows function. (Some examples of various approaches to newspaper design are shown in figures 3.44 through 3.48.)

Graphic solutions that come right to the point.

JACK ROTHMAN • GRAPHIC DESIGNER

Jack Rothman, designer of the cover, logo,
and introductory pages of this Graphic Arts Manual.
Available for all phases of graphic design.
From concept to printed piece.

15 East 26th Street, New York 10010 • 212/679-0199

**Our Designs
Work for You**

Concept through Completion

Catalogues, corporate identity, logo,
brochures, mailers, advertisements,
posters, packaging

Communigraphics
21 West 58th Street
New York, NY 10019
212/223-0985

CORPORATE IDENTITY
Kenneth D. Love, ANSPACH GROSSMAN PORTUGAL, INC.

Visual symbology associated with the promotion of services or products has been around for a long time. As long as people have had something to sell, there have been signs to advertise the fact. We all have a mental picture of the traveling salesman in his brightly painted wagon, peddling patent medicines to the horse-and-buggy households of our emerging nation. He epitomized the future of business in American life—highly visible, extremely mobile, and adaptable to rapid change. Other vanishing symbols of embryonic marketing are the symbol/signs associated with pawn shops, dry goods establishments and tailors, barber shops, shoe repair concerns, and gunsmiths. All of these used the most direct and literal interpretation of what they offered the public. Some still do.

As our society became more sophisticated, however, small businesses grew diverse and complicated, and so

Figure 3.49: Coca-Cola logotype. Logotype is shown as it is used today and as it appeared in a 1905 advertisement. *Courtesy of Archives, The Coca-Cola Company, Atlanta, Ga.*

did the way they identified themselves. The singular sign above the door no longer sufficed for the modern company. Two familiar forms of modern-day corporate identity, International Harvester and Coca-Cola, are both internationally known by corporate designs conceived decades ago. Although both companies recently updated their corporate design programs to fit current media needs, their identifying signs still retain an extremely close resemblance to the original concepts.

Coca-Cola, which was born and essentially remains a one-product company, has retained its familiar script signature from the earliest days of advertising. In fact, the original Coca-Cola logotype was designed in the late 1890's (see figure 3.49).

International Harvester, however, was created from several smaller companies and because of its great variety of products—mostly for the agriculture, construction, and transportation industries—chose a strong, dynamic "alphabet mark" to symbolize its existence. The bold *I* within the *H* was introduced in 1944 and can be considered one of the first modern-day corporate designs that has survived the test of time (see figure 3.50).

The first published concepts of the value of corporate design appeared in 1924 in a book entitled *A Book of American Trade-Marks and Devices*. It outlined the basic rules for corporate identity, recognizing that a trademark could set the character of a company and influence the appearance of a product, as well as printed material. The rules, which were illustrated by more than 300 trademarks, simply stated that a good mark had to be simple, yet unique, and flexible enough to suit all anticipated situations. Those points basically characterize successful corporate designs today.

While isolated examples of corporate designs which were developed in the early part of this century are still in evidence today, the 1960's produced a multitude of changes affecting graphic design for industry. During this period, large numbers of companies felt the need to update their public image by improving their visual communications. The primary reason for this corporate search for identity was the dilution, via multiple

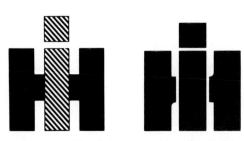

Figure 3.50: International Harvester logo. Symbol is shown as it originally appeared in 1944 (left) and in its present form. *Courtesy of International Harvester Company.*

IC Industries

ARISTAR

BFGoodrich

ESMARK

PRANGES

Figure 3.51: Logotypes.

mergers and acquisitions, of their public image. This trend did not cease during the economically turbulent 1970's. Today the number of changes in corporate structures appear to be as numerous as in the sixties. In addition, the role of the corporate entity has become more complex, both in scope of operations and in the range of products and services offered. During the past 25-year period, we have seen the rise of the "multinational" corporation, the "conglomerate," and the "service" company.

At the same time, there has been increasing concern with government regulation, consumer pressures, and environmental problems. The combination of these factors has made corporations extremely concerned with their public image and the manner in which they communicate this image. Undoubtedly, another cause has to do with the intangible motivation of "change for the sake of change." There exists an ever-present corporate need to keep up with competition; yet coincidental with a desire to remain one up is the need for conformity. The aim is to appear new and progressive at all times, whatever the cost, but within the limits of contemporary acceptability.

DESIGN TERMINOLOGY

The term *corporate identity* is often used to refer to the total impression a company makes on the public; however, it is more properly defined in a more specific sense. Three basic terms can be used to describe aspects of a company's total identity program: *corporate image, corporate identity,* and *visual communications.*

Corporate image is the conception that people have of a company. In order to form this mental image, people must become aware of the company's existence and character in one or more ways: by reputation (they can hear about it from another person); by direct experience (by working for it, doing business with it, or using its products or services); by direct observation (they see visible evidence of the company, such as factory buildings, signs, trademarks, products, advertisements, and the like). The people who form an impression of a company can be classified into various groups—customers, suppliers, stock brokers, financial analysts, shareholders, competitors, journalists, the general public, and the company's employees and management. Their conceptions are as frequently influenced by prejudices and emotions as they are by knowledge and reason.

Corporate identity refers to the visible elements which can be used to identify a company. The basic elements are the symbol and the logotype; it is important to note the difference between them.

A *logotype* as defined by most graphic designers is typography set in a unique style to identify a company or organization. Therefore, Mobil Oil Corporation's distinctive *Mobil* is considered a logotype, as is the script signature associated with Coca-Cola. (Some logotypes are illustrated in figure 3.51.)

A *symbol* is defined as a mark which by its association with a corporation or organization represents that entity by reason of relationship. When designers use the term *symbol,* it is usually to describe any element that is not the written word. For example, Eastern Airlines, Irving Bank Corporation, and the Continental Can Company utilize identifying marks which are usually referred to as graphic symbols. (Some graphic symbols are shown in figure 3.52.)

The corresponding typeface used to spell out the company name in conjunction with the symbol is the logotype. A symbol can be used singularly and solely as an identifying element or in conjunction with a logotype. Logotypes in many instances are used without symbols for the same purpose. A *trademark* (symbol and/or logotype) is a legally registered identifying element of a company (see "Copyrights, Patents, Trademarks, and Trade Secrets," page 599).

The symbol and logotype may be used in a wide variety of applications: on a company's products, equipment, stationery, and so on. A company can have a carefully planned, concise, and easily understood identity or one that is unplanned, unarticulated, and confusing. Considering identity as a whole image composed of diverse yet consistently similar parts is a major step toward the establishment of a corporate identity.

Visual communications are the tools which may be used to create and maintain a planned corporate identity. Every element of a company which is of a visible

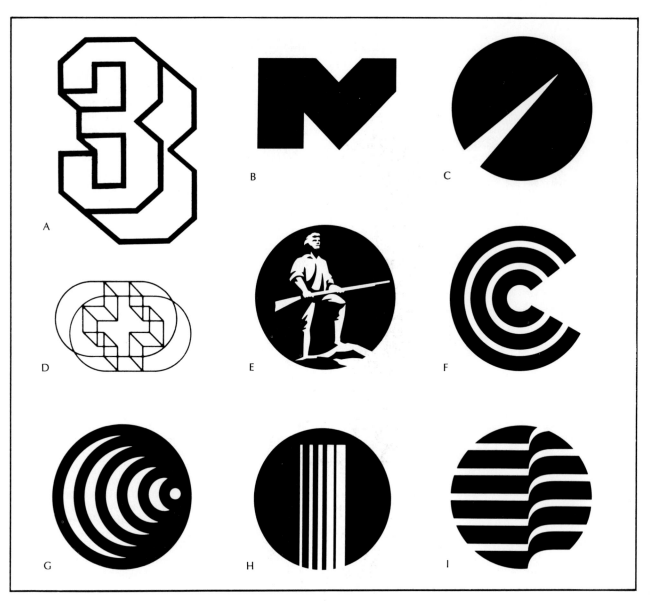

Figure 3.52: Graphic symbols. (A) Three Rivers Stadium, (B) Merit Oil Corporation, (C) Multibanco Comermex, (D) Curtis & Davis, Architects, (E) Sentry Insurance, (F) The Continental Group, (G) Ohio Center Entertainment Complex, (H) Irving Bank Corporation, (I) South Carolina National Bank.

nature can and should be used to reflect a consistent, accurate, and favorable identity. Visual communications can include brochures, advertisements, exhibits, business forms, letterheads, business cards, products and packages, labels, signs, offices, factories, reception rooms, delivery trucks, and other elements.

All elements of a company's visual communications system are important, simply because they are often the only form of contact that many people have with a company. Initial visual impressions are usually lasting impressions, and the fact that almost 80 percent of the information conveyed to us comes through just one of our senses—sight—proves the need for careful planning and proper design of a company's visual communications. If people see an antiquated symbol, poorly maintained buildings, deteriorating signs, or unimaginative advertisements, they will subconsciously endow the company with the same characteristics. Market research studies confirm that how people visualize a company has a marked effect on the sales of its products or services. Robert W. Sarnoff, former chairman of RCA Corporation and a staunch believer in strong graphics, once said: "A company's identity is at the heart of its marketing effort. Other things being equal, the customer's impression of a business firm can make the difference between a sale or no sale, between profit and loss."

The core of a well-planned corporate identity/visual

communications system is the design of the symbol and company name. These two primary elements of visual communication should be evaluated in several ways:

• Do they accurately and favorably represent the true nature and scope of the company now and as related to future plans?

• Are they distinctive enough to be easily recognized by customers and potential customers?

• Do they distinguish the company from its competitors?

• Do they suggest that the company is up-to-date and progressive, or do they suggest that the company is old-fashioned?

• Is there consistency in the use of symbol and name so that a single identity is constantly projected?

• Can the symbol and company name be easily reproduced in all media?

• Do the symbol and company name coordinate well with secondary trade names and symbols used to identify products, brands, or services so that these auxiliary names strengthen and support one identity?

If the answer to even one of the above questions is negative, it may be that the symbol and company name should be reevaluated. However, it may well be that an evolutionary, rather than a revolutionary, change may be the proper approach because of certain valuable equities that have accrued to a symbol and name over the years. In such cases, a modified design can serve to correct certain deficiencies while these equities are maintained and strengthened.

It is not enough to merely look "modern and progressive," nor will it do to "rubber stamp" a symbol and logo on signs, letterheads, labels, packages, and the like, without considering the design aspects of each item in the corporation's visual communication system.

The planning and design of a visual communications system is a job for an experienced professional designer, not a talented artist. The planning of visual communications in a total sense is the major contribution that a consultant designer can make in a corporate identity program. Few, if any, people in a company have the opportunity to see the company's total corporate identity, and it usually comes as a real surprise, indeed often a shock, when management is exposed to all factors of its existing visual communications. Frequently there is a marked absence of consistent design, lack of control, and unnecessary duplication that went unrecognized for a long period of time.

Symbols and logos should not be designed as abstract visual expressions. They always appear in the context of some specific application, such as a letterhead, a calling card, a building sign, a product nameplate, advertising, and the like. The designer must, therefore, consider applications concurrently with the other criteria which the symbol and logo must meet.

In each application, the overall design should harmonize with and reinforce the primary elements of corporate identity. An individual is primarily known by his name and his face, but he also comes to be recognized by his height, build, style of dress, and mannerisms. In the same sense a company's letterhead, for example, is recognized not only by the name and symbol printed on it, but also by the additional elements

of color, typography, layout, and paper stock. The same analogy can be applied to all types of visual communications.

Groupings of like or similar categories of visual communications should also share the same basic characteristics of design, so that the corporate identity is reinforced by a "family look." A well-planned system assures an optimum corporate identity.

A well-designed corporate identity/visual communications system provides many benefits:

• It allows management to precisely control the company's identity and to project the exact kind of identity that it wants the company to have.

• It provides the framework within which future acquisitions, new products, and new services can be quickly integrated under one common identity.

• It saves money in both production and inventory budgets—often enough to pay the initial design and implementation costs within the first year of use.

CORPORATE DESIGN PROGRAM

Most design programs are initiated with a research and orientation phase. Before beginning any work, however, the designer should chart a project schedule indicating periodic review sessions with management. This will save time and money and will automatically involve corporate management when critical decision points are reached.

Research and orientation phase

During the research phase of work, the designer (with management assistance) will establish criteria for a corporate identity system. This is done through management interviews which acquaint the designer with the workings of the company and its patterns of thinking. In addition to an in-depth understanding of company function, the research establishes what new direction the company may be taking in terms of diversification, acquisitions, and markets. A successful trademark should be a timeless symbol of the company's existence, as should the design of a corporate identity program.

During this initial phase of development, the designer should collect and photograph all existing graphic applications, as well as review all design work the company has produced. This will gauge the value of the items now in existence and will allow the designer to observe where current problems exist. For example, a company with an acceptable symbol or logotype may lack a satisfactory design program because of poor internal direction. Suggestions on better design application of existing elements may save the cost of a new identity. If a new identity is needed, preliminary research will set the pace and provide an outline for an overall design program. It will assist by narrowing the choice of alternate approaches before design is initiated.

Even though the designer is basically concerned with corporate communications, he must analyze the company's attitudes and goals in order to fully understand the corporation. Outlining corporate objectives is possible only after conference with the company's top management, and since most members of management usually see the objectives in different ways, a consensus must be reached.

After the research is completed and basic objectives are determined, the designers should translate these goals into the elements that represent the firm. These items are as varied as the corporations they represent. Certainly there would be a big difference between an identity program for a large university and an international oil company, or a small architectural firm and a major metropolitan department store.

The basic elements of a corporate design program could include any number of the following:
- Corporate mark (symbol, logotype, color)
- Typography
- Environmental design (office architecture, plant architecture, retail outlets, exhibits)
- Product design
- Package design
- Advertising
- Sales promotion
- Paper items (stationery, business forms, labels, containers, envelopes)
- Architectural signage
- Vehicle identification and uniforms
- Graphic standards manual (guidelines and regulations for use of the corporate identity elements)

Some of the applications of four corporate identity programs are shown in figures 3.53 through 3.56.

Conceptual design phase

Once the goals are established, the conceptual design phase can be initiated. During this phase alternate designs for symbol, logotype, and typography are developed. Preliminary designs are usually developed in black and white, in both positive and negative form. If the symbol or logotype is visually acceptable in this form, it is easy to add color and vary the line quality and other refinements later, after basic design principles are established. The symbol or logotype should be analyzed in both large and small scale, as a design that works on a company truck will not necessarily read well on a cafeteria matchbook. After the unsuccessful preliminary designs have been eliminated and a favored design direction has been established, the sym-

Figure 3.53: Logotypes and graphic symbols used in architectural signage.

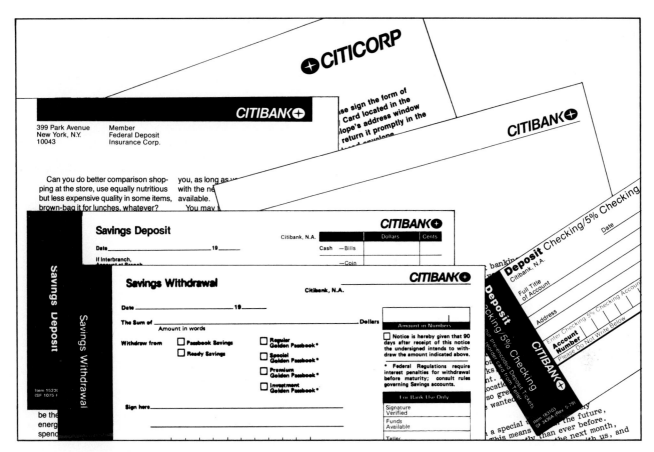

Figure 3.54: Logotype and graphic symbol used on paper items.

bol or logotype can be refined to include color. If the company name is to be used in conjunction with a symbol, typography should be selected, proportioned, and scaled to complement the symbol. At this time it should be determined whether symbol and logotype are flexible enough to fit all applications. They must be scaled to work with subsidiary divisions, affiliates, and all corporate applications which involve visual communications.

During this phase, periodic review sessions with management will keep them informed of progress and insure that the symbols and logotypes being explored are legally acceptable and can be registered and copyrighted.

Final design phase

The third phase of a corporate identity program is the final design phase. Once the basic symbol or logotype, typography, and colors have been mutually accepted by the designer and client, the major design elements are developed for a variety of applications in a comprehensive fashion. Applications would depend on the company's size and type of business but would generally include advertisements and other promotional pieces, stationery and business forms, products and packages, vehicle identification, signs, and other important visual aspects associated with the firm. The mock-up articles should be done in a finished manner

as realistically as possible to illustrate to management that the program represents their company with a clear and consistent image. They should be photographed and presented to the client through the use of 35mm slides in order to show them in their actual environment and to scale. For example, if a matchbook is illustrated, it should be photographed in someone's hand or adjacent to an ashtray or similar item to establish scale. Similarly, a corporate sign should be placed in the area for which it was designed, whether it be a reception area or a warehouse facility. The management of the corporation can begin to evaluate the importance and impact of the program only if the presentation shows the design as a total system.

Slides also allow the designer to maintain a consistent presentation. Usually, he will have to present the program to several layers of management, and slides provide a flexible system for communication. If changes or additions to the concept are made or the designer finds it necessary to alter the presentation because of a shift in the audience, slides provide the best vehicle for this purpose. It is also much easier to control an audience through the use of slides by allowing the viewer to concentrate on one subject at a time.

Graphic standards manual

Once the final design has been accepted, the next step is the development of the graphic standards man-

81

Figure 3.55: Logotype used in packaging design.

ual or guidelines. While this phase would be unnecessary for a small architectural firm with only a few items to be designed, it is mandatory for a large utility or a national airline which must communicate with a large and diverse internal organization, as well as the public. The manual sets forth rules and regulations for use of the visual elements of the corporation as a system. It describes the construction and use of the symbol or logotype, color applications, typographic style, and corporate nomenclature. It should describe in detail the use of these elements for all aspects of the system, including stationery, business forms, vehicles, signs, and promotional material such as print and broadcast media. The breadth of this manual will depend on the complexity of the organization, and its use and success will largely depend on the implementing body within the organization. A good, comprehensive design manual will not ensure a successful design program. A successful program depends upon consistent use of the manual by the corporation.

The graphic standards manual will assist the company with day-to-day design questions, although it will be necessary to update aspects of it as time goes by. There are always special situations and projects requiring design consultation, and there must be a con-

stant and religious policing of the program to insure that no errors in design are being introduced. Someone within or outside the corporate framework will always attempt to introduce some "new" element in order to give a personal touch to the system. Enough of these additions to the program will send management back to ground zero, and they can prepare themselves to start the design process all over again.

SUCCESSFUL CORPORATE DESIGN

Good design is good business. The visual characteristics of a business are as important as the development of new products, advanced engineering, quality control, manufacturing efficiencies, and aggressive marketing programs. All of these factors contribute substantially to the effectiveness and, consequently, the success of a company. Since the planning of a corporate identity program is a highly creative activity interrelated with corporate policy and planning, it requires the personal attention and judgment of a company's top management plus the skills, talents, and experience of professional corporate graphic designers.

There is no real mystery about what makes a corporate identity system succeed. It must be unique, it

Figure 3.56: Logotype used on annual report cover and matchbook.

must not go out of style, it must be workable for all applications, it must represent the corporation appropriately, and it must be clearly understood by the corporation's public. It must be well planned and used in a clear and consistent manner.

Since the integrity of the corporation is on the line, all elements involving visual communication must be of the highest quality, and the design should reflect a strong character and a definite style. After all the research, interviews, testing, and guidelines have been analyzed, as noted design critic Ada Louise Huxtable has said, "it is only the design that counts."

ANNUAL REPORTS
Bob Salpeter, LOPEZ SALPETER, INC

The thousands of publicly owned corporations in the United States that publish annual reports each year do so basically because they have to. The Securities and Exchange Commission requires some form of yearly financial report and has some hard-and-fast rules not only about what must be in it but even about such details as type sizes. As long as twenty years ago, some companies realized that annual reports could also fill a public relations need. Today, many companies have learned that annual reports can be valuable in the areas of recruitment, acquisitions, product sales, and, of course, sale of a company's stock.

Pick up almost any major annual report and you will find certain standard elements: a "Letter from the President," "Financial Highlights," the required "Financial Statements with Footnotes," and usually a list of "Directors and Officers." A designer generally starts an annual report knowing that these elements must be

included. Hopefully, the designer also has been given some overall corporate objectives such as emphasis on research, overseas facilities, the youthful outlook or, conversely, the years of experience of its executives. In an annual report designed for the American Cancer Society, for example, the organization wanted to stress the positive aspects of its work with particular emphasis on research. So an assortment of photographs was used to show how the ACS's dollars were put to work in aiding research throughout the United States (see figure 3.57).

Ideally, the day after a corporation mails out its annual report it should start planning and organizing its next one. This would assure a good selection of photographs of important events as they occurred, such as plant openings, breakthroughs in research, and other newsworthy events. Every designer would like to be brought in on a corporation's annual report early

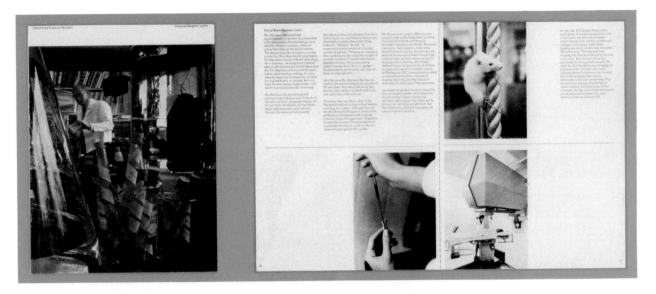

Figure 3.57: American Cancer Society Annual Report. The theme of this annual report was "Great Expectations." Research efforts throughout the United States were shown in photographs and discussed in text. Shown here are front cover (left) and an inside two-page spread. *Courtesy of the American Cancer Society.*

enough to arrange for high-quality photographs of these events. But this seldom happens, so annual report designers have learned to work around the problem by using other techniques to make the final report look good and work well.

SIZE

Generally, a company will insist on a standard 8½" x 11" size for their annual report, although sometimes a smaller or larger rectangle can be used. One good reason behind this is that financial analysts, stock brokers, and accountants—who are a vital audience—will want to keep annual reports in a normal-sized file folder. Some notable exceptions in large-sized annual reports have occurred over the past few years.

An example of a smaller size was an annual report designed for IBM World Trade Corporation (the international division of IBM). Paul Rand, the designer for IBM Corporation's annual report, had decided that a size other than 8½" x 11" would be a refreshing change after years of the standard size, so the international division followed suit in designing the international report. Of course, there was also a saving in paper costs. (See figure 3.58.)

COVER AND CONTENT

The design for the cover can often say something new or important about the company. For example, when the cover for Polychrome Corporation's 1973 Annual Report was being designed, the company had developed Flexomer, a new platemaking technique, and Uvimer, a family of liquid resins. It was decided that news of these products should be featured. Normally a vial of resin and a printing plate are not very exciting to look at; but the annual report cover was

designed with a dramatic square of metallic silver leaf debossed to suggest the back of a printing plate. Inside the cover was the front of the printing plate, and on the first page was the copy exactly as it would reproduce from the plate (see figure 3.59). Opening the cover in effect simulated the process of printing the page. The result was simple and dramatic, and the accompanying explanation of the two new products on the inside front cover seemed perfectly logical.

Sometimes the best approach is a basic presentation of the financial facts with no embellishment. In such cases, an elegant execution can reflect and enhance the quality of the company. An example of this is an an-

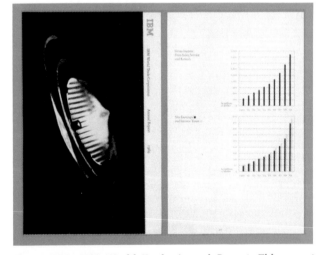

Figure 3.58: IBM World Trade Annual Report. This report was designed in smaller than usual size. Simple graphs of income, earnings, and taxes speak for themselves. Shown are cover and an inside page. *Courtesy of International Business Machines Corporation.*

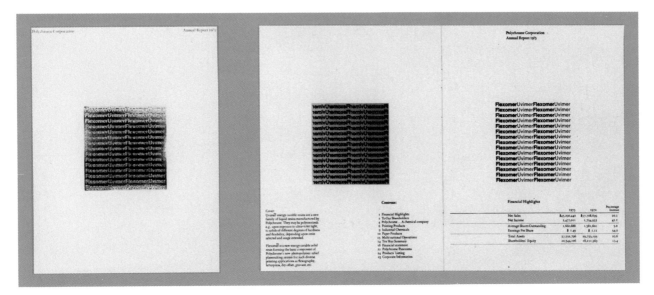

Figure 3.59: Polychrome Corporation Annual Report. On front cover (left), metallic silver leaf is debossed to suggest the back of a printing plate. The front of the plate is repre- sented on the inside cover, and the theme is continued on the first page, which shows the printed result. *Courtesy of Polychrome Corporation.*

nual report for the stock brokerage firm, Shearson, Hammill & Co., Inc. (now Shearson Hayden Stone, Inc.). To convey a feeling of solid progress in a time of rapid change in the securities industry, the pages of the report were printed on sedate, buff-colored stock with no photographs, charts, or drawings. The cover design was simply the name of the company formed by a series of horizontal lines embossed on a dull coated white cover stock (see figure 3.60).

Another way to use a cover as a basic design element is shown in an annual report system devised for Lord Abbett, an investment firm with a number of funds, each of which required a report. Here the idea

to be conveyed was of four different funds within a single company. Four separate booklets were designed, one for each fund, all having the same basic style and format and similar content. A color was assigned to each fund and used as a tint behind an appropriate photograph on the cover of the booklet discussing that fund. The same color was used inside each report as a second color to highlight important statements in the text and to make the charts more readable. Thus color was used both as a thematic element within each individual report and as a unifying style element to link all four funds.

One thing that all annual reports have in common

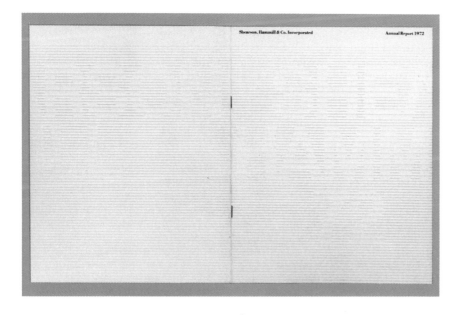

Figure 3.60: Shearson, Hammill Annual Report cover. The white embossed cover contrasts with buff-colored stock used for inside text, to convey a solid, businesslike look. *Courtesy of Shearson Hayden Stone, Inc.*

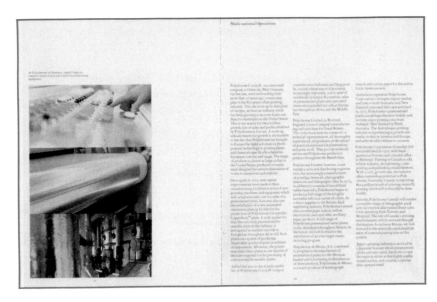

Figure 3.61: Use of grid in Polychrome report. As with most well-designed annual reports, a grid was used for the Polychrome annual report. There is a unity throughout the report, yet each spread has a look of its own. *Courtesy of Polychrome Corporation.*

is that financial data must be shown. In some cases it is in the form of bar charts, line graphs, and similar devices (see "Charting: The Basic Facts," page 264). Entire books have been written on the subject of graphic presentation of financial data. The aim is always to present the figures in an understandable way and to make the presentation fit in with the rest of the annual report.

FORMAT

Annual report designers have learned to work with a minimum of time and a maximum of last-minute changes. Even beginning with as much as two months' design and production time, which is a luxury, a designer usually finds change after change being made, as the deadline nears, in everything from the financial tables to the photograph of the president and the chairman of the board. So if there is one word to remember in annual report design, it is *flexibility*.

To cope with last-minute changes as the year's re-

sults are figured out, a layout based on a grid system is essential (see "The Grid System," page 39). Otherwise, the printed report is likely to look disorganized and leave a confusing impression. When a grid has been developed, all changes can be effected without wasted effort and without endangering the unity of the report. If the company needs to add something vital after the report is in type and positioned in the mechanical, the designer can work within the grid to position the new element without destroying the design of the page and may even arrive at a better format.

A grid does not necessarily make every page look the same. It is only a framework within which a designer works and which serves to help hold the entire report together visually. The Polychrome report is a good example of how the various spreads can have both unity and an individual look (see figure 3.61).

Annual reports may be something that corporations have to do, but for all their restrictions they offer exciting creative challenges to the designer.

are your designs eye-catching

kathleen jackson studio • 160 front street, n.y.c. 10038 • 425-1948

BROCHURES AND CATALOGS
Bob Salpeter, LOPEZ SALPETER, INC.

A designer working on a brochure or catalog is confronted with a set of interesting challenges. Generally, a considerable amount of information must be organized logically and presented in a readable and understandable manner, with a uniform style that is in keeping with the subject matter. But if the designer merely meets these criteria, he or she may well end up with a finished piece that, while thorough and complete, fails to meet another vital requirement. Starting with the cover, the brochure or catalog must in some way get the reader interested and intrigued and involved. (In a sense, the cover is an advertisement for the brochure itself.) Some people receiving the piece may be interested enough in the subject to devour the information regardless of how it is presented. However, considering the extraordinary volume of printed material passing through people's hands today, it is evident that the piece must meet rigorous standards in order to receive the attention necessary to do its job of informing and of helping, directly or indirectly, to sell the product or service covered.

BROCHURES

A brochure designed for the IBM 72 Composer used a provocative cover to attract the reader and to suggest a theme which was to be carried through the brochure: the combining of new and efficient technology with traditional standards of typographic excellence. The cover was meant to speak for itself, but without using a single word. It showed a "golf ball" font of type from the IBM Composer sitting in a "California job case," normally used in composing rooms to hold a complete alphabet of metal type. To the audience, most of whom had already heard of the IBM 72 Composer, the cover evoked a feeling of tradition and quality typesetting and told in a glance what the new product could do for them. (See figure 3.62.)

Inside the brochure, the theme was continued. The first spread showed the reader that the machine was like a normal electric typewriter in appearance and stressed efficiency and high quality. The second spread pointed out that the machine continued the traditions of classic typography by offering all five of the basic major type styles. The brochure went on to describe the versatility and ease of operation of the machine. A short note told the reader that all the copy in the brochure had been set by the IBM 72 Composer. Lastly, the cover was die cut to hold the business card of the IBM sales representative.

Another way to use a brochure to illustrate a product in action is shown by a piece designed for the Gold Bronze Powder Council entitled "The Golden Touch," which promoted the use of metallic gold bronze in visual communications. While the cover of the previous brochure used a photograph with no words, here the cover showed only the three words of the title printed on a large expanse of metallic gold bronze.

Figure 3.62: IBM 72 Composer brochure. A provocative cover was used to get readers interested in the informational aspects of the product, detailed within. *Courtesy of International Business Machines Corporation.*

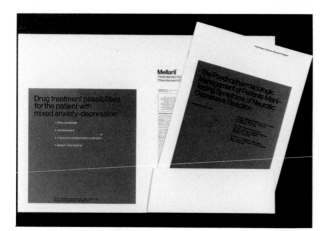

Figure 3.63: Sandoz Pharmaceuticals brochure. Literature on Mellaril used basic folder to hold printed pieces, allowing literature to be tailored and updated. *Courtesy of Sandoz Pharmaceuticals.*

Once again, the cover was designed to be provocative. Because it was assumed that the readers—designers, printers, and art directors—would be primarily interested in examples of the product at work, the text was limited to short-fold pages. The brochure showed examples of gold bronze ink in a variety of applications: for illustration, photography, line drawing, and so on. The text, which discussed the technique of using gold bronze powder, was kept separate from the actual samples, allowing full pages for effective presentation of the illustrations. Different paper was used for text and illustrations in order to highlight the metallic printing, which after all was the hero of the piece. The back cover held removable samples of the four basic gold bronze colors.

Another printed piece which used a cover with no words was done for Sandoz Pharmaceuticals on a drug called Mellaril. Here the cover consisted of head-on photographs of four faces selected to show anxiety and depression. Inside were a brief listing of indications for which Mellaril was effective and a detailed listing of such factors as precautions and contraindications.

Since the brochure would go to a number of different physician audiences, each of which might be interested in a different feature of Mellaril, it was designed as a folder that a Sandoz representative could tailor for his prospect by adding appropriate material. One such piece was a booklet showing a preliminary clinical research report which used charts and graphs to show the results of a double-blind study. (See figure 3.63.) This is an example of literature that can be updated or adjusted to meet specific needs at reasonable cost.

One aspect of printed pieces often ignored by designers is the element of time. Turning the pages of a booklet brings this element into play, so that it is possible to simulate a slide presentation or other kind of time continuum. An example of this is a simple eight-page booklet for IBM announcing "Closeup," a radio series on computers. As shown in figure 3.64, the right-

Figure 3.64: IBM radio program promotion booklet. Cover of closed booklet is shown at top; subsequent two-page spreads follow below. As the pages of the booklet are turned, the word "close-up" appears to move closer and closer, graphically illustrating the title and concept of a series of short radio programs on computers. *Courtesy of International Business Machines Corporation.*

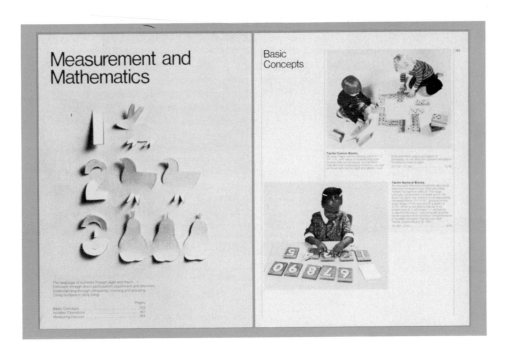

Figure 3.65: Childcraft cata-log. Spread shows paper sculpture and first page of "Measurement and Mathe-matics" section of catalog. *Courtesy of Childcraft Education Corp.*

hand pages bring the word *closeup* closer and closer with each turn of the page, suggesting a recurrence over a period of time and illustrating graphically the name of the program.

CATALOGS

While brochures such as those discussed offer the designer a fairly wide field in which to work, catalogs are generally more restricting. A client has a large number of items he wishes to illustrate and almost always has existing photographs he plans to use in order to keep costs down to a manageable level. Working within such a framework presents a considerable challenge to the designer because the options are limited. If the designer can tie the elements together in a meaningful way, however, it is often possible to end up with a piece that presents the client's products in a new and inviting manner.

An example is a catalog for Childcraft, a company which makes educational toys. The company wanted a piece of literature that would present their thousands of products so that educators and parents would clearly see the importance of the toys during a child's growing years. A full-color cover was designed that showed a group of youngsters, each peering out from one of a dozen hinged openings. The cover offered to the reader an invitation to enter the world of children. Inside, the catalog was separated into 14 categories such as "Environment for Learning," "Active Play," "Eye-Hand Coordination," and "Language Development." Each category was introduced with a photograph of a piece of paper sculpture relating to the products presented in that section. Throughout the catalog, the toys were shown being used by children who were completely caught up in what they were doing. The catalog conveys the impression that the toys are meaningful and durable yet avoids an overly pedantic approach (see figure 3.65).

Sometimes a catalog must be done with no photographs or illustration. To prevent it from being merely a dry listing of products or services, some idea must be developed. An example is a catalog of films prepared for IBM World Trade Corporation. Since most IBM films covered more than one subject, the brochure had an alphabetical table of contents listing the films, plus a convenient chart-like device providing cross-indexing by subject (see figure 3.66). After finding the films that included something on the subject in which he was interested, the reader could refer to the page number

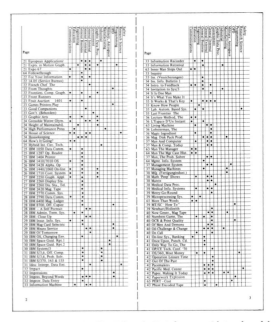

Figure 3.66: IBM Audio Visual Catalogue. List of subjects across the top of each page of the alphabetical table of contents helped the reader to locate films of interest. *Courtesy of International Business Machines Corporation.*

listed with the name of each film to find a complete description.

The problem of organizing a large body of information in an interesting and meaningful way faces the designer in developing both brochures and catalogs.

While the emphasis may be different and the amount of flexibility allowed the designer may vary, the concept of unity is essential to an effective printed piece of any size.

DIRECT MAIL DESIGN
Jim Cokeley, FREE-LANCE COPYWRITER

Direct mail is a specific discipline within the advertising industry. It is one of the oldest forms of advertising, yet it is often considered the newest: in recent years, direct mail has been rediscovered. Direct mail encompasses a wide variety of advertising materials, such as letters, postcards, brochures, and catalogs, which are intended to sell a product to a specific audience. It is a most effective medium for selectively pinpointing a market—doctors, nurses, retired people, teenage girls, or golfers, for example.

Direct response—a broader concept than direct mail—is the use of any advertising medium (which can include radio, television, newspapers, magazines, and even matchbooks, as well as mail) to get a direct reaction, specifically an order or inquiry, from the reader or listener. Through such response, advertisers can build a core of dependable future customers for follow-up sales, and for the sales of additional products. But the broad direct response media do not enjoy the high degree of selectivity that is possible with direct mail.

With direct mail, each market is pinpointed and each effort is precisely measured in terms of results. It is not enough to scatter a message broadly, or to create an image, or to develop good will, or even simply to assume that the direct mail campaign is doing its job. Direct mail must continually be refined until it produces the lowest cost per inquiry or the lowest cost per order. A difference of one-half of one percent in response might not be a matter of major concern to a general advertiser (or even be measurable), but that percentage can make or break a direct mail advertiser.

Direct mail can be used well, and it can be used badly (as it often is). Perhaps even more significantly, it is often completely overlooked when its unique effectiveness could be invaluable.

From a graphics point of view, direct mail has too often been viewed with disdain. (After all, haven't the most effective mailing envelopes, proved time and time again, proudly announced the same old words *new, news,* or *free?*) On the other hand, direct mail can be approached as an exciting challenge. Many successful practitioners are proving that this challenge can be met with advertising that is both practical and interesting, both effective and exciting. It can be highly inventive, and highly challenging to the art director. However, direct mail cannot be satisfied to win awards (although

it may) or win the plaudits of other art directors (although it may do that, too). The best direct mail exhibits effective graphic ideas and distinctive design, but it uses these within a specific discipline that must produce measurable results.

ADVANTAGES

Before moving into specific graphic treatments, it might be well to review the major advantages of direct mail. Direct mail offers something special to its recipients; this may be why it sells over fifty million dollars' worth of goods and services a year.

Convenience is one of the main advantages offered by direct mail. For many products and services, buying by mail is uniquely convenient. This important aspect of direct mail should be worked into the design, format, and verbal message of direct mail materials. Direct mail allows people to use credit cards to make their purchases; this affects the presentation of the offer and the reply device. Shopping by mail saves on gas and transportation costs, an important selling point today. It eliminates the inconveniences of crowds, time-consuming shopping trips, parking, "out-of-stock" problems, nighttime shopping worries. It is especially important to senior citizens, the handicapped, and shut-ins: awareness of this audience should affect the designer's thinking about the design of direct mail pieces.

Direct mail is unique in the way it reaches its reader. The graphics used should fit into and enhance the following specific advantages of direct mail:

• Direct mail is selective. It can address itself very specifically to an audience: retired school teachers, women lawyers, football coaches, or people who own Volkswagens. It can pinpoint a market and talk directly to that market.

• It is person-to-person. Whether it is computerized to "Mr. Phillips" or addressed to "Dear Subscriber" or "Dear Customer," the message is distinctly personal.

• It is basic for testing. Direct mail is perfect for the small-scale, controlled testing of ideas, concepts, creative approaches, offers, prices, product features, design.

• It receives undivided attention. If the message and the recipient are properly selected, the mailer wins the full attention of the reader, free of competition from entertainment, other messages, and other advertising.

• It allows ideal timing. Direct mail can be used precisely at the most effective time, without concern for publication dates or other restrictions.

• It allows for great variety in format. There is no limitation to the page or minute, as in print or broadcast media, and there is opportunity for creative variety. Of course, there are postal and budget restrictions, but there is great flexibility in terms of unusual shapes and designs, attention-getting devices, and enclosures.

• It allows variation in copy length. Direct mail offers unusual flexibility in communication; its verbal message may be long or short. Usually, direct mail copy is plentiful, providing reasons for buying and advantages of the product in persuasive detail.

• It includes reply devices. Direct mail is best known for the fact that it asks for the order immediately. An important consideration in design is a way of making response easy—enclosing a postage-paid reply card, for example. Providing vague instructions or saying "see your nearby dealer" is not effective enough. The point is to act now, send now, do it now.

While graphics are extremely important in direct mail, design has to be considered within these basic direct response considerations. Creative ideas in direct mail are extremely important and are challenging to the designer, but they generally begin from a broader base than copy or art or graphics alone.

FORMAT

When an overall idea for a direct mail piece has been established, one of the main design problems is establishing a format. The most basic of direct mail formats is the letter. Of course, a letter is not automatically the best answer to a marketing problem (direct response, as mentioned earlier, may make use of an array of media ranging from television to matchbooks), but letters are basic in direct mail. A letter is a personal communication; it will interest the reader if the subject matter is of concern to her or him.

However, many things can be done with a letter. Is the letter worth the cost of computer personalization? Should it be one page or four pages? Should the direct mail package "tease" the reader on the envelope or straightforwardly tell him something he wants to know? Would a plain, simple envelope be more credible to the reader than a colorful, obviously more designed envelope? Should something special be done with the letter? Would an unusual concept or graphics handling increase response effectively and economically? Some common variations of the basic letter format are:

Letter with enclosure. There is an almost unlimited possibility for enclosures, but the basic ones are folders, broadsides, booklets, brochures, and circulars. These are methods of providing "reason why . . . *more* reason why."

Self-mailer. This means that there is no separate envelope—simply one piece, ranging from a postcard or single page to a multi-page folder.

Catalogs and price lists. These range from the simplest listing of prices to the most complex, colorful catalog. Readers who have been well selected—whether coin collectors or boat owners or buyers of clothing—will enjoy seeing a "menu" of offerings.

Special "newsletter," bulletin, report format. People love to read "news" when it applies to them.

Product samples. When the product lends itself to sampling, this has long been a most effective technique.

Couponing. Offering a special money-off incentive can also be an effective technique.

READER INVOLVEMENT

There are many reader involvement techniques. Direct mail pieces can get the reader to "do something" by many methods. It can pop up, punch out, paste on, or demonstrate. Direct mail can provide the reader with a "stamp" to tear out and send back; it can request him to send back his opinion as part of a research project; it can give him samples to experiment with and gadgets to play with.

Consider these examples of creative direct mail design:

• One highly successful mailing, which required the respondent to check an area of interest, included a pencil to do the checking off with. This technique provided a free sample and involved the reader in the mailing piece.

• Another successful mailing aimed at persuading nursing-school graduates to consider an Army nursing career used a recording of comments by Army nurses in active conversation. These comments were completely candid, not "professionally written," and believable. Results were gratifying.

• A mailing to employers from a temporary employment service used a "panic button" on the envelope, for the recipient to push. The message, of course, was that the service provides an alternative to pushing that button when sudden needs for extra help occurred.

• A manufacturer wanted to introduce a new floor tile that needed no waxing. To demonstrate rather than merely state this advantage to architects and contractors, the company sent out a complete "demolition kit" that included a sample of the product, a ball-point pen, a crayon, a cigarette, and a book of matches. The recipients were invited to try to ruin the tile. A buffer pad was included for repairing the damage. This was an outstanding example of establishing believability through actual demonstration and reader involvement; it achieved outstanding success.

Through graphics, the designer tries to capture the reader's interest and make him a participant in a project. In this way, the graphic concept can make an important contribution to the impact of the direct mail piece. However, it is important not to jump into direct response with undisciplined creativity alone, without thorough study of the medium, its successes, and its less-than-successes. It is imperative to obtain the counsel of experienced professionals.

MANUSCRIPT PREPARATION

4

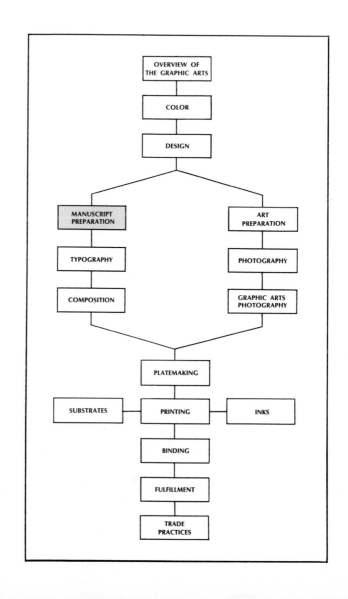

OVERVIEW OF
THE GRAPHIC ARTS

COLOR

DESIGN

MANUSCRIPT
PREPARATION

ART
PREPARATION

TYPOGRAPHY

PHOTOGRAPHY

COMPOSITION

GRAPHIC ARTS
PHOTOGRAPHY

PLATEMAKING

SUBSTRATES — PRINTING — INKS

BINDING

FULFILLMENT

TRADE
PRACTICES

THE EDITING PROCESS
Stanley E. Loeb, FREE-LANCE EDITOR

Editing is the process of getting an author's work ready for typesetting and publication. The editorial group in any publishing unit is responsible for the following general tasks: (1) preparing manuscript (often called *copy*) for production, working closely with the author(s), designer, and manufacturing coordinator; (2) handling galley and page stages, including correcting proofs and resolving design (dummy) and art layout problems; (3) approving final composition stages and performing attendant in-house tasks related to publicity and publication itself.

These general tasks assume different proportions in different publishing enterprises. A trade book editor's job may involve a great deal of publicity and promotion, while a technical journal editor may not perform any promotional work. The editor of comic books may concentrate on art and design, the newspaper editor on written copy.

Editorial responsibilities are divided in several ways, depending on the publication medium, the kind of publishing house, and even the type of department within a large house. Some editors—usually chief editors, managing editors, or acquiring editors—have heavy responsibility for evaluating and accepting material from authors, while others work only in the later stages of copy preparation. In some newspapers, magazines, and in-house company publications, the editors also are the writers.

MANUSCRIPT PREPARATION

An editor reads every manuscript (1) to assess the author's organization, logic, style, strengths, and weaknesses, and (2) to perfect the punctuation, grammar, and usage as set up by the house or its designated authority.

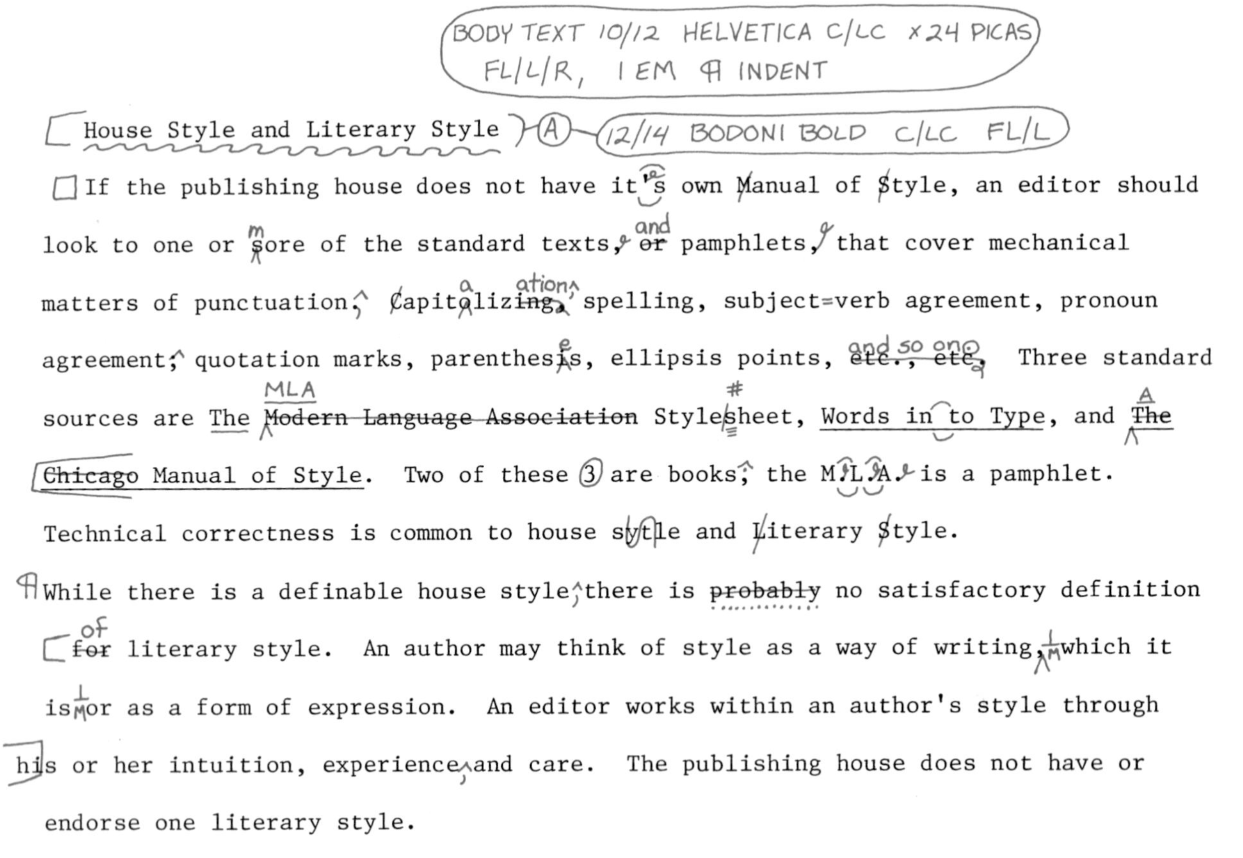

BODY TEXT 10/12 HELVETICA C/LC x 24 PICAS
FL/L/R, 1 EM ¶ INDENT

[House Style and Literary Style — (A) — 12/14 BODONI BOLD C/LC FL/L

□ If the publishing house does not have its own Manual of Style, an editor should look to one or more of the standard texts, and pamphlets, that cover mechanical matters of punctuation, capitalization, spelling, subject=verb agreement, pronoun agreement, quotation marks, parentheses, ellipsis points, and so one. Three standard sources are The Modern Language Association (MLA) Stylesheet, Words in to Type, and The Chicago Manual of Style. Two of these 3 are books; the MLA is a pamphlet. Technical correctness is common to house style and literary style.

¶ While there is a definable house style, there is no satisfactory definition for literary style. An author may think of style as a way of writing, which it is, or as a form of expression. An editor works within an author's style through his or her intuition, experience, and care. The publishing house does not have or endorse one literary style.

Figure 4.1: Sample page of edited manuscript.

The editor's first task may be to determine whether or not a manuscript is "satisfactory"—whether it meets the publisher's needs, intents, and standards. Often a book editor sends the manuscript to outside readers, authorities on the subject, for advice on its timeliness, accuracy, and freshness.

The manuscript editor also compiles suggestions, observations, and questions that will enable the author to tighten the organization, recast sections, add facts, and so on. In book publishing, the editor usually does not attempt to rewrite or substantially add to the manuscript, except where he or she is an expert and has the author's trust and permission. In the journalistic media, the editor rewrites as a matter of routine. Deletions and simplifications are routinely undertaken by editors in every type of publishing, as are modifications of sentence style.

When the overall content of the manuscript is satisfactory, style and content are refined. More specific aspects of language—such as grammar, capitalization, spelling, and punctuation—are perfected. These elements are usually called *copy editing*. Often copy editing is performed by a person other than the editor who makes content decisions. The copy editor usually works directly on the manuscript, writing in corrections in standard form. Figure 4.1 is a sample of how a manuscript page is edited.

While the material is being edited, attention must be given to the final form in which it will be presented. In book publishing, after the author and editor agree upon the organization and development of the manuscript, the editor requests preliminary design of the material. In conference with an art director and/or a designer, the editor presents the major characteristics, needs, and goals of the book. Sample pages are drawn and set for the editor's approval.

In other media, the design of the publication may be predetermined. On a newspaper, for example, all headlines are designed to standard specifications; the editor simply selects one specific style and writes the head to fit the specifications. Similarly, page makeup involves the assembly of type and illustrations preset to standard measures; the newspaper makeup editor simply sketches a rough diagram or dummy of the page, arranging these standardized units on the basis of content, length, and importance. Many magazines and other media make extensive use of standardized design but permit some freedom for customized layouts in certain sections. Typically in a magazine the treatment of front and back matter is standardized so that editors can handle this material without consulting designers, but the feature section is designed page by page with editors and designers collaborating closely.

Editors do not dictate to designers; a well-designed book or article reflects their mutual understanding. A design must also make economic sense, taking into account information from a manufacturing coordinator about type, paper, printing method, and schedules. Either the editor or the designer later marks the copy-edited manuscript for composition, specifying all the elements of the agreed-upon design, as in figure 4.1.

In addition to preparing the text, the editor may work closely with the designer in selecting illustrations and reviewing artwork for technical accuracy in relation to the text. The editor may assist the photo researcher, making final selections and preparing captions as necessary. While art credits and photo permissions are usually assembled by members of the art department staff, the inclusion of these credits in the publication is the editor's responsibility. Further, it is an editorial task to secure or oversee all permissions relating to the text, whether these are requested by the author or by the editorial staff. Inclusion of such credits are often last-minute matters that demand close attention and accuracy.

When the manuscript is released by the editor for composition, it bears the standard markings of copy editing and copy marking. Questions of fact and author's idiosyncrasies have been discussed and settled. Changes in typeset materials are so expensive that the editor needs to release as perfect a manuscript as possible.

RESPONSIBILITIES DURING COMPOSITION

The editor's responsibility does not cease when the manuscript is sent to composition. The first proof, usually in galley form (see "The Composition Process," page 190), is sent by the editor to a proofreader, to the designer if a dummy layout of pages is to be prepared, and sometimes to those responsible for publicity, who may engage the editor in their campaign. In the book industry and sometimes in other types of publishing, proofs are sent to the author as well. The editor reads this first proof with extreme care, marking three kinds of corrections: printer's errors (P.E.); author's alterations (A.A.); and minor line alterations—sometimes called house alterations—to distinguish them from author's changes—to justify column lengths on pages, to remove widows (very short lines at ends of paragraphs), and to accommodate the text to page breaks, art inserts, and other non-text demands. When all sets of galleys bearing changes are in hand, the editor transfers the changes to the printer's set, stamped "master." A wise editor will make a duplicate of the master.

The compositor's own proofreader reads and marks the master proof before it is sent to the editor, directing queries to the editor and corrections to the compositor, but seldom picks up all typographical errors, transposed lines, or inappropriate word breaks. It is usually a good idea for the editor to mark the master galleys in a color different from that used by the supplier's proofreader. Corrections are marked in the margins of the galley proofs, using proofreaders' symbols (see figures 4.2 and 4.3).

Page proofs, or second-stage proofs, should reflect all changes called for on the master galleys; the editor reviews these changes and works with the designer to resolve all problems of fit. Page proofs enable work to begin on the index and the front matter of a book.

In periodical publication, the final approval of page proofs is typically the last step before the editor sees the finished product. In book production, however, several additional checking steps may be performed by the editor, depending on the project.

Reproduction proofs are the camera copy from which the book will be photographed. They are printed on

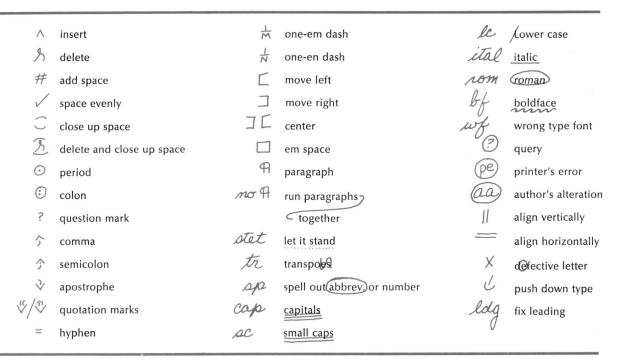

∧	insert	⊥/M	one-em dash	*lc*	lower case
⅄	delete	⊥/N	one-en dash	*ital*	italic
#	add space	⊏	move left	*rom*	(roman)
✓	space evenly	⊐	move right	*bf*	boldface
⌢	close up space	⊐⊏	center	*wf*	wrong type font
⅄	delete and close up space	▢	em space	(?)	query
⊙	period	⁋	paragraph	(pe)	printer's error
⊙	colon	*no* ⁋	run paragraphs together	(aa)	author's alteration
?	question mark			‖	align vertically
↱	comma	*stet*	let it stand	=	align horizontally
↱	semicolon	*tr*	transpose	×	defective letter
↓	apostrophe	*sp*	spell out (abbrev.) or number	↲	push down type
⁇	quotation marks	*cap*	capitals	*ldg*	fix leading
=	hyphen	*sc*	small caps		

Figure 4.2: Standard proofreaders' marks. Symbols are shown, followed by their meanings. In cases where one symbol is usually used in the margin and another within the text area, the latter is shown to the right.

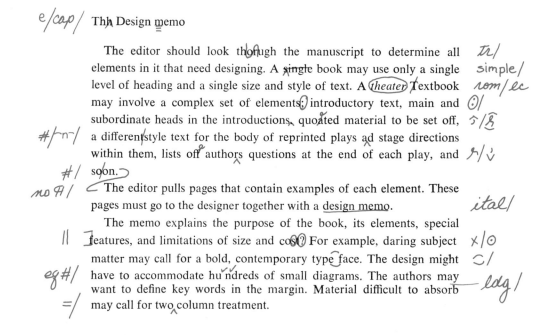

Figure 4.3: Sample galley as marked by proofreader.

coated paper on which the editor marks errors, if any, in a nonreproducing light blue. Repro patching can often be handled by the art department, giving the editor the assurance of final release of correct proofs. Otherwise, corrected repros are sent to the editor for confirmation. Release of camera-ready repros marks the last step of the compositor's involvement with the material, but may not be the editor's.

Often the printer sends photographic prints made from negatives used in platemaking; these blues (or browns, or silvers, or ozalids, as they may also be called) enable the editor to see that all art and text are in proper position and that pages are in sequence—in short, that the contents are as planned (see "Color Proofing," page 365). Checking of this stage is always rapid; sometimes the printer waits only for telephoned approval to begin printing.

The first printed sheets of a book that the editor may see, unless he or she visits the printing plant when the book is run, are folded and gathered sheets. These sheets are checked for completeness and sequence: sometimes a signature is upside down, or omitted, or included twice. Only flagrant or distorting errors can be corrected at this stage. When folded sheets are approved, the editor's involvement is finished. The book is then bound and shipped to the warehouse or to the distributor. The editor will see that the author is sent a copy as soon as possible.

COPY PREPARATION AND MARK-UP

Liz Stalcup, FREE-LANCE EDITOR

Good copy preparation and mark-up depend mainly upon attention to details. If the end product is to reflect the desires and judgment of the person preparing the copy, then little should be left to the judgment of others. Every "author's alteration" is an admission of faulty copy preparation, and many a "printer's error" is due to ambiguity of editing or to the poor physical quality of the original copy.

APPEARANCE OF THE MANUSCRIPT

Text materials should be typed to standard measure, with a clear and easily readable impression. If the typeset character count per line is known, it is convenient to type to that number of characters, particularly for captions and display material. Normally, manuscript is typed double-spaced on 8½" x 11" good-quality paper (not the "erasable" kind, on which ink is easily blurred), with margins of about 1¼" to 1½" on all four sides. Faded typewriter ribbons and photocopies that are not sharp and clear invite trouble: Is that name spelled with an e or an o? Is that number a 3 or an 8 or even a 5? Is that punctuation mark a comma or a semicolon? Striking over incorrect letters to correct a typing mistake produces copy that is hard to read and may result in errors in typesetting; incorrect letters or words should be erased or crossed out, and corrections should be typed in place of them or above them.

All editorial changes must be clearly and legibly indicated. Extensively edited material should be retyped. Ambiguous indications must be avoided. Stetting must be made clear: Should the copy be typeset as it appeared originally, or does the indication mean "stet as edited"? Most typewriter faces do not distinguish between a zero and a capital o. If the copy calls for both in any possibly confusing usage, the capital letter should be identified by three short under-scores; the number should be labeled with a circled word zero. The letter l and the numeral 1 should be distinguished similarly. Another problem is that typists have not yet standardized the format for the long or em dash; some use "xx - xx," some "xx-xx" or "xx--xx." All three should be marked 1/M.

If the material has been typed flush rather than with indented paragraphs, and paragraph indentions or spacing will be used in the typeset material, they must be indicated or clarified. For example, if the last line of the preceding page runs the full width of the page, is the first flush line of the next page a new paragraph, or not?

Editorial and proofreading marks (as shown in figure 4.2) are a form of shorthand that is remarkably flexible. For example, a new paragraph could be marked or a series of capitals could be lowercased in several ways. The simplest, neatest, and most informative form always should be used.

EDITORIAL STYLE

Consistency of editorial style depends on two practices. First, the copy editor should follow an authority on style, preferably a company style manual. Failing that, the editor should develop a consistent personal system of usage and a preference for particular authorities. Second, for each job of any length, the editor should make an individual style sheet or style cards, recording special words used frequently in the material, unusual spellings, standard abbreviations, hyphenation of compound words, spelling of names, and so forth. A preliminary style sheet sometimes is drawn up for the author's or managing editor's approval, before copy editing proceeds in earnest. The final style sheet is used to conform captions, front matter, index, and related books such as an Instructor's Manual to the style of the text. A copy should go to the compositor in the hope that the typesetter or the proofreader will pick up any inconsistencies that the editor has missed.

Accepted and/or preferred usage varies according to the idiosyncrasies of editors and the audience for which the material is intended. The punctuation, sentence structure, and vocabulary in a scholarly journal are different from those in a juvenile hobby journal. Certain fundamentals of grammar are generally agreed upon, but even here there is argument between the "open" or "modern" or "minimal" school of punctuation and the "full" or "closed" school.

Accepted "authorities" include *A Manual of Style* of the University of Chicago Press; the U.S. Government Printing Office *Style Manual; Words into Type*, published by Appleton-Century-Crofts; and the Modern Language Association's *MLA Style Sheet*. Good books on writing style include *A Dictionary of Modern English Usage* by Fowler (Oxford University Press), *Usage and Abusage* by Partridge (Penguin), *Art of Plain Talk* by Flesch (Collier-Macmillan), and *The Elements of Style* by Strunk and White (Macmillan). All style manuals have been written to meet specific needs, which may or may not be yours *in toto*, so do not hesitate to borrow when and where you must; simply remain consistent.

MARK-UP FOR THE TYPESETTER

Ideally, all text material runs in perfect sequence of numbered pages, each identified with a story or job slug or short title. Manuscript page numbers should run from beginning to end of the entire manuscript, not of chapters or sections. If pages are inserted into a previously numbered sequence, the page before the insertion should have a notation reading "pages 00A–00X follow" and the page following should be marked "follows page 00X."

Material other than text, such as tables, footnotes, and bibliographies, is usually assembled separately from the text. If typed separately, a table should be labeled with the number of the manuscript page it is to accompany. Footnotes, similarly, are put at the end of the manuscript and labeled by chapter. The position of all such material must be marked in the text.

If copy is keyed to a display layout, the blocks of text should be keyed to match the layout indications in some logical sequence—left to right, for example.

Typographic instructions should be clearly written in a highly visible area such as a margin and should be repeated as frequently as necessary. Instructions for text type should give the typeface, type size, leading, line length, and justification. If a lengthy manuscript is to be keyboarded for metal composition, the text-type instructions should be repeated at least at the beginning of each chapter; job tickets do not always travel as they should through a plant. Other elements such as chapter titles, heads and subheads, tabular matter, extracts, and captions are also marked with type specifications, indentions, and spacing above and below. Each set of instructions is often accompanied by a key letter, number, phrase, or color code that will designate all recurrences of that element. Except in ambiguous situations, this *key marking* usually eliminates having to repeat instructions. However, elements that recur at infrequent intervals should always be respecified.

Compositors who use photographic, tape, computer, or computer-assisted technologies vary greatly in how they want their customers to indicate typefaces and measures. Because of the complexity of instructions needed for such methods, and therefore the greater possibility of costly errors, some prefer that the customer indicate only the face by name or number and the measure in picas or inches. Others insist that the customer learn the symbolic codes for field indications and use them in marking copy instructions (see "Mark-up for Computer Processing," following). Some scanner/computer operations recognize only certain typewriter faces typed on specified paper. The compositor who requires such specialized input will supply the codes, instructions for their use, specifications for typing, and so forth. These instructions must be followed, for they are determined not by the quirks of an individual but by the limitations of the equipment used.

Typographic esthetics belong with the customer. The editor or art director must plan and clearly indicate any special treatment of the type. For example, if art is inserted in the type area, how many lines will run around the art, and to what measure or measures will they be set? Is the copy to be set line for line? If it is typed in paragraphs or in any way other than with the desired line breaks, slashes should be inserted at the places where the lines are to break, and a notation should be made for the typesetter to "set line for line as marked."

The editor must anticipate the need for "sorts"—accented letters, mathematical symbols, superior and inferior figures, and so on—so that the compositor may be advised in advance. Not all typefaces come with a full complement of such incidentals. Decisions to use different, compatible faces and symbols should not be left entirely to the compositor.

For any lengthy job a sample page, or preferably several sample pages, of the material should be typeset. The material chosen for such samples should include both typical and atypical problems. Sample pages can be well worth their cost. They show up the gaps in preparation—or the thoroughness and completeness of it.

MARK-UP FOR COMPUTER PROCESSING

Paul D. Doebler, PUBLISHING MANAGEMENT CONSULTANT

With the entry of computer systems into the field of composition, the process of marking copy with typesetting instructions has become more complex. Careful and complete mark-up is more difficult and more important than in older typesetting systems.

In conventional typesetting procedures, copy often is marked with broad or basic instructions by the copy editor or designer, and the composing room "fills in" the details of the specifications. Sometimes typesetting machine operators make these decisions as they set the type. More often in better-managed composing rooms, the copy is first put through a mark-up operation by the department's most skilled compositors; they analyze the job and mark the detailed instructions on the copy, often copyfitting difficult portions exactly in the process. This system assures consistency when the job is set by more than one typesetting machine operator.

In commercial composing rooms using computerized composition systems, the mark-up function has typically been expanded and strengthened because errors in specifications entered into a computerized system can cause many new and difficult problems. More complete mark-up is also required because, in a computerized system, every last typographic decision must be encoded specifically. A computer cannot handle con-

Code	Command
QL	Quad left: Set line flush left and terminate line.
QR	Quad right: Set line flush right and terminate line.
QC	Quad center: Center line and terminate it.
QM	Quad middle: Insert blank space.
□	Leave an em space or paragraph indent.
½	Leave an en space, same width as digits.
¦	Leave a thin space.
SS	Use supershift, a third case in addition to lower case and upper case.
⊄	Type an opening bracket, when surrounded by SS and ↓.
↓	Return to lower case.
ⓒ	Format call: Execute a predefined set of commands.
[F1]ⓒ	Execute commands defined as F1.
[CA5]	Increase the leading after the line where it appears.
[CL10]	Change to 10-point leading.
[CP9]	Change to 9-point type.
[CT1]	Change to typeface 1
[CT3,9]	Change to typeface 3 and 9-point type; convenient for subheads when no other details change.
[CW13]	Change to 13-pica column width or line length.
[ORC]	Set text ragged right and left, no hyphens.

Code	Command
[ORL]	Set text ragged left, no hyphens.
[ORR]	Set text ragged right, no hyphens.
[OH]	Allow hyphenation.
[ON]	Disable hyphenation.
[OW]	Disable letterspacing.

Tabulated matter

Code	Command
	Commands to establish tab stops within existing line length (assume 20 picas):
[T5,10,15]	Set tab stops at 5, 10, and 15 picas, creating four columns.
[TC4]	Set up four equal columns; tab stops will be set automatically at 5, 10, and 15 picas.
[TP3,2,3,2]	Set three tab stops at intervals that match the proportions specified; tab stops will be set at 6, 10, and 16 picas, forming four columns.
	Single-key functions to set text in tabulated columns:
ⓉⒸ	Tab center: Center text in column and advance to beginning of next column.
ⓉⓁ	Tab left: Set text flush left in column and advance to beginning of next column.
ⓉⓇ	Tab right: Set text flush right in column and advance to beginning of next column.

Figure 4.4: Some machine codes used in one computer-based mark-up system. *Courtesy of Bru-El Graphics, Inc.*

tingencies outside of its instructions, nor can it notice wrong instructions as a human operator can.

In some instances today, mark-up of the detailed machine codes to be set by the typesetting keyboard operators has been taken back into the office of the customer, giving the editor better control over the details of styling copy and saving the work of a separate mark-up operation in the composing room. This trend is likely to accelerate greatly as another new trend spreads through the graphic arts—using computer-based editing facilities in the offices of publishers and other customers of traditional composing rooms (see ''The Electronic Systems Revolution,'' page 242). Therefore, editorial and design personnel in the future will need a basic understanding of copy mark-up for composition by electronic systems.

CODING INSTRUCTIONS

The need for extraordinarily detailed mark-up in computerized typesetting, of course, comes from the fact that the machine system cannot think for itself— it requires that every last instruction be written out correctly and encoded into machine language before the system can set the type. Because the machine system must have a unique code for every function to be performed, a variety of symbols and abbreviations has been developed. Unfortunately, computer-based systems are still so new that no consensus has yet developed on a standard set of symbols. However, mark-up systems are all based on the same principles and show certain similarities. The basic procedure followed in most mark-up systems is to write special symbols on the manuscript that the keyboard operator can type into machine codes along with the actual text.

Figure 4.4 shows a partial listing of the most often used commands in one system, the mark-up symbols used to represent them on the copy, and the actions they cause.

The symbols are usually written on the copy in the position or sequence in which they should be typed—preceding or following characters and words, between lines and paragraphs, and so on—not on separate specification sheets or even in the margins. Figures 4.5 and 4.6 show two kinds of copy coded for typesetting. One example is a short passage; the second is a table. Along with the marked copy, the typeset versions are shown. These examples are taken from actual copy which was set for *Publishers Weekly*, a book industry

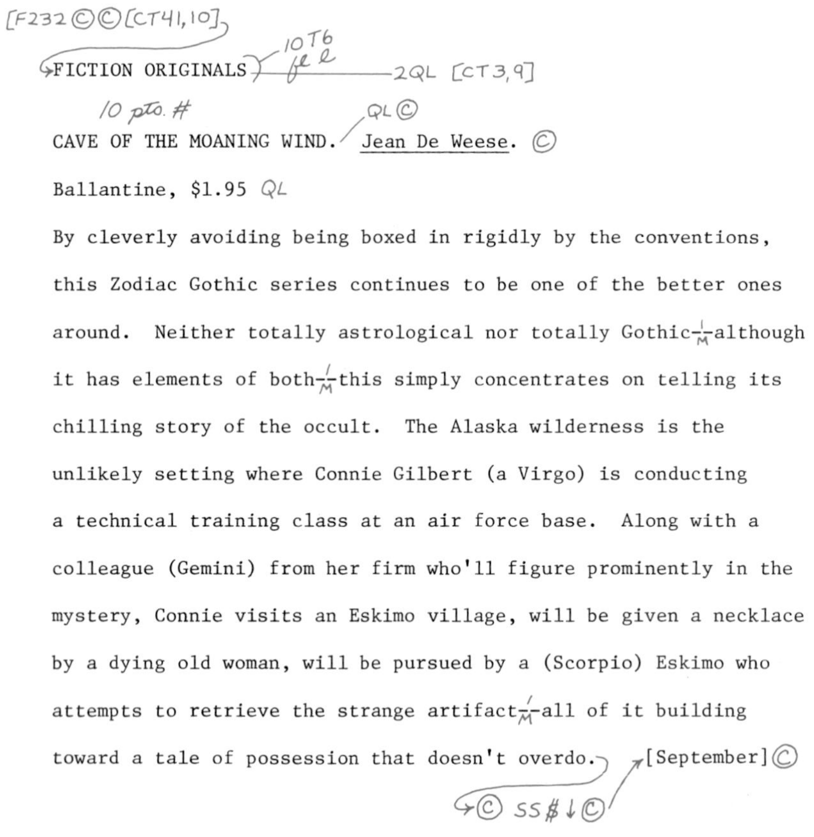

[F232 ©© [CT41,10]

→FICTION ORIGINALS ⟩   10 T6 fll ll   2QL [CT3,9]

10 pts. #   QL ©

CAVE OF THE MOANING WIND. / Jean De Weese. ©

Ballantine, $1.95 QL

By cleverly avoiding being boxed in rigidly by the conventions, this Zodiac Gothic series continues to be one of the better ones around. Neither totally astrological nor totally Gothic—although it has elements of both—this simply concentrates on telling its chilling story of the occult. The Alaska wilderness is the unlikely setting where Connie Gilbert (a Virgo) is conducting a technical training class at an air force base. Along with a colleague (Gemini) from her firm who'll figure prominently in the mystery, Connie visits an Eskimo village, will be given a necklace by a dying old woman, will be pursued by a (Scorpio) Eskimo who attempts to retrieve the strange artifact—all of it building toward a tale of possession that doesn't overdo. [September] ©

© ss# ↓ ©

FICTION ORIGINALS

CAVE OF THE MOANING WIND.
Jean De Weese. Ballantine, $1.95
By cleverly avoiding being boxed in rigidly by the conventions, this Zodiac Gothic series continues to be one of the better ones around. Neither totally astrological nor totally Gothic—although it has elements of both—this simply concentrates on telling its chilling story of the occult. The Alaska wilderness is the unlikely setting where Connie Gilbert (a Virgo) is conducting a technical training class at an air force base. Along with a colleague (Gemini) from her firm who'll figure prominently in the mystery, Connie visits an Eskimo village, will be given a necklace by a dying old woman, will be pursued by a (Scorpio) Eskimo who attempts to retrieve the strange artifact—all of it building toward a tale of possession that doesn't overdo.   [*September*]

Figure 4.5: Sample text passage for computerized typesetting. Left, manuscript marked with coding instructions; right, resulting typeset copy. *Courtesy of Publishers Weekly and Bru-El Graphics, Inc.*

[CT 43,10] TABLE 3 Price Trends by Customer Category 2QC [CP9] [TP 4,8,1,8]

[TP4,2,1,2,1,2,1,2,1,2] (TL)

Consumer Books	1974 Price Change	Market Share	Weight	1975 Price Change	Market Share	Weight
Trade	7.4%	39.0%	2.9	12.1%	37.0%	4.5*
Book Clubs	17.6%	21.0%	3.7	15.5%	21.0%	3.2
Mass Market Paper	14.3%	22.0%	3.1	13.3%	23.0%	3.1
Mail Order		18.0%	0*	5.2%	19.0%	1.0
Avg. Price Incr.			9.7%			11.8%
Avg. Dollar Sale Incr.			9.6%			9.3%
Est. Unit Change			−2.4%			−2.7%

[CP9] Educational Books (TC) QL [CP8] [CA5]

Educational Books	1974 Price Change	Market Share	Weight	1975 Price Change	Market Share	Weight
Professional	11.2%	31.0%	3.4	11.1%	30.0%	3.3
College*	14.2%	30.0%	4.3	12.5%	32.0%	4.0
Elhi*	8.9%	39.0%	3.5	13.2%	38.0%	5.0
Avg. Price Incr.			11.2%			12.3%
Avg. Dollar Sale Incr.			12.9%			10.3%
Est. Unit Change			−2.2%			−0.9%

*includes workbooks, tests, manuals, etc. 2QC

TABLE 3 Price Trends by Customer Category

Consumer Books	1974 Price Change x	Market Share =	Price Weight	1975 Price Change x	Market Share =	Price Weight
Trade	7.4%	39.0%	2.9	12.1%	37.0%	4.5
Book Clubs	17.6%	21.0%	3.7	15.5%	21.0%	3.2
Mass Market Paper	14.3%	22.0%	3.1	13.3%	23.0%	3.1
Mail Order		18.0%	0	5.2%	19.0%	1.0
Avg. Price Incr.			9.7%			11.8%
Avg. Dollar Sale Incr.			9.6%			9.3%
Est. Unit Change			−2.4%			−2.7%
Educational Books						
Professional	11.2% x	31.0% =	3.4	11.1% x	30.0% =	3.3
College*	14.2%	30.0%	4.3	12.5%	32.0%	4.0
Elhi*	8.9%	39.0%	3.5	13.2%	38.0%	5.0
Avg. Price Incr.			11.2%			12.3%
Avg. Dollar Sale Incr.			12.9%			10.3%
Est. Unit Change			−2.2%			−0.9%

*includes workbooks, tests, manuals, etc.

Figure 4.6: Sample page of tabulated material for computerized typesetting. Top, manuscript marked with coding instructions; bottom, typeset copy. *Courtesy of* Publishers Weekly *and Bru-El Graphics, Inc.*

magazine composed by Bru-El Graphics, Inc., a commercial composition house using an advanced electronic composition system and the code shown in figure 4.4.

The code marks seem cryptic until we understand their origins. Virtually all current mark-up systems build code marks out of abbreviations and symbols representing basic items or functions. For example, "T" might be assigned to represent the word "typeface" in such a scheme, and each font in the typesetting machine might be given its own number; to tell the machine to set copy in "typeface number 12," the code "T12" would be marked immediately preceding the material to be set in this face, so that the code would be keyboarded into the machine at the right time.

To the left of the title in figure 4.6, for example, the command "[CT43,10]" specifies that the title for the table is to be set in typeface 43 in the 10-point size. The designation "2QC" following the title causes proper positioning and spacing. The "QC" tells the machine to center the title in the overall measure. The "2" tells the keyboard operator to strike the "QC" command key twice; this action causes the machine to leave an extra line of white space between the title and the next type line. (The machine system is programmed to automatically set the line as instructed and then advance the film one line before executing the next instruction; thus when the operator strikes the "QC" key twice, the machine centers the title, advances the film, then centers the following line, which has no characters in it, and advances the film once more.)

The code "[TP4,8,1,8]" specifies the positions of the column headings in the following line, in preparation for their setting (this code is explained in figure 4.4 under the heading "tabulated matter"). This system of locating column positions across the table is much like that used on conventional typewriters; each tab stop position in the typesetting machine is assigned a numerical designation that can be specified in a code.

The technique for constructing the rest of the table can be deduced from the mark-up codes. To have the headings and the figures set within the individual columns, for example, the mark-up person first calculated the widths of the columns in tab units. The beginning and ending points for each column were then given in the master "TP" code at the upper left just above the heading "Consumer Books." The heading and figures in each column were then aligned by "TC" commands, telling the machine to center the type within the tab limits for that column. Where the figures were to align vertically but the first line contained one less digit than the other lines, the mark-up person called for a fixed space the width of a numeral by writing "½," which stands for a half-em (or en) space.

EXPANDING THE CODE

Some instructions can be encoded simply by striking one appropriate key; for example, the quadding codes "QL," "QR," and "QC" have their own special keys. There are relatively few key positions available for such codes on most typesetting keyboards, however, and

computer-based systems must contain some provision for building additional codes out of conventional alphabetical and numerical characters on the keyboard.

This problem is solved by selecting one or two little-used characters on the keyboard and programming the computer to recognize that they signal the presence of a command rather than the presence of ordinary characters to be set in type. In many computer composition systems the "$" or the "£" are used for this purpose. The system illustrated here uses brackets. In the command code "[CP9]," for example, the opening bracket tells the machine system that "CP9" immediately following it is to be read not as characters to be set in type but as an instruction to "change to 9-point type size." The closing bracket tells the system that material following it is to be regarded again as characters to be set in type, not as further instructions.

The use of brackets in this manner, of course, means that these same keys cannot specify brackets to be set in type as characters; other keys must be used. In this system, a special code—the "$" surrounded by format call, supershift, and unshift instructions—is used to set brackets; this code is illustrated at the end of figure 4.5, where the month is set inside brackets.

FORMAT CODING

A great many command codes are required for setting complex material such as tables. Compare the number of command characters on the table in figure 4.6 to the relatively few required for the text passage in figure 4.5. The number of typeset characters in the two examples is about equal. This problem with complex matter became evident early in the history of computerized composition systems, and equipment manufacturers have developed a basic technique for greatly reducing the number of codes that must be marked up and keyboarded. The technique, called *format coding*, has become one of the most powerful tools available for simplifying the handling of copy for computerized systems.

Format coding consists of substituting a very simple code for a series of more complex codes in such a way that the computer can later resubstitute the complex series for the simple code. The complex series is established at the beginning of a job to describe completely a typographic format that repeats at various places in the job. This kind of code series typically includes such specifications as typeface, size, extra spacing top and bottom, and position on the line (flush left, right, or center). Such a series need not be limited to a single line of type; all of the specifications for a display area, such as a chapter opening in a book or a section of a display advertisement in a newspaper, can be preprogrammed in the code series. The series of commands is assigned a single simple code—such as "F1" for "format number 1"—and then keyboarded and stored in the computer.

From then on, the mark-up person writes the simple format code "F1" every time that particular typographic treatment is to be used in the job, and the keyboard operator types "F1" into the machine system instead of the longer complex code series. Whenever the computer receives the command "F1," it automatically pulls the complex code series out of memory and applies it to the material being processed.

Examples of format codes can be found in a number of places in figures 4.5 and 4.6; one example occurs at the beginning of figure 4.5, where "[F232]" is used to establish the basic specifications for the setting of single-column text matter. In many computer-based systems, these codes can be made to parallel ordinary key marking. For example, if a publisher marks various styles of headlines by using letters or numbers, these same markings can be programmed into the computer as the simple format codes recognized by the machine.

With such techniques as these, and the increasing responsiveness of electronic systems to editorial needs today, the process of marking copy in editorial offices for handling by electronic systems is becoming greatly simplified and very similar to the copy-making symbols and techniques long used in the graphic arts.

COPYFITTING

Edward M. Gottschall, INTERNATIONAL TYPEFACE CORPORATION

Copyfitting is the process of determining how much space will be occupied by a manuscript or piece of typewritten copy when it is typeset. A number of systems, gauges, and booklets on the market are designed to make this job easier and the results more accurate. Most are based on the average number of characters of a given face and size that will fit into one pica—the *characters per pica* count, or *cpp*. The cpp is multiplied by the number of picas in the column width as specified for the job to give the number of characters that will fit in a typeset line.

ESTIMATING MANUSCRIPT LENGTH

To determine the space that the manuscript copy will fill when set in type, it is necessary to estimate the number of characters, including punctuation and spaces, in the copy. This process is called *casting off*. Characters can be counted one by one, or typewritten lines can be measured with a ruler. Pica typewriters have 10 characters (or spaces) to the inch; elite typewriters have 12. The number of characters can be estimated by finding the average number of characters in a typewritten line and multiplying by the number of lines in the copy. The characters in the short lines at the ends of paragraphs should be counted separately and a new count begun for each paragraph for more accurate results. Dividing the total number of characters in the manuscript by the number of characters per typeset line for the typeface to be used will give the number of lines that the final typeset copy will occupy.

To simplify the process, it is useful to have the manuscript typed in lines containing approximately the same number of characters as in an average line of typeset copy, or a multiple of that number. For example, if the column width will take 40 characters, the manuscript would be typed with 40, 60, or 80 characters per line; thus each typewritten line will equal 1, 1½, or 2 lines of type. This process yields directly an estimate of the number of lines that the copy will occupy in the final typeset version.

If it is not possible to type the manuscript line for line, a convenient way of approximating that method is to count out the number of characters per typeset line on one line of the manuscript and then draw a vertical line down the page at that point. Because all characters and spaces are the same width on a standard typewriter, every typed line to the left of the vertical line will contain the correct number of characters. The leftover characters to the right of the vertical line can be counted or measured separately.

Whatever way the number of typeset lines is determined, it is then possible to find the actual space to be occupied by the typeset copy. It is necessary to know only the number of lines of type in the particular typeface and size, including leading, that will fit in the column depth to be used. The final estimate must take into account, of course, the number of columns per page, space for illustrations or large headings, and any other variables.

COPYFITTING SYSTEMS

In recent years the proliferation of photographic and CRT systems has given a new flexibility to word spacing and thus to the number of characters that will fit in a pica or line. In earlier systems such as Linotype composition, the variations due to word breaks and space bands could be averaged out. Today, however, because of the tight letter and word spacing possible with film systems, the copyfitter's job becomes more complicated.

Many copyfitting systems have been produced to aid the copyfitter. Most systems list current typefaces in various sizes; using accompanying gauges or charts, the copyfitter can find either the cpp or the number of characters per line for the pica width to be used. In addition, many typographic services supply copyfitting data and instructions in their type books for the faces they feature.

A system that deals with the problem of rapidly proliferating typeface designs is the Unitype Copy Fitter, manufactured by Baumwell Graphics in New York. This system can be used for any typeface in any size and

105

Alphabet length in points	cpp	6	8	10	12	14	16	18	20	22	24	26	28	30	32	34	36	38	40	42
													Line length in picas							
61	5.60	34	45	56	67	78	90	101	112	123	134	146	157	168	179	190	202	213	224	235
62	5.51	33	44	55	66	77	88	99	110	121	132	143	154	165	176	187	198	209	220	231
63	5.42	33	43	54	65	76	87	98	108	119	130	141	152	163	173	184	195	206	217	228
64	5.34	32	43	53	64	75	85	96	107	117	128	139	150	160	171	182	192	203	214	224
65	5.26	32	42	53	63	74	84	95	105	116	126	137	147	158	168	179	189	200	210	221
66	5.18	31	41	52	62	73	83	93	104	114	124	135	145	155	166	176	186	197	207	218
67	5.10	31	41	51	61	71	82	92	102	112	122	133	143	153	163	173	184	194	204	214
68	5.02	30	40	50	60	70	80	90	100	110	120	131	141	151	161	171	181	191	201	211
69	4.95	30	40	50	59	69	79	89	99	109	119	129	139	149	158	168	178	188	198	208
70	4.88	29	39	49	59	68	78	88	98	107	117	127	137	146	156	166	176	185	195	205
71	4.81	29	38	48	58	67	77	87	96	106	115	125	135	144	154	164	173	183	192	202
72	4.75	29	38	48	57	67	76	86	95	105	114	124	133	143	152	162	171	181	190	200
73	4.68	28	37	47	56	66	75	84	94	103	112	122	131	140	150	159	168	178	187	197
74	4.62	28	37	46	55	65	74	83	92	102	111	120	129	139	148	157	166	176	185	194
75	4.56	27	36	46	55	64	73	82	91	100	109	119	128	137	146	155	164	173	182	192
76	4.50	27	36	45	54	63	72	81	90	99	108	117	126	135	144	153	162	171	180	189
77	4.44	27	36	44	53	62	71	80	89	98	107	115	124	133	142	151	160	169	178	186
78	4.38	26	35	44	53	61	70	79	88	96	105	114	123	131	140	149	158	166	175	184
79	4.32	26	35	43	52	60	69	78	86	95	104	112	121	130	138	147	156	164	173	181
80	4.27	26	34	43	51	60	68	77	85	94	102	111	120	128	137	145	154	162	171	179
81	4.22	25	34	42	51	59	68	76	84	93	101	110	118	127	135	143	152	160	169	177
82	4.17	25	33	42	50	58	67	75	83	92	100	108	117	125	133	142	150	158	167	175
83	4.12	25	33	41	49	58	66	74	82	91	99	107	115	124	132	140	148	157	165	173
84	4.07	24	33	41	49	57	65	73	81	90	98	106	114	122	130	138	147	155	163	171
85	4.02	24	32	40	48	56	64	72	80	88	96	105	113	121	129	137	145	153	161	169
86	3.97	24	32	40	48	56	64	72	79	87	95	103	111	119	127	135	143	151	159	167
87	3.93	24	31	39	47	55	63	71	79	86	94	102	110	118	126	134	141	149	157	165
88	3.88	23	31	39	47	54	62	70	78	85	93	101	109	116	124	132	140	147	155	163
89	3.84	23	31	38	46	54	61	69	77	84	92	100	108	115	123	131	138	146	154	161
90	3.80	23	30	38	46	53	61	68	76	84	91	99	106	114	122	129	137	144	152	160
91	3.75	23	30	38	45	53	60	68	75	83	90	98	105	113	120	128	135	143	150	158
92	3.71	22	30	37	45	52	59	67	74	82	89	96	104	111	119	126	134	141	148	156
93	3.67	22	29	37	44	51	59	66	73	81	88	95	103	110	117	125	132	139	147	154
94	3.63	22	29	36	44	51	58	65	73	80	87	94	102	109	116	123	131	138	145	152
95	3.60	22	29	36	43	50	58	65	72	79	86	94	101	108	115	122	130	137	144	151
96	3.56	21	28	36	43	50	57	64	71	78	85	92	100	107	114	121	128	135	142	150
97	3.52	21	28	35	42	49	56	63	70	77	84	92	99	106	113	120	127	134	141	148
98	3.48	21	28	35	42	49	56	63	70	77	84	90	97	104	111	118	125	132	139	146
99	3.45	21	28	35	41	48	55	62	69	76	83	90	97	104	110	117	124	131	138	145
100	3.42	21	27	34	41	48	55	62	68	75	82	89	96	103	109	116	123	130	137	144
102	3.35	20	27	34	40	47	54	60	67	74	80	87	94	101	107	114	121	127	134	141
104	3.28	20	26	33	39	46	52	59	66	72	79	85	92	98	105	112	118	125	131	138
106	3.22	19	26	32	39	45	52	58	64	71	77	84	90	97	103	109	116	122	129	135
108	3.16	19	25	32	38	44	51	57	63	70	76	82	88	95	101	107	114	120	126	133
110	3.10	19	25	31	37	43	50	56	62	68	74	81	87	93	99	105	112	118	124	130
112	3.05	18	24	31	37	43	49	55	61	67	73	79	85	91	98	104	110	116	122	128
114	3.00	18	24	30	36	42	48	54	60	66	72	78	84	90	96	102	108	114	120	126
116	2.94	18	24	29	35	41	47	53	59	65	71	76	82	88	94	100	106	112	118	123
118	2.89	17	23	29	35	40	46	52	58	64	69	75	81	87	92	98	104	110	116	121
120	2.85	17	23	29	34	40	46	51	57	63	68	74	80	86	91	97	103	108	114	120
122	2.80	17	22	28	34	39	45	50	56	62	67	73	78	84	90	95	101	106	112	118
124	2.75	17	22	28	33	39	44	50	55	61	66	72	77	83	88	94	99	105	110	116
126	2.71	16	22	27	33	38	43	49	54	60	65	70	76	81	87	92	98	103	108	114

with any variation in intercharacter spacing. It is necessary to know the length of the lowercase alphabet in typeface and size to be used and with the correct intercharacter spacing. The alphabet is measured on a gauge to find a key number, which refers to a scale showing the number of characters per line for a range of line lengths.

AN ALTERNATE SYSTEM

If you do not have access to such type books or copyfitting systems, you can use tables 4.1 and 4.2 instead. Table 4.1 gives approximate characters per line for most systems and typefaces. To use the table, determine the alphabet length (in points) of the typeface in the size to be used. This information may be avail-

Alphabet length in points	cpp	6	8	10	12	14	16	18	20	22	24	26	28	30	32	34	36	38	40	42
128	2.67	16	21	27	32	37	43	48	53	59	64	69	75	80	85	91	96	101	107	112
130	2.63	16	21	26	32	37	42	47	53	58	63	68	74	79	84	89	95	100	105	110
132	2.59	16	21	26	31	36	41	47	52	57	62	67	73	78	83	88	93	98	104	109
134	2.55	15	20	26	31	36	41	46	51	56	61	66	71	77	82	87	92	97	102	107
136	2.51	15	20	25	30	35	40	45	50	55	60	65	70	75	80	85	90	95	100	105
138	2.47	15	20	25	30	35	40	44	49	54	59	64	69	74	79	84	89	94	99	104
140	2.44	15	20	24	29	34	39	44	49	54	59	63	68	73	78	83	88	93	98	102
142	2.40	14	19	24	29	34	38	43	48	53	58	62	67	72	77	82	86	91	96	101
144	2.37	14	19	24	28	33	38	43	47	52	57	62	66	71	76	81	85	90	95	100
146	2.34	14	19	23	28	33	37	42	47	52	56	61	66	70	75	80	84	89	94	98
148	2.31	14	18	23	28	32	37	42	46	51	55	60	65	69	74	79	83	88	92	97
150	2.28	14	18	23	27	32	36	41	46	50	55	59	64	68	73	78	82	87	91	96
155	2.20	13	18	22	26	31	35	40	44	48	53	57	62	66	70	75	79	84	88	92
160	2.13	13	17	21	26	30	34	38	43	47	51	55	60	64	68	72	77	81	85	89
165	2.07	12	17	21	25	29	33	37	41	46	50	54	58	62	66	70	75	79	83	87
170	2.01	12	16	20	24	28	32	36	40	44	48	52	56	60	64	68	72	76	80	84
175	1.95	12	16	20	23	27	31	35	39	43	47	51	55	59	62	66	70	74	78	82
180	1.90	11	15	19	23	27	30	34	38	42	46	49	53	57	61	65	68	72	76	80
185	1.84	11	15	18	22	26	29	33	37	40	44	48	52	55	59	63	66	70	74	77
190	1.80	11	14	18	22	25	29	32	36	40	43	47	50	54	58	61	65	68	72	76
195	1.75	11	14	18	21	25	28	32	35	39	42	46	49	53	56	60	63	67	70	74
200	1.71	10	14	17	21	24	27	31	34	38	41	44	48	51	55	58	62	65	68	72
205	1.66	10	13	17	20	23	27	30	33	37	40	43	46	50	53	56	60	63	66	70
210	1.62	10	13	16	19	23	26	29	32	36	39	42	45	49	52	55	58	62	65	68
215	1.59	10	13	16	19	22	25	29	32	35	38	41	45	48	51	54	57	60	64	67
220	1.55	9	12	16	19	22	25	28	31	34	37	40	43	47	50	53	56	59	62	65
225	1.52	9	12	15	18	21	24	27	30	33	36	40	43	46	49	52	55	58	61	64
230	1.48	9	12	15	18	21	24	27	30	33	36	38	41	44	47	50	53	56	59	62
235	1.45	9	12	15	17	20	23	26	29	32	35	38	41	44	46	49	52	55	58	61
240	1.42	9	11	14	17	20	23	26	28	31	34	37	40	43	45	48	51	54	57	60
245	1.39	8	11	14	17	19	22	25	28	31	33	36	39	42	44	47	50	53	56	58
250	1.36	8	11	14	16	19	22	25	27	30	33	35	38	41	44	46	49	52	54	57
260	1.31	8	10	13	16	18	21	24	26	29	31	34	37	39	42	45	47	50	52	55
270	1.26	8	10	13	15	18	20	23	25	28	30	33	35	38	40	43	45	48	50	53
280	1.22	7	10	12	15	17	20	22	24	27	29	32	34	37	39	41	44	46	49	51
290	1.17	7	9	12	14	16	19	21	23	26	28	30	33	35	37	40	42	44	47	49
300	1.14	7	9	11	14	16	18	21	23	25	27	30	32	34	36	39	41	43	46	48
320	1.06	6	8	11	13	15	17	19	21	23	25	28	30	32	34	36	38	40	42	45
340	1.00	6	8	10	12	14	16	18	20	22	24	26	28	30	32	34	36	38	40	42
360	.95	6	8	10	11	13	15	17	19	21	23	25	27	29	30	32	34	36	38	40
380	.90	5	7	9	11	13	14	16	18	20	22	23	25	27	29	31	32	34	36	38
400	.85	5	7	9	10	12	14	15	17	19	20	22	24	26	27	29	31	32	34	36
425	.80	5	6	8	10	11	13	14	16	18	19	21	22	24	26	27	29	30	32	34
450	.76	5	6	8	9	11	12	14	15	17	18	20	21	23	24	26	27	29	30	32
475	.72	4	6	7	9	10	12	13	14	16	17	19	20	22	23	24	26	27	29	30
500	.68	4	5	7	8	10	11	12	14	15	16	18	19	20	22	23	24	26	27	29
550	.62	4	5	6	7	9	10	11	12	14	15	16	17	19	20	21	22	24	25	26
600	.57	3	5	6	7	8	9	10	11	13	14	15	16	17	18	19	21	22	23	24
650	.52	3	4	5	6	7	8	9	10	11	12	14	15	16	17	18	19	20	21	22
700	.48	3	4	5	6	7	8	9	10	11	12	12	13	14	15	16	17	18	19	20
750	.45	3	4	5	5	6	7	8	9	10	11	12	13	14	14	15	16	17	18	19
800	.42	2	3	4	5	6	7	8	8	9	10	11	12	13	13	14	15	16	17	18

able from the type shop, or the alphabet may be run off and measured. In film systems, where minus-1 or minus-½ unit spacing may be used, the alphabet should always be run off with the spacing to be used; otherwise the resulting data will be inaccurate.

Table 4.1 also shows cpp values corresponding to the alphabet lengths listed. These values have been cal-culated by using a conversion factor of 28.5, which ac-counts for the letter-use frequency of uppercase letters, wide and narrow letters, and punctuation. This factor is multiplied by 12 to convert from points to picas. The resulting product, 342, is divided by the alphabet length to yield the corresponding characters per pica count.

TABLE 4.2: LINES PER COLUMN

Column depth in inches	Type size including leading, in points														
	6	7	8	9	10	11	12	13	14	15	16	17	18	19	20
¼	3	2	2	2	1	1	1	1	1	1	1	1	1		
½	6	5	4	4	3	3	3	2	2	2	2	2	2	1	1
¾	9	7	6	6	5	4	4	4	3	3	3	3	3	2	2
1	12	10	9	8	7	6	6	5	5	4	4	4	4	3	3
2	24	20	18	16	14	13	12	11	10	9	9	8	8	7	7
3	36	30	27	24	21	19	18	16	15	14	13	12	12	11	10
4	48	41	36	32	28	26	24	22	20	19	18	16	16	15	14
5	60	51	45	40	36	32	30	27	25	24	22	21	20	18	18
6	72	61	54	48	43	39	36	33	30	28	27	25	24	22	21
7	84	72	63	56	50	45	42	38	36	33	31	29	28	26	25
8	96	82	72	64	57	52	48	44	41	38	36	33	32	30	28
9	108	92	81	72	64	58	54	49	46	43	40	38	36	34	32
10	120	102	90	80	72	65	60	55	51	48	45	42	40	37	36
11	132	113	99	88	79	72	66	60	56	52	49	46	44	41	39
12	144	123	108	96	86	78	72	66	61	57	54	50	48	45	43
13	156	133	117	104	93	85	78	72	66	62	58	55	52	49	46
14	168	144	126	112	100	91	84	77	72	67	63	59	56	53	50
15	180	154	135	120	108	98	90	83	77	72	67	63	60	56	54
16	192	164	144	128	115	104	96	88	82	76	72	67	64	60	57
17	204	174	153	136	122	111	102	94	87	81	76	72	68	64	61
18	216	185	162	144	129	117	108	99	92	86	81	76	72	68	64
19	228	195	171	152	136	124	114	105	97	91	85	80	76	72	68
20	240	205	180	160	144	130	120	110	102	96	90	84	80	75	72
21	252	216	189	168	151	137	126	116	108	100	94	88	84	79	75

With some newer type styles brought out for photographic systems, the use of 28.5 as a conversion factor is not reliable. In such cases, the typesetter should be consulted; if available, the correct cpp, rather than alphabet length, should be referred to in the table. After you locate the appropriate alphabet length or cpp, simply read across to the column corresponding to the line length to be used. This number indicates the average number of characters that will fit in a line.

Table 4.2 is used to determine the number of lines that will fit in a given column. At the top of the table, find the size of the type to be used, plus the leading. For example, a 9-point typeface with 1-point leading ("9 on 10") will have a value of 10. Then read down the column to the line corresponding to the appropriate column depth.

TYPOGRAPHY 5

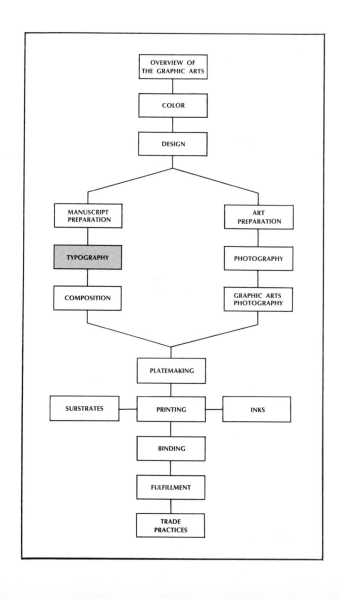

OVERVIEW OF
THE GRAPHIC ARTS

COLOR

DESIGN

MANUSCRIPT
PREPARATION

ART
PREPARATION

TYPOGRAPHY

PHOTOGRAPHY

COMPOSITION

GRAPHIC ARTS
PHOTOGRAPHY

PLATEMAKING

SUBSTRATES

PRINTING

INKS

BINDING

FULFILLMENT

TRADE
PRACTICES

THE FUNDAMENTALS OF TYPE

Paul D. Doebler, PUBLISHING MANAGEMENT CONSULTANT

Although typesetting processes and machinery are going through a revolution today, type design and use and the mechanics of type remain firmly rooted in traditional principles. Before the art of typography can be effectively employed by graphic designers, regardless of the typesetting process used, the basic mechanics of type must be thoroughly understood. These mechanics include the structure of letterforms, the basic measurements used in typesetting and composition, the principles of spacing used to position type characters in lines, and the classification structure within which all typefaces are organized.

LETTERFORMS

Individual pieces of type originated with Gutenberg, of course, who invented the process of casting a raised character on the top of a rectangular block of metal. Although newer typesetting processes have taken over the vast majority of typesetting, some foundry type is still used today, and much of modern type terminology comes from the original hand-set metal type. Figure 5.1 shows the various parts of a piece of modern-day foundry type.

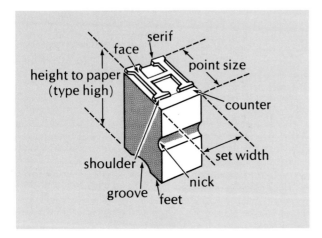

Figure 5.1: A piece of foundry type.

The most important of the terms used in typography today are those having to do with the typeface itself and the rectangular area on the printed page that it occupies, for these terms apply to all typefaces regardless of the process by which they are set into lines. In figure 5.1, these terms are: *face, serif, point size,* and *set width.* In addition, several other terms should be understood; these are shown in figure 5.2 along with

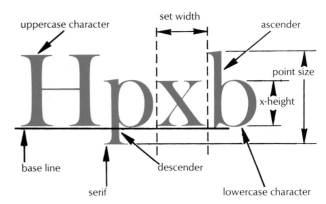

Figure 5.2: Fundamental type design elements.

those from figure 5.1. At this point, some important definitions are needed:

Face: The printed area which forms the character itself.

Point size or body: The vertical depth of the space occupied by the character.

Set width: The horizontal width of the space occupied by the character.

Base line: The line along the bottom of the character to which all characters in the particular design and size are aligned.

x-Height: The vertical height of the small x above the base line; the line to which the main parts of all small letters are aligned at the top.

Ascender: Any part of a small letter which extends above the x-height line.

Descender: Any part of any letter that extends below the base line.

In addition, two other commonly used terms originating with hand-set type should be noted. The term *lowercase* refers to all small letters in the alphabet, while *uppercase* denotes all capital letters. These terms arose in the early days of typesetting when two cases or trays were used to hold hand-set metal type on a rack within easy reach of the typesetter. The case for capitals was positioned above the case for small letters.

It is important to understand that the character itself can be positioned within its assigned space as the typeface designer chooses. Thus, the base line for one typeface may not necessarily align with the base line of another face of the same point size, nor will they necessarily have the same x-height, nor do the ascenders and descenders have to be the same length. This is illustrated in figure 5.3, which shows the *h* in a variety of typefaces, all of them 24-point types. In most typefaces, however, the ascenders and descenders usually extend to nearly the full point-size depth, making it possible to tell what size a typeface is by measuring from the

Figure 5.3: Comparison of 24-point h from different typefaces. Letter sizes vary even though all are 24-point faces.

tops of the capitals and ascenders to the bottoms of the descenders.

In addition, space can be added or subtracted from the depth and/or width of the space in which the character is positioned. In practice, the vertical depth or body is usually made either the same as the point-size designation for the typeface, or larger—and on rare occasions it is made smaller. The horizontal set width, too, often is varied either wider or narrower than the normal width established by the original typeface designer.

In metal typesetting, machine constrictions led to the almost universal adoption of *top alignment*—that is, the tops of all capitals and most ascenders in all typefaces were positioned at the top edge of the metal body. Reductions of set widths and point sizes to less than the normal or standard point-size designations were not made very often because they required cutting of metal in many instances. (An exception to this is found in Monotype setting, which can cast characters on a smaller-than-normal body.)

In the new photographic typesetting machines, however, these constrictions no longer apply. Because characters can be easily positioned optically in the space they will occupy, great freedom is available. Most phototypesetters now have adopted the convention of *base-line alignment*, in which the position of the base line is standardized for all faces of the same point size. This makes the mixing of different faces in the same line much easier. Set widths, too, may be varied; increasing use of photocomposition has permitted much more experimentation with different set widths to achieve new typographic effects.

THE POINT SYSTEM OF MEASUREMENT

Typesetters throughout the world have developed a number of measuring systems over the years, including the point system used in this country and the United Kingdom and the Didot system used on the European continent. The two basic units in the point system are:

The point: A linear measurement .0138 inch long. There are approximately 72 points in an inch (actually, 72 points measures .9936 inch, which is close enough to assume for practical purposes that 72 points equals 1 inch).

The pica: One pica is made up of 12 points, and there are approximately 6 picas to the inch.

Not only are type sizes designated in points, but so are all spacing dimensions and instructions such as the widths of type lines, depths of pages, amounts of space to be allowed between columns and other elements on the page.

An additional measure often used in connection with display advertising space in publications is the *agate line.* The term *agate* is the old name for 5½-point type, coming from the days when all of the basic type sizes were referred to by names rather than by point size

(12-point type, for example, was called "pica," and 6-point type was called "nonpareil"). An agate line of advertising space today is actually ⅟₁₄ of an inch deep, slightly less than the full 5½-point line of old. An agate line of advertising space also is understood to be one column wide (the actual width of the single column will vary from publication to publication, but it is most often within the range of 11 to 13 picas).

THE EM MEASUREMENT AND CHARACTER FITTING

While these measurements are all based on the point system, another measurement extremely important to typeface design is the *em.* An em often is defined as the square of the point size of a given face—in other words, the em for a 12-point size would be 12 points wide and 12 points deep. Although this is often the case, it is, however, an incorrect definition.

The em actually is the rectangular area occupied by the capital *M* of the typeface. In regular width versions of the face, the em may actually be a perfect square, but in condensed and expanded versions, the *M* of the face will be narrower or wider than the vertical point-size depth.

This is an extremely important principle of good type design and typography because the widths of all characters for a given typeface are related to the width of the capital *M* or em, not to the square of the point size, to achieve the optimum aesthetic effect when characters are assembled side by side into lines. Lateral character fitting is one of the most subtle and important parts of type design, and poor designs are very likely to err in this respect.

Typefaces are divided into two kinds depending on how their characters are related to the em: *non-unit faces* and *unit faces.* The choice for a given type design depends on the kind of *justification* system used in the typesetting equipment.

In most typesetting of text matter, all lines are *justified* by making the ends of each line align at the maximum specified measure. Since the various combinations of characters and spaces in lines rarely add up exactly to the maximum measure, the line is first filled with as many characters as possible (while still observing the rules of word endings and syllabic hyphenation) and then extra space is added between words to make the lines come out even at the ends. Extra space can also be added between characters of a word, but this normally is not done in fine printing except for special effects, which are discussed later.

In virtually all hand-setting methods and in the hot metal linecasting process of typesetting, justification is achieved by non-counting methods—space is added either by eye or, in linecasting, by tapered wedges which are automatically expanded to fill any remaining space. Types for these processes can be designed as non-unit faces, which impose no limitation other than aesthetics on the type designer in choosing various character widths. These may be established at any individual dimension within the maximum em size.

If the typesetting machine must count and add up the widths of characters and spaces in order to compute the space to be added for justification, however, unit typefaces must be used on the machine. In this case, the type designer divides the em into a number

111

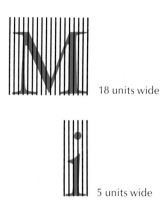

18 units wide

5 units wide

8 units wide

Figure 5.4: Unit-designed type using the 18-units-to-the-em system.

of increments of equal width, or *units*, and each character is designed to occupy a chosen number of units. Naturally, the finer the division of the em into units, the more flexibility the type designer will have in producing a well-proportioned face. An 18-units-to-the-em system is illustrated in figure 5.4.

The number of units to the em used in such designs has ranged from one for the standard typewriter to a hundred or more in some computer systems. In proportional-spacing typewriters used extensively for strike-on composition, faces are often designed for three to five units to the em, and some very good results have been obtained considering the severe limitations placed on the designer. However, such limited unit systems work well only with a very few type styles, and even with these designs they cannot yield the much finer quality achieved by other forms of typesetting. The most common system in use for typefaces today is the 18-unit system on which the Monotype method of typesetting is based. Over the years, Monotype has proven that the 18-unit system is capable of very fine typography, and most of the present-day photocomposition systems have adopted the 18-unit system as their standard.

SPACING

In addition to the positioning and spacing considerations dealt with by the original type designer, four kinds of spacing must be handled by those who use type in the design of jobs and those who set type in composing rooms. These are *letterspacing*, *kerning*, *word spacing*, and *line spacing*.

Letterspacing

Letterspacing is the placement of additional space between characters in a line. In lesser quality typesetting, and especially in very short line measures, letterspacing is used to fill out and justify lines; this, however, is generally considered poor practice. Very narrow

measures should be avoided if possible, or the type should be set ragged on one edge to preserve proper character spacing. Very fine letterspacing in small increments—fractions of a point—can be used between all characters in a line to justify it in fine typesetting in some cases, if not too much extra space must be added, but this is painstaking work which slows down the machine operator.

Letterspacing is best used in setting display type in all capitals. The shapes of capital letters are not uniform and create unequal optical spaces between them even though they are positioned carefully by the type designer. As figure 5.5 shows, the space between the *M* and the *N* is a minimal thin sliver, while the space between the *A* and the *T* is broad. To compensate for this, a good compositor will "optically" letterspace the line —that is, add enough space between the closely positioned letters to make their spacing look equal to the

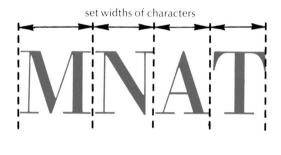

set widths of characters

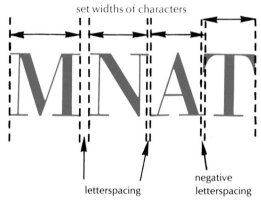

set widths of characters

letterspacing

negative letterspacing

Figure 5.5: Use of letterspacing to adjust intercharacter spacing optically.

others. Figure 5.5 also shows how the addition of space between some letters provides an evenly composed line.

There is no fixed rule as to how much additional space should be added between each combination of two characters. This will vary with the design of each individual typeface. Nor are there any rules about how much a display word may be spread out across a page by letterspacing—this is an artistic judgment to be made by the designer of the job.

Kerning

Kerning is the opposite of letterspacing, in that space is subtracted from the area occupied by a character to

set widths of characters

Unkerned

set widths of characters

Kerned

Figure 5.6: Use of kerning to achieve better optical appearance of type, particularly italics.

bring another character closer. It can be used instead of letterspacing to improve the appearance of all-capital display lines, but it also is very important in certain lowercase situations as well. Certain lowercase letters, notably the *f*, have ascenders or descenders that project out horizontally from the main part of the character, as shown in figure 5.6. By tucking these ascenders or descenders over or under adjacent characters (that is, kerning them over or under), the appearance of the line is greatly improved, as figure 5.6 also shows.

In phototypesetting, this is easy to do because characters can be positioned by optical projection. In metal typesetting, however, the body on which the character is positioned is a fixed block of metal which is not easily reduced to allow kerning. The exception to this is the Monotype system, which can cast an individual character on a narrower body and thus kern characters. But even there, as in almost all other typesetting systems, it has proven desirable to create special new

Figure 5.7: Four commonly used standard ligatures.

characters for special situations in which two characters should fit closer together. These special characters, which combine two standard characters on one body, are called *ligatures*. In general use, there are four standard ligatures which combine *f* with *i* and *l* (see fig. 5.7), as well as the double *f*. Unusually elaborate typefaces may have special ligatures, such as *Qu*, in which a long tail on the capital extends under the lowercase letter. In metal typesetting systems, ligatures were essential to fine typesetting; in photographic typesetting, the use of special ligature characters sometimes is replaced by kerning on the machine.

Word spacing

Word spacing in fine typesetting follows one basic rule—use as little space as needed between words while still providing a clear optical break between them. Too little space can be used between words, of course, but by far the greater problem is the tendency of many compositors to use too much space. Wide word spacing not only tends to break up the even flow of the individual line and interrupt eye movements; it also tends to create *rivers,* or streaks of white space down the column, when several word spaces occur over one another in a series of lines. A *river* is illustrated in figure 5.8.

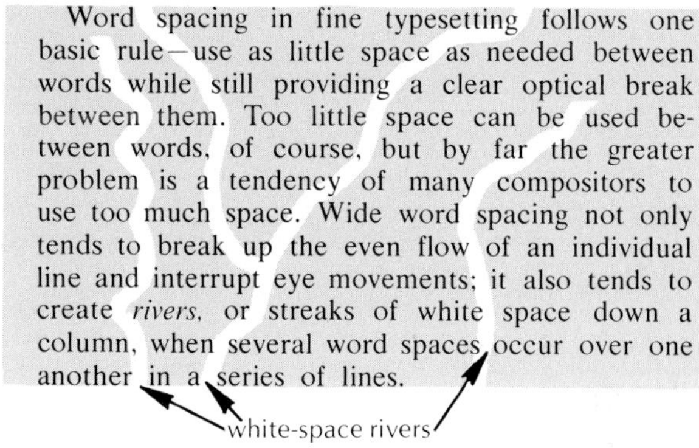

Word spacing in fine typesetting follows one basic rule—use as little space as needed between words while still providing a clear optical break between them. Too little space can be used between words, of course, but by far the greater problem is a tendency of many compositors to use too much space. Wide word spacing not only tends to break up the even flow of an individual line and interrupt eye movements; it also tends to create *rivers,* or streaks of white space down a column, when several word spaces occur over one another in a series of lines.

white-space rivers

Figure 5.8: Type set with word spacing that is too wide, creating rivers.

Line spacing

Line spacing is the amount of space added between type lines in addition to the point size of the body. This is often called *leading,* a term which comes from metal composition in which thin lead strips one point or two points thick are inserted between lines to add the space. The term has carried over into photocomposition.

Line spacing is very much a choice which the designer of the job makes to suit the overall effect being sought. In large amounts of text, however, line spacing rarely exceeds three points. Special effects for very short copy blocks, on the other hand, often are set with far larger line spacing. Figure 5.9 shows the effects of several line spacings on the same sample of text.

TYPE CLASSIFICATIONS

Over the last 500 years, a rather elaborate classification structure has developed to identify different kinds of type. This structure ranges from such mechanics as

Line spacing is the amount of space added between type lines in addition to the point size of the body. This is often called *leading*, a term which comes from metal

No line spacing

Line spacing is the amount of space added between type lines in addition to the point size of the body. This is often called *leading*, a term which comes from metal

1-point line spacing

Line spacing is the amount of space added between type lines in addition to the point size of the body. This is often called *leading*, a term which comes from metal

2-point line spacing

Line spacing is the amount of space added between type lines in addition to the point size of the body. This is often called *leading*, a term which comes from metal

Figure 5.9: **Examples of different line spacings used with one typeface.**

type sizes and the number of characters in a complete set or font to type design families and groups of families.

Type sizes

Type size generally is measured in points, although some very large sizes are sometimes said to be so many "lines" (agate lines) high. The "line" designation, however, was used in the last century with wooden types and is not often encountered today.

While theoretically there is no limit to the number of type sizes that can be created (with photocomposition enlargement procedures, a typeface could be varied infinitely in size), a practical range of specific point sizes has emerged as more or less standard. In hot metal, the cost of producing different sizes required standardization of such a range, and this has carried over into the newer photocomposition systems for which equipment costs are lowered by using fixed enlarging ratios rather than an infinitely variable optical system.

The most commonly used type sizes range from 5-point to 72-point. Within that range, sizes are usually available in 1-point increments from 5-point through 12-point, and sometimes in ½-point increments such as 5½-point. Above 12-point, most sizes are 6 points apart in size, with a few exceptions. The common sizes above 12-point are: 14, 18, 24, 30, 36, 42, 48, 60, and 72. There have been a few 16-, 20-, 22-, and 28-point sizes manufactured, just as on the low end of the scale there are some sizes less than 5-point, but these are generally used only in special situations.

Bodoni
Bodoni

Bodoni
Bodoni Italic

Bodoni
Bodoni Book

Bodoni
Bodoni Book Italic

Bodoni
Bodoni Bold

Bodoni
Bodoni Bold Italic

Bodoni
Bodoni Bold Condensed

Bodoni
Bodoni Ultra

Bodoni
Bodoni Ultra Italic

Bodoni
Bodoni Ultra Extra Condensed

Bodoni
Bodoni Open

Figure 5.10: **Examples of various typefaces from the Bodoni type family.**

Character sets

A complete set of all the characters required in one design and size to set type is called a *font*. At the very minimum, a font includes all uppercase and lowercase letters, numerals *0* through *9*, the most-used punctuation marks, and usually a few special characters such as ligatures. In addition, other characters may be included, such as superior and inferior figures, fractions, special bibliographic symbols, accented characters for foreign languages, and others.

Hot metal typesetting requires a separate font of *matrices* (or character molds) for each different size of a given typeface. However, to increase the ability of linecasting machines to handle more faces, a single set of matrices normally is *duplexed*—that is, it carries the molds for two different faces of the same size, providing two typefaces from the same set of matrices. The term *font* can be used to refer to a single set of typeface characters, to a duplexed set of hot metal linecasting matrices, or to a set of Monotype or linecasting matrices carrying only one typeface.

In photocomposition, where a single set of character images is normally used to project a series of enlarged or reduced type sizes, the term *font* has come gradually to refer to the set of master images only, with the sizes available on the machine specified separately. Thus, a phototypesetter is described as handling 4 fonts (or different typefaces) in 10 sizes, or 18 fonts in 22 sizes, at one time.

Regardless of the typesetting process, a range of different sizes from smallest to largest for a given typeface design is called a *series*.

Type designs

Beyond these mechanical classifications, typefaces are grouped according to their aesthetic design relationships and characteristics into families and broad period or character groupings.

A type family is made up of all the variations of a fundamental type style or design. For example, the Bodoni typeface was originally designed as a single font by Bodoni. This basic graphic design was then varied in a number of ways to create many additional styles in other fonts, but all of these styles are unmistakably derived from the original Bodoni design. Figure 5.10 illustrates just some of the variations developed in the Bodoni family, one of the oldest and most durable typefaces ever created.

Each of the variations usually is named to indicate the dimension in which it varies from the original. Thus Bodoni Condensed is the name given to a squeezed-together version of the basic face, and *extra condensed* describes a font that is even more squeezed. *Extended* or *expanded* describes fonts wider than the original design. Differences in weight—the thickness of lines making up the characters—are expressed in a series of terms such as *light, medium, demibold, bold, extra bold, black,* and the like. Faces that slant or lean to the right at an angle are usually called *italic,* but they also can be named *oblique.* Thus any typeface can be identified by its family and its position in that family by adding to the basic design name the appropriate descriptive words.

The broad spectrum of basic typeface designs or families generally is grouped into a number of rather loose classifications which express either the period in which they were designed or the special nature of their design which sets them apart in some distinctive way. The most widely used groupings, illustrated in figure 5.11, are as follows:

Text. The first letterforms used by Gutenberg when

Text letters (Goudy Text)

Oldstyle (Garamond)

Modern (Bodoni)

Transitional (Century)

Square serif (Stymie)

Sans serif (Helvetica)

Script (Commercial Script)

Decorative (Comstock)

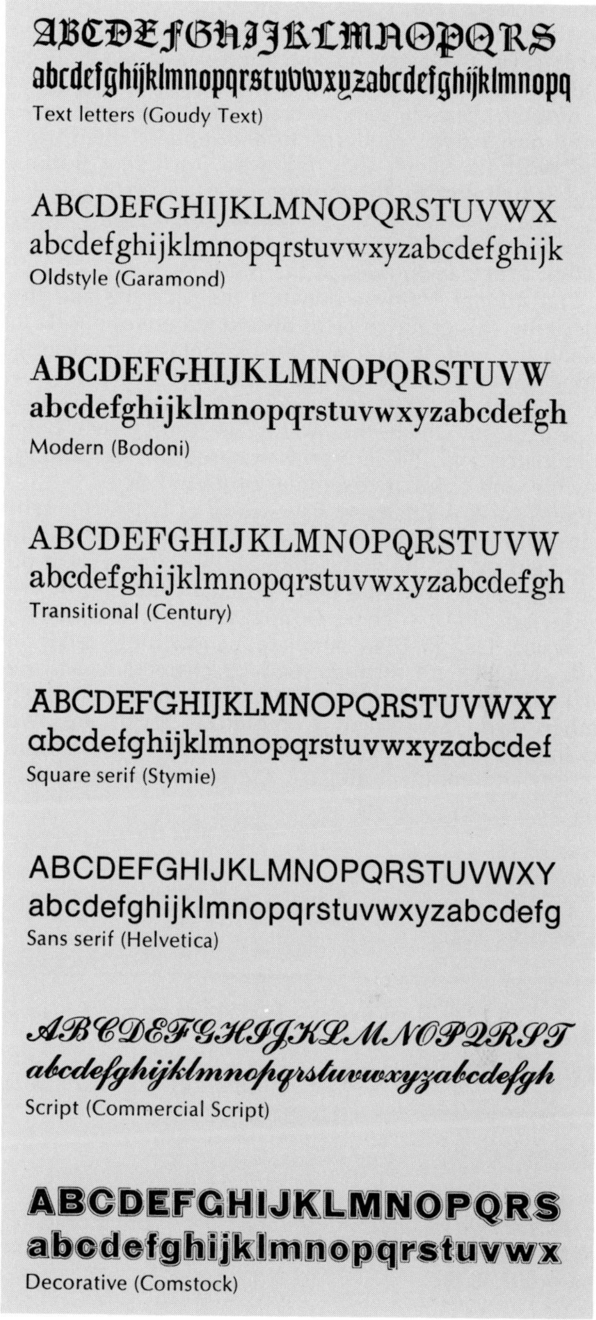

Figure 5.11: Major period and style groups used to classify type designs.

he first cast his movable type, text characters are patterned directly after the hand-drawn letters of the early scribes who, before the invention of printing, reproduced books by hand in the monasteries of the Middle Ages. Common names for text faces today are Old English and Engravers Text.

Oldstyle. This group of faces followed the text faces within a relatively few years and grew out of the classic Roman letterforms used in inscriptions. The great old-

115

style designs are some of the most readable and aesthetically expressive typefaces ever created, and faces such as Garamond and Caslon are widely used today in a broad range of applications.

Modern. These faces, actually 200 years old now, were designated "modern" to differentiate them from the oldstyles which they followed. Including Bodoni and Scotch Roman, the modern faces are distinguished by their mechanically perfected designs with every line and stroke precisely drawn, as compared to the softer, irregular outlines of the oldstyles.

Transitional. Halfway between the oldstyles and the moderns, this group of faces developed out of efforts to blend the best of both worlds. Examples of the transitional group are Century and Baskerville.

Square serif. This is a gradually growing group of typefaces in which the points on serifs have been eliminated and the serif ends squared off. Clarendon, Stymie, and Cairo are examples of these faces.

Sans serif. A relatively new group of typefaces, sans serifs have grown very rapidly in popularity and use in this century. As the name implies, these faces have no serifs at all. Among the more popular examples in use today are Univers, News Gothic, and Futura.

Script. Designed to simulate handwriting, faces in this category are distinguished by characters that are shaped like handwritten letters and that join each other. Typo Script and Commercial Script are two examples. A distinction often is made between true scripts and another category, the so-called "cursives,"

whose characters are patterned after handwriting but whose connecting strokes do not actually join up. Bernhard Cursive and Coronet are two such faces.

Decorative. Also known as "novelty" types, these faces include just about everything that does not fall within the other categories. Such typefaces usually have very unusual shapes, intended primarily for use in eye-catching display lines. Use of these faces changes rapidly with the fads and fashions of the moment.

In all, there are estimated to be well over 40,000 different typefaces in existence today, including all the different condensed and expanded versions and weight variations of basic designs. Moreover, this roster has been growing rapidly in recent years as the ease of producing new faces photographically has made it inexpensive to manufacture and market new designs. Unfortunately, photographic manufacture also has made it easy to "pirate" existing type designs by simply altering minutely a few dimensions of the characters, rephotographing the face, and marketing it under a new name. This has led to an effort to place typeface designs under copyright protection, but the move has stirred up a great deal of opposition and debate. In any event, the increasing use of photographic typesetting most likely will continue to spur rapid growth in typeface designs as designers explore the new dimensions which these processes open up to them for creating new graphic communications techniques.

TYPOGRAPHIC LEGIBILITY

Eugene M. Ettenberg, GRAPHICS CONSULTANT

This article has been reprinted from Typographic "i" *published by International Typographic Composition Association, Inc.*

Let us first agree on the meaning of the word *legibility,* for it has been given many names—among them discernibility, readability, and visibility—some having the same meaning, others only partially describing its qualities.

Legibility, as it has come to be understood, is the combining of visibility (the quality of being seen) with comprehension (understanding). Hence, an oversimplified but working definition would be: Alphanumeric symbols are legible when they have those inherent qualities that make them read with ease and contribute to their meaningfulness to a reader.

Perception, a word much favored by psychologists, has also to do with legibility. It is that complex process

by which we select, interpret, and organize sensory stimuli into coherent pictures of all that is about us. At first, we hazily distinguish shapes; then these shade into perception as we relate what we see and feel with past experiences.

Typographers and graphic designers, whose business it is to work with symbols of language, have invariably bridled when their opinions on legibility have been doubted, particularly by laymen. But the more honest of them would have to admit that their intuitive knowledge was not enough, that their opinions on legibility were not only unreasoned but unsupported by evidence and made up of hunches and hand-me-down rules acquired in the dim past.

Those who prefer to base their judgments on a firmer foundation may, with profit, study the results of various scientific investigations of legibility, some of which are to be found at the end of this article.

THE READING PROCESS

For more than 100 years, researchers have been attempting to better understand this subject. Their findings are not as definitive as one would like, nor are they all in accord, but many of their conclusions are significant. The intensity and extensiveness of these studies are evidenced by the more than 3,000 reports on various aspects of the reading process alone.

At first, efforts were directed at saving the eyesight of school children, who, it was felt by such men as the French ophthalmologists Cohn, in 1865, and Javal, in 1878, were being blinded by the size, weight, and style of typefaces then used in schoolbooks. Subsequently, observations were made of the eye movements of children and adults in the act of reading (Erdman & Dodge, 1898). These disclosed that the eye moves from left to right in short, jerky (saccadic) motions, pausing for the duration of a split second (fixation). When the reader was unsure of the meaning of what he had read, words or sentences were reread. These return eye movements are known as *regressions,* and by counting their number, the investigator was able to arrive at an index of how difficult the reader found the tested reading matter.

At this point in the research, all elements of the printed page were considered piecemeal in the attempt to isolate the causes of reading difficulties. One by one, type styles were tested, as were type sizes, type widths, leading, margins, effect of colored inks, light source intensities, and kinds of printing papers. Having compiled a lengthy list of variables that affected legibility, the researchers noted that only half of these factors were subject to control. Those that could be held in check by the typesetter or graphic designer were size of page; style, size, and width of type; spacing between letters, words, and lines; indentions and margins. The choice of printing papers, color of ink, and the presswork could be controlled by production people and printers. The remainder rested literally in the hands and eyes of the reader himself.

Legibility is affected by and dependent upon the visual acuity of the reader; his age, reading ability, and mood of the moment; his esthetic preference in color, texture, and proportion; the degree of interest he has in the subject matter. Further uncontrollable factors of legibility might be the angle at which he holds his newspaper or book and whether he is seated quietly in an easy chair with adequate light or is reading on a moving train, jiggled about and distracted by the noise of the environment.

Then there is habit, a factor stressed in the studies of the English psychologist, Sir Cyril Burt. The reader, that investigator was convinced, found most legible those types that he had most frequently encountered in his reading experience. As an extension of this thought, it is possible that typeface styles impressed on a child's consciousness during his first four years of schooling when he is being taught to read may well be those he finds most legible as an adult. Another interesting speculation might be that the typefaces a child had become accustomed to in his reading matter at age ten (when, as Bushness found in 1930, the eye movements of children become stabilized) would ever after be most legible to him.

DISPLAY LEGIBILITY

The vast majority of types for display or headline use, one need not be told, are quite different from those used for text. What is said about the legibility of text type applies only in slight degree to display type. The designer or typographer who employs letters which are to be read on directional signs, posters, billboards, or for use in newspapers has, as indeed he should have, considerable license in their use. Confined, as such a message usually is, to a few words or a short sentence, its function is to challenge a reader's interest, to cause him to consider its meaning, and so to persuade him to read on. Because of this, novelty and inventiveness on the part of the designer in the choice of type style and arrangement, within sensible limits, may well override the demands of legibility. When sufficiently intrigued, the reader will go to great lengths to puzzle out the meaning of a printed message. To quote Miles Tinker, an authority on legibility, "The human visual mechanism has the capacity to adjust to a bewildering variety of situations requiring visual discrimination."

TEXT LEGIBILITY

But we are here concerned with the legibility of text types and only with those factors that can be controlled.

The ingredients of a legible typeface, as concluded by Edwin Shaar of Harris Corporation, are:

Alignment of type. A variation of one or two thousandths of an inch is noticeable.

Optically corrected face. Optical correction compensates for failure of the eye to differentiate realities from illusions. An example is the need to slightly increase the size of round letters over that of square letters.

Uniform letter proportions in font. This involves thickness of stroke, length of serif, and evenness of color when seen in mass.

Contrast within font. Italic and boldface contrast with the regular weight of roman.

Clear symbol identification. All symbols should be clearly distinguished so that the numeral *1* cannot be mistaken for *7* or cap *I* or lowercase *l,* or a *G* confused with an *O* or a *Q.* The upper half of letters should be particularly recognizable.

Fitting. Good linkage of one letter to another when composed together.

Large x-height. The x-height should be as large as possible without unduly sacrificing the size of ascenders and descenders.

Printability. No ink traps; open counters in *b, d, o, p, q, a, e,* and *g.*

Familiarity of form. The typeface should have no strange mannerisms, should offer no distractions, and should appear easy and warm to the reader.

LEGIBILITY RESEARCH FINDINGS

Research done over the years has pinpointed factors which enhance or detract from legibility depending on how they are handled. Many of these findings confirm subjective judgments made by designers and passed

117

on as "rules of thumb." Some of the more important findings are discussed below.

Size of type

Size, as well as leading, is dependent on measure, but generally 10-, 11-, and 12-point type were most favored by researchers. The apparent size, dependent upon x-height, is more than point size. In testing, Granjon 11-point was found more legible than 8-, 9-, 10-, or 12-point (Tinker, 1963). Using scientific journals as reading matter, 11 on 13 points by 30 picas wide was found superior to three other sizes tested (Poulton, 1959); 8 on 9 and 8 on 10 were most readable in an 18-pica line (Paterson & Tinker, 1946). Fixations decreased from 8.5 to 7.8 as type was increased from 4 to 10 points in size (Luckiesh & Moss, 1941).

Boldness and slant

Italics reduce speed of perception (Tinker, 1953). Medium weight of Memphis is more legible than light, bold, and extra bold versions (Luckiesh & Moss, 1940).

Shape and contour

Distinctive tops of letters, particularly ascenders of lowercase characters, contribute to legibility. Also, the greater the enclosed white space (bowls and counters) the greater the legibility (Tinker, 1963). All researchers agree legibility is impaired when a letter has extreme contrasts in its thicks and thins, has heavy and overlong serifs, or is overly narrow.

Serifs

Short triangular serifs improve legibility (Sanford, 1888; Tinker, 1963). Most investigators regard types with serifs as more legible than those without terminals. However, significantly, Zachrisson in 1965 found that children are more favorably disposed to sans serif types than adults.

Line measure

Ideally, the measure should be 20 to 25 picas long, which gives the fewest hyphenated lines. Most opinions give the optimum line as 22 picas. Using 10-point Textype, readability increased as line width increased from 13 to 21 picas and decreased with 25- to 29-pica lengths (Luckiesh & Moss, 1941). Text was read more rapidly in 16½-pica widths than in 9-pica or 30-pica widths (Starch, 1923).

Spacing

All the researchers agree that some leading increases legibility—with normal ascenders and descenders, 1 point; when they are short, 2 or 3 points. Using the typeface Textype, 3 points of leading with 10-point type gave optimum readability (Luckiesh & Moss, 1938). Tinker gives as "safety zones" 2- to 4-point leading for 6-point type set from 14 to 28 picas; 1- to 4-point leading for 10-point type set from 14 to 21 picas; 1- to 3-point leading for 11-point type set from 16 to 34 picas. Indention of the first line of a paragraph improves legibility by 7% (Tinker, 1963). Margins should be 50% of the total area of a page (Tinker, 1963). Use of 3-to-em or 4-to-em word spaces is recommended to keep rivers of white out of type masses.

Text type arrangement

Highest ranking scores in Sweden went to typographic arrangements with which readers were most accustomed. Appropriateness to subject was found to be more important than whether the type was symmetrical or asymmetrical in arrangement.

Background

Yellowish tinted papers were preferred by Javal in 1878. By 1898, papers considered ideal were hard-surfaced, unglazed, opaque, and handmade.

In 1925, the paper most preferred by the researchers had no gloss and was as white as possible—so that it took a clean impression and had no show-through. Since then, glossy and dull finished papers have been found equal in properties affecting legibility, but it is stressed that reading should be done under diffused light. Black type on white reads 42% more rapidly than white on dark gray (Starch, 1923). Brightness difference between type symbol and background is the chief determinant of legibility (Miyake, Dunlap & Cureton, 1930). Poorest legibility is black on red and red on black; highest legibility is black on yellow (Luckiesh, 1933; Paterson & Tinker, 1931).

Conclusions

No single typographic difference affects objective legibility of types in ordinary reading (Pyke, 1923), and all common types are equally legible (Ovink, 1938). Letterforms are less important than size, weight, spacing, and shape of adjacent letters (Roethlein, 1912). However, "when several undesirable typographical factors are combined, they operate together to produce inefficient oculomotor patterns." (Paterson & Tinker, 1944).

Factors that most influence legibility are size, simplicity or complexity of a type's outline, stroke width, shading and hairlines, bowls and counters, distinguishing parts of a letter (Tinker, 1963).

X-HEIGHT

Steve Byers, MERGENTHALER LINOTYPE COMPANY

One aspect of letterform important to the creative designer or user of type is lowercase x-height. It is the principal element of visual size and readability; it affects word and line composition and paragraph color.

The x-height of a typeface is the top-to-bottom measurement of the lowercase x. The same measure applies approximately to all lowercase letters that align with the x, such as a, e, m, and c. However, since many of these letters may extend beyond the exact base and upper lines (the top and bottom curves of the o, for example), the x is the only consistently accurate measure of this space. The measure does not include the descending elements of the g, y, and j; nor does it apply to the ascending strokes of the h, b, d, or t.

To permit comparison of groups of typefaces by x-height, the measurement is expressed as a percentage of the height of the capital letters in a particular typeface. For example, in 18-point type the x-height of Clarendon Roman is .120 inch, and the height of a capital R is .170 inch; that is, the lowercase x is 70 percent of the height of the capitals.

X-height varies greatly from typeface to typeface and from family to family. (See figure 5.12.) Nineteenth-century oldstyle typefaces such as Caslon Old Face 2, Scotch 2, and Cloister Roman have x-heights of 54%, 55%, and 58% of their respective capital letters. More recent gothic typefaces such as Helvetica, Univers, and Optima measure 70%, 72%, and 69% respectively. Galliard, a new serif typeface, and Video, a new sans serif typeface, were both designed by Matthew Carter.

54%	Caslon Old Face 2
55%	Scotch 2 Roman
58%	Cloister Roman
69%	Optima Medium Roman
70%	Helvetica Roman
71%	Galliard Roman
72%	Univers 55 Roman
72%	Video Roman

Figure 5.12: Comparison of x-heights of various 18-point typefaces in terms of percentage of capital height.

Video has an x-height of 72% of its capital letters, and Galliard has an x-height of 71% of its capitals. The trend seems to be toward a larger x-height for text typefaces. The use of large x-heights in new type designs may be in part a matter of fashion, but the favorable effect of a large x-height on the readability and legibility of a typeface and on economy of space makes the trend a sound one.

Since lowercase characters make up 95 percent of the text in normal English-language composition, the legibility of a setting and the overall look of the copy will be determined largely by these letterforms. Generally, a small x-height will give a more open look, since a smaller percentage of the height of the line is occupied by the lowercase letters. A large x-height will give a "darker color" to the copy and increased readability, and there will be less unfilled space. Of course, other factors such as the design of the typeface itself, the leading, and the fit of the letters will affect the appearance of the printed page, but x-height has a significant effect and should be taken into account.

As influential as x-height is on the visual color of a text setting, however, it is not the normal vertical measure used by book designers. This normal measure is the *body height* of the typeface—the vertical space within which the typeface is positioned, and which is expressed in points. Because of the variation in the relation between x-height and capital height and between x-height and point size from one typeface to another, it is important to consider x-height as a separate element in type design and use. Since the proportion of overall height to lowercase height varies by more than 20 percent through the various typeface designs, a 10-point typeface with a small x-height can be the legibility equivalent of an 8-point typeface with a large x-height. (See figure 5.13.) The height of a lowercase character in 10-point Baskerville is just about 4 points. The lowercase height of 8-point Helvetica is also just about 4 points. Thus we have the same x-height (within .001") and an equally readable lowercase alphabet with a 2-point saving in line depth through substitution of one typeface for another. This example projected through a text setting of book length has an implied economic importance which graphic designers, editors, and publishers should keep in mind. Whether such a substitution is made or is even desirable is a question of design and editorial judgment. However, it is the responsibility of a good typographer to understand that such options are available.

The relation of x-height to overall size may vary even among faces with the same x-height to cap height ratio because of variations in design. Ascenders, for example, are not always the same height as capital letters; in some faces they go a bit beyond the height of the

Helvetica Roman 8-point	Baskerville Roman 10-point
Helvetica Roman 10-point	Baskerville Roman 10-point
Helvetica Roman 8-point	Baskerville Roman 8-point

Figure 5.13: Effect of x-height on legibility. Helvetica in 8-point is equivalent to 10-point Baskerville; when both are in the same point size, Helvetica appears more legible.

capitals and occasionally substantially beyond. Some metal faces even have alternate sets of characters with long and short descenders, to be used at the designer's discretion to achieve different effects. There are additional variations among equivalent typefaces in foundry, machine-set, and photoset type. Some photo systems, for example, simply enlarge and reduce one master for a number of point sizes, while metal types almost always have subtle reproportioning of the letters from one type size to another.

These minor variations also relate to the space between the x-heights of successive lines of type, which is of course an important element in the visual effect of the printed piece. This space will be determined not only by the leading between lines plus the ascenders and descenders, but also by any variations between the point size and the actual overall height of the characters.

Because of all the factors affecting the final typeset copy, it is not advisable to base the choice of typeface and type size on the point size alone. It is important to consider which x-height will best fulfill the requirements of the job, in terms of visual effect, legibility, and economy. The luxury of trial settings, always the ideal solution, is not always possible, so the more knowledge brought to the job by everyone involved—the typographer, the designers, the editor, the publisher—the more intelligent will the decisions be and the more satisfactory the results—both visually and in terms of production costs.

TYPE "WHYS"

Edward M. Gottschall, INTERNATIONAL TYPEFACE CORPORATION

The popularity of a typeface may depend upon any of a number of factors—fashion, distinctive design, wide availability on many kinds of typesetting equipment, and various practical design advantages such as high readability, tightness of fit, and wide scope of family. Some of the faces that have become popular in recent years are the Helveticas, Windsor, the Times family, Optima, Melior, Avant Garde Gothic, and Palatino. Of course there are others, but an examination of what brought these to the fore may help to reveal the major considerations in the minds of today's type designers and type specifiers. (Samples of these seven popular typefaces are shown in figure 5.14.)

WHY HELVETICA?

For a while Helvetica was by far the most widely used typeface, and no doubt it was overused because it was in fashion. However, it is a soundly designed face that will live long after its fashion phase is over.

M. Miedinger designed Helvetica to be highly legible. At one time, sans serif faces were considered less legible than serif faces, especially those of the so-called "legibility" group. As new generations of readers grew up, however—readers who had been familiar with serifless types from childhood—it was found that sans serifs as a class were at least as readable as serif faces and that the element of familiarity, not considered in earlier legibility studies, was a significant factor in readability. Part of Helvetica's legibility is due to extreme cleanness of design. The counters are open, and in the small sizes this prevents fill-in and helps characters retain their visual identity. Readability is enhanced by good alignment, which eliminates eccentricities in setting, and by the proper fit of virtually any combination of letters.

Another factor in Helvetica's popularity is its large x-height. Each letter occupies a large volume of space relative to the type body. The printed character and the space around it take the same space on the page as a character of another style of the same size, but the printed character itself is larger and the surrounding space less. (See "X-Height," page 119.)

The combination of large x-height, relatively short ascenders and descenders, and cleanness of design make for tight copyfitting and maximum readability. In fact, Helvetica is so legible that it is often used in a size

120

The popularity of a typeface may depend upon any of a number of factors—fashion, distinctive design, wide availability on many kinds of typesetting equipment, and various practical design advantages such as high readability, tightness of

Helvetica

The popularity of a typeface may depend upon any of a number of factors—fashion, distinctive design, wide availability on many kinds of typesetting equipment, and various practical design advantages such as high readability, tightness of fit, and wide scope of family.

Windsor

The popularity of a typeface may depend upon any of a number of factors—fashion, distinctive design, wide availability on many kinds of typesetting equipment, and various practical design advantages such as high readability, tightness of fit, and wide scope of

Times Roman

The popularity of a typeface may depend upon any of a number of factors—fashion, distinctive design, wide availability on many kinds of typesetting equipment, and various practical design advantages such as high readability, tightness of fit, and

Optima

The popularity of a typeface may depend upon any of a number of factors—fashion, distinctive design, wide availability on many kinds of typesetting equipment, and various practical design advantages such as high readability, tightness of fit, and wide

Melior

The popularity of a typeface may depend upon any of a number of factors—fashion, distinctive design, wide availability on many kinds of typesetting equipment, and various practical design advantages such as high readability, tightness of fit, and

Avant Garde Gothic Book

The popularity of a typeface may depend upon any of a number of factors—fashion, distinctive design, wide availability on many kinds of typesetting equipment, and various practical design advantages such as high readability, tightness of fit, and wide scope of

Palatino

Figure 5.14: Samples of seven popular typefaces.

smaller than many other faces, and additional copyfitting is gained without sacrificing readability.

Adding to Helvetica's popularity is its large family—a wide range of sizes, weights, condensed and expanded versions—and its universal availability. It can be found all over the world in foundry type, on metal casting machines, and in film.

WHY WINDSOR?

Partly as a reaction to the overly wide use of the Helvetica and Univers families, there is a recurring interest in serif faces. One of these is Windsor. Designed at the turn of the century by Elisha Peshey, Windsor is certainly not a new typeface, but it offers a distinctive look within the traditional serif style. Windsor is characterized by its beak-like serifs, large bowls in the uppercase P, R, and B, and the splayed legs of the uppercase M.

Windsor has other features sought by today's designer. Tight packing of characters gives a high character count and a generally tight appearance in the copy mass. There is enough variety within the family (regular, light, condensed, elongated, and outline), and the range of sizes carries it through many text and display needs. When contrast with sans serif text faces is wanted, Windsor makes a good display choice.

WHY TIMES?

The Times family is possibly the most widely used of the serif styles. It is highly readable, featuring a large x-height that permits the use of a 10-point type, for example, that reads like a 12. It is compact without appearing condensed. Unlike the monotone "legibility" faces designed for newspapers in the 1930's, Times has visual sparkle with contrasting thick-and-thin strokes and sharp, angled serifs. It is available virtually all over the world and on a wide variety of equipment. The family is large, including two versions of the bold; and in metal it ranges in size from 4½ to 48 points. Another asset is its wide range of special characters.

Times was created by Stanley Morison for the *Times* of London as a highly readable face, and some consider that in this respect it has no peer. Introduced over 40 years ago, it is fading out as a newspaper face but is thriving in communication graphics and book work. It seems to strike many as a safe face—contemporary yet classic; distinctive yet not eccentric. Many designers, when in doubt, specify Times.

WHY OPTIMA?

Optima has many of the virtues of Helvetica and Times—large x-height, high readability, wide availability, tight fitting, large family, and a font with foreign accents. It is especially liked for its ability to combine well with almost any other typeface. This is because it is eclectic—it is a sans serif with a sparkle due to thick-and-thin stroke design.

Designed by Hermann Zapf, Optima appeared on the American scene in 1960. Unlike other serifless thick-and-thins (Radiant, Lydian, Stellar), it was available in foundry and on the machine, so it instantly became available for both text and display setting.

WHY MELIOR?

Melior, like Optima, was designed by Hermann Zapf and is also an eclectic design. It is a thick-and-thin square serif or "Egyptian" typeface. Like so many of today's most popular types, Melior has a large x-height, is highly readable (it originated as a newspaper face), and has an excellent character count. It is unique in design, featuring openness, no excess thins, sharp curves, and slightly rounded-off stroke ends, and it is relatively condensed. Although Melior does not mix as easily as Optima does with other faces, it is widely used where a combination of distinction and readability is sought.

WHY AVANT GARDE GOTHIC?

More than most other widely used typefaces, Avant Garde Gothic owes much of its popularity to newness and distinctiveness. It is in fashion. Designed by Herb Lubalin and Tom Carnese, it was marketed in 1970 and was the first typeface introduced by International Typeface Corporation. Because ITC markets its faces to all equipment manufacturers, it became quickly available across the board in film systems. Its wide availability and visual distinction helped it to achieve quick acceptance. Although unavailable in metal, it is widely available in film and on dry transfer sheets.

Avant Garde Gothic is an even-toned face in five weights; the weights intermix well for varieties of contrast. Large x-height, tight-fitting characters, and special ligatures compensate for round o's and wide, angular letters, so that the face fits despite its wide look. It is distinguished by ascenders and descenders that are not only short but tucked in tightly to the body, as with the lowercase g.

WHY PALATINO?

Unlike some of the other of today's popular faces, Palatino has only normal x-height and copyfitting characteristics. It is not obviously contemporary, like Avant Garde Gothic; its appeal lies in its classic beauty and distinction. Hermann Zapf, who designed Palatino in the late 1940's, derived its form from the edged pen's natural motion. It is an oldstyle face designed for twentieth-century photographic and electronic typographic composition systems. It is widely available in a range of text and display sizes, and has good character fitting and special ligatures to give copy blocks the even color so much in demand today. The designer, among others, feels that the Linofilm version shows off the face at its best, compared with previous metal versions.

WHERE NOW?

While each of these faces has its own appeal, the common characteristics wanted in today's market are apparent: good x-height, good character fitting, clean lines, compatibility with other faces, and distinctive, classic design. Photographic typesetting has opened up many opportunities for new type designs, and a host of new faces will come into vogue. Most will be fads, dropping from use after a year or two; a few great faces will live indefinitely. In addition, we will always see revivals of old favorites designed to work on new equipment and to meet new graphic needs.

SURPRINT AND REVERSE VISUALIZER

The typographic visualizers on the following pages are reprinted from Typographic "i" *published by International Typographic Composition Association, Inc.*

A common problem in the use of type is the need to superimpose the type over an illustration or background of some kind. If both background and typeface are not chosen carefully to coordinate with each other, the designer runs the risk of creating hard-to-read, or even unreadable, presentations. While this factor must be considered when using one color of type against another color background, the problem is usually much more difficult when type is integrated into a halftone background which will be printed in the same color.

There are two ways to superimpose type on a halftone background. Generally, in both, the type appears as a solid area without any halftone dots, while the surrounding areas are halftone. In the first method, the type appears as a solid color, or a *surprint*; in the second, the type appears as a clear unprinted area called a *reverse image*. Both forms of lettering must be sufficiently different in contrast from the surrounding halftone areas to be readily visible.

Another factor that is important to good legibility of the type is the relationship of screen ruling to size of the characters. Finer line screens provide better definition of character edges. If relatively coarse screens are used with type having fine serifs, the serifs can be lost to the eye even though the type may contrast well with the overall halftone background.

To illustrate these principles, and to provide the designer with a quick reference guide to these effects, the following pages reproduce some of the more popular typefaces in both surprint and reverse against varying degrees of halftone shading. By finding a type similar to that which will be used in the job, the designer can get a good approximation of the final effect he will achieve in his piece.

Surprint visualizer, from 10% to solid in 10% steps; 133-line screen.

Futura Light, 6 pt. See for yourself how this face surprints or reverses over the entire spectrum of tone values, with fine
Futura Light, 8 pt. See for yourself how this face surprints or reverses over the entire spectrum of tone val
Futura Light, 10 pt. See for yourself how this face surprints or reverses over the entire spa
Futura Light, 12 pt. See for yourself how this face surprints or reverses over

Futura Book, 6 pt. See for yourself how this face surprints or reverses over the entire spectrum of tone values, with fine
Futura Book, 8 pt. See for yourself how this face surprints or reverses over the entire spectrum of tone values, w
Futura Book, 10 pt. See for yourself how this face surprints or reverses over the entire spe
Futura Book, 12 pt. See for yourself how this face surprints or reverses over th

Futura Medium, 6 pt. See for yourself how this face surprints or reverses over the entire spectrum of tone values,
Futura Medium, 8 pt. See for yourself how this face surprints or reverses over the entire spectrum of t
Futura Medium, 10 pt. See for yourself how this face surprints or reverses over the
Futura Medium, 12 pt. See for yourself how this face surprints or revers

Futura Demi, 6 pt. See for yourself how this face surprints or reverses over the entire spectrum of tone values, w
Futura Demi, 8 pt. See for yourself how this face surprints or reverses over the entire spectrum of
Futura Demi, 10 pt. See for yourself how this face surprints or reverses over th
Futura Demi, 12 pt. See for yourself how this face surprints or reverse

Futura Bold, 6 pt. See for yourself how this face surprints or reverses over the entire spectrum of
Futura Bold, 8 pt. See for yourself how this face surprints or reverses over the entire spe
Futura Bold, 10 pt. See for yourself how this face surprints or reverse
Futura Bold, 12 pt. See for yourself how this face surprints

News Gothic, 6 pt. See for yourself how this face surprints or reverses over the entire spectrum of
News Gothic, 8 pt. See for yourself how this face surprints or reverses over the entire v
News Gothic, 10 pt. See for yourself how this face surprints or reverses ov
News Gothic, 12 pt. See for yourself how this face surprints or r

News Gothic Bold, 6 pt. See for yourself how this face surprints or reverses over the entire spectrum
News Gothic Bold, 8 pt. See for yourself how this face surprints or reverses over the e
News Gothic Bold, 10 pt. See for yourself how this face surprints or revers
News Gothic Bold, 12 pt. See for yourself how this face surprints

News Gothic Cond., 6 pt. See for yourself how this face surprints or reverses over the entire spectrum of tone va
News Gothic Cond., 8 pt. See for yourself how this face surprints or reverses over the entire spectrum
News Gothic Cond., 10 pt. See for yourself how this face surprints or reverses over the en
News Gothic Cond., 12 pt. See for yourself how this face surprints or reverses over t

News Gothic Bold Cond. (Alt #2), 6 pt. See for yourself how this face surprints or reverses over the entire spect
News Gothic Bold Cond. (Alt #2), 8 pt. See for yourself how this face surprints or reverses over the e
News Gothic Bold Cond. (Alt #2), 10 pt. See for yourself how this face surprints or reve
News Gothic Bold Cond. (Alt #2), 12 pt. See for yourself how this face surprints o

Helvetica Light, 6 pt. See for yourself how this face surprints or reverses over the entire spectrum of tone val
Helvetica Light, 8 pt. See for yourself how this face surprints or reverses over the entire spe
Helvetica Light, 10 pt. See for yourself how this face surprints or reverses o
Helvetica Light, 12 pt. See for yourself how this face surprints or

Helvetica, 6 pt. See for yourself how this face surprints or reverses over the entire spectrum of tone values
Helvetica, 8 pt. See for yourself how this face surprints or reverses over the entire spectr
Helvetica, 10 pt. See for yourself how this face surprints or reverses ov
Helvetica, 12 pt. See for yourself how this face surprints or re

Helvetica Semi Bold, 6 pt. See for yourself how this face surprints or reverses over the entire spectrum of
Helvetica Semi Bold, 8 pt. See for yourself how this face surprints or reverses over the e
Helvetica Semi Bold, 10 pt. See for yourself how this face surprints or r
Helvetica Semi Bold, 12 pt. See for yourself how this face sur

Reverse visualizer, from solid to 10% in 10% steps; 133-line screen.

Futura Light, 6 pt. See for yourself how this face surprints or reverses over the entire spectrum of tone values, with fine or coarse screens. See for yourself how this face
Futura Light, 8 pt. See for yourself how this face surprints or reverses over the entire spectrum of tone values, with fine or coarse screens. See for you
Futura Light, 10 pt. See for yourself how this face surprints or reverses over the entire spectrum of tone values, with fine or co
Futura Light, 12 pt. See for yourself how this face surprints or reverses over the entire spectrum of tone valu

Futura Book, 6 pt. See for yourself how this face surprints or reverses over the entire spectrum of tone values, with fine or coarse screens. See for yourself how this face sur
Futura Book, 8 pt. See for yourself how this face surprints or reverses over the entire spectrum of tone values, with fine or coarse screens. See for yourself how
Futura Book, 10 pt. See for yourself how this face surprints or reverses over the entire spectrum of tone values, with fine or coa
Futura Book, 12 pt. See for yourself how this face surprints or reverses over the entire spectrum of tone values

Futura Medium, 6 pt. See for yourself how this face surprints or reverses over the entire spectrum of tone values, with fine or coarse screens. See for yourself how
Futura Medium, 8 pt. See for yourself how this face surprints or reverses over the entire spectrum of tone values, with fine or coarse screens. See
Futura Medium, 10 pt. See for yourself how this face surprints or reverses over the entire spectrum of tone values, with
Futura Medium, 12 pt. See for yourself how this face surprints or reverses over the entire spectrum of

Futura Demi, 6 pt. See for yourself how this face surprints or reverses over the entire spectrum of tone values, with fine or coarse screens. See for yourself how
Futura Demi, 8 pt. See for yourself how this face surprints or reverses over the entire spectrum of tone values, with fine or coarse screens.
Futura Demi, 10 pt. See for yourself how this face surprints or reverses over the entire spectrum of tone values
Futura Demi, 12 pt. See for yourself how this face surprints or reverses over the entire spectrum of

Futura Bold, 6 pt. See for yourself how this face surprints or reverses over the entire spectrum of tone values, with fine or coarse screens.
Futura Bold, 8 pt. See for yourself how this face surprints or reverses over the entire spectrum of tone values, with fine or coa
Futura Bold, 10 pt. See for yourself how this face surprints or reverses over the entire spectrum of
Futura Bold, 12 pt. See for yourself how this face surprints or reverses over the enti

News Gothic, 6 pt. See for yourself how this face surprints or reverses over the entire spectrum of tone values, with fine or coarse screens.
News Gothic, 8 pt. See for yourself how this face surprints or reverses over the entire spectrum of tone values, with fine or
News Gothic, 10 pt. See for yourself how this face surprints or reverses over the entire spectrum of tone
News Gothic, 12 pt. See for yourself how this face surprints or reverses over the entire sp

News Gothic Bold, 6 pt. See for yourself how this face surprints or reverses over the entire spectrum of tone values, with fine or coarse screens
News Gothic Bold, 8 pt. See for yourself how this face surprints or reverses over the entire spectrum of tone values, with
News Gothic Bold, 10 pt. See for yourself how this face surprints or reverses over the entire spectrum of
News Gothic Bold, 12 pt. See for yourself how this face surprints or reverses over the entire

News Gothic Cond., 6 pt. See for yourself how this face surprints or reverses over the entire spectrum of tone values, with fine or coarse screens. See for yours
News Gothic Cond., 8 pt. See for yourself how this face surprints or reverses over the entire spectrum of tone values, with fine or coarse scree
News Gothic Cond., 10 pt. See for yourself how this face surprints or reverses over the entire spectrum of tone values, with fine
News Gothic Cond., 12 pt. See for yourself how this face surprints or reverses over the entire spectrum of tone values

News Gothic Bold Cond. (Alt #2), 6 pt. See for yourself how this face surprints or reverses over the entire spectrum of tone values, with fine or coarse screens.
News Gothic Bold Cond. (Alt #2), 8 pt. See for yourself how this face surprints or reverses over the entire spectrum of tone values, with fine or
News Gothic Bold Cond. (Alt #2), 10 pt. See for yourself how this face surprints or reverses over the entire spectrum of tone
News Gothic Bold Cond. (Alt #2), 12 pt. See for yourself how this face surprints or reverses over the entire spectru

Helvetica Light, 6 pt. See for yourself how this face surprints or reverses over the entire spectrum of tone values, with fine or coarse screens. See for yours
Helvetica Light, 8 pt. See for yourself how this face surprints or reverses over the entire spectrum of tone values, with fine or coar
Helvetica Light, 10 pt. See for yourself how this face surprints or reverses over the entire spectrum of tone
Helvetica Light, 12 pt. See for yourself how this face surprints or reverses over the entire sp

Helvetica, 6 pt. See for yourself how this face surprints or reverses over the entire spectrum of tone values, with fine or coarse screens. See for yourse
Helvetica, 8 pt. See for yourself how this face surprints or reverses over the entire spectrum of tone values, with fine or coarse
Helvetica, 10 pt. See for yourself how this face surprints or reverses over the entire spectrum of tone
Helvetica, 12 pt. See for yourself how this face surprints or reverses over the entire sp

Helvetica Semi Bold, 6 pt. See for yourself how this face surprints or reverses over the entire spectrum of tone values, with fine or coarse screens. See
Helvetica Semi Bold, 8 pt. See for yourself how this face surprints or reverses over the entire spectrum of tone values, with fi
Helvetica Semi Bold, 10 pt. See for yourself how this face surprints or reverses over the entire spectr
Helvetica Semi Bold, 12 pt. See for yourself how this face surprints or reverses over the

124

Futura Light, 6 pt. See for yourself how this face surprints or reverses over the entire spectrum of tone values, with fine or coarse screens.
Futura Light, 8 pt. See for yourself how this face surprints or reverses over the entire spectrum of tone values, with fine or coarse screens.
Futura Light, 10 pt. See for yourself how this face surprints or reverses over the entire spectrum of tone values, with
Futura Light, 12 pt. See for yourself how this face surprints or reverses over the entire spectrum of

Futura Book, 6 pt. See for yourself how this face surprints or reverses over the entire spectrum of tone values, with fine or coarse screens.
Futura Book, 8 pt. See for yourself how this face surprints or reverses over the entire spectrum of tone values, with fine or coarse screens.
Futura Book, 10 pt. See for yourself how this face surprints or reverses over the entire spectrum of tone values, with
Futura Book, 12 pt. See for yourself how this face surprints or reverses over the entire spectrum of

Futura Medium, 6 pt. See for yourself how this face surprints or reverses over the entire spectrum of tone values, with fine or coarse screens.
Futura Medium, 8 pt. See for yourself how this face surprints or reverses over the entire spectrum of tone values, with fine or coarse screens.
Futura Medium, 10 pt. See for yourself how this face surprints or reverses over the entire spectrum of tone values.
Futura Medium, 12 pt. See for yourself how this face surprints or reverses over the entire spectrum

Futura Demi, 6 pt. See for yourself how this face surprints or reverses over the entire spectrum of tone values, with fine or coarse screens.
Futura Demi, 8 pt. See for yourself how this face surprints or reverses over the entire spectrum of tone values, with fine or coarse screens.
Futura Demi, 10 pt. See for yourself how this face surprints or reverses over the entire spectrum of tone
Futura Demi, 12 pt. See for yourself how this face surprints or reverses over the entire spectrum

Futura Bold, 6 pt. See for yourself how this face surprints or reverses over the entire spectrum of tone values, with fine or coarse screens.
Futura Bold, 8 pt. See for yourself how this face surprints or reverses over the entire spectrum of tone values, with
Futura Bold, 10 pt. See for yourself how this face surprints or reverses over the entire spectrum
Futura Bold, 12 pt. See for yourself how this face surprints or reverses over the

News Gothic, 6 pt. See for yourself how this face surprints or reverses over the entire spectrum of tone values, with fine or coarse screens.
News Gothic, 8 pt. See for yourself how this face surprints or reverses over the entire spectrum of tone values.
News Gothic, 10 pt. See for yourself how this face surprints or reverses over the entire spectrum
News Gothic, 12 pt. See for yourself how this face surprints or reverses over the entire

News Gothic Bold, 6 pt. See for yourself how this face surprints or reverses over the entire spectrum of tone values, with fine or coarse screens.
News Gothic Bold, 8 pt. See for yourself how this face surprints or reverses over the entire spectrum of tone values.
News Gothic Bold, 10 pt. See for yourself how this face surprints or reverses over the entire spectrum
News Gothic Bold, 12 pt. See for yourself how this face surprints or reverses over the

News Gothic Cond., 6 pt. See for yourself how this face surprints or reverses over the entire spectrum of tone values, with fine or coarse screens.
News Gothic Cond., 8 pt. See for yourself how this face surprints or reverses over the entire spectrum of tone values, with fine or coarse
News Gothic Cond., 10 pt. See for yourself how this face surprints or reverses over the entire spectrum of tone values.
News Gothic Cond., 12 pt. See for yourself how this face surprints or reverses over the entire spectrum of

News Gothic Bold Cond. (Alt #2), 6 pt. See for yourself how this face surprints or reverses over the entire spectrum of tone values, with fine or co
News Gothic Bold Cond. (Alt #2), 8 pt. See for yourself how this face surprints or reverses over the entire spectrum of tone values.
News Gothic Bold Cond. (Alt #2), 10 pt. See for yourself how this face surprints or reverses over the entire spectra
News Gothic Bold Cond. (Alt #2), 12 pt. See for yourself how this face surprints or reverses over the entire

Helvetica Light, 6 pt. See for yourself how this face surprints or reverses over the entire spectrum of tone values, with fine or coarse screens.
Helvetica Light, 8 pt. See for yourself how this face surprints or reverses over the entire spectrum of tone values, with
Helvetica Light, 10 pt. See for yourself how this face surprints or reverses over the entire spectrum
Helvetica Light, 12 pt. See for yourself how this face surprints or reverses over the

Helvetica, 6 pt. See for yourself how this face surprints or reverses over the entire spectrum of tone values, with fine or coarse screens.
Helvetica, 8 pt. See for yourself how this face surprints or reverses over the entire spectrum of tone values, with fine
Helvetica, 10 pt. See for yourself how this face surprints or reverses over the entire spectrum
Helvetica, 12 pt. See for yourself how this face surprints or reverses over the

Helvetica Semi Bold, 6 pt. See for yourself how this face surprints or reverses over the entire spectrum of tone values, with fine or coarse screens.
Helvetica Semi Bold, 8 pt. See for yourself how this face surprints or reverses over the entire spectrum of tone values.
Helvetica Semi Bold, 10 pt. See for yourself how this face surprints or reverses over the entire
Helvetica Semi Bold, 12 pt. See for yourself how this face surprints or reverses

Reverse visualizer, from solid to 10% in 10% steps; 65-line screen.

Futura Light, 6 pt. See for yourself how this face surprints or reverses over the entire spectrum of tone values, with fine or coarse screens. See for yourself how this face
Futura Light, 8 pt. See for yourself how this face surprints or reverses over the entire spectrum of tone values, with fine or coarse screens. See for you
Futura Light, 10 pt. See for yourself how this face surprints or reverses over the entire spectrum of tone values, with fine or coa
Futura Light, 12 pt. See for yourself how this face surprints or reverses over the entire spectrum of tone valu

Futura Book, 6 pt. See for yourself how this face surprints or reverses over the entire spectrum of tone values, with fine or coarse screens. See for yourself how this face ap
Futura Book, 8 pt. See for yourself how this face surprints or reverses over the entire spectrum of tone values, with fine or coarse screens. See for yourself h
Futura Book, 10 pt. See for yourself how this face surprints or reverses over the entire spectrum of tone values, with fine or coa
Futura Book, 12 pt. See for yourself how this face surprints or reverses over the entire spectrum of tone values

Futura Medium, 6 pt. See for yourself how this face surprints or reverses over the entire spectrum of tone values, with fine or coarse screens. See for yourself how
Futura Medium, 8 pt. See for yourself how this face surprints or reverses over the entire spectrum of tone values, with fine or coarse screens. See
Futura Medium, 10 pt. See for yourself how this face surprints or reverses over the entire spectrum of tone values, with
Futura Medium, 12 pt. See for yourself how this face surprints or reverses over the entire spectrum of

Futura Demi, 6 pt. See for yourself how this face surprints or reverses over the entire spectrum of tone values, with fine or coarse screens. See for yourself how
Futura Demi, 8 pt. See for yourself how this face surprints or reverses over the entire spectrum of tone values, with fine or coarse screens.
Futura Demi, 10 pt. See for yourself how this face surprints or reverses over the entire spectrum of tone values
Futura Demi, 12 pt. See for yourself how this face surprints or reverses over the entire spectrum of

Futura Bold, 6 pt. See for yourself how this face surprints or reverses over the entire spectrum of tone values, with fine or coarse screens.
Futura Bold, 8 pt. See for yourself how this face surprints or reverses over the entire spectrum of tone values, with fine or see
Futura Bold, 10 pt. See for yourself how this face surprints or reverses over the entire spectrum of
Futura Bold, 12 pt. See for yourself how this face surprints or reverses over the enti

News Gothic, 6 pt. See for yourself how this face surprints or reverses over the entire spectrum of tone values, with fine or coarse screens.
News Gothic, 8 pt. See for yourself how this face surprints or reverses over the entire spectrum of tone values, with fine or
News Gothic, 10 pt. See for yourself how this face surprints or reverses over the entire spectrum of tone
News Gothic, 12 pt. See for yourself how this face surprints or reverses over the entire sp

News Gothic Bold, 6 pt. See for yourself how this face surprints or reverses over the entire spectrum of tone values, with fine or coarse screens.
News Gothic Bold, 8 pt. See for yourself how this face surprints or reverses over the entire spectrum of tone values, with
News Gothic Bold, 10 pt. See for yourself how this face surprints or reverses over the entire spectrum of
News Gothic Bold, 12 pt. See for yourself how this face surprints or reverses over the entire

News Gothic Cond., 6 pt. See for yourself how this face surprints or reverses over the entire spectrum of tone values, with fine or coarse screens. See for your
News Gothic Cond., 8 pt. See for yourself how this face surprints or reverses over the entire spectrum of tone values, with fine or coarse scree
News Gothic Cond., 10 pt. See for yourself how this face surprints or reverses over the entire spectrum of tone values, with fine
News Gothic Cond., 12 pt. See for yourself how this face surprints or reverses over the entire spectrum of tone values

News Gothic Bold Cond. (Alt #2), 6 pt. See for yourself how this face surprints or reverses over the entire spectrum of tone values, with fine or coarse screens.
News Gothic Bold Cond. (Alt #2), 8 pt. See for yourself how this face surprints or reverses over the entire spectrum of tone values, with fine or
News Gothic Bold Cond. (Alt #2), 10 pt. See for yourself how this face surprints or reverses over the entire spectrum of tone
News Gothic Bold Cond. (Alt #2), 12 pt. See for yourself how this face surprints or reverses over the entire spectru

Helvetica Light, 6 pt. See for yourself how this face surprints or reverses over the entire spectrum of tone values, with fine or coarse screens. See for you
Helvetica Light, 8 pt. See for yourself how this face surprints or reverses over the entire spectrum of tone values, with fine or con
Helvetica Light, 10 pt. See for yourself how this face surprints or reverses over the entire spectrum of tone
Helvetica Light, 12 pt. See for yourself how this face surprints or reverses over the entire sp

Helvetica, 6 pt. See for yourself how this face surprints or reverses over the entire spectrum of tone values, with fine or coarse screens. See for your
Helvetica, 8 pt. See for yourself how this face surprints or reverses over the entire spectrum of tone values, with fine or coarse
Helvetica, 10 pt. See for yourself how this face surprints or reverses over the entire spectrum of tone
Helvetica, 12 pt. See for yourself how this face surprints or reverses over the entire sp

Helvetica Semi Bold, 6 pt. See for yourself how this face surprints or reverses over the entire spectrum of tone values, with fine or coarse screens. See
Helvetica Semi Bold, 8 pt. See for yourself how this face surprints or reverses over the entire spectrum of tone values, with fi
Helvetica Semi Bold, 10 pt. See for yourself how this face surprints or reverses over the entire spectr
Helvetica Semi Bold, 12 pt. See for yourself how this face surprints or reverses over the

Clarendon, 6 pt. See for yourself how this face surprints or reverses over the entire spectrum of tone values,

Clarendon, 8 pt. See for yourself how this face surprints or reverses over the entire spectrum of tone

Clarendon, 10 pt. See for yourself how this face surprints or reverses over the entire

Clarendon, 12 pt. See for yourself how this face surprints or rev

Melior, 6 pt. See for yourself how this face surprints or reverses over the entire spectrum of tone values, with fine or coarse

Melior, 8 pt. See for yourself how this face surprints or reverses over the entire spectrum of tone values

Melior, 10 pt. See for yourself how this face surprints or reverses over the entire spectrum of

Melior, 12 pt. See for yourself how this face surprints or reverses over the entire

Baskerville, 6 pt. See for yourself how this face surprints or reverses over the entire spectrum of tone values, with fine or coarse

Baskerville, 8 pt. See for yourself how this face surprints or reverses over the entire spectrum of tone values,

Baskerville, 10 pt. See for yourself how this face surprints or reverses over the entire spectrum of

Baskerville, 12 pt. See for yourself how this face surprints or reverses over the entire

Bookman, 6 pt. See for yourself how this face surprints or reverses over the entire spectrum of tone values, with fine or coarse

Bookman, 8 pt. See for yourself how this face surprints or reverses over the entire spectrum of tone values, with fine

Bookman, 10 pt. See for yourself how this face surprints or reverses over the entire spectrum or

Bookman, 12 pt. See for yourself how this face surprints or reverses over the entire

Caslon, 6 pt. See for yourself how this face surprints or reverses over the entire spectrum of tone values, with fine or coarse screen. See for yourself

Caslon, 8 pt. See for yourself how this face surprints or reverses over the entire spectrum of tone values, with

Caslon, 10 pt. See for yourself how this face surprints or reverses over the entire spectrum of tone values

Caslon, 12 pt. See for yourself how this face surprints or reverses over the entire

Garamond, 6 pt. See for yourself how this face surprints or reverses over the entire spectrum of tone values, with fine or coarse

Garamond, 8 pt. See for yourself how this face surprints or reverses over the entire spectrum of tone values, with fine

Garamond, 10 pt. See for yourself how this face surprints or reverses over the entire spectrum of tone val.

Garamond, 12 pt. See for yourself how this face surprints or reverses over the entire

Times Roman, 6 pt. See for yourself how this face surprints or reverses over the entire spectrum of tone values, with fine

Times Roman, 8 pt. See for yourself how this face surprints or reverses over the entire spectrum of tone

Times Roman, 10 pt. See for yourself how this face surprints or reverses over the entire spectrum of

Times Roman, 12 pt. See for yourself how this face surprints or reverses over the entire

Optima, 6 pt. See for yourself how this face surprints or reverses over the entire spectrum of tone values, with fine or coarse

Optima, 8 pt. See for yourself how this face surprints or reverses over the entire spectrum of tone values

Optima, 10 Pt. See for yourself how this face surprints or reverses over the entire spectrum of

Optima, 12 pt. See for yourself how this face surprints or reverses over the entire

Century Expanded, 6 pt. See for yourself how this face surprints or reverses over the entire spectrum

Century Expanded, 8 pt. See for yourself how this face surprints or reverses over the entire spectrum

Century Expanded, 10 pt. See for yourself how this face surprints or reverses over

Century Expanded, 12 pt. See for yourself how this face surprints or reverses

Bodoni Book, 6 pt. See for yourself how this face surprints or reverses over the entire spectrum of tone values, with fine or coarse

Bodoni Book, 8 pt. See for yourself how this face surprints or reverses over the entire spectrum of tone values

Bodoni Book, 10 pt. See for yourself how this face surprints or reverses over the entire spectrum

Bodoni Book, 12 pt. See for yourself how this face surprints or reverses over the entire spectrum

Palatino, 6 pt. See for yourself how this face surprints or reverses over the entire spectrum of tone values, with fine or coarse

Palatino, 8 pt. See for yourself how this face surprints or reverses over the entire spectrum of tone values

Palatino, 10 pt. See for yourself how this face surprints or reverses over the entire spectrum of tone

Palatino, 12 pt. See for yourself how this face surprints or reverses over the entire

Caledonia, 6 pt. See for yourself how this face surprints or reverses over the entire spectrum of tone values, with fine or coarse

Caledonia, 8 pt. See for yourself how this face surprints or reverses over the entire spectrum of tone values, with fine

Caledonia, 10 pt. See for yourself how this face surprints or reverses over the entire spectrum of to

Caledonia, 12 pt. See for yourself how this face surprints or reverses over the entire

Clarendon, 6 pt. See for yourself how this face surprints or reverses over the entire spectrum of tone values, with fine or coarse screen
Clarendon, 8 pt. See for yourself how this face surprints or reverses over the entire spectrum of tone values, wi
Clarendon, 10 pt. See for yourself how this face surprints or reverses over the entire spectru
Clarendon, 12 pt. See for yourself how this face surprints or reverses over the

Melior, 6 pt. See for yourself how this face surprints or reverses over the entire spectrum of tone values, with fine or coarse screens. See for your
Melior, 8 pt. See for yourself how this face surprints or reverses over the entire spectrum of tone values, with fine or
Melior, 10 pt. See for yourself how this face surprints or reverses over the entire spectrum of tone valu
Melior, 12 pt. See for yourself how this face surprints or reverses over the entire spectru

Baskerville, 6 pt. See for yourself how this face surprints or reverses over the entire spectrum of tone values, with fine or coarse screens. See for yourself ho
Baskerville, 8 pt. See for yourself how this face surprints or reverses over the entire spectrum of tone values, with fine or coarse scree
Baskerville, 10 pt. See for yourself how this face surprints or reverses over the entire spectrum of tone values,
Baskerville, 12 pt. See for yourself how this face surprints or reverses over the entire spectrum of

Bookman, 6 pt. See for yourself how this face surprints or reverses over the entire spectrum of tone values, with fine or coarse screens. See for yourself
Bookman, 8 pt. See for yourself how this face surprints or reverses over the entire spectrum of tone values, with fine or coarse sc
Bookman, 10 pt. See for yourself how this face surprints or reverses over the entire spectrum of tone values, w
Bookman, 12 pt. See for yourself how this face surprints or reverses over the entire spectrum

Caslon, 6 pt. See for yourself how this face surprints or reverses over the entire spectrum of tone values, with fine or coarse screens. See for yourself how this face surprints or reverses
Caslon, 8 pt. See for yourself how this face surprints or reverses over the entire spectrum of tone values, with fine or coarse screens.
Caslon, 10 pt. See for yourself how this face surprints or reverses over the entire spectrum of tone values, with fine or
Caslon, 12 pt. See for yourself how this face surprints or reverses over the entire spectrum of

Garamond, 6 pt. See for yourself how this face surprints or reverses over the entire spectrum of tone values, with fine or coarse screens. See for yourself ho
Garamond, 8 pt. See for yourself how this face surprints or reverses over the entire spectrum of tone values, with fine or coarse screens.
Garamond, 10 pt. See for yourself how this face surprints or reverses over the entire spectrum of tone values, with fine or
Garamond, 12 pt. See for yourself how this face surprints or reverses over the entire spectrum of tone value

Times Roman, 6 pt. See for yourself how this face surprints or reverses over the entire spectrum of tone values, with fine or coarse screens. See for
Times Roman, 8 pt. See for yourself how this face surprints or reverses over the entire spectrum of tone values, with fine or co
Times Roman, 10 pt. See for yourself how this face surprints or reverses over the entire spectrum of tone values
Times Roman, 12 pt. See for yourself how this face surprints or reverses over the entire spectru

Optima, 6 pt. See for yourself how this face surprints or reverses over the entire spectrum of tone values, with fine or coarse screens. See for yourself h
Optima, 8 pt. See for yourself how this face surprints or reverses over the entire spectrum of tone values, with fine or coarse scr
Optima, 10 Pt. See for yourself how this face surprints or reverses over the entire spectrum of tone values
Optima, 12 pt. See for yourself how this face surprints or reverses over the entire spectru

Century Expanded, 6 pt. See for yourself how this face surprints or reverses over the entire spectrum of tone values, with fine or coarse screens.
Century Expanded, 8 pt. See for yourself how this face surprints or reverses over the entire spectrum of tone values,
Century Expanded, 10 pt. See for yourself how this face surprints or reverses over the entire spectr
Century Expanded, 12 pt. See for yourself how this face surprints or reverses over the e

Bodoni Book, 6 pt. See for yourself how this face surprints or reverses over the entire spectrum of tone values, with fine or coarse screens. See for yourself
Bodoni Book, 8 pt. See for yourself how this face surprints or reverses over the entire spectrum of tone values, with fine or coarse
Bodoni Book, 10 pt. See for yourself how this face surprints or reverses over the entire spectrum of tone values, with
Bodoni Book, 12 pt. See for yourself how this face surprints or reverses over the entire spectrum of to

Palatino, 6 pt. See for yourself how this face surprints or reverses over the entire spectrum of tone values, with fine or coarse screens. See for your
Palatino, 8 pt. See for yourself how this face surprints or reverses over the entire spectrum of tone values, with fine or coarse
Palatino, 10 pt. See for yourself how this face surprints or reverses over the entire spectrum of tone values
Palatino, 12 pt. See for yourself how this face surprints or reverses over the entire spectrum

Caledonia, 6 pt. See for yourself how this face surprints or reverses over the entire spectrum of tone values, with fine or coarse screens. See for
Caledonia, 8 pt. See for yourself how this face surprints or reverses over the entire spectrum of tone values, with fine or coar
Caledonia, 10 pt. See for yourself how this face surprints or reverses over the entire spectrum of tone value
Caledonia, 12 pt. See for yourself how this face surprints or reverses over the entire spectrum o

128

Clarendon, 6 pt. See for yourself how this face surprints or reverses over the entire spectrum of tone values, with fine or
Clarendon, 8 pt. See for yourself how this face surprints or reverses over the entire spectrum of tone v
Clarendon, 10 pt. See for yourself how this face surprints or reverses over the entire
Clarendon, 12 pt. See for yourself how this face surprints or reverses ov

Melior, 6 pt. See for yourself how this face surprints or reverses over the entire spectrum of tone values, with fine or coarse screens
Melior, 8 pt. See for yourself how this face surprints or reverses over the entire spectrum of tone values, w
Melior, 10 pt. See for yourself how this face surprints or reverses over the entire spectrum of t
Melior, 12 pt. See for yourself how this face surprints or reverses over the entire s

Baskerville, 6 pt. See for yourself how this face surprints or reverses over the entire spectrum of tone values, with fine a
Baskerville, 8 pt. See for yourself how this face surprints or reverses over the entire spectrum of tone values, with fine or
Baskerville, 10 pt. See for yourself how this face surprints or reverses over the entire spectrum of ton
Baskerville, 12 pt. See for yourself how this face surprints or reverses over the entire spe

Bookman, 6 pt. See for yourself how this face surprints or reverses over the entire spectrum of tone values, with fine or coarse screens. See
Bookman, 8 pt. See for yourself how this face surprints or reverses over the entire spectrum of tone values, with fine
Bookman, 10 pt. See for yourself how this face surprints or reverses over the entire spectrum of tone
Bookman, 12 pt. See for yourself how this face surprints or reverses over the entire s

Caslon, 6 pt. See for yourself how this face surprints or reverses over the entire spectrum of tone values, with fine or coarse screens. See for yourself how this
Caslon, 8 pt. See for yourself how this face surprints or reverses over the entire spectrum of tone values, with fine or re
Caslon, 10 pt. See for yourself how this face surprints or reverses over the entire spectrum of tone values, w
Caslon, 12 pt. See for yourself how this face surprints or reverses over the entire spec

Garamond, 6 pt. See for yourself how this face surprints or reverses over the entire spectrum of tone values, with fine or coarse screens. See f
Garamond, 8 pt. See for yourself how this face surprints or reverses over the entire spectrum of tone values, with fine or co
Garamond, 10 pt. See for yourself how this face surprints or reverses over the entire spectrum of tone values, w
Garamond, 12 pt. See for yourself how this face surprints or reverses over the entire spectrum of te

Times Roman, 6 pt. See for yourself how this face surprints or reverses over the entire spectrum of tone values, with fine or coarse or
Times Roman, 8 pt. See for yourself how this face surprints or reverses over the entire spectrum of tone values, with
Times Roman, 10 pt. See for yourself how this face surprints or reverses over the entire spectrum of to
Times Roman, 12 pt. See for yourself how this face surprints or reverses over the entire

Optima, 6 pt. See for yourself how this face surprints or reverses over the entire spectrum of tone values, with fine or coarse screens. See
Optima, 8 pt. See for yourself how this face surprints or reverses over the entire spectrum of tone values, with fine, co
Optima, 10 Pt. See for yourself how this face surprints or reverses over the entire spectrum of tor
Optima, 12 pt. See for yourself how this face surprints or reverses over the entire

Century Expanded, 6 pt. See for yourself how this face surprints or reverses over the entire spectrum of tone values, with fine or coar
Century Expanded, 8 pt. See for yourself how this face surprints or reverses over the entire spectrum of te
Century Expanded, 10 pt. See for yourself how this face surprints or reverses over the entir
Century Expanded, 12 pt. See for yourself how this face surprints or reverses ove

Bodoni Book, 6 pt. See for yourself how this face surprints or reverses over the entire spectrum of tone values, with fine or coarse screens
Bodoni Book, 8 pt. See for yourself how this face surprints or reverses over the entire spectrum of tone values, with fine
Bodoni Book, 10 pt. See for yourself how this face surprints or reverses over the entire spectrum of tone val
Bodoni Book, 12 pt. See for yourself how this face surprints or reverses over the entire spectr

Palatino, 6 pt. See for yourself how this face surprints or reverses over the entire spectrum of tone values, with fine or coarse screens
Palatino, 8 pt. See for yourself how this face surprints or reverses over the entire spectrum of tone values, with fine
Palatino, 10 pt. See for yourself how this face surprints or reverses over the entire spectrum of to
Palatino, 12 pt. See for yourself how this face surprints or reverses over the entire sp

Caledonia, 6 pt. See for yourself how this face surprints or reverses over the entire spectrum of tone values, with fine or coarse scre
Caledonia, 8 pt. See for yourself how this face surprints or reverses over the entire spectrum of tone values, with fi
Caledonia, 10 pt. See for yourself how this face surprints or reverses over the entire spectrum of to
Caledonia, 12 pt. See for yourself how this face surprints or reverses over the entire spe

Clarendon, 6 pt. See for yourself how this face surprints or reverses over the entire spectrum of tone values, with fine or coarse screen.
Clarendon, 8 pt. See for yourself how this face surprints or reverses over the entire spectrum of tone values, w
Clarendon, 10 pt. See for yourself how this face surprints or reverses over the entire spectrum
Clarendon, 12 pt. See for yourself how this face surprints or reverses over the

Melior, 6 pt. See for yourself how this face surprints or reverses over the entire spectrum of tone values, with fine or coarse screens. See for your
Melior, 8 pt. See for yourself how this face surprints or reverses over the entire spectrum of tone values, with fine or
Melior, 10 pt. See for yourself how this face surprints or reverses over the entire spectrum of tone valu
Melior, 12 pt. See for yourself how this face surprints or reverses over the entire spectrum

Baskerville, 6 pt. See for yourself how this face surprints or reverses over the entire spectrum of tone values, with fine or coarse screens. See for yourself h
Baskerville, 8 pt. See for yourself how this face surprints or reverses over the entire spectrum of tone values, with fine or coarse scree
Baskerville, 10 pt. See for yourself how this face surprints or reverses over the entire spectrum of tone values
Baskerville, 12 pt. See for yourself how this face surprints or reverses over the entire spectrum of

Bookman, 6 pt. See for yourself how this face surprints or reverses over the entire spectrum of tone values, with fine or coarse screens. See for yourself
Bookman, 8 pt. See for yourself how this face surprints or reverses over the entire spectrum of tone values, with fine or coarse sc
Bookman, 10 pt. See for yourself how this face surprints or reverses over the entire spectrum of tone values, w
Bookman, 12 pt. See for yourself how this face surprints or reverses over the entire spectrum

Caslon, 6 pt. See for yourself how this face surprints or reverses over the entire spectrum of tone values, with fine or coarse screens. See for yourself how this face surprints or re
Caslon, 8 pt. See for yourself how this face surprints or reverses over the entire spectrum of tone values, with fine or coarse screens
Caslon, 10 pt. See for yourself how this face surprints or reverses over the entire spectrum of tone values, with fine or
Caslon, 12 pt. See for yourself how this face surprints or reverses over the entire spectrum of

Garamond, 6 pt. See for yourself how this face surprints or reverses over the entire spectrum of tone values, with fine or coarse screens. See for yourself ho
Garamond, 8 pt. See for yourself how this face surprints or reverses over the entire spectrum of tone values, with fine or coarse screen
Garamond, 10 pt. See for yourself how this face surprints or reverses over the entire spectrum of tone values, with fine or
Garamond, 12 pt. See for yourself how this face surprints or reverses over the entire spectrum of tone value

Times Roman, 6 pt. See for yourself how this face surprints or reverses over the entire spectrum of tone values, with fine or coarse screens. See for
Times Roman, 8 pt. See for yourself how this face surprints or reverses over the entire spectrum of tone values, with fine or co
Times Roman, 10 pt. See for yourself how this face surprints or reverses over the entire spectrum of tone values,
Times Roman, 12 pt. See for yourself how this face surprints or reverses over the entire spectru

Optima, 6 pt. See for yourself how this face surprints or reverses over the entire spectrum of tone values, with fine or coarse screens. See for yourself ho
Optima, 8 pt. See for yourself how this face surprints or reverses over the entire spectrum of tone values, with fine or coarse. See
Optima, 10 Pt. See for yourself how this face surprints or reverses over the entire spectrum of tone values.
Optima, 12 pt. See for yourself how this face surprints or reverses over the entire spectru

Century Expanded, 6 pt. See for yourself how this face surprints or reverses over the entire spectrum of tone values, with fine or coarse screen
Century Expanded, 8 pt. See for yourself how this face surprints or reverses over the entire spectrum of tone values
Century Expanded, 10 pt. See for yourself how this face surprints or reverses over the entire spectr
Century Expanded, 12 pt. See for yourself how this face surprints or reverses over the e

Bodoni Book, 6 pt. See for yourself how this face surprints or reverses over the entire spectrum of tone values, with fine or coarse screens. See for yourself
Bodoni Book, 8 pt. See for yourself how this face surprints or reverses over the entire spectrum of tone values, with fine or coarse
Bodoni Book, 10 pt. See for yourself how this face surprints or reverses over the entire spectrum of tone values, with
Bodoni Book, 12 pt. See for yourself how this face surprints or reverses over the entire spectrum of to

Palatino, 6 pt. See for yourself how this face surprints or reverses over the entire spectrum of tone values, with fine or coarse screens. See for your
Palatino, 8 pt. See for yourself how this face surprints or reverses over the entire spectrum of tone values, with fine or coarse
Palatino, 10 pt. See for yourself how this face surprints or reverses over the entire spectrum of tone values
Palatino, 12 pt. See for yourself how this face surprints or reverses over the entire spectrum

Caledonia, 6 pt. See for yourself how this face surprints or reverses over the entire spectrum of tone values, with fine or coarse screens. See for
Caledonia, 8 pt. See for yourself how this face surprints or reverses over the entire spectrum of tone values, with fine or coar
Caledonia, 10 pt. See for yourself how this face surprints or reverses over the entire spectrum of tone value
Caledonia, 12 pt. See for yourself how this face surprints or reverses over the entire spectrum o

Souvenir Light, 6 pt. See for yourself how this face surprints or reverses over the entire spectrum of tone values, with fine or coarse screens. See for yourself how this face
Souvenir Light, 8 pt. See for yourself how this face surprints or reverses over the entire spectrum of tone values, with fine or coarse
Souvenir Light, 10 pt. See for yourself how this face surprints or reverses over the entire spectrum of to
Souvenir Light, 12 pt. See for yourself how this face surprints or reverses over the entire

Souvenir Medium, 6 pt. See for yourself how this face surprints or reverses over the entire spectrum of tone values, with fine or coarse screens. See for yourself how
Souvenir Medium, 8 pt. See for yourself how this face surprints or reverses over the entire spectrum of tone values, with fine
Souvenir Medium, 10 pt. See for yourself how this face surprints or reverses over the entire spectrum
Souvenir Medium, 12 pt. See for yourself how this face surprints or reverses over t

Souvenir Demibold, 6 pt. See for yourself how this face surprints or reverses over the entire spectrum of tone values, with fine or coarse screens. See for
Souvenir Demibold, 8 pt. See for yourself how this face surprints or reverses over the entire spectrum of tone values
Souvenir Demibold, 10 pt. See for yourself how this face surprints or reverses over the entire
Souvenir Demibold, 12 pt. See for yourself how this face surprints or reverses

Avant Garde Extra Light, 6 pt. See for yourself how this face surprints or reverses over the entire spectrum of tone values, with fine or coarse screens. See for
Avant Garde Extra Light, 8 pt. See for yourself how this face surprints or reverses over the entire spectrum of tone values
Avant Garde Extra Light, 10 pt. See for yourself how this face surprints or reverses over the entire
Avant Garde Extra Light, 12 pt. See for yourself how this face surprints or reverses

Avant Garde Medium, 6 pt. See for yourself how this face surprints or reverses over the entire spectrum of tone values, with fine or coarse screens. See fo
Avant Garde Medium, 8 pt. See for yourself how this face surprints or reverses over the entire spectrum of tone values
Avant Garde Medium, 10 pt. See for yourself how this face surprints or reverses over the entire s
Avant Garde Medium, 12 pt. See for yourself how this face surprints or reverses ove

Avant Garde Book, 6 pt. See for yourself how this face surprints or reverses over the entire spectrum of tone values, with fine or coarse screens. See for yourse
Avant Garde Book, 8 pt. See for yourself how this face surprints or reverses over the entire spectrum of tone values, with fin
Avant Garde Book, 10 pt. See for yourself how this face surprints or reverses over the entire spec
Avant Garde Book, 12 pt. See for yourself how this face surprints or reverses over th

Avant Garde Demibold, 6 pt. See for yourself how this face surprints or reverses over the entire spectrum of tone values, with fine or coarse screens. Se
Avant Garde Demibold, 8 pt. See for yourself how this face surprints or reverses over the entire spectrum of tone v
Avant Garde Demibold, 10 pt. See for yourself how this face surprints or reverses over the
Avant Garde Demibold, 12 pt. See for yourself how this face surprints or rever

Avant Garde Bold, 6 pt. See for yourself how this face surprints or reverses over the entire spectrum of tone values, with fine or coarse screens
Avant Garde Bold, 8 pt. See for yourself how this face surprints or reverses over the entire spectrum of tone valu
Avant Garde Bold, 10 pt. See for yourself how this face surprints or reverses over the enti
Avant Garde Bold, 12 pt. See for yourself how this face surprints or reverses

Stymie Light, 6 pt. See for yourself how this face surprints or reverses over the entire spectrum of tone values, with fine or coarse screens. See for yourself
Stymie Light, 8 pt. See for yourself how this face surprints or reverses over the entire spectrum of tone values, with fine or coa
Stymie Light, 10 pt. See for yourself how this face surprints or reverses over the entire spectrum of tone
Stymie Light, 12 pt. See for yourself how this face surprints or reverses over the enti

Stymie Medium, 6 pt. See for yourself how this face surprints or reverses over the entire spectrum of tone values, with fine or coarse screens. See for
Stymie Medium, 8 pt. See for yourself how this face surprints or reverses over the entire spectrum of tone values, wi
Stymie Medium, 10 pt. See for yourself how this face surprints or reverses over the entire spe
Stymie Medium, 12 pt. See for yourself how this face surprints or reverses over

Stymie Bold, 6 pt. See for yourself how this face surprints or reverses over the entire spectrum of tone values, with fine or coarse screens. See for yo
Stymie Bold, 8 pt. See for yourself how this face surprints or reverses over the entire spectrum of tone values,
Stymie Bold, 10 pt. See for yourself how this face surprints or reverses over the entire spe
Stymie Bold, 12 pt. See for yourself how this face surprints or reverses ove

Korinna, 6 pt. See for yourself how this face surprints or reverses over the entire spectrum of tone values, with fine or coarse screens. See for yourself ho
Korinna, 8 pt. See for yourself how this face surprints or reverses over the entire spectrum of tone values, with fin
Korinna, 10 pt. See for yourself how this face surprints or reverses over the entire spectrum o
Korinna, 12 pt. See for yourself how this face surprints or reverses over the ent

Korinna Bold, 6 pt. See for yourself how this face surprints or reverses over the entire spectrum of tone values, with fine or coarse screens. See for yo
Korinna Bold, 8 pt. See for yourself how this face surprints or reverses over the entire spectrum of tone values, w
Korinna Bold, 10 pt. See for yourself how this face surprints or reverses over the entire spe
Korinna Bold, 12 pt. See for yourself how this face surprints or reverses over the

Reverse visualizer, from solid to 10% in 10% steps; 133-line screen.

Souvenir Light, 6 pt. See for yourself how this face surprints or reverses over the entire spectrum of tone values, with fine or coarse screens. See for yourself how this face surprints or rever
Souvenir Light, 8 pt. See for yourself how this face surprints or reverses over the entire spectrum of tone values, with fine or coarse screens. See
Souvenir Light, 10 pt. See for yourself how this face surprints or reverses over the entire spectrum of tone values,
Souvenir Light, 12 pt. See for yourself how this face surprints or reverses over the entire spectru

Souvenir Medium, 6 pt. See for yourself how this face surprints or reverses over the entire spectrum of tone values, with fine or coarse screens. See for yourself how this face surp
Souvenir Medium, 8 pt. See for yourself how this face surprints or reverses over the entire spectrum of tone values, with fine or coarse
Souvenir Medium, 10 pt. See for yourself how this face surprints or reverses over the entire spectrum of tone
Souvenir Medium, 12 pt. See for yourself how this face surprints or reverses over the entir

Souvenir Demibold, 6 pt. See for yourself how this face surprints or reverses over the entire spectrum of tone values, with fine or coarse screens. See for yourself how
Souvenir Demibold, 8 pt. See for yourself how this face surprints or reverses over the entire spectrum of tone values, with fin
Souvenir Demibold, 10 pt. See for yourself how this face surprints or reverses over the entire spectru
Souvenir Demibold, 12 pt. See for yourself how this face surprints or reverses over t

Avant Garde Extra Light, 6 pt. See for yourself how this face surprints or reverses over the entire spectrum of tone values, with fine or coarse screens. See for yourself how th
Avant Garde Extra Light, 8 pt. See for yourself how this face surprints or reverses over the entire spectrum of tone values, with fine or
Avant Garde Extra Light, 10 pt. See for yourself how this face surprints or reverses over the entire spectrum
Avant Garde Extra Light, 12 pt. See for yourself how this face surprints or reverses over the

Avant Garde Medium, 6 pt. See for yourself how this face surprints or reverses over the entire spectrum of tone values, with fine or coarse screens. See for yourself how
Avant Garde Medium, 8 pt. See for yourself how this face surprints or reverses over the entire spectrum of tone values, with fine
Avant Garde Medium, 10 pt. See for yourself how this face surprints or reverses over the entire spectrum
Avant Garde Medium, 12 pt. See for yourself how this face surprints or reverses over the en

Avant Garde Book, 6 pt. See for yourself how this face surprints or reverses over the entire spectrum of tone values, with fine or coarse screens. See for yourself how this face
Avant Garde Book, 8 pt. See for yourself how this face surprints or reverses over the entire spectrum of tone values, with fine or coarse
Avant Garde Book, 10 pt. See for yourself how this face surprints or reverses over the entire spectrum of to
Avant Garde Book, 12 pt. See for yourself how this face surprints or reverses over the entire

Avant Garde Demibold, 6 pt. See for yourself how this face surprints or reverses over the entire spectrum of tone values, with fine or coarse screens. See for yourself
Avant Garde Demibold, 8 pt. See for yourself how this face surprints or reverses over the entire spectrum of tone values, with
Avant Garde Demibold, 10 pt. See for yourself how this face surprints or reverses over the entire sp
Avant Garde Demibold, 12 pt. See for yourself how this face surprints or reverses ove

Avant Garde Bold, 6 pt. See for yourself how this face surprints or reverses over the entire spectrum of tone values, with fine or coarse screens. See for yourse
Avant Garde Bold, 8 pt. See for yourself how this face surprints or reverses over the entire spectrum of tone values, with fin
Avant Garde Bold, 10 pt. See for yourself how this face surprints or reverses over the entire spect
Avant Garde Bold, 12 pt. See for yourself how this face surprints or reverses over the

Stymie Light, 6 pt. See for yourself how this face surprints or reverses over the entire spectrum of tone values, with fine or coarse screens. See for yourself how this face sur
Stymie Light, 8 pt. See for yourself how this face surprints or reverses over the entire spectrum of tone values, with fine or coarse screens.
Stymie Light, 10 pt. See for yourself how this face surprints or reverses over the entire spectrum of tone values,
Stymie Light, 12 pt. See for yourself how this face surprints or reverses over the entire spect

Stymie Medium, 6 pt. See for yourself how this face surprints or reverses over the entire spectrum of tone values, with fine or coarse screens. See for yourself how thi
Stymie Medium, 8 pt. See for yourself how this face surprints or reverses over the entire spectrum of tone values, with fine or co
Stymie Medium, 10 pt. See for yourself how this face surprints or reverses over the entire spectrum of
Stymie Medium, 12 pt. See for yourself how this face surprints or reverses over the ent

Stymie Bold, 6 pt. See for yourself how this face surprints or reverses over the entire spectrum of tone values, with fine or coarse screens. See for yourself how this
Stymie Bold, 8 pt. See for yourself how this face surprints or reverses over the entire spectrum of tone values, with fine or
Stymie Bold, 10 pt. See for yourself how this face surprints or reverses over the entire spectrum of
Stymie Bold, 12 pt. See for yourself how this face surprints or reverses over the enti

Korinna, 6 pt. See for yourself how this face surprints or reverses over the entire spectrum of tone values, with fine or coarse screens. See for yourself how this face sur
Korinna, 8 pt. See for yourself how this face surprints or reverses over the entire spectrum of tone values, with fine or coarse
Korinna, 10 pt. See for yourself how this face surprints or reverses over the entire spectrum of tone va
Korinna, 12 pt. See for yourself how this face surprints or reverses over the entire spec

Korinna Bold, 6 pt. See for yourself how this face surprints or reverses over the entire spectrum of tone values, with fine or coarse screens. See for yourself how this
Korinna Bold, 8 pt. See for yourself how this face surprints or reverses over the entire spectrum of tone values, with fine or
Korinna Bold, 10 pt. See for yourself how this face surprints or reverses over the entire spectrum of
Korinna Bold, 12 pt. See for yourself how this face surprints or reverses over the entire s

Souvenir Light, 6 pt. See for yourself how this face surprints or reverses over the entire spectrum of tone values, with fine or coarse screen. See for yourself how this face

Souvenir Light, 8 pt. See for yourself how this face surprints or reverses over the entire spectrum of tone values, with fine or coarse

Souvenir Light, 10 pt. See for yourself how this face surprints or reverses over the entire spectrum of tor

Souvenir Light, 12 pt. See for yourself how this face surprints or reverses over the entire

Souvenir Medium, 6 pt. See for yourself how this face surprints or reverses over the entire spectrum of tone values, with fine or coarse screen. See for yourself how

Souvenir Medium, 8 pt. See for yourself how this face surprints or reverses over the entire spectrum of tone values, with fine

Souvenir Medium, 10 pt. See for yourself how this face surprints or reverses over the entire spectrum

Souvenir Medium, 12 pt. See for yourself how this face surprints or reverses over th

Souvenir Demibold, 6 pt. See for yourself how this face surprints or reverses over the entire spectrum of tone values, with fine or coarse screens. See for

Souvenir Demibold, 8 pt. See for yourself how this face surprints or reverses over the entire spectrum of tone value

Souvenir Demibold, 10 pt. See for yourself how this face surprints or reverses over the entire

Souvenir Demibold, 12 pt. See for yourself how this face surprints or reverses

Avant Garde Extra Light, 6 pt. See for yourself how this face surprints or reverses over the entire spectrum of tone values, with fine or coarse screen. See for yourself how

Avant Garde Extra Light, 8 pt. See for yourself how this face surprints or reverses over the entire spectrum of tone values

Avant Garde Extra Light, 10 pt. See for yourself how this face surprints or reverses over the entire s

Avant Garde Extra Light, 12 pt. See for yourself how this face surprints or reverses o

Avant Garde Medium, 6 pt. See for yourself how this face surprints or reverses over the entire spectrum of tone values, with fine or coarse screens. See for

Avant Garde Medium, 8 pt. See for yourself how this face surprints or reverses over the entire spectrum of tone values. See for

Avant Garde Medium, 10 pt. See for yourself how this face surprints or reverses over the entire s

Avant Garde Medium, 12 pt. See for yourself how this face surprints or reverses over

Avant Garde Book, 6 pt. See for yourself how this face surprints or reverses over the entire spectrum of tone values, with fine or coarse screens. See for yourself

Avant Garde Book, 8 pt. See for yourself how this face surprints or reverses over the entire spectrum of tone values, with fine

Avant Garde Book, 10 pt. See for yourself how this face surprints or reverses over the entire spec

Avant Garde Book, 12 pt. See for yourself how this face surprints or reverses over th

Avant Garde Demibold, 6 pt. See for yourself how this face surprints or reverses over the entire spectrum of tone values, with fine or coarse screens. Se

Avant Garde Demibold, 8 pt. See for yourself how this face surprints or reverses over the entire spectrum of tone v

Avant Garde Demibold, 10 pt. See for yourself how this face surprints or reverses over the e

Avant Garde Demibold, 12 pt. See for yourself how this face surprints or reverse

Avant Garde Bold, 6 pt. See for yourself how this face surprints or reverses over the entire spectrum of tone values, with fine or coarse screens

Avant Garde Bold, 8 pt. See for yourself how this face surprints or reverses over the entire spectrum of tone valu

Avant Garde Bold, 10 pt. See for yourself how this face surprints or reverses over the enti

Avant Garde Bold, 12 pt. See for yourself how this face surprints or reverses o

Stymie Light, 6 pt. See for yourself how this face surprints or reverses over the entire spectrum of tone values, with fine or coarse screen. See for yourself h

Stymie Light, 8 pt. See for yourself how this face surprints or reverses over the entire spectrum of tone values, with fine or coa

Stymie Light, 10 pt. See for yourself how this face surprints or reverses over the entire spectrum of to

Stymie Light, 12 pt. See for yourself how this face surprints or reverses over the enti

Stymie Medium, 6 pt. See for yourself how this face surprints or reverses over the entire spectrum of tone values, with fine or coarse screens. See for y

Stymie Medium, 8 pt. See for yourself how this face surprints or reverses over the entire spectrum of tone values, wit

Stymie Medium, 10 pt. See for yourself how this face surprints or reverses over the entire spe

Stymie Medium, 12 pt. See for yourself how this face surprints or reverses over

Stymie Bold, 6 pt. See for yourself how this face surprints or reverses over the entire spectrum of tone values, with fine or coarse screens. See for you

Stymie Bold, 8 pt. See for yourself how this face surprints or reverses over the entire spectrum of tone values, a

Stymie Bold, 10 pt. See for yourself how this face surprints or reverses over the entire spe

Stymie Bold, 12 pt. See for yourself how this face surprints or reverses over t

Korinna, 6 pt. See for yourself how this face surprints or reverses over the entire spectrum of tone values, with fine or coarse screens. See for yourself ho

Korinna, 8 pt. See for yourself how this face surprints or reverses over the entire spectrum of tone values, with tin

Korinna, 10 pt. See for yourself how this face surprints or reverses over the entire spectrum o

Korinna, 12 pt. See for yourself how this face surprints or reverses over the ent

Korinna Bold, 6 pt. See for yourself how this face surprints or reverses over the entire spectrum of tone values, with fine or coarse screens. See for yo

Korinna Bold, 8 pt. See for yourself how this face surprints or reverses over the entire spectrum of tone values, wit

Korinna Bold, 10 pt. See for yourself how this face surprints or reverses over the entire spe

Korinna Bold, 12 pt. See for yourself how this face surprints or reverses over the

Reverse visualizer, from solid to 10% in 10% steps; 65-line screen.

Souvenir Light, 6 pt. See for yourself how this face surprints or reverses over the entire spectrum of tone values, with fine or coarse screens. See for yourself how this face surprints or rever
Souvenir Light, 8 pt. See for yourself how this face surprints or reverses over the entire spectrum of tone values, with fine or coarse screens. See
Souvenir Light, 10 pt. See for yourself how this face surprints or reverses over the entire spectrum of tone values,
Souvenir Light, 12 pt. See for yourself how this face surprints or reverses over the entire spectru

Souvenir Medium, 6 pt. See for yourself how this face surprints or reverses over the entire spectrum of tone values, with fine or coarse screens. See for yourself how this face sur
Souvenir Medium, 8 pt. See for yourself how this face surprints or reverses over the entire spectrum of tone values, with fine or coarse
Souvenir Medium, 10 pt. See for yourself how this face surprints or reverses over the entire spectrum of tone
Souvenir Medium, 12 pt. See for yourself how this face surprints or reverses over the enti

Souvenir Demibold, 6 pt. See for yourself how this face surprints or reverses over the entire spectrum of tone values, with fine or coarse screens. See for yourself how
Souvenir Demibold, 8 pt. See for yourself how this face surprints or reverses over the entire spectrum of tone values, with fin
Souvenir Demibold, 10 pt. See for yourself how this face surprints or reverses over the entire spectru
Souvenir Demibold, 12 pt. See for yourself how this face surprints or reverses over t

Avant Garde Extra Light, 6 pt. See for yourself how this face surprints or reverses over the entire spectrum of tone values, with fine or coarse screens. See for yourself how
Avant Garde Extra Light, 8 pt. See for yourself how this face surprints or reverses over the entire spectrum of tone values, with fine or
Avant Garde Extra Light, 10 pt. See for yourself how this face surprints or reverses over the entire spectrum
Avant Garde Extra Light, 12 pt. See for yourself how this face surprints or reverses over the

Avant Garde Medium, 6 pt. See for yourself how this face surprints or reverses over the entire spectrum of tone values, with fine or coarse screens. See for yourself how
Avant Garde Medium, 8 pt. See for yourself how this face surprints or reverses over the entire spectrum of tone values, with fine
Avant Garde Medium, 10 pt. See for yourself how this face surprints or reverses over the entire spectrum
Avant Garde Medium, 12 pt. See for yourself how this face surprints or reverses over the en

Avant Garde Book, 6 pt. See for yourself how this face surprints or reverses over the entire spectrum of tone values, with fine or coarse screens. See for yourself how
Avant Garde Book, 8 pt. See for yourself how this face surprints or reverses over the entire spectrum of tone values, with fine or coarse
Avant Garde Book, 10 pt. See for yourself how this face surprints or reverses over the entire spectrum of to
Avant Garde Book, 12 pt. See for yourself how this face surprints or reverses over the entire

Avant Garde Demibold, 6 pt. See for yourself how this face surprints or reverses over the entire spectrum of tone values, with fine or coarse screens. See for yourself
Avant Garde Demibold, 8 pt. See for yourself how this face surprints or reverses over the entire spectrum of tone values, with
Avant Garde Demibold, 10 pt. See for yourself how this face surprints or reverses over the entire sp
Avant Garde Demibold, 12 pt. See for yourself how this face surprints or reverses ove

Avant Garde Bold, 6 pt. See for yourself how this face surprints or reverses over the entire spectrum of tone values, with fine or coarse screens. See for yourse
Avant Garde Bold, 8 pt. See for yourself how this face surprints or reverses over the entire spectrum of tone values, with fin
Avant Garde Bold, 10 pt. See for yourself how this face surprints or reverses over the entire spect
Avant Garde Bold, 12 pt. See for yourself how this face surprints or reverses over the

Stymie Light, 6 pt. See for yourself how this face surprints or reverses over the entire spectrum of tone values, with fine or coarse screens. See for yourself how this face sur
Stymie Light, 8 pt. See for yourself how this face surprints or reverses over the entire spectrum of tone values, with fine or coarse screen
Stymie Light, 10 pt. See for yourself how this face surprints or reverses over the entire spectrum of tone values,
Stymie Light, 12 pt. See for yourself how this face surprints or reverses over the entire spect

Stymie Medium, 6 pt. See for yourself how this face surprints or reverses over the entire spectrum of tone values, with fine or coarse screens. See for yourself how this
Stymie Medium, 8 pt. See for yourself how this face surprints or reverses over the entire spectrum of tone values, with fine or co
Stymie Medium, 10 pt. See for yourself how this face surprints or reverses over the entire spectrum of
Stymie Medium, 12 pt. See for yourself how this face surprints or reverses over the ent

Stymie Bold, 6 pt. See for yourself how this face surprints or reverses over the entire spectrum of tone values, with fine or coarse screens. See for yourself how this
Stymie Bold, 8 pt. See for yourself how this face surprints or reverses over the entire spectrum of tone values, with fine or
Stymie Bold, 10 pt. See for yourself how this face surprints or reverses over the entire spectrum of
Stymie Bold, 12 pt. See for yourself how this face surprints or reverses over the enti

Korinna, 6 pt. See for yourself how this face surprints or reverses over the entire spectrum of tone values, with fine or coarse screens. See for yourself how this face sur
Korinna, 8 pt. See for yourself how this face surprints or reverses over the entire spectrum of tone values, with fine or coarse
Korinna, 10 pt. See for yourself how this face surprints or reverses over the entire spectrum of tone va
Korinna, 12 pt. See for yourself how this face surprints or reverses over the entire spec

Korinna Bold, 6 pt. See for yourself how this face surprints or reverses over the entire spectrum of tone values, with fine or coarse screens. See for yourself how this
Korinna Bold, 8 pt. See for yourself how this face surprints or reverses over the entire spectrum of tone values, with fine or
Korinna Bold, 10 pt. See for yourself how this face surprints or reverses over the entire spectrum of
Korinna Bold, 12 pt. See for yourself how this face surprints or reverses over the entire s

Surprint visualizer, from 10% to solid in 10% steps; 133-line screen.

Goudy, 6 pt. See for yourself how this face surprints or reverses over the entire spectrum of tone values, with fine or coarse screens.
Goudy, 8 pt. See for yourself how this face surprints or reverses over the entire spectrum of tone values, with fine or coarse screens.
Goudy, 10 pt. See for yourself how this face surprints or reverses over the entire spectrum of tone values.
Goudy, 12 pt. See for yourself how this face surprints or reverses over the entire spectrum.

Goudy Bold, 6 pt. See for yourself how this face surprints or reverses over the entire spectrum of tone values, with fine or coarse screens.
Goudy Bold, 8 pt. See for yourself how this face surprints or reverses over the entire spectrum of tone values.
Goudy Bold, 10 pt. See for yourself how this face surprints or reverses over the entire spectrum.
Goudy Bold, 12 pt. See for yourself how this face surprints or reverses over the entire.

Goudy Extrabold, 6 pt. See for yourself how this face surprints or reverses over the entire spectrum of tone values, with fine or coarse screens.
Goudy Extrabold, 8 pt. See for yourself how this face surprints or reverses over the entire spectrum of tone.
Goudy Extrabold, 10 pt. See for yourself how this face surprints or reverses over the entire.
Goudy Extrabold, 12 pt. See for yourself how this face surprints or reverses.

Aster, 6 pt. See for yourself how this face surprints or reverses over the entire spectrum of tone values, with fine or coarse screens.
Aster, 8 pt. See for yourself how this face surprints or reverses over the entire spectrum of tone values.
Aster, 10 pt. See for yourself how this face surprints or reverses over the entire spectrum.
Aster, 12 pt. See for yourself how this face surprints or reverses over the entire.

Aster Italic, 6 pt. See for yourself how this face surprints or reverses over the entire spectrum of tone values, with fine or coarse screens.
Aster Italic, 8 pt. See for yourself how this face surprints or reverses over the entire spectrum of tone.
Aster Italic, 10 pt. See for yourself how this face surprints or reverses over the entire spectrum.
Aster Italic, 12 pt. See for yourself how this face surprints or reverses over the.

Trump Medieval, 6 pt. See for yourself how this face surprints or reverses over the entire spectrum of tone values, with fine or coarse screens.
Trump Medieval, 8 pt. See for yourself how this face surprints or reverses over the entire spectrum of tone.
Trump Medieval, 10 pt. See for yourself how this face surprints or reverses over the entire.
Trump Medieval, 12 pt. See for yourself how this face surprints or reverses.

Trump Medieval Bold, 6 pt. See for yourself how this face surprints or reverses over the entire spectrum of tone values, with fine or coarse screens.
Trump Medieval Bold, 8 pt. See for yourself how this face surprints or reverses over the entire spectrum.
Trump Medieval Bold, 10 pt. See for yourself how this face surprints or reverses over the.
Trump Medieval Bold, 12 pt. See for yourself how this face surprints or reverses.

Vladimir, 6 pt. See for yourself how this face surprints or reverses over the entire spectrum of tone values, with fine or coarse screens.
Vladimir, 8 pt. See for yourself how this face surprints or reverses over the entire spectrum of tone values.
Vladimir, 10 pt. See for yourself how this face surprints or reverses over the entire.
Vladimir, 12 pt. See for yourself how this face surprints or reverses over the.

Vladimir Bold, 6 pt. See for yourself how this face surprints or reverses over the entire spectrum of tone values, with fine or coarse screens.
Vladimir Bold, 8 pt. See for yourself how this face surprints or reverses over the entire spectrum of tone.
Vladimir Bold, 10 pt. See for yourself how this face surprints or reverses over the.
Vladimir Bold, 12 pt. See for yourself how this face surprints or reverses over.

Friz Quadrata, 6 pt. See for yourself how this face surprints or reverses over the entire spectrum of tone values, with fine or coarse screens.
Friz Quadrata, 8 pt. See for yourself how this face surprints or reverses over the entire spectrum of tone values.
Friz Quadrata, 10 pt. See for yourself how this face surprints or reverses over the.
Friz Quadrata, 12 pt. See for yourself how this face surprints or reverses.

Friz Quadrata Bold, 6 pt. See for yourself how this face surprints or reverses over the entire spectrum of tone values, with fine or coarse screens.
Friz Quadrata Bold, 8 pt. See for yourself how this face surprints or reverses over the entire spectrum of.
Friz Quadrata Bold, 10 pt. See for yourself how this face surprints or reverses over the.
Friz Quadrata Bold, 12 pt. See for yourself how this face surprints or.

Melior, 6 pt. See for yourself how this face surprints or reverses over the entire spectrum of tone values, with fine or coarse screens.
Melior, 8 pt. See for yourself how this face surprints or reverses over the entire spectrum of tone values.
Melior, 10 pt. See for yourself how this face surprints or reverses over the.
Melior, 12 pt. See for yourself how this face surprints or reverses over.

Melior Bold, 6 pt. See for yourself how this face surprints or reverses over the entire spectrum of tone values, with fine or coarse screens.
Melior Bold, 8 pt. See for yourself how this face surprints or reverses over the entire spectrum of tone.
Melior Bold, 10 pt. See for yourself how this face surprints or reverses over the entire.
Melior Bold, 12 pt. See for yourself how this face surprints or reverses.

Goudy, 6 pt. See for yourself how this face surprints or reverses over the entire spectrum of tone values, with fine or coarse screens. See for yourself how this face surprints or reverses over
Goudy, 8 pt. See for yourself how this face surprints or reverses over the entire spectrum of tone values, with fine or coarse screens. See for yourself how
Goudy, 10 pt. See for yourself how this face surprints or reverses over the entire spectrum of tone values, with fine or c
Goudy, 12 pt. See for yourself how this face surprints or reverses over the entire spectrum of tone value

Goudy Bold, 6 pt. See for yourself how this face surprints or reverses over the entire spectrum of tone values, with fine or coarse screens. See for yourself how this face
Goudy Bold, 8 pt. See for yourself how this face surprints or reverses over the entire spectrum of tone values, with fine or coarse scre
Goudy Bold, 10 pt. See for yourself how this face surprints or reverses over the entire spectrum of tone value
Goudy Bold, 12 pt. See for yourself how this face surprints or reverses over the entire spectrum of tone

Goudy Extrabold, 6 pt. See for yourself how this face surprints or reverses over the entire spectrum of tone values, with fine or coarse screens. See for yourself h
Goudy Extrabold, 8 pt. See for yourself how this face surprints or reverses over the entire spectrum of tone values, with fine o
Goudy Extrabold, 10 pt. See for yourself how this face surprints or reverses over the entire spectrum of
Goudy Extrabold, 12 pt. See for yourself how this face surprints or reverses over the entire sp

Aster, 6 pt. See for yourself how this face surprints or reverses over the entire spectrum of tone values, with fine or coarse screens. See for yourself how
Aster, 8 pt. See for yourself how this face surprints or reverses over the entire spectrum of tone values, with fine or coarse scr
Aster, 10 pt. See for yourself how this face surprints or reverses over the entire spectrum of tone values, wit
Aster, 12 pt. See for yourself how this face surprints or reverses over the entire spectrum of

Aster Italic, 6 pt. See for yourself how this face surprints or reverses over the entire spectrum of tone values, with fine or coarse screens. See for yourse
Aster Italic, 8 pt. See for yourself how this face surprints or reverses over the entire spectrum of tone values, with fine or coar
Aster Italic, 10 pt. See for yourself how this face surprints or reverses over the entire spectrum of tone value
Aster Italic, 12 pt. See for yourself how this face surprints or reverses over the entire spect

Trump Medieval, 6 pt. See for yourself how this face surprints or reverses over the entire spectrum of tone values, with fine or coarse screens. See for yours
Trump Medieval, 8 pt. See for yourself how this face surprints or reverses over the entire spectrum of tone values, with fine or coa
Trump Medieval, 10 pt. See for yourself how this face surprints or reverses over the entire spectrum of tone val
Trump Medieval, 12 pt. See for yourself how this face surprints or reverses over the entire sp

Trump Medieval Bold, 6 pt. See for yourself how this face surprints or reverses over the entire spectrum of tone values, with fine or coarse screens. See for yourself how this
Trump Medieval Bold, 8 pt. See for yourself how this face surprints or reverses over the entire spectrum of tone values, with fine o
Trump Medieval Bold, 10 pt. See for yourself how this face surprints or reverses over the entire spectrum of ton
Trump Medieval Bold, 12 pt. See for yourself how this face surprints or reverses over the enti

Vladimir, 6 pt. See for yourself how this face surprints or reverses over the entire spectrum of tone values, with fine or coarse screens. See for yourself how this
Vladimir, 8 pt. See for yourself how this face surprints or reverses over the entire spectrum of tone values, with fine or coarse screen
Vladimir, 10 pt. See for yourself how this face surprints or reverses over the entire spectrum of tone values, with
Vladimir, 12 pt. See for yourself how this face surprints or reverses over the entire spectrum

Vladimir Bold, 6 pt. See for yourself how this face surprints or reverses over the entire spectrum of tone values, with fine or coarse screens. See for yourself how
Vladimir Bold, 8 pt. See for yourself how this face surprints or reverses over the entire spectrum of tone values, with fine or coarse
Vladimir Bold, 10 pt. See for yourself how this face surprints or reverses over the entire spectrum of tone values,
Vladimir Bold, 12 pt. See for yourself how this face surprints or reverses over the entire spect

Friz Quadrata, 6 pt. See for yourself how this face surprints or reverses over the entire spectrum of tone values, with fine or coarse screens. See for yourself how this face surprints
Friz Quadrata, 8 pt. See for yourself how this face surprints or reverses over the entire spectrum of tone values, with fine or coarse scree
Friz Quadrata, 10 pt. See for yourself how this face surprints or reverses over the entire spectrum of tone valu
Friz Quadrata, 12 pt. See for yourself how this face surprints or reverses over the entire sp

Friz Quadrata Bold, 6 pt. See for yourself how this face surprints or reverses over the entire spectrum of tone values, with fine or coarse screens. See for yourself how this fac
Friz Quadrata Bold, 8 pt. See for yourself how this face surprints or reverses over the entire spectrum of tone values, with fine or c
Friz Quadrata Bold, 10 pt. See for yourself how this face surprints or reverses over the entire spectrum o
Friz Quadrata Bold, 12 pt. See for yourself how this face surprints or reverses over the

Melior, 6 pt. See for yourself how this face surprints or reverses over the entire spectrum of tone values, with fine or coarse screens. See for yourself how this
Melior, 8 pt. See for yourself how this face surprints or reverses over the entire spectrum of tone values, with fine or coarse scree
Melior, 10 pt. See for yourself how this face surprints or reverses over the entire spectrum of tone values
Melior, 12 pt. See for yourself how this face surprints or reverses over the entire spec

Melior Bold, 6 pt. See for yourself how this face surprints or reverses over the entire spectrum of tone values, with fine or coarse screens. See for yourself how
Melior Bold, 8 pt. See for yourself how this face surprints or reverses over the entire spectrum of tone values, with fine or coarse
Melior Bold, 10 pt. See for yourself how this face surprints or reverses over the entire spectrum of tone va
Melior Bold, 12 pt. See for yourself how this face surprints or reverses over the entire

Surprint visualizer, from 10% to solid in 10% steps; 65-line screen.

Goudy, 6 pt. See for yourself how this face surprints or reverses over the entire spectrum of tone values, with fine or coarse screens. See for yourself how this face surprints
Goudy, 8 pt. See for yourself how this face surprints or reverses over the entire spectrum of tone values, with fine or coarse screens. See for
Goudy, 10 pt. See for yourself how this face surprints or reverses over the entire spectrum of tone values, w
Goudy, 12 pt. See for yourself how this face surprints or reverses over the entire spectrum of t

Goudy Bold, 6 pt. See for yourself how this face surprints or reverses over the entire spectrum of tone values, with fine or coarse screens. See for yoursel
Goudy Bold, 8 pt. See for yourself how this face surprints or reverses over the entire spectrum of tone values, with fine or
Goudy Bold, 10 pt. See for yourself how this face surprints or reverses over the entire spectrum of t
Goudy Bold, 12 pt. See for yourself how this face surprints or reverses over the entire spectrum

Goudy Extrabold, 6 pt. See for yourself how this face surprints or reverses over the entire spectrum of tone values, with fine or coarse screens. See
Goudy Extrabold, 8 pt. See for yourself how this face surprints or reverses over the entire spectrum of tone values,
Goudy Extrabold, 10 pt. See for yourself how this face surprints or reverses over the entire spe
Goudy Extrabold, 12 pt. See for yourself how this face surprints or reverses over the e

Aster, 6 pt. See for yourself how this face surprints or reverses over the entire spectrum of tone values, with fine or coarse screens. See for
Aster, 8 pt. See for yourself how this face surprints or reverses over the entire spectrum of tone values, with fine or
Aster, 10 pt. See for yourself how this face surprints or reverses over the entire spectrum of tone va
Aster, 12 pt. See for yourself how this face surprints or reverses over the entire spec

Aster Italic, 6 pt. See for yourself how this face surprints or reverses over the entire spectrum of tone values, with fine or coarse screens. S
Aster Italic, 8 pt. See for yourself how this face surprints or reverses over the entire spectrum of tone values, with f
Aster Italic, 10 pt. See for yourself how this face surprints or reverses over the entire spectrum of t
Aster Italic, 12 pt. See for yourself how this face surprints or reverses over the enti

Trump Medieval, 6 pt. See for yourself how this face surprints or reverses over the entire spectrum of tone values, with fine or coarse screens
Trump Medieval, 8 pt. See for yourself how this face surprints or reverses over the entire spectrum of tone values, wit
Trump Medieval, 10 pt. See for yourself how this face surprints or reverses over the entire spectrum of
Trump Medieval, 12 pt. See for yourself how this face surprints or reverses over the e

Trump Medieval Bold, 6 pt. See for yourself how this face surprints or reverses over the entire spectrum of tone values, with fine or coarse screens. See for
Trump Medieval Bold, 8 pt. See for yourself how this face surprints or reverses over the entire spectrum of tone values, w
Trump Medieval Bold, 10 pt. See for yourself how this face surprints or reverses over the entire spectru
Trump Medieval Bold, 12 pt. See for yourself how this face surprints or reverses over

Vladimir, 6 pt. See for yourself how this face surprints or reverses over the entire spectrum of tone values, with fine or coarse screens. See for your
Vladimir, 8 pt. See for yourself how this face surprints or reverses over the entire spectrum of tone values, with fine or co
Vladimir, 10 pt. See for yourself how this face surprints or reverses over the entire spectrum of tone val
Vladimir, 12 pt. See for yourself how this face surprints or reverses over the entire s

Vladimir Bold, 6 pt. See for yourself how this face surprints or reverses over the entire spectrum of tone values, with fine or coarse screens. See for
Vladimir Bold, 8 pt. See for yourself how this face surprints or reverses over the entire spectrum of tone values, with fin
Vladimir Bold, 10 pt. See for yourself how this face surprints or reverses over the entire spectrum of ton
Vladimir Bold, 12 pt. See for yourself how this face surprints or reverses over the enti

Friz Quadrata, 6 pt. See for yourself how this face surprints or reverses over the entire spectrum of tone values, with fine or coarse screens. See for yourself how t
Friz Quadrata, 8 pt. See for yourself how this face surprints or reverses over the entire spectrum of tone values, with fine or co
Friz Quadrata, 10 pt. See for yourself how this face surprints or reverses over the entire spectrum of
Friz Quadrata, 12 pt. See for yourself how this face surprints or reverses over the e

Friz Quadrata Bold, 6 pt. See for yourself how this face surprints or reverses over the entire spectrum of tone values, with fine or coarse screens. See for yourself
Friz Quadrata Bold, 8 pt. See for yourself how this face surprints or reverses over the entire spectrum of tone values, wi
Friz Quadrata Bold, 10 pt. See for yourself how this face surprints or reverses over the entire spe
Friz Quadrata Bold, 12 pt. See for yourself how this face surprints or reverses o

Melior, 6 pt. See for yourself how this face surprints or reverses over the entire spectrum of tone values, with fine or coarse screens. See for you
Melior, 8 pt. See for yourself how this face surprints or reverses over the entire spectrum of tone values, with fine or co
Melior, 10 pt. See for yourself how this face surprints or reverses over the entire spectrum of ton
Melior, 12 pt. See for yourself how this face surprints or reverses over the enti

Melior Bold, 6 pt. See for yourself how this face surprints or reverses over the entire spectrum of tone values, with fine or coarse screens. See for
Melior Bold, 8 pt. See for yourself how this face surprints or reverses over the entire spectrum of tone values, with fine
Melior Bold, 10 pt. See for yourself how this face surprints or reverses over the entire spectrum a
Melior Bold, 12 pt. See for yourself how this face surprints or reverses over the

Goudy, 6 pt. See for yourself how this face surprints or reverses over the entire spectrum of tone values, with fine or coarse screen. See for yourself how this face surprints or reverses over

Goudy, 8 pt. See for yourself how this face surprints or reverses over the entire spectrum of tone values, with fine or coarse screen. See for yourself how

Goudy, 10 pt. See for yourself how this face surprints or reverses over the entire spectrum of tone values, with fine or c

Goudy, 12 pt. See for yourself how this face surprints or reverses over the entire spectrum of tone value

Goudy Bold, 6 pt. See for yourself how this face surprints or reverses over the entire spectrum of tone values, with fine or coarse screens. See for yourself how this face

Goudy Bold, 8 pt. See for yourself how this face surprints or reverses over the entire spectrum of tone values, with fine or coarse scre

Goudy Bold, 10 pt. See for yourself how this face surprints or reverses over the entire spectrum of tone value

Goudy Bold, 12 pt. See for yourself how this face surprints or reverses over the entire spectrum of tone

Goudy Extrabold, 6 pt. See for yourself how this face surprints or reverses over the entire spectrum of tone values, with fine or coarse screens. See for yourself h

Goudy Extrabold, 8 pt. See for yourself how this face surprints or reverses over the entire spectrum of tone values, with fine o

Goudy Extrabold, 10 pt. See for yourself how this face surprints or reverses over the entire spectrum of

Goudy Extrabold, 12 pt. See for yourself how this face surprints or reverses over the entire sp

Aster, 6 pt. See for yourself how this face surprints or reverses over the entire spectrum of tone values, with fine or coarse screens. See for yourself how

Aster, 8 pt. See for yourself how this face surprints or reverses over the entire spectrum of tone values, with fine or coarse scr

Aster, 10 pt. See for yourself how this face surprints or reverses over the entire spectrum of tone values, wit

Aster, 12 pt. See for yourself how this face surprints or reverses over the entire spectrum of

Aster Italic, 6 pt. See for yourself how this face surprints or reverses over the entire spectrum of tone values, with fine or coarse screens. See for yours

Aster Italic, 8 pt. See for yourself how this face surprints or reverses over the entire spectrum of tone values, with fine or coar

Aster Italic, 10 pt. See for yourself how this face surprints or reverses over the entire spectrum of tone value

Aster Italic, 12 pt. See for yourself how this face surprints or reverses over the entire spect

Trump Medieval, 6 pt. See for yourself how this face surprints or reverses over the entire spectrum of tone values, with fine or coarse screens. See for yours

Trump Medieval, 8 pt. See for yourself how this face surprints or reverses over the entire spectrum of tone values, with fine or coa

Trump Medieval, 10 pt. See for yourself how this face surprints or reverses over the entire spectrum of tone val

Trump Medieval, 12 pt. See for yourself how this face surprints or reverses over the entire sp

Trump Medieval Bold, 6 pt. See for yourself how this face surprints or reverses over the entire spectrum of tone values, with fine or coarse screens. See for yourself how this

Trump Medieval Bold, 8 pt. See for yourself how this face surprints or reverses over the entire spectrum of tone values, with fine o

Trump Medieval Bold, 10 pt. See for yourself how this face surprints or reverses over the entire spectrum of ton

Trump Medieval Bold, 12 pt. See for yourself how this face surprints or reverses over the enti

Vladimir, 6 pt. See for yourself how this face surprints or reverses over the entire spectrum of tone values, with fine or coarse screens. See for yourself how this

Vladimir, 8 pt. See for yourself how this face surprints or reverses over the entire spectrum of tone values, with fine or coarse screen

Vladimir, 10 pt. See for yourself how this face surprints or reverses over the entire spectrum of tone values, with

Vladimir, 12 pt. See for yourself how this face surprints or reverses over the entire spectrum

Vladimir Bold, 6 pt. See for yourself how this face surprints or reverses over the entire spectrum of tone values, with fine or coarse screens. See for yourself how

Vladimir Bold, 8 pt. See for yourself how this face surprints or reverses over the entire spectrum of tone values, with fine or coarse

Vladimir Bold, 10 pt. See for yourself how this face surprints or reverses over the entire spectrum of tone values,

Vladimir Bold, 12 pt. See for yourself how this face surprints or reverses over the entire spect

Friz Quadrata, 6 pt. See for yourself how this face surprints or reverses over the entire spectrum of tone values, with fine or coarse screens. See for yourself how this face surprint

Friz Quadrata, 8 pt. See for yourself how this face surprints or reverses over the entire spectrum of tone values, with fine or coarse scree

Friz Quadrata, 10 pt. See for yourself how this face surprints or reverses over the entire spectrum of tone valu

Friz Quadrata, 12 pt. See for yourself how this face surprints or reverses over the entire sp

Friz Quadrata Bold, 6 pt. See for yourself how this face surprints or reverses over the entire spectrum of tone values, with fine or coarse screens. See for yourself how this fac

Friz Quadrata Bold, 8 pt. See for yourself how this face surprints or reverses over the entire spectrum of tone values, with fine or c

Friz Quadrata Bold, 10 pt. See for yourself how this face surprints or reverses over the entire spectrum o

Friz Quadrata Bold, 12 pt. See for yourself how this face surprints or reverses over the

Melior, 6 pt. See for yourself how this face surprints or reverses over the entire spectrum of tone values, with fine or coarse screens. See for yourself how this

Melior, 8 pt. See for yourself how this face surprints or reverses over the entire spectrum of tone values, with fine or coarse scree

Melior, 10 pt. See for yourself how this face surprints or reverses over the entire spectrum of tone values

Melior, 12 pt. See for yourself how this face surprints or reverses over the entire spec

Melior Bold, 6 pt. See for yourself how this face surprints or reverses over the entire spectrum of tone values, with fine or coarse screens. See for yourself how

Melior Bold, 8 pt. See for yourself how this face surprints or reverses over the entire spectrum of tone values, with fine or coarse

Melior Bold, 10 pt. See for yourself how this face surprints or reverses over the entire spectrum of tone va

Melior Bold, 12 pt. See for yourself how this face surprints or reverses over the entire

HOW TIGHT IS TOO TIGHT?

This article has been reprinted from Typographic "i" *published by International Typographic Composition Association, Inc.*

How tight should spacing between characters be? There is no one rule. It depends on the purpose of the line or the copy block. It depends on the designer and the effect he must achieve.

For some, "tightography" is graphic fun and distinction; for others, it's functional. It can increase legibility and readability, or it can catch the eye at the expense of readability. Whether your typesetting shop does it for you or you blow it up and razor-blade it yourself, it's your judgment and touch that matter the most.

When you are deciding how tight is right, forget the "rules" but remember your objectives and assign them priorities. For example, what's primary: legibility? color? design? modernity? coordination with text types or other graphic elements? For execution to match your specifications, blend your judgment with the taste, know-how, and facilities of a good typographic service.

These 24-point showings of some widely used faces illustrate how they appear when set normally (first setting in each group) and in various degrees tighter than normal. Following these showings are examples of how some designers are getting tight with type.

How tight is right depends on the

How tight is right, depends on the ef

How tight is right, depends on the effe

How tight is right, depends on the effect

How tight is right, depends on the effect

HELVETICA BOLD

(Normal)
How tight is right,
depends on the effect

(Tight)
How tight is right,
depends on the effect

(Very tight)
How tight is right,
depends on the effect

(Butting)
How tight is right,
depends on the effect

(Overlapping)
How tight is right,
depends on the effect

OPTIMA

**How tight is right,
depends on the effect**

**How tight is right,
depends on the effect**

**How tight is right,
depends on the effect**

**How tight is right,
depends on the effect**

**How tight is right,
depends on the effect**

OPTIMA SEMIBOLD

How tight is right,
depends on the eff

How tight is right,
depends on the effec

How tight is right,
depends on the effect

How tight is right,
depends on the effect

How tight is right,
depends on the effect

NEWS GOTHIC

**How tight is right,
depends on the ef**

**How tight is right,
depends on the effe**

**How tight is right,
depends on the effec**

**How tight is right,
depends on the effect**

**How tight is right,
depends on the effect**

NEWS GOTHIC BOLD

The Ultimate Power: Seeing 'Em Jump

Headline from *New York* magazine; Milton Glaser, Design Director.

Studebaker Worthington Inc.

Letterhead. Note handling of crossbar on *t*.
Designer: Aron & Falcone, Inc.

Bubbling Bath Oil
Bubbling Milk Bath
Deluxe Dusting Powder

Tight letterspacing can emphasize verticality of letters.
From a DuBarry promotion; Manfred Ender, Art Head.

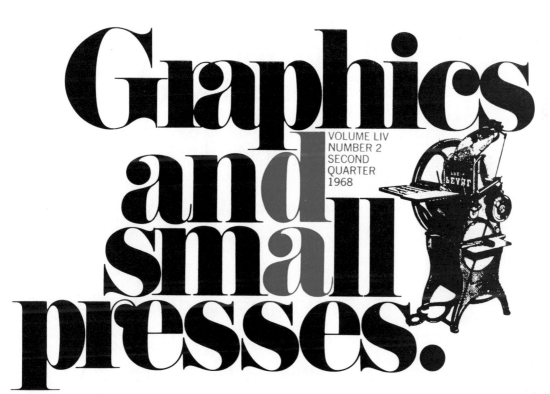

Graphics and small presses.

VOLUME LIV
NUMBER 2
SECOND
QUARTER
1968

You can join 'em and kern 'em, butt them and lap them, and make one out of two. Note the
r and *a* in *Graphics*. Mo Lebowitz, Design Organization, for cover of *Direct Advertising*.

EUROPECRAFT

simplified regimen

Designer flexibility. Some characters are close; some link. Note how crossbar on *f* links up left and right and how descender on *p* makes a unit of a two-line head. For CIBA by Aron & Falcone, Inc.

Despair and

Part of running head in *Singer Light,* quarterly of the Singer Co. Designer: Milt Simpson.

lowers blood pressure
plus helps
protect the kidney
by increasing
renal blood flow

lowers blood pressure
plus helps
protect the brain
hydralazine component
increases or maintains
cerebral blood flow

Tight spacing emphasizes copy blocks. For CIBA by Aron & Falcone, Inc.

142

RULES, BORDERS, AND ORNAMENTS

Dan X. Solo, SOLOTYPE TYPOGRAPHERS

The use of rules, borders, and ornaments to contain, separate, and decorate type matter is as old as printing itself. Older, in fact—for the scribes who copied manuscripts by hand used these same devices in their work. The first printers, having no art of their own, imitated the scribes.

Until the nineteenth century, rules were seldom more than a simple line, or pair of lines, and decorative borders were limited to a row of "printer's flowers" around a page. The development of more elaborate rules and more sophisticated borders paralleled the development of ornamented typefaces, both of them reaching their fullest flower (literally!) just before the end of the century.

Early printers formed rules from sheet brass sheared into type-high strips. The thickness of the brass determined the weight of the printed line. With the Industrial Revolution came techniques for milling and planing and stamping patterns into the printing surface of the rule. Hundreds of patterns were offered, ranging from a simple hairline to a half-inch-wide Scotch plaid.

The twentieth century brought automatic casting machines that produced the equivalent of brass rule in type metal. Supplied in two-foot lengths, easily cut to size as needed, this material is inexpensive enough to discard once used. The typographer today will have on hand a variety of this material, selected from among the hundreds of patterns available at the type foundry.

In use, the selected pattern will be cut to length on a printer's saw and, if a complete box is being formed, the corners will be mitered at a 45° angle on another machine. Where patterns are involved, some expertise is required to miter the corners pleasingly.

At the height of the Victorian age, printers were offered ornamental border types of every conceivable design. These were of two general types: piece borders, consisting of the same character repeated a sufficient number of times to border the page, often with a special version of the character for use at the corners; and combination borders, consisting of anywhere from a half dozen to a hundred different characters, which could be assembled into a wide variety of elaborate shapes.

Even by relaxed Victorian standards, combination borders were time-consuming to assemble, and by the end of the century they had fallen into disuse. Piece borders survive to this day, though not much used. They have been replaced by the ubiquitous acetate sheet, which is quick to use, never gets worn out or battered, and is inexpensive. Some of the borders available on acetate sheets are shown in figures 5.15 and 5.16.

Ornaments, the generic name for a wide array of decorative spots, corners, dashes, vignettes, pointers, flourishes and so on *ad infinitum*, have been made from the very beginning of printing. At any given time, the new productions reflected the current design interest:

classic, floral, art nouveau, art deco, etc. But the previous designs were kept also, so that by the middle of the twentieth century there were countless thousands of ornaments available from the world's typefounders. Not many are offered today, because photographic typesetting is rapidly making foundry type a thing of the past.

Like borders, many of the old ornaments are being reproduced on acetate sheets which can be cut up and assembled right at the drawing board. (Formatt, in particular, specializes in decorative material.) Figure 5.17 shows some of the ornaments available on acetate.

Borders are printed in foot-long lengths, with an appropriate corner piece at each end. A single sheet will contain four to eight patterns of border, depending upon their width, and will include at least four strips of each, which is enough to border a typical page.

The printed acetate sheet is backed with a light coating of pressure-sensitive adhesive and laid down on a chemically treated backing sheet. This sheet is tough enough to withstand the knife when cutting out a particular section of border or an ornament, and the coating allows the adhesive to release easily when lifting the cut out piece.

In preparing a mechanical, non-reproducing blue guidelines are drawn to accurately indicate the dimensions of the border. The strips of acetate are then placed over these guidelines and burnished into place. Unlike the typographer, the artist is not limited to rectangles or other straight-line shapes. It is an easy matter to cut the individual border units apart and dispose them around a circle or an oval, or even an irregular shape. The pieces can be overlapped slightly, forming a continuity of pattern that would be the envy of a printer who works with rigid type. (See figure 5.18.)

The various borders and ornaments available on acetate can be combined at the discretion of the artist to form elaborate "built up" borders, box headings, backgrounds, etc. Recently introduced is the "step-and-repeat" background pattern, a sheet containing a single decorative element repeated over its entire surface. These are much like the dot and line pattern shading sheets, but highly decorative. (See figure 5.19.)

Acetate art "aids," as they are called, are available at commercial art supply houses, and lavish catalogs from the manufacturers are supplied without charge. At least one manufacturer sells a special binder in which the sheets can be stored—a good investment if many sheets are kept on hand, as it prevents them from becoming dog-eared and damaged.

Those who like to haunt used-book stores and similar dens of iniquity should check the stacks of old sheet music for lavish oldtime borders. Some of these are the highest form of the lithographic engraver's art; others are elaborate typographic constructions. Either way, they will be a bargain at the prices usually charged.

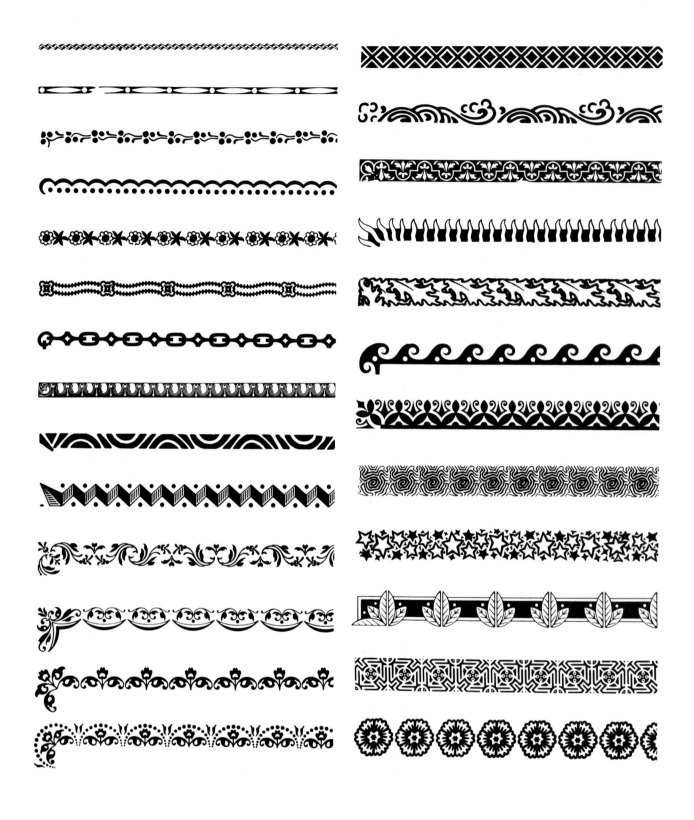

Figure 5.15: Sample borders. Hundreds of borders are now available on printed acetate with adhesive back. In use, a non-reproducing blue line is drawn to indicate the confines of the border. The cut out strips of the design are placed along this line, with special attention to matching the corners. Sometimes it is necessary to change the desired dimensions slightly to conform to the increments of the border, for a better fit.

Figure 5.16: Additional borders. The designs available today are selected from those available in all parts of the world, many from patterns long in disuse. Before being offered on a printed acetate sheet, each design element is enlarged to three inches in height and cleaned up by an artist. When reduced and repeated to form a border, it is crisp and sharp to a degree that usually surpasses the original engraving.

Figure 5.17: Sample ornaments. Countless thousands of typographic ornaments have come and gone in the past five centuries of printing. Today, many are available once again in the form of printed acetate art aids. Each sheet contains ornaments in a variety of sizes, but related by theme—classic, rococo, art nouveau, etc.—or by similarity of use—fists, brackets, patriotic motifs, etc.

Figure 5.18: Finished borders. Most printed acetate borders have their own corners, but some must be mitered. To properly miter a certificate border, the artist must locate strips on light blue guidelines symmetrically, overlapping the corners (lower right), and then must cut a 45° angle, removing the excess. Rosettes (center) are formed the same way, by carefully mitering over a segmented circle. Multi-lined brass rules can be butted, overlapped, chamfered, etc.

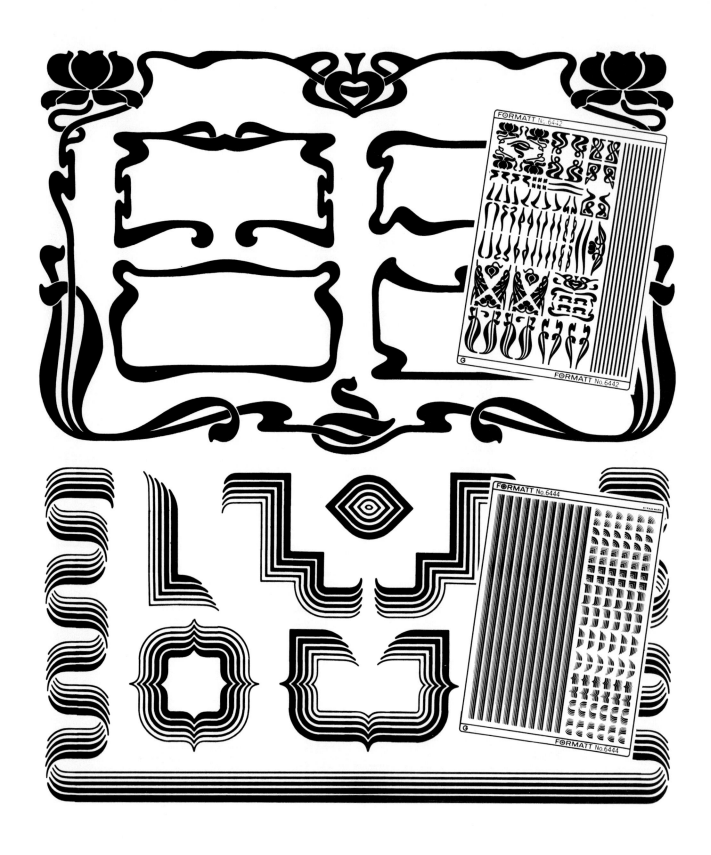

Figure 5.19: Combination borders. Creative artists can express themselves in the endless arrangements possible with combination borders. Corner and median ornaments are supplied with lengths of matching rule. The transparent nature of the acetate base makes it easy to try various placements of the elements. Once all pieces are in place, a final burnishing attaches them permanently to the board.

148

DECORATIVE TYPES OF THE NINETEENTH CENTURY

Dan X. Solo, SOLOTYPE TYPOGRAPHERS

The rise and fall of ornamental printing types fits very neatly into the framework of the nineteenth century. The few decorative types made before 1800 were, for the most part, crude and not particularly novel in design. They were often produced by engraving flowers or scrollwork on the face of existing large types, which in themselves were of limited variety.

Advertising as we know it today began to take on recognizable form early in the century, and with it came the need for bolder, more compelling types. By 1810, the "fat face" was clearly established; by 1820, the three-dimensional effect had been added; by 1830, highly decorated styles were being offered.

Developments of the Industrial Revolution gave the typefounders increased capabilities, so that by the time of the Civil War, there was nothing beyond their grasp. Prior to 1840, all types began their existence as steel punches, laboriously cut by hand at an average rate of one letter per day. The production of three or four sizes of a new type could easily occupy the better part of a year. In 1840, the process of electrotyping—duplicating objects in copper by electroplating—was developed. This was immediately applied to copying types, and soon typefounders around the world were pirating each other's designs without the labor of punch-cutting.

At about the same time, the typecasting machine made its appearance. Instead of pouring metal into a hand mold, the molten fluid was now forced in under pressure, giving a sharper, more detailed cast. Fine lines, previously hard to hold, now became practical. Fantastic designs began to appear, involving external shadows, rims, and rays, and internal shading, scrolls, and flowers. Sometimes all of these devices appeared in a single design. (Some of the developments in the uses of these decorative type designs are illustrated in figures 5.20 through 5.23.)

By 1870, decorative types and their use had become, among the better printers at least, codified. The Victorians applied certain principles to the decorative arts generally. The first and most obvious of these was con-trast, the arranging of components to provide relief and break the monotony of surfaces. Every wall must have its pictures, every window its lambrequin, every ceiling its fresco. The printer achieved contrast with variety of type, disparate sizes, ornaments to break up leftover white space, and—where the budget would allow—two or more colors in the printing.

The second principle, adapted from nature, was the curved line. The printer could draw from a practically endless well of borders and ornaments based on nature. Scrolls, filigree, leaves, vines, flowers—these were the basis for the bulk of the printer's ornamentation. Brass rule, originally developed for printing straight lines, was curved and twisted with pliers and other tools made for the purpose. Special curved spacing material made it possible to set type in arches or serpentine patterns.

Whether or not the Victorian printer was successful in applying these principles depended in great part upon his sense of proportion, which, of course, is another important factor in design. Not all printing of that day was of prize-winning quality. Then, as now, the trade had its "blacksmiths." But when it was good, late nineteenth-century typography was superb, showing a degree of craftsmanship that not many printers of today could equal.

The demise of this work was remarkable in its suddenness. Reaching its peak about 1890, it was soon to be replaced by a plain, workmanlike, uncluttered style executed in a whole new assortment of types undreamed of twenty years earlier.

Some of the reasons for this turn-around are almost forgotten today. Shortly before 1890, the typefounders of America adopted an entirely new system of body measurement. This was a boon to printers, making their work easier, but many of the old styles could not be adapted to the new bodies. Others had passed their prime, and were not worth putting on the new system.

A second factor is that, by 1890, the typefounding business was mired in a hopelessly cutthroat competition from which no one was making any money. In 1892, the major foundries got together, forming a single company known to this day as American Type Founders Company. It was to the advantage of this new firm to phase out many of the old styles, cutting inventory. Around 1900, they hit upon the idea of type "families," in which a basic style is issued in a variety of weights and widths, with matching italics. This was a complete departure from the old idea of variety, and printers embraced it.

Theodore DeVinne, a successful printer and pundit of the profession at the turn of the century, wrote:

> The old craving for highly ornamented letters seems to be dead; it receives no encouragement from typefounders. Printers have been surfeited with ornamented letters that did not ornament and did degrade composition, and that have been found, after many years of use, frail, expensive, and not attractive to buyers. They listen with more respect to the teachings of men who hold that the proper function of types is to convey instruction, and that they are not improved by decoration, any more than a trowel is by painting or a saw by gilding.

Of course the ultimate factor in the demise of Victorian types, overriding commercial and mechanical considerations, was the continuing change in taste—the swing of the pendulum. The time had come for a change; that the change was more abrupt than usual was due to circumstances. It would have come anyway,

149

just as recent years have seen the pendulum swing back to the use of ornamentation in type. Here again, the swing was rather swift, due to the advent of the photo-display typesetting machine for which new typefaces can be produced at relatively minor cost. These machines incorporate prisms and lenses which can alter the weight, width, size, slope and other aspects of the design, giving endless variation to what is already a superabundance of available styles. (See "Photomodifications," page 154.)

Just think what the Victorians could have done with that!

FOREIGN EDITIONS

SHADED TUSCAN

TRUE MOSAIC WORKS

COLORED PICTURES

CHOICE Engravings

NERVOUS SYSTEMS

MODERN TIMES

EDINBURGH

Drafts & Cheques

BRIGHT SHADE

CRESSES

EIGHTY YEARS SINCE

FINEST EDITION

STARS OF NIGHT

CHORAL UNIONS

LONDON Ornaments

SELECT MUSIC

FLOWER BORDERS

THE English Operas

SELECT MUSIC

FOUNTAIN

HORSES

Figure 5.20: Early decorative typefaces. The typefaces on this page are representative of the Industrial Revolution era, 1830 to 1860. Except for a few basic names drawn from architectural orders, such as Ionic, Doric, and Corinthian, most types were identified by number. No two foundries used the same system, so that one maker's "Ornamented No. 34" would be different from another's.

Figure 5.21: Elaborate type designs. These spectacular floriated styles were a product of the years just before 1850. The originals were engraved by hand on end-grain boxwood and then pressed into plaster of Paris to form a mold, called a matrix. Molten type metal was poured into the matrix to cast the finished type. The process destroyed the plaster matrix, and a new one was required for each casting.

Figure 5.22: Applications of ornamental type. Here is a typical selection of mid-Victorian job work that points up one of the often overlooked ingredients in ornamental typog- **raphy: time. Even in a well-equipped shop, an elaborate piece like the "Florida Water" label would take a journeyman compositor at least half a day to design and set up.**

Discoverer of America

THE TRADE NEWS

Wildcats ❀ Reformed

Curious · Form · Lately · Cast

Rain · Water · Remark

GRACELAND ARTS

Combat ✠ of ✠ Kilkenny

Concert Opens

Association for Encouraging Habit

Third Southern Company Failed

Foreign Editions

Merchants Donate

Tattered Prince

SCIENTIFIC REPORTS

Harm Prevails

Excited Citizens

Enjoying Festive

South of Nation

BANQUET Tactic

No Gambling in Church

Impressive · Services

Graphic ⚡ Arts ⚡ Handbook

Figure 5.23: Later type designs. True Victoriana, the types above were, for the most part, designed and used during the 1870's, 1880's, and 1890's. During this time, the naming of designs came into vogue, and printers came to know such styles as Nymphic, Ringlet, Kitcat, Minaret, Monkish, Japanesque, Lady Text, Gazelle, and even Greenback.

PHOTOMODIFICATIONS

George Sohn, PHOTO-LETTERING, INC.

Modification of letterforms, although it is not a new technique, remains for many in the graphic arts an unknown or misunderstood subject. *Photomodification* refers basically to the changing of the form or proportions of typographic material using photographic techniques. An almost unlimited range of effects may be achieved through photomodification of type. Modification may be applied to a complete alphabet; to a single letter to fit a specific layout requirement; or to a finished mechanical, including overlays and halftones, to conform to a new format or page size.

MODIFICATION OF ALPHABETS

Phototypesetting equipment and methods have made the modification of complete alphabets or individual characters a relatively simple process. Variations in alphabet designs need no longer be cut in metal, involving tedious and expensive operations. Now they are photographed and plated for testing in a matter of hours. The proof may be evaluated; problems in design, weight, or fit noted; and the corrections incorporated into the original artwork. The new master alphabet is again photographed, plated, and run for a second proving. This may be done three or four times until the desired effect is achieved and approved; but in any event the final form will be only two steps away from the original, much to the satisfaction of designers and buyers. The original may be the copy supplied by the client or one of the alphabets in the working file of the studio.

Anamorphic lenses

The first photolettering services were offered in the mid-1930's. One of the tasks of the earliest display photocompositors was to match the hand letterer's ability to fit a prescribed headline layout area for both height and width. The solution was modification of the proportions of letters by the incorporation of a new type of optical lens into the Rutherford photolettering machine. Anamorphic reproportioning lenses gave a single alphabet font master the capability of thousands of variations. The use of anamorphic lenses in photodisplay composition (and occasionally in text) is now a routine procedure. These lenses expand, condense, oblique, and backslant master letters as they are photographed. (See figure 5.24.)

A convenient way to visualize the effects produced by an anamorphic lens is to picture a letter printed on a small piece of very flexible rubber. This rubber may be stretched or compressed horizontally or pulled diagonally from corner to corner. As the rubber increases or diminishes in width, the letter on it expands (widens) or condenses (narrows), and the weight of its vertical strokes increases or diminishes in exact proportion to the amount of expansion or condensation. The letter's horizontal strokes do not change at all. Thus a style like Helvetica takes on a thick-and-thin appearance when it is expanded; it begins to look a little like Radiant. The diagonal stretch of the rubber results in either a forward or backward slanting effect, with the weight of the vertical and horizontal strokes of the letters being redistributed according to the direction of the stretch.

Reproportioning

Most alphabets can be reproportioned up to 25 percent wider or 17 percent narrower than their original width without seriously disturbing the quality or readability of the design. (See figure 5.25.) Even within these percentages, however, some correction to the letterform may be necessary; therefore lightening (taking weight away from the letter) or weighting (adding weight to the letter) may be performed to retain the look of the original design.

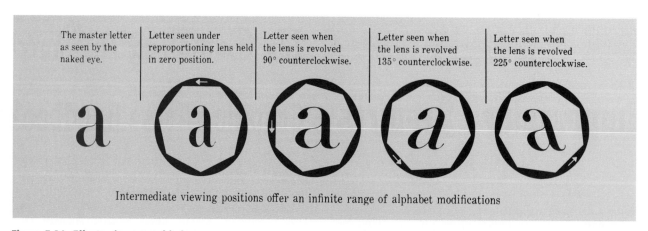

| The master letter as seen by the naked eye. | Letter seen under reproportioning lens held in zero position. | Letter seen when the lens is revolved 90° counterclockwise. | Letter seen when the lens is revolved 135° counterclockwise. | Letter seen when the lens is revolved 225° counterclockwise. |

Intermediate viewing positions offer an infinite range of alphabet modifications

Figure 5.24: Effects of anamorphic lens.

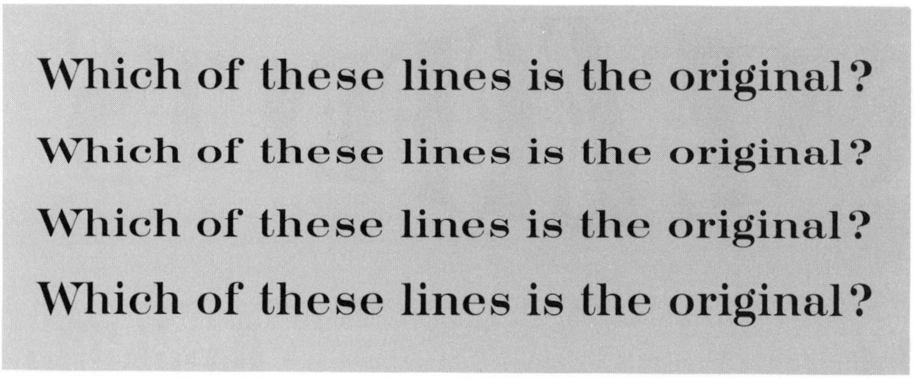

Which of these lines is the original?

Which of these lines is the original?

Which of these lines is the original?

Which of these lines is the original?

Figure 5.25: Reproportioning. Alphabets may be condensed or expanded without affecting the readability of the original typeface. In the example above, it is impossible to determine which is the original alphabet and which are modifications.

Occasionally the weighting or lightening effect when applied to an alphabet or line of composition will give a significantly different flavor to the style. (See figure 5.26.) Such derivatives, when explored further using good taste and judgment, can become the basis for a new design or series of designs.

Lightening and weighting techniques are also applied to line art that is simply wanted heavier or lighter. Photographic weight modifications provide greater flexibility and control than "tight" and "open" positive stats.

A word of caution: Sans serif monoweight alphabets such as Futura, Bauhaus, and Busorama, with perfectly drawn round characters such as the o or c, lose much of their "look" when reproportioned. This is particularly true when they are condensed. To do justice to the design, such letters should be used in their normal proportion or with slight expansion. When expanded these typefaces become thick and thin (like the typeface Radiant); when they are condensed the weights fall in the wrong areas, with the vertical strokes becoming lighter than the horizontal ones (somewhat suggesting a Barnum).

Obliquing

Obliquing, or slanting, of designs is still another form of modification which can be achieved through the use of anamorphic lenses. A pleasing angle of italic slant varies from 8° to 12°. Slants of 20° or 30° will give the letter a dramatic feeling of speed, known as the "zip effect," simulating motion. A forward slant is usually more successful than a backward one. A drawn italic design should rarely, if ever, be backslanted to an upright position. Backing up an italic produces an unbalanced and asymmetrical design.

OPTICAL CAMERA EFFECTS

Optical effects achieved through the use of cameras and other special equipment are also considered photomodifications. They include reproportioning, circoflairing, ogee curving, perspectives, contours, outlining, shadows, step-and-repeats, antiquing, spherography, and obliquing. (Various effects are illustrated in figures 5.27 through 5.38.) The original copy may be the studio's photolettering proofs or the client's type proofs or mechanicals. Reproportioning, curving, and perspective effects are perhaps the three services that require

further explanation. They provide an unusual and inexpensive way of saving a job from resetting or more expensive revision costs.

Reproportioning

Reproportioning is used to change the dimensions of the original typeset copy or mechanical. First, a precision photographic film negative reduction or enlargement of the line art is made to one of the final dimensions wanted. The negative is then, by direct contact onto photographic paper, expanded or condensed to the other final dimension. The result is a high-quality photographic print ready for paste-up, or, if the client prefers, a precision film negative for direct platemaking. The range for condensing and expanding is very wide—limited only by considerations of readability and taste.

Curving

Curving effects require equipment and methods that are more advanced and complex than those used for reproportioning. There are two basic kinds of curving—circoflairing and ogee curving.

The circoflairing service can be as simple as taking a single line of lettering and photographically curving it around a design or logo, or as complex as taking a block of copy and curving it to fit precise arcs in packaging labels. One aspect of circoflairing that makes it professionally and esthetically satisfying is that the let-

Figure 5.26: Weighting and lightening effects.

155

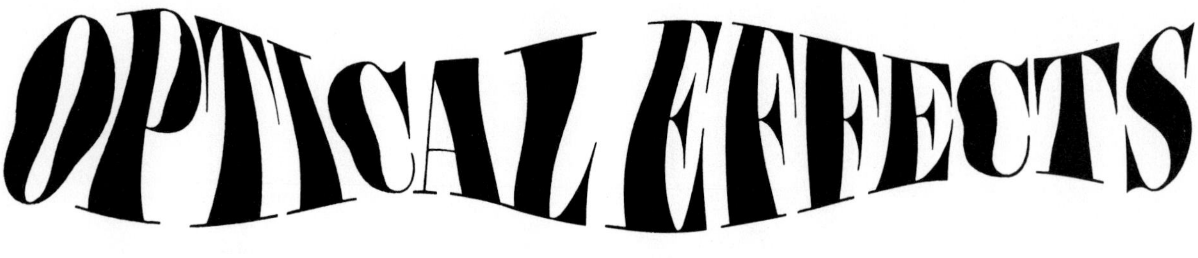
OPTICAL EFFECTS

Figure 5.27: Optical effects of line art (above).

Figure 5.28: Circoflairing (left).

Figure 5.29: Multiple reproportioning (right).

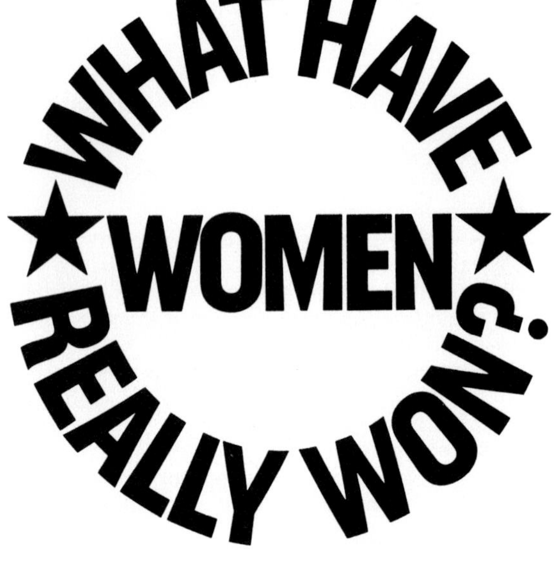
WHAT HAVE
WOMEN
REALLY WON?

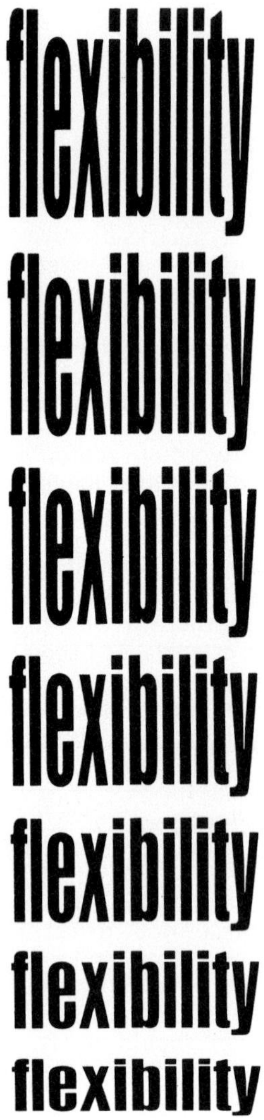
flexibility
flexibility
flexibility
flexibility
flexibility
flexibility
flexibility

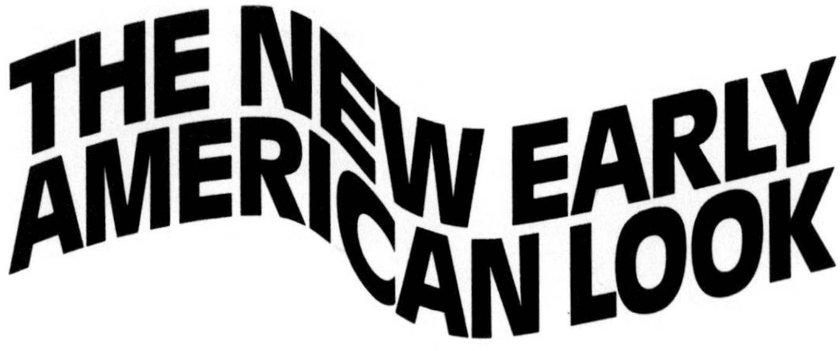
THE NEW EARLY
AMERICAN LOOK

Figure 5.30: Arch/dip, ogee curve.

Figure 5.31: Perspective tapering to right.

FLYING SAUCER

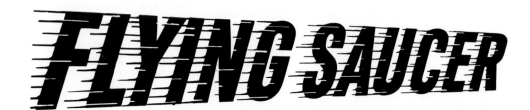

Figure 5.32: Perspective, top converging.

ENKALURE II
THE NEW
CARPET FIBER
THAT HIDES SOIL
NOT
PROFITS!

Figure 5.33: Radiations in sequence giving top-taper effect.

ANNOUNCING THE
OPENING DAY
SPECTACULAR
SALE OF SALES!

Figure 5.35: Step-and-repeat.

Figure 5.36: Cylindrical curve.

Figure 5.37: Spherography. On the left is the original art; on the right, the final spherography effect.

Figure 5.38: Dip/arch, backslant, perspective tapering to left.

Figure 5.34: Outlining with hand effects (left).

157

ters curve at the base to the desired degree of the arc rather than simply being staggered around the curve, as in a cut-apart paste-up. Circoflairing also enhances the letter shape with a subtle flair so that the letters fit well rather than having the noticeable gaps that may appear in a mechanical paste-up.

Ogee curving, although base-curved to any arc or curve, keeps the uprights of the letters vertical—much like the appearance of a picket fence running up and down over hilly terrain.

Perspectives

Perspectives of line art are perhaps the most difficult and time-consuming of all camera modifications. The client should supply a tissue indicating the area that the final perspective must fit into. A perspective must start with composition set in a rectangle fairly close in proportion to what is finally needed. For example, for a deep perspective a condensed type would probably be better for the initial setting than an expanded type. Anywhere from one or two lines of type to an entire page can be used, and the perspective can take off in any direction. The perspective effect is obtained either through the use of special lenses or by photographing the copy at an angle using adjustable boards and cameras.

Extremely tapered perspectives present problems in letter weight distribution. Without correction, letters in the spread side of the perspective become much heavier than those in the vanishing side. To counteract this problem, a "varigam" process—a continuous variation of the width of the letters—is used before processing the perspective. Varigam redistributes the weight and proportion of the characters, making the side to be spread lighter and narrower than the vanishing side. This pre-modification process balances out the line for color and stroke weight.

USING THE PHOTOLETTERING SERVICE

All special effects are custom operations performed by highly skilled technicians. The user of these services should also be aware, however, of his or her role in obtaining the best possible results. The client may provide only a rough layout, or he may supply a mechanical accompanied either by a layout showing how the final copy should look or by specific instructions as to the exact changes required—the amount of expansion of the type, for example, or the space requirements of the final copy. If the client does not provide the typeset copy or mechanical, the studio can match a rough layout or specifications as closely as possible using one of the typefaces in its files. It is usually easier, however, if the client designates a particular typeface from the studio's catalog.

Photomodifications solve certain problems satisfactorily and at nominal cost. Other problems are solved more economically and efficiently through hand lettering. Correctly used, photomodifications will often provide highly professional and satisfying results.

NICETIES OF PHOTOCOMPOSITION

Victor Spindler, SPINDLER SLIDES, INC.

We all have been "future shocked" by the abundant discussions of where typography is going and what the future of phototypography holds. But what the designer and production person really need to know today is where the state of the art is right now and what can presently be expected from suppliers.

The first point to remember about phototypography today is that, while its development and capabilities are based on the same principles as metal type, photocomposition is not limited by what is possible with metal systems. Neither is it true to say, however, that phototypesetting can do anything that metal typesetting can do. While similar in principle, the two processes differ in significant ways. Perhaps the best way to understand the capabilities of phototypesetting is to compare them to those of metal processes.

The first point of difference is simply the appearance of phototypeset material as against metal composition.

The photographic job, if done properly, should look sharper. There is no ink spread from the impression, nor are there any broken characters. (See figure 5.39.) Because the typeface manufacturers know there will be no ink spread on the final print used by the artist or printer, they alter the drawings of characters to allow as best they can for this fact; however, there is still a difference. (See figure 5.40.)

In addition, the size of a metal letter in different fonts of the same point size often varies substantially at the whim of the designer or typefounder. For example, there is a 4-point difference in height between 24-point Times Roman and 24-point Optima in metal fonts. Most photographic typesetting systems, however, have standardized the heights of fonts in a given point size, so that the heights of all 24-point fonts would be nearly the same. (See figure 5.41.) This is a very handy feature when a job is being produced completely in

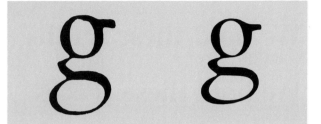

Figure 5.39: Effect of ink spread in letterpress-printed character (left) versus photographically set and lithographically printed character (right).

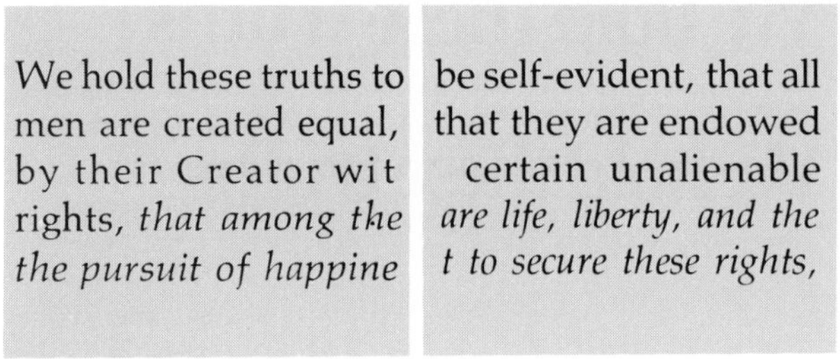

We hold these truths to
men are created equal,
by their Creator wit
rights, *that among the*
the pursuit of happine

be self-evident, that all
that they are endowed
certain unalienable
are life, liberty, and the
t to secure these rights,

Figure 5.40: Metal type (left) compared with photocomposition. Even after compensating for ink-spread effects, there is a difference.

photocomposition, but when a client sends along a print of metal type and asks that it be reproduced exactly, a phototypesetter cannot do it.

Another difference between the two typesetting methods is that kerning is not always possible in metal. Often when it is, it costs a great deal, and the metal type must be specially cut, permanently reducing its future usefulness. In photocomposition, on the other hand, kerning is accomplished by simply projecting the characters on the film or photographic paper with less space between them, without any loss of production speed or material. (See figure 5.42.)

The major fundamental advantage of photocomposition over metal typesetting, in fact, is the great new freedom offered the typographer in spacing type characters both horizontally and vertically. This new facility ranges all the way from simple kerning up through letterspacing, word spacing, and interline spacing, to formatting of entire areas in columns or on pages.

The keys to this new capability over metal are twofold. First, the photographic process allows the quick and easy placement of characters at any point on the film or photo paper, limited only by the mechanics of the typesetting machine. Today's better machines place very few limitations on the graphic designer once he understands how to get what he wants from them.

Second, the development and use of encoded tapes and pre-specified command code structures enable the designer to precisely define just what he wants and to instruct the machine exactly. Currently, the most popular system is to punch a coded paper tape on a keyboard-equipped perforator unit and then to use this tape to control all typesetting machine operations. Along with the coded letters and other characters, command codes specifying typefaces, sizes, spacing,

Metal type

WE HOLD THESE TRUTHS
Bodoni

WE HOLD THESE TR
Bookman

WE HOLD THESE TRUTHS
Optima

WE HOLD THESE TRUTH
Times Roman

Photocomposition

WE HOLD THESE TRUTHS
Bodoni

WE HOLD THESE TRUTH
Bookman

WE HOLD THESE TRUTHS
Optima

WE HOLD THESE TRUTHS
Times Roman

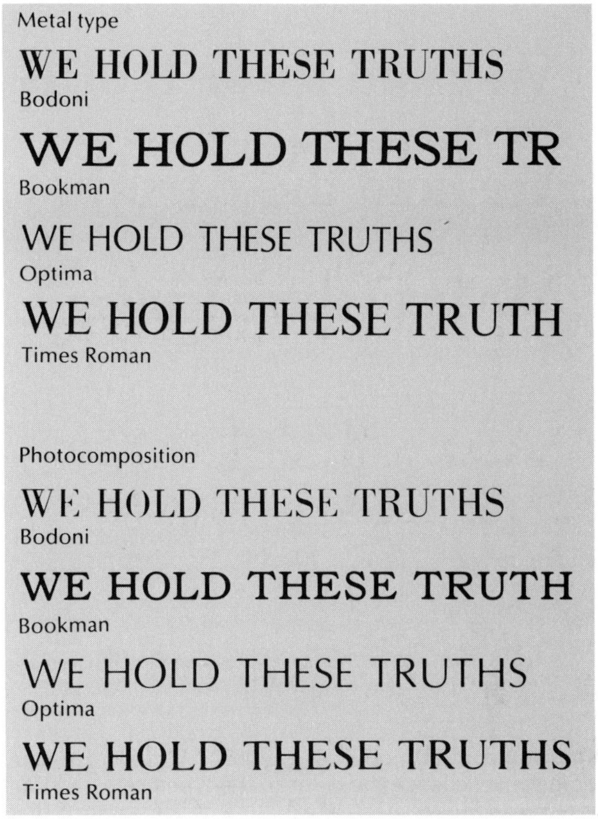

Figure 5.41: Variations in typefaces designed for metal and photographic typesetting. All are in the same point size.

and the like are also punched into the tape. These command codes carry the designer's original instructions, as marked on the copy, through the rest of the process with great precision. Moreover, the designer can often change many of his instructions at a later time, after the copy has been keyboarded, to adjust the

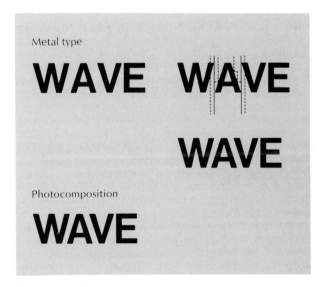

Metal type

WAVE   WAVE

WAVE

Photocomposition

WAVE

Figure 5.42: Use of kerning to equalize optical space.

We hold these truths
Normal

We hold these truths
Minus one-half unit

We hold these truths
Minus one unit

We hold these truths
Normal

We hold these truths
Minus three ninths

We hold these truths
Minus six ninths

We hold these truths
Minus nine ninths

We hold these truths
Minus twelve ninths

Figure 5.43: Subtraction of space between characters for tight setting. Older phototypesetting systems (left) offered only whole-unit and half-unit spacings; newer systems (right) use increments as small as one-ninth of a unit.

appearance of the job once he sees it in type. He can, for instance, change the color of the typeface by adding or removing letterspace, generating an appearance that will set the project apart from the ordinary. On some modern phototypesetting systems, these increments of space that are added or subtracted can be as fine as one-ninth of a unit on which the typeface design is based (18 units to the em is an often-used unit system), compared to older phototypesetters which offered only whole-unit or half-unit intercharacter spacings. (See figure 5.43.)

Similarly, word spacing can be preselected to establish a desired range within which the machine will stay, thus enabling the typographer to adjust word spacing to complement any changes made in letterspacing from the norm established for the face by the manufacturer. Generally four different word-spacing specifications can be adjusted: average word spacing, maximum allowable word spacing, minimum word spacing, and the amount of word spacing allowed before automatic letterspacing is used to justify a line. Variable word spacing can often be cancelled altogether and fixed-size spaces used instead for ragged composition.

Word spacing depends in part on the hyphenation of words at the ends of lines, and machines that offer these word-spacing options often also offer automatic hyphenation facilities. These machines have a small internal computer programmed with logic rules for breaking words into syllables. The logic, however, is not perfect in its accuracy because English is not a completely logical language. In most cases the logic is correct, and in special cases the incorrect break is simply corrected afterwards or the exceptional words are typed originally with "discretionary" hyphenation codes. These codes are inserted at all places in the word where a correct break can be made, and the

computer chooses the one that best suits the need for justification, overlooking all of the others in that word.

A second approach to the illogical hyphenation problem is the use of a larger computer which can store an "exception-word" dictionary with illogical words pre-hyphenated. In hyphenating a word, the computer first scans the exception dictionary to see if anything stored there should be used. If it does not find the word there, the program then hyphenates the word logically. These programs run automatically and provide the basis for being able to specify very tight typesetting on high-speed equipment.

Another refinement routinely possible on some phototypesetters is "hanging" punctuation (fig. 5.44), a typographic nicety that formerly was considered to be too expensive for most metal jobs.

Vertical spacing, or *leading*, can be built into a typesetting job as it is produced from the phototypesetting machine, just as additional leading can be provided in the metal processes. However, in metal this leading is generated by casting the type on a larger size slug, such as a 10-point type cast on a slug 12 points deep; there is no way to remove that extra leading once it is cast onto the slug, and the job must be completely rekeyboarded to get a smaller size body. In phototypesetting, on the other hand, an original instruction to set the type on a given body size usually can easily be overridden and a different body size specification inserted in the typesetting machine. Thus even if the job has already been keyboarded into tape and set once on one body size, a new body size can be specified and the tape rerun to produce the new type. The keyboarding cost is not incurred again—only the running time of the phototypesetter, which normally is much less. Vertical spacing on phototypesetting equipment usually can be varied in half-point increments, although some machines will handle much finer increments.

160

We hold these truths to be self-evident, that all men are created equal, that they are endowed by their Creator with certain unalienable rights, that among these are life, liberty, and the pursuit of happiness. That to secure these rights

We hold these truths to be self-evident, that all men are created equal, that they are endowed by their Creator with certain unalienable rights, that among these are life, liberty, and the pursuit of happiness. That to secure these rights

Figure 5.44: Use of "hanging" punctuation at ends of lines. Top paragraph is set without hanging punctuation, bottom paragraph with hanging punctuation.

Expanding on this theme, it is often possible to change lines or blocks of copy from justified to flush left, flush right, or centered—or vice versa—by changing only a couple of typesetting codes for each change made. (See figure 5.45.) In some cases, the typesetter can, if asked, change the font master in the machine and reset the entire job in a new typeface from a tape produced for the original face.

By using a little imagination, the typographer can now set some jobs completely on the typesetting machine that formerly he would have done by manual paste-up of type elements, such as unusual logotypes or display compositions. (See figures 5.46 and 5.47.) Since these machines have small computers in them, they can be made to do tabulations and set complete tables. The typographer can define up to 20 or so individual columns and specify that type in each column be set flush left, flush right, centered, or justified. (See figure 5.48.)

Special characters, too, are often easier to insert on the phototypesetting machine. A special symbol or emblem can be photographically added to a master

Figure 5.46: Special display effect created by overlapping type lines.

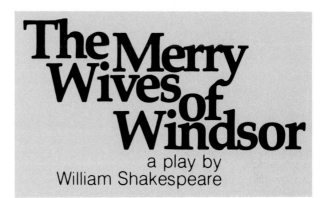

Figure 5.47: Original logotype created by unusual placement of characters and lines.

We hold these truths to be self-evident, that all men are created equal, that they are endowed by their Creator with certain unalienable rights, that among these are life, liberty, and the pursuit of happiness. That to secure these rights,
Justified

We hold these truths to be self-evident, that all men are created equal, that they are endowed by their Creator with certain unalienable rights, that among these are life, liberty, and the pursuit of happiness. That to
Flush left, ragged right

We hold these truths to be self-evident, that all men are created equal, that they are endowed by their Creator with certain unalienable rights, that among these are life, liberty, and the pursuit of happiness. That to
Centered

We hold these truths to be self-evident, that all men are created equal, that they are endowed by their Creator with certain unalienable rights, that among these are life, liberty, and the pursuit of happiness. That to
Flush right, ragged left

Figure 5.45: Justification changes created by running same typesetting-machine tape through unit with different machine settings.

Most comfortable store for personal clothes shopping

	$15,000 & over	$10,000-14,999	Under $10,000
Department store	41%	35%	26%
National chain	18	23	30
Discount store	8	12	14
Specialty store	23	26	24
Other	10	4	6

Figure 5.48: Tabular matter set from single set of typographic instructions for the machine.

Figure 5.49: Special characters or symbols inserted automatically by typesetting machine.

font grid and carried in the machine, where it is set in position like any other character. (See figure 5.49.) This eliminates the need to later strip or paste in such special items manually. The special photographic masters for such characters can be made by the typeface manufacturer if adequate time is available, but sometimes overnight service is possible if a cooperative slide house is close by.

Repetitive formatting is another powerful technique available on most phototypesetting machines today. What does formatting mean? Very simply, it is the process of specifying typography—faces, sizes, line measures, quadding or justification, or spacing around lines and/or copy blocks. In many kinds of work, the formatting for the job is designed by the typographer and then must be recopied many times before the original type is completed. Repetitive formatting techniques permit the typographer to establish the original specifications and then have these entered into computer memory in the typesetter for automatic execution every time each particular format style is needed.

For example, the typographer might want every headline in a job in Serif Gothic Bold, 12 on 13 point, minus one-half unit letterspacing, on a 25-pica measure. Without repetitive formatting capability in the typesetting machine, the keyboard operator would have to retype all of the individual command codes for each of these instructions every time one of the headlines had to be set—a total of perhaps 20 or so

keystrokes for every headline. With repetitive formatting, however, the operator would first type in the command codes along with a special "format" code which would be assigned to that string of commands. Then when each headline was set in the copy, the operator would type only the one format code along with the characters to be set.

In the typesetting unit, the format code plus the string of command codes would first be read into memory. Then when each headline was to be set, the format code accompanying it would tell the computer to insert all the command codes to produce the headline in the correct format. (See figure 5.50.)

Everything discussed here is the current state of the art in photocomposition today. But there are some things of which typographers and designers should be aware and/or wary in trying to use these techniques.

First it must be said that many typesetting shops will not want to take the extra care necessary to produce the refinements outlined here, so the designer must use care and discretion in choosing both the supplier to be used and the job to be produced. Do not start with the biggest rush job for the best account in the house—get your feet wet with a smaller, less important job. You may have to learn some new terminology; ask your supplier to define these terms for you in language you can understand, not the language of technicians.

With photocomposition, fewer proofs may be required than with metal repros—photoproofs cannot be smeared and will not offset if left together.

The state of the art is changing rapidly in this field, and more and more new things are becoming possible every day. Stay alert to the new developments. Even now, computer programs have been developed to permit economical setting of runarounds. Folios, running heads, and kerning in some instances can now be set completely automatically, so that the keyboard operator need not even think about them. A number of machines can now *reverse lead*, that is, set one column and then back up the film or photo paper to set a second or third column beside the first. This, in effect, enables the phototypesetter to potentially make up complete pages inside the machine.

At this point, today's state of the art meets the future, which is the subject of other articles. However, that future is not too far away.

ZAYRE DEPT. STORES
All Stores

GRANT CITY DEPT. STORES
Hometown, N.J.

WOOLCO STORES
Nationwide

Figure 5.50: Repetitive format in which repeated items are set automatically by reusing instructions for first item.

TYPOGRAPHY AND TECHNOLOGY
Bently Raak, TYPOGRAPHIC CONSULTANT

Rapidly changing technology in composition will affect type design greatly in the future. Many new trends have already begun. The new technology is bringing to the typographic field greater freedom in manipulating type images, and as at the beginning of any major movement, the new techniques have been used both badly and well. Some of today's trends will prove transitory, while others hold more promise for basic change than most of us yet realize.

TRENDS IN TYPEFACE USAGE
The most obvious and widely discussed impact of new technology on type design is its potential for developing new faces and new versions of existing designs. The use of photographic images has made it far easier to convert a new design into a machine font than it used to be when metal punches had to be cut and casting matrices stamped in brass. The growing family of video-tube typesetters, which are controlled completely electronically, make possible the easy distortion of letterforms on the tube face to form oblique and unusually shaped characters.

There has been much talk of totally new typefaces coming into widespread use to replace the classic "metal" faces. However, letterforms in all languages and alphabets have evolved over centuries of use, and the requirements of recognition and readability place severe restrictions on the range of desirable design manipulation. Today's crop of new typefaces must resemble to some degree the work of type designers over the last 500 years because few possibilities for radically new designs exist. The design of new faces that stand the test of time, in fact, is more a process of subtle adaptation and reinterpretation than of building all new from the ground up.

As might be expected, a survey of typeface usage in the major areas of commercial typesetting shows the continuing heavy usage of a relatively few favored faces which have proven themselves over the years.

Books
Over the approximately 50 years that the American Institute of Graphic Arts has sponsored the Fifty Books of the Year exhibition, Baskerville has been used in more books than any other typeface, followed by Caslon, Janson, Garamond, Granjon, Bodoni, Caledonia, Bembo, and Scotch Roman. Only about 4½ percent of the books have used sans serif faces such as Helvetica, Univers, and Futura. These sans serifs were used primarily in art and photography books, mainly for captions, not for text. In the last several years, Caslon has dropped almost out of sight and is being replaced by Janson, another Dutch-oriented design which has more weight in the thin stems and a better design throughout.

General job work
The two most popular faces for the vast range of general work—magazines, catalogs, bulletins, brochures, notices, and the like—are Times and Helvetica. Close behind are Janson, Bodoni, Caledonia, News Gothic, Garamond, Bembo, and Palatino. Souvenir is gaining popularity; Univers is definitely on the decline. For setting catalogs, the condensed versions of Helvetica and News Gothic rank very high, with Times in third place. The tested standard designs seem to be holding their position in this field, too.

Advertising
The advertising field makes the most use of new typefaces. Advertising art directors are always looking for something new, even if it is not better typographically. In this field, newness is a stronger requirement than high readability.

National magazine advertising currently shows new interest in serif types for text, after a long period of favoring sans serifs. A recent count of typefaces used in ads showed approximately equal use of serif and sans serif faces. Serif faces are being used for text in ads now even with sans serif heads in the same ad.

In other forms of advertising, there is increasing use of Souvenir and some of the other "non-type-foundry" faces—faces designed and issued by people outside of type foundries. Other designs of this kind that are proving popular are Avant Garde, Serif Gothic, Korinna, and Tiffany. Faces like these usually have a relatively short life as fads in advertising change.

MODIFICATION OF TRADITIONAL FONTS
The vast majority of typesetting is done in book production, general job work, and newspaper printing, which, unlike advertising, rely on proven designs. Therefore, the main thrust of technological innovation in typography will be toward enhancing and improving classic designs rather than toward providing a greatly enlarged inventory of typefaces.

Technology is bringing change to traditional type in two important ways. It is now easy to make subtle alterations in proven designs, and to create more efficient and flexible font arrangements, avoiding the severe restrictions metal typesetting imposes.

Altering existing faces
Readability research and new type designs in this century have shown certain principles to be very important in making typefaces as legible as possible. Many of the older faces, however, were designed before these principles were understood or before modern typesetting practices emphasized the need to observe them stringently. Many of the older faces could be improved for certain applications if they

were modified in ways not apparent to the eye but important to legibility.

One example of a limitation on readability is the relatively small x-height of a face like Garamond or Janson. Janson in particular is finding increased use now, and a slightly larger x-height—only a few thousandths of an inch—would significantly improve its ratio of x-height to ascenders and descenders without materially affecting the appearance of the Janson design. This modification can be made easily through photographic means; a variety of test characters and fonts can be made and test copy can be set at modest cost to verify the proper design. The expense of making such test fonts in metal would be prohibitive.

New font arrangements

Compared with metal typesetting, the photographic process and photographic typesetting machinery provide a hitherto undreamed-of ability to expand character sets in fonts and to intermix special characters and different fonts in the same line. One of the earliest developments was the expansion of the standard font from the 90-character set required for linecasting machines to larger sets of over 100 characters. The number of characters in a font is no longer standard; it is limited only by the mechanism in the phototypesetting machine that selects individual characters for exposure. Manufacturers have developed machines with different capabilities for different applications.

Many phototypesetting machines now put virtually an entire type library within the touch of a few keys on the typesetting keyboard. These machines may use individual fonts or they may place a variety of fonts on a single photographic master such as a rotating disc. In either case, these masters are inexpensive enough to permit typesetters to set up customized arrangements for specialized material. Custom-made font masters have been produced to order for almost every purpose imaginable, from the composition of foreign languages, mathematics, and chemistry to set-

ting business cards and type for rubber stamps.

Phototypesetting machine manufacturers also have developed various "standard" font arrangements for certain kinds of composition. AM Varityper, for example, has a basic jobbing font arrangement or format for setting booklets, publications, leaflets, programs, and other miscellaneous work; a news format for newspaper editorial material; an advertisement format with extra bullets, boxes, and dingbats; a book format with small caps and other refinements; a catalog format with oversized superior and inferior figures and a kerned slash line to produce more readable fractions in 6-point and 7-point type; and a mathematics format with normal, superior, and inferior roman and italic fonts, lower and uppercase Greek letters, bold sans serif caps, and about 60 mathematical symbols. Figure 5.51 shows how the 448 different characters in a mathematics layout can be set from a single typewriter-style keyboard through the use of a shift and supershift mechanism.

CHARACTER SPACING

New electronic control and photographic exposure technologies have also provided complete freedom to place characters on a page in any position desired. This freedom has given the graphic designer the opportunity to create spectacular new typography-based display graphics. Unfortunately, it has also enabled people without an understanding of type design and principles of readability to abuse the fitting of characters next to one another in text matter.

Since the late 1960's, there has been a strong tendency to set type tighter than normal—an option made possible by phototypesetting. Tight setting goes all the way to overlapping the characters in some instances. The trend started in the larger advertising typography shops, where the technicians of this new typesetting technology tried to do things differently, and it has been filtering down slowly to the smaller composing

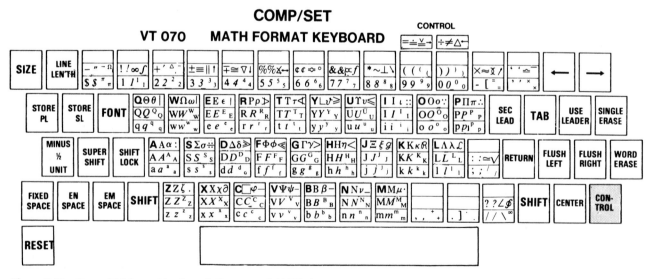

Figure 5.51: Comp/Set format keyboard. *Courtesy of AM Varityper.*

rooms. Extra-tight setting is effective and appropriate for display headlines and some advertising copy blocks where stylish treatment is important, but it is a highly questionable practice in books and other reading text because it impedes reading. To the extent that extra-tight setting is a fad of the advertising world, it will not last for more than a few years. Tight setting was a swing away from traditional limitations, and when the advertising typographers have exhausted their scope for experimentation someone will come up with another trend to return character spacing to normal.

However, a reversal of this trend will not solve the entire problem of too-tight or uneven character spacing. The new freedom in letterspacing has also been used by technicians, computer programmers, and other "non-type-educated" typographers to produce justified text matter with greater ease. By squeezing the characters in the line together, they sidestep the hard-to-resolve hyphenation problems at the ends of lines.

This particular problem may disappear in time as new computer memory units with far greater capacity make possible more sophisticated, accurate hyphenation programs. However, the larger problem of poor character spacing can only be solved if today's typeface producers learn the art of character fitting, an art well known to the metal type foundries but dying out with them.

CHARACTER FITTING

Character fitting involves much more than specifying that more or less space be used between characters in a line of type. It is a process of adjusting the set widths of various characters, or the lateral spaces in which they are positioned, so that the characters appear evenly spaced and the proper average distance apart when set in different combinations in various words. The most beautiful alphabet design in the world is no good for typesetting unless the characters have been properly fitted to go together in words without undue crowding or gapping. Good fitting is essential to good readability.

In the fitting process, each character is first positioned with what appears to be the right amount of white space on each side. Then each letter is checked by placing it between two letters with the two basic letter shapes. Lowercase characters, for example, are placed between lowercase n's, which have straight vertical lines, and then between lowercase o's, which have the basic rounded shape used throughout the alphabet. Such test lines would look like the following:

nnn nanbncndnenfngnhninjnknlnmnonpn
nqnrnsntnunvnwnxnynzn nnn

ooo oaobocodoeofogohoiojokolomonopo
oqorosotouovowoxoyozo ooo

The capital letters are checked between *H* and *O* in the same manner, and figures are checked between zeros. All punctuation marks are checked with both lowercase and capital letters.

Every individual design, weight, and width variation has different fitting requirements and must be fitted separately. In the days of metal type design, each size also was fitted a little differently from other sizes in a series (the characters were designed slightly differently in each size, for that matter). In photocomposition, however, in which many sizes are projected from the same master font, fitting each size separately poses major mechanical problems in the typesetting machine, so it is not done often. On a few machines, a compromise has been adopted by using two, three, or four different-size font masters of the same face, each projecting only a limited range of sizes. For the most part, however, photocomposition fonts must be fitted so they can be used to set a relatively wide range of sizes, which adds to the difficulty of the basic fitting job.

The number of character combinations possible in a full font of type suggests the complexity of the fitting task, which is essentially a trial-and-error process. It is very tedious and time-consuming: of the total man-hours invested in creating a properly fitted new typeface, about 85 percent goes into the fitting process. In a few cases, type designers have also done their own fitting. However, fitting is a highly specialized skill, and most designers have relied on people known as justifiers in the type foundries to do the fitting work. While the great type designers have become famous, their fitters have remained unknown.

Fitting skills are disappearing as the number of metal type foundries dwindles. The manufacturers of phototypesetting equipment are engineers by background and most have no real contact with the classic processes of producing type. In many cases, therefore, the type available on phototypesetting machines today is not fitted well according to the traditional aesthetic principles of typeface production.

Unfortunately, there is little literature on the subject. Perhaps the earliest book, and still one of the most authoritative, to record the alignment and fitting of letters is Joseph Moxon's *Mechanick Exercises*, published in London in 1683, with many pages devoted to the justification of type matrices. The foundry justifiers, however, were a secretive group, and they all kept "little black books" with notes on the techniques they had learned from years on the job. A designer would instruct a justifier to fit a new face in the way that a similar face was fitted and to show samples of a few characters. When the samples were approved, the justifier would fit the rest of the font accordingly. Proofs were examined, changes were made, and settings of trial words were examined for final approval. In this process, the justifier often would make several "errors" in the positioning of matrices which only he knew how to correct. Thus, if other people tried to use this fitting data, they would produce an unacceptable product. The "little black books" were guarded as trade secrets, and their accumulated knowledge has not become available to the type-designing community at large.

With the advent of phototypesetting, graphic designers took over much of the responsibility for fitting which the foundry justifiers formerly held, but without the necessary experience or access to it. The phototypesetting industry must now train its designers in the art of character fitting, an art that will take years to learn.

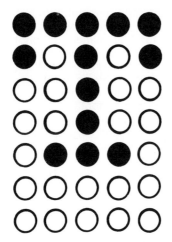

Figure 5.52: The letter T formed by a set of dots on a matrix of five dots by seven dots.

VIDEO-SCREEN TYPOGRAPHY

So far we have examined the impact of technology on traditional type design and typography. Typographic considerations are having an impact on machine designs as well, particularly in the area of video-screen typography.

Most type displayed on the video screens used for editing and typesetting has been designed by the engineers who built the equipment. Tentative steps have been made by a few manufacturers to develop something more sophisticated than the blueprint-style block lettering most often used, but alternative styles are still in their infancy.

The dot matrix

A major constraint on the design of characters on a video screen is the *dot matrix* which is used to generate them. The characters are formed by a set of dots of light, as shown in figure 5.52. The area in which the character is positioned is a rectangle with rows of dots which can either be lighted or unlighted. These dot matrices can have various numbers of dots in them, such as five dots across and seven dots down, seven dots across and ten dots down, and other combinations. The more dots in the matrix, the finer the refine-

ments can be in character shapes; but a matrix with more dots costs more in internal circuitry in the machine, and most of today's equipment is strictly limited in the size of its dot matrices.

Still, early efforts to design more readable type characters based on present-day dot matrices have produced great improvements over the first primitive block letters. Experience has shown that judicious forming of characters is effective in overcoming matrix limitations. There is no reason to accept the original poor letterforms as a requirement on video terminal screens.

Special characters

Another dimension of video-screen typography which has not yet received adequate attention is the need for special characters to set foreign languages, mathematics, chemistry, and other special material. With the growth of international business and commerce, foreign language composition facilities are becoming important.

Early video editing equipment had little facility for holding and displaying large fonts with many characters beyond the basic alphabet, figures, and punctuation. Special characters were indicated by showing all manner of blinking, underlined, struck-through, and double-bright characters which had to be interpreted by the machine operator; or a dollar sign followed by a regular character was used as a substitute for the special character.

Now machines with much greater capacity to generate the special images directly on the screen are emerging. The key to this capacity is the Programmable Read-Only Memory (PROM), an integrated circuit that can store any character pattern and deliver it to the screen instantly on command. This new memory circuit permits special images to be programmed for individual machines at reasonable cost.

A number of electronic composition systems now can generate some accented characters for language composition on video screens. A complete set of accented characters for all languages set in the Roman alphabet is available for use on AM Varityper Comp/Set systems. Figure 5.53 shows an early version of this character set, photographed from the video screen. Video-screen character sets are also available for the Cyrillic, Arabic, and Hebrew alphabets.

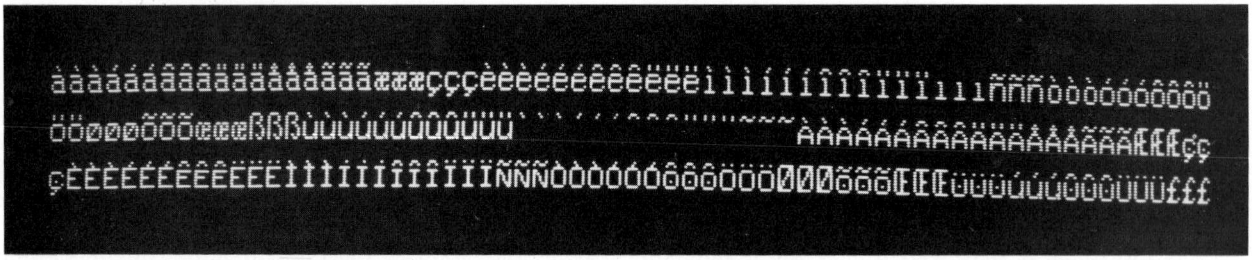

Figure 5.53: Set of accented characters for all languages using the Roman alphabet, photographed from a video screen. *Courtesy of AM Varityper.*

COMMONLY USED TYPEFACE NAMES

Alexander S. Lawson and Archibald D. Provan, ROCHESTER INSTITUTE OF TECHNOLOGY

With the rapid expansion of photographic methods in typesetting, there has also come an explosion of new typefaces readily produced by photographic means. A great many of these typefaces, however, are simply adaptations of the most preferred basic type designs, altered to work with a specific equipment manufacturer's machinery and marketed under a new name. The resulting proliferation of typeface names has caused confusion among designers and editors.

This compilation is designed to provide a quick reference to the most commonly used typeface names, both old and new, showing which faces are actually related adaptations of other faces. This kind of correlation is necessarily somewhat inexact, however, because the technological needs of equipment and the personal preferences of type designers do result in some differences between faces shown here as being equivalent. These differences can be particularly important if an equivalent face of one manufacturer is used to set insertions or corrections for material set in the equivalent face of another manufacturer. While the differences may not be apparent when the two faces are used in separate jobs, they are likely to become unacceptable when the types are intermingled.

In the left-hand column of the listing below, some 250 frequently encountered typeface names are listed alphabetically, including those names considered original designations (indicated by italic type) and those considered variations or equivalents. If the name is an original designation, it is followed in the right-hand column with all its variations found in this list. If the typeface in the left-hand column is itself a variation or equivalent, it is followed in the right-hand column only by the original designation of its design; other related variations, if any, can easily be found by looking up the original name in the alphabetical listing. (Whenever an original designation appears in either column, it is printed in italics for easy identification.)

It should be noted that complete agreement does not exist among all authorities on the derivation of certain designs. This is particularly true among the newspaper readability faces, where basic designs are all fairly similar. It is possible that a few typeface names listed here as variations or equivalents might, by some authorities, be considered original designs.

In this list, no attempt has been made to separate or identify typefaces according to the type foundry or composing machine manufacturer which markets them.

A

Ad Bold	*Dom Casual*
Aigrette	*Bernhard Tango*
Airport	*Futura*
Akzidenz Grotesk	Standard
Alpha Gothic	*News Gothic*
Alphavers	*Univers*
Alternate Gothic	Gothic No. 1
Andover	*Palatino*
Annonce Grotesque	*Venus Extrabold Extended*
Anzeigen Grotesk	*Aura*
Aquarius	*Corona*
Aries	*Univers*
Arrighi	Centaur Italic
Aster	Astro
Astoria	*Comstock*
Astro	*Aster*
Atlantic	*Plantin 110*
Aura	{ Anzeigen Grotesk / Aurora Bold Condensed
Aurora Bold Condensed	*Aura*
Aurora Condensed	Wotan Extra Condensed
Avant Garde Gothic	Cadence

B

Ballardville	*Melior*
Bank Gothic	{ Banker's Gothic / Commerce Gothic / De Luxe Gothic / Stationer's Gothic
Banker's Gothic	*Bank Gothic*

Baskerline	*Baskerville*
Baskerville	{ Baskerline / Beaumont
Beacon Bold	*Bernhard Modern Bold*
Beaumont	*Baskerville*
Bedford	*Imperial*
Bernhard Cursive	{ Bridal Script / Liberty / Lotus
Bernhard Modern Bold	Beacon Bold
Bernhard Tango	Aigrette
Bem	*Bembo*
Bembo	{ Bem / Griffo
Bikini Script	*Trafton Script*
Blado	Poliphilus Italic
Bodoni	Brunswick
Bodoni Extrabold Condensed	*Onyx*
Bologna	Verona
Bookface	*Bookman*
Bookman	Bookface
Boston	*Univers*
Bridal Script	*Bernhard Cursive*
Brunswick	*Bodoni*
Busorama	De Ville

C

Cadence	*Avant Garde Gothic*
Caledo	*Caledonia*

Caledonia	Caledo
	California
	Cornelia
	Edinburgh
	Gemini
	Highland
	Laurel
California	Caledonia
Cambridge	Century Expanded
Cambridge Light	Century Schoolbook
Canterbury Capitals	Floriated Capitals
Casual	Dom Casual
Centaur	Centaurus
Centaur Italic	Arrighi
Centaurus	Centaur
Century	Century Expanded
Century Expanded	Cambridge
	Century
	Century Light
	Century X
Century Light	Century Expanded
Century Modern	Century Schoolbook
Century Schoolbook	Cambridge Light
	Century Modern
	Century Text
	Century Textbook
	Schoolbook
Century Text	Century Schoolbook
Century Textbook	Century Schoolbook
Century X	Century Expanded
Chelmsford	Optima
Cheltenham	Cheltonian
	Gloucester
	Winchester
Cheltonian	Cheltenham
Clarendon	Clarique
	Craw Clarendon
Clarendon Modern	Craw Modern
Clarique	Clarendon
Claro	Helvetica
Cochin	Le Cochin
Commerce Gothic	Bank Gothic
Comstock	Astoria
Concord	Deepdene
Cooper Black	Pittsburgh Black
	Rugged Black
Copper Light	Copperplate Gothic
Copperplate Gothic	Copper Light
	Formal Gothic
	Lining Plate Gothic
Cornelia	Caledonia
Corona	Aquarius
	Crown
	News No. 3
	Quincy
Corvinus	Elegis Medium
	Glamour
Corvus	Helvetica
Craw Clarendon	Clarendon
Craw Modern	Clarendon Modern
	Deane
Crown	Corona

D

De Luxe Gothic	Bank Gothic
De Ville	Busorama
Deane	Craw Modern
Deepdene	Concord

Dom Casual	Ad Bold
	Casual
	Polka
Doric	Ionic

E

Edinburgh	Caledonia
Elegante	Palatino
Elegis Medium	Corvinus
Empira	Regal
English	Times Roman
Eros	Venus
Eurogothic	Eurostile
Europe	Futura
Eurostile	Eurogothic
	Microgramma
Eve	Rivoli
Eve Bold	Paramount

F

Fairfield	Fairmont
Fairmont	Fairfield
Floriated Capitals	Canterbury Capitals
Folio	Haverhill
Fontales	Fontanesi
Fontanesi	Fontales
Formal Gothic	Copperplate Gothic
Franklin	Franklin Gothic
Franklin Gothic	Franklin
	Pittsburgh
Futura	Airport
	Europe
	Photura
	Sirius
	Spartan
	Techno
	Tempo
	Twentieth Century
	Utica

G

Galaxy	Univers
Garamond	Garamont
	Grenada
Garamont	Garamond
Gemini	Caledonia
Geneva	Helvetica
Glamour	Corvinus
Gloucester	Cheltenham
Gold Rush	Klondike
Gothic No. 1	Alternate Gothic
Gothic No. 2	Metro
Gothic No. 3	Metro
Gothic No. 4	Metro
Goudy Light	Goudy Old Style
Goudy Old Style	Goudy Light
	Number 11
Granite	Lydian
Grenada	Garamond
Griffo	Bembo

H

Hanover	Melior
Haverhill	Folio
Helios	Helvetica

Helvetica	Claro
	Corvus
	Geneva
	Helios
	Megaron
	Newton
	Vega
Highland	Caledonia

I

Imperial	Bedford
	News No. 2
	Taurus
Ionic	News Text Medium
	Doric

K

Kabel	Sans Serif
Kaufmann Bold	Swing Bold
Kennerley	Kentonnian
Kentonnian	Kennerley
Klondike	Gold Rush

L

Latine	Meridien
Laurel	Caledonia
Le Cochin	Cochin
Liberty	Bernhard Cursive
Libra	Libretto
Libretto	Libra
Lining Plate Gothic	Copperplate Gothic
London Roman	Times Roman
Lotus	Bernhard Cursive
Lydian	Granite
Lyra	Melior

M

Mallard	Melior
Medallion	Melior
Megaron	Helvetica
Melier	Melior
Melior	Ballardvale
	Hanover
	Lyra
	Mallard
	Medallion
	Melier
	Uranus
	Ventura
Meridien	Latine
Metra	Metro
Metro	Gothic No. 2
	Gothic No. 3
	Gothic No. 4
	Metra
Microgramma	Eurostile
Minstral	Mistral
Mistral	Minstral
Musica	Optima

N

News Gothic	Alpha Gothic
	Record Gothic
	Toledo
	Trade Gothic
News No. 2	Imperial

News No. 3	Corona
News Text Medium	Ionic
Newton	Helvetica
Nitetime	Venus Extrabold Extended
Noontime	Venus Bold Extended
Number 11	Goudy Old Style

O

Olympus	Trump Mediaeval
Onyx	Bodoni Extrabold Condensed
Optima	Chelmsford
	Musica
	Oracle
	Orleans
	Ursa
	Zenith
Oracle	Optima
Orleans	Optima

P

Palatino	Andover
	Elegante
	Palladium
	Patina
	Pontiac
Palladium	Palatino
Paramount	Eve Bold
Patina	Palatino
Pegasus	Times Roman
Photura	Futura
Pittsburgh	Franklin Gothic
Pittsburgh Black	Cooper Black
Plantin 110	Atlantic
Poliphilus Italic	Blado
Polka	Dom Casual
Pontiac	Palatino
Primer	Rector

Q

Quincy	Corona

R

Record Gothic	News Gothic
Rector	Primer
Regal	Empira
Rivoli	Eve
Roman Stylus	Typo Roman Shaded
Royal	Vela
Rugged Black	Cooper Black
Rustic	Rustic Shaded
Rustic Shaded	Rustic

S

Sans Serif	Kabel
Saphir	Sapphire
Sapphire	Saphir
Schoolbook	Century Schoolbook
Sirius	Futura
Society Text	Wedding Text
Spartan	Futura
Standard	Akzidenz Grotesk
Stationer's Gothic	Bank Gothic
Stylon	Vogue
Swing Bold	Kaufmann Bold

T

Taurus	*Imperial*
Techno	*Futura*
Tempo	*Futura*
Times New Roman	*Times Roman*
Times Roman	⎧English ⎪London Roman ⎨Pegasus ⎩Times New Roman
Toledo	*News Gothic*
Torina	*Torino*
Torino	Torina
Trade Gothic	*News Gothic*
Trafton Script	Bikini Script
Triumph	*Trump Gravur*
Trump Gravur	Triumph
Trump Imperial	*Trump Mediaeval*
Trump Mediaeval	⎧Olympus ⎩Trump Imperial
Twentieth Century	*Futura*
Typo Roman Shaded	Roman Stylus

U

Univers	⎧Alphavers ⎪Aries ⎨Boston ⎪Galaxy ⎩Versatile
Uranus	*Melior*

V

Vega	*Helvetica*
Vela	*Royal*
Ventura	*Melior*
Venus	Eros
Venus Bold Extended	Noontime
Venus Extrabold Extended	⎧Annonce Grotesque ⎩Nitetime
Verona	*Bologna*
Versatile	*Univers*
Vogue	Stylon

Ursa — *Optima*
Utica — *Futura*

W

Walbaum	Waverley
Waverley	*Walbaum*
Wedding Text	Society Text
Winchester	*Cheltenham*
Wotan Extra Condensed	*Aurora Condensed*

Z

Zenith — *Optima*

TYPEFACE SPECIMENS

Many of the following one-line typeface specimens have been reproduced from Visual Graphics Corporation's *Alphabet Library*. Others have been supplied by various typeface manufacturers, including Alphatype-Filmtype Sales Corp., Compugraphic Corporation, Dymo Graphic Systems, Harris Corporation, International Typeface Corporation, and Mergenthaler Linotype Company. This list does not attempt to be all-inclusive but provides examples of the wide range of typefaces available.

Abbott Old Style
ABRAMESQUE
Accolade Semibold
Accolade Semibold Italic
Accolade Semibold Condensed
Ad Lib
AESTHETIC
AETERNA
AGENCY GOTHIC OPEN
AKI LINES
Akzidenz Grotesk
Akzidenz Grotesk Medium
Albertus
Albertus Inline
Albertus Outline
ALBERTUS TITLING
ALBERTUS BOLD TITLING
ALBERTUS BLACK
Alfereta
Algonquin Shaded
Allegro

Alpin Gothic No.1
Alpin Gothic No.2
Alpin Gothic Italic No.2
Alpin Gothic No.3
Alternate Gothic No.1
Alternate Gothic No. 2
Alternate Gothic No. 2 Italic
Alternate Gothic No. 3
Amelia
American Gothic Light
American Gothic Medium
American Gothic Bold
American Text
American Typewriter LIGHT
American TYPEWRITER MEDIUM
American TYPEWRITER BOLD
American Typewriter LIGHT CONDENSED
American Typewriter MEDIUM CONDENSED
American Typewriter BOLD CONDENSED
American UNCIAL & INITIALS
American UNCIAL & INITIALS BOLD

American UNCIAL & INITIALS OPEN
Americana
Americana Italic
Americana Bold
Americana EXTRABOLD
Americana OUTLINE
Andrich Minerva
Andrich Minerva It.
Anglo
Antikva Margaret LIGHT
Antikva Margaret
Antikva Margaret ITALIC
Antikva MARGARET EXTRA BOLD
Antikva MARGARET BLACK
Antique #1
Antique #1 Italic
Anzeigen Grotesk Bold
Aquarius 2
Aquarius 4
Aquarius 5
Aquarius 6

Aquarius 7

Aquarius 8

Aquarius Outline

ARBORET

Arnholm Sans Medium

Arnholm Sans Bold

Arpad Light

Arpad Medium

Arpad Bold

Arpad Outline

Arrow

Art Gothic

Art Script

Aster

Aster Italic

Aster Bold

Aster EXTRABOLD

Aster Outline

Astur

Athenaeum

Atlantic

Atlantic Italic Tru-Cut

AUGUSTEA

AUGUSTEA INLINE

Auriga Roman

Auriga Italic

Auriga Bold ROMAN

Aurora Condensed

Aurora Bold Condensed

Aurora Grotesk IX

Aurora Grotesk EXTRA CONDENSED VIII

Avant Garde GOTHIC EXTRA LIGHT

Avant Garde GOTHIC BOOK

Avant Garde GOTHIC MEDIUM

Avant Garde GOTHIC DEMI

Avant Garde GOTHIC BOLD

Avant Garde GOTHIC BOOK CONDENSED

Avant Garde GOTHIC MEDIUM CONDENSED

Avant Garde GOTHIC DEMI CONDENSED

Avant Garde GOTHIC BOLD CONDENSED

BAGHDAD

Baker Argentina No.1

Baker Argentina No.1 Italic

Baker Argentina No.2

Baker Argentina NO. 2 ITALIC

Baker Argentina No.3

Baker Argentina No.3 ITALIC

Baker Argentina No.4

Baker Argentina No.4 ITALIC

Baker Argentina No.5

Baker Argentina NO. 5 ITALIC

Baker Argentina No.6

Baker Argentina NO. 6 ITALIC

Baker Danmark 1

Baker Danmark 2

Baker Danmark 3

Baker Danmark 4

Baker Danmark 5

Baker Danmark 6

Baker Danmark Outline

Baker Danmark Shaded

Baker Sans FINELINE LIGHT

Baker Sans DISPLAY LIGHT

Baker Sans MONO LIGHT

Baker Sans FINELINE REGULAR

Baker Sans DISPLAY REGULAR

Baker Sans MONO REGULAR

Baker Sans FINELINE MEDIUM

Baker Sans DISPLAY MEDIUM

Baker Sans MONO MEDIUM

Baker Sans FINELINE BOLD

Baker Sans DISPLAY BOLD

Baker Sans MONO BOLD

Baker Signet

ABCDEFGHIJKL BALLÉ INITIALS

BALLOON LIGHT

BALLOON BOLD

BALLOON EXTRA BOLD

Balzac

Bamboo

BANCO

BANK GOTHIC MED.

BANK NOTE ITALIC

Bank Script

P.T. Barnum

Barry Light

Barry Medium

Barry Bold

Basilea

Baskerville

Baskerville Italic

Baskerville BOLD

Baskerville BOLD ITALIC

Bauer Bodoni

Bauer Bodoni ITALIC

Bauer Bodoni BOLD

Bauer Bodoni BOLD ITALIC

Bauer Bodoni EXTRABOLD

Bauer Bodoni EXTRABOLD ITALIC

BAUER BODONI TITLE

Bauer Classic ROMAN

BAUER TEXT INITIALS

Bauer Topic Medium

Bauer Topic Medium ITALIC

Bauer Topic Bold

Bauer Topic Bold ITALIC

Bauhaus Light

Bauhaus Medium

Bauhaus Demi

Bauhaus Bold

Bauhaus Heavy

Bauhaus Heavy Outline

Beads

Bedford

Bedford Bold

Belgian

Bembo

Bembo Italic

Berling Semibold

Bernase Roman

Bernhard Gothic Light

Bernhard Gothic MEDIUM

Bernhard GOTHIC EXTRA HEAVY

Bernhard Tango WITH *Swash* INITIALS

Bernhard Book

Bernhard Roman

Bernhard Italic

Bernhard Modern Roman

Bernhard Modern Italic

Bernhard Modern Bold

Bernhard Modern Bold ITALIC

Bernhard Cursive

Bernhard Cursive Bold

Bessellen

Beton Medium CONDENSED

Beton Bold

Beton Bold CONDENSED

Beton Extra BOLD

Bijou

Billy Beck System 1

Billy Beck System 2

Billy Beck System 3

BILLY BECK SYSTEM 4

Binder Style Bold

Bisque

Blado (Poliphilus Italic)

Bloc

Bodoni Book

Bodoni Book Italic

Bodoni

Bodoni Italic

Bodoni Bold

Bodoni Bold ITALIC

Bodoni Bold CONDENSED

Bodoni Bold Modified

Bodoni Ultra

Bodoni Ultra ITALIC

Bodoni Ultra EXTRA CONDENSED

Bodoni Open

Bolt Bold

Bon Aire

Book Jacket Italic

LSC Book REGULAR ROMAN

LSC Book REGULAR ITALIC

LSC Book BOLD ROMAN

LSC Book BOLD ITALIC

LSC Book EXTRABOLD ROMAN

LSC Book EXTRABOLD ITALIC

173

Bookman Light
Bookman Light Italic
Bookman
Bookman Italic
Bookman Medium
Bookman Medium ITALIC
Bookman Demi
Bookman Demi ITALIC
Bookman Bold
Bookman Bold ITALIC
Bookman Outline
Bookman Contour
Boulevard
Bradley
Bradley Outline
Britannic
Britannic Italic
Britannic Bold
BROADWAY
BROADWAY ENG.
Brody
BRUCE MIKITA
Brush
Bubble Light
Bubble
Bubble Dubble
Bubble Outline
Bubble Shadow

BUFFALO BILL
Bulletin Typewriter
Bulmer
Bulmer Italic
Burgondy Right
BURMESE BLACK
BUSORAMA LIGHT
BUSORAMA MEDIUM
BUSORAMA BOLD
BUSORAMA BOOK
Cactus Light
Cactus Bold
Cactus Extrabold
Cactus Black
Cairo
Cairo Italic
Cairo Medium
Cairo Medium Italic
Cairo Bold
Cairo Bold Italic
Cairo Heavy
Cairo Bold Condensed
Caledonia
Caledonia Italic
Caledonia Bold
Caledonia Bold It.
CALYPSO
Campanile

CANTERBURY INITIALS
CAROLUS ROMAN
CAROLUS ROMAN BOLD
CAROLUS ROMAN OUTLINE
Carpenter
CARTOON BOLD
Caslon Adbold
Caslon Antique
Caslon Antique Italic
Caslon 471 Roman
Caslon 471 Swash Characters
Caslon No. 471 Italic
Caslon No. 540
Caslon No.540 Italic
Caslon No. 641
Caslon, New
Caslon Italic, New
Caslon Bold
Caslon Bold Italic
Caslon Bold Condensed
Caslon Extra Condensed
Caslon Headline
A B C D E F G H CASLON INITIALS
Caslon Old Face
Caslon Old Face Italic
Caslon Old Face 2
Caslon Old Face 2 Italic
Caslon Old Face HEAVY

Caslon Openface

Caslon Shaded

LSC Caslon Light NO. 223

LSC Caslon LIGHT NO. 223 ITALIC

LSC Caslon Reg. NO. 223

LSC Caslon BOLD NO. 223 ITALIC

LSC Caslon EXTRABOLD NO. 223

LSC Caslon EXTRABOLD NO. 223 ITALIC

Catalina

CAXTON INITIALS

CAXTONIAN

CELTIC ORNATE

Centaur

Centaur Italic

CENTAUR TITLING

Centennial Script

Century Book Roman

Century Book Italic

Century Expanded

Century Expanded It.

Century Oldstyle

Century Oldstyle ITALIC

Century Oldstyle BOLD

Century Schoolbook

Century SCHOOLBOOK ITALIC

Century SCHOOLBOOK BOLD

Century Bold

Century Bold Italic

Century Bold Condensed

Century Bold Condensed It.

Century Nova

Century Nova Italic

Century Ultra Roman

Century Ultra Italic

Champion

Charme Light

Charme Bold

Cheltenham Book

Cheltenham Book Italic

Cheltenham Medium

Cheltenham Medium It.

Cheltenham Bold

Cheltenham Bold It.

Cheltenham Bold Condensed

Cheltenham Bold Cond. It.

Cheltenham Bold Extra Cond.

Cheltenham BOLD EXTENDED

Cheltenham Bold Open

Cheltenham Ultra ROMAN

Cheltenham Ultra ITALIC

Cheltenham Old Style

Cheltenham Old Style Cond.

CHEQUE

Chester Cursive

Chevalter

CHINA

Chisel

Chisel EXPANDED

CICERO

Cigno

City Light

City Medium

City Bold

Civilite

Clarendon Regular

Clarendon Medium

Clarendon Semi BOLD

Clarendon Bold

Claudius

Clearface Bold

Clearface Extra BOLD

Clearface Extra BOLD ITALIC

Cloister Old Style

Cloister Roman

Cloister Italic

Cloister Bold

Cloister Bold Italic

Cloister Black

 CLOISTER INITIALS

Cochin Old Style NO. 61

Codex

Columbia

Columbia Italic & SWASH

Columbia Bold

Columbia Bold It.
Columbia Bold Cond.
Columbus
COLUMNA
COLUMNA (SOLID)
Commercial Script
COMPUTER
COMPUTER OUTLINE
Comstock
LSC Condensed
LSC Condensed Italic
CONDENSED TITLE GOTHIC NO.11
Congress
Consort
ABCDEFGHI CONSTANZE INITIALS
Contact Bold Condensed
Contact Bold Condensed It.
Contempo
Contempo Bold
Continental
Continental Italic
Continental Black
Contura
Cooper Old Style
Cooper Old Style Italic
Cooper Black
Cooper Black It.
Cooper Black Cond.

Cooper Black CONDENSED OUTLINE
COPPERPLATE GOTHIC LIGHT
CORNBALL
Coronet
Corona
Corona Italic
Corvina Black
Corvinus Skyline
Corvinus Medium
Corvinus Medium ITALIC
Corvinus Bold
Craw Clarendon
Craw Clarendon BOOK
Craw Clarendon Cond.
Craw Modern
Craw Modern It.
Craw Modern BOLD
Crayon
Crayonette
CRISTAL
CRT Gothic Light Roman
CRT Gothic Medium Roman
CRT Gothic Bold Roman
CRT Gothic Black ROMAN
Daisyland
DAVIDA BOLD
Deepdene
Deepdene Italic

DELPHIAN
Delphin No. 1
Delphin No. 2
Delta Medium
Delta Medium Italic
Delta Bold
Derby
De Roos Roman
De Roos Italic
De Roos Semibold
DE ROOS INLINE INITIALS
DEUTSCH BLACK
DEUTSCH BLACK OPEN
Didi
Discus
Discus Semibold
Dom Casual
Dom Diagonal
Dom Bold
Dominante
Dominante Italic
Dominante Bold
Domino
Domning Antiqua
DRESDEN
DUO SOLID
DUO OUTLINE
DUTCH INITIALS

176

Dynamic

Edrik

Egiziano

Egizio Roman Med.

Egizio Italic Med.

Egizio Medium Condensed

Egizio Bold

Egizio Bold Italic

Egmont Light

Egmont Light Italic

Egmont Medium

Egmont Medium Italic

Egmont Bold

Egmont Bold Italic

EGYPTIAN

Egyptian 505 LIGHT

Egyptian 505

Egyptian 505 MED.

Egyptian 505 BOLD

Egyptian 505 OUTLINE

Egyptian Bold CONDENSED

Egyptian BOLD EXTENDED

Egypt EGYPTIAN EXPANDED OPEN

Eight Ball

Eight Ball Open

Electra

Electra Italic

Electra Cursive

Electra Bold

Electra Bold Cursive

Elizabeth Roman

Elzevir

Elzevir Italic

Emphasis Italic

Enge Etienne

Engravers Old English

ENGRAVERS ROMAN

Engravers Text

ERASMUS Initial Series 1

ERASMUS Initial Series 2

ERBAR INITIALS

Erbar Light Condensed

Erbar Bold Condensed

Estro

Eurostile

Eurostile EXTENDED

Eurostile Bold

Eurostile Bold Condensed

Eurostile BOLD EXTENDED

Eurostile BOLD EXTENDED OUTLINE

Eve

Eve Italic

Eve Bold

Eve Bold Italic

Eve Heavy

Excelsior Script

Excelsior Script Semi Bold

Exempla

Fairfield

Fairfield Italic

Fairfield Medium

Fairfield Medium Italic

Fancy Celtic

Fantail

FARGO

Fat Face

Firenze

Firmin Didot Roman

Firmin Didot Italic

Firmin Didot Bold

Flex

Flirt

Florentine

Florentine Cursive

FLORIATED CAPITALS

Folio Light

Folio Medium

Folio Medium EXTENDED

Folio MEDIUM EXTENDED ITALIC

Folio Bold

Folio Bold Condensed

Folio Bold EXTENDED

Folio Extrabold

Folio Extra BOLD OUTLINE

Folkwang

FONTANESI

Fortuna Light

Fortuna Bold

Fortuna Bold It.

Fortuna EXTRABOLD

FORUM I

FORUM II

Fox

Fraktur (GERMAN TEXT)

Franklin Gothic

Franklin Gothic It.

Franklin Gothic Cond.

Franklin Gothic Cond. It.

Franklin Gothic Extra Cond.

Franklin GOTHIC WIDE

Freehand

FRENCH FLASH

Friz Quadrata

Friz Quadrata Medium

Friz Quadrata DEMI BOLD

Friz Quadrata Bold

FRY'S ORNAMENTED

Futura Light

Futura Light Oblique

Futura Book

Futura Medium

Futura Medium Oblique

Futura Medium Condensed

Futura Demibold

Futura Demibold OBLIQUE

Futura Bold

Futura Bold OBLIQUE

Futura Bold Condensed

Futura Bold Condensed OBLIQUE

Futura Extra BOLD

Futura Extra BOLD OBLIQUE

Futura Extra Bold COND.

Futura Extra Bold COND. OBLIQUE

Futura Black

Futura Display

FUTURA INLINE

GALLIA

Garamond Old Style

Garamond Old Style Italic

Garamond Bold

Garamond Bold Italic

Garamond Book Roman

Garamond Book Italic

Garamond Ultra Roman

Garamond Ultra Italic

GARDENIA

Gavotte

Gazelle

Germain

Gerstner Program Light

Gerstner Program LIGHT OBLIQUE

Gerstner Program LIGHT EXPANDED

Gerstner Program MEDIUM

Gerstner Program MEDIUM OBLIQUE

Gerstner Program MEDIUM CONDENSED

GerstnerProgram MEDIUM EXPANDED

Gerstner Program SEMIBOLD

Gerstner Program SEMIBOLD OBLIQUE

Gerstner Program SEMIBOLD EXPANDED

Gerstner Program BOLD

Gerstner Program BOLD OBLIQUE

GerstnerProgram BOLD EXPANDED

Gill Sans Light

Gill Sans Light Italic

Gill Sans

Gill Sans Italic

Gill Sans Bold

Gill Sans Bold Italic

Gill Sans Bold Cond.

Gill Sans Bold Extra Condensed

Gill Sans Extra BOLD

Gill Sans Ultra BOLD

Gillies Gothic Bold

GIORGIO

GIORGIO OUTLINE

Girder Heavy

Glenn

GLYPHIC SERIES

GLYPHIC SERIES ITALIC

GLYPHIC SERIES BACKSLANT

GLYPHIC SERIES COND.

GLYPHIC SERIES OUTLINE

GLYPHIC SERIES OUTLINE ITALIC

GLYPHIC SERIES OUTLINE CONDENSED

GOLD RUSH

Goodger Pointy

Gorilla

GOTHIC OUTLINE TITLE NO. 61

Gotina

Goudy Old Style

Goudy Old Style Italic

Goudy Catalogue

Goudy Cursive

Goudy Bold

Goudy Bold Italic

Goudy Extra Bold

Goudy HEAVYFACE

Goudy HEAVYFACE ITALIC

Goudy Heavyface CONDENSED

Goudy Handtooled

Goudy Mediaeval

Goudy Text

Goudy Thirty

GOUDY TITLE

Granjon

Granjon Italic

Granjon Bold

GRAPHIQUE

GRECIAN BOLD

Grizzly

Grotesque No. 6

Grotesque No. 8

Grotesque No. 9

Grotesque No. 9 Italic

Grotesque No. 18

Grotesque NO. 66

Grouch

HADRIANO STONECUT

Hallo Italic

Harry Thin

Harry Plain

Harry Heavy

Harry Fat

Harry Obese

Harry Obese Squeezed

Hellenic WIDE

Helvetica Light

Helvetica Light Italic

Helvetica Thin

Helvetica

Helvetica Italic

Helvetica Italic Out.

Helvetica Regular Cond.

Helvetica Reg. EXTENDED

Helvetica Medium

Helvetica Medium ITALIC

Helvetica Medium OUTLINE

Helvetica Bold

Helvetica Bold COMPACT ITALIC

Helvetica Bold Out.

Helvetica Bold Condensed

Helvetica Bold Cond. Out.

Helvetica Bold EXTENDED

Helvetica Extrabold Cond.

Helvetica Extrabold CONDENSED OUTLINE

Helvetica EXTRABOLD EXTENDED

Helvetica Compressed

Helvetica Extra Compressed

Helvetica Ultra Compressed

HELVIN

HELVIN BLACK

Heritage

Herold Condensed

HESS NEOBOLD

HIDALGO

Hobo

Hogarth

Holla

Holland Seminar

Holland Seminar Italic

Honda

HOPKINS·WOOD

Horizon Light

Horizon Light Italic

Horizon Medium

Horizon Bold

Horizon Bold Condensed

Houghton

Howland Open

Huit Light

Huit Medium

Huit Medium Italic

Huit Bold

Impact

INFORMAL GOTHIC

Information

Ingrid

Inserat Grotesk

Inverserif Light

Inverserif Light Italic

Inverserif Regular

Inverserif Regular Italic

Inverserif Heavy

***Inverserif* HEAVY ITALIC**

Inverserif Condensed

***Inverserif* CONDENSED ITALIC**

IVY LEAGUE

IVY LEAGUE OPEN

Ionic 1

Jana

Janson

Janson Italic

Japanette

Jay Gothic Light

Jay Gothic

Jay Gothic Bold

Jay Gothic Extrabold

Jay Gothic Outline

JIM CROW

Kabel Light

Kabel Medium

Kabel Bold

Kabel Bold Condensed

Kabel Heavy

Kabel Stencil

Kabel Stencil Heavy

Kalina Light

Kalina Light Italic

Kalina Medium

KALINA Medium cond.

Kalina Bold

Kalina Bold Italic

KALINA Openface

Kap-Antiqua Light

Kap-Antiqua Italic

Kap-Antiqua Standard

Kap-Antiqua Bold

Kap-Antiqua EXTENDED

Karen

Karen Bold

Karen Extrabold

Karen Extrabold CONDENSED

Karen EXTRABOLD EXPANDED

Karen Black

Karen Black EXPANDED

Karen Black Condensed

Karnac

Karnak Black Condensed

Karnak Black Condensed It.

Karolys Romain

Karolys Italique

Kaufmann Script

Kaufmann Bold

Keller Antiqua Light

Keller Antiqua Outline

Kennerley Oldstyle

Kennerley Oldstyle Italic

Kennerley Bold

Kennerley Bold Italic

Kismet

Kompakt

Korinna

Korinna Bold

Korinna Extra Bold

Korinna Heavy

Korinna Outline

L&C Hairline

Lafayette

LANEFIXT

LARGO LIGHT

LARGO BOLD

LARGO EXTRABOLD

LARGO OPEN

Lariat

Latin Elongated

Latin Bold

Latin Bold Condensed

Latin Wide

LAVINIA
Lee
Lee Italic
Lee Bold
Legend
LEXINGTON
Liberty
LIBRA
Lightline Gothic
Lilith
LINCOLN GOTHIC
Lisbon
Lisbon Italic
Litho Light Roman
LITZENBURG
ABCDEFGh LOMBARDIC INITIALS
Lubalin Graph EXTRA LIGHT
Lubalin Graph Book
Lubalin Graph MEDIUM
Lubalin Graph DEMI
Lubalin Graph Bold
Lucian
Lucian Bold
Lydian
Lydian Italic
Lydian Bold
Lydian Bold Italic
Lydian Bold Condensed
Lydian Bold Condensed Italic

Lydian Cursive
MACHINE
MACHINE BOLD
Mademoiselle
MADISON
Makart
MANDARIN
Mandate
ISC Manhattan
Manila
MARBLEHEART
Markus Roman
Maxime
MAXIMUS
mediator
Melior
Melior Italic
Melior Semibold
Melior Semibold ITALIC
Melior Semibold OUTLINE
Melior Bold
Melior Bold Cond.
Melior Bold Outline
Memphis Light
Memphis Light Italic
Memphis Medium
Memphis Medium Italic
Memphis Medium Condensed
Memphis Bold

Memphis Bold Italic
Memphis Bold Condensed
Memphis Extrabold
Memphis Extrabold Italic
Memphis Extra Bold Condensed
Meridien Light
Meridien Medium
Meridien Bold
Meridien EXTRABOLD
Meridien Black
Metrothin 2
Metrolite 2
Metromedium 2
Metroblack 2
Metropolis Bold
MICHELANGELO
MICROGRAMMA NORMAL
MICROGRAMMA CONDENSED
MICROGRAM MICROGRAMMA EXTENDED
MICROGRAMMA BOLD
MICROGRA MICROGRAMMA BOLD EXTENDED
Microstyle
Microstyle Bold
Microstyle EXTENDED
Microstyle BOLD EXTENDED
Milano Roman
Mistral
Modern No. 20
Modern No. 20 Italic

181

Modula
Modula Medium
Modula Bold
Modula Extra Bold
MOLE FOLIATE
MONASTIC
Monogram
Monogram Stencil
Moon Light
Moon Medium
Moon Bold
Moon Black
Moore Combo
MOORE COMPUTER
MOORE LIBERTY
Moore Swash for TIMES ROMAN BOLD
MOSAIK
Murray Hill Bold
Neil Bold
Neil Bold Open
NEON
NEULAND OUTLINE NO. 1
NEULAND OUTLINE NO. 2
NEULAND INLINE
NEULAND
NEULAND BLACK
Nevison Casual
News Gothic
News Gothic Condensed

News Gothic Extra Condensed
News Gothic Bold
Newtext Light
Newtext Light Italic
Newtext Book
Newtext Book Italic
Newtext Regular
Newtext Regular Italic
Newtext Demi
Newtext Demi Italic
Nicolini Broadpen
Nobel Light
Nobel Light Italic
Nordia Light
Nordia Medium
Nordia Bold
Normal Grotesk Demibold
Normal Grotesk BOLD
Normande
Normande Italic
Normande Condensed
Normande Cond. Outline
Normandia OPEN
Nova Augustea
Nubian
Nymphic with Swash Caps
OCTIC EXTENDED
OLD BOWERY
Old English

Old Gothic Bold ITALIC
Old Town No. 536
Olden
Olive Antique
Olive Antique Italic
Olive Antique Narrow
Olive Antique Med.
Olive Antique BOLD
Olive Antique BLACK
Olive Ant. BLACK EXTENDED
Olive Ant. BLACK EXTENDED ITALIC
OLYMPIC
Ondine
Onyx
Onyx Italic
OPEN ROMAN CAPITALS
Optima
Optima Italic
Optima Semibold
Optima Semibold It.
Optima Semibold OUTLINE
Optima Bold
Orbit-B
Orbit-B Outline
Orbit-B Out. Shadow
ORCANDA LIGHT
ORCANDA
ORCANDA BOLD
Orion Roman

Orion Italic

ORLEANS OPEN

Ornata

Orpheus Roman

Orpheus Italic

Orpheus Bold

ORPLID

Oscar

Outline Gothic Condensed

ABCDEFG PAGEANT INITIALS

Palatino

Palatino Italic

Palatino Semibold

Palatino Semibold OUTLINE

Palatino Bold

Pamela

Pantagraph

Parisian

Park Avenue

Pascal

Patricia Bold

Peak

PEIGNOT LIGHT

PEIGNOT DEMI BOLD

PEIGNOT BOLD

Pekin

Permanent

Permanent Medium

Permanent MEDIUM EXTENDED

Permanent Bold

Permanent Headline with LOWER CASE

Permanent Headline Italic

Permanent Headline Open with LOWER CASE

Permanent Massiv

PERPETUA TITLING LIGHT

Perpetua Roman

Perpetua Italic

PERPETUA TITLING MEDIUM

Perpetua Bold

Perpetua Bold It.

PERPETUA TITLING BOLD

Perpetua EXTRA BOLD

Perpetua Black

Phidian

PIONEER

PISA

Pistilli Roman

Pistilli Roman BOLD

Pistilli Roman BLACK

Pistilli OPEN NO. 1

Pistilli OPEN NO. 2

Plantin Light

Plantin Light Italic

Plantin

Plantin Italic

Plantin Bold

Plantin Bold Italic

Plantin Bold Condensed

Plantin Bold Cond. Out.

PLANTIN TITLING

Playbill

Plymouth

POINTILLE

POLIPHILUS TITLING

Post Italic

Post Mediaeval Lt.

Post Mediaeval Lt ITALIC with SWING CAPS

Post Mediaeval Med.

Post Roman Light

Post Roman Medium

Post Roman Bold

Post Roman EXTRA BOLD

Post Roman OLDSTYLE NO. 2

Post Oldstyle Italic

Post Oldstyle Condensed

Précis Medium

Précis Bold

Précis Slim

Précis Extended

Primer

Primer Italic

Primus

PRISMA

PROFILE

PUBLICITY GOTHIC

Quill

Radiant Medium

183

Radiant Bold	ROMANTIQUE NO. 4 (DANDY)	*Sans Serifs Italic, Condensed*
Radiant Bold Condensed	ROMANTIQUE NO. 5 (BRACELET)	**SANS SERIFS NO. 1,** CONDENSED
Radiant Bold Extra Condensed	Ronda Light	**San Serifs No. 6, Condensed**
Radiant Heavy	Ronda	Sans Serifs No. 7, Condensed
ABCDEFGH RAFFIA INITIALS	**Ronda Bold**	Sans Serifs No. 12, Condensed
RAILROAD GOTHIC	Rondo Bold	SANS SERIFS, ELONGATED
Recherche	Ronsard Crystal	SANS SERIF LINED
Regal 1	Roslyn Gothic Medium	SANS SERIFS SHADED
Regal 1 Bold	**Roslyn Gothic Bold**	SAPPHIRE
REGINA	Roslyn Gothic Outline	Satellite
Reiner Black	Royal	**Satellite Bold**
Reiner Script	*Rusinal* (CURSIVA)	Scandor Thin
RELIEF	Russell Square Extralight	Scandor Norm
Renaissant	*Russell Square* EXTRA LIGHT ITALIC	Schadow Antiqua
Rhapsodie with Initials	Russell Square Light	*Schadow Antiqua* ITALIC
RICCARDO	*Russell Square Light* ITALIC	**Schadow Ant.** BOLD
Ringlet	Russell Square	**Schadow Ant.** SEMIBOLD
Rococo	*Russell Square Italic*	**Schadow Antiqua** BOLD CONDENSED
Rodin	Russell Square Bold	Schadow Werk
Rodin Italic	**Russell Square** EXTRA BOLD	SCOT GOTHIC
Rodin Condensed	RUSTIC	Scotch 2 Roman [9]
Rodin Extended	Rustikalis Light	*Scotch 2 Italic* [9]
Roman Compressed No. 3	Rustikalis Semibold	SCOTFORD UNCIAL
ROMAN SHADED ELONGATED	**Rustikalis Bold**	Serif Gothic Light
Romana Normal	**Rustikalis Black**	Serif Gothic Regular
Romana Bold	Rustikalis MODERNIZED GOTHIC	Serif Gothic Bold
ROMANTIQUE NO. 1 (CARNET de BAL)	St. Clair	Serif Gothic Extra Bold
ROMANTIQUE NO. 2 (CARNIVAL)	Salto	**Serif Gothic Heavy**
ROMANTIQUE NO. 3 (HARMONY)	**Samson**	**Serif Gothic Black**

Serif Gothic Open Bold	Solitaire Thin	stan control NO. 3
Serpentine Light	Solitaire	stan compr COMPROMISE NO. 1
Serpentine MEDIUM	Solitaire Bold	stan compr COMPROMISE NO. 2
Serpentine BOLD	Solon Antiqua Light	Stan Conform
Serpentine ITALIC	Solon Antiqua Normal	stan free
SHADOW	Solon Antiqua Semibold	Standard Extra LIGHT EXTENDED
SHOTGUN	Solon Antiqua Bold	Standard Light
SHOTGUN DOUBLE BARREL	Soul Light	Standard Light EXTENDED
SHOTGUN LOADED	Soul Medium	Standard
SHOTGUN BLANKS	Soul Bold	Standard Condensed
Signal Medium	Soul Open	Standard EXTENDED
Signum	SOUTACHE	Standard Medium
SIMPLEX	SOUTHERN CROSS	Standard Medium Condensed
sintex 1	Souvenir Light	Standard Bold
sintex outline	Souvenir Light Italic	Standard Bold Condensed
SISTINA TITLING	Souvenir Med.	Standard Extrabold Cond.
Skin & Bones	Souvenir Medium It.	Standard EXTRABOLD EXTENDED
Skjald	Souvenir Demi	Stark Debonair
Skylark	Souvenir Demi It.	Stark Debonair Monobold
Slenderella	Souvenir Bold	Stark Debonair Semibold
Slenderella Refined	Souvenir Bold ITALIC	Stationers Semiscript
Slogan	Souvenir Outline BOLD	STEELPLATE GOTHIC BOLD
Smoke	Spazio Light	STENCIL
Snell Roundhand	Spazio Medium	STEPHEN ORNATE
Sol Thin	Spazio Black	Stettler
Sol Plain	Spazio Deep Black	Stop
Sol Heavy	Spazio Outline	Stradivarius
Sol Fat	Stan Control No.1	STREAMLINE
SOLEMNIS	stan control NO.2	STRIDON

Studio
Studio Bold
Stylescript
L&C Stymie Hairline
Stymie Light
Stymie Medium
Stymie Bold
Stymie Extra Bold
Stymie Obelisk Medium Condensed
STYMIE OPEN
STYMIE OPEN COND.
SUMMER
SUPERBA ILLUSTRA
Syntax
Syntax Bold
Syntax Ultrabold
Tangier
Tarantella
Tavern
TEA CHEST
Tempo Heavy Condensed
Tempo Black
Tempo Black Cond.
Textype
Textype Italic
Textype Bold
Textype Bold Italic
T.H. ALPHABET SOUP
T.H. Grandee

T.H. Grandee Swash
TH TUBE
T. H. UNCLE SAM
Thompson Quillscript
THOR
Thorowgood ROMAN
Thorowgood ITALIC
THUN THUNDERBIRD
THUNDERBIRD EXTRA CONDENSED
Tiffany Light
Tiffany Medium
Tiffany Demi
Tiffany Heavy
Time Script
Time Script Semibold
Time Script Bold
Times Roman
Times Italic
Times New Roman SEMIBOLD
Times Roman Bold
Times Roman Bold ITALIC
Times Bold MODIFIED NO. 1
Times Bold MODIFIED NO. 2
Times Roman Black
TIMES TITLING
TIMES HEAVY TITLING
TIMES EX EXTENDED TITLING
TITLE GOTHIC EXTRA CONDENSED NO. 12
Tom's Roman

TOO MUCH CLEAR
TOO MUCH SHADOW
TOO MUCH OPAQUE
Torino Roman
Torino Italic
Tower
Trafton Script
Trajanus
Trajanus Italic
Trajanus Semibold
Treasury Open
TROCADERO
Trooper Roman Light
Trooper Roman Light ITALIC
Trooper Roman
Trooper Roman Italic
Trooper Roman Bold
Trooper Roman EXTRABOLD
Trooper Roman Black
Trooper Grotesque
TRUMP GRAVUR
Trump Mediaeval
Trump Mediaeval ITALIC
Trump Mediaeval SEMI BOLD
Trump Mediaeval SEMIBOLD COND
Trump MEDIAEVAL BOLD
Trump MEDIAEVAL BOLD ITALIC
TRYLON SHADED
TRYLON SHADED OBLIQUE

186

TUSCAN GRAILLE
Typo Roman Light
Typo Roman
Typo Roman Shaded
Typo Shaded
Typo Upright
Typo Upright Bold
Typo Script
Typo Script EXTENDED
Typo Text
UMBRA
Union Pearl
Univers 39
Univers 45
Univers 46
Univers 47
Univers 48
Univers 49
Univers 53
Univers 53 Outline
Univers 55
Univers 55 Outline
Univers 56
Univers 57
Univers 57 Outline
Univers 58
Univers 58 Outline
Univers 59
Univers 59 Outline

Univers 63
Univers 65
Univers 65 Outline
Univers 66
Univers 66 Outline
Univers 67
Univers 67 Outline
Univers 68
Univers 68 Outline
Univers 73
Univers 73 Out.
Univers 75
Univers 75 Outline
Univers 76
Univers 76 Outline
Univers 83
Univers 83 Out.
Upright Neon
Upright Regular
Velve'
Vendome
Vendome Italic
Vendome Bold
Venture
Venus Light
Venus Light Italic
Venus Light Condensed
Venus Medium
Venus Medium Italic

Venus Medium EXTENDED
Venus Bold
Venus Bold Italic
Venus Bold Condensed
Venus Bold EXTENDED
Venus Extrabold
Venus Extrabold Condensed
Venus EXTRABOLD EXTENDED
Vero Block
Vero Block Medium
Vero Semi Block
Vero New Antiqua
Vero Fat Antiqua
Vero Tall Antiqua
Vero Italiano
Vero Square
Vineta
Vineta Italic
Vineta Open
Vineta OPEN ITALIC
Vineta Narrow
Vineta NARROW ITALIC
Vineta NARROW OPEN
Vineta NARROW OPEN ITALIC
Vineta MIDDLE
Vineta MIDDLE ITALIC
Vineta MIDDLE OPEN
Vineta MIDDLE OPEN ITALIC
Vineta 70

Vineta 70 ITALIC
VINETA ORNAMENT
Vintage
Virtuoso 1
Virtuoso 2
Visa
Vivaldi
Vladimir
Vladimir Bold
Vladimir Cond.
Vladimir Bold Cond.
Vogue
Vogue Oblique
Vogue Bold
Vogue Bold Oblique
Vogue Extrabold
Vogue Extrabold Oblique

Vogue Condensed
Vogue Bold Condensed
Walbaum
Walbaum Italic
Walbaum Medium
Wedding Text
Weiss Roman
Weiss Italic with REGULAR & SWASH CAPS
Weiss Roman Bold
Weiss Roman Extra BOLD
WEISS INITIALS SERIES I
WEISS INITIALS SERIES II
WEISS INITIALS SERIES III
Wexford
Wexford Medium
Wexford Bold
Wexford Ultra Bold

Whedons Gothic Outline
Whitin Black
Whitin Black Cond.
Whitin Black Cond. OUTLINE
Willow
Windsor Light Condensed
Windsor Elongated
Windsor
Windsor Outline
Windsor Heavy CONDENSED
WINTER
Wolf Antiqua
York
York Bold
York Black
ZEBRA

COMPOSITION 6

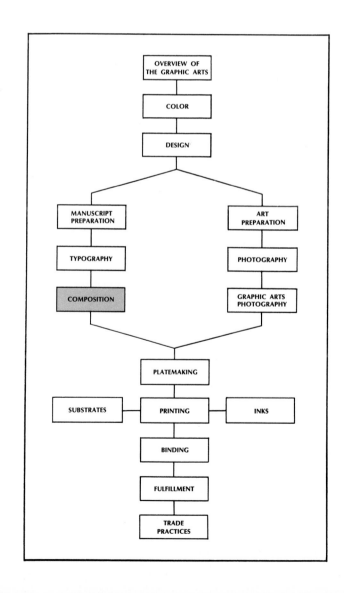

THE COMPOSITION PROCESS
Paul D. Doebler, PUBLISHING MANAGEMENT CONSULTANT

Composition is the process of converting words into type and arranging the type into pages along with various illustrative materials. Thus the composition stage is the point at which the elements of a printed piece converge prior to printing. Typesetting technology—the machinery and methods used to assemble type characters into lines and columns of typeset matter—is only part of the composition process. Many additional operations are involved: proofreading, correcting of typeset material, makeup of pages and forms, and a substantial amount of handling of materials in and out of storage. All of these operations require a great deal of manual effort despite the use of sophisticated typesetting machinery, and composition is therefore one of the most sensitive, complex, and error-prone areas in the graphic arts.

EVOLUTION OF COMPOSITION TECHNOLOGY

The composition process is older than printing itself, if one considers hand-lettered scrolls, manuscripts, and illuminated books to have been "composed" by the artisans who produced them. However, composition first appeared as a separate and distinct series of operations in the production of graphic works with the advent of composition technology, beginning with the invention of movable type in the early 1400's, probably in Holland. Capitalizing on earlier efforts, Johannes Gutenberg, in the 1440's in Germany, perfected the process of casting individual metal type characters from brass molds and thus became known as the principal inventor of movable type. Before then, the procedure of assembling graphic images had been performed by artisans who crafted each image individually. The separate technology of typesetting permitted non-artisans to convert the writings of authors into high-quality graphic presentations through the mechanical operations of assembling mass-produced, predetermined images in proper sequence.

This initial technology of composition, the hand assembly or *hand setting* of individual metal type characters, remained fundamentally unchanged for almost 400 years. Then, in the midst of the Industrial Revolution, inventors finally created typesetting machinery which began to automate and speed up parts of the composition process. In the 1880's the Linotype appeared, followed in the 1890's by the Monotype and other auxiliary devices for producing set type. These machines all cast new type from brass character molds on command from their operators, eliminating the *distribution* operation required in hand setting. It was no longer necessary to use precast metal type which had to be disassembled after every use and redistributed into the cases in which it was held. The machine-produced type was simply melted down after printing, and the metal was reused in the typesetting machines to cast new type for the next job. The Linotype and Monotype used keyboard-operated mechanisms to select the brass character molds for casting the new type, greatly speeding the process of assembling characters into proper sequence.

A second kind of typesetting technology, the *impact* or *strike-on* method, also had its beginning in the mid-1800's when the typewriter was invented. This method of composing characters into lines and pages was generally thought of as a transcription process rather than a typesetting method until the middle of this century. However, with the development of inexpensive offset duplicating machinery for use in offices, as well as improvements in the quality of typed images, strike-on composition became widely used for many kinds of economy-grade printed products such as reports, manuals, advertising flyers, booklets, and even some books. The equipment is much less costly and easier to operate than metal typesetting machinery.

These first mechanized typesetting systems established two fundamental directions in technological development which continue even today and are chiefly responsible for the current reshaping of the composition process. One of these directions is the automated assembly of type images (and eventually graphics such as halftones and line illustrations) into lines, columns, and pages. The second is the mechanization of preparatory functions in the composition process to speed their performance or to eliminate redundant operations altogether.

After the development of typecasting machines such as the Linotype and Monotype, the technology of image assembly took its next major leap forward with the introduction of photographic projection systems which placed characters in position on photographic film or paper, rather than casting them in metal. The first phototypesetting machines were introduced in the 1940's, and today phototypesetting is rapidly replacing metal typesetting, as well as impinging on strike-on. However, metal and strike-on typesetting still account for a great deal of composition work and will continue to be used for years to come.

The chief advantages of phototypesetting over metal and strike-on typesetting are two: the ability of photographic equipment to project images of various sizes precisely in position in a page or other area to be made up, and the ability of such equipment to operate at high speeds directed by electronic signals from computer-based systems. Given appropriately organized electronic signals from a computer system, today's most modern phototypesetting machinery can produce a completely typeset page automatically in a matter of minutes. Metal composition, on the other hand, is inherently limited to the machine production of lines and columns of type which must then be assembled by hand into made-up pages. Strike-on typesetting is similarly limited, and in addition cannot produce the superior quality images offered by phototypesetting.

190

The growth of phototypesetting has been heavily dependent on developments in the second area of technological evolution—the mechanization of preparatory functions—which permitted the required electronic command signals to be encoded and recorded prior to typesetting. The operation of typesetting machines from coded commands actually began in the Monotype system, which employed a punched paper ribbon to link two separate machines. A *keyboard unit* was used to produce the punched tape; as the operator struck the keys, a set of punches produced rows of holes in the tape. When mounted on the *casting unit*, the tape was fed through a sensing device which determined which characters were to be cast by "reading" the various combinations of holes in the tape. This separation of keyboard from typesetting machine proper was later applied to the Linotype through development of the Teletypesetter (TTS) system, to some strike-on typesetting systems, and to most photographic typesetting systems. Over the years, the use of two separate units has permitted keyboarding and the actual setting of type to proceed at their own optimum speeds, unhindered by delays which one part of the process may impose on the other.

With the advent of the computer in typesetting in 1964, the split between keyboarding and typesetting operations became much more important. The computer began to take over routine tasks formerly performed by the keyboard operator, such as determining line endings and hyphenation points within words, insertion of strings of instruction codes on command from a single keystroke by the operator, and the merging, deleting, and positioning of material on command from the operator working at a keyboard. Computerizing such functions reduced the amount of work the keyboard operator had to perform and made it much more economical to prepare the instruction sets for producing completely typeset pages from phototypesetting machines.

These developments have been only a prelude, however, to even more radical changes which are now emerging in composition procedures. In addition to automating and speeding keyboarding operations, computer-based technology has also made it possible to mechanize heretofore manual operations such as correcting errors and arranging type into pages. In addition, time-honored sequences of composition operations can now be changed to eliminate redundant handling of material at various stages of the process.

From the 1400's until the early 1960's technological development in composition was concentrated almost exclusively in the areas of typesetting and the preparatory function of keyboarding characters into lines and copy blocks. In recent years, however, the application of sophisticated technology has spilled over into every operation in the process, causing the most fundamental change in composition since the invention of movable type.

BASIC COMPOSITION PROCESS

While new composition techniques have evolved to match new technologies, the basic composition process has remained essentially unchanged. In the first step of the process, type characters are assembled into proper sequences of words, sentences, and paragraphs. The character string is then broken into segments of the proper length to form type lines when set in a particular type font and to a specified line length or *measure*. Columns of type are formed from the lines when the depth of each line is specified and the type is set accordingly. Finally, in *page makeup*, type lines and columns are assembled into pages by placing them in position in an area the size of the page and anchoring them in some manner. During this phase, decorative and illustrative elements such as rules, ornaments, halftones, and line illustrations are also positioned in the page with the type.

Often, more than one function is combined into a single operation. For example, characters may be typed into a typesetting machine in correct sequence until enough have been assembled to fill a line; at that point an end-of-line function is performed before the next line of characters is typed. The typesetting machine will produce a running column of type as it sets the lines because the appropriate line depth was programmed into the system before keyboarding was begun. Thus the first three phases of the process are accomplished at one time. However, as composition technology has developed in recent years, particularly with the use of computers to perform some functions automatically, the trend has been toward splitting functions apart and performing them in discrete steps.

Composition would be a relatively straightforward process if it were not for the fact that virtually every step is error-prone. Despite the development of highly sophisticated technology, the key operations in composition today remain essentially manual processes which are susceptible to human oversight or misinterpretation. Because of this, the composition process also includes a great deal of checking, verification, and correction, which also are essentially manual operations subject to error themselves. Checking or proofreading operations and accompanying correction operations are performed after all major stages of assembly. Sometimes several cycles of proofreading and correction are required to eliminate all errors and satisfy the purchaser of the composition job that it has been well designed and well produced. The number of proofreading and correction cycles employed in producing different kinds of work varies greatly. Newspapers, because of time pressures, usually proofread and correct editorial material only once, without checking corrections that are made in the first cycle. Books, on the other hand, are typically proofread by many people—by the composing room proofreaders, by the publisher's editors, by the author—and these people will usually check several revisions. Some of these proofreading and correction operations take relatively little time to perform, but their large number can easily bring the total time spent on them to more than the time spent on any other kind of operation in the composition process. The resulting work flow when correction and revision cycles are included can become very complex. Figure 6.1 illustrates a typical flow which jobs might follow in an average commercial composition shop.

Over the years, this basic process of assembling, proofreading, and correcting in repetitive cycles has

TYPESETTING
DEPARTMENT

PROOFREADING
DEPARTMENT

MAKEUP
DEPARTMENT

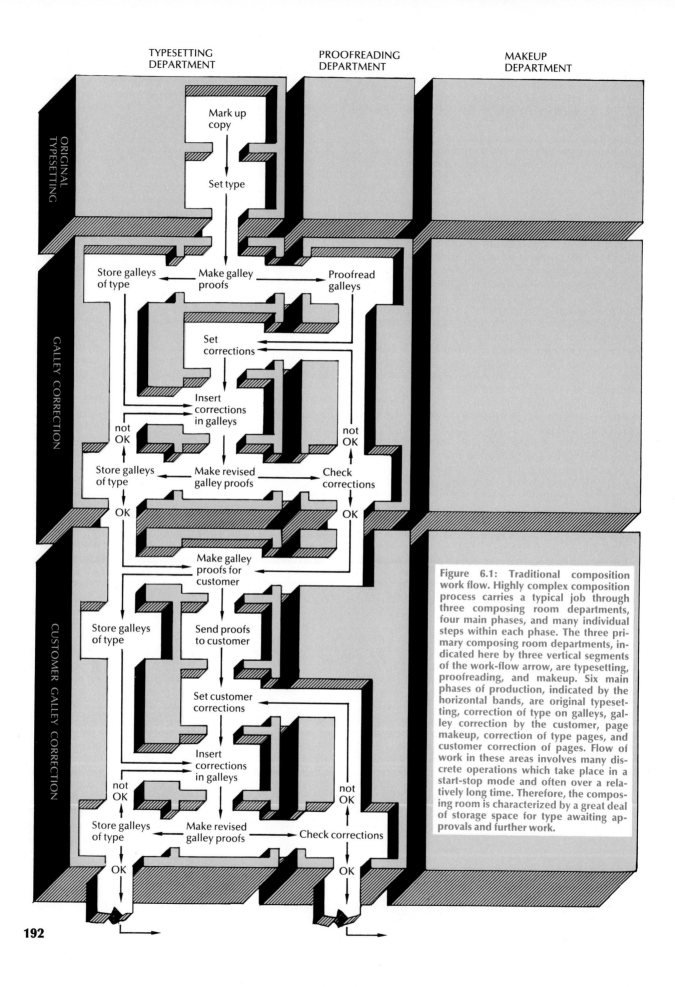

ORIGINAL TYPESETTING

GALLEY CORRECTION

CUSTOMER GALLEY CORRECTION

Mark up copy

Set type

Store galleys of type

Make galley proofs

Proofread galleys

Set corrections

Insert corrections in galleys

not OK

Store galleys of type

Make revised galley proofs

Check corrections

not OK

OK

OK

Make galley proofs for customer

Store galleys of type

Send proofs to customer

Set customer corrections

Insert corrections in galleys

not OK

not OK

Store galleys of type

Make revised galley proofs

Check corrections

OK

OK

Figure 6.1: Traditional composition work flow. Highly complex composition process carries a typical job through three composing room departments, four main phases, and many individual steps within each phase. The three primary composing room departments, indicated here by three vertical segments of the work-flow arrow, are typesetting, proofreading, and makeup. Six main phases of production, indicated by the horizontal bands, are original typesetting, correction of type on galleys, galley correction by the customer, page makeup, correction of type pages, and customer correction of pages. Flow of work in these areas involves many discrete operations which take place in a start-stop mode and often over a relatively long time. Therefore, the composing room is characterized by a great deal of storage space for type awaiting approvals and further work.

192

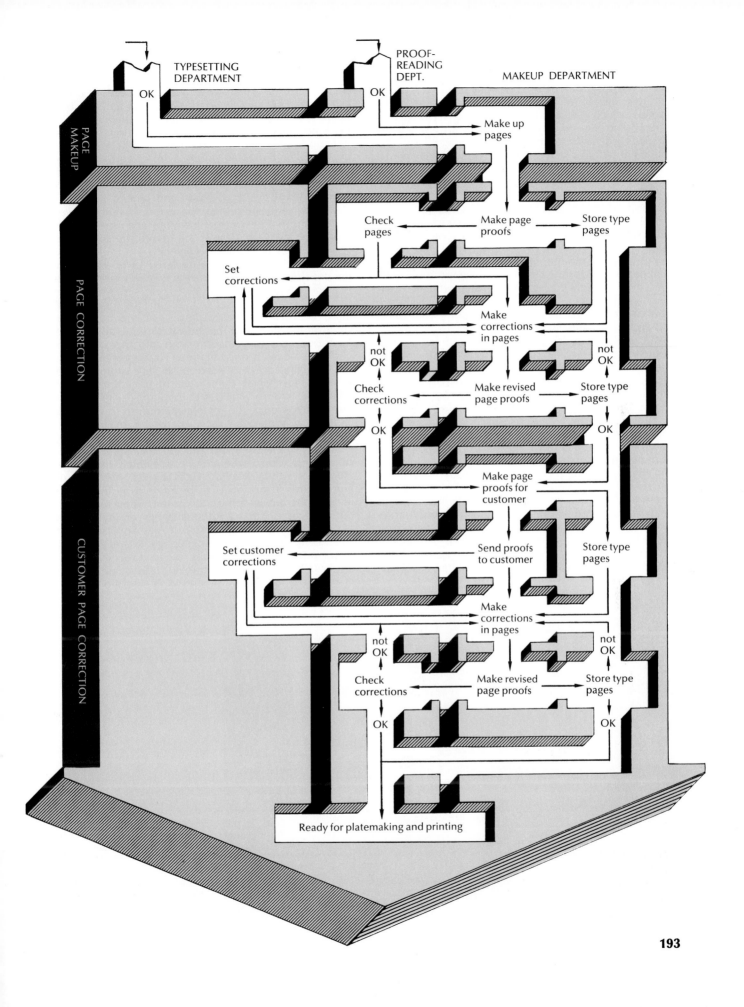

TYPESETTING DEPARTMENT

PROOF-READING DEPT.

MAKEUP DEPARTMENT

PAGE MAKEUP

PAGE CORRECTION

CUSTOMER PAGE CORRECTION

OK

OK

Make up pages

Check pages ← Make page proofs → Store type pages

Set corrections

Make corrections in pages

not OK

not OK

Check corrections ← Make revised page proofs → Store type pages

OK

OK

Make page proofs for customer

Set customer corrections ← Send proofs to customer → Store type pages

Make corrections in pages

not OK

not OK

Check corrections ← Make revised page proofs → Store type pages

OK

OK

Ready for platemaking and printing

taken two traditional forms, based on the kind of type involved. One is the assembly of metal type; the second is the assembly of type on film or paper. Today, with the advent of computerized photocomposition systems which can produce a finished typeset page directly from the typesetting machine, a third process has emerged which permits complete assembly of type while it is still in the form of electronic signals within the computerized system.

COMPOSITION BY METAL CONSTRUCTION

Procedures, techniques, and equipment in metal composition are based on the need to handle heavy metal type. Because metal composition is the oldest process, much of the terminology used throughout the composition field comes from metal composition practices, even though the equipment and products handled are different in other kinds of composition. Figure 6.2 shows a typical metal composing room scene, with its heavy equipment and type.

The repetitive cycles of assembly, proofreading, and correcting are generally divided into two major phases of operations: *typesetting* and *makeup*. Metal composing rooms generally are divided into separate areas for these activities. Within each area, both the original assembly work and the correction work are performed. Proofreading for both these phases, however, is usually separated from the work centers and performed in a *proofroom* equipped with appropriate desks, soundproofing, and reference materials.

In the typesetting phase, incoming copy normally is first reviewed and *marked up* with instructions for the typesetting machine operators. The job is then set, and the type is placed in columns on long, narrow trays called *galleys*. Next, each galley of type is placed on the bed of a *proof press* and a printed copy is made of the column of type. Typically, several such printed *proofs* are made for various uses including proofreading; they are known as *galley proofs*.

After proofreading, during which the proofs are examined to detect errors made in typesetting, they are returned to the typesetting area for correction. If special instructions are required, the proofs are sent back to the mark-up desk before going to the typesetting machine operators; if not, they go directly to the operators, who reset the portions of type with errors in them. The corrected portions are given to a printer, who inserts them in place of the incorrect type in the galleys. In most cases, a new set of galley proofs, called *revised proofs,* is made and sent to the proofroom for verification that the errors have been corrected and that new errors have not been made in the process. If additional errors are found, the correction/verification cycle usually is repeated.

When the type is finally declared to be correct by the proofreaders, a set of *customer* galley proofs often is made for submission to the customer. More often than not, the customer will return the proofs with more changes and corrections, and the correction/verification cycle will be repeated until all changes have been correctly incorporated into the job. If the customer finds an error made in the typesetting process, it is labeled a *printer's error*. If the customer makes other changes which differ from the original copy from which the type was first set, they are designated *author's alterations*; the composition firm is normally entitled to impose an extra charge for making these changes.

The type is next moved into the makeup area of the composing room, where it is assembled into pages along with other elements such as rules, borders, and illustrations. If the job is to be printed by letterpress, illustrations are added at this point. They may be in the form of original photoengravings or in the form of duplicate plates such as stereotypes or plastic plates (see "Letterpress Platemaking," page 381). If the job is to be printed by lithography or gravure, illustrations are usually put in later; however, spaces are inserted in the page for them. To reserve the positions where

Figure 6.2: Composing room for metal composition. Heavy machinery predominates in the metal typesetting process. Here compositors work at Linotype machines casting new type. *Courtesy of Royal Composing Room, Inc.*

Figure 6.3: Composing room for film/paper composition. In contrast with heavy equipment used in metal composing rooms, film/paper composition facilities utilize photographic equipment, drafting and layout tables, and file cabinets. Here a layout/paste-up artist assembles images on pieces of photographic paper into a finished page. *Courtesy of Royal Composing Room, Inc.*

these illustrations will be added and to hold all the other elements in place, *spacing material* is inserted. Spacing material is not as high as the type and other printing elements, so it will not print when put on a press. It usually consists of type metal cast into long rectangular strips of various thicknesses, which are cut into the exact lengths needed to fill in around the printing elements. When finished, the pieces of the made-up page should fit together well enough so that later, after the final correction stages, it can be *locked up*—that is, squeezed tightly on all four sides in a steel frame called a *chase*—and lifted off the working surface in one piece.

The made-up page is then put through a second round of proofing, proofreading, and correcting similar to the cycle for galley proofs, except that the proofs are now called *page proofs*. When the proofreaders have now approved all pages in the job, a set of customer page proofs is made and submitted for approval, after which any corrections or author's alterations (which are again charged for separately) are incorporated through a final round of correction and verification.

At this point, the finished pages may go in one of several directions. If duplicate letterpress plates are to be made, the made-up type and illustrations are sent to the appropriate platemaking department. If letterpress printing is to be done directly from the type, it is locked up by the composing room, along with illustrative materials, into a printing *form*. If printing will be done by lithography or gravure, the composing room makes *reproduction proofs*, often called *repros* for short, from the type. Sometimes other *conversion* methods are used instead to obtain proofs which, like repro proofs, can be photographed for use in photomechanical platemaking.

A form is composed of the type (enclosed in the chase) and additional spacing material called *furniture*, which is made of wood or metal. The type is squeezed or locked into place tightly by means of wedges called *quoins* so that the entire form can be lifted and moved from the composing room to the press. Although other printing methods do not employ actual locked type forms, the term *form* is used throughout the printing industry to denote a complete set of pages or print-

ing images arranged in type or on a printing plate to print one side of a sheet of paper.

Reproduction proofs are produced on a special proof press capable of high-quality reproduction from type and letterpress plates. Actually, repros are very often made from galleys of type as well as made-up pages. When page repros are made, they are sent directly to the camera department for photographic conversion of the images into film negatives. When galley repros are produced, they are sent to an art department (either the customer's or the printer's) where *mechanical artists* or *paste-up personnel* cut out lines and blocks of type and paste them up into finished pages or other arrangements. These *paste-ups* or pieces of *mechanical art* are then sent to the printer's camera department for conversion into negatives. (Assembly of paste-ups and mechanicals is discussed in "Art Production," page 256.)

COMPOSITION BY FILM OR PAPER PASTE-UP

With photocomposition and strike-on typesetting methods, type is set directly on paper or on film, and makeup consists of pasting or stripping elements together. As in metal composition, the basic assembly, proofreading, and correcting operations are organized within typesetting, makeup, and proofreading sections of the composition department. The work flow follows a sequence of steps very similar to the steps in metal composition. The major differences lie in the equipment on which type is set (as described in other articles in this section) and the materials which are handled in subsequent operations.

While a metal composing room resembles an industrial plant, a strike-on or photocomposition department looks more like an art studio. Figure 6.3 shows a typical scene in a film or paper composition department, where heavy equipment is replaced by artists' boards and office furnishings. Paste-up and stripping operations are done on artists' drafting boards and light tables, using drafting instruments, adhesive tapes, and various glues. Additional equipment may include special waxing machines which coat the back of the paper with a sticky wax for speeding paste-up, as well as photocopying devices of various sizes and kinds for making proofs. Rather than heavy storage racks for holding galleys of type in metal composing rooms, a strike-on or photocomposition department has storage cabinets with lightweight drawers which can hold far more typeset material. Typically, a strike-on or photocomposition department is more compact than a metal composing room.

Mark-up of copy for film or paper composition is similar in nature to that for metal composition. However, it must often be much more extensive, particularly for phototypesetting in which complex display material is to be composed in position within a given area, such as a section of an advertisement or a chapter opening of a book. The addition of spacing during the keyboarding operation in order to place type in exact position vertically as well as horizontally requires further instructions.

Typesetting may be done on typewriter-style equipment—in the case of strike-on composition—to produce type on paper, or on phototypesetting equipment to produce type on photographic paper or film. Proofs of typeset material are then made via one of the photocopying processes.

Corrections in film or paper composition are cut into position in the film or paper, or sometimes pasted over incorrect lines in paper composition. These processes are more difficult than replacing one character or slug of metal with another. Thus, correction has been a more costly part of film and paper composition, and a great deal of attention has been directed toward developing new and better methods of making corrections.

Makeup, on the other hand, can provide economies. Whereas metal makeup requires the cutting and placing of spacing material to fill in the areas around printing elements in a page, the pasting of paper or stripping of film onto a substrate requires only the positioning of the elements themselves. (Of course, when galley repros made from metal type are assembled into pages by an artist, the process is the same as for other paper paste-up.)

Rules, borders, and other simple line graphics can be drawn directly on a paper paste-up and sometimes can be inked onto or scribed into film positives and negatives. Preprinted decorative borders and ornaments are widely available and often are simply pasted or stripped into position with the type.

The final result of composition on paper is a paste-up of the final page or other arrangement, which is sent to the camera department for conversion to a photographic negative. Halftones and complex line illustrations are normally added after conversion to negative form. During paste-up, pieces of red or black paper are pasted in the positions to be occupied by the illustrations. When the paste-up is photographed, the pieces of paper leave clear windows in the negatives. Illustration films, which have been previously prepared in the camera department, are then taped over the windows, or the windows are cut out and the illustrations cut and taped into position. Quite often, in commercial printing plants, the work of inserting illustrations in the windows is done in the stripping department rather than the composing room (see "Image Assembly," page 369).

In film makeup, the film coming from the phototypesetter is positive; that is the characters are black on a clear background. Illustrations very often are made in positive film form in the camera department and simply stripped onto the type assembly in the composition department or the stripping department. Pages composed in positive film can be assembled directly into flats for platemaking if film positives are required by the platemaking process. For use with negative-working plates, film pages can go through a contact printing step to produce film negatives.

COMPOSITION BY ELECTRONIC MANIPULATION

With the advent of the computer in composition processes, it has become possible to perform various composition steps while material is in the form of electronic codes prior to actual typesetting. With appropriate electronic equipment, it is much more economical to perform many composition operations while material is in coded form in a computerized system than it is to manually move metal type around or to cut and paste bits and pieces of paper or film. Such equipment as video display terminals and computer sorting and merging facilities have been particularly helpful in reducing the cost of making corrections. New techniques using electronic equipment have also been developed to permit area and full-page makeup within computer systems, and additional facilities are under intensive development in this field. Figure 6.4 shows one of the makeup systems now in operation.

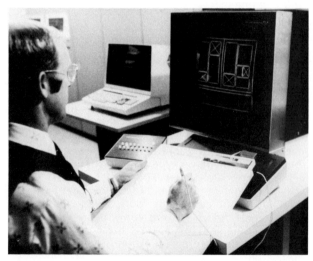

Figure 6.4: Electronic composition facilities. Both metal construction and film/paper paste-up are replaced here by computer generation of the image of the page on a video screen. The layout artist making up the page can manipulate the image by means of the sketch pad and wired pen or through a keyboard attached to the terminal. Once the page is completed, the electronic system will drive a phototypesetter to produce the page in type, with all elements except illustrations in exact position on a single piece of film or paper. Such electronic makeup systems are new developments; the system pictured here has been developed for production of the World Book Encyclopedia. © *Field Enterprises Educational Corporation.*

Material to be composed is entered into an electronic system by some form of keyboarding—by typing on a keyboard connected directly to the computerized system, by preparing tape to be read into the system, or by preparing typed pages in a special typeface that can be read optically into the system by an electronic reader. Once in the system, the material can then be manipulated under the control of computer programs very rapidly and at little additional cost for each additional manipulation. Material in the system is displayed for visual reading by those who operate the system via video displays or by printing out the material onto paper. Finally, when all possible processing has been done within the electronic system, the electronic signals are sent to a phototypesetting machine which produces finished set type. The material may be fed to the typesetter by use of coded tape, or the typesetter may be connected directly to the rest of the system by wires. Depending on how extensively the machinery is programmed, the typesetter may produce type in galleys, which are then put through the basic paste-up or stripping process for makeup into pages, or it may produce completely made-up pages with spaces left for other graphics such as illustrations.

Initial attempts to use computer-based technology in composition were aimed at simply speeding up existing operations by substituting computer processing for operations formerly done manually, such as determining the ending point in a line or selecting the appropriate point in a word for hyphenating it. Gradually, however, it was found that computers permitted the rearrangement of operations from the time-honored sequences followed in traditional composition. (Compare the steps for computer-based composition, illustrated in figure 6.5, with those in the flow chart in figure 6.1.) The most prevalent of these changes so far has been the movement of correction operations, and in some instances makeup operations, to positions prior to actual typesetting. Because more manipulation is done before typesetting, costs are lowered: making changes in set type has always been more expensive than getting everything in correct condition before typesetting. Another major movement now developing is the operation of electronic equipment directly by people who make the creative decisions—writers, editors, and even graphic designers in some instances. This eliminates the need for composition department production workers to perform tasks such as keyboarding which repeat work done in other departments.

The field of electronically based composition is still very young, and new concepts such as the reordering of long-standing procedures are developing with great rapidity. Because of favorable economics, computer-based composition promises to become the dominant composition system, replacing almost entirely the

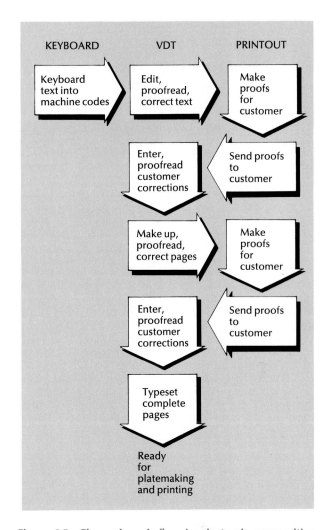

Figure 6.5: Changed work flow in electronic composition system. Use of computer-based video terminals permits major changes to be made in the time-honored work flow pictured in figure 6.1. Because material to be typeset is held in electronic storage, it can be proofread, edited, and typographically formatted before actual setting occurs, greatly reducing time required for checking and correcting set and made-up type and permitting many steps in the conventional composition process to be rearranged or even eliminated.

metal composing room and a large part of the paste-up/stripping kind of operation. Along with it, photo-typesetting will become the dominant typesetting process because it is the only method of setting type that lends itself to the high-speed, error-free operation required to match the operating patterns of computerized systems.

METAL TYPESETTING

Frank J. Romano, GRAPHIC ARTS MARKETING ASSOCIATES

For over 500 years, beginning with Gutenberg's perfection of movable type, the process of casting type in metal was the primary means of setting type for reproduction. In the last century, the metal typesetting processes were mechanized and partially automated; in the last decade or so, photographic methods have been replacing them. Soon metal typesetting will be very much the minority process compared to photographic and other means. However, since a great deal of typesetting tradition and practice derive from metal typesetting, an understanding of the process will still be important to those who work in the graphic arts.

Metal type is cast by a variety of procedures and machines using *type metal*. Type metal is composed mainly of lead, and in fact is often called *lead*; it also contains tin and antimony to improve its casting properties and its hardness after casting. Different ratios of lead, tin, and antimony are used for type cast by the various kinds of typesetting machines.

All metal type consists of a *body* or rectangular base on which is positioned a raised printing character or characters. Figure 6.6 illustrates a single-character piece of type and a slug containing an entire line of characters. The type images on the top of the body are laterally reversed, or *wrong-reading*; when they are coated with ink and printed on paper, they produce images which are *right-reading*.

The same basic casting principles are used in all forms of typecasting, regardless of the kinds of type produced or the various machines employed. Three main elements are required to cast a piece of type: a mold of the character to be cast, another mold which forms the body of the type, and a melting pot and pump to hold molten type metal and force it into the mold cavity. These elements are brought together as shown in figure 6.7. The appropriate character mold forms the top of the casting cavity, the body mold

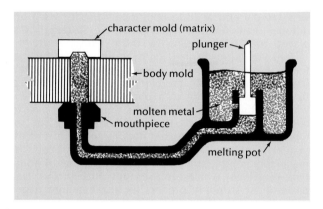

Figure 6.7: Casting process used in metal type production. A character mold, called a matrix, is locked against a second body mold in the typecasting machine. The mouthpiece of a metal pot containing molten type metal is locked tightly against the bottom of the body mold. A pump then forces molten type metal into the mold, where it solidifies within a second or two to form the metal type.

provides the sides, and the mouthpiece of the melting pot becomes the bottom. Metal is forced up into the cavity through the mouthpiece and hardens in seconds; then the melting pot and the character mold are removed, and the piece of type is forced out of the body mold by an ejector blade in the typecasting machine.

The body mold and the melting pot are mounted firmly in the typecasting machine. Body molds often are adjustable or interchangeable so that different body sizes can be cast, but such changeovers require manual operations and are not usually made between castings of individual pieces of type; they are made

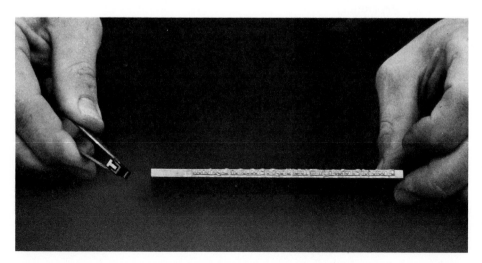

Figure 6.6: Pieces of metal type. Foundry type and type cast by the Monotype process contain only one character on each piece of metal, as shown at left. Linotype process produces a complete line of characters on one bar or slug of metal, as shown at right. Ludlow process also produces lines of characters on a single slug (not shown here). *Courtesy of Royal Composing Room, Inc.*

198

between jobs or production runs. The character molds, which are made of brass and are called *matrices*, are changed each time a new piece of type is cast, and typesetting machines are designed either to speed their manual handling or to automate entirely their removal and replacement with other matrices.

Although all metal type is manufactured by casting, it can be cast either before setting the characters in specific sequences in lines or afterward, depending on the specific machine process used. Originally type characters were cast individually by type foundries and sold to printers who used them over and over. Now most metal type is set on machines that permit the character matrices to be assembled first and then the type cast from them. In this situation, the cast type is rarely saved and used again in different jobs; it is simply remelted and used to cast new type.

All metal typesetting can be classified as either *hand-set* or *machine-set*, depending on the method by which the characters are assembled into lines. In hand setting, the typesetter must pick up individual pieces of type or the matrices from which they are cast and place them in order in a special holder. In machine setting, a keyboard is used to select the character matrices desired, along with appropriate operating commands for the machine. This keyboarding in turn causes the typesetting machine to assemble the matrices and cast the type. In addition, the machine-set category can be further divided into manually operated machines and mechanized or semiautomated systems which use code-controlled mechanisms to run the typecasting machines.

HAND-SET TYPE

In the metal process, hand-set type generally is divided into two categories: *foundry* and *Ludlow*.

Foundry type

Foundry type is cast by a type foundry and packaged into fonts. Typographers, printers, and typesetters purchase these fonts in complete packages or assortments of characters as needed. Each font contains a complete collection of letters in both capitals and lower case, along with figures and punctuation marks, all in one size and type style. The number of duplicates of each character provided depends upon the frequency of use of that particular character. Also included in the font are blank units of various widths called *spaces* and *quads*. The *em quad* is a space equal in width to the em of the font (the em is discussed in "The Fundamentals of Type," page 110). The *en quad* is a space equal to one-half the em. Other widths of spacing material are simply called *spaces*.

Foundry type is stored in type cases. The typesetter picks out individual letters one at a time and assembles them into a line in a *composing stick* (see figure 6.8), which can be set to the desired line length or *measure*. When the typesetter has assembled all of the characters that will fit within the line measure, he spaces the characters out to fill the remaining space in the measure by inserting additional spaces between words. This process of making each line fill the full measure so that it is of equal length to other lines is called *justification*. Lines also can be justified by placing extra

Figure 6.8: Hand-set type in composing stick. Individual pieces of metal type are placed in a special holder, the composing stick. Pieces of metal spacing material of various widths are added between words to fill the measure. *Courtesy of Royal Composing Room, Inc.*

spaces on either side of the line of type for centering or positioning to the right or left. This procedure is often referred to as *quadding out* the line. Quads and spaces also are used to establish uniform paragraph indentions, tabular alignments, and other special positions. Lines also are spaced out vertically by inserting metal strips, called *leads* and *slugs*, between lines. Leads usually are manufactured in 1-point and 2-point thicknesses; slugs are thicker spacing materials of 6, 12, or more points.

After a job set in foundry type has been printed, the type must then be broken apart and distributed back into the type case compartments before it can be reused. Distribution can take almost as long as the original setting.

Hand setting of foundry type is slow and laborious, and not much used these days except for setting display type in unusual faces not available on a typesetting machine. Until the late nineteenth century, however, it was the only way type could be composed.

Ludlow

The Ludlow Typograph machine is another hand setting method. It was developed in the early 1900's and still finds some use today in the production of display composition. The Ludlow machine produces a solid slug with type on the top surface. The slug is cast from brass matrices, which are hand assembled in a special holder or stick (see figure 6.9). The matrices are shaped so that the typesetter can pick up several in sequence and transfer the group to the stick, thus speeding the assembly process over that of foundry type. Spacing materials are added between words, and the stick is locked to hold the matrices during casting. The locked stick is inserted in the machine, which then casts the line. After casting, the matrices are distributed back into their case. After printing, the slug of type is melted down for recasting.

The Ludlow machine can cast as many duplicate

Figure 6.9: Ludlow stick and matrices. Large display type often is set and cast new for each use by placing Ludlow matrices in a special composing stick. The stick with the assembled line is then inserted in the Ludlow machine, where type is cast. After casting, matrices are redistributed into the case from which they were assembled to await reuse. *Courtesy of Ludlow Typograph Co.*

lines from a single assembled stick of matrices as desired. For this reason, and because only small numbers of matrices are assembled and cast at one time, an unlimited amount of type can be produced from a very limited set of matrices.

The Ludlow system can produce type from 6-point to 144-point. However, the different size faces are cast on a standard size body, either 6 points or 12 points in depth, with the balance of larger size characters projecting or *overhanging* beyond the body. Metal spac-

Figure 6.10: Ludlow line with underpinning. Ludlow type is always cast on a standard-width body slug regardless of type size; characters overhang or project out beyond top and bottom of the body slug. Additional metal material is inserted beneath overhang portions to support them, as shown. *Courtesy of Ludlow Typograph Co.*

ing material or slugs are then placed beneath the overhangs of the characters to support them, as shown in figure 6.10. This principle permits many sizes of type to be cast without having to change the body mold in the typecasting machine.

Although not as fast as keyboard-equipped machine systems, the Ludlow enjoys the advantage in display work. It is faster than hand setting of foundry type, produces new type every time, and allows multiple castings of a line from one assembly of matrices.

MACHINE-SET TYPE

The first major breakthrough in typesetting technology since Gutenberg came in the 1880's with the successful development of keyboard-controlled typecasting machines. Two basic systems were developed: the *Monotype* and the *Linotype*. The Monotype casts individual characters, while the Linotype casts complete lines. The Linotype became by far the most widespread method and in turn spurred the development of several competitive machines which work on the same principles.

Figure 6.11: Monotype keyboard. By typing out characters on the keyboard, the operator causes unique character codes to be punched into a ribbon of paper mounted at top of machine. *Courtesy of Royal Composing Room, Inc.*

Monotype

The Monotype system was perfected in 1887 by Tolbert Lanston of Washington, D.C., and is still used today in certain specialized areas of typesetting. The system employs two separate machines, a typecaster and a keyboard unit. The keyboard unit, shown in figure 6.11, generates a punched paper tape which is used to control the casting machine.

200

Like foundry type, the Monotype system uses individual pieces of type. In fact, characters cast on Monotype machines sometimes are put into cases for hand setting and referred to as foundry type. However, true foundry type is cast from a type metal mixture that produces much harder type than does Monotype metal.

Unlike foundry type, Monotype composition is cast in line sequence of characters and spaces according to the manuscript or copy. The lines come from the caster fully justified because the spaces are custom-cast to the exact size needed to justify the line.

Monotype setting takes place in two separate operations: keyboarding and casting. In the first, an operator types out the copy to be set on the keyboard, inserting into the stream of text characters various spacing, line-ending, and justification codes at appropriate points. As the operator works, the machine perforates little holes in a paper ribbon 4½" wide, forming codes which uniquely identify each key struck on the keyboard. The paper tape looks very much like the old-time player piano ribbons and operates basically the

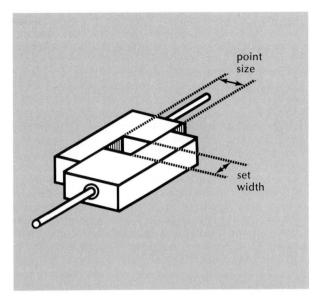

Figure 6.13: Monotype mold. Body mold in the Monotype casting machine is made of two pieces which slide against each other in the machine, as shown. This permits characters of different widths to be cast on appropriately sized bodies.

same way when placed in the casting unit.

When keyboarding of a job is completed, the ribbon is removed from the keyboard unit and placed in the caster. As the ribbon is advanced past a sensing point, air is forced through the holes one row at a time, causing the machine to automatically position a set of character matrices over the body mold and cast the appropriate character. (A set of character matrices is shown in figure 6.12.) The mold is also adjusted automatically to cast characters of different set widths, as shown in figure 6.13.

Separate operation of the keyboard and caster units permits each to be run at its own optimum speed. A keyboard operator may type in erratic patterns, while the casting of characters runs continuously as fast as 140 characters per minute.

The Monotype system offers important advantages over other metal typesetting systems and many phototypesetting systems as well. These include:
• The large number of characters which can be set directly from the keyboard. Monotype matrix cases contain between 225 and 272 characters and spacing matrices, depending on the model of the machine used—far more than other metal typesetting machines and many phototypesetters.
• The ability to precisely position characters at several places on the body of the type.
• The use of a justification system which computes the values of spaces in the line.
• The ability to correct individual characters instead of whole lines.

These factors permit the setting of highly complex material with great precision because the position of each character can be computed and specified and a great many special symbols can be handled. In addition, Monotype offers superior facility for correcting complex tables. Entire lines do not have to be reset as in other typesetting processes; individual characters

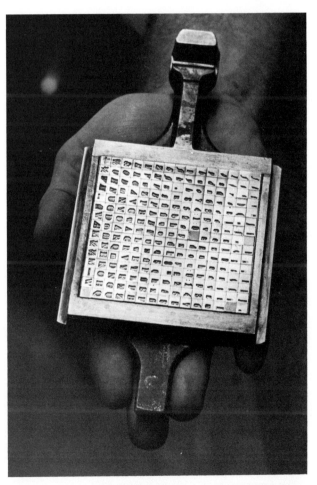

Figure 6.12: Monotype matrix case. Individual character matrices are inserted into a special case and locked in position. Case is then mounted on Monotype casting unit, which in turn positions the proper character matrix over the machine's body mold for casting of characters. *Courtesy of Royal Composing Room, Inc.*

may simply be substituted. Thus the Monotype system became over the years the favored method of setting complicated tables and mathematical and chemical formulas. Not until the more recent developments in electronically controlled phototypesetting equipment was Monotype seriously challenged in this area.

Linotype

The Linotype machine, developed by Ottmar Mergenthaler, was first used successfully at the New York *Tribune* on July 3, 1886, and became the fastest metal typesetting method. After the turn of the century, when Mergenthaler's patents began to run out, the competitive International Typographic Company (which later became the Intertype Company) was formed. The Intertype machine was based on the same system as the Linotype, and both have come to be known as *linecasting* machines. The name *Linotype* and the term *linecasting* are derived from the main principle of operation—the fact that the machine casts a complete line of type at one time rather than single characters. Because type is produced in slugs or bars, it is much easier to handle than either Monotype or hand-set foundry type.

In linecasting, the keyboard is combined with the casting unit to form a single machine. The machine can be run directly by an operator typing on the keyboard or by remote control through a punched paper tape and a special control unit attached to the keyboard. (A few machines in recent years were built without a keyboard, with a control unit only for tape operation.) The speed of operation can be 4 to 20 times faster than that of hand setting.

The linecasting machine uses the principle of circulating matrices. The operator manipulates the keyboard, and matrices are dropped out of a storage *magazine* and assembled in a line. When the line is completely assembled, it is transported automatically to the casting section of the machine. After the slug is cast, the matrices are automatically returned and redistributed in the magazine for reuse in subsequent lines. The type line, meanwhile, is ejected onto a receiving tray in sequence with other lines. (Matrix circulation is illustrated in figure 6.14.)

Justification spacing is automatic but not computed. Instead of selecting a space from a case, as might be done in setting type by hand, the operator strikes a *spaceband* key, and a wedge-shaped device falls into the line of matrices to be cast. When the line is sent to the casting section, the wedge-shaped spacebands are driven upward, forcing the matrices apart until they come in contact with two jaws which are positioned precisely to the line measure being set. Once the matrices are wedged firmly between the jaws, the line is cast.

Because this justification system does not compute the exact amount of space between characters or words in the line, the setting of tabular material requires use of special fixed-width spaces, which are provided as special matrices in the magazine. These matrices are inserted between columns of a table to standardize column spacing. However, there are limitations on how many columns can be set on a single slug of type, depending on whether the columns are justified and how they are positioned. Complex tables

Figure 6.14: Phantom view of Linotype matrix circulation. When the operator strikes a key on the keyboard, the appropriate matrix drops from the magazine (upper right) into a special assembler (at base of diagonal belt). Spacebands are dropped into the line from a box immediately above the assembler. When a line is assembled, the operator presses a lever, lifting the assembler up and triggering a series of transfer devices which move the line of matrices and spacebands in front of a body mold (mounted in the large disc, lower left). Here the line is cast. Afterward, matrices and spacebands are lifted to a separation point; spacebands are carried to the right, back to their box above the assembler, and matrices are taken to the top of the machine and placed on a special distributor bar across the top of the magazine. Screws carry the matrices along the bar until they reach appropriate points at which each character is dropped down into a grooved channel which holds it until needed again. *Courtesy of Mergenthaler Linotype Co.*

set by linecasting machines often must be made up by butting two or more slugs together endwise to form longer lines.

In addition, all linecasting typefaces are *top aligning*—that is, the tops of the capital letters align with the top of the body slug. Unless special matrices are used, the alignment of characters cannot be shifted to another point in the line, making composition of more complex formulas extremely difficult. The top alignment principle also means that matrices from different fonts cannot be mixed in the same line unless both fonts have been designed to the same dimension from the tops of the capital letters to the base line (see "The Fundamentals of Type," page 110).

Linecasting machines can hold from one to eight magazines of matrices depending on the model of the machine (usually four is the maximum). Magazines are of two types: standard and auxiliary. Standard-size magazines hold 90 different kinds of matrices, while auxiliary magazines hold 34 different kinds of matrices. On a machine equipped with auxiliary magazines, the main magazines normally house the standard fonts while the auxiliaries are used for short fonts and special characters. Literally thousands of special combinations are available using such machines. However, because the mechanics of setting up special layouts are very expensive, they are normally used only when there is sufficient work on a continuing basis to pay for the investment.

Each standard linecasting machine magazine is said to contain a font of type. However, this font of 90 different kinds of matrices usually contains two typefaces on the matrices, not one. The font of matrices is said to be *duplexed*. The two faces must, of course, be positioned within the same set width, but otherwise they can be completely different. In most cases, however, the roman of a given typeface is duplexed with the italic or boldface version of the same face, in the same point size. A line of duplexed matrices is shown in figure 6.15.

Duplexed matrices can be positioned in the linecasting machine so that characters in both the upper and lower positions can be cast in the same line. Therefore, each magazine on the machine makes available 180 characters from the keyboard. Additional *mixing* facility is provided on some machines designed as *mixers*. They permit the dropping of matrices from two vertically adjacent magazines into the same line and will redistribute the matrices back to the correct maga-

zines. This increases the characters available from the keyboard at one time to 360 if two standard magazines are used on a mixer, and to 496 characters if two auxiliary magazines are also employed.

A final way to obtain additional special characters on linecasting machines is through the use of *sorts* or *pi matrices*. These are inserted into the assembled line by hand and are sent during distribution back to a special pi chute which returns them to a holder beside the machine operator. Hand insertion of pi matrices slows down operating speed, but character selection is limited only by the availability of matrices.

AUTOMATION OF METAL TYPESETTING MACHINES

Automation in metal typesetting processes has largely meant the use of punched coded tape to control the operation of machines previously operated manually. Since the Monotype system has used punched paper ribbons from the beginning, the term *automation* when applied to metal typesetting has come to mean tape control of linecasting machines.

It was a Monotype operator, Walter Morey, who was responsible for the first step in automation of the linecasting process. With the backing of newspaper publisher Frank Gannett and the company which manufactured most of the wire communications equipment in the United States, Morey adapted to the linecasting process the principle of perforating a tape on a separate keyboard unit and then running it through a special control unit on the typecaster. The group founded the Teletypesetter Corporation to manufacture the special tape-punching keyboards and linecasting-machine control units. This system is known today as the *Teletypesetter (TTS)* system.

As in the Monotype system, the essential automation principle behind the TTS system is the separation of keyboarding from actual typesetting, which permits both functions to proceed at their optimum speeds unhindered by delays or interruptions from the other. It is a principle which has been carried into all of the newer composition technologies that have since emerged.

The TTS keyboard resembles that of a conventional typewriter rather than that of the linecasting or Monotype machine—another innovation in typesetting which has remained through all subsequent system development. Justification of lines in the TTS system is still done with spacebands on the linecasting machine, but some method had to be provided on the keyboard to tell the operator when a line was full and could be ended and justified. A modification of the Monotype computational method of justification was used. A counting device in the keyboard adds up the width values of characters as they are typed and punched into the tape; two pointers on a scale on the front of the machine indicate when the line is full enough to be justified.

The system of counting and adding up width values requires that linecasting machine type fonts used with the TTS system be manufactured in standard unit widths such as those used in Monotype. These are known as *unit* faces (see "The Fundamentals of Type," page 110). Some non-unit faces not manufactured to the TTS standard unit system have been used with

Figure 6.15: Line of Linotype matrices and spacebands. Most matrices are "duplexed"; that is, they have two type characters impressed into their casting edges. Either character can be positioned for casting within the line by means of special controls on the Linotype machine. Spacebands are composed of two inverted wedges which slide against each other, causing space between words to become larger or smaller as required to justify the line. *Courtesy of Mergenthaler Linotype Co.*

TTS equipment, but the use of non-unit faces allows room for error in counting and works reasonably well only for composition set to long measures with many characters per line.

Although typists with minimal training in typesetting can produce TTS tape, operating a TTS keyboard requires more effort than regular typing. There are 19 additional keys for various function codes, and the operator must keep an eye on the justification pointers as well as the copy to be set. Also, the tape itself often must be scanned by the operator to catch and correct possible errors. Nevertheless, the use of TTS keyboards generally produced significantly higher production rates than keyboarding of lines directly on linecasting machine keyboards, and operating speeds on the linecasting machines also were materially increased.

The TTS system was first introduced in the 1920's and grew steadily in the 1930's. But it was not until the 1950's that the automation movement really became widespread, and then mainly in newspapers. The development of TTS equipment was closely related to that of Teletype equipment used extensively in wire transmission of typed messages. In 1951 the Associated Press inaugurated a special TTS news service which allowed stories to be punched into TTS tape in a central office and transmitted to client newspapers by press wire. The tape received in the newspaper offices could be put directly on the linecasting machines and the type set without keyboarding in the local plant. When newspapers began using this service, they also equipped their composing rooms with perforating keyboards for processing local copy via TTS.

The next major advance came in the 1960's with the insertion of electronic computers into the processing stream between the TTS keyboard and the linecasting machine. The computer was used to automatically hyphenate words and justify lines under control of a computer program. This permitted the keyboard operator to produce so-called "idiot" tape with no end-of-line codes or other instructions; the characters alone could be typed in a continuous stream at top speed without the interruptions required for justifying lines at the keyboard. Substantial gains in typing speed were obtained, but the cost of computer equipment was high, so the net gain from this step was not as dramatic as some early pioneers of computerized typesetting systems had hoped.

Most of the computers applied to linecasting operations in these years were general-purpose machines supplied by the major computer manufacturers. Several special-purpose devices were developed for specific typesetting applications, however, and these proved very successful. The first was a machine for translating the raw data in telephone book listings into fully coded tape that could drive linecasters. The machine accepted the text characters and added all punctuation, capitalization, and typesetting commands. Another machine automatically justified lines until a word had to be hyphenated, at which point the word was displayed on a video screen for an operator to specify the break point. A third device provided hyphenation of words under the control of a computer program and also permitted data on two different tapes to be correlated and merged into one corrected tape. All of these functions could be performed on the general-purpose machines, but the cost of the special-purpose equipment was lower.

Other attempts to automate the linecasting process in the 1960's included development of attachments which would shift magazines and body molds and make other setup adjustments on command from coded tape. Machines equipped with these devices were able to produce automatically a much wider variety of type, such as was needed for advertisements.

By the end of the 1960's, however, it became clear that the metal typesetting processes were inherently limited in important respects compared to phototypesetting. Regardless of the amount of automation, the end products were still lines of type on galleys, and makeup remained a manual operation. Metal processes were error-prone, while electronic systems could retain material in an error-free state once it was in the system. In addition, there was little chance that operating speeds of metal typesetting equipment could be increased. As a result, several years ago the major manufacturers of linecasting machines stopped making all but a few machines, concentrating instead on phototypesetting systems. While metal typesetting will remain in use for a long time, it will account for a declining share of all composition in the future.

CONVERSION SYSTEMS
Paul D. Doebler, PUBLISHING MANAGEMENT CONSULTANT

With the growth of lithography and the widespread use of photographic technology in making printing plates of all kinds, the need arose to link metal composition processes with film images. The traditional means of converting raised metal printing surfaces to film images has been the reproduction proof, but a number of special conversion processes were also developed. Some were essentially proofing techniques in which special materials and/or equipment were used instead of standard proofing paper and presses. Others were camera systems in which the metal type itself was photographed directly.

At one time, a considerable variety of conversion systems was available on the market. Today, however, the growth of phototypesetting to replace hot metal composition has greatly reduced the need for conversion processes, and only a few, such as Scotchprint and Cronapress, remain in use.

STANDARD REPRODUCTION PROOFS

The conventional *reproduction proof,* a high-quality print made specifically to be photographed, is still one of the most widely used conversion methods. These proofs, called *repros* or *repro proofs* for short, are made on special proofing presses equipped with precision impression cylinders and inking systems. The type is aligned and locked in position on the bed of the press, and proofs are pulled one at a time. A high-quality letterpress "kiss" impression is sought—a rich black print without excessive pressure or punch-through on the sheet. Heavy-weight coated papers are usually used for repro proofs, and paper mills have developed special coatings that will absorb ink and press pressures well without excessive squeeze-out of ink around the edges of the type. Repro proofs must be handled carefully in subsequent operations to prevent smearing; sometimes they are sprayed with artists' protective plastic films.

Repro proofs may be made of complete pages of type with all elements in final position, but in a great many cases proofs are made of type in galley format. These galley repros are given to an artist who cuts out individual lines and blocks of type and pastes them down as part of an art mechanical.

SCOTCHPRINT

One of the earliest of the special conversion processes to be developed was Scotchprint, a product of the 3M Company, which is still being used today. Scotchprint is a special proofing material—a dimensionally stable plastic sheet with a special ink-receptive surface on one side—which can withstand substantially more distortion during impression than paper proofing stocks.

The Scotchprint process of arriving at a film negative involves two steps—proofing and exposing. A Scotchprint proof is pulled in essentially the same manner as an ordinary repro proof. Then it is normally exposed to film by contact printing (although Scotchprint proofs also can be photographed on a copyboard if desired). When placed before a strong light, the Scotchprint material permits light to pass through it in areas not covered by the inked image; thus a sheet of film can be exposed as if from a film positive. Scotchprint therefore reduces the time and capital investment required in the exposure stage of conversion.

205

CRONAPRESS

A method of obtaining a film negative directly from the type form without using photography is Du Pont's Cronapress conversion system. This system does not use a standard proof press; it uses instead a special machine equipped with thousands of tiny lead balls which vibrate against pressure-sensitive film laid over the type.

The special pressure-sensitive film has a micro-sponge-like coating which is relatively opaque. When the coating is compressed, the bubbles collapse, forming transparent areas which will pass light. After the image areas have been compressed in the machine, called a *clarifier,* the film is coated with dye. The dye is absorbed by the uncompressed areas, forming a negative.

The film can be compressed only by the application of very high pressures, far in excess of those possible on a conventional proof press. The clarifier machine accomplishes this by vibrating the tiny lead balls, causing them to bounce against the film and the type. Although the lead pellets are very small, each time one of them strikes the film and type it achieves immense pressure in a pinpoint area, enough to clarify that area. By vibrating thousands of lead pellets over the film and form for five or six minutes, the clarifier produces millions of impacts which overlap each other and clarify all image areas.

The process is very precise and can pick up the finest detail with excellent fidelity. Very fine wood grains and the finest halftone dots are succcessfully rendered as a film image with the process. Of special importance in type conversion work is the ability of the tiny lead balls to conform to irregular surfaces and pick up fine detail; this has enabled the process to be used extensively to convert worn standing type forms to negatives.

STRIKE-ON TYPESETTING

Paul D. Doebler, PUBLISHING MANAGEMENT CONSULTANT

Although the invention of the typewriter preceded the invention of the keyboard-operated Linotype and Monotype, it was only within the last 35 years that the typewriter came to be considered a typesetting device. Prior to World War II, it was thought of essentially as a transcription machine, even though it was used for years before that to compose characters on mimeograph stencils for use in duplicating.

The identification of the typewriter strike-on principle as a distinct typesetting process occurred when another printing process, offset lithography, moved from the printing plant into the office to challenge the mimeograph in the duplicating field. The far superior reproduction quality of offset duplicating equipment (it could print all manner of images, including halftones, which prior duplicating processes could not) quickly created a demand for better images to duplicate. Because most material to be duplicated was and still is text, and because metal typesetting technology (photocomposition was largely unavailable at the time) was far too expensive and complex for office use, the lowly typewriter was rapidly upgraded to produce more attractively composed text.

DEVELOPMENT OF STRIKE-ON TECHNOLOGY

The basic principle of strike-on typesetting, of course, is a raised metal character striking an inked ribbon and pressing it sharply against the paper to leave an imprint of the character on the sheet. Early typewriter ribbons made of fabric, however, produced very poor images for reproduction purposes. The thread patterns in the fabric created rough edges on the typed characters, and the resulting fuzziness was accentuated in the final printed product. To produce a better quality image, the *carbon ribbon,* a thin plastic film with a fine layer of carbon black, was developed. When this ribbon is struck by the key, the carbon compound is transferred to the paper, depositing a clearly defined image. The carbon ribbon is used only once so that the quality is always uniform.

The original typewriter faces were designed for efficient production and legibility with fabric ribbons. With better reproduction capability, however, it became possible to successfully imprint faces with the subtler lines of metal type, and a number of faces, mostly serif, were developed for typewriters.

While standard typewriters could be equipped with these new faces, special kinds of strike-on typesetting typewriters were also developed and marketed to accommodate them. The VariTyper machine (shown in figure 6.16) became the most widely used of these strike-on typesetters, although a good number of Friden Flexowriters found use in typesetting situations.

No typesetting system can compute and insert space between words to justify lines until all of the characters in the line have been set. On a typewriter, characters are typed on the paper as the keys are struck; therefore, justified composition requires a second typing to produce the final typeset copy. On the Vari-

Figure 6.16: VariTyper machine. This device for many years was the mainstay of strike-on composition. *Courtesy of AM Varityper.*

Typer, the operator typed the line once for fitting and then typed it again for reproduction on the final page. The Flexowriter system, however, used two machines, one a typewriter for encoding text on punched paper tape and the other a machine through which the tape was run back to produce the typeset material. The operator performed only the first keyboarding step; the second typing was done automatically by the machine.

The VariTyper, however, offered an advantage over the Flexowriter and the standard typewriters of the day which accounted for its popularity—it allowed type fonts to be changed very simply at any time. Type characters for a complete font were contained on a curved metal plate which snapped into place on an impression mechanism. The machine automatically moved the plate vertically and horizontally to position the correct character for typing. Font plates could be removed and inserted at any time, so that different type designs could be mixed in the same job.

The IBM Magnetic Tape Selectric Composer (MT/SC) system, introduced in the 1960's, incorporated principles used in both of the earlier machines. Apart from the standard office typewriter, the MT/SC became the leading strike-on composition facility of recent years. It is composed of two units, a keyboarding device and a retyping unit (see figure 6.17), and offers interchangeable type fonts, using the Selectric "golf ball" principle (see figure 6.18).

In addition to the usual typing facilities, the keyboarding unit has a magnetic tape recording and reading capability which allows revision and correction of text previously typed. Thus a job can be encoded on magnetic tape in a tape cassette, stored for a period of time, returned to the machine and changed by an operator working at the keyboard, and then placed on the retyping unit for final setting in justified format. This system was the forerunner of today's *editing typewriter*, which is the cornerstone of the word processing movement, a trend that is leading to a basic reorganization of offices and office procedures throughout business today.

STRIKE-ON TYPE AND TYPOGRAPHY

The typographic quality of strike-on composition has been improved over the years by a number of developments, to the point where some very good results can now be achieved with appropriate equipment. Some strike-on typesetting, in fact, rivals moderately good quality typesetting by other methods. Fine typography, however, will always lie beyond the reach of strike-on equipment because of its inherent limitations.

One improvement was the development of the *mul-*

Figure 6.17: IBM MT/SC system. Many of these systems are used today for strike-on composition, although much of this kind of work also is done on specially equipped standard electric typewriters. The MT/SC allows recording and revision of typeset material on magnetic tape, has special format controls, and offers other additional features. *Courtesy of IBM Office Products Division.*

Figure 6.18: IBM Selectric "golf ball" typing element. This small ball containing all characters of a type font mounts on the typing head of the IBM Selectric Typewriter. Typing elements can be changed quickly and easily, permitting use of many typefaces in one job. *Courtesy of IBM Office Products Division.*

207

tiple-unit escapement, a device which permits the use of typefaces designed on a multi-unit basis similar to that used in metal and photographic type. The escapement on a typing machine determines how far the carriage moves to position the paper for the next character to be typed. Most typewriters provide only a single escapement travel distance for all characters; the multiple-unit escapement will move the carriage different distances for different characters. Thus, type for the multiple-unit escapement machine can be designed with characters of different widths. Because of mechanical limitations in the design of escapement devices, however, multiple-unit strike-on typefaces are still limited to about three to five units to the em, whereas metal and photographic typefaces are commonly designed with 18 or more units to the em.

An alternative approach which became more widely used was the development of new typefaces with characters optimally fitted to a single escapement width, a severe restriction but one which has been overcome surprisingly well in many instances. Serif types have worked best in this situation because the horizontal projections on the narrower letters can be manipulated to help fill the spaces between adjacent letters. Sans serif types work poorly under such circumstances.

Most typewriters not designed especially for typesetting do not have typographic refinements demanded in better grades of composition, such as ligatures. Machines designed for typesetting, however, such as the VariTyper and the MT/SC, do have such extra characters. On a few machines, such as the IBM Selectric "golf ball" typewriter, interchangeable fonts of type make it possible to have a wide range of special symbols and characters, as well as multiple type designs, available for setting in a single job.

Extensive formatting facilities have also been built into some modern strike-on composing machines. In the MT/SC, typographic controls have been largely separated from the typing function by including them in a special control console on the composer unit. From this panel, the operator can control the merging of two tapes and specify the number of lines to be set in a given area or page. Line measure, indentions, leader spacing, and quad spacing can also be set from the console. An automatic hyphenation logic routine is available to break words at line endings automatically if desired.

Character, word, and line spacing are also controlled from the console of the MT/SC. An escapement lever is used to set character spacing for different point sizes of type as well as for letterspacing. Maximum and minimum tolerances can be established for interword spacing, and a leading dial permits selection of vertical spacing. A tabulating stop system can be set up to produce complex multicolumn composition from a minimum of typing on the original input keyboard.

In recent years, a number of these typesetting control features have been adapted and incorporated into IBM's line of typewriters, permitting certain kinds of typesetting to be produced efficiently from machines other than the full MT/SC configuration. For example, the IBM Magnetic Tape Selectric machine, which is essentially the front or input half of the MT/SC system, also permits magnetic tapes to be revised and updated, and then retyped on the unit's typewriter.

When material is retyped off the tape to a new line measure, the machine will remove previously inserted hyphens from words broken at the ends of lines.

Although other IBM Selectric typewriter models have interchangeable type fonts, they do not offer a full range of type sizes. On the newer Selectrics, however, a dual-pitch adjustment does permit the machine to use either a 10-point elite face with 12 characters to the inch or a 12-point pica face with 10 characters to the inch.

With these developments, and with the growing use of photocomposition in situations formerly dominated by strike-on composition, it would appear that strike-on typesetting probably has reached a plateau of technical development which it may not exceed in the future. The basic mechanics of the process and its equipment place limitations on its further refinement, while phototypesetting processes afford much greater potential for development. This does not mean, however, that strike-on composition will not continue to be used extensively. It will undoubtedly remain the most economical process for many kinds of lower and moderate grade typesetting work without further technological advances in machinery and methods, at least for some time to come.

COMPUTER PRINTOUTS

A form of strike-on composition which has been used extensively for certain kinds of data, lists, and other reference materials is the computer printout. When computers came into use for compiling such material, the most direct route to its publication was to produce a printout of the material on a printout device and then photograph it for lithographic platemaking. The most common printout devices at that time were the electric typewriter and the chain printer, sometimes called a line printer because it types a complete line at a time on a continuous web of paper. Chain printers were most popular because of their high speeds of 300 or more lines per minute. In a chain printer, the type characters are carried in an endless chain past punches which tap the characters at the right moment to print the characters on the paper in proper position.

A major drawback to such printouts, however, is the space occupied by the type. Characters are widely spaced and often are available only in capital letters. Pages produced on chain printers thus occupy several times the area that a typeset page containing the same material would occupy, and this materially increases paper, printing, and binding costs. In recent years, therefore, there has been a trend to preparing such computer-generated material for typesetting via photocomposition rather than chain printer. As the ties between computers and phototypesetting systems continue to increase, chain printer composition of pages for reproduction will decrease.

DEVELOPMENT OF WORD PROCESSING

Although the technology of producing strike-on images themselves may stabilize at the present state of the art, other facets of typewriter technology are moving ahead rapidly. The most evident of these developments is the expanding use of the editing and revision principles established in the MT/SC system in situations other than typesetting. In the last several years, this trend has coalesced under the name of *word processing,* and it has caught the attention of the general business community as a means of reordering office work and upgrading office productivity.

An important emerging development in the word processing field at the present time is the use of tapes prepared on editing and correcting typewriter equip-ment similar to the MT/SC system to drive photocomposing machines. This permits the office staff to obtain film typesetting directly from their keyboarding efforts, thus raising the quality of typesetting available to them while eliminating the cost of rekeyboarding and proof-reading the material in the typesetting shop. This coupling of phototypesetting and word processing systems will become a predominant controlling feature of future composition systems and will greatly influence the amounts of other kinds of typesetting used.

PHOTOTYPESETTING

Frank J. Romano, GRAPHIC ARTS MARKETING ASSOCIATES

Typesetting by photographic means, commonly viewed as the new technology in typesetting, is on its way to replacing most metal composition. Yet it took almost three decades for this new technology to gain its present momentum. For phototypesetting to become economically advantageous, the convergence of several fundamental technological trends was required. Among these were:

• The growth of offset lithography and gravure, which over these years took a major share of the total printing market away from letterpress. Letterpress used the raised printing images of metal type, but lithography and gravure demanded photographic media for their platemaking processes. Today even letterpress, with its photomechanically made plates, requires photographic originals.

• The growth of electronic technology, particularly computerized systems, which provided new possibilities for controlling the composition process.

• The rising cost of manual labor compared to the lowering cost of technological automation in the composition area.

With these forces at work, phototypesetting systems enjoy a fundamental advantage over metal typesetting systems. In addition, photography is a technology well-matched to the operating characteristics of electronics, while metal typesetting is essentially mechanical and is severely limited in the development of new principles of operation.

EVOLUTION OF PHOTOTYPESETTING EQUIPMENT

All of this was not apparent during World War II, however, when phototypesetting first got its start. There are differing opinions as to the birthday and the father of photographic typesetting. There were probably several of both.

In 1944, an ITT engineer in France, René A. Higon-net, visited an offset printing plant in Lyon and observed the difficulty of adapting hot metal composition to the photolithographic process. Recalling a technical paper on the use of flash tubes to study high-speed mechanisms such as airplane propellers, he discussed the application of this principle with a friend, Louis Moyroud. By 1945, they had put together a simple machine to demonstrate that flash was fast enough to project on a plate a clear image of a character from a revolving disc. The second problem, line justification, was solved by April, 1946, in a unit that composed lines on film from a selection of 82 characters. The main components of the machine were:

• A manual typewriter with permutation bars and contacts to give each character a unique binary code.

• A memory register to record the codes on a revolving drum. Solenoid-controlled pins could be set for either of two positions.

• A counter/justifier to accumulate character widths and determine word-space increments after each line had been typed.

• Control circuitry composed of telephone relays.

• A photographic unit made up of a film carriage and a continuously rotating disc with 82 clear characters on a black background (a photographic positive).

In May, 1946, Higonnet visited the United States and interested Lithomat Corporation in his machine. A second version was demonstrated in July, 1948. This unit had 88 characters, improved speed, and one of the first electric typewriters, an Electromatic. A variable escapement mechanism permitted a selection of 18 character widths. In 1949, the machine was shown to the industry.

In September, 1950, at the Graphic Arts Exposition in Chicago, Intertype unveiled the Fotosetter, a machine that composed type on film or photosensitive paper instead of hot metal slugs. To the naked eye, the Fotosetter was a linecaster, except that the pot of molten lead was replaced by camera equipment. It contained 114 instead of 90 keys and used a matrix, called a Fotomat, which was very similar in outward appearance to the linecasting matrix, except that it had a photonegative character imbedded in its side. Characters were photographed one at a time. The 12-point characters in the Fotomat could be reduced or enlarged to a number of sizes from 6- to 36-point at the turn of a dial which changed lenses in the machine. Thus, complicated mixing of sizes and typefaces was greatly simplified over the metal process, where a separate magazine was necessary for each size in each typeface.

At the same exhibition, Mergenthaler Linotype Company showed a version of the linecasting machine which used matrices with highly visible ebonite characters on them. The line was set and justified with spacebands as in linecasting and then photographed all at once. Linofilm, as it was called, went back to the drawing boards and never reappeared in this version, but the other two machines went on to commercial sales in the industry.

It was the Higonnet-Moyroud machine which pioneered most of the lasting principles of modern-day phototypesetting devices. Lithomat, which later changed its name to Photon, continued development of the machine. It was operated from a standard typewriter-style keyboard with all additional controls located at the keyboard position. The device indicated when a line was full enough for justification and performed the justification operation automatically when the operator hit an end-of-line key. The machine could set lines up to 42 picas, and choice of line length was controlled by a dial at the keyboard. The machine could hold 16 fonts of type and set them in 12 sizes, mixing all faces and sizes within the same line if desired. All quadding functions (flush right, center, flush left, and insertion of space and leaders in the middle of a justified line) were handled automatically with the touch of a key. In late 1955, the Photon Model 200 was introduced.

About three years later, the name Linofilm reappeared on the market, but this time the system paralleled the concepts of the Photon machine. Interchangeable master font grids were used with an optical system that could project a variety of type sizes. The photographic unit could hold 16 font grids and mix faces freely. The Linofilm system also enabled the operator to add or subtract minute units of space from the set widths of characters, permitting high-quality letterspacing from the keyboard at virtually no extra cost. In addition, very significantly, the system departed from the concept of *direct entry*, with the keyboard attached directly to the photographic unit. Instead, the *stand-alone* keyboard unit produced a 15-level punched paper tape which was then used to control the photo unit. Production of lines from this unit jumped substantially, so that it became necessary to think of a phototypesetting installation as one in which several keyboards were required to keep a single typesetting unit busy.

Linofilm was not the only early equipment to use tape in phototypesetting. The Monotype Company brought out the Monophoto system, which retained the same 31-level tape and keyboarding system used for its metal casting process; a photographic typesetter was simply substituted for the metal caster. American Type Founders developed a small two-unit phototypesetting system using the Friden Flexowriter, a tape-punching typewriter-style keyboard, to prepare 7-level tape to drive a table-top style of photosetting device. In the early 1960's, following the rapid acceptance of tape-controlled phototypesetting systems in the late 1950's, Photon joined the trend by adapting the Model 200 to operation by tape. Soon after, it brought out its first completely tape-driven machine, the Model 540, which was simply the Model 200 photo unit separated from the keyboard. The machine was driven by 8-level tape produced on the now separate Model 200 keyboard.

The 1960's and early 1970's were years of tremendous expansion in the variety of phototypesetting equipment that was made available. New manufacturers came into the market with competitive equipment, and early suppliers retired their first models in favor of much more advanced machinery, until today there is a phototypesetting machine available to fit virtually any kind of composition requirement. Costs of today's equipment have dropped to a fraction of those for the early equipment, while typesetting capabilities have risen greatly.

Despite the diversity in phototypesetting equipment, however, it can be categorized into several basic groups for better understanding. The first major distinction, as in metal typesetting, is between what amounts to hand composition (even though it often must be done on certain kinds of machines) and machine-based composition. The essential difference between these two categories is the use in machine setting of a keyboard that permits typing action and speed in operating machinery. Within the machine-based area, three "generations" of equipment have evolved. The first generation was the photographic typesetter built on the principles of linecasting machines, including the initial Fotosetter and the aborted first Linofilm; these first-generation machines are no longer made. Second-generation machines use other kinds of electromechanical systems for positioning and exposing type characters, and constitute by far the largest category of phototypesetting equipment presently in use. Third-generation machines, the most rapidly growing kind of equipment, employ all-electronic means, such as cathode ray tubes and lasers, for forming and exposing characters.

HAND PHOTOCOMPOSITION

The term *hand photocomposition* is a somewhat loose designation, for it encompasses a number of diverse procedures and processes. It can refer to *dry transfer* or *"rub-on" lettering*, or it can indicate type set on *photolettering machines*, some of which can perform precise and intricate functions.

Rub-on transfer art and lettering are purchased on transparent carrier sheets. One sheet usually contains a font of type, although all kinds of special symbols and ornaments are also available. Type is set by positioning the appropriate character and rubbing the surface of the carrier sheet to make the character stick to the supporting art surface. When the carrier sheet

Figure 6.19: Phototypesetting machines for hand setting photographic type. Representative of the numerous machines available in this classification are the Staromat (left) and the VGC Photo Typositor 3000 (right). *Courtesy of Berthold of North America, Inc., and Visual Graphics Corp.*

is lifted, the character remains on the supporting surface. Since it is transferred from the carrier sheet, each character can be used only once.

Dry transfer lettering requires careful alignment when complete words are being set. The slow composition process—alignment, rubbing the character to properly transfer it from the font sheet, and finally again rubbing the assembled typeset material to assure that the transferred letters will all adhere to the layout board—makes transfer lettering totally impractical for text setting. Artists find transfer lettering most useful for setting small label-style captions into artwork.

The more mechanized version of hand photocomposition is the use of equipment such as the Vari-Typer Headliner, Photo Typositor, Staromat, Compugraphic 7200, and other such machines which produce type on long continuous strips of photographic paper or film. (Two of these machines are illustrated in figure 6.19.) In these machines, fonts are carried on strips of film or on discs. The operator moves the font strip or disc by means of dials or levers to position a chosen character for exposure and then exposes the character onto the photographic paper or film. He then moves the font strip or disc to the next desired character and repeats the exposure process.

This process, too, is slow, but it offers several advantages. First, cost of equipment is low compared to any keyboard-operated system. Second, spacing between characters can be manipulated very easily, permitting unusual effects to be readily achieved. Third, the cost of master type fonts is very small compared to other forms of machine-based phototypesetting, and this permits the acquisition of many fonts

of unusual design and in many sizes. These machines are therefore used essentially to produce display-size type for headlines and unusual needs.

SECOND-GENERATION PHOTOTYPESETTERS

Second-generation phototypesetting machines are the most numerous and the most varied in design and capabilities. In all of them, however, typeset material is produced from master characters stored photographically in master fonts in the machine. Also, all of the machines have a number of major subsystems, including input sources, character selection, image output control, and interline spacing (as diagrammed in figure 6.20). Although the basic principles used by all manufacturers are similar, numerous variations in design complexity and configuration present a vast array of alternative methods for setting type.

Input sources

Phototypesetters use codes from input sources to activate machine responses that produce typeset copy. The codes identify parameters that control the operation, including characters to be typeset, desired fonts and point sizes, interword spacing for line justification, and desired interline spacing.

Input sources for second-generation devices include a keyboard attached directly to the typesetting machine, keyboard-produced perforated paper tape or floppy disc, computer-produced magnetic tape, and magnetic media from other devices.

Early systems used entry by keyboards directly interfaced with the machine and were designed for use by

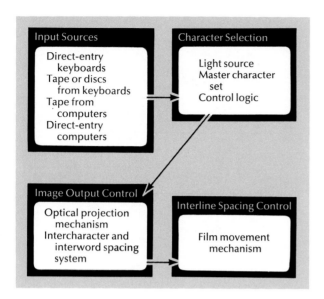

Input Sources
- Direct-entry keyboards
- Tape or discs from keyboards
- Tape from computers
- Direct-entry computers

Character Selection
- Light source
- Master character set
- Control logic

Image Output Control
- Optical projection mechanism
- Intercharacter and interword spacing system

Interline Spacing Control
- Film movement mechanism

Figure 6.20: Second-generation phototypesetting machine principles. Basic functions performed by second-generation machines are shown in the sequence in which they occur.

skilled operators who understood the function codes required to typeset copy and who could divide the copy into justified lines. This method was slow because end-of-line justification and extra coding strokes had to be handled manually. (In recent years, much improved small direct-entry machines have been developed for light-duty applications. Two of these are illustrated in figure 6.21.)

As faster and more flexible phototypesetters became available, the use of keyboard perforating units for paper tape became more popular. These units changed keyboard text entry into an off-line operation and made possible the use of multiple keyboards with a single phototypesetter. This method allowed the typesetter to operate at its maximum speed rather than at the speed of the keyboard operator. (Two systems that use paper tape are illustrated in figure 6.22.)

Most of today's input and editing devices utilize magnetic media consisting of a substrate coated with a metal oxide that can be magnetized so that information can be recorded or read. Most often used are *floppy discs,* flexible pieces of Mylar impregnated with metal oxide, which can be stored in standard filing folders for later use.

Magnetic tape may also be generated either by general-purpose computers, which are adapted to typesetting work by means of special programs, or special-purpose computers designed specifically for this application. However, most phototypesetters today are connected on-line to the computer.

Computers can sometimes be used to bypass the keyboarding step in typesetting by taking the material to be set from an encoded data base already stored in a computer system. The typesetting computer then processes this material to perform typesetting functions, adding to the final tape all necessary codes to operate the typesetter. Catalogs, directories, and other products which are heavily revised and reissued are especially suited to such handling. Elimination of the keyboarding step greatly enhances the economy, efficiency, and accuracy of the total system, as keyboard entry has traditionally been an error-prone bottleneck in photocomposition.

Character selection

The basic character-selection subsystem consists of a light source, a master character set, and a control logic to synchronize the light source and character set.

The light source is of high intensity and may be continuous or may operate stroboscopically with a flash duration of one or two microseconds (millionths of a second). The light source normally used is a xenon flash lamp or flash tube. For larger point sizes, the lamp is flashed twice (multi-flash) to assure that the film is fully exposed for uniform character blackness (density).

Master character sets are transparent negatives (clear characters on opaque backgrounds) which supply character images in the typeface or font desired. Master character sets may be stored on rotating discs, rotating drums with interchangeable film strips, rotating turrets, or stationary grids. In all cases, master character sets

Figure 6.21: Direct-entry phototypesetters. Two representative machines in this class are the EditWriter 7500 (left) and the Comp/Edit (above). *Courtesy of Compugraphic Corporation and AM Varityper.*

Figure 6.22: Tape-driven phototypesetters. Two commonly used machines in this classification are the V-I-P (above) and the UniSetter (right). *Courtesy of Mergenthaler Linotype Company and Compugraphic Corporation.*

are interchangeable to permit insertion of desired fonts not already in the machine. Some phototypesetters offer multiple character arrays with up to five discs or 18 grids.

The process of character selection begins with reading of coded information from the input source into the machine's control logic. As the logic unit recognizes the character and font code, it determines where the desired font is located in relation to the light sources. In machines with single character-set arrays, all available fonts are located in front of the light source. Multiple character-set arrays may find the desired font elsewhere and move it into position before the light source. Simultaneously, the logic unit is selecting the proper light source, when more than one is available, and positioning the apertures, mirrors, and lenses used to isolate the desired character.

As the proper character image approaches the light source, most systems use a series of timing marks on the master character set or timing pulses to synchronize action between the light source and the character image. On some machines the timing mechanism will cause the character to stop in front of the light source. However, on most machines the extremely fast stroboscopic light source is sufficient to obtain high-quality output by simply flashing at the exact moment the character image is in front of the light source. Once the proper character is selected and its image is optically initiated, image output control begins.

Image output control

The image-output-control subsystem positions the character image on the output medium. Components

of the subsystem include an optical projection mechanism to focus, direct, and magnify the projected light rays, and a spacing mechanism to accurately provide intercharacter and interword spacing.

Character projection. Optical projection mechanisms vary significantly among phototypesetting machines. Rotating character sets normally carry several fonts around the rotating surface. The stroboscopic light flash illuminates a complete row of characters rather than isolating individual characters. A series of apertures, mirrors, or lenses moves into a unique set of positions in response to function codes on the input tape. The desired character image is thus guided into the optical path while all others are deflected away. As the number of fonts on an individual rotating character set increases so does the complexity of the optical system required to isolate and project individual characters.

Stationary grid systems are the most complicated systems of all for optical character isolation. Since character images on the grids are stationary and not rotating past the light source, a continuous light source is used. Light is distributed evenly over the grid by condenser lenses specifically designed for this purpose. The effect is illumination of an entire matrix of character images rather than a single row. The light rays from each character are formed into a beam of virtually parallel rays by a series of lenses called a collimator assembly. The rays then enter a series of eight pairs of optical wedges designed to isolate the desired character image. Directed by codes on the input tape, the wedges move to a unique set of positions for that character. The refractive angles on the wedges guide

213

light rays from the appropriate character along the optical path and deflect all others away. A decollimator assembly is used to converge the parallel light rays and restructure the character on the output medium.

Character sizing. All phototypesetters have available a range of character point sizes, called the point-size range, but machines differ significantly in the number of specific sizes available and the method for changing point size. Systems vary from manual insertion of new font masters to highly automatic selection of sizes accomplished by changing the projection mechanism.

Systems that require manual changing of point size permit by far the most straightforward and inexpensive design of the image-output-control subsystem. In most of the low-priced text-oriented machines no mechanism to control point size is required, as the master character set and the set-width gears must be changed manually. In several machines, manual adjustment of point size is accomplished by the setting of levers to correspond to the desired point size. Movement of the levers causes lenses in the main optical system to change position and vary magnification of the master font.

In the Fototronic system, variations in magnification are accomplished automatically by movement of two lenses. Directed by function codes on the input tape, the movable lenses are driven along the optical axis by motors until positioned in the appropriate locations for the desired magnification.

The most commonly used methods of obtaining different point sizes are the multilens turret and the zoom lens. The turret normally holds eight or more lenses which provide a range of magnification levels. Each magnification level relates to a specific point size. The appropriate lens is rotated into position in response to a coded command from the input tape. Lens turrets provide good typographic flexibility with reasonable photomechanical simplicity. Zoom lenses provide a greater number of sizes in less space.

Intercharacter and interword spacing. There are numerous methods by which proper intercharacter or interword spacing can be achieved. Two basic components are involved: the mechanism that physically sets and advances character images across the output medium, and the logic system which controls the amount of advance and synchronizes it with the stroboscopic light source.

A lens carriage which moves laterally across the output medium to locate the character properly along the typeset line is the most common method for placing characters along the line. After each character is set, the lens carriage advances a distance equal to the appropriate character width and is ready for the next character image. Master character widths are either permanently hardwired into the circuitry of the phototypesetter or are available through changeable width circuits called *width plugs* or *width tapes*. The character widths are then applied to the carriage advance.

Another simple method which is also becoming popular is a positioning mirror that rotates to deflect the image the desired amount. Character focus is maintained by a focusing lens that moves in synchronization with the mirror. Rotation of the positioning mirror is controlled by a second optical system that generates electrical pulses to indicate the amount of

rotation occurring. Rotation will stop when image deflection equals the appropriate character width. Perforated program tapes are used to load character widths into the machine memory in coded form. A new character width tape must be read into memory for each change in point size.

A third technique for correctly positioning characters along the line of copy involves a carriage that advances the light source and master character set laterally in relation to the output medium. The carriage advance is determined by the character width contained in the device's memory. Loading of the memory from special coded tapes before typesetting begins is again used.

Another method for proper character placement is a complex version of the original traveling lens carriage. In this system a carriage containing a lens and a fixed mirror travels laterally in relation to the output medium. However, the carriage is advanced only after several characters have been set on the film or paper. The task of proper character placement while the carriage remains stationary falls jointly to the character-selection subsystem and the mechanism which isolates the desired character image along the optical path.

Immediately adjacent to the master character set are two movable apertures, one with two horizontal slits and one with a single vertical slit. Light passes through these apertures only at the intersection of the slits. Directed by the machine's control logic, the apertures are positioned so that light rays from only the desired character image pass through the intersection. However, because of the control circuitry built into the machine, the projection of a specific character's image need not originate in precisely the same location each time the character is used. Timing of the flash and movement of the apertures can be controlled to vary the optical path between the displacement limits. Character width, interword spacing, and intercharacter spacing are all considered during movement of the optical path. Only after maximum displacement of the optical path has occurred will the carriage advance.

Interline spacing

The interline-spacing subsystem establishes the *leading*—the vertical distance separating sequential lines of typeset copy. After each line is set, the end-of-line function code from the input source triggers a mechanism that advances the film or paper the proper distance. Leading information is often entered through a manual setting on inexpensive phototypesetters but is generally entered as a function code on larger, more versatile machines.

Capabilities and configurations

In describing and rating the performance characteristics of phototypesetting machines, a number of criteria are used. These include speed of operation, size range of type handled, number of sizes, number of styles or fonts, number of characters per font, line length, and leading. In addition, special capabilities may also be considered.

Speeds of typesetting machines most often are expressed in lines per minute. To further standardize this parameter, the expression *lines per minute* has come to mean single-column newspaper text lines of about 30 characters. Even this is not a very precise

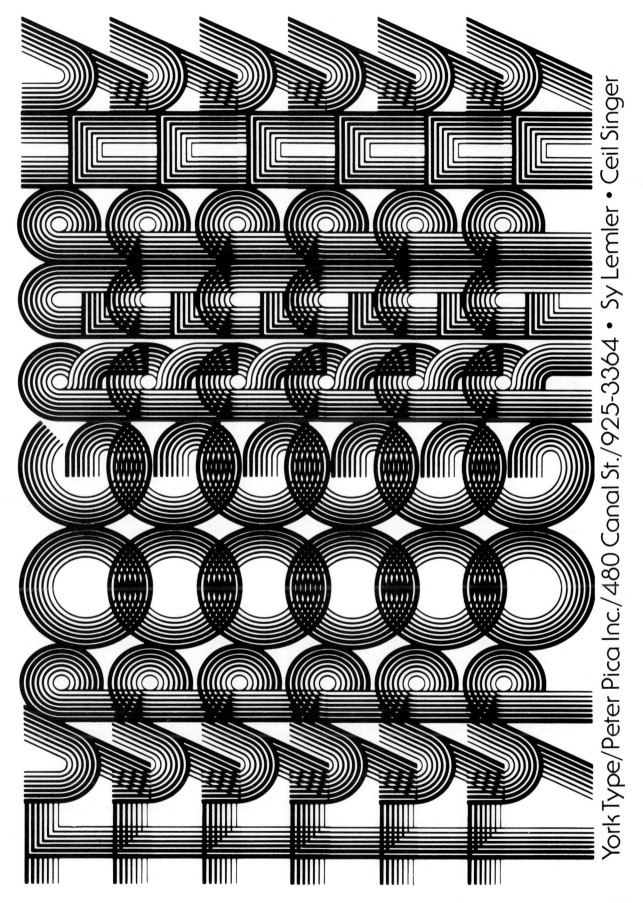

York Type/Peter Pica Inc./480 Canal St./925-3364 • Sy Lemler • Ceil Singer

measure of performance because the setting of display composition in which machine settings are changed often within lines or between lines introduces variables which are independent of the mechanics of simply laying down characters. Lines per minute, however, is the best available expression of relative speed available today and is used widely.

Second-generation phototypesetters vary from 18 to 150 lines per minute in operating speeds. Most, however, fall into an intermediate range of 25 to 60 lines per minute, with only a minority of the devices ranging above that. The higher speeds are associated with the larger machines also offering more comprehensive ranges of type sizes and styles.

Type sizes that can be set on second-generation equipment range between a low of 4 to 6 points to an upper limit of 18, 24, 36, 48 or 72 points depending on the particular model of machine. Most machines fall into two distinct groups, one which offers an upper limit of 24- to 36-point type and another which extends its range to 72-point. The actual number of type sizes offered within these ranges varies widely, from a single size up to 138 or more different sizes. There is no particular level within this range at which most machines have been standardized.

The number of styles of fonts which a machine can hold at one time, however, is highly concentrated in the area of 2 to 6. A smaller group of machines, the larger devices, has a font capacity in the area of 16 to 18, and a few phototypesetters handle 10, 12, or 15 fonts simultaneously.

The number of characters per font in second-generation machines ranges from 84 to 120, with most machines handling either 96-character fonts or 110- to 112-character fonts.

Maximum line lengths set by these machines range from 33 picas to 100 picas, almost wide enough to set a line the width of a full standard-size newspaper page. Many second-generation machines, however, have adopted a maximum line length of 45 picas. (It should be noted that these line-length parameters apply primarily to tape-operated machines and some direct-entry units designed for setting text. Other direct-entry machines, which are essentially keyboard-operated display setting devices, produce single lines on a continuous strip of very narrow film or paper and can have an infinite line length.)

All presently available second-generation phototypesetters offer very fine interline spacing. The vast majority offer ½-point leading increments, and a few offer ¼-point.

Special capabilities which may also be found in certain phototypesetters include automatic justification and hyphenation facilities, format storage, and other items. These are all functions of computerized systems and are accomplished by use of a minicomputer built into the "front end" of the machine. The computers range from very small units to quite sizable ones which have the ability to perform surprisingly sophisticated operations.

Hyphenation programs for these machines are of two types: *logic* and *logic-plus-dictionary*. All of the programs use logical rules to determine points where words may be hyphenated to end lines. However, no purely logical system can hyphenate all words correctly, and dictionaries of frequently used words that are exceptions to the rules sometimes supplement the logic program. The computer first checks the dictionary to see if the word to be broken is stored there. If it is, that hyphenation is used; if not, the word is broken logically.

An added feature of some hyphenation programs is the *discretionary hyphen*, inserted by the keyboard operator during original input keyboarding wherever words may be broken. When the computer must break the word, it chooses one of the discretionary points so identified and ignores the others.

Format storage has been developed to save substantial amounts of keyboard work in the setting of complex matter such as tables and certain types of repetitive display material. All of the specific instruction codes are typed only once at the beginning of the job. The set of codes for each specific format is stored in its own computer memory slot in the typesetting machine. At any point during keyboarding when that particular type specification is needed for a bit of copy, the keyboard operator can type a single format identification code. This code in the typesetting machine's computer causes all of the associated operating codes stored in the format slot to be withdrawn and used to control the machine in setting that copy. Format coding has become a powerful feature of modern phototypesetting machines. Some applications are described in "Niceties of Photocomposition," page 158.

One additional recent development of special importance is the *reverse leading* capability found on some second-generation machines. This is, simply, the ability to back the film up in the machine automatically without losing its position registration. Thus one column of type can be set and the film backed up to set another alongside the first. This ability to make up multicolumn formats by backing up the film saves considerable computer time and space when producing full pages from the machine and makes full-page composition on one piece of film or paper far more practical. Reverse leading is increasingly important as typesetters are required to accept material directly from

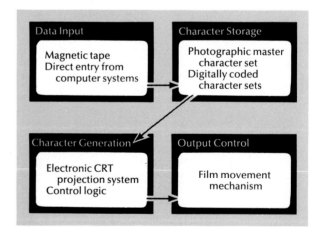

Figure 6.23: **Third-generation phototypesetting principles.** Basic functions performed by third-generation cathode ray tube typesetters are illustrated in the sequence in which they occur.

Figure 6.24: Third-generation phototypesetters. Two current types of third-generation machines are the Linotron 606 (left) and the Harris 7400. *Courtesy of Mergenthaler Linotype Co. and Harris Corporation, Composition Systems Division.*

electronic editing and display composition systems which can completely prepare material for full-page output.

THIRD-GENERATION PHOTOTYPESETTERS

Third-generation CRT, or "digitized," phototypesetters produce typeset material by electronically selecting character images and exposing them on the face of a cathode ray tube (CRT). The major subsystems making up a CRT phototypesetter include data input, character storage, character generation, and output control (as diagrammed in figure 6.23).

Input

Most CRT phototypesetters presently operate in an off-line mode, with computer-generated magnetic tape as their input source. The tape contains the same character, function, and interline spacing codes associated with second-generation devices. Magnetic tape is also used for loading fonts into those CRT phototypesetters using digital character storage. (Two third-generation machines are illustrated in figure 6.24.)

Character storage

Character storage in third-generation phototypesetters is either photographic or digital.

Photographic storage requires the positioning of master character sets in an optical path. The photographic images are then scanned and converted to digital signals for use in operating the character-generation subsystem. Access to fonts not already stored within the machine requires manual changing.

Digital storage defines character shapes by digital coding which is read and processed by a computer. The information required to describe all of the characters digitally is so voluminous that peripheral mag-

netic disc systems are required to maintain a reasonable font selection within control of the computer typesetting system. Magnetic disc systems may be directly interfaced with the main computer system or with the phototypesetter.

Character generation

Generation of character images for CRT phototypesetters occurs from electronic projection of character descriptions stored within the machine. Phototypesetters that use photographic storage employ two CRT's to generate character images. One CRT is a scanning device that describes the character shape, while the second translates this pattern and displays the character in the correct size and position for exposure onto the output medium. Machines that store characters digitally use a single display CRT.

Characters can be formed on the face of the video tube of a CRT typesetter by a number of techniques, but they all are methods of scanning—that is, moving an electron beam across the face of the tube and turning it on and off at appropriate times to form the character image or images on the screen. Characters are in a sense "painted" on the screen by strokes of light. The electron beam is very small in diameter and is highly focused on the tube face, creating very fine strokes. When high-quality definition is required, a text character may be composed of a hundred or more such lines. Despite the large number of strokes required to form a character, the extremely fast operating speeds of electronic systems permit as many as 1,000 or more such characters to be produced on the tube face in a second.

To generate type characters, three basic methods or principles are used: stroke, line, and page.

In the *stroke* method, only vertical deflection of the electron beam is used. Each stroke displayed on the face of the CRT is located in exactly the same position. No horizontal movement of the electron beam occurs at any time. A mechanically driven prism lays down each vertical slice of the character side by side, one at a time. A series of timing lines synchronizes movement of the prism with generation of each stroke.

The *line* method utilizes horizontal as well as vertical deflection of the electron beam to typeset a complete line and a mechanical system to advance the film or paper between lines. This method is much faster than the stroke method because electronic beam deflection is faster than mechanical action. However, the extra speed is achieved at the cost of a more expensive, larger CRT and more complicated circuitry to compensate for distortion of the electron beam as it moves away from the center of the tube.

The *page* method uses both horizontal and vertical deflection of the electron beam to set a complete area or page of type without any mechanical movement. The output film or paper is advanced only between pages. Although the fastest typesetting method of all, it is the most expensive.

The Fototronic CRT uses a combination of the line and page methods. It combines beam motion with motion of the output film or paper for both horizontal and vertical placement of characters. Horizontal character placement is accomplished by beam deflection across the full 11.5-inch width of the CRT display tube. In addition, the output film or paper is on a carriage that can be shifted sideways if a wider line is required.

Also part of character generation for CRT phototypesetters is the system used to change point sizes. In scanning systems, height adjustments are made by changing the length of the scan stroke. Width changes are more complex and must be accomplished either by increasing the dimensions of the electron beam while spacing the strokes farther apart, or by maintaining a constant electron beam size and using more strokes to describe the character.

CRT phototypesetters designed for photographic character storage vary point size by using a constant stroke width in the display CRT and increasing or decreasing the number of strokes used to create the character. This is done by varying spacing of the vertical scan lines in the scanning CRT in relation to the point size. For example, for a 5-point width, the master character image would be scanned in half as many strokes as used for a 10-point width. When combined with a constant beam width in the display CRT, the result is a character width or point size in proportion to the number of scanning strokes.

Output control

As in second-generation machines, the final system component is a film-holding mechanism which permits the film to be moved as type is set. While film can be advanced between lines, many CRT machines are designed to set entire pages in one film position, moving the film only between pages.

Capabilities and configurations

CRT typesetters generally are designed for large-scale, high-speed composition installations; machines for small shops, such as direct-entry devices, are not available. All CRT machines are "slave" devices; that is, they are operated under the control of coded tape or floppy disc or from signals transmitted directly from a computer by wire.

Because these machines operate at very high speeds —anywhere from 400 to 5,000 newspaper text lines per minute—they generally must contain all the fonts required to set a large amount of type without stopping for manual changeovers. CRT typesetters, therefore, typically provide a complete range of type sizes from 4-point to 48-point or 72-point; one machine even goes up to 80-point. They also offer many sizes within the range, from 22 on up to several hundred. In number of fonts or type styles offered, however, some machines are as limited as many second-generation machines, offering only four or five. Other machines, however, will hold a dozen or more font styles at one time, providing virtually a complete composing room in one machine. Being computer-oriented, these machines also often provide some kind of "front-end" computer capability for hyphenation and/or format control.

A major trend in typesetting machine development today among CRT machines is toward longer maximum line lengths. Several new devices can set lines as long as 100 picas, long enough to produce a full eight-column newspaper page at one time on one piece of film or paper. Such full-page machines will become the output mechanisms for the new computer-based editorial, classified, and display ad production systems which are now moving into newspapers across the country. They will "set" halftones and line art in place on the page as well as type, as is now being done for *U.S. News & World Report*.

Ultimately, however, technologists foresee that even these full-page film typesetters will be replaced by printing-plate engraving machines operated directly from coded computer data, producing press plates directly and bypassing the film stages of processing. This, in turn, will require the inclusion of illustrative material (including halftones) in the computer-based system for setting on the plate via the engraving machine. Such things have been done experimentally, and two first-generation newspaper plate engraving machines are now being marketed commercially.

KEYBOARDS

Frank J. Romano, GRAPHIC ARTS MARKETING ASSOCIATES

Futurists have been predicting a day when the spoken word might be translated automatically into machine codes, but so far the act of striking keys on a keyboard to activate an encoding mechanism remains firmly entrenched as the basic method of initially getting text material into electronic form for later manipulation and typesetting. Keyboarding shows no sign of being displaced from this role in the foreseeable future. Even such advanced technologies as optical character recognition and video displays do not eliminate keyboarding of most informational material —they simply reduce the amount of keyboarding required or speed subsequent processing.

Keyboards were the earliest means employed to automate the manual processes of converting written words to printed forms. Both the typewriter and the first typesetting machines, invented in the 1800's, used the striking of keys to assemble character images in proper sequence at several times the speed of writing or setting type by hand.

The first keyboard machine is generally credited to Dr. William Church, who invented a typesetting device in 1822. By the end of the 1800's, two typesetting systems, the Linotype and the Monotype, had joined the typewriter as keyboard-operated machines for encoding written language into other forms for reproduction and dissemination.

Since then, many kinds of keyboards have been developed and used in many industries—keypunch units for computer input, teletypes for communications transmission, and the like. All of these have remained

Figure 6.26: Stand-alone keyboard. Keyboard unit produces coded tape which is then used to control a separate type-setting machine. *Courtesy of AM Varityper.*

closely tied to original keyboard principles, however, and keyboards for graphic arts use have retained many of the fundamental characteristics of those two earliest typesetting keyboards.

The Linotype machine, for example, has a keyboard built into it as an integral part of the machine; such machines are known today as *direct-entry units* (see figure 6.25). The Monotype, on the other hand, divides keyboarding from the actual casting of type by using a *stand-alone* keyboard (see figure 6.26) and a typecaster. A punched paper tape or ribbon is used to record keyboarded codes and transfer them to the typecaster. In this configuration, called *off-line* operation, neither the keyboard nor the caster is limited by the mechanics of the other unit, and each can be operated at its own optimum speed.

In the 1920's, Walter Morey proposed the Teletypesetter (TTS) system of operating linecasting machines from punched paper tape in much the same manner as Monotype casters, but from distant locations. His method adapted Teletype keyboards used for wire transmission to the production of punched paper tape, which was then run through a special tape-reading and control unit mounted on the linecasting-machine keyboard.

These ideas have been carried through to modern typesetting systems, with certain elaborations and refinements. In addition to the major division between

Figure 6.25: Direct-entry keyboard. Keyboard is built into a single unit with the rest of the typesetting machine. *Courtesy of Compugraphic Corp.*

219

direct-entry keyboards, which are permanently attached to their associated typesetting machines, and off-line or stand-alone keyboards, the important characteristics which keyboards possess can be grouped into four categories: counting capabilities, coding structures and keyboard arrangements, visual displays, and output forms.

COUNTING CAPABILITIES

Counting capability in a keyboard is the ability of the machine to add up the widths of the characters being typed in a line and to indicate when the line is full enough for the typesetting machine to justify it. Keyboards range all the way from no counting ability whatsoever to sophisticated multicolumn justification capabilities.

Keyboards with no counting capability at all are properly called *non-counting* keyboards, but are sometimes referred to as *idiot* machines. The output from these units is a string of machine codes for the characters to be set without any end-of-line or justification codes interspersed at the proper points. Before the output of a non-counting keyboard can be used to drive a typesetting machine, these additional codes must be inserted by a subsequent operation such as a pass through a computer hyphenation and justification (H & J) program. If desired, most keyboards with counting ability can also be used as non-counting keyboards.

All keyboards with counting ability are called *counting* keyboards regardless of their capacities to handle simple or complex justification problems. Specific counting systems used in these keyboards vary, but in principle most employ a subtraction process. The line measure is entered in memory, and as each character is struck its width value is subtracted from the line length. The number of variable spaces in the line also is totalled. When the remaining space left in the line to be filled moves within the maximum and minimum limits to which the spaces can be varied, the machine will indicate that the line can be justified (see figure 6.27). When the operator sees or hears this indication, he selects an appropriate ending point for the line—either a word space or a point where the word can be hyphenated—and types an end-of-line code key. This causes an end-of-line code to be inserted in the output stream and the counting mechanism to be reset for a new line.

If the line is not ended properly within the justification zone, the machine will signal an *overset* condition, requiring that some characters be taken out of the line until it will fit. The justification zone—that is, the range between the minimum and maximum width values of all the spaces in the line—can be preset on many keyboards to produce tighter or looser spacing between words. Tighter spacing using word spaces with less expansion capability produces better quality typesetting, but the use of wider spaces between words makes it easier to justify lines which may have awkward breaks at the end.

In order for keyboard counters to count character widths, they must be supplied with the various width values for the characters in the fonts being set. The many thousands of type fonts in use today vary widely

Figure 6.27: Line-length/justification indicator. Used on a counting keyboard, indicator displays numerically the amount of space left in a line and signals the operator when the line can be justified by the typesetting machine. *Courtesy of Compugraphic Corp.*

in size and shape of their characters, and there is no standard set of width values that applies across the board to all fonts. Some fonts have been designed specifically to standard unit systems (see "Fundamentals of Type," page 110), but most unit-designed fonts still contain variations which prevent these units from being used easily in counting mechanisms. Therefore, counting keyboards generally provide means for inserting custom sets of character-width values for each type font being used.

A number of systems have been used for changing character-width values. The Monotype system, the first to set type from a counting keyboard, used interchangeable justifying scales on drums to accommodate different fonts. The Teletypesetter system made use of changeable width plugs which had unit values for specific typefaces wired in as electrical contacts. A commonly used method of portable character-width storage in today's keyboards is the printed circuit board, which plugs into electronic sockets in the equipment. Keyboards equipped with computer-type memory units can be programmed with the appropriate character widths by recording width codes on a tape and running it through a tape reader on the machine to read the values into memory.

The ability of a counting keyboard to justify various kinds of typeset material automatically without the direction of an operator depends on the complexity of the computing circuitry provided. Simpler keyboards provide only a single justification computation; any tabular or indented setting with aligned columns within the overall line length is left to the keyboard operator, who must insert fixed and variable spaces individually by mentally calculating how many to place in each position in the line and then striking every space key required. More complex keyboards, however, enable the operator to simply strike one or two keys which will cause the machine to automatically compute and insert more complex spacing codes for the typesetter.

Many counting keyboards today offer automatic *leadering* and *quadding*. Leadering is the process of setting dots in a listing of items with two or more columns, such as a table of contents, so that the dots lead the eye from the appropriate line in the first column to the associated line in the second. Automatic leadering lets the operator specify that this is desired by striking one key, after which the machine will calculate how many such leader dots must be inserted to fill out the space between the two lines of type. Quadding, similarly, is the process of inserting space on either side of a line to position it at the left or the right or in the center of the total line measure. A keyboard with automatic quadding will compute and produce all output codes required to accomplish this on a typesetting machine upon a single keyboard command from the keyboard operator.

Advanced counting features in keyboards can range up to the ability to formulate all of the commands for setting complete areas of display composition, such as chapter openings of books, standardized parts of display advertisements, or the different submeasures and typefaces to be used in a multicolumn table. With such facilities in a keyboard, a good operator can actually encode all of the material to produce finished typeset pages from a phototypesetting machine.

With the addition of some computer-type memory capacity, some keyboards can now store and call back predetermined *formats,* or sets of typographic instructions, for insertion in the output stream at appropriate points. The storing of such formats greatly reduces the amount of typing required of the operator on jobs containing many changes in typefaces, sizes, and measures. The operator simply types out the detailed instruction codes for each format at the beginning of the job and stores these in memory. A master code character is associated with each stored format. When a particular format is needed, the operator strikes only the master code, and this in turn causes all of the stored operating codes to be inserted in the output stream automatically.

CODING STRUCTURES, KEYBOARD ARRANGEMENTS

One general rule governs the number of codes and keys required on a keyboard: the more characters and/or machine commands required in a typeset job, the more codes and keys required on the keyboard. There are only a few options open to designers of keyboards for obtaining additional characters and codes, and the debates over which technique is best have at times been heated.

Although there are a number of different machine-code structures used in the computer, communications, and graphic arts industries, all of them are constructed on the same principles. The basic Teletypesetter (TTS) code, used as the basis for most of today's graphic arts keyboards, illustrates these principles. In TTS perforated paper tape, the presence or absence of holes in the tape represents encoded *bits* of information. Each bit is assigned a specific position on the tape. The presence of a hole represents one kind of information recorded in the bit position; the absence of a hole represents another kind of information in that bit position. When several bit positions are grouped together into a vertical row, complex codes can be built up.

In figure 6.28, the TTS code is shown as having six bit positions, called *levels.* Each level can hold either a hole or a blank space, representing two kinds of information. One level, then, can represent two different conditions, or in the case of type, two different characters. If another level is combined with the first, however, the number of unique bit combinations possible doubles to four; if a third is added, the number of possible combinations doubles again to eight; and so on until a code of any desired size is created. The TTS code, with six levels, contains 64 different bit combina-

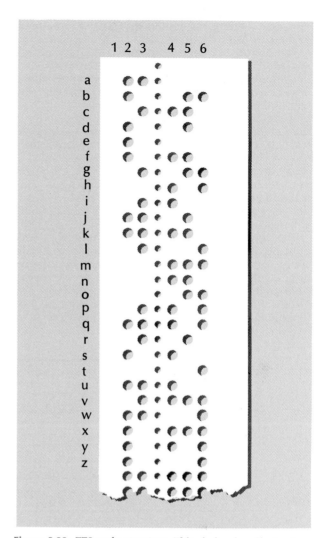

Figure 6.28: TTS code structure. This six-level code structure is a portion of the Teletypesetter (TTS) code used widely in typesetting systems. All codes are made up of six data positions. On typesetting tapes, these positions are arranged across the tape, and different characters are represented by the presence or absence of various data bits. Each character or command code has its own unique combination of bits. On paper tapes, holes are punched to represent data bits; on magnetic tapes, the data bit areas are magnetized.

tions, and each character in the type font is assigned one of these combinations as its very own code.

Type fonts typically have many more than 64 characters, however, and the TTS system accommodates them all by use of a *shift* or *precedence* code. One of the 64 basic codes is reserved for the shift function rather than being assigned to a character; when it is used, it causes the machine to change the meaning of the codes immediately following so that they stand for characters different from those which would be represented if the shift code had not been present. Thus the code for the lowercase a, if preceded by the shift code, becomes instead the code for the uppercase A. This shift technique virtually doubles the capacity of the six-level TTS code structure to represent different characters. Sometimes a third *supershift* code is also used, adding yet another potential 62 characters to the keyboard repertoire.

The precedence-code technique is also used to obtain additional control or command codes, particularly in computer-based systems which use relatively simple keyboard units to prepare input for computers that will further process the material for typesetting. Here one symbol such as a dollar sign or asterisk often is used before conventional character codes to designate machine commands. The characters used are usually chosen to represent shorthand expressions of the full terms involved in the command, to make the coded instructions readable to the human eye. Thus a command to set a given line in 12-point type on a 24-pica line measure might read: *p12*L24. Such symbolic abbreviations are called *mnemonics*.

The only alternative to use of the precedence-code principle in obtaining more characters and command codes from a keyboard is to add more keys to the machine. Several keyboards developed over the years have gone to the extreme of one key per code generated, the oldest of these being the Monotype keyboard which has more than 250 keys on it. The other

extreme, of course, is the straight typewriter keyboard with a minimum of 44 keys for the alphabet, punctuation, numerals, a few special symbols, and a shift. Both of these extreme examples have been used successfully to input material into computer and typesetting systems.

The trade-off in operator time consumed is subtle. Use of the shift principle requires more keystrokes by the operator to set a given piece of material, but the length of reach required to hit various keys is reduced. Use of many more single-code keys requires only one stroke per character set, but on a keyboard such as the Monotype the length of reach often results in a hunt-and-peck kind of keyboarding rather than the faster typewriting style. Advocates of the larger number of keys, on the other hand, claim that finding special characters on shift-style keyboards often is just as time-consuming. The debate has raged for many years without clear resolution. Most keyboard arrangements today begin with use of the standard typewriter layout, including the primary shift for capital letters; but beyond this each achieves its own compromise between more keys and more shifting. The number of keys on

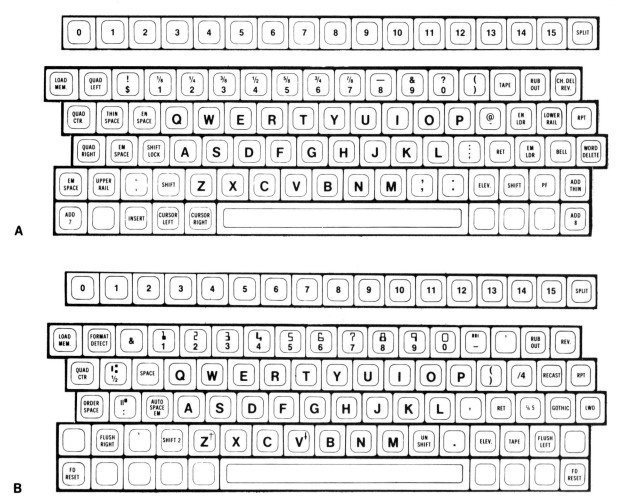

Figure 6.29: Four keyboard layouts to fit different typesetting requirements: (a) layout designed for newspaper work; (b) layout suited to setting OCR type for bank checks; (c) layout for book and general job composition set on a Comp/

222

most of today's graphic arts keyboards designed specifically for typesetting ranges from 68 to 157. Of these, the number of command or function keys (as opposed to character-setting keys) ranges from none at all to 99.

While keyboard layouts may be limited to compromises of this type, code structures are not. The six-level TTS code structure has been widely used for a long time in the graphic arts, but there is a movement under way toward eight-level codes, which are more efficient in subsequent machine processing and which better fit modern computer code configurations based on 8, 12, or 16 bits of information per character. An eight-level code, for example, contains four times as many unique character or command designations as a six-level code, and it can be processed in a single machine cycle rather than the two required by a precedence-code system.

The higher level code structures place no limitations on keyboard layout designs or on the use of shift or precedence coding. The keyboard unit is simply equipped with relatively inexpensive electronic circuits which take the signals from both shift keys and character or command keys and combine them into a single unique eight-level code for the output stream.

Finally, keyboard arrangements vary in one other important way—the special characters they can encode. Despite the fact that large keyboards can accommodate several hundred different characters, there are so many thousands of characters available today that no keyboard could possibly handle them all simultaneously. Therefore, specific keyboard layouts with special combinations of characters to fit individual jobs or types of jobs are very common. Figure 6.29 shows four layouts designed to meet different requirements. Quite often a keyboard will be purchased with special character assignments built into it by the manufacturer. On other keyboards, special interchangeable overlay templates are used to show which keys will encode special characters used in different jobs. Obviously, in such situations the layout of code structure and fonts in the typesetting machine must be coordinated with these special keyboard layouts. The planning of character/key assignments on keyboards often is one of the most time-consuming planning tasks in setting up a new typesetting system.

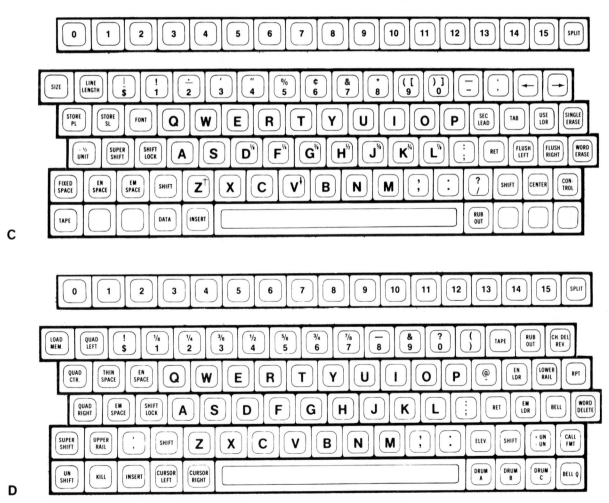

Set 500; (d) another layout for job work. Basic typewriter layout is standard, but special characters and commands vary with application.
Courtesy of AM Varityper.

Figure 6.30: Hardcopy keyboard display. Hardcopy is a typed version of material to be typeset, produced by a typing mechanism built into the keyboard or from a separate print-out device attached to the typesetting system. *Courtesy of IBM Office Products Division.*

VISUAL DISPLAYS

Visual display facilities on a keyboard unit permit the operator to see what is being typed, just as a typist can see the characters being struck on the paper in a typewriter. Some typesetting keyboards, in fact, employ typewriter-style keybars, platens, and paper to actually produce a typescript of the keyboarded work. Other keyboards use different means of showing the characters, while some include no visual display of the work at all. Keyboards that have no visual display of any kind are called *blind* keyboards. Those using the typewriter mechanism are called *hardcopy* keyboards because they produce a permanent physical copy of what was typed into the machine (see figure 6.30). A

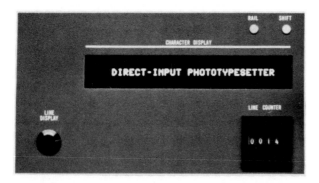

Figure 6.31: Visual keyboard display. Last several characters or words typed into the machine are displayed electronically on the indicator panel. As each new character is typed at one end of the panel, all displayed characters move down one position and the oldest character disappears from the other end of the display. *Courtesy of Compugraphic Corp.*

third classification consists of keyboards with *soft* displays—that is, characters projected on a video screen or formed by electronic diode matrices. These character images are not permanent but change as each new character is struck.

Soft displays are of several types. The simplest is the *last code* type, which shows only the last code entered into the machine. The *floating* display shows a number of characters and function codes on a one-line electronic display (see figure 6.31). As new characters are added to one end of the line, previously typed characters move toward the other end and disappear. The *cathode ray tube* or *CRT* display is a television-like screen on which several lines of text can be shown (see figure 6.32.) As lines are completed, the previously set lines are advanced and disappear one at a time off the screen. CRT displays generally are used on equipment that permits editing and correction of the material as well as original keyboarding, so that anything displayed on the screen normally can be changed

Figure 6.32: VDT keyboard display. A number of lines of text, up to a full manuscript page, are displayed on a video screen. Usually such devices will also allow the operator to change any character on the screen after it has been typed. The oldest line moves off the screen as each new line is begun. *Courtesy of AM Varityper.*

via keyboard control even if the operator has typed well beyond the point at which the correction is to be made. Such devices are usually classified as video display terminals (VDT's) for editing and correction rather than as input keyboards, even though such terminals are being used increasingly today for original input operations. (VDT's are discussed in greater detail in "Video Display Terminals," page 230.)

The need for visual displays on keyboards has been another greatly debated subject over the years. A great deal depends on the specific working patterns in the individual typesetting system, and there are no firmly established general rules about the need for and use of such displays.

OUTPUT FORMS

The coded output of graphic arts keyboards can be in one of several forms: perforated paper tape, magnetic tape, typewritten sheets of machine-readable copy, or electronic impulses which can be fed directly into other machines in the typesetting system.

Six-level punched paper tape has been the most widely used output medium for many years, primarily because of the widespread use of the TTS system. This is changing, however, with the introduction into the typesetting process of computers and higher level code structures. While paper tape still accounts for a majority of keyboard output, it will eventually be replaced by magnetic media, by machine-readable typing, or by wiring input keyboards directly to other typesetting equipment.

One kind of magnetic output medium is magnetic tape—either reels of computer tape or the smaller cassettes used also for audio recording. The use of magnetic tape cassettes has been spurred significantly by the development of the *word processing* field, a movement to automate and streamline office-type operations. As the name implies, word processing involves the origination and manipulation of text material. One of its chief tools is the *input revision typewriter* (IRT), a machine which records on magnetic tape as it types on paper. The tape can then be played back through the unit and corrections made in the recorded material. Such devices are now being used for preparing material for typesetting.

While most IRT's today use the magnetic tape cassette as their primary storage medium, another magnetic device, the floppy disc, may in the future take part of this task. The floppy disc is a magnetic storage disc housed in a portable plastic envelope. It slips easily in and out of a slot in the keyboard machine, affording quick random access to any material recorded on it. Tape, on the other hand, must be run sequentially through the reader until the desired material is found. Floppy discs are now available with a few IRT's and with a few computer-based typesetting systems.

Typewritten sheets of machine-readable copy are intended for use with an optical character recognition (OCR) device, which scans the typed images, recognizing the unique characters and translating them into machine-readable codes. OCR systems are discussed more completely in "Optical Character Recognition" (following). It should be noted here that keyboards for OCR input consist essentially of electric typewriters equipped with special OCR-recognizable type fonts, plus whatever additional counting and formatting capabilities are desired. The OCR fonts are readable to the human eye as well as to the machine, so that the typed hardcopy can also be proofread.

As more complete electronic systems for editing and typesetting are developed and installed, the number of input keyboards connected directly to the rest of the system by wire will increase. However, there will always be a need for off-line keyboards, and the other output media will continue to be widely used.

OPTICAL CHARACTER RECOGNITION

Frank J. Romano, GRAPHIC ARTS MARKETING ASSOCIATES

As the computer industry grew, it became evident that a major limitation of systems operations was the relatively slow speed of keyboarding required to enter material into computer systems—a process shared with the typesetting field. Over the years, a number of technological avenues have been explored to either reduce or eliminate keyboarding effort. One of the first was *optical character recognition* (OCR), now one of the most widely used methods. OCR has also found application in typesetting, as the computer has moved into this field. Two OCR machines used in the graphic arts are shown in figure 6.33.

Optical character recognition is a process in which the OCR device "sees" what is written or printed on paper, reads the characters, and translates them into codes which can be handled by machines. As such, OCR does not directly replace keyboarding. If material has been typed or printed previously for another purpose in a typeface which an OCR unit can recognize, then a second keyboarding can be avoided by simply letting the unit read the material from the previously printed documents. However, if the material to be encoded is not in OCR-readable form, then it must be rekeyboarded on a typewriter equipped with an OCR-readable type font.

There have been many general business and commerce applications in which OCR has eliminated keyboarding. For example, bank checks preprinted ahead of time can be optically read after they are written and cashed, for updating of bank records. Tests with answer spaces which are filled in with special soft pencils can be marked and graded automatically by machine through optical reading of the answers. Data imprinted from credit cards onto charge slips when items are purchased can be read off by machines for processing of account records. Information printed in certain specified areas of forms can be selectively extracted by optically reading only those areas designated by the controlling program in the OCR unit.

In graphic arts, the possibility has existed for a long

time of reading previously printed material into machine code for further processing and republication. However, because most published material is new or extensively rewritten, this application has not become a major factor. Instead, most OCR applications in graphic arts have involved keyboarding in an OCR-readable face. In newspaper work, for example, it has been possible to have reporters write their stories originally on OCR-font typewriters, so that the copy does not have to be rekeyed in the composing room. In other situations, copy has been typed for OCR entry rather than another form of entry because OCR-typed copy can be read into systems at very high speeds compatible with other computer operations.

THE OCR PROCESS

To permit processing of a manuscript by an OCR system, the typed pages or documents must satisfy the criteria of the OCR reader. Some of these constraints are:

· The type style must be one that the OCR reader "knows."

· The character set used should not exceed the character library in the OCR unit.

· The paper or document material must be acceptable to the reader.

· The line length and line placement must be appropriate for the reader.

Most optical character recognition machines consist of four basic units: the document transport unit, the reading unit, the recognition unit, and the format and control unit (as diagrammed in figure 6.34).

The transport unit moves the documents from an input hopper or feed roll past one or more scanning units to one or more output stackers. In certain equipment the documents are read while still moving, but in most cases the document is stopped and read. Document transports employ combinations of vacuum, air blast, and friction to separate and feed individual documents, while belts and rollers are used to transport the documents past the scanning unit.

The speed of most OCR systems is limited by the speed of the document transport. The scanning unit determines the speed of the OCR unit when the amount of data per document is large.

Based on the types of input documents they handle, OCR units are classified into two groups: *document readers* and *page readers*. Document readers generally can read one to five lines of data from a small-size document such as a coupon or stub card. Page readers normally handle larger sheets of paper such as manuscript pages and are designed to take in a widely variable amount of alphanumeric information typed in regular page format.

Reading of characters in OCR systems is done by scanning techniques. A single point of light is moved over the character image, and the light and dark portions of the scanning pattern are fixed on a matrix. The dark portions of the image represent dots on the matrix, and it is then possible to assign X and Y coordinates to the dots. Thus, the character image is converted to a dot pattern, and each of the dots can be represented numerically in the electronic system as an X-Y coordinate.

Figure 6.33: OCR machines. Two typical character recognition units used in graphic arts applications are the Compu-Scan Alpha (top) and the ECRM Autoreader (bottom). *Courtesy of CompuScan, Inc. and ECRM, Inc.*

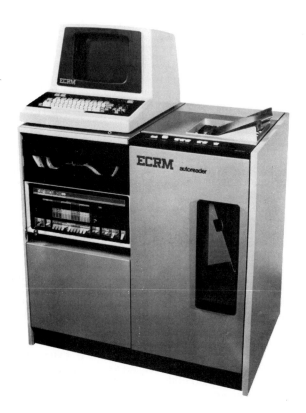

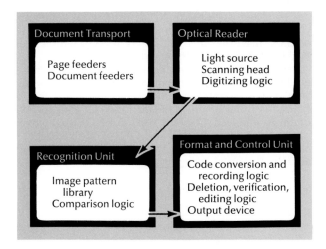

Figure 6.34: OCR machine principles. Basic functions performed by optical character recognition machines used in typesetting are shown in the sequence in which they occur.

OCR readers scan several hundred lines to the inch in each of the two planes to achieve fairly high levels of resolution. The process of reducing the image shape to dots on a matrix is sometimes called *digitizing*, or converting the image to digital representation.

Scanners are either mechanical or electronic. Mechanical scanners control the movement of the light point by means of mirrors. Some mechanical scanners position the document on a drum and rotate the document to derive one plane; a mirror establishes the other plane. Electronic scanners use CRT (cathode ray tube) principles and control the light point by electronic deflection plates.

Once the character image has been digitized, it is then passed on to the recognition stage, where the character being read is compared to a library of all known image patterns. This is called *correlation*. When a reasonable comparison is achieved, the character is identified.

The identified character is now passed on to the format and control section, where the information is organized for proper recording on the output tape. The control and format section also takes care of such things as discarding characters that were marked by the typist or editor for deletion. Some systems also utilize a small video screen on which unidentifiable characters are shown. If the reader scans a character but cannot find a comparison in the character library, the operator can interpret the image on the screen, insert the correct character back into the system via a keyboard, or take other appropriate action.

The output of OCR systems may be magnetic tape, punched paper tape, or signals sent to a computer directly over wires. Magnetic tape is usually used on higher speed machines because of the higher recording speeds, but paper tape can also be used if the speed sacrifice is not important.

OCR TYPE FONTS

Optical character recognition devices read a wide variety of images, all the way from simple pencil marks to a variety of printed typefaces and, in a few instances, even stylized handwritten characters. The more elaborate the character design and the more designs to be read, the more complex and costly the machinery must be. OCR systems can be classified into three groups based on the kinds of marks or fonts they can read: *optical mark readers, stylized-font readers,* and *multifont readers.*

Optical mark readers are an improvement over the mark sensing techniques in which the location of graphite pencil marks was determined by measuring the electrical conductivity of the pencil mark. Now, most mark reading is done optically. At one time, optical mark readers were used primarily in scoring tests and questionnaires and in survey applications. Today, they are also used as data acquisition devices in payroll, inventory control, meter reading, and similar applications.

For use in preparing text input to composition systems, a variation of the mark reading idea has been developed. This is the so-called *bar-code* or *associated-code* reader which recognizes bar-like symbols typed on the manuscript page along with the roman alphabet characters they represent. The characters are readable by people; the bar codes are readable by the machine. Actually the codes need not be bars, although many are; they may also be dot patterns or other special marks. Some systems use typewritten pages to feed into the OCR unit, but others type the text and codes onto continuous strips of paper tape which are then fed into the reader. Using special codes for machine reading instead of scanning the characters directly makes possible a lower cost machine, but it also can make editing of the OCR copy prior to scanning more difficult.

Most OCR systems used in the graphic arts are stylized-font readers. As the name implies, these readers recognize conventional alphabet characters, but only if they have been designed especially to match the recognition patterns built into the machine. Some of these units are multifont readers in the sense that they can recognize several stylized fonts. Other multifont readers are capable of reading nonstylized typefaces used in conventional printing or typing. The much higher cost of nonstylized-font readers, however, weighs heavily in favor of using stylized-font machines to read copy typed on typewriters equipped with the special OCR faces.

The number of OCR stylized typefaces has grown in recent years. There are today about 50 major type fonts in common use on typewriters and computer printout devices, two of the main sources of OCR input. To hold down the cost of OCR machines and to improve the error rates in recognizing characters, OCR manufacturers have gradually developed their own stylized faces instead of using the existing faces. Unfortunately, a lack of standardization in OCR faces has severely limited the growth and acceptance of OCR as an input technique, and only recently have two OCR faces gained enough widespread support to become adopted as industry-wide standards.

The more widely used of these two OCR faces is one commonly called OCR-A, which was adopted as a United States standard by the USA Standards Institute. It is suitable for both OCR scanning and for conventional typing of correspondence and other documents, so that typewriters equipped with the font can be used for a variety of purposes. Almost all font-reading OCR systems can accept OCR-A today.

The second commonly used font is ISO-B, which has been designated OCR-B in this country by USASI. The font was developed and adopted by the International Standards Organization as a standard throughout the world and is now being considered for adoption as a standard in this country. It differs greatly from OCR-A and is closer in design to conventional typefaces. While more readable to humans, OCR-B requires more complex machine recognition systems. (Samples of OCR-A and OCR-B are shown in figure 6.35.)

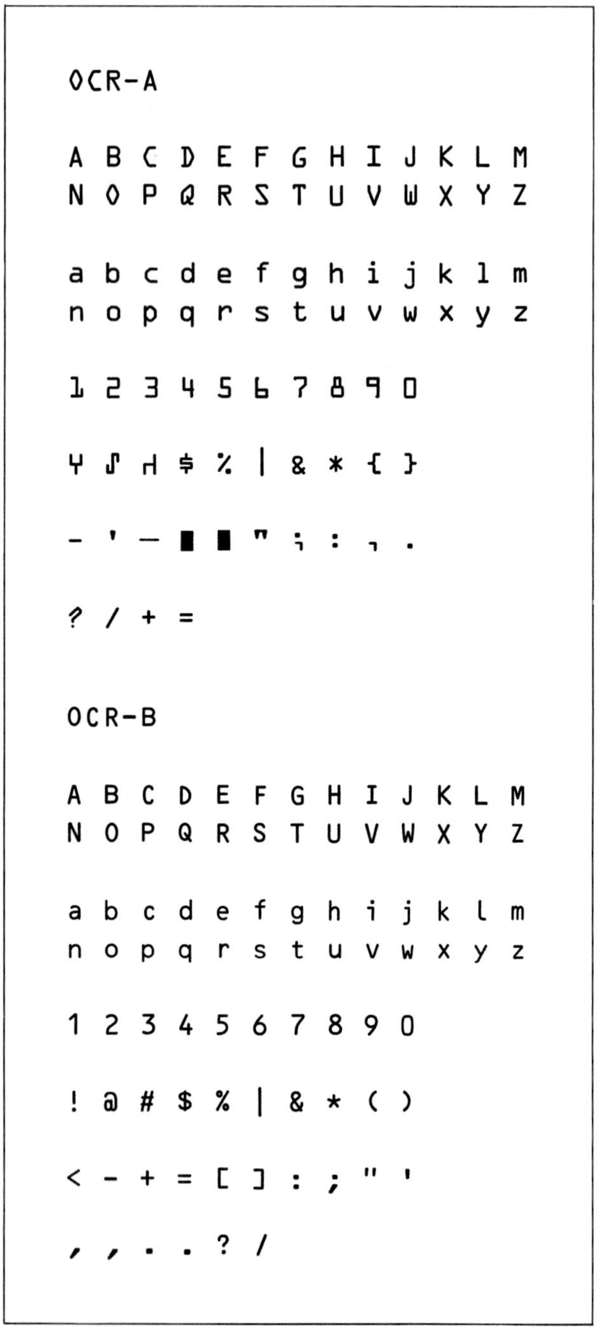

Other OCR faces have been developed and marketed by specific machine manufacturers. In addition, some names used in certain places actually refer to one or the other of the standard fonts. OCR-C, for example, is simply a 14-point version of OCR-A, which is a 10-point face. OCR-A and OCR-C are sometimes called ANS I and IV after the agency that sponsored their development, the American National Standards Institute.

OPERATING SPEEDS AND ERROR RATES

Readers that handle documents of one size are easy to rate for performance because their throughput of material is predictable. It is more difficult to state in simple terms the performance of readers that handle different-size documents and variable-size data fields.

Three ways of measuring the performance of optical readers are by documents handled per minute, lines read per minute, and characters read per second. The documents-per-minute rating is usually most applicable to mark and bar-code readers, as well as to character readers that read only one or two lines from each document. The lines-per-minute rating is usually most meaningful for readers of journal tapes such as those from cash registers. The scanning rate in characters per second is probably the most meaningful measure for machines that read whole pages of text.

Careful evaluation of timing information, which often becomes quite complex, is necessary to accurately predict the performance of the more sophisticated character readers. The size of the document, the amount and location of data on the document, and processing of the data can all affect the rate at which documents proceed through the reader. On-line units can be affected by other activities of the computer, if running in a multiprogramming environment, or by poor programming of input/output functions.

In most graphic arts situations, however, operating speeds of the scanning reader are not a limiting factor on system productivity. An OCR reader operates far faster than the capacity of an average group of keyboard operators to prepare material for it. Most often, any critical problem in matching operating speeds of an OCR reader to other system parts will occur in connecting this device on-line to a computer which can operate at similar or even faster speeds.

Error rates of OCR readers, on the other hand, are a much more vital concern in graphic arts applications because uncorrected material allowed to proceed beyond this stage is often costly to correct later. There are three principal types of error sources of concern to users of optical character readers: ambiguous characters, invalid data, and documents in poor condition.

Characters may be ambiguous—that is, the reader cannot decipher them—for a variety of reasons. Typically, the characters are broken or poorly formed, or stray dirt and other marks are picked up by the reader. Handling of this situation varies with the reader and with programming. Many readers automatically rescan an ambiguous character. Some substitute a standard

Figure 6.35: OCR type fonts. Two special stylized typefaces designed especially for machine reading are OCR-A (top) and OCR-B (bottom). These are the most commonly used in graphic arts. *Courtesy of CompuScan, Inc.*

U&lc is free to all users of typesetting/ word processing equipment.

U&lc, the International Journal of Typographics is a one-of-a-kind blend of graphic inspiration, fun (that's right, fun) and typographic information. It is unlike any other publication you now receive.

It is tabloid size, published quarterly and you can have a free subscription to it (if you don't already have one) by completing the form below and mailing it to U&lc.
Do it now. This will be the best investment you ever made.

character for all unreadable characters and continue. Others display the character on a CRT screen for operator determination; sometimes adjacent data is also displayed to give the operator a context for making the decision. Printing quality and paper quality can drastically affect the incidence of this type of error.

OCR users quickly learned that the inclusion of checks in the data is extremely useful for insuring that no incorrect data is entered into the computer system. The check frequently takes the form of repeated data fields, particularly for numeric entries. The technique is applicable only if the data can be processed and the actions of the reader controlled on the basis of the result.

Another commonly employed check is the check digit. The digits of a numeric field are manipulated (there are several standard formulas to do this) to generate a check digit. This digit is included in the input. The reader or associated processor generates another check digit while reading and compares it to the one read in. Failure of this check normally causes the documents to be rejected.

Documents that have extraneous items on them (such as stamps) or that have been badly mutilated can cause misfeeding and/or jams. The typical character reader is far less susceptible to this kind of jam than the average card reader, but people are much more likely to "fold, spindle, or mutilate" OCR documents than punched cards.

EDITING

Because material processed for typesetting in the graphic arts is so error-prone and revision-prone, the manufacturers of OCR systems used in the graphic arts have found it desirable to provide some kind of editing capability in scanning systems. These can be classified into several groups according to level of sophistication.

First, most OCR systems can be instructed to ignore items such as characters, words, lines, and even whole blocks of typed material. This is done either by writing a special code onto the manuscript in the proper position to deactivate the scanner, or by simply marking through the material to be deleted with a special black marking pen. This level is known as *deletion editing*.

The second level is *insertion editing*, or the ability to accept and insert in the data stream corrections and new material typed between lines of copy. The desired position of the inserted material in the main text line is indicated by means of a caret or other special symbol typed in the proper position. Unlike additions in ordinary manuscript, which are often handwritten above the main line, additions in OCR-typed copy are typed in the OCR typeface, usually immediately below the line in which they are to be inserted.

A third level of editing capability is available in some OCR equipment through the use of a video display screen and keyboard. Such systems allow the operator to see the scanned and encoded copy and change it via the keyboard. Video screens are also used for ambiguous character recognition by an operator, as already noted. Video display terminals, however, may not be required as part of the OCR system if the system feeds material into a computer-based editing system which also uses video terminals. This kind of post-scanning editing can then be done in the editing system as part of other editing work.

VIDEO DISPLAY TERMINALS

Frank J. Romano, GRAPHIC ARTS MARKETING ASSOCIATES

The first video display terminals were introduced to the graphic arts in 1970. In the relatively short time since then, the VDT has become a central component in editing and composition systems and has proven to be one of the most flexible tools available for processing material to be typeset.

Basically, a video display terminal is a special kind of television set with a keyboard attached so that the images on the face of the video tube can be manipulated by typing on the keyboard. There are more than 200 video display terminals of various kinds on the commercial market today. Some kinds are alphanumeric—that is, they show numbers, letters, and other special symbols on their screens. Others are "graphic" terminals with the ability to display two- or three-dimensional line drawings. Only a handful of these 200-plus machines are well suited to graphic arts uses, however—most of these having been tailored specifically for such applications. (A typical video display terminal is shown in figure 6.36.)

OPERATING PRINCIPLES

The video tube in a VDT operates on the same principles as the character-generation tube in a cathode ray tube (CRT) typesetter. An electron gun projects a stream of electrons onto a phosphor coating on the face of the tube, causing the coating to glow where the electrons strike it.

Character formation

Characters are formed by controlling this electron beam in one of several ways:
• Characters may be created out of a series of dots arranged into a rectangle or *dot matrix*. This is the most popular method of generating VDT characters.

Figure 6.36: Video display terminal. Typical VDT unit consists of keyboard and display screen, with associated electronics to store and manipulate coded text. *Courtesy of Mergenthaler Linotype Co.*

Most commercial VDT's employ a matrix five dots wide and seven dots deep, but it is difficult to design legible lowercase letters within these constraints. In many applications, lower case is not an important requirement, but for graphic arts uses it is essential. Therefore, VDT's for editing and composition systems generally use a matrix of seven dots by nine dots, or larger (see "Typography and Technology," page 163). The dot matrix principle is well suited to work with the kind of fixed scanning used in television sets, making it possible for virtually any TV set to become a display device for text matter.

• Characters can be created out of a series of line segments drawn on the screen and linked together. This method is much more complex than the dot matrix principle because the lines must be curved at all angles to achieve the letter shapes; more complex programming in the terminal is thus necessary to control the electron beam accurately. This principle is the least commonly used.

• Characters may be "painted" on the screen with a series of horizontal or vertical strokes of the electron beam. While more complicated than the dot matrix, this method is simpler than the line segment method. It is the same principle used in CRT phototypesetters, except that in a VDT a much lower resolution (fewer strokes per character) would be used.

The number of characters which may be displayed on the tube at one time is a function of the resolution of the tube. The more addressable points there are on a tube and the fewer addressable points required to describe each character, the greater the number of characters that will fit on the screen at one time. The size of the tube itself is of relatively little consequence in determining how much information will fit on the screen. The same number of scanning lines are used to cover the face of a 7-inch tube as are used on a 21-inch tube. The 21-inch tube may be larger, but all it really shows is an enlarged and more legible version of the same picture.

Character sets

Most commercially available VDT's are not aimed specifically at the typesetting market and have limited character sets—often about 64 separate symbols, including only uppercase characters and very few special symbols. Increasingly, greater numbers of upper- and lowercase alphanumeric terminals are coming on the market. Most of these will display over 96 separate symbols. Some will display as many as 128.

There is no theoretical limit to the number of different characters that could be generated on a VDT screen, given a dot matrix or other point-locating system with enough resolution to handle the shapes involved, and provided the machine were equipped with enough electronic memory capacity to store them. Recent moves in the design of some graphic arts terminals indicate that many more special characters will soon be available on VDT screens for direct reading by the operator. A number of suppliers have programmed their equipment to generate some accented characters for foreign language composition, and moves are under way to develop standard universal sets of special characters such as mathematical signs and symbols as well as accents. It is also possible to get unique symbols programmed for custom applications in many standard units. (See also "Typography and Technology," page 163.)

Character generation and refresh logic

To generate characters on VDT screens, hold them there, and manipulate them, all VDT's have three basic electronic sections: character generation, refresh logic, and editing logic (as diagrammed in figure 6.37). Character codes entering the terminal via coded tape, on-line wire, or direct keyboarding by an operator are stored in the refresh logic memory. The codes are then read by the character generation unit, which matches them against associated dot matrix patterns stored in memory. The appropriate dot pattern for each code is then displayed on the screen in proper position.

Because the glowing phosphor image on the screen will fade away a short time after the electron beam has moved on, these images must be restored or *refreshed* periodically if the image is to remain on the screen indefinitely until changed by the operator. To accomplish this, the character information stored in the refresh memory is repeatedly scanned by the machine logic to regenerate the images on the face of the tube. This refreshing action takes place 60 or more times a second, and in a well-designed VDT it is free of flicker and invisible to the human eye.

Editing functions

The character generation and refresh logic alone will produce an indefinite static image on the screen. To alter that image, editing logic is also required. Basically, editing logic must provide the operator with two kinds of capability—the ability to locate on the screen

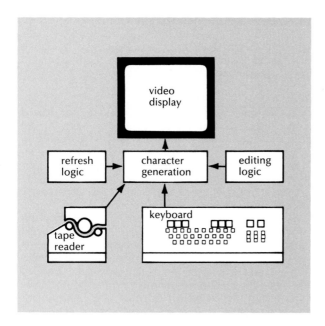

Figure 6.37: VDT operating principles. Character generation memories and logic sections link keyboard, display screen, and input and output devices.

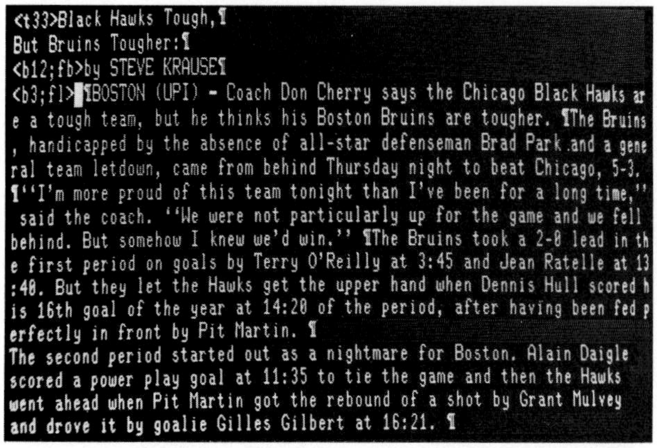

Figure 6.38: Cursor on VDT screen. A bright spot of light, called a cursor, is used to identify the spot on the display screen where action will take place when keys are struck. Cursor here is located before the word "Boston" in upper left-hand corner. *Courtesy of Hendrix Electronics, Inc.*

the point at which an action is to take place, and the ability to specify exactly what action is to be taken.

There are several ways in which location on the screen can be designated. One of the oldest methods is the *light pen*—a pencil-like device with a wire running from one end to the terminal logic, and a light-sensing cell in the other end. When pointed to a spot on the screen, the pen registers the exact time at which the electron beam sweeps by and energizes its light cell. The VDT then remembers this location and performs subsequent action at that point. Thus, the operator can simply point the pen at a selected character on the screen and then specify what is to be done to it by hitting keys on the keyboard.

Two other methods of location are more widely used now, but they follow the same principles. The most popular is a *cursor*, or spot of light on the screen (see figure 6.38). This spot of light can be made to move up, down, left, or right by the manipulation of four direction keys on the keyboard. Some machines even have a *home key* which will return the cursor directly to a predetermined place on the screen, such as the upper left-hand corner. Additional special commands may move it directly to the end of the nearest paragraph or to other special locations. Cursors can be of various shapes and kinds—an underline beneath the character, a square of light overlaying it, a caret-shaped mark. Some blink continuously to more forcefully call attention to their location.

The other locational method, more useful in "graphics" oriented terminals which display diagrams and the like, is the *electronic* or *sonic tablet*. This device provides a sketching area in which diagrams or other manually sketched graphics can be drawn, in the manner that an artist or draftsman would use a piece of drawing paper. As the drawing pen or other instru-

ment is pressed onto the tablet, its position on the tablet is sensed in two directions, vertically and horizontally. The tablet mechanism then converts the vertical and horizontal distances from the edges of the tablet into numerical X-Y coordinate values and transmits them via wire to the terminal's electronic logic sections.

The final element in a basic VDT system is the structure of actual commands that cause action, including such functions as "insert," "delete," "move," and the like. Each of these commands is normally given a separate key on the keyboard (see figure 6.39), and the operator need only strike that key to cause the action to take place. Striking the key activates a particular computer logic routine in the editing logic section. As the action takes place inside the machine, the display on the screen changes almost instantaneously to show what the machine has done in response to the command. Thus the operator sees immediately the results of his work and can evaluate them on the spot and make any necessary corrections without having to

Figure 6.39: VDT keyboard showing control keys. Keys to right of main keyboard permit operator to perform a variety of special operations which show on video screen. Four keys with arrows permit movement of cursor in any desired direction. *Courtesy of Hendrix Electronics, Inc.*

wait for proofs to be made or other time-consuming intermediate steps to take place. This instantaneous response and verification capability which the VDT offers is the most important factor in its success. If properly used, VDT's can eliminate most of the cost of corrections in modern typesetting systems.

SYSTEM CONFIGURATIONS

The basic video display terminal itself is a relatively simple device. The wide variations in VDT capability to perform different tasks in editing and composition systems are dependent essentially on the amount of computer power—both hardware (equipment) and software (programming)—to which the terminal is connected. Actually, no VDT device is used all by itself; every terminal must have some additional facilities to form a complete system for processing material, even though the complete assembly may be referred to as simply a terminal. Such VDT assemblies can be classified into two general groups, although the dividing line between them is not always clear-cut. One is the so-called *stand-alone* terminal; the second is the *on-line* terminal.

Stand-alone terminal

A stand-alone terminal incorporates a complete processing system from input to output, along with a single display screen and keyboard, within one machine unit (see figure 6.40). Many stand-alone terminals have a punched paper tape reader which is used to enter material keyboarded previously on a tape-perforating keyboard. Their output device is usually a paper-tape punch which produces tape ready either for further processing in a computer or for use directly in a typesetting machine. In the present marketplace, however, paper tape has been replaced by the floppy disc—a portable magnetic recording disc that looks much like a 45 rpm phonograph record—for both input and output media.

Stand-alone terminals also normally have some

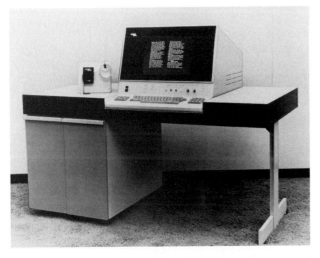

Figure 6.40: Stand-alone terminal. Machine can be operated independently of other devices; it accepts coded tape as input and produces a second coded tape as output. *Courtesy of Harris Corporation, Composition Systems Division.*

Figure 6.41: On-line terminal. Machine must be wired to a control computer in order to operate. Input material to be worked on can be received by wire from the control computer. Output material is sent by wire to the computer. *Courtesy of Harris Corp., Composition Systems Division.*

computer and memory facilities in addition to the bare minimum described previously to handle the basic editing functions. Most often this additional capacity is used to handle more text than can be shown on the video screen, but in some cases the facilities are powerful enough to provide sophisticated formatting functions for specifying complex typography.

On-line terminal

In contrast to the stand-alone terminal, the on-line terminal (see figure 6.41) is dependent on another computer system: it is connected by wire to a separate computer which usually is connected in turn to still other system components. These additional components can include other VDT's, large-size memory storage units, printout devices, tape readers, tape punches or recorders, and the like. Typically such systems include more than one VDT so that two or more operators can work simultaneously with material in the system. Such multiterminal systems are usually known as *storage and retrieval* systems because of their large-scale capacity for storing material indefinitely until needed again on the screen of a VDT.

The on-line VDT itself is normally a much simpler device than its stand-alone counterpart, even though more complex tasks often can be performed on it. The on-line VDT can be controlled by a program in the central computer, not simply by the instructions built into the terminal itself. This central program can be far larger and more sophisticated than the instruction set that can be built into a terminal's own memory and logic.

These two classifications of terminals tend to overlap to some degree in terms of capabilities. Some of the more powerful stand-alone terminals have computers in them that could also serve as the core for small multiterminal systems, and some of the functions performed by certain stand-alone terminals are not available in multiterminal systems using computers of comparable size. Generally, however, the medium-

Some of the most relevant characters in New York hang out here.

Take, for instance, the comma, half-sister to the period. Or again, their cousins, the colon and semi-colon. How shall we dispose of the hyphen, the quotation mark or apostrophe? "Give them their very own place in the sun. Nourish their hungry egos," plead those of more gentle persuasion. "Hang them, hang them all," demand the hard liners. Here, at Baumwell, we daily (and most expertly) reconcile the warring points of view. Fearlessly and without favor —be it with Korinna, Souvenir, Serif Gothic, Friz Quadrata, Avant Garde, Olivette, or any of the faces you see in U&lc (along with many more)— we staunchly, albeit carefully, march down both sides of the road, arm-in-arm with a host of happy designers. Care to join the ranks? Start by asking (on your letterhead, please) for our expanded Catalog of Available Faces.

MJ BAUMWELL TYPOGRAPHY
461 8TH AVENUE
NEW YORK NY 10001
(212) 868-0515

size and larger multiterminal systems are much more powerful tools than the stand-alone terminals.

FUNCTIONAL CAPABILITIES

The various editing and composition operations which can be performed on video display terminals range all the way from simple text editing to the makeup of complex pages. These can be considered most easily under three headings: text entry and editing, galley formatting, and area or page makeup.

Text editing

The simplest and most common functions are those for text editing. These include the basic four—insert, delete, move, and change—as well as others which may or may not be found in various terminals. In most instances each command requires the striking of a separate key, but in certain situations operations can be simplified by combining two functions into one keystroke. One example is the so-called *write-over* method of changing characters, in which the cursor is placed in position at the character to be changed and the new character key struck; the old character is deleted automatically and the new character inserted. Whether this kind of feature is desirable, however, depends on the particular application. If an additional character were to be inserted within a word, for instance, this particular feature would require that the rest of the word be retyped. Therefore, this feature would be desirable in work requiring many changes of characters, but would not in work involving the insertion of many new characters within words or other material.

The basic four commands can be applied to manipulate individual characters, words, lines, and copy blocks; but not all terminals are set up to manipulate all four of these elements. In addition, terminals may or may not be equipped to provide other text handling features such as *scrolling* and *searching*. Scrolling is the ability to move material off the screen vertically in one direction so that new material can be moved on at the other end of the screen. Some machines can scroll forward only; others can scroll both backward and forward. Search, or *autosearch* as it is sometimes called, is the ability of the machine to scan through the material on command and pick out pre-specified characters, words, or other features being sought.

Formatting

A step beyond text editing and handling is typographic formatting. Formatting as used in this sense includes the insertion of typesetting machine command codes to produce type set in continuous columns. The typesetting commands involved range from the elementary specification of typeface, size, and line measure up to those required for multiple indentations, tabular setting, and special characters.

A special function within typographic formatting is the automatic hyphenation and justification of type lines under the control of computerized logic. Available for many years in full-scale computerized typesetting systems, this capability is also provided today by some of the larger stand-alone terminal systems.

Sophistication and accuracy of the H & J programs varies from machine to machine, but the terminal provides means for changing incorrect hyphenations when they occur.

Another dimension of columnar formatting is the ability to control vertical spacing of type lines. Both body leading and individual discrete spaces can be added independently between type lines and copy blocks on some machines. This enables operators of such terminals to make up certain kinds of simple pages which are columnar in structure—that is, single or multicolumn pages in which all columns have identical vertical depths in terms of the number of type lines they contain. Columnar formatting, however, generally stops short of the ability to space vertically to an absolute measurement such as picas and points or inches.

Page makeup

The ability to space vertically to absolute measurements is one of the salient features of page makeup VDT's and systems. Other characteristics are the ability to show the complete made-up page on the video screen at one time and the ability to change any part of the layout as well as the text and display copy at will.

Some programs have been written for larger storage and retrieval systems to permit makeup of display advertisements on the screens of terminals designed primarily for text editing; copy can be fitted to absolute vertical dimensions as well as to line measures, but the type itself is shown on the terminal screen in a single text size, and the spacing between lines and copy blocks is not represented with perfect precision.

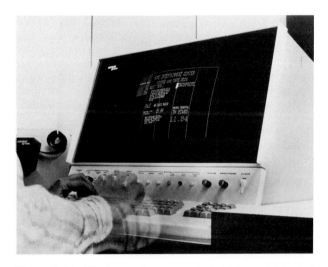

Figure 6.42: Display makeup terminal. This sophisticated VDT and its control computer permit the operator to display text in a wide range of type sizes and to position each line anywhere on the screen. Specific typefaces are chosen by the operator, and characters on the screen are shown in exact widths they will occupy when set. The unit thus enables the operator to make up typeset material on the screen and change it easily until the layout is perfected. Then the machine codes are sent to a phototypesetter to direct it in producing the completely made-up area on one piece of photographic film or paper. *Courtesy of Harris Corporation, Composition Systems Division.*

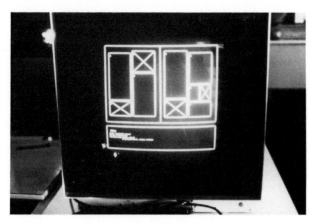

Figure 6.43: Video screen of page makeup terminal. This VDT system has been programmed to display a complete page diagram similar to the sketched layout an artist would draw for a page to be sent to a conventional composition department. Screen here shows a double-page spread for a book with two columns of type per page. Illustrations are indicated by boxes with crosses in them. The layout artist creates a diagram on the screen, using a method similar to that for producing a pencil-and-paper layout. The horizontal box at the bottom of the screen is reserved for writing in special notes and instructions about the page. © *Field Enterprises Educational Corporation.*

The true makeup terminal generally shows type in the actual size it will be set and positioned with enough precision on the screen so that the operator can confidently place it in position simply by looking at it.

The first full-scale makeup VDT's were designed to handle newspaper display advertisements and had a screen about one-quarter the area of a full newspaper page (see figure 6.42). Page-size ads are made up on these machines by producing subsections for later paste-up assembly. These units include much more than the VDT itself. Because makeup operations require extensive separate computer and memory storage facilities, the makeup systems often take the form of several VDT's connected to a central "controller" computer and on-line disc-pack storage. There are now makeup VDT's that can handle a complete newspaper page on the screen at one time. Figures 6.43 and 6.44 show two approaches to displaying page-makeup images on terminal screens.

Because the application of VDT's to display makeup is still so new, no consensus has emerged in the industry as to basic operating modes. Some makeup systems project ruled diagrams of pages on the screen and then enable operators to fit type to these ruled boxes.

Figure 6.44: Page View Terminal showing portion of newspaper page. This system displays text in position using a representative typeface in the point size to be used. It has the ability to show an entire newspaper page. *Courtesy of Mergenthaler Linotype Company.*

Others project the type itself on the screen in reduced size; when an area of small print must be read by the operator, that specific area is automatically enlarged to reading size at the push of a button. While some of the early makeup equipment operates in a stand-alone mode, with tapes used for input and output, newer equipment is being designed primarily for on-line connection with central storage and retrieval systems.

With the advent of display makeup VDT's that can handle full-size newspaper pages, the VDT has claimed a place in all phases of preparing material for typesetting. It can be used as a direct input device, an editing device, and a typographic specification device. Thus it has become the most versatile of all the available input and control devices for handling material in electronic composition systems.

236

FACSIMILE TRANSMISSION

Daniel M. Costigan, BELL LABORATORIES

Facsimile communication, or "fax," is an electronic process for dispatching graphics by wire and radio. It is similar in principle to television, which it preceded by many years. As with the electric telegraph, newspaper publishers were among the earliest users of the process. By the turn of the century, when fax was already more than 50 years old, it was being used to send pictures over wires for short distances, and by the middle 1920's, when television was still just a crude laboratory curiosity, photographs were being transmitted across the Atlantic by radiofacsimile.

Fax has since survived every revolution in communications technology and has found several additional uses in the publishing industry, which can be classified into two types:

• *Message fax,* the transmission of copy the quality of typed manuscript or photocopies. Message fax includes filing of stories and graphics by reporters covering events distant from the home office and exchange of copy between central and satellite editorial offices or between editorial and printing facilities.

• *Repro fax,* transmission of reproduction-quality page proofs for automatic production of photographic masters or actual plates at a satellite printing site.

OPERATING PRINCIPLES

Fax is similar in principle not only to slowed-down television but also to other types of electronic scanning systems used in graphic arts for platemaking and color separation. The major difference is that in fax the input scanning operations and the output recording operations are separated into two different machines located many miles apart and are connected by some kind of communications link such as telephone lines. Figure 6.45 illustrates the similarities and differences.

The photoelectric scanning process, basic to platemaking and color-separation scanners as well as fax, consists of a pinpoint of light "sweeping" the original graphics in the same manner that our eyes sweep or scan a line of text as we read it. Just as the eye moves downward after each line of text, the scanning light spot in a fax transmitter makes each successive sweep along an axis slightly displaced from that of the previous sweep. Thus eventually—after perhaps a thousand successive sweeps—the scan spot will have covered the entire surface of the original.

Equally essential to the basic scanning process is the photoelectric receptor, which picks up the "bounced" light from the scan spot and converts it to electricity. Assuming that a black ink sketch on white paper is the object being scanned, the light of the scan spot will be absorbed whenever it hits a black portion of sketch, so that little or no bounced light will reach the receptor. Conversely, a considerable proportion of the scan spot's light energy will be reflected to the receptor from a white portion of the sketch. From this information, the receptor—more accurately called a *transducer,* since it converts one form of energy to another—produces a pulsating current that amounts to an electrical model or analog of the density variations of the sketch within each scan stroke: a high level of output for the white portions and a low level for the black.

In the typical platemaking or color-separation scanner, the scanner output is reconverted to an analogous pulsating light source in another part of the same machine so that the original art can be reproduced on a photosensitive surface. The fax system differs fundamentally in that the scanning and reproduction functions are separated from each other by large distances and are linked together by communication circuits. Therefore, the scanner output must be processed to make it compatible with the type of communication circuit used, such as a telephone line or radio channel. Similarly, at the receiving end of the system, which may be several thousand miles away, the incoming signal must be boosted and reprocessed into an electric current or modulated light source capable of reproducing ("recording") the transmitted graphics on sensitized paper or film, or directly on an ink-printing medium.

The geographical separation of scanning and reproducing functions in the fax system imposes the need to synchronize the relative positions of the scan spot and recording spot (or stylus) within a stroke at a given point in time. In the typical commercial fax system, precision electric power sources assure that the separated scanning and recording mechanisms run at speeds that are as stable and as nearly equal as possible. A pretransmission exchange of special electrical pulses insures that the separated mechanisms start and end their scan strokes at the same relative positions on the paper or film surface. (Without this assurance, a split image might result at the receiver.)

RECORDING

A number of electrical "printing" techniques are used to reproduce the scanned image in fax systems.

Two of the more popular ones, the burn-off and electrolytic processes, are *direct* processes, in which the image is formed directly without additional processing steps. In the *burn-off* process, a metal stylus in contact with the paper surface responds to the varying voltage potentials of the amplified picture signal by discharging sparks of varying intensity. This "arcing" penetrates the white coating of the special electrosensitive paper to reveal a black underlayer, thereby directly reproducing the transmitted image elements. Similarly, in the *electrolytic* process, paper saturated with a liquid electrolyte turns black in proportion to the electric current that passes through it.

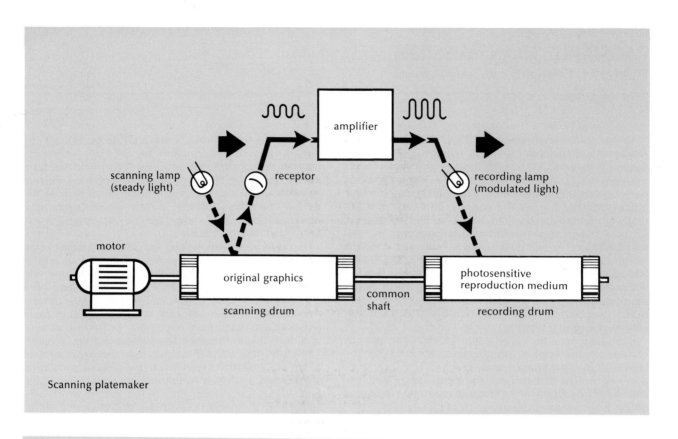

Scanning platemaker

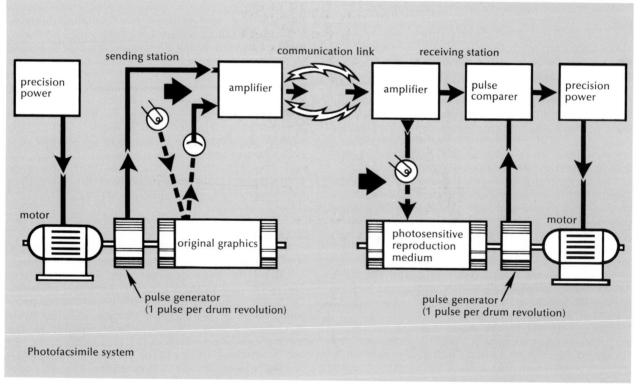

Photofacsimile system

Figure 6.45: Simplified comparison of a scanning platemaker and a fax communication system. The basic distinction is that input and output are performed by two separated machines. Means must be provided to ensure that the separated scan- ning and recording drums continue to move relative to each other as if both were still on a common shaft. The large arrows indicate the direction in which the scanning and recording light beams move along the drums.

Another direct process, the use of which has declined in recent years, reproduces the image on plain paper by the interposition of ordinary carbon paper between it and a mechanically vibrating stylus.

Various attempts have been made to use quick-drying liquid ink directly in the fax recording process, but they have failed to catch on. RCA pioneered the use of modulated ink jet techniques in fax systems many years ago, and the Rudolf Hell Company of West Germany more recently used a wet-ink impact process in one of its commercial business fax systems.

While the response speed of the traditional direct processes is generally adequate for rates of a few thousand pulses per second (1,300 is the maximum normally transmitted by phone lines in conventional analog business fax systems), *electrostatic techniques* are favored for the newer high-speed digital data compression systems, such as the Dacom and Rapifax systems. Inasmuch as the electrostatic process involves a latent image which must be developed by application of charged ink or toner, it is not considered a direct process in the usual sense.

In *photofacsimile systems*, the reprocessed picture signal modulates a light source, and the scanning process is, in effect, reversed. The traditional light source is a special lamp capable of rapid fluctuations in intensity. Recently, however, optically modulated lasers have been adopted for the purpose. In either case, a concentrated spot of modulated light produces a latent image on photosensitive paper or film for subsequent development.

Gray tones

Most fax systems in use today are capable of reproducing varying degrees of gray as well as discrete black and white tones. In fact, by nature, an analog fax system has a tonal capability that is continuously variable from black to white. The reproduction process is the chief limiting factor. Although the photographic process is hard to surpass in tonal latitude, some of the more direct processes are capable of excellent tonal rendition.

The desire to reproduce shades of gray becomes a problem with the adoption of digital transmission techniques. Inasmuch as digital communication is based on binary (two-state) coding, it is ideally suited to the transmission of black and white picture elements; the natural analog output of the scanner is *thresholded* so that all gray tones above a certain threshold are transmitted as black and all those below are transmitted as white. If gray-scale reception is desired, the gray must be *quantized;* that is, a separate threshold must be established for each of the discrete number of gray tones desired. Experience has shown that any fewer than 14 quantization levels results in discernible quantization "noise"—visually, a patchwork effect resulting from divisions between discrete gray shades.

The need to quantize so large a number of gray shades in order to avoid noise increases the number of code "words" necessary to define the content of the original graphics, and transmission efficiency suffers accordingly. The answer to the problem may lie in some of the electronic halftone screening techniques that are just beginning to emerge.

Color reproduction

Pictures can be transmitted and received in color as well as black and white, using some method of synchronized sequential filtering or wide-band channels that can be subdivided among the separate color signals. Regardless of the particular technology—whether the three colors are scanned and transmitted sequentially or simultaneously—the transmission time required for a three-color system is theoretically three times that of a straight black-and-white system. In actual practice, there is some trading-off of resolution for speed, with the result that a professional-quality 8" x 10" three-color print (nominally 100 lpi resolution along both axes) can be received via a "Telephoto" voice-grade circuit in as little as 13 minutes.

Muirhead of England and at least two other companies currently produce color fax equipment suitable for graphic arts applications. Some of these systems use conventional color print paper in roll form as the recording medium, whereas others are designed to take standard Polaroid color film packs. Three separate light sources (of appropriate colors and intensities) are required to produce the latent image. Perhaps eventually some of the special processes developed for color copiers will find application in fax reception.

GRAPHIC ARTS APPLICATIONS

Facsimile transmission has been used in various areas of the graphic arts for some years, and its use continues to grow.

Transmitting news photographs

As previously mentioned, the transmission of news photographs by wire and radio was one of the earliest practical applications of the fax principle. It remains virtually unchallenged as the means by which the wire services supplement news text with pictures. As a distinctive branch of the fax art, it is known technically in this country as *telephotography* (an unfortunate choice, since it also means the taking of pictures through a telescopic lens) and in Europe as *phototelegraphy*. A broader term, *photofacsimile*, refers to all fax applications in which recording is by modulated light on photosensitive surfaces. Such uses include reception of cloud-cover pictures from weather satellites and reception of newspaper page proofs at branch printing plants.

News pictures are typically scanned at resolutions ranging from 100 to 200 scan lines per inch. Both the equipment and special transmission circuits are designed to handle a continuous gray range of at least 16 tones. (Business fax systems, by contrast, range from 64 to 100 lpi resolution and seldom reproduce more than four or five discernible gray tones.)

Typically, it takes 8 to 12 minutes to send an 8" x 10" photo (with caption) over specially conditioned telephone lines, plus an additional few minutes for photographic processing. Some modern receivers have built-in processing capabilities.

Among the newer developments in news picture equipment is the use of laser recording, the immediate advantage of which is that it permits use of less complex photocopying processes for image reproduction.

The Associated Press's pioneering Laserphoto system, for example, uses 3M "dry silver" paper as the recording medium and develops the latent image instantly by heat rather than by liquid chemicals. When the Laserphoto system is implemented fully, it will also be capable of higher resolution reproduction than is obtainable currently with conventional photofacsimile systems and at higher transmission speeds than are now practical.

Another recent advance has been the substitution of electrostatic techniques for photofacsimile in the reception of news pictures. United Press International is in the process of implementing its "Unifax II" electrostatic system, which offers simplified news picture reception at reduced costs.

Message fax

Reporters can file news stories by fax from outlying news bureaus and remote sites. Fax is also used as a link between the main newsroom and satellite offices. *The Wall Street Journal*, for example, uses fax to dispatch copy from its Washington Bureau to the newsroom in New York.

Filing of stories from remote locations permits relaying of graphic materials as well as text. A reporter can, for example, transmit a rough sketch depicting a complex chain of events that may be easier to explain graphically than verbally. New lightweight battery-operated fax machines with built-in acoustic couplers make it possible to transmit from any phone booth.

Periodical publishers have used fax for transmitting material between geographically separated departments. Manuscripts to be set in type may be transmitted from editorial offices to the printer, who can return galley or page proofs of the typeset material for proofreading. Fax has proved useful in expediting the checking and correcting of editorial and ad proofs by publishing personnel remote from their printing facilities or by customers of commercial printers. With the ability to send a page of text in minutes, the potential savings in time, transportation costs, and other respects are obvious. The major drawback has been the lack of assurance that proofs will remain legible after a round trip across relatively inexpensive fax terminals.

Repro fax

Perhaps the most interesting of all current fax applications in the graphic arts is the long-distance transmission of whole newspaper page proofs for the automatic production of offset printing masters at a satellite plant. Dow-Jones, one of the earlier and more persistent advocates of the use of fax in publishing and printing, has built a nationwide network for page proof transmission between plants printing *The Wall Street Journal*.

As is still standard for the news picture nets, page proofs are received by photofacsimile techniques. But instead of prints, the normal output is high-quality photographic negatives for subsequent production of lithographic plates. Resolution requirements are high (300 to 1000 lpi), not so much for text legibility as to avoid moiré from interference of scan lines with dot arrays in reproduced halftones.

Dow-Jones and some other users of page proof fax systems have recently installed new terminals that yield at least fourfold increases in transmission speed by the technique of scanning rapidly over the blank portions of the copy. Alternatively, these data compression systems (developed by Dacom Incorporated and Litton-Datalog, among others) can be used on lower bit rate, less expensive circuits at no change in speed, or on existing circuits at higher resolution instead of higher speed.

With conventional binary/analog equipment, it takes about six minutes to send a full 14" x 21" page over a 240 kilohertz transmission channel. In the Dacom system now in operation at *The Christian Science Monitor*, a page is sent in six minutes by 50 kilobit data channels.

As an alternative to data compression for increased transmission speed or for higher resolution reproduction, the terminals can be linked together by digital carrier facilities intended for bulk handling of telephone calls. A special data set introduced by the Bell System in 1971 permits use of these facilities for high-speed data transmission at the rate of 1.344 megabits per second (nearly 30 times the single channel voice rate). Pulitzer Publishing was the first to take advantage of the new service in a network linking four sending terminals at the main plant in downtown St. Louis with four receivers at a suburban offset plant 20 miles away. A full page of the *Post-Dispatch* can now be sent in 2½ minutes at 600 lpi resolution, or in slightly more than 4 minutes at 1,000 lpi. Besides terrestrial links, earth-orbiting communication satellites now also provide wideband transmission paths for page proof fax systems. Since 1975, Dow-Jones has been transmitting *The Wall Street Journal* daily from Chicopee, Mass., to Orlando, Fla., by satellite.

These page proof systems can, of course, also transmit multiple smaller periodical pages in one shot and, with provision for transparencies as the input and for precision pin registration, can now effectively transmit color separations as well.

Another recent advance has been the introduction of laser recording to the page proof fax systems but for somewhat different reasons than its adoption for news picture reception. In the high-speed page proof systems, the laser can solve the problem of the drastically shortened life span of more conventional glow-modulator (discharge) tubes when they are made to operate at high impulse rates. Tests have shown that a helium-neon laser lasts 100 times as long as a discharge tube (5,000 hours as compared with 50). Moreover, the laser makes it possible to record directly on litho film at high speeds, thereby offering certain material and production economies. Even more importantly, in the long view, the laser also permits recording directly on metal or polymer plates, thus eliminating a step in the platemaking process.

THE FUTURE

A number of recent and forthcoming technological advances ensures not only the continued use of fax in the graphic arts but some interesting changes in the way it is used. In the distribution of photographs by the wire services, for example, it is anticipated that by the middle of the 1980's editors will be accessing pictures from computer storage via interactive CRT terminals that will permit electronic cropping and enhancing prior to reception. The technology exists; the main obstacle to implementation is economic.

This "store and forward" approach to the accessing of graphic information applies to the preparation of ad copy as well. Standard logos and trade names can be put by facsimile scanners into compacted computer storage where they may be intermixed with other information for automatic composing, and then the resulting composite can be printed out as fax copy (on paper or film) for use in page makeup. The National Weather Service is already applying the principle to the computer generation of weather maps. Fax input of "background" graphics is mixed with current data; the output, a composite digital bit stream, is simultaneously transmitted to multiple receiver stations where conventional fax recorders print it out as complete weather maps.

The use of fax to expedite the exchange of editorial and ad proofs between geographically separated facilities could benefit from the recent introduction of high-speed digital data compression fax terminals. The systems currently available provide a transceiving capability on conventional phone circuits at an average speed six times faster than conventional analog systems at a selection of resolutions ranging as high as 200 lines per inch. Such systems seem perfectly suited to proof-checking applications, with two possible limitations: (1) the received copy is strictly binary (no grays), and (2) a relatively high day-to-day usage volume would be required to justify the comparatively high terminal rentals (more than $200 a month per station initially). At present, the systems appear to be catching on for business applications requiring comparatively high transmission volumes by the telephone dial network. Assuming continuation of this trend and considering the potential for competition in this new sector of the fax market, terminal costs (excluding the inflation factor) could conceivably decline in the future.

As for the transmission of page proof masters to remote offset printing plants, there are four current trends that are certain to yield eventual economic benefits: (1) the adoption of laser recording, (2) the growth of satellite communications and transmission networks designed specifically for digital communication, (3) the maturing of graphic data compression techniques, and (4) the merging of photocomposing and fax transmission technologies in a single system.

Digital communication—transmission of discrete pulses—by facilities specifically tailored for that purpose benefits customer and carrier alike because the less subtle signalling format is more efficient and economical. In the Bell Telephone System there are already over one million miles of short-haul digital circuits (T-1 carrier) in metropolitan areas and a steady growth in long-haul (T-2 carrier) mileage between cities. By combining this digital transmission capability with data compression techniques at the terminals, transmission efficiency can be improved still further.

Apart from those advances in transmission technology, considerable progress has been made in electronic composition of whole pages, both text and pictures, by manipulation of data held in temporary computer storage. This technique opens the way to the remote creation of first-generation page masters by transmission of a composite computer output to a high-resolution fax receiver. Time Inc.'s PDI subsidiary has developed a remote electronic composing system with color graphic capabilities.

On a less sophisticated plane, it has been proposed that the newspaper page proof systems be used to expedite national distribution of periodicals by "broadcasting" the same set of proofs to several contract printers simultaneously in various sectors of the country. This concept, together with the increasing transmission speeds possible with such systems, holds promise of dramatic improvements in distribution efficiency.

Two additional technological advances could contribute to a general reshaping of electronic graphic communications technology in the not-too-distant future: (1) the perfection of solid-state scanning devices using the "charge-coupling" technology developed at Bell Laboratories, and (2) the reception of "hard" graphics on an electronically erasable medium. Solid-state scanning offers the advantage of greatly simplified scanner design, while an erasable recording medium will permit obvious savings in materials and image processing.

One such erasable recording medium is a special ceramic material called *PLZT* (coined from abbreviations of the chemical symbols for lead, lanthium, zirconium, and titanium), which is capable of retaining a light image by changing its refraction properties in proportion to the amount of light striking it. The material is light-sensitive only while an electric potential is applied to it. For this reason, the recorded image may be rendered permanent simply by cutting off the applied voltage and may subsequently be erased simply by reapplying the voltage and exposing the material to a flash of light. The image is made visible by projection onto a viewing screen or onto a photosensitive surface for subsequent chemical development.

THE ELECTRONIC SYSTEMS REVOLUTION

Paul D. Doebler, PUBLISHING MANAGEMENT CONSULTANT

Electronic editing and composition systems are the most important advance in composition technology for publishing since Gutenberg's invention of movable type in the 1400's made mass publication possible in the first place. Unlike any previous advance in composition technology since Gutenberg, today's new electronic systems are opening up new dimensions for publishers to do new things in new ways for readers. The publishing industries are still a long way from realizing all of the potential such systems promise (the movement into first-generation systems is barely beginning in most areas of publishing), but even now these systems are creating a revolution within the editorial, design, and composition processes.

The key to understanding this change—so radical compared to previous developments in composition such as the Linotype, Monotype, or phototypesetting machines—lies in the fact that the new electronic systems deal with the entire process of moving text from the writer's hand to the finished typeset page. Until now, technological development concentrated on typesetting, the assembly of individual characters into lines and columns of type; the rest of the work has remained manual and is still performed in the same sequence as in Gutenberg's time. The "up-front" functions of writing, editing, and graphic design, which take place outside of the composing room in the offices of authors and publishers, have never before been included in attempts to improve the process. Computer technology is changing all that. For this technology promises no less than the elimination of most composing room operations by enabling the electronic system to produce finished composed pages directly from the work of writers, editors, and designers without intermediate handling by compositors, proofreaders, and others.

Composition and creation have intermingled of necessity from the beginning. Composition is nothing more than a conversion of original text and typographic designs into a medium capable of being mass-reproduced through printing. Projects have traditionally passed back and forth between those doing this conversion and those doing writing, editing, and layout.

This system is error-prone, laborious, and costly. Not only are the mechanics of keyboarding, proofreading, and inserting and assembling pieces of type highly susceptible to human error, but those in the composing room must also make interpretations of what the original creator wanted, and these second-guessings of intent are often incorrect. Meanwhile delays in composition can cause the creative people to have second thoughts about their work; often they must update it by the time it has been typeset. Making these corrections and revisions has become progressively more difficult and costly as typesetting technology has advanced. But the new electronic technology—which can now encompass the creative functions as well as the mechanical assembly of type—affords the first significant opportunity to simplify the time-honored "write-edit-compose" process.

THE SYSTEM CONCEPT

This technology is based on the idea of a complete electronic write-edit-compose system as opposed to the traditional view of composition as discrete processes performed by separate machines. Most of the machinery for an electronic write-edit-compose system is discussed in detail in other articles in this section. The system concept deals with how these individual devices are linked to form a complete facility for use by a graphic arts organization. Although the details of specific systems differ greatly, the diagram in figure 6.46 can be used to understand the basic principles of any write-edit-compose system.

All such systems are made up of six basic types of facilities, each with a certain function to perform. The center of such a system is a computer to which the other facilities are connected. The computer serves as a system control unit, containing all the programs required to perform various actions and directing traffic as data in the system moves from one place to another.

The two input functions to the left of the central control computer are used to get material into the system. Original copy that has not yet been encoded in machine language must be keyboarded by someone working on one of the devices shown in the upper *original input* section. Material that has previously been translated into machine code may be entered into the system by one of the methods indicated in the lower *transfer input* section.

Once in the system, copy is manipulated—added to, changed, deleted, or formatted—by the devices shown in the *manipulation* section. The video display terminal has become the predominant device for this function because of its capability for letting operators make instantaneous changes. This unique characteristic of the VDT, more than anything else, has made the new kind of write-edit-compose system possible.

When no work is being done on material in the system, it is stored in the *memory storage* section. Other parts of the system have limited memory storage capacity as well, but they are generally designed for special purposes, such as holding active working blocks of copy or special items such as computer programs. The main memory storage facilities, indicated at the top of the diagram, are very large mass-storage files which hold all of the material in the system when not being processed.

The *output* section of the system provides one or more means of getting material out of the system when needed. The two most common forms of output from

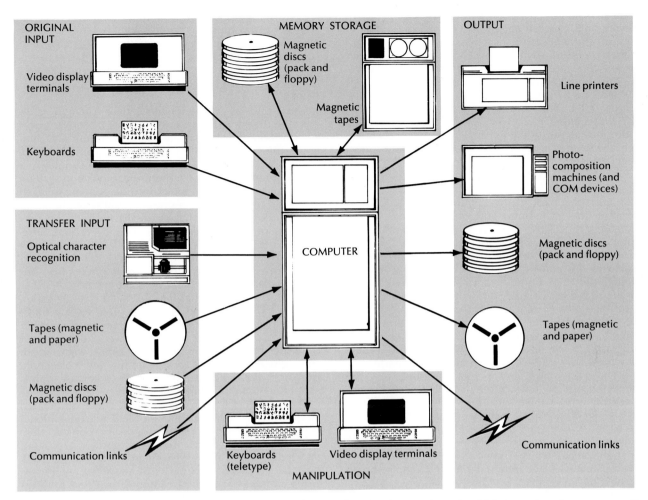

ORIGINAL INPUT

Video display terminals

Keyboards

MEMORY STORAGE

Magnetic discs (pack and floppy)

Magnetic tapes

OUTPUT

Line printers

Photo-composition machines (and COM devices)

TRANSFER INPUT

Optical character recognition

Tapes (magnetic and paper)

Magnetic discs (pack and floppy)

Communication links

COMPUTER

Magnetic discs (pack and floppy)

Tapes (magnetic and paper)

Communication links

Keyboards (teletype)

Video display terminals

MANIPULATION

Figure 6.46: The basic "write-edit-compose" system configuration. All types of equipment in such electronic systems can be classified under one or more of six fundamental functional areas through which typeset matter passes on its way from the writer's hand to the finished page.

a write-edit-compose system, of course, are photo-composed galleys or pages of type and printouts from line printers. In addition to standard-size photocomposition machines producing full-size type, other photocomposing devices known as COM (computer-onto-microfilm) units can be used to set miniaturized type directly into miniature microfilm-size pages. Finally, such a system can also be equipped to produce data output in machine-coded form on media such as discs, tapes, or communications links.

HISTORICAL DEVELOPMENT

In the most dramatic new systems today, electronic signals can be transmitted instantly from one unit in the system to another. This on-line continuous processing means that people operating the system's keyboards and video display terminals can make any change they wish in the material in the system and see the results of their work instantly. This mode of operation is not the only one in use today; computer-based editing and composing systems have evolved to this kind of operation through many years of development.

Early systems

The earliest application of computer facilities to the process of moving copy into typeset pages came in 1959, when Dr. Michael P. Barnett, working at the Massachusetts Institute of Technology, produced technical reports by using a keypunch unit, a computer, and a phototypesetting machine directed by an experimental computer program he had written. His experiments quickly caught the attention of people in the graphic arts. A number of newspapers and book printers within the next few years attempted to apply computers in their composition departments in order to mechanize certain steps of typesetting. The most widespread use of computers at the time was in automating the justification and hyphenation of type lines once they had been keyboarded.

Barnett's experiments, however, also indicated the possibility that computers might automatically assemble type into columns, tables, and pages by having machines sort and arrange material under the direction of a computer program. During the 1960's, a new kind of typesetting service developed many programs and computer facilities for this kind of work. However, the cost of initial entry and processing, compared to conventional typesetting, proved to be the same or more for the first setting of a product, and the bulk of typeset products—which are set once and never revised—remained in conventional composing rooms. The computerized facilities proved effective for products that were revised periodically—directories, catalogs, and the like—because once in the computer, only the changes had to be keyboarded and inserted in the master file. Although the first-edition cost was high, the savings in succeeding editions far outweighed the initial investment.

Batch processing

At the time these systems were being developed, not all of the technology indicated in figure 6.46 was available. Optical character recognition equipment, although available, was far too expensive for widespread use before 1970. The video display terminal did not appear in the graphic arts in a form suitable for text editing until 1970. Computers suitable for simultaneous on-line operation of many terminals and other devices were not available at a cost appropriate for composition systems until the late 1960's. Therefore, these early systems were designed to operate quite differently from today's on-line continuous processing mode. They operated *off-line* in a *batch-processing mode*.

Off-line operation means that machines are not connected directly to each other; each operates independently and is linked to other units in the system by means of portable memory. Most such systems use paper or magnetic tape for this portable memory. Individual machines are equipped with tape readers for input, and with tape punches or recorders to get finished material out onto a tape for transporting to the next unit.

Because it is not economical to carry small bits of tape from machine to machine and process them, batch processing is the predominant mode of operation. Work is grouped in sizable batches for efficient handling at each processing stage. First a batch of copy is keyboarded, and the coded material is recorded on tape. Then, when a sufficiently large volume of work has accumulated, a batch of tapes from the keyboard is run into the computer. When changes are to be made, they are batched for keyboarding onto tape; once a large batch has been keyboarded, the corrections are run into the computer and merged into the original file. When it is time to produce the typeset copy, a batch run is made to put the material through a typesetting program, which arranges it in proper sequence and inserts instructions for the typesetting machine. The typesetting machine may be wired directly to the computer, but more often still another tape is produced by the computer and run through the typesetting device in a final batch processing.

Batch processing provides efficiency in running the machines, but it requires staffs of computer specialists to program and operate the equipment, and it often takes a substantial amount of time for work to proceed through the various queues that precede each processing step. Off-line batch processing systems are still in wide use today and will probably be used for some time to come. But the major growth trend in compu-

terized editing and composition systems has been in the on-line continuous processing systems because they overcome a great many of the speed, cost, and specialized knowledge problems of former systems.

COSTS

The best way to understand these changes is to examine the comparative cost structure of conventional composition and the new technology. Figure 6.47 diagrams the cost structures for three types of composing room operations: traditional hot metal technology, a contemporary computerized photocomposition system, and a possible future computerized system. In each case, the complete bar represents 100% of the composition cost, and the bar segments indicate the percentages of the total cost consumed by various functions. Note that the actual total dollar costs for each alternative will be different. Dollar costs for the second and third types of operation, for example, will be significantly less than for the hot metal operation. Another point of difference is that the hot metal cost allocation is for book composition, in which proofreading traditionally plays a greater role than it does in many other kinds of composition, while the two allocations for computer-based systems are for periodical work, which generally receives less proofreading and correction. However, these allocations still illustrate key points about the nature of composition costs.

The first bar shows the limited effect automated equipment has on reducing the cost of conventional composing room operations despite its sophistication. These allocations for hot metal composition are based on studies made some years ago by a leading book manufacturer who used the most advanced equipment and techniques, including computers for line justification, word hyphenations, and formatting, as well as fully automated linecasting machines that could change fonts, measures, and type sizes from taped commands. Although some cost savings were made, all of this automation failed to radically change the basic "one-third rule" illustrated in figure 6.47—that total composition cost for the books they produced divided down into about one-third for original keyboarding and correcting of galleys, one-third for proofreading of all kinds, and one-third for making up and correcting pages. The reason, of course, was that operation of the computer and the tape-driven linecasting machines was but a small fraction of the first one-third cost segment. The rest of the cost was for manual work that could not be automated and that was limited to the speeds at which people can perform it.

Computer-based photocomposition systems employing video display terminals and other new equipment have produced savings over hot metal systems in printers' composing rooms and trade typesetting plants primarily because this new technology permits the rearrangement of certain steps to eliminate other work. The second bar in figure 6.47 shows this rearrangement and the resulting percentage allocation of the total cost. This cost allocation was given by G. William Teare, president of Bru-El Graphics, a commercial typesetting firm specializing in periodical and book work, in an article published in the July 1976 issue of

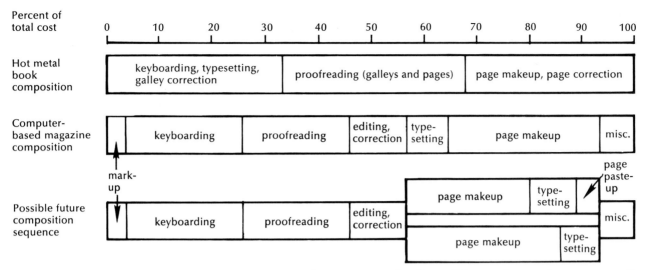

Figure 6.47: Cost structure comparison for three types of composing room operations. Bar segments indicate approximate sequence of operations but not exact occurrences; some proofreading, editing, and correction costs actually occur after typesetting and page makeup.

Association Management. The major realignment is the placement of actual typesetting later in the sequence, after the initial proofreading and correction (but not after the introduction of author's alterations), as opposed to the traditional hot metal or photocomposition sequence in which typesetting is done during or immediately after original keyboarding and is followed by proofreading and correction.

The objective of these and other changes in work flow sequence, of course, is to achieve something that has eluded writers, editors, and compositors alike since Gutenberg—to get the copy in perfect shape before it is set in type, after which changes are very costly. For the first time, with these new systems, the cost of making changes in copy is minimal as long as they are made while the material is electronically stored.

THE WORK FLOW SEQUENCE

Let us examine improvements in the work flow in more detail. Type is set in these new systems after proofreading and correction operations. How is the type proofread before typesetting? The answer is that the actual type itself is not proofread; instead, a reliable replica of the type is read and corrected. This substitute for the material yet to be typeset is the image generated on a video display terminal screen or on a printout from the computer's line printer. If printouts are used for proofreading, these documents are created immediately after the copy has been keyboarded into the system; they are read and corrected and then given to VDT operators who insert the corrections as they view the master file of copy on the terminal screen. If the uncorrected copy is proofread directly from images projected on the VDT screen, the proofreaders simply make corrections in the copy while reading it. Not until the copy is completely corrected (including incorporation of author's alterations marked on printouts sent to the authors) is the material sent through the typesetting machine.

The process of making corrections on video display terminals is much faster than the conventional process of setting new lines in type and then inserting them accurately into the original galleys of type, even when the corrections are first marked on printouts and later transcribed by special VDT operators. Making corrections directly on the VDT's during proofreading, of course, is even more economical. The use of printouts is essentially an example of speeding up operations; there are still separate proofreading and correction steps in this sequence. Proofreading directly on VDT screens, however, is an example of eliminating steps completely. The separate step of making corrections is simply collapsed into the proofreading operation. This change saves virtually all of the time required in a separate correction operation because the actual act of making a correction on a VDT takes a very small amount of time; the bulk of the time in a separate correction operation employing a special terminal operator is consumed by carrying proofs around and handling them, scanning them to find corrections, reading the proofreader's marks to decipher what is to be done, and waiting for work when none is available.

Further economies from changes in the work flow sequence are anticipated in the near future when new technology becomes available. The page makeup VDT, now under development, will permit a complete page arrangement of type to be projected onto the video terminal screens (see "Video Display Terminals," page 230). On such a terminal, the operator will be able to position and size type from the keyboard or a sketch pad wired into the machine, and the image on the screen will show the new makeup instantly. VDT systems for the makeup of areas smaller than page size are widely used in composing newspaper advertisements and other products.

This type of terminal is intended to replace conventional makeup operations such as paper paste-up or film stripping in photocomposition systems. The typesetting operation will then be moved even farther

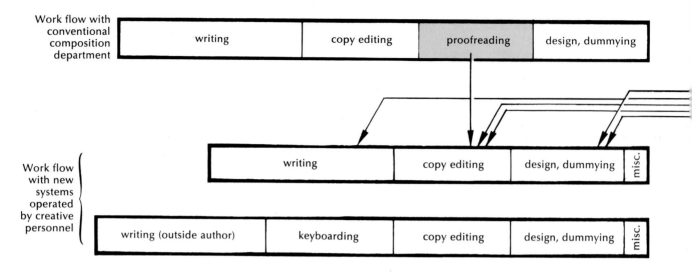

back in the process, behind makeup, as shown in the third bar in figure 6.47. Actually, this bar indicates two possible makeup sequences likely to come into popular use. In the first (the top segment of the two makeup alternatives), the typographic specifications required to produce completely formatted columns of type (including vertical justification) will be entered by the VDT, then type will be set, and finally the finished columns will be pasted into position with a minimum of cutting and fitting. The text editing terminals of several on-line systems on the market can already be used in this manner for page makeup if appropriate programs are purchased with the equipment.

The second alternative involves use of the true page makeup terminal; in this case, all page makeup will be moved ahead of the typesetting operations, and page proofs will be provided before typesetting by using a special kind of plotter-printer to make graphic print-outs of the pages. The typesetting machine will then produce completely made-up type pages lacking only illustrations, film for which will be inserted into spaces left for them by the typesetting machine. Sometime in the 1980's, it is expected that the phototypesetting machine will be replaced by devices which will produce printing plates directly from the coded signals provided by the computer. Then the system will also be equipped to accept digital versions of halftones and line illustrations and to process and transmit these to the platemaking machine along with type matter.

The new work flow offers a great advantage in speed. Because typesetting, when it finally occurs, can take place rapidly and produce pages ready for printing, deadlines for editing and revising copy can be moved closer to the printing date for periodicals or books. Thus, a new management strategy is now possible for publishing—put copy into the electronic system at the earliest possible moment; edit and manipulate it at will until the last possible moment; then typeset, plate, and print it so quickly it cannot become outdated. Even without the special page makeup VDT, on-line electronic systems are being used in this manner

today by composition houses and printers' composition departments serving magazine and book publishers.

ELIMINATING THE COMPOSING ROOM

The newspaper industry, which has pioneered these new systems, has found even more radical departures from time-honored practices to be even more desirable. These departures involve placing the electronic system's terminals directly in the hands of editorial and other personnel rather than composition department operators—eliminating the composing room entirely. This principle is being explored and designed into several systems in book and magazine publishing, and it appears to have widespread application in a host of other organizations, such as corporations and professional societies, which engage in a great deal of editorial and publishing activity.

Eliminating the composition department essentially amounts to eliminating the conversion operations that have always been intertwined with the creative editorial and design work of publishing. In the days before large publishing organizations, editors and designers were also the printers who set and published newspapers, books, magazines, and the like. But as the major publishing industries arose as separate businesses, the creative decisions on editorial content and graphic design moved from the printer to the publishing office. These decisions now had to be written down as instructions for compositors, who remained in the printing plant and had highly specialized skills needed to operate typesetting equipment and perform the other mechanics of composition. The new generation of electronic write-edit-compose systems, however, has made it possible to build into the system all of the mechanics of assembling type into composed pages; all the operator of such equipment need do today is give the system the appropriate instructions—instructions that originate with the writer, editor, and designer, not the compositor. Thus, by receiving the original creative decisions directly from those who

246

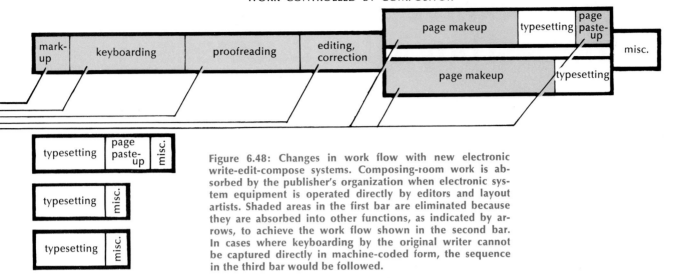

Figure 6.48: Changes in work flow with new electronic write-edit-compose systems. Composing-room work is absorbed by the publisher's organization when electronic system equipment is operated directly by editors and layout artists. Shaded areas in the first bar are eliminated because they are absorbed into other functions, as indicated by arrows, to achieve the work flow shown in the second bar. In cases where keyboarding by the original writer cannot be captured directly in machine-coded form, the sequence in the third bar would be followed.

make them, then remembering these decisions without error, and finally using them to produce finished typeset pages at the appropriate time, the new electronic systems can eliminate the costly conversion work traditionally performed in the composing room.

Newspapers have gone farthest with this movement, placing OCR typewriters and video display terminals on the desks of writers and editors. The newspaper's reporters write original articles directly on the OCR keyboards or the more popular VDT's, and the copy is stored directly in the system's memory. Editors call stories out on their terminals, edit them, write the headlines and other additional material to go with them, and send them on to typesetting. When page makeup terminals are available, the articles will be laid out by the publication's makeup editors on the video screens prior to typesetting. Similar procedures are being implemented today in certain magazine and book publishing houses.

Absorbing composition functions

Some idea of how the composing room's conversion work can be absorbed into publishing office functions is provided by figure 6.48, a bar chart like figure 6.47. The top bar shows a separation of the major functions in the complete write-edit-compose process. On the left side are the activities that occur prior to composition. On the right are the composition functions as they would occur in a composing room equipped with an electronic system that included page makeup terminals (the third arrangement shown in figure 6.47). The second bar shows the functions that would remain in the total write-edit-compose work flow if publishing personnel working directly with the system's equipment took over composition operations.

The shaded functions are those that would be eliminated or absorbed into other functions; the arrows indicate where the replacement work would be done (in effect, at what point the original decisions would now be made). Keyboarding previously done in the composing room would be replaced by capturing

the typing of the original writers. Proofreading and correction operations would be done by the copy editors as they edit the material (note that separate proofreading in the publishing office also would be saved in addition to proofreading in the composing room). Typographic markup of copy as well as makeup operations would be performed by layout artists or designers. At first glance, it might seem that the publisher's staff—particularly copy editing and design—would have to be enlarged greatly to accommodate extra work to perform some of these composition functions. However, copy editors and layout people in publishing offices now spend a great deal of time marking corrections and instructions on copy and making paste-up dummies of page layouts for the composing room. In a new electronic system, the work of inserting instructions into the system would simply replace the previous effort expended on preparing marked copy and dummies for the composing room.

The work flow portrayed by the second bar is found in newspapers and other publishing houses that employ writers on their editorial staffs. In other instances, particularly some magazine and most book publishing, copy is written by outside authors and submitted in manuscript form. Many people have assumed that electronic write-edit-compose systems would not prove economical in this situation because copy would have to be rekeyboarded to enter it into the system. However, the third bar in figure 6.48, showing the work flow which would occur if copy from outside authors were to be encoded by a special keyboarding operation, indicates that other savings in editing and makeup still easily outweigh the loss of savings due to special keyboarding.

Remaining work for compositors

Figure 6.48 also shows some residual work—the operation of typesetting equipment—remaining in the composition house or printing plant. This work is shown in two versions, one for systems with makeup terminals and one for those without. Systems without

Why a Comp/Edit phototypesetter is the best buy in the business.

To get all this power in any other typesetter, you'd have to pay twice as much.

A Comp/Edit system gives you 16 type faces and 138 sizes on-line.

You get a 40-line display screen with an 8,000-character scrolling buffer. And editing power that's backed by 80K of memory, the biggest of any machine in its price range.

You'll cut down on time-consuming paste-up operations, too, because our 70-pica line length and 16-inch reverse leading let you do big jobs in one piece.

With all this power, the Comp/Edit system is easy-to-learn and easy-to-use. And it's backed by the largest service force in the industry.

We'd like to tell you more about how a Comp/Edit system can help your business. (We've only begun to describe all of its features.)

So call toll-free today, and we'll send you our new copyfitting calculator, absolutely free. Call (800) 631-8134, except in Alaska and Hawaii. From New Jersey, (201) 887-8000 extension 666.

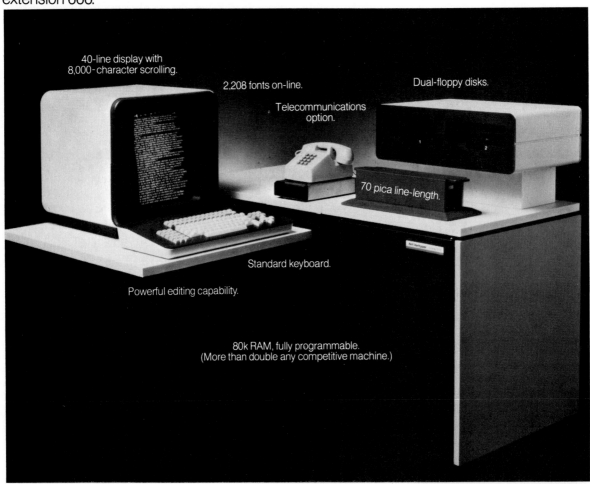

40-line display with 8,000-character scrolling.

2,208 fonts on-line.

Telecommunications option.

Dual-floppy disks.

70 pica line-length.

Standard keyboard.

Powerful editing capability.

80k RAM, fully programmable. (More than double any competitive machine.)

A/// Varityper
the Informationists.

makeup terminals would require a small amount of manual paste-up, as noted earlier. However, even this work need not remain in the composing room if the publisher chooses to install phototypesetting equipment (and paste-up facilities if needed) in order to handle the entire job, sending finished pages directly to the printer's camera department for film processing.

On the other hand, the publisher may elect not to bring all composition operations in-house, depending on circumstances. For example, many published products today are already stored in the computer systems of composition service firms and are designed typographically to be reset for each edition by running the data file through the service firm's formatting and makeup programs. Some publishers have installed only input and editing systems in their offices to permit their own people to update these standing files. In such an operation, the file from the previous edition is recorded on tape by the composition house and sent to the publisher, who places it in the editing system memory. After the file has been revised by editors, the publisher records the new version on tape and sends it back to the composition house for processing through its typographic programs and setting into pages. Thus the publisher continues to make use of previous investments in existing programs and data files, while limiting new investment to facilities that will provide additional economy.

Smaller publishers may not have the capital to invest in a complete on-line system in their own offices. Such publishers might invest only in equipment to perform the earlier functions in the write-edit-compose process, such as input and editing, leaving the insertion of typographic instructions to mark-up personnel in a composition service firm or the composition department of the printer. Or the publishers might perform some typographic functions on their equipment, such as formatting of galleys or columns of type, but leave the insertion of page makeup instructions to the compositor. Most probably, a range of options will become available to publishers, including perhaps the rental or even free use of input and editing equipment supplied by compositors who wish to tie in closely with their customers' operations.

STAND-ALONE EQUIPMENT

An important trend in technological evolution is likely to greatly influence how these options develop. That is the growth of smaller systems which can attain a large part, if not all, of the performance available in the larger and more powerful on-line systems. In particular, this trend includes new kinds of *stand-alone equipment*, complete minisystems designed as work stations for use by a single person. Such equipment does not offer the extra features of larger systems, but it often does include all of the basic functions required to get a certain job done at an acceptable level of efficiency in a small organization.

Some stand-alone terminal equipment, for example, now includes programming for text editing, tabular construction, and a certain amount of specification, copyfitting, and positioning of display type in relation to the text. The output of such equipment is a tape which can be used directly to drive a compatible phototypesetting unit. On the other side, certain typesetting machines and keyboard units have now been equipped with keyboard-controlled programming which permits a certain amount of editing and tabular construction to be done before actually setting the type; video screens are used on several of these increasingly versatile "typesetting" keyboards.

Although these units first were limited primarily to producing punched paper tapes to drive typesetting machines, most now use other forms of memory, notably floppy discs. The "unitizing" of memory in this manner—in standard, inexpensive packages of storage capacity that can be easily handled—makes possible a new form of system, the off-line multi-unit system providing a hybrid type of continuous processing on batches of material. As in the earlier batch-processing computerized composition systems, material would be carried between various pieces of equipment and the different operating steps by means of magnetic cassettes or discs. During each operation, however, all of the material available on a particular cassette or disc would be available immediately in random order to the machine operator for processing in any manner.

This type of small stand-alone equipment is less costly than a completely wired on-line system, yet can be used to achieve most of the benefits of the larger system in a small operation. It promises to bring electronic write-edit-compose systems within reach of all but the smallest producers of published materials within the next few years.

FUTURE PRODUCTS AND SERVICES

The development and installation of write-edit-compose systems in publishing offices will take a number of years to complete, well into the 1980's at least. Once in use, these systems will go beyond providing economies in composition; they will give their operators opportunities to create new kinds of informational products and services that are impossible with conventional composition techniques. Writers and editors will be able to rearrange and recompile existing files into new forms and products, adding new information in the process. It will also be possible to generate new material by processing existing files—for example, by computing new reference data from programs and calculations developed by editors working with terminals. In addition, telephone links will allow operators to reach outside the editorial office to electronically stored data bases maintained and marketed by others and to scan and purchase data as needed. Publishers will be able to market data files directly from their own systems through electronic dissemination facilities, such as telephone lines and data recordings on tapes and discs. Such new uses of write-edit-compose systems have already been attempted experimentally by organizations that have led the way into the electronic systems; ultimately they can be expected to become the cornerstone for new forms of publishing.

ART
PREPARATION

7

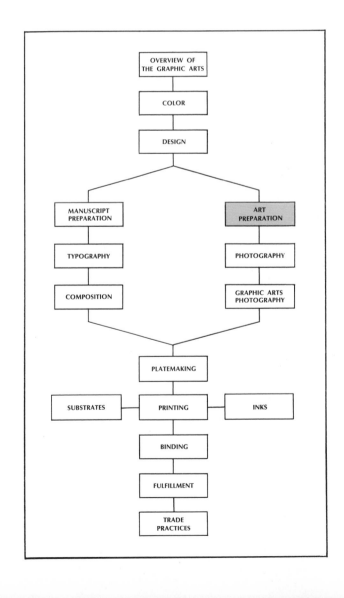

BASIC ART MATERIALS AND TECHNIQUES

Murray A. Falick, FALI-CO ART STUDIOS, INC.

The words *art* and *copy* are used loosely to refer to anything that comes to the printer for reproduction. In this article, we shall limit discussion of artwork to hand-done illustration.

The simplest art is the *sketch* or *rough* used by the artist to first get his ideas down on paper. These bear little resemblance to the final piece prepared for reproduction, the only purpose being to set out a number of images as rapidly as possible to provide a basis for discussion, selection, and refinement—the evolutionary process by which an idea is translated into a printed piece.

The materials used at this point are unimportant so long as they work smoothly and freely. For this reason soft graphite pencils and felt-tip pens are most favored, the color choices available in the latter making them particularly suitable if the artist needs the dimension of color as well as shape to set forth his conception.

The end purpose of the illustration largely defines the technique of rendering to be followed. The treatment of surfaces, whether the softness of a girl's face or the brittle luster of a new auto, will call for a technique quite different from the bold outline of a fashion illustration intended for newspaper reproduction.

Pencil

Pen and ink

Scratch board

Felt-tip pen

Figure 7.1: Common types of line art.

Within each technique, however, there are so many individual variations and combinations that it is futile to consider any hard-and-fast rules for guidance. "Daring" departures from the expected will sometimes yield striking results, but it is best to approach these situations with caution, as the surprise quickly wears off with repeated exposure.

LINE ART

Among the first decisions to be made is whether the illustration is to be reproduced in *line* or in *tone*. The nature of the subject matter usually is the determining factor, although the reproduction process and differences in cost may influence the decision. Line art is often the simplest to prepare and is generally the most economical for reproduction, as it can be photographed along with any type that is pasted in position.

Pen and ink is the most common form of line art. Pencil and felt-tip pens can be rendered in line if the paper used is smooth and the lines are drawn sufficiently dark and even. Scratch board is another way to prepare line art and is particularly convenient for illustrations that depend on the fineness of the white lines, or uninked areas, for their visual impact. Some common types of line art are illustrated in figure 7.1.

The spacing and thickness of the lines provide the shading and sense of dimension when such is required. Additional aids are the self-adhering preprinted shading materials such as the familiar benday tints. Textures and other variations are also available to give a wide

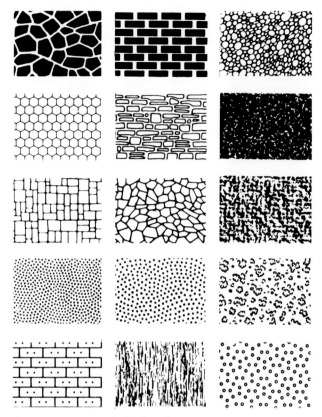

Figure 7.3: Patterned shading sheets.

range of effects simply and quickly. Shading materials are illustrated in figures 7.2 and 7.3.

Color can be used, as well, in line art. Any solid color to be matched by printing inks is best prepared on a separate overlay. Most useful for this purpose are the "peel-off" materials coated on a transparent base. These are supplied in sheets of frequently used sizes in red and amber, both of which photograph as black.

The color material is translucent enough to be placed over a key or line drawing, and the shape cut away with a swivel knife or razor blade and straightedge. The unwanted material is easily peeled off, leaving smooth, sharp edges for reproduction. The ease with which the material can be worked permits extremely intricate configurations.

For each color used in reproduction, a separate overlay is made, and, of course, overlapping register marks must be centered outside the work area. The printer can also be instructed to place film tints behind the "windows" that appear in the negative to create a number of distinct tones from each solid color used in printing.

If process inks are used, a full gamut of colors can be obtained by varying the tint values. Such use of overlays to represent the process colors is referred to as *fake process*. Since it is preseparated, it is usually far more economical than the usual four-color process separations. If the subject matter lends itself to this treatment, the results are cleaner and smoother than if the art had been prepared as a full-color piece for process separation. (See "Techniques for Preseparated Color," page 263.)

Figure 7.2: Benday tint sheets.

Pencil

Felt-tip pen

Wash drawing

Charcoal or pastel

Paint

Air brush

Figure 7.4: Common types of continuous-tone art.

CONTINUOUS-TONE ART

Borrowing from the terminology of photography, we can refer to artwork in which the intermediate tones between black and white are not created by discrete spaces as *continuous tone*. Wash drawings are an example of this, where the depth of the tone is proportional to the concentration of the dye. In charcoal and pastel, variations in pressure create the range of tones. Some common types of continuous-tone art are illustrated in figure 7.4.

With the exception of the collotype or photogelatin process, however, the tones cannot be reproduced in a continuous fashion but necessitate the introduction of a screen.

If charcoal or pencil drawings are rendered on a rough enough paper, the surface texture itself can provide a random-pattern screen allowing the illustration to be reproduced in line. The critical requirement is that the specks of black and white be large enough to be resolved by the copy camera. Since it is difficult for the artist to do this uniformly, the reproductions tend to be muddy, especially in the darkest areas, and the results are unpredictable.

For most purposes, a smooth white illustration board provides the best working surface. The copyboard lighting in graphic arts photography is adjusted to minimize surface irregularities such as paper texture, and illustrations which lean heavily on rough surfaced papers for their visual impact are likely to be disappointing when finally printed. The effect is better simulated by preparing the art on a smooth surface and then printing on paper of the desired texture.

Opaque materials, as well as transparent washes, can render tone, the chief difference being that they are applied in a layer of more or less uniform thickness and concentration. The changes in value are made by varying the proportion of black to white or by selecting from a set of prepared grays. Airbrush technique permits an infinite number of intermediate values to be created from a single color by adjusting the size of the orifice, air pressure, and the distance the brush is held from the paper. Both transparent and opaque materials can be used in an airbrush, although the latter is more common.

A sophisticated use of black with another color lies in a technique often referred to as *two-color process*. The artist prepares a palette of grays and selected values of a single hue. The second color should be clean and bright, such as orange, light blue, or green. Dark colors like brown and purple should be avoided, as they tend to restrict the range of brightnesses. Another color to be avoided is yellow, since the combination of yellow and black gives a displeasing khaki color.

Very effective illustrations can be made in this manner. The economy comes about through the use of only two colors in printing; the art, not being preseparated, must go through photographic separation techniques with little if any saving over conventional four-color process separations. This is not to be confused with a duotone which is only a photographic simulation prepared from black-and-white copy. Here the art itself is rendered in two colors.

With sufficient skill, of course, all full-color art could be preseparated into overlays with each value of gray corresponding to the amount of the printing primary required to make the full color. Such was actually the method used in the early days of color printing. The artist would submit a full-color sketch which was faithfully redrawn in black and white on lithographic stones. Each stone carried values determined by the skill and experience of the lithographic artist as the best representation of the contribution made by a particular primary. For the highest fidelity more than three primaries were required, and the use of as many as eight separate stones was not uncommon.

The ability to visualize a color in terms of three or more primaries is no small feat, and the skills of the lithographic artist have been replaced by color-separation photography. One ingenious method which still permits the artist to prepare separations himself is the Bourges process. The four primaries of the printing process—cyan, magenta, yellow, and black—are deposited as ink films on a transparent support. By scratching, burnishing, applying solvents, and other hand manipulation, the unwanted colors are removed. The transparent materials can be laid over each other as the work proceeds to give a final full-color image at each stage. The finished films are sent to the printer where exposure through appropriate color filters yields separate images ready for plating.

FULL-COLOR ARTWORK

The bulk of color illustration is provided as final art using the customary methods of watercolor, oils, acrylics, crayon, etc. The rendering is presented to the printer just as it will finally appear. This gives the artist maximum flexibility in preparation, as he is not concerned with overlays, register, and all the attendant photomechanical problems. Attached to this, of course, are the expenses of four-color process separation.

There are very few restrictions in preparation since the camera will "see" whatever is placed before it just as the viewer sees it. The artist has at his disposal, however, a larger palette of potential colors than the printer, who is limited to the gamut produced by three primary inks plus black. Some printers provide a chart showing a sample of the colors obtainable with the commonly used printing inks. This is worth some careful study. It will be noted that the very purest colors which the artist can obtain quite directly from a tube are somewhat cleaner than those obtainable in process reproduction. These are potential problem areas, and the artist should avoid fine distinctions in color purity and subtleties which are beyond the limits of the printing process. The use of fluorescent or Day-Glo colors may add a lot of "pizzazz" to the original rendering, but the printed results are likely to be disappointing unless similar fluorescing inks are used. Metallic pigments such as silver and bronze, or colors with metallic luster, should also be avoided. The lustrous effect in the original rendering is dependent upon the viewing angle with respect to the light source, as well as the diffuseness of the lighting. Copyboard lighting in graphic arts photography is set at a fixed angle to eliminate surface reflections and glare, and in so doing it effectively eliminates the reflections that give these pigments their distinctive lustrous quality.

Artwork should also be prepared whenever possible

as close to final size as practical. Reductions of up to one-half are permissible and will help obscure slight imperfections. Contrary to popular belief, detail is not added by making oversize originals and excessive reductions. A two-thirds reduction, or, as it is sometimes called, "a third off," is sound general practice. Enlargement ratios of more than 150% can produce particularly unpleasant results if the illustration is dependent upon fine brushwork or texture for its effect. Such pictures seem "bloated" in reproduction since the scale is unexpected and unnatural.

NOVEL TECHNIQUES

Art prepared in other than traditional ways is also acceptable for four-color process reproduction. Transparent and opaque films and papers, bits of wire, yarn, and other materials can be assembled as collage. However, direct reproduction imposes some restrictions. The assembly must be kept very close to a plane surface since it is pressed under glass in the camera copyboard. Mounting it on the front surface of the glass copyboard does not provide a solution, as the lenses used in copy work do not have sufficient depth of field to keep the entire object in sharp focus. Furthermore, the standard 45° lighting casts harsh shadows. Foil, tinsel, and other metallic objects will photograph as black. Heavily textured surfaces will appear much flattened. If the collage is essentially a three-dimensional object, it should be converted to a color transparency since the studio photographer has complete control over his lighting.

Certain products such as fabric swatches, paint chips, tile samples, and other two-dimensional colored objects can be assembled as final art. If scaling and other considerations permit, this is preferable to first making a color transparency. Higher color fidelity and better detail are obtained, and there is no need to correct for the inaccuracies introduced by the color transparency.

Previously printed reproductions should not be used as artwork as the double screen pattern will almost certainly produce moiré (see "Color Reproduction," page 346). Screen angles can be adjusted to eliminate the pattern in single-color reproductions but seldom with full color.

There is also the large field of "cameraless" photography to be explored, where the artist uses the light-sensitive materials of photography as his medium. Geometric patterns of great intricacy can be "painted with light" directly on the film, as well as unusual abstractions of light and shade from polished reflecting surfaces. Du Pont's Cromalin materials, introduced as a method of prepress proofing, use a tacky surface as the image-forming device. Powdered color toners stick to the surface according to the amount of light that has been permitted to strike it. The toners can be applied by hand with a cotton swab. The possibilities for combining a controlled application of color with photographic images are endless.

Whether these hybrids are the province of "art" or "technology" is an academic question. The artist and the printer have always been greatly dependent upon each other, and the introduction of new materials for the creation of graphic images will create new opportunities for both to explore.

ART PRODUCTION
Jack Golden, DESIGNERS 3, INC.

The graphic arts industry blends a unique harmony of craftsmanship—design, art, photography, retouching, and mechanical production—on the one hand, and a multiplicity of mechanical processes on the other, to achieve a finished product through any number of printing processes. The ultimate objective must constantly be borne in mind through every step of the creative process from design through mechanical.

Too often we forget that we must work within prescribed limitations, and that we must accommodate these limitations as dictated by the requirements of a specific printing process. For example, it would be foolish to expect that a facsimile of Helvetica light, particularly in smaller sizes, could be held clean and sharp in screen printing or die stamping. And it would certainly look quite different in gravure or letterpress than in lithography or steel-die engraving.

Foresight is always better than hindsight; thus it would be wise to consider an analysis of design ob-

jectives related to printing capabilities as a prerequisite to all important design efforts. Avoiding the pitfalls that lead to poor reproduction can invariably be accomplished by prepress analysis with a printer or production specialist. In the long run it saves time and money. The traditional routine of preparing mechanicals is well entrenched, almost everyone producing them in his own individual manner. Inaccuracies that occur are hopefully caught in the blueprint stage. When they are not caught at this stage, but caught on press, corrections can become quite expensive. Can we do something to prevent such costly errors? Yes, by establishing a disciplined routine of checking and rechecking the mechanical as we progress each step of the way. It sounds simple, yet it is doubtful that it is done methodically all the time, every time. This may be because the individual has such faith in his own accuracy that he does not think checking is necessary, or because he feels that he can skip it because the job is in a rush and he cannot afford the extra time. How impractical! We would never eliminate proofreading, no matter how accurate we felt the typographer was. And how often do typos occur even after two or three people proofread the copy. Checking a mechanical every step of the way does not really take so much extra time, once it is made part of a routine.

Following is an outline for a production system. Although where the human element is involved one can hardly consider any system foolproof, this one would go a long way toward eliminating many of the errors that somehow inadvertently creep into mechanicals.

A systematic approach to production should include the following steps:

1. Scaling all material to proper sizes
2. Checking accuracy of sizing
3. Checking availability of elements for assembly
4. Checking layout against original copy
5. Ruling the boards, drawing guide lines
6. Checking the sizes ruled
7. Paste-up of various elements
8. Checking paste-up alignments, squaring, correct positioning
9. Preparing overlays where necessary, positioning register guides
10. Writing instructions, color keying

SCALING

The scaling of original art to fit the layouts can be done in several ways. The most cumbersome and time-consuming is the *diagonal line method,* illustrated in

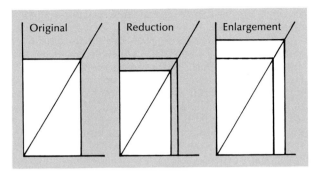

Figure 7.5: Diagonal line method for scaling art. To find enlargement or reduction size: trace the borders of the original art on a tissue overlay and draw a diagonal line bisecting the rectangle; measure one of the final dimensions and mark this distance either from the horizontal line to the diagonal (if height is known) or from the vertical line to the diagonal (if width is known); complete the rectangle to obtain final enlargement or reduction size.

figure 7.5. The *proportional scale,* a circular scale consisting of two rotating wheels, as in figure 7.6, is the most common and the fastest way to get proportional sizes. Great care should be used in reading the sizes beyond 12″ on the circular scale. If sizes less than 1″ are to be enlarged (when scaling from 35mm transparencies particularly), it is necessary to double or

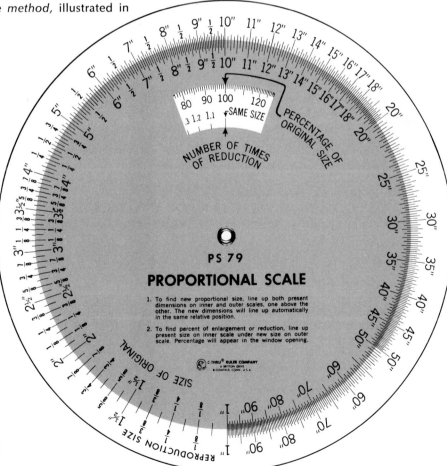

Figure 7.6: Proportional scale. To find new proportional size, line up both dimensions of original art on inner and outer scales. Dimensions in the same proportions will align automatically around the scale. To find percentage of enlargement or reduction, align original size of one dimension on inner scale with reproduction size of same dimension on outer scale. Percentage aligns with arrow in the window opening. *Courtesy of The C-Thru Ruler Company.*

257

triple the size and then reverse the process with the enlarged size.

An easy way to scale art is to use the *proportional border device* (see figure 7.7), which is based on the diagonal line method. By loosening the knobs on the diagonal rod we can set the borders to conform to the finished size required; then by tightening the knobs we can slide the borders back and forth over the art or photograph until we have determined the exact cropping desired. It is the most foolproof method for seeing exactly how the art will crop. The ruler on each side of the border will give the sizes to designate for the photostatter and printer to follow.

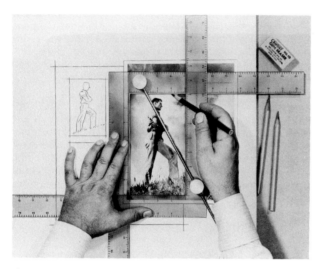

Figure 7.7: Proportional border device. *Courtesy of The Brandt Corporation.*

When making photostats of original art, it is important to realize that stats can never be perfectly accurate because of stretch or shrinkage. They should be considered as a guide for position only, and the printer should follow the specifications on the art. Since this occurs with glossy stats as well, instructions must be given to the photostatter to produce an exact size when the stats are being used as finish art.

It would be wise to consider all the options before scaling original material to fit the layout. One should consider a layout as a working tool and not necessarily be slavish in conforming to it, for aesthetic considerations may dictate that slight modifications be made for improvement.

CHECKING ACCURACY OF SIZING

It is not always necessary to use stats of art or photos for positioning on a mechanical, particularly when square halftones are indicated. When only keylines are provided, however, checking of sizes becomes more important. Eliminating photostats can save money, but no savings are effected when engravings are made to incorrect sizes.

Checking all sizes before sending material out also provides the opportunity to reconsider certain sizes that have been established.

CHECKING AVAILABILITY OF ELEMENTS

Checking to see that all the necessary materials are available is more a time-saver than anything else. It is advisable to start a mechanical with all the elements at hand. Checking the layout against everything provided would obviously indicate the pieces that are missing. When such portions are essential for accuracy (such as a silhouette photograph and type to conform to the silhouette) it is wise to wait before proceeding.

It is at this point also that type is checked for broken letters, poor proofing, and correct sizing. Type should have been proofread for accuracy. Photographs should be checked for cracks and imperfections, as well as for spots.

Photographs or stats of line art to be used for reproduction should be clean and sharp and not unevenly curled. Flat photographs or stats are absolutely essential; if not supplied that way, they should be returned to the supplier for refinishing.

Where logos are required and stats are supplied by the client, be sure that they are sharp and clean and in a usable size. It is not unusual to receive a stat that is smaller than the final size, requiring a blowup. It would be wise to request a stat that can be reduced in size rather than enlarged.

CHECKING LAYOUT AGAINST COPY

Checking the layout against the copy may seem an obvious step, but it is an important one. It ensures that nothing will be left out of the mechanical that appears in the original copy, particularly the minutiae—such as trademark and copyright symbols, asterisks, footnotes, code numbers, etc. We are not infallible, and the eye sometimes does skip over things that are very obvious.

It is also wise to check sequence of paragraphs when several galleys of type are used. Inadvertently, when galleys are cut apart, the sequence may be lost, and the only way to ensure accuracy is to check against the original copy. It is very awkward, for example, to find that two paragraphs of Section 3 of an annual report are under Section 6. This would probably require pulling the entire mechanical apart, which becomes unnecessarily expensive and time-consuming.

Errors in keying captions to photos crop up constantly, and again can be prevented by checking with the copy.

As a matter of fact, it is important to check every piece of the paste-up against the copy while the mechanical is being put together.

RULING THE BOARDS, DRAWING GUIDE LINES

Mechanicals should be produced on illustration board, except when clients require copies of the mechanical for proofreading and checking. A new wrinkle to producing mechanicals, on flexible two-ply sheets instead of board, was devised not only to save the cost of photostats but to save time. What makes this possible is a copying machine utilizing a roll of paper instead of individual sheets, such as the Remington R-3, which can copy 11″ x 17″ spreads (or 11″ x 24″ or 30″ or any length, if necessary) very expeditiously.

The advantage of this method is very obvious when

producing an annual report, since, in most instances, a client could request anywhere from 10 to 40 copies to circulate among board members, executives, lawyers, accountants, and others involved.

There actually is no difference in production, except that after the two-ply sheet has been copied, it is taped down on illustration board. It should not be cemented down, since if corrections are to be made subsequently, taping will permit the sheets to be lifted off the board and put through the copying machine again.

Before any actual guide lines are ruled, it would be a good idea to make sure that the page size is accurate, that it has not changed from the original layout. If, when estimating, a printer should recommend a size change of 1/8″ or 1/4″ (or more) larger or smaller than the original layout to accommodate a press size and at the same time save money, the change should be noted on the layout immediately.

In instances where the change to a new size is more radical (such as enlarging to 6″ x 9″ from 5″ x 8″), all measurements will change, requiring changes all the way down the line.

When producing more than one mechanical for an assignment, make certain that all the boards are first cut to the same standard size. An 11″ x 17″ spread, for instance, would work well on a 15″ x 20″ board, allowing ample area for writing instructions. (Two-ply sheets are cut to fit the size requirements of the copying machine.) Skimping on the size of a board is very unprofessional. Every mechanical should allow at least 2″ beyond the outside dimensions of the page.

Prior to inking, all ruling should be done in light pencil. Guide lines for positioning of type, photography, art, etc., should be drawn very lightly, but legibly, and always beyond the areas involved.

When drawing with a ruling pen, it is better to draw clean, crisp lines beyond the area involved than to try to come right up to each edge. (Cleaning up the edges with white paint is simple to do.) This procedure is unnecessary with Rapidograph pens, which come in a variety of sizes. It is good practice, when ruling for reproduction, to do the pieces separately and assemble them later, as you would with stats and type. This method gives greater flexibility, allowing for size changes when required.

CHECKING THE SIZES RULED

Checking at this point is another safeguard against redoing mechanicals. Check page sizes to be sure that all are the same, that all margins are consistent, that folds are indicated properly. A cursory examination of all sizes is most important particularly when alignments throughout a book are to be consistent.

PASTE-UP

Most paste-ups at this time are being done on boards, but as phototypesetting becomes more widespread, more and more mechanicals are being prepared on film, particularly by film typographers.

Mechanicals on boards

It may seem too obvious to mention, but it would be wise to check the square of T squares and triangles regularly before doing mechanicals. Screws holding squares in position have been known to loosen, and if not checked for accuracy T squares can wreak havoc in production. Also, instruments used for ruling lines must never be used as cutting edges. Use a separate set for cutting only, and always use metal triangles, never plastic ones for such purposes.

Pens such as ruling and Rapidograph pens should always be kept clean and in working order so that no time will be lost in preparation for work. This will increase speed and efficiency and will obviously reduce costs.

Before proceeding with the paste-up for a saddle-stitched booklet involving photographs that will jump gutters, a check of production requirements should be made. An 8- or 12-page book is less of a problem in binding than a 32-page one. Horizontal alignments are always a problem, and the safest method of avoiding misalignments is to prepare boards by spreads in continuous sequence, not according to a printer's imposition. Mechanicals can be prepared to an imposition, and stripping costs can be saved, but it is far safer to prepare mechanicals by spreads.

The narrow edges that show through on subsequent pages when photos jump gutters are very unsightly and are a more difficult problem to solve. In books of 16 pages or more, no matter how accurate the binding, some creep does tend to take place. To avoid this, do not paste right up to the gutter, but allow approximately 1/32″ from each side of the gutter; or discuss with the printer what he would allow and have him make the adjustments when stripping.

Aside from accuracy, neatness and cleanliness are the mark of the true professional in preparing a paste-up. It may be easier to cut type without using a straightedge, but it is more efficient to use one. Without a straightedge, one is never quite sure of the parallel. Arbitrary cutting of type proofs causes them to look optically out of square, even though they may not be. Mechanicals are easier to check when all cuts are made neatly on the square.

Figure 7.8 shows a mechanical with elements pasted into position.

Figure 7.8: Elements pasted into position on board.

Figure 7.9: Blacking the edges of reversal elements.

When using proofs from metal, be sure that they are sprayed with a clear plastic to prevent smearing and smudging. Even after a day or two some inks do not dry completely. Play it safe and spray at all times. This is not necessary, of course, when using film typography.

When supplying reverse areas for reproduction, savings can be effected by preparing everything in reverse for the camera. Sharp negative photostats of lettering, type, or line art are cemented into position as a complete paste-up on the black areas on the mechanical. This eliminates the need for the cameraman to make separate reversals from positive copy, as well as the need for stripping. All individual elements must be blackened at the cut edges, to prevent white strip lines from showing on the film, which would entail handwork by the stripper. (See figure 7.9.)

Checking to see that everything is pasted down firmly, so that nothing can lift off accidentally, is extremely important. This is particularly true of the very small elements. Be very careful when pasting down on glossy photostats or prints. Making fine-line prints from film negatives of the complete paste-up will eliminate any anxiety about pieces lifting off after the mechanical has left the studio.

Avoid picking up and repasting again and again, unless you use cement thinner to lift up the material. If a residue of cement buildup occurs because of constant repositioning, it would be advisable to remove it completely with cement pickup and start afresh.

Once all the art is down in position, place a sheet of heavy tracing paper (or any heavy paper) over the entire mechanical and with the edge of a triangle glide over the art with a steady pressure to press all the elements down on the board firmly. If any portions do not stay down, use one-coat cement under those areas and firmly press down again. If any portion is not pasted down securely, it could crease or tear during handling at the engraver's.

There are several types of adhesives that can be used for paste-ups. Most popular is the one-coat rubber cement, permitting fairly easy lift-up and repositioning. The new 3M Spra-Mount comes in an aerosol can and when used properly will permit even greater flexibility for repositioning material. It can be lifted up many times without using cement thinner and without losing adhesion.

To be sure that no rubber cement dirt specks or streaks are reproduced, cleaning up all pasted areas is a must. The printer is expected to opaque all of these unwanted dirt specks, but if he does not catch them all (and they are most difficult to find in type areas) or if they are not caught in the blueprint, they will show up in the printed piece. Initially, rubber cement residue is not visible, but with repeated handling, dirt begins to adhere; so the last step before turning the mechanical over to the printer should be running your fingers over the paste-up areas and feeling for the sticky cement spots, particularly in the areas of typography.

Mechanicals with film

Until the advent of phototypesetting, mechanicals made on boards with paper type proofs were the only way to go. The offset printer would convert the mechanical to film, strip the halftones where necessary, and show a client blueprints for approval.

Phototypesetting has changed all that. Although the change has not become universal, the absolute need for making mechanicals on boards no longer prevails. Many typesetters will provide phototypeset copy in film form rather than on paper. Since the ultimate objective is to create a film positive for the printer or photoengraver, why convert film to paper and come back to what you started with?

In essence, providing a film mechanical saves the cost of shooting and stripping by the printer, as well as time. Since costs in the graphic arts industry are skyrocketing, film mechanicals become very attractive.

However, one must completely reorient his thinking about producing mechanicals. Paste-ups are done on acetate, not on board. A light table is required, not a drawing board. Transparent tape is used very often instead of rubber cement (3M Spra-Mount is another efficient method for paste-up).

One can stop at providing a line positive, with indications of where art or photos go, and let the engraver do the rest; or if simple black-and-white halftones are required, these can be procured and stripped into position with the line material. Where two or more colors are indicated, it would still be preferable to let the engraver take over.

At the present time phototypesetters are providing this service, particularly to ad agencies. Since more and more magazines are being produced by offset, mailing costs are drastically reduced because film is cheaper to mail than electros.

Producing film mechanicals is, in essence, no more difficult than producing mechanicals on board. It requires reorienting your approach to the materials and the method of paste-up. The film mechanical is in its infancy, at present, in most art departments, although it is catching on at magazines. It will not be too long, however, with a greater and greater use of phototypesetting, before this will become the accepted way to make mechanicals.

CHECKING THE PASTE-UP

At this stage, it would again be wise to check the paste-up. First, check the mechanical against the layout and original copy to be sure that nothing has been left out and that the proper captions appear with the proper photos.

Secondly, check all type, to see that there are no broken letters and no misalignments. This is particularly important with phototype. Because the proof is made from film, dirt specks and paste-up marks can show up on the proofs; and it is not unusual to find type out of alignment because of a careless paste-up by the film typographer.

Where type corrections have been made, such as cutting numbers, words, or even letters, be sure they are pasted down very securely, so that they will not fall off.

Running the T square up and down the mechanical with a triangle to check alignments and squaring is a must.

PREPARING OVERLAYS, REGISTER GUIDES

Preparing overlays is the last step in the production process, aside from writing the instructions to the printer. Depending upon requirements, overlays are necessary where overprinting or line and halftone combinations are required and/or where two or more colors are called for, other than four-color process.

It is advisable that acetate overlays be used in all instances, although heavy vellum overlays can be used when accurate register is not a requisite. When a good deal of ruling is to be done, *prepared* clear or frosted acetate is an absolute must, to assure perfect register. Ruling does not necessarily have to be done on the acetate. It can be done separately on white one-ply and cemented into position.

It should be remembered that positioning cemented elements on acetate is not as easy as on board, since cement grabs the smooth surface of the acetate more tenaciously. Positioning elements while the cement is not quite dry gives greater maneuverability.

Line and halftone combination

Halftone and benday areas should be put on the board and all line material registered in position on the overlay. It is easier to see exactly what you are doing through the acetate.

There will be many occasions when all halftone material will remain the same but there will be different sets of type on the overlays. In such cases a *separate* overlay is required for each type change. Where a "knockout" from the halftone is necessary and a surprint is indicated on the knockout, two separate overlays will be required, one for the knockout and one for the surprint, the surprint being the top overlay.

When grouping several photos on a page that require black or white borders between photos, do not trim the photos to exact size; butt all the photos up to each other, and draw the separation borders on the overlay. The engraver will use these either as a surprint or knockout. (See figures 7.10 and 7.11.)

Overlays for two or more colors

The same technique discussed above applies for color overlays. However, since registration becomes of prime consideration you must decide whether to prepare your own color keys or leave it to the engraver.

Figure 7.10: Butting photographs.

It is often quite possible to prepare all the art on one mechanical and prepare tissue overlays to indicate color breakup. Simple tint blocks may be indicated, as in figure 7.12. Because the outlines are simple and registration of colors is not much of a problem, these color areas could also be prepared on acetate overlays for direct shooting by the engraver. Tissue overlays are needed more often for art with irregular outlines which must trap one against another. In such cases, it is best

Figure 7.11: Addition of acetate overlay with borders for photographs indicated.

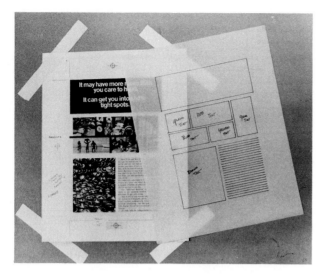

Figure 7.12: Tissue overlay indicating color.

Figure 7.13: Register marks.

to rely on the camera and stripping techniques of the printer. Cameramen can make all the necessary adjustments, including the line-width "overlaps" required when one color registers with another.

For complex color areas, indications should be made carefully by coloring in the full areas with felt-tip markers or crayon pencils, not just by marking diagonal strips. Being as accurate and complete as possible when preparing a color tissue is the best way to ensure perfect color plates.

When preparing overlays for a book with many pages, some or all of which have similar color indications, it is safer to make color tissues for each page than to make one tissue with instructions to the engraver to repeat where necessary.

Four-color process

In preparing art for four-color printing, only a tissue overlay for color indications is necessary unless surprints and knockouts are involved, and all the elements can be put on one board, as discussed above.

Register marks

At least three register marks are required on a mechanical. The simplest method is the use of register strip rolls available from an art-supply dealer (see figure 7.13). In preparing acetate overlays, it is imperative to keep the acetate from shifting when applying the register marks. When more than one overlay is required, check very carefully that all marks are dead center, one over the other.

WRITING INSTRUCTIONS

One of the most important things to remember, before sending your mechanicals to the printer, is to be as explicit and comprehensive as possible in communicating with him. Instructions should be simple and easy to read, not ambiguous. Leave nothing to the imagination. If possible, put all your instructions on the board, not on the tissues. Instructions for acetate belong on acetate. (See figure 7.14.)

One should be most exacting when it comes to ben-

day tint instructions. There are many color reference guides that can be used to assure accuracy in determining the precise percentages desired. These should be used religiously when two-color tints are necessary. Remember, however, that this still does not assure an accurate color rendition, since slight tint variations will occur from printer to printer.

When tints of three or more colors are required, on a four-color process job, it is essential to secure one of the many process tint sheets, for coated and uncoated papers. Although standards for four-color letterpress printing for magazine publishing were set many years ago, and those for magazines printed by offset lithography were established in 1975, no accepted standards exist for commercial four-color printing. Consequently, it would be advisable to consult with the printer producing your job before specifying tints in process colors. Color charts used for specifying will vary from printer to printer, depending upon the process inks used.

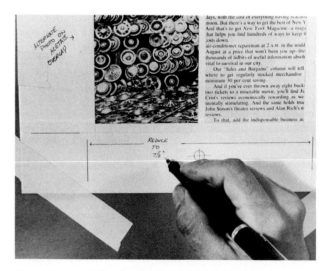

Figure 7.14: Writing instructions on mechanical.

262

Also bear in mind that color will vary on various types of paper. When indicating color for a coated paper, for example, remember that the color will be different on a Kromekote than a regular coated or dull coated stock. With enough experience, you can use your discretion to make slight changes from your color chart to accommodate the paper being used. Naturally the same will hold true for uncoated papers. A smooth matte paper may require different instructions than a standard uncoated offset.

Finally, when providing a color swatch, it could be very helpful to use a matching system, such as the Pantone system (see "Color Matching," page 508). The choice of colors is very extensive, though by no means complete. Colors not available in the Pantone Formula Guide can be obtained by increasing or decreasing the amounts in a specific formula after discussion with the printer.

Last but not least, it is advisable to go over your instructions with the printer, making sure that he understands them completely, allowing no room for error or misunderstanding.

TECHNIQUES FOR PRESEPARATED COLOR
Ellen Greene, WATSON-GUPTILL PUBLICATIONS

A steep rise in production costs has spurred renewed interest in the field of preseparated color reproductions. Art which has been prepared on separate overlays by the artist enables the printer to use less complicated, and therefore less expensive, photographic procedures to make the printing plates. In addition, preseparated art techniques provide effects not possible with conventional color printing.

Art prepared in full color must be photographically separated so that four plates may be made, each of which will print in one of the four process-color inks. One way to use preseparated color techniques is to create an overlay to represent the areas where each of the process colors will print so that there is no need for a photographic separation step. However, the artist is not restricted to combinations of process inks. One of the important advantages of preseparated art is that the artist may choose any colors he or she wishes to use, whether flat, process, or a combination. When using flat colors, the artist may specify the exact color desired by providing the printer with a swatch of the color to be matched or by designating a number from the Pantone Matching System or another color matching system. The surest way to match to a standard is to provide a sample on the substrate to be used. Whether process or flat inks are used, the expensive camera separation step is avoided, because a separate overlay is created for each color.

Economy is not always the only consideration: there are many instances in which reproduction quality can be improved through thoughtful preparation by the artist. Illustrations for juvenile books, for example, are frequently prepared as black line drawings with the fill colors on a separate overlay. Magenta, yellow, and cyan plates are made from the overlay in the conventional manner, with the black plate made from the outline supplied by the artist. Because the black outline is carried on the black plate only, and not on all plates as in regular process printing, there are two large advantages. First, there is no register problem, and the black outline remains clear and sharp. Secondly, the other colors print clean and bright since no black is carried to muddy them.

CHOICE OF MATERIALS

An important factor in successful preseparation is the quality of the materials used. When fine register is necessary, overlay materials should be dimensionally stable; that is, they should neither shrink nor stretch when exposed to heat or humidity, nor with the passage of time. Materials of this type, such as Mylar, are more expensive but are worth the extra cost. Alternatively, an attempt should be made to use materials within a single piece of art that will all react in the same way. A line key prepared on board with acetate overlays is a setup for possible trouble. If the key is also prepared on acetate, the likelihood is that all elements will change size together, preventing troublesome fit problems.

Zipatone and similar masking materials can be used when there are large solid areas that would require tedious handwork with a brush. The sheet of Zipatone is adhered to the overlay, and non-printing areas are cut to shape and peeled away. Remaining areas can be printed solid, or a percentage of color can be indicated for the printer to follow.

Another method of preseparation involves the use of balanced gray opaques—paints specially prepared in various strengths of gray. These are used to represent percentages of color on the overlay, which is then photographed in halftone and printed in the color specified.

A factor to keep in mind when working with preseparated art is that both red and black are seen as black by the camera. Therefore, separations prepared in either of these colors will photograph well. They can, of course, be printed in any color specified.

CARE IN PREPARATION

The savings gained through the use of preseparation techniques can be lost unless the artist works neatly, carefully, and thoughtfully, as errors will have to be corrected by the printer. If possible, the artist should work over a light table. The first step should be to make the key, whether for black or another color, and then all overlays should be registered to the key—not to each other. In this way, small, unavoidable errors will not be cumulative. Registration should be carefully indicated, using either a pin system or paste-on register marks. If trapping (the overlapping of two or more colors) is required, it is a good idea for the artist to create it rather than to rely on the printer. All overlays should be prominently marked with the name of the color in which they are to print.

When a line key is used, any type matter which will print in the same color can be pasted into position on the key, creating a type mechanical as well.

The main difficulty for the artist when creating separations is that he must work in tones of black, while picturing the art in combinations of the colors of the different inks that will be used. There are many artists who do beautiful work in full color but cannot preseparate their work. In such cases, the best solution is to hire an artist who specializes in creating separations, or, of course, to have camera separations made. When available, however, preseparated art is a useful production technique. Preseparated art gives the artist a good deal of choice and control over how the final piece will look and, when carefully done, can reduce costs and problems in printing while producing clean, attractive illustrations that would be difficult to achieve with the conventional methods of process separation.

CHARTING: THE BASIC FACTS

Steve J. Reiter, THE CHARTMAKERS, INC.

If a picture is worth a thousand words, then a chart is worth two thousand. It strips away all that is extraneous and leaves only the basic information that we need to help us analyze problems and make complex decisions. In this computer age, enormous amounts of information are made available to us. Much of it lies buried under mountains of figures and printouts.

Charts are graphic representations of data. Their purpose is to make information easier to understand and to communicate it more effectively. There are several basic types of charts used to convey different kinds of information, and it is essential that we select the type which will do the particular job best. Curves, bars, and pie charts all have their special uses. From these simple forms we can elaborate so that the chart has added interest and dimension. These charts may be thought of as "super graphics" since we have added design elements that further enhance the facts.

TYPES OF CHARTS

In the following 14 charts and accompanying text, we are attempting to show some of the ground rules for graphic charting as well as a few of the many possible graphic styles which may be used. Figures 7.15 through 7.23 are examples of *curve* charts (figures 7.22 and 7.23 are also known as *layer* or *area* charts); figures 7.24 and 7.25 are *bar* charts; figure 7.26 is a *pie* chart; and 7.27 and 7.28 illustrate the use of "super graphics."

Curve charts

An examination of the first six charts shows that, although they present different pictures, they are based on the same two sets of figures. Let us analyze which of these have shown us realistic comparisons. The broken line in each chart represents the population of New York City; the solid line shows the population of New York State.

In figures 7.15 and 7.16, a curve is plotted on an appropriate scale; each chart shows an individual picture. The scales on both charts start at zero (the zero base is a must for nearly all charts). The two charts do not relate to each other visually, however, and if they are presented side by side as they are here the wrong impression will result.

This is evident in figure 7.17, where we have combined the first two charts, keeping their own individual scales. The first impression of this chart would suggest that the population of New York City was higher than that of the state during recent years. If we consult the scales, we can see that these have been treated as two completely separate sets of figures, simply placed on the same chart. This is usually a technique to be avoided, since it gives a completely misleading picture if the two sets of figures are at all related. If they have no relation to each other, then placing them on the same chart suggests that there should be some relationship. Except in rare instances, this is a form to be avoided. If the figures are intended to be compared,

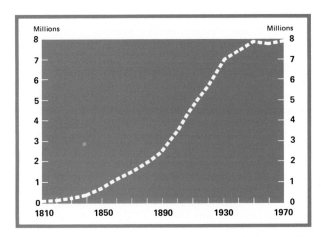

Figure 7.15: Curve chart representing population of New York City from 1810 to 1970. A set of figures is plotted at ten-year intervals on a scale that is appropriate for the figures involved.

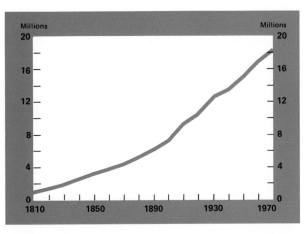

Figure 7.16: Curve chart representing population of New York State from 1810 to 1970. Here a different set of figures is plotted at ten-year intervals for the same period of time but on a scale that is appropriate for these figures.

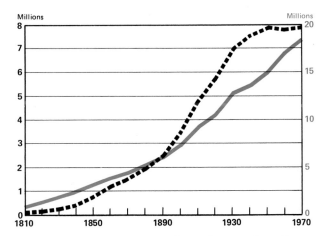

Figure 7.17: Misleading comparison of curves from figures 7.15 and 7.16. The curves have their own individual scales at opposite sides of the grid and are duplicates of the curves in the previous charts.

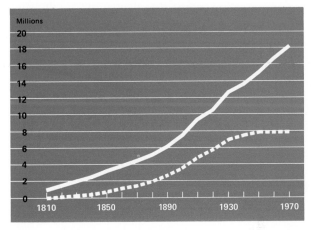

Figure 7.18: Logical comparison of curves in figures 7.15 and 7.16. The same two sets of figures are plotted, but on a common scale.

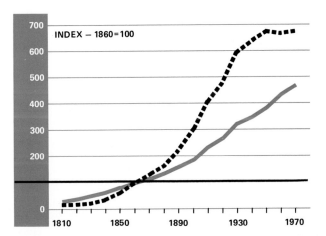

Figure 7.19: Curve chart using figures for the year 1860 as an index. Both sets of figures have been converted in relation to 1860 = 100.

the scale used should reflect an honest comparison, as in the following chart.

Figure 7.18 gives us a logical picture of the comparative trends of New York City and New York State populations on an arithmetic scale. As opposed to figure 7.17, this chart compares accurately the sizes of the populations of the city and state because both curves are based on the same scale. We can get a direct comparison at ten-year intervals of the relationship between the two—the accelerated growth of the city population up to 1950 and its leveling off, compared to the continued growth of the state population.

In figure 7.19, by converting these figures to an index, we have related all figures to the year 1860. We have treated 1860 as a basis for comparison of the growth of the city and state. Thus we can determine that in 1950, for example, the state population was almost four times what it was in 1860, while the city population had increased almost sevenfold.

In figure 7.20 we have used a logarithmic scale for the figures and an arithmetic scale for the years. This is known as a semilogarithmic scale. Each curve shows a rate of change from the previously plotted figure. In other words, a 10% change would always look the same. An increase of 3,000 to 3,300 which is a 10% increase, would have the same angle or slope as an increase of 3,000,000 to 3,300,000, which is also a 10% rise.

A semilogarithmic scale shows this and this only, and should never be confused with a chart such as figure 7.18, where an increase of 300,000 would show a fantastic rise compared to an increase of 300. Inasmuch as most people are more familiar with the arithmetic scale, the semilogarithmic scale is a dangerous one to use unless it is properly explained or the viewer is familiar with the technique being used and understands its purpose.

In figure 7.21, we have added the population figures for the United States to those of New York State and New York City on the semilogarithmic chart (fig. 7.20). We have removed the logarithmic scale and have arbitrarily placed the United States curve between the other two curves. The scale was dropped because we are not presenting comparative figures, but are showing

instead only a graphic comparison of rates of growth. This, too, is a legitimate charting practice provided the viewer understands what the chart has to say, as well as its limitations.

In figure 7.22, we have simply taken the two curves that were drawn in figure 7.18 and filled in the areas. By doing this, we have shown a more definite picture. The bottom area shows us the New York City population as it has increased to 1970. The area directly above it gives us a comparison with New York State, excluding New York City. The top line gives us the total of the two—the entire population of the state.

Figure 7.23 compares New York City's population to that of the state on a percentage basis. The population of New York State has been considered as 100% for each year plotted, and New York City's relation to the state population is all that we show here. This chart does not illustrate New York City's growth, New York State's growth, or anything relative to the rest of the country.

Bar charts

In figure 7.24, we have plotted the same data as that in figure 7.18, except that we have drawn bars instead

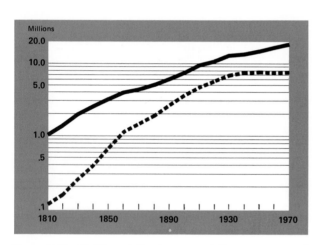

Figure 7.20: Plotting of the two sets of figures on a semilogarithmic scale.

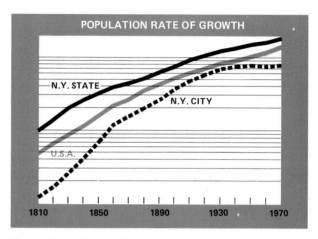

Figure 7.21: Curve chart comparing rates of population growth.

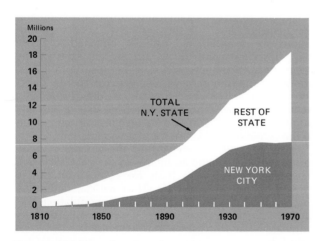

Figure 7.22: Area chart based on the two curves drawn in figure 7.18.

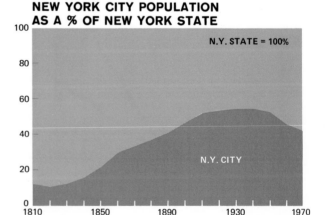

Figure 7.23: Area chart showing one set of values as a percentage of the other.

266

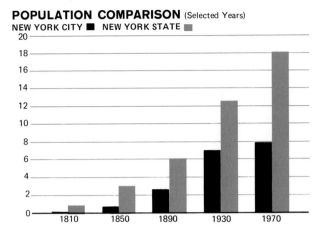

POPULATION COMPARISON (Selected Years)
NEW YORK CITY ■   NEW YORK STATE ▩

Figure 7.24: Bar chart showing population comparison. This emphasizes the comparison for each year rather than the trend over a period of time.

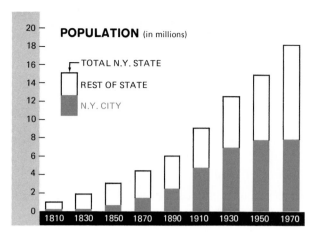

POPULATION (in millions)

TOTAL N.Y. STATE
REST OF STATE
N.Y. CITY

Figure 7.25: Bar chart based on figure 7.18.

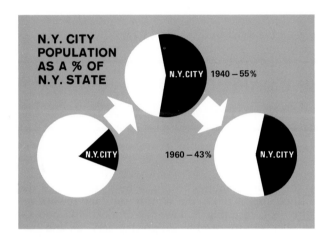

Figure 7.26: Pie chart comparing population percentages in three different years.

of connecting the points to form curves. Because of space limitations, we have plotted only 40-year intervals. This chart form tends to direct one's attention to a comparison of the figures for each year plotted rather than toward the trends. Therefore, the bar chart is usually considered as the form to use for direct comparisons, while curve charts are preferred for demonstrating trends.

It is as important in bar charts as in curve charts that the time scale be drawn at equal intervals. Otherwise, a distorted picture will result. While the prime purpose of the chart is a direct comparison of figures, the trend does show and should be represented accurately. If you do not care to show figures for equal intervals, then the spacing of the bars should be adjusted proportionately to fit the time scale using a true arithmetic progression.

In figure 7.25, we have converted the data in figure 7.22 into bar chart form. We have placed the rest of New York State on top of New York City's population to show the total for the state. As in figure 7.22, we have used the information that we are most interested in (the city's population) at the base, because we get

the best comparison of the population from one year to the next in the segment adjacent to the base line.

Pie charts

Figure 7.26 illustrates the use of pie charts. As in figure 7.23, the state population is considered as 100%, and the city population as a percentage of the state's. Here the state population is represented by the whole circle or "pie," and the city population shows up graphically as a percentage of the whole. Three years have been selected: one in which the city population was a small percentage of the state's; a second in which the city population reached its highest level in relation to the state; and finally a recent comparison of the two populations. While this does not show a trend, it gives a fine picture of the relationship for the years selected.

Super graphics

Figures 7.27 and 7.28 are examples of the "super" chart forms. In such charts, the basic facts are enhanced by the utilization of a photograph which illustrates the content of the chart. This aids the graphic

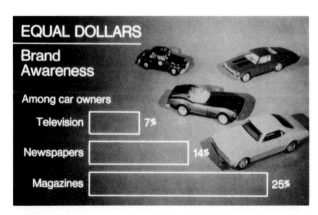

Figure 7.27: "Super" bar chart. *Reprinted from* Weight of Evidence . . . , *with permission of Magazine Publishers Association.*

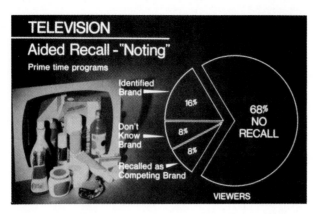

Figure 7.28: "Super" pie chart. *Reprinted from* Weight of Evidence . . . , *with permission of Magazine Publishers Association.*

form aesthetically as well as in recognition of the content.

CHART FOR EACH PURPOSE

It can be seen that each of these charts shows a definite picture, and, with the exception of figure 7.17, each is an accurate and fair representation of the data. Whatever point you are making, there is one chart form which will best tell your story.

An important point to keep in mind is the final form the chart will take—printed form for technical papers or annual reports, or slides for presentation. Today's sales meetings, stockholders' meetings, and technical seminars may have audiences of 1,000 people or more. Slides may be used to project a chart, making it visible to these large audiences. No matter what method of presentation is used, the basic rules outlined above still apply.

COMPUTER TECHNOLOGY FOR THE GRAPHIC ARTIST

Dave A. Ware, GENERAL ELECTRIC COMPANY

The traditional methods of creating and producing commercial art have not changed substantially in many years. The artist working with a variety of materials—colored paper, rub-on lettering, adhesive-backed colored tapes, rubber cement—does rough layouts and then executes the finished flat art in accordance with his client's wishes. This process can take from one to four hours for each piece of art used in a business presentation, depending upon its complexity.

Certain phototypesetting techniques have been introduced that have improved the layout efficiency of words and numbers. The basic problem with these techniques is internal communication: the art director must communicate with two or more of his assistants before all the different factors are harmoniously synchronized. All too frequently, the artist must move among several locations to complete the photographic process and to set up the necessary overlays that call for painstaking attention to detail by both the artist and the photographer.

In the traditional method of artistic creation, the artist has to visualize the final product, make a rough sketch, and attempt to sell this unfinished concept to his client. It is not until after the rough sketch or the comp rendering that a final judgment can be made. If there is not general agreement as to the approach, or if a significant number of alterations must be made, it is usually more efficient to redo the entire piece than to try to alter the various elements.

The key elements in this age-old creative process that have not seen any substantial improvement are

(1) the time it requires to create both roughs and the finished product; (2) the almost constant rework requirement, resulting in lowered productivity; and (3) the necessity for sizable supporting services and materials inventory. Let us look at the ways in which burgeoning advances in computer technology are changing this picture.

Within the last few years, there has been considerable attention focused on computer-generated art. It was first viewed as a novelty in the aesthetic world of fine art and was used to generate almost accidental textures and patterns. More recently, computer art has been applied to such practical tasks as circuit design and other engineering layouts where a simple linear expression can convey the necessary information. This kind of system, the calligraphic system, is a point-to-point line generator. It is a monochromatic display that offers no aesthetic value but is perfectly suitable for structural analysis and other drafting-type applications. This system, available from a number of manufacturers, is a limited system of little interest to an artist.

In 1971, it became apparent to General Electric that there was a tremendous potential for the application of more sophisticated computer-generated visuals for business and professional presentations. And that is when Genigraphics was conceived.

Complex, interrelated hardware and computer programs had to be developed. A team of graphic art and electrical engineers was assembled to do the necessary work to produce a system that would significantly improve the unimproved key areas of a commercial

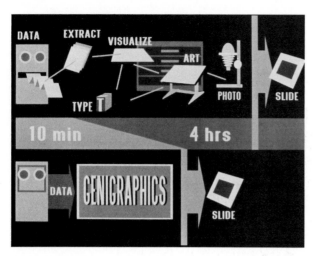

Figure 7.29: Flow chart comparing Genigraphics system with conventional art preparation. The chart illustrates how a business graphic can be created and photographed in an average time of ten minutes, compared to an average of four hours using conventional methods. In this example, the graphic is created from a customer's computer data base and translated in one step into reproducible art using the Autochart service. Information for the flow chart was provided by Admaster, Inc., and the flow chart was created on the Genigraphics image generation system.

artist's life—time, productivity, the need for supporting services and materials inventory—and do it in a way that not only would make life easier for an artist, but would not require him to become a technician. The result is a computer-based image generation system, marketed by General Electric under the name Genigraphics, which can be operated by an artist with training in the operation of the Genigraphics system but with no technical knowledge or ability. Artwork can be produced in a fraction of the time required by the conventional system, as illustrated in figure 7.29.

The Genigraphics system is geared to an artist. It accommodates his traditional frame of reference—a drawing board—while offering him advantages no single pair of hands could ever possess. The basic system consists of three elements: an artist's console, a digital computer, and a camera coupled with a high-resolution cathode ray tube. The artist, seated at the console, can create artwork right from scratch by quickly generating basic elements, such as circles, squares, and straight lines; or he can select from a variety of preprogrammed images stored in the computer which he can resize, color, and position freely, allowing him practically unlimited composition and layout. Once the artist has the various graphic elements in harmonious composition, he can photograph the image immediately and store it on magnetic tape for later recall. (See figure 7.30.)

Because the image can be stored and changed at any time without the necessity of completely redrawing the entire piece of art, the artist's time is freed for additional creative work. All the basic elements for most management charts—typefaces, line and bar graphs, and the rest—are stored in the computer, so the artist need never recreate any piece of art once he has con-

ceptualized it. He can build a library of design elements and finished art that can instantly be accessed for any job. Items can be individually enlarged, reduced, stretched, recolored, repositioned, and duplicated within the artwork. The entire piece can then be changed in the same way. In short, the Genigraphics system relieves the artist of the drudgery of rework, enables him to do basic business presentations with new efficiency, and gives him additional creative time.

The system also lessens the need for support services and materials inventory by condensing the work load. An artist working with the Genigraphics system can produce slides at a rate of almost eight to one over the traditional method. He literally has everything he needs right at his fingertips. Moreover, the equivalent of approximately 100 art flats can be stored on a single, inexpensive floppy disc. The saving in storage space alone almost makes the system economically feasible for any organization that does numerous visual presentations. The greatest advantage, however, is that the artist can alter part of his creation without having to redraw the whole.

Genigraphics dramatically alters the artist's frame of reference. Unlike the calligraphic technique of computer-generated art, the Genigraphics system uses the raster scan technique, which allows the manipulation of areas, as well as lines, and offers color. That is a considerable leap forward because it offers the freedom to create the more sophisticated shapes and forms that are a requirement of business-type graphics.

In addition to supplying the artist with a new tool, the Genigraphics system offers various ways to access the variety of images in the computer. By use of a catalog showing prepared graphic formats, the artist can order business slides or charts from a book. By specifying the particular artwork he wishes, the artist can get customized charts processed by a computer located at a production center without ever leaving his

Figure 7.30: Genigraphics control console. Designed for use by an artist, the control console consists of a keyboard and controls labeled with terms an artist understands, and a color television monitor which displays the art immediately. The artist can alter and manipulate instantly both the color and graphic elements.

office. This catalog contains the most commonly used business formats, such as single and multiple bar charts, pie charts, trend-line charts, and a variety of others. The variety and flexibility provided by the catalog are sufficient to cover the majority of business chart requirements.

If there are alterations that have to be made, the image can be recalled from the floppy disc on which it has been stored and new artwork created in far less time than it took to create the original.

There is yet another routine that can be followed in the Genigraphics system. This one, called the Autochart service, is for certain types of constantly recurring statistical presentations, such as monthly financial projections. A particular format can be created to customer specifications and stored on a floppy disc. Once this format has been established, it can be updated on a continuing basis by means of a floppy disc, cassette, or data phone. The user of the Autochart prepares his data and submits it in whatever processed form he finds most convenient, and the production center makes a single-step conversion of this data into management graphics. This is a form of computer-generated graphics that is both time and cost efficient for presentation of recurring business information.

We have discussed the capability of Genigraphics in terms primarily of slides, as they are the basic business communication unit. But there are other applications of the system. For instance, it is possible to take whatever design is created and render it via a 4,000-line screen on black-and-white or full-color film for print. The whole graphic arts picture has changed—and for the better, as any overworked commercial artist will readily agree.

271

PHOTOGRAPHY

8

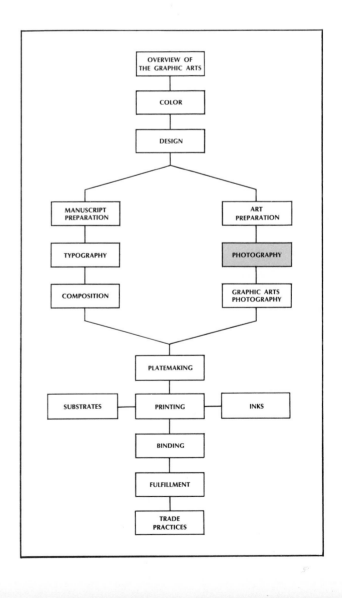

THE PHOTOGRAPHIC PROCESS
Robert Loekle, COLOR REPRODUCTION CONSULTANT

A literal translation of photography is "drawing with light." Today photography has permeated every aspect of the graphic arts—from preparing the original pictorial matter, through the setting of type, to the making of the final printing plate. So dependent are the contemporary printing processes on the principles of "drawing with light" that they may be considered as really a highly specialized branch of photography, distinguished only by the manner in which the inked image is transferred to paper. In this respect, it is interesting to remember that it was the early nineteenth century printers who, in their search for a light-sensitive engraving resist, initiated the chain of discoveries from which photography developed.

The first requirement of a photograph is some method for forming an optical image. It had long been known that a lens placed in the wall of an otherwise darkened room would project a full scene of the outdoors on the wall opposite. This *camera obscura*, or darkened room, was a source of entertainment to the ancients, and from it is derived our modern camera, in principle as well as in name.

While the use of a glass lens is the most common method of forming an optical image, it is by no means the only possible way. Astronomical telescopes employ curved mirrors, and the familiar "pinhole" camera requires only a tiny opening about 1mm in diameter to form a crude image. The common medical X ray is the direct projection of the "shadows" formed by objects with varying opacities to the radiation. The electronic scanner used in photomechanical processes detects brightness differences as each point of the original passes before a small opening. These are converted to electrical current which by activating a small glow lamp at the output end reconstructs the image.

PHOTOGRAPHIC LENSES
Far and away the most important method of image formation in photography makes use of the light-bending properties of the glass lens. Compound lenses consist of several elements differing in refractive index and the radius of curvature to which they are ground. By controlling these two variables, the lens maker determines the image characteristics of the lens. Lens design is too technical an area to summarize in a few paragraphs, but some understanding of its importance can be gained from considering the special requirements to be met. A distinguishing characteristic of each lens is its *focal length*, or the distance between lens and image when a distant object is in sharp focus. From this one measurement a number of other characteristic properties of the lens can be inferred.

The image size depends upon the focal length of the lens. This is a vital consideration, of course, because an image to be recorded on 8" x 10" film must be large enough to fill the entire area. The field angle, or area of the subject which will be covered, is also a function of the focal length (see figure 8.1). Lens design determines the absolute values for each lens, but the general rule is that image size varies directly and field angle inversely with focal length.

The light-gathering ability, or *speed,* of a lens is expressed by its *f*/number, or the ratio of focal length to apparent lens diameter. The lower the *f*/number, the faster the lens. This is an important consideration in the choice of a lens when lighting levels are low, or if the subject calls for high shutter speeds. Practical considerations limit the fast lenses to small, hand held cameras with their short focal length lenses. An *f*/2 lens for the copy camera used by printers would call for a lens perhaps 16 inches in diameter!

When a lens is focused on a distant object, say 50 feet or more, all objects at a farther distance will appear to be in equally sharp focus. However, as the distance between the object and lens decreases, both foreground and background will become blurred. The distance between the planes in which the foremost and rearmost objects appear to be in sharp focus is called *depth of field*. Depth of field decreases the closer the lens is to the subject, the longer the focal length of the lens used, and the larger the relative aperture (see figure 8.2). The effect is widely used to emphasize features of interest in close-up photography; however, it can be troublesome if treatment of the subject calls for sharp focus throughout the entire picture.

The subject of the photograph and the conditions under which it must be made largely determine the choice of lens and camera. The 8" x 10" studio camera is the standby of advertising illustration, particularly fashion, products, and interiors. On the other hand, the spontaneity of models in the presence of a small, hand held camera, the need for a number of shots taken in rapid succession, or the ease of transporting equipment when on location may call for a 35mm camera. The smaller formats require higher skills and a more elaborate technology on the part of the printer if image quality is to be maintained. For this reason, many printers used to attach penalty charges to 35mm copy or outrightly refuse to accept it for reproduction. This situation has changed dramatically in the last few years, in large measure because of the increased availability of electronic color scanners. Improved technology has freed the art director from the considerations of reproduction and allowed him to concentrate his skills on the visual message he is trying to communicate. There is no valid reason today to anticipate compromises in reproduction quality when submitting small-size films to the printer—provided they have been made with the same care and professional competence found in studio illustration.

Figure 8.1: Field angle varies inversely with focal length. The subject has been photographed three times from the same standpoint using lenses with different focal lengths: top, 21mm (wide angle) lens; middle, 50mm (normal) lens; bottom, 250mm (telephoto) lens. *Courtesy of E. Leitz, Inc.*

Figure 8.2: Depth of field varies inversely with relative aperture. The subject has been photographed at two different f/stops: top, f/22 (smaller aperture); bottom, f/2.8 (larger aperture).

PHOTOCHEMICAL REACTIONS

The second requirement for photography is a method of recording the image formed by the lens. A number of compounds exhibit photosensitive properties. *Photosensitivity* may very roughly be described as the ability of a substance to rearrange its internal atomic or molecular structure by the absorption of light. Certain salts of iron have this ability and are the photosensitive agent in the common blueprint. Alkaline dichromates are capable of tanning gelatin, a phenomenon taken advantage of in the deep-etch platemaking process and in collotype printing. Diazo compounds are decomposed into products which can be coupled with dyes, or, as in lithographic platemaking, made oleophilic or ink accepting.

The most important of the compounds exhibiting photosensitive properties are the silver salts, particularly the halogens iodine, chlorine, and bromine. A suspension of these salts in gelatin, known as an *emulsion*, coated on either a paper or film support provides the great bulk of photosensitive materials manufactured.

When light strikes this emulsion, a photochemical reaction takes place and a *latent image* is formed. Such an image is invisible, consisting only of a change in the internal structure of the molecules, and requires further treatment to render it visible. This step is provided by *development*, the selective reduction to metallic silver of those grains struck by light. Further chemical treatment and washing remove the unexposed materials and render the image permanent.

The image at this point consists of finely divided particles of silver which appear black, as indeed any substance will if the particles are sufficiently small. The extent of the blackening is proportional to the amount of light received at any point, and the tones are thus reversed in value from the orginal scene. Such an image is referred to as *negative*. To produce a final *positive* image the negative is placed in contact with, or projected upon, another sheet of photosensitive material, and the process is repeated. The materials used in the two steps are essentially the same, and both are *negative working*, the product of the two negative steps, of course, being positive.

There are several ways in which positive images can be gotten directly in the silver halide system. The emulsion can be manufactured to yield a positive image, such materials being known as *direct positive films*. There are limited applications for such materials, however, and they have been developed largely to meet specific needs; the contact films used in graphic arts are an example. The *diffusion transfer* process produces both a positive and negative simultaneously, the negative generally being discarded after the transfer stage. This is the method used in Polaroid photography.

Conventional negative-working materials can also be converted to positive during the processing stage. After the silver image is formed from the first development, it is bleached away. The unexposed silver halides remain in proportion to the amount of light which they did not receive; as such they may be thought of as a positive record of darknesses in the original scene. To make the image visible, the unexposed areas are given a fogging exposure to render them developable and then are reduced to silver in the second development. This technique for obtaining a positive image is known as *reversal processing*, and although it is of minor importance in general black-and-white photography it is the basis for dye formation in the most common of the color processes.

Silver halide emulsions are inherently sensitive to radiation in the ultraviolet and blue regions of the spectrum. By the addition of sensitizing dyes to the emulsion, this sensitivity can be increased through the red and even into the infrared. Films which correspond roughly to the spectral sensitivity of the eye are called *panchromatic*. This characteristic is essential if colored objects are to be rendered in monotone.

COLOR PHOTOGRAPHS

Photography in color makes use of the same photosensitive properties of the silver halides and takes advantage of an additional property: their ability to be coupled with dyes during development. However, before discussing the mechanism by which colored images are produced photographically it would be helpful to examine the way in which the human visual mechanism constructs a colored image. Color vision is an immensely complex subject, but we are concerned only with those aspects that will help explain why color photography is possible.

It is believed that the eye contains three receptors, each of which is sensitive to one of the three large areas of the spectrum roughly identified as red, green, and blue. All the other colors we see are the result of stimulating these receptors in various proportions. The eye then can be considered an *analytical* instrument, separating each color into its primary components and

transmitting the information by way of the optical nerves to the brain for *synthesis,* or reconstruction of the image. (See Section 2, *Color.*)

Color photography is a physical imitation of this physiological process. A lens is used to form an image in much the same way as its counterpart in the eye. Substituted for the retinal receptors are light-sensitive films which by various means can be made independently sensitive to red, green, and blue. The three separate images gotten in this fashion are records of the original scene in terms of its red, green, and blue reflectances at each point. Synthesis then consists of using these records in such a manner that the eye is presented with stimulations equivalent to the original scene.

The first experimental demonstration of image reconstruction was performed by James Clerk Maxwell, an English physicist perhaps best known for his work in electricity, over one hundred years ago. Maxwell's experiment consisted of an original scene, actually a small segment of a multicolored ribbon, of which three photographs were made in succession through red, green, and blue filters held in front of the camera lens. These were processed to yield positive images; that is to say, where red reflectance was high in the original, the red-filter record showed clear areas in the film, progressively darkening as red reflectance decreased.

The three images so obtained were placed in separate magic lanterns and projected through the same filters through which they were photographed so that the clear areas let the light of each color through. When the images were superimposed on a screen in a darkened room, the eye was presented with the same stimuli that prevailed in the original scene. The result was a full-color photographic reproduction.

Until the advent of color television there was no feasible technology to reconstruct the image in the manner just described. Color television and Maxwell's experiment both start off with a darkened screen and provide the stimuli directly by the addition of colored light. When starting with a piece of paper or a viewing box, we are presented with a bright field, which for the sake of the argument we will call white. "White" is the sensation we receive when the three retinal receptors are highly stimulated, and to approximately the same degree. This creates a somewhat different problem, but the solutions really amount to the same thing only approached from the opposite end. To give rise to the sensation of red, for example, we require only a method of reducing the stimulation of the blue and green receptors. This is easily accomplished by the use of filters which block the passage of the blue and green components of white light. The only critical requirement is that each filter control one—and only one—of the three primary components, red, green, and blue. As described in "Color and Light" (page 14), the color which absorbs the red component but freely transmits the green and blue is called cyan, and the green and blue absorbers are magenta and yellow, respectively. To create the sensation of redness, we filter out first the green component by the use of magenta, and then the blue component by the use of the yellow.

For these filters can be substituted pigments dispersed in a transparent medium, or, as in the case of photography, dyes suspended in gelatin. Analysis al-

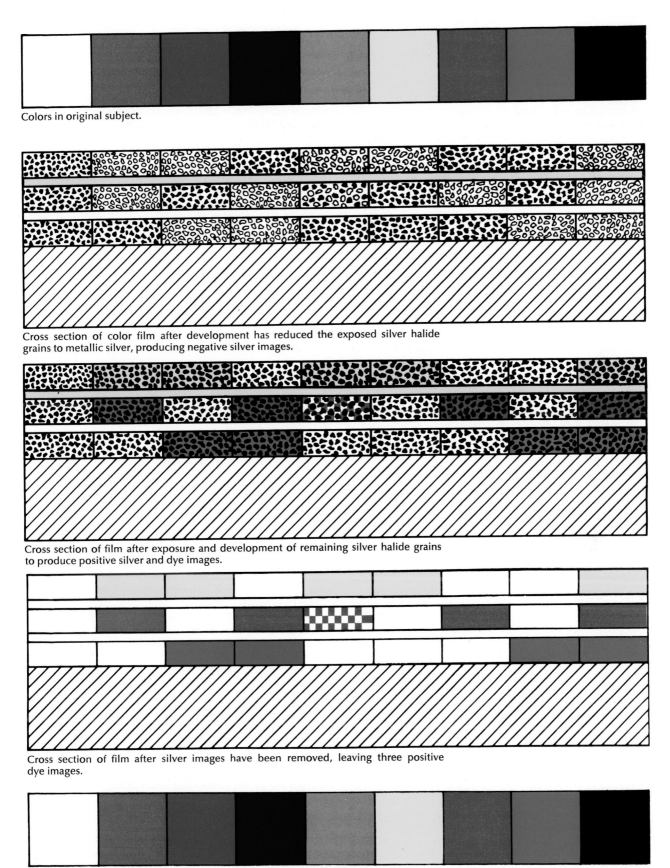

Colors in original subject.

Cross section of color film after development has reduced the exposed silver halide grains to metallic silver, producing negative silver images.

Cross section of film after exposure and development of remaining silver halide grains to produce positive silver and dye images.

Cross section of film after silver images have been removed, leaving three positive dye images.

Dye images as they appear when the film is viewed by transmitted light.

Figure 8.3: Reproduction of colors by a reversal color film.

277

ways makes use of red, green and blue. Synthesis may use either those colors if we are adding light to the system, or their complements if we are subtracting light from the system.

The analytical method of Maxwell, which used successive exposures, is not without drawbacks. The subject cannot be in motion, of course, or the images will not register. (In color separation for graphic arts use this is not a restriction, and the practice of sequential exposure is maintained.) A number of ingenious methods were proposed to overcome this, the object being to have all three records exposed simultaneously on one piece of film.

The principle employed in Kodachrome, which was commercially introduced in 1935, was the coating of three separate emulsions on one support, each layer being sensitive to only one of the primary components. The inherent sensitivity of photographic films, as previously mentioned, extends from the ultraviolet into the blue area of the visible spectrum. The top layer of the color film consists of an emulsion with such sensitivity. This emulsion forms the blue record and is unaffected by red and green, which are transmitted to the layers below. Some blue light would also be transmitted, and since the emulsions below are sensitive to blue, a yellow dye layer is introduced which permits the red and green to pass through while removing

the unwanted blue. The next layer is sensitive to green and blue. No blue light reaches it, however, so a single record of the green is formed. Green and red light are again transmitted to the bottom layer, which, being sensitive mainly to red, forms the final record.

Independent red, green, and blue records are now contained in the separate layers. Conversion to a positive dye image is made in a sequence of processing steps. The film is first developed in a solution which reduces all the exposed grains to metallic silver just as in black-and-white photography. The unexposed grains form a positive latent image. During development, a by-product is formed in the developer which can be further combined to form a colored dye. The unexposed grains are then given an overall exposure to light, and, during the second or color development, dye amounts are produced in proportion to the amount of silver reduced. The yellow filter layer is destroyed in the processing so that no overall yellow cast will remain. The metallic silver is bleached out, leaving the three dye images which can then be viewed by transmitted light.

The color of the dye image is complementary to the color of the light recorded in each layer. The processing steps and the reproduction of a colored image can be better understood by examining the diagram of a reversal color film, shown in figure 8.3.

COLOR FILMS AND PRINTING PAPERS

Robert Loekle, COLOR REPRODUCTION CONSULTANT

Materials used in color photography may be conveniently divided into two categories: *positive working* and *negative working*. This distinction, irrelevant in black-and-white photography because of the limited application of positive-working materials, separates the two paths that can be taken to obtain photographic images in full color. The types of color images and the various ways of arriving at them using these two basic methods are discussed in the following article and diagrammed in figure 8.4.

POSITIVE-WORKING MATERIALS

For photographs which are to be reproduced photomechanically, the positive-working materials are far more widely used. Of these, the *color transparency*, intended for viewing by projection in a darkened room or illuminated from the rear by a light box, is the most familiar example. The use of *transparency* in this discussion is restricted to a positive color image produced on a clear film base, and unless stated otherwise it implies an original image direct from the camera. The reason for this is to avoid confusion when discussing other ways, such as duplicating, to get positive film images.

Transparencies are made by causing dyes to form in the unexposed areas, and the mechanism for producing the positive image is known as *reversal processing* (see "The Photographic Process," page 274). In the first color films, dye formation was caused by dye couplers included in the developers. Three different developers, one to form each dye layer, were required, and the process was so exacting that the exposed film had to be returned to the manufacturer. The introduction of films in which the dye couplers were incorporated into the emulsion at the time of manufacture permitted dye formation to take place in a single step, and although requiring extremely careful control the processing can be done by professional color labs and the usual commercial sources. The availability of simplified processing greatly increased the areas of usefulness, and transparencies, particularly in the "professional" sizes, 4" x 5" and larger, soon became the customary color copy for photomechanical reproduction.

Making good color transparencies is inherently more difficult than obtaining a good black-and-white print. First of all, there is no intermediate negative step where compensation for errors in exposure can be introduced. Exposure latitude is also sharply reduced since there are three layers which differ in their degree of reciprocity

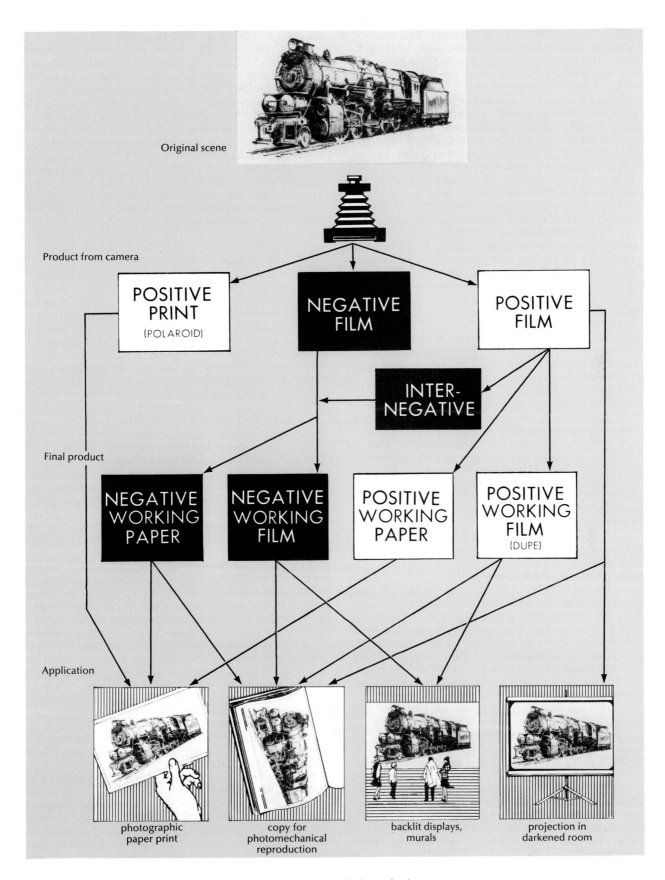

Original scene

Product from camera

POSITIVE PRINT (POLAROID)

NEGATIVE FILM

POSITIVE FILM

INTER-NEGATIVE

Final product

NEGATIVE WORKING PAPER

NEGATIVE WORKING FILM

POSITIVE WORKING PAPER

POSITIVE WORKING FILM (DUPE)

Application

photographic paper print

copy for photomechanical reproduction

backlit displays, murals

projection in darkened room

Figure 8.4: Negative and positive photographic processes for producing color images.

failure with exposure time. To maintain color balance, processing must be carried out under standardized conditions. The color of the light source illuminating the scene also has a profound effect on color rendering. Walking from out-of-doors into a room illuminated totally by incandescent tungsten, we may be aware for a short interval of an overall yellowness imparted to all colors; but this soon vanishes and we accept the colors as being very much the same as if viewed out-of-doors even though the actual spectral distribution of the light reaching our eyes may be very different.

This is a psychological adaptation, and while the phenomenon of *color constancy* is vital to our ability to process information under widely different sources of illumination, it creates havoc in photography. Film and camera cannot make psychological adaptations: the spectral qualities are recorded according to the sensitivities built in during manufacture. For this reason there are two color balances to accommodate the qualities of daylight and incandescent tungsten, with intermediate or other values obtainable by special color filters placed over the lens.

Let us assume, however, that we have managed to obtain a transparency to our liking. As such it is well suited for photomechanical reproduction so far as reproduction quality is concerned, but there may yet be difficulties in production and handling.

A common requirement is that more than one color transparency be available, either for insurance in case of damage, or to send simultaneously to several printers, or for other good reasons. Another requirement may be that the transparency be to final printing size so that more economic advantages can be gained by "ganging" or making transparency assemblies. For multiple copies and size changes, *transparency duplicating* provides an answer (see "Manipulation of Color Transparencies," page 284).

Obviously, the film used for the duplicate must be positive working if the duplicate is to be made in one step, and at first thought it might seem logical to use the same material as used for the original. All color materials, however, have inherent color error, caused mainly by the inability of the colorants to control their assigned part of the spectrum independently of each other. The transparency is one step removed from the original scene, and the small errors may pass unnoticed —particularly when one considers the difficulty of making a side by side evaluation of the transparency with the original scene. In duplicating, however, the difference between the original transparency and the "dupe" is noticeable and objectionable. Since films designed for camera use have high contrast, the errors are further exaggerated. These errors can be corrected by masking, but this is a time-consuming and therefore expensive extra step.

Special positive-working duplicating films are manufactured for this purpose. The contrast is reduced to minimize the color errors and to provide a range more suitable for photomechanical reproduction. Most of these are reversal process materials and can produce high-quality duplicates at reasonable cost. Duping is also widely used in conjunction with 35mm transparencies. The advantage of small-format originals is maintained, and those selected for reproduction may be enlarged. Enlargement also gives the printer the advantage of working with a larger image.

Color prints can also be made from transparencies using a positive-working paper. This material, like the film, is coated with three emulsions and works on the same principle of dye formation and reversal processing. The main difference between papers and films is the thickness of the dye layers, lesser thicknesses being required for paper since the light is absorbed both on its way through the dye and again when reflected from the white support. Positive-working papers suffer the same disadvantage of inherent color error, and exhibit considerable degradation and darkening of blues and greens. They are seldom used as copy for photomechanical reproduction but are used mainly for color "stats" or comprehensive mechanicals.

NEGATIVE-WORKING MATERIALS

When negative images are formed in color materials, not only are the brightness values reversed, but the hues of the colors are complementary to those of the positive image. No reversal exposure is required since the formation of dyes must take place in the exposed rather than the unexposed areas. Negative-working materials are based on the same principles as positive ones, having three layers sensitive to red, green, and blue and using silver halides as the photosensitive agent, the difference being where the dyes are caused to form.

To make this clearer, let us consider an original scene which contains a red apple, and to simplify the discussion let us suppose that the color of the apple is such that only wavelengths in the red part of the spectrum are reflected from it, the blue and green parts of the spectrum being totally absorbed. In both positive- and negative-working materials the photochemical reaction takes place in the layer sensitive to red, and in our hypothetical example no reaction takes place in the other layers since neither green nor blue light from the apple reaches them.

In the positive process, no cyan dye will be formed in the red-sensitive layer, but the maximum amount of magenta and yellow dyes will be formed in the green and blue layers. The subtractive combination of magenta and yellow is red, and the image is thus positive with respect to the original. In the negative process, cyan dye is formed directly in the red-sensitive layer and in proportion to the extent of exposure. Such an image is negative, and if it is exposed in turn to a similar material the process will be repeated. However, since the reversal has been twice repeated, the image will again be positive in respect to the original.

Negative materials for camera use are, of course, always coated on a transparent film base, as they are intended as a step in the process of obtaining a final positive image and never as an end in themselves. Negative-working materials that act as receivers and produce the positive end result may be coated on either film or paper. Films may be used for making a number of duplicate transparencies, which for all practical purposes are indistinguishable from those made on positive materials and may be used for the same purposes. An important use is in the preparation of large, back-lighted displays.

Negative papers are the most widely used method

More than
meets the eye.

You can get more than quality products from Kodak. You can get expert technical assistance and advice from Kodak representatives—who, in turn, are backed by the technical resources and facilities of Kodak. See your dealer in Kodak products for more information. Kodak products include materials for:

Copy prep
Phototypesetting
Color duplicating
Camera
Contacting
Platemaking
Printing

Graphics Markets Division, Eastman Kodak Company,
Rochester, N.Y. 14650

for obtaining color prints. They are increasingly popular for amateur use, as paper prints require no apparatus or darkened rooms for viewing. The color quality of prints cannot be properly compared with projected transparencies because of the different range of luminances and the effect of darkened surroundings, but prints made in this fashion compare favorably with those using more complicated procedures. Individualized or custom color processing provides image quality entirely suitable for photomechanical reproduction.

Another negative-working material is the *internegative*, designed for converting from positive transparencies to the system of negative-working films and papers just described. The original color positive transparency is exposed to a color negative material to produce the internegative, which provides a color-corrected image which can be reexposed to a negative-working material, either film or paper. The internegative process yields superior reproductions and is commonly used to go from a positive transparency to a color print or a color-corrected film positive, including mural-size back-lighted displays. This technique is often used to improve a poor transparency, since it offers an additional step to modulate tone reproduction and color balance.

NEGATIVE VERSUS POSITIVE SYSTEMS

Since the end result of both positive- and negative-working systems is a positive color image, one is tempted to ask why the process should not be done as directly as possible in all cases with transparencies in one step from the camera. Transparencies certainly are the most widely used materials for photomechanical reproduction; however, there are arguments for the expanded use of negative materials.

Transparencies are intended to be viewed by transmitted light. This mode of viewing calls for a range of densities considerably greater than a print, and since accurate reproduction is impossible under those circumstances it has been suggested that the best original copy for reproduction would be a print. This is a compelling argument, and there is ample evidence that when both original and reproduction are viewed in the same mode, greater reproduction accuracy is obtainable. However, whether reproduction excellence is judged on fidelity to the original or some other, less exacting criterion is debatable. Certainly, the required tone scale compression has not been a major source of difficulty for either the printer or buyer in using transparencies for copy.

The introduction of an extra step does provide an extra point of control. In a negative system, errors in color balance can be corrected when the print is made. (*Print* can refer to either film or paper.) For this reason, negative films do not require "daylight" or "tungsten" balance—one material is sufficient and the difference is made up in printing. Adjustment for under- and over-exposure is also possible to a limited degree. Negative films have greater latitude than positive transparencies; this can be a marked advantage under difficult shooting conditions.

All subtractive color reproduction methods have inherent errors stemming from the unwanted absorptions of the dyes used. This is corrected by a technique known as *photographic masking* (see "Manual and Photographic Color Correction," page 353). This should be distinguished from the common opaque mask used for bordering. Photographic masking is the superimposition of a full-scale image on the original to provide selective tone modulation. The technique is cumbersome, requires skill and experience, and therefore may add considerable cost to the process. In a first-generation color image, such as a positive transparency, the errors may not be objectionable. In subsequent transferral, however, the cumulative effect is too great and corrective masking is in order. The advantage of negative systems is that this masking function can be incorporated into the film at the time of manufacture. Film prints or paper prints made from these incorporated color-correcting masks show much improved color rendition.

Color negatives are suitable copy for photomechanical reproduction without the need for positive prints. Color separation techniques must be adjusted accordingly, however, and since few printers seem able to cope with the problems, negatives are seldom used.

In summary, both reversal positive color transparencies and the color positives produced by negative-working materials are well suited for photomechanical reproduction. The overwhelming use of transparencies suggests that they serve the need very well and that there is no clamor for change. However, the possibilities of negative systems should not be overlooked when complex jobs are encountered and when there is a need for more than one end use of the photography. Paper prints, multiple copy transparencies, photocomposed assemblies, and enlarged transparencies for dis-

Checkmate your costs with the single-set of seps strategy.

The name of the game is controlling costs . . .without sacrificing quality. The best move to make is the reproduction duplicate assembly. From your multiple originals Crandall will give you back a one-shot, one-focus assembly which requires only a single-set of color separations. The strategy is simple: you see your ad or page before it's printed. You also know that it will separate properly because each dupe has been color corrected and balanced for density. You know, too, that each element is properly sized, cropped, and in position to your layout. You've saved time and money, and assured yourself of quality and accuracy.

ROBERT CRANDALL ASSOCIATES, INC.
306 EAST 45 STREET, NEW YORK, N.Y. 10017   (212) 661-4710

play all can be made from a single color negative, and all will be reasonably in agreement with each other, free of the distortions introduced when positive transparencies are subjected to repeated copying. A panchromatic black-and-white paper is even made so that accurate monotone reproductions can be obtained from a color negative.

DYE TRANSFER

Properly speaking, color photography consists of the use of *integral* materials, the color-separation function being incorporated into the film or paper. *Dye transfer* uses color-separation negatives made on black-and-white films to provide the red, green, and blue records. This is the same technique used in photomechanical reproduction, the only difference being the application of a dye image to paper instead of printing ink.

The separation negatives are exposed to a special material called matrix film and processed to give a positive relief image of gelatin. The matrices are placed into dye baths of cyan, magenta, and yellow, and absorb the dye in proportion to their thickness at a given point. These are transferred one at a time in register to a prepared paper and result in a continuous-tone color print. The matrices may be reused for additional prints.

Dye transfer prints provide excellent color reproductions, both for display and for photomechanical reproduction. They will accept substantial retouching, and the three separation negatives from which they are made provide an additional step of control for color correction since they can be manipulated independently of each other. Although somewhat more expensive than single-step photographic processes, they serve a variety of needs for advertising illustration and are not likely to be soon replaced.

MANIPULATION OF COLOR TRANSPARENCIES
Robert S. Crandall and John R. Battiloro, Jr., ROBERT CRANDALL ASSOCIATES, INC.

The first premise of good color transparency duplication is a faithful reproduction of the original transparency, but this is only the starting point: the flexibility of the process permits improvements to be made when the original is not of the desired quality, and editorial changes can be made by removing parts of the original image and substituting new subjects in its place.

The basis of this kind of color transparency manipulation is the *repro-dupe*, a duplicate transparency prepared especially for reproduction by one of the printing processes. Such dupes are created in the color duplication lab, a special workshop which uses a number of techniques to alter and combine original transparencies as they come from the photographer into finished illustrations ready for color separation. They are a critical link in the production chain that stretches from original creative photography to the printed sheet. By integrating many of the separate preparatory steps such as color, density, and contrast control into a single, useful form suitable for photomechanical reproduction, the color dupe allows for a minimum of work following the separation step.

The manipulation of transparencies involves a number of stages—making of duplicates, assembly of these into final composite illustrations by one or more techniques, and retouching. All of these operations are performed at an early stage in the complete chain of reproduction events, providing maximum flexibility prior to committing the work to the more expensive processing stages that occur in the printing plant.

MAKING OF DUPLICATES

Transparency duplicates must not only meet the requirements for viewing by rear illumination, they must also satisfy the technical requirements of the color separator and the printing process.

For the color separator to treat a number of individual shots as one, they all must closely approximate one another in both highlight and shadow densities. Obviously, in original transparencies this is seldom the case because of variation in lighting conditions, exposure, color emulsions, and other factors. In the process of duplication, each original can be made to conform to the highlight and shadow densities specified by the printer. This can be done while still retaining the integrity and mood of the original. Color imbalances between different originals can also be restored if desired, so that all the dupes will appear to have been photographed under similar conditions. Very pale color filters, called color-correcting or "CC" filters, can be held over the original until the client feels that the color balance is correct. This effect can be closely reproduced in the dupe without guesswork. Further correction can be made by selective bleaching of dye layers or by adding dyes by hand to local areas.

Duplicates also serve the advertiser when a series of ads are to be produced simultaneously in different places. The scheduling problem is alleviated when a number of exact duplicates are sent to each production center at the same time, rather than having to wait for the original to travel from one place to the next.

284

A

B

C

D

E

Figure 8.5: Cut and butt method for transparency assembly. Steps for dropping an image into a new background are shown. (A) Car is cut out of old background. (B) Car is taped to new background; background is scored around edge of car. (C) Car is removed; emulsion and base are cut through on score line. (D) Car is placed in hole; edges are cemented. (E) Final assembly can be treated as a single piece of film.

TECHNIQUES FOR ASSEMBLY

There are three basic methods of assembling transparencies. Two are done manually by the stripper: the *cut and butt* method, which is the more common one, and the *emulsion stripping* or *emulsion floating* method, used less often because of its complexity, the unavailability of skilled technicians, and higher cost of materials. For these methods, duplicates must first be made, checked against the printer's specifications, and corrected for compatibility with each other. The third method, *photocomposition*, is a more exacting process which involves photographing multiple subjects on a single piece of film during the duplicating process rather than after it. These methods are described below, and their advantages and disadvantages are summarized in table 8.1 (page 288).

Cut and butt

The cut and butt method is so named because it requires cutting and cementing together of the elements of the illustration. The chromes to be assembled are positioned over the film layout, or tissue, and taped to the stripping table on one or two sides. The edge to be butted is placed over a sheet of acetate so the blade will not cut the other sheet of film or the table, and a T square is aligned with the line for the cut. The cut is made with a stainless steel razor blade. The cut edge is covered with a strip of acetate. The chrome to be butted to the first one is also positioned, taped, and cut. A sheet of absorbent tissue is inserted under the cut edge of both chromes, and they are sealed together with a solvent cement.

Other shapes, of course, are also possible. In fact, rather intricate cuts can be made, provided the image has a clearly defined edge to follow. For example, it

may be desirable to strip a photograph of an automobile into an entirely different background. The edge of the automobile is followed with a razor blade, cutting clear through to the base. The cut out piece is placed in correct position over the background. The shape is followed to make the hole into which the automobile will exactly fit, and then the elements are cemented together. Figure 8.5 illustrates the steps in the assembly process.

Emulsion stripping

The emulsion stripping process is more complicated, requiring a sealed, dust-free room with a strong exhaust system, as well as many more chemicals and materials than are used for the cut and butt method. The chromes to be assembled are taped to a sheet of glass with their emulsions facing the glass, and the bases are dissolved. The emulsions are cut free of the glass and in a semi-wet state floated onto a new support in the proper positions. Images to be butted are overlapped, and one cut goes through the emulsion of both films, resulting in a butt join. To drop one image into another, one film is placed upon the other in position. During one cutting operation, both emulsions are cut through. The areas not being used are removed. Both films are moistened, and the image is floated into position and worked around until the edges seal up. When all images are in position, a sheet of stripping film is cemented over the finished assembly to protect it and to keep the elements in position. Figure 8.6 shows some of the steps in putting together an assembly by emulsion stripping.

Photocomposing

The methods described above are fine for images with well-defined edges. However, if the borders of the

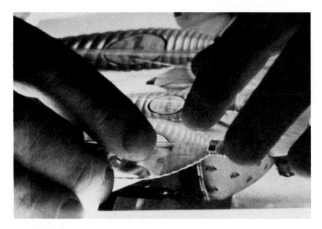

A. When the image has been positioned correctly, the emulsion is cut to the desired shape.

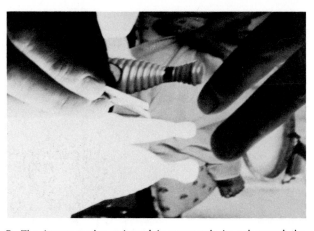

B. The image to be stripped is removed; its edge and the edge of the hole are checked for cleanliness.

C. Stripping cement is applied to the assembly, and the element being stripped is placed on the assembly and squeegeed into position to remove air pockets.

D. When all elements of the assembly have been stripped, the entire assembly is moistened with liquid gelatin and covered with a stripping film emulsion.

E. The stripping film emulsion is squeegeed down to remove all air pockets, dried, and taped all around with clear tape.

F. The completed assembly is on a new film base and will not come apart.

Figure 8.6: Emulsion stripping method of image assembly. Steps for dropping an image into a new background are shown. *Courtesy of Avon Products, Inc.*

image are not clearly defined—for example, if standing by the car there were a woman, and the wind were blowing her hair to create a soft edge—these methods will not usually produce satisfactory results. The cut will create a definite line where the subject has an indefinite edge.

For such problems, photocomposition is the solution. During duplication, the images are exposed separately on the same sheet of film with protective masks defining the edge shapes. These can be made in a manner that will blend soft edges into the background so that no joining line shows. An example of the effects that can be achieved using the photocomposing process is shown in figure 8.7.

Photocomposition techniques lend themselves to a variety of special effects that could be done in no other way. Photomontages, vignetting, and overlapping images can be created with precision and certainty during the duplicating process. Because of the number of masks required, and the skill, care, and time needed for photocomposing, the cost is higher than for stripping processes; it is, therefore, not a substitute.

ADVANTAGES OF TRANSPARENCY ASSEMBLY

The production staffs of most large catalog houses and book publishing companies have realized enormous economies with the proper utilization of assemblies. For the catalog people, assemblies have provided a way of coping with heavy volume and tight schedules. They are able to view a finished page that has had flesh tones balanced, all retouching corrections done, garments completely matched to swatches, and all elements put in their proper positions, prior to releasing it for separation.

Book publishers have several basic reasons of their own for having originals duplicated and assembled:
• They can have densities, contrast, and color of their stock originals corrected to reproducible and pleasing balance.
• The assembly will be to final size and position.
• They can see their pages assembled for effect prior to submission for separation.
• They can return original transparencies to the stock libraries and avoid a holding fee.
• They can budget their cost because duplicating

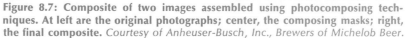

Figure 8.7: Composite of two images assembled using photocomposing techniques. At left are the original photographs; center, the composing masks; right, the final composite. *Courtesy of Anheuser-Busch, Inc., Brewers of Michelob Beer.*

Process	Advantages	Disadvantages
Cut and butt	The cut and butt method is fast. A page of six or seven elements with straight butts could be produced in 1½ to 2 hours.	No matter how well butted and cemented, the assembly may come apart in time if not handled with care.
	Bleaching and retouching can be done on any one of several images in the finished page.	An assembly consisting of many small elements could break when wrapped around a scanning drum. Butt lines and lines around dropped-in images will also be exaggerated.
	One or more elements can be removed or replaced if necessary. A drop-in may be replaced if necessary, as long as the replacing image completely covers the old one.	Original 2¼″ and 35mm films cannot be butted with sheet film because of the difference in thickness of the base.
Emulsion stripping	The finished assembly is on a new film base and cannot break apart.	A page of six or seven elements will take approximately 2½ to 3 hours if the lab is set up and ready to go. If not, it could take longer.
	The assembly is ideal for scanning and overseas shipping.	Bleaching cannot be done on the finished assembly.
	Originals in 2¼″ and 35mm can be stripped with cut sheet film.	In most cases, once an element is stripped, it cannot be removed or replaced.
	Additive retouching or color correction can be done on the finished assembly.	Elements could be out of position, slightly out of square, and distorted, because of the pliability of the emulsion when floating it onto the new base.
		The loss rate of chromes being assembled is greater than with the cut and butt method.
Photo-composition	The photocomposed subjects are all on one sheet of film and can never break apart.	The exposing time for a final two-element photocomposition is approximately 1 hour, as compared to 30 minutes for two elements that are to be assembled.
	There is virtually no butt line, making the assembly suitable for scanning, and the meeting point, or line around a subject, can be controlled to produce a sharp, soft, or vignetted edge.	The time required to produce a set of masks for a two-element photocomposite of a subject and background is approximately 2 to 4 hours, depending on the complexity of the subject.
	One photocomposite may contain subjects having soft and blend joins as well as hard and straight.	If an error is made on one subject during shooting, or if a subject is damaged during processing, the entire photocomposite must be reshot.
	The meeting point between subjects may be retouched to either soften or sharpen.	
	The density and/or color of one subject may be altered slightly without affecting the others by using adhesive or liquid friskets.	

with color correction and assembly is a basic charge.
• Changes can be made quickly and easily prior to the separation process.
• They can project schedules.

With prior planning and full communication among art director, color preparation studio, separator, and printer, the special needs of all involved can be satisfied through the use of color assemblies.

RETOUCHING

A good retoucher is a good artist. The only difference is that when an artist finishes you can see what he has done, but when a retoucher is finished you should not be able to. One could define retouching as "the only line of endeavor that pays so well for doing something that cannot be seen." Unfortunately, there are some "retouchers" who are paid extremely well for producing work that can not only be seen but that shows up very clearly when the material is copied or separated.

Retouching probably began very shortly after the first photographs were produced, starting with nothing more than the use of lampblack on a light spot or area of a print, and developing into the industry it is today.

Prior to the 1930's, the only retouching of any volume was done in the portrait studios. All material for advertising and mail-order catalogs was produced by drawings and wash, or oil painting, rather than photographs. When most of the catalog artists went out on strike in 1934, large catalog houses pressed for the use of more photographs. Some artists saw the trend and turned their talents from illustration to the improvement of the quality of photographs. From this point on, the use of art was on its way out, and photography and the newly developed retouching techniques were here to stay.

Even with the development of early color photographic techniques, such as dye toning, Carbo prints, and Wash-Off Relief, retouching did not change radically from the techniques first used for black-and-white prints. With the Kodachrome transparency, however, came a whole new approach to retouching. A dark area could no longer be lightened by scratching but had to be bleached slowly and carefully and then built back up with dye. The use of opaque colors as a quick cover-up ceased to exist. A further radical change came with the introduction of Ektachrome in 1947. Most of the bleaches and techniques that had been developed for Kodachrome would not work the same way on Ektachrome. The emulsion side changed color when wet, so color could not be added. With each new film that has been introduced, the transparency retoucher has had to run extensive tests to establish the proper bleaches and dyes capable of standing up in reproduction.

The art of transparency retouching has now developed to a point where it equals the possibilities that can be obtained on dye transfer prints. The few limitations are more likely to be caused by the small size of the transparency with which the artist must work, rather than a lack of ability. Using dyes and bleach, the retoucher can modify the colors in a transparency or change the details of the picture, adding hair to a bald head, for example, or changing the collar of a shirt.

When retouching is to be done on a dye transfer, a 20" x 24" print can be made, allowing the detail to be handled more easily. When it is reduced for reproduction no retouching errors will show. Small-size transparencies can be enlarged during duplication, and some of the more difficult corrections can be made during this step. Additional work can be done on the larger size dupe, producing finished art that separates well.

On the left in figure 8.8 is an unretouched transparency. Unfortunately, the original did not match the garment, so a custom dupe was made (right). The garment was colored to match the swatch, and the flesh tone was normalized. Enlarged to final page size, the dupe is ready for assembly with other elements.

Poor photographs can often be saved by careful retouching. This does not mean that the original should not be reshot if possible, but there are many times on location when that is impossible, and the answer has to be found in retouching. As much as possible, correction should be incorporated into the duping stage. Corrections that can be handled at this point include the problems of over- and underexposure and poor color balance that are most difficult to correct by hand. The retoucher is then free to concentrate on the details which the camera cannot supply.

If retouching appears good on the transparency but shows up blotchy or off-color in the reproduction, the

Figure 8.8: Color corrections made using retouching techniques. On the left is the original; on the right, the retouched duplicate. *Courtesy of J. C. Penney Co., Inc.*

odds are that the retouching has been done with incompatible dyes. The dyes used ought to have characteristics very close to those of the dyes used in the transparency, and even then they may not photograph the same just because they look the same to the eye. Special dyes are made for transparency retouching, and they are the only ones that should be used.

Another key to good results in retouching lies in the communication with the client, which involves more than just giving instructions to the retoucher. The client should communicate background data on the job and its intended final use. The best way to formulate instructions is to visualize the job as it should look and to think the corrections through step by step. The client must be able to implant his vision in the mind of the retoucher so that they both "see" the same thing. With creativity and good communications, retouching can help make a masterpiece; without them, a monster.

SPECIAL PHOTOGRAPHIC APPLICATIONS

The photographic process is characterized by its immense flexibility, and it is not surprising, therefore, to find many specialized applications. In the whole spectrum of photographic applications, graphic arts itself represents but one narrow field which has developed its own special films, materials, equipment, and methods to meet a unique set of requirements. In preparing copy for printing, two specialized applications are of particular significance: the *photostat* and the *screened print*. They serve as an important link between the needs of the graphic designer and the technical requirements of the printing process.

Other articles in this section begin with the assumption that the most desirable photograph is one which most faithfully reproduces the original scene. *Line conversion* is a special photographic application which breaks through the restrictions imposed by "photographic fidelity" and imposes careful and deliberate distortion on the image. This may be used to simulate the appearance of other art media such as pen-and-ink line renderings, charcoal sketches, or the compressed tone scale characteristic of poster art. It may be used to effect economies in reproduction so that pictorial subject matter can be printed along with line work without resorting to halftone techniques. And in its most imaginative form it draws from effects peculiar to photographic technology itself to create new images of striking impact, adding an additional dimension to what is already familiar.

PHOTOSTATS
Mark Harberman, FINLEY PHOTOGRAPHICS, INC.

In the preparation of a mechanical, it is often necessary to change the size of display type as supplied by the typographer. Editorial changes or some new design considerations appearing after the type has been specified must be dealt with quickly and economically. Final-size prints of pictorial copy are also needed for cropping, paste-up, and marking with instructions for the printer to indicate dropouts, line insets, silhouetting, and so on. The prints need not be of reproduction quality; time and economy are the paramount considerations.

These needs are filled by the *photostat*, which is distinguished generally from conventional photography by its use of a paper negative. If reversals are called for, negatives of type can be pasted in directly, since all stats whether positive or negative are made right-reading. Image quality of pictorial matter is usually not adequate for reproduction, but serves its intended purpose well enough.

Photostats are usually designated by their paper surface, either *glossy* or *matte*. This can lead to confusion since the important characteristic being referred to is the image contrast rather than surface properties. Glossy stats are of high contrast and suitable for line reproductions such as type. The matte finish is of lower contrast and yields a continuous-tone image suitable for pictorial matter. There are a number of intermediate grades with overlapping uses—and overlapping nomenclature—so it is advisable to request samples from your supplier along with his suggestions for recommended use.

Direct positive photostats are also available. The absence of an intermediate negative reduces both the cost and processing time; obviously, however, it is useless where reversals are called for. Direct positive stats are the sharpest form of photostat reproduction. The image quality is sufficiently high for many display purposes.

"Stat houses" usually are able to provide a number of additional photographic services such as color prints, continuous-tone prints, mural-size prints, screened prints, posterizing, line-tone renditions, and textured screens, as well as mounting, matting, and finishing.

SCREENED PRINTS
Bernard Fein, SCOTT SCREEN PRINTS, INC.

A screened print, or "velox" as it is more commonly known, differs from an ordinary photographic print in that the halftone pattern has been incorporated at the start of the reproduction process. As such, it can be pasted into position on the mechanical along with the line elements and photographed together. This eliminates the need for a special halftone negative made by the printer which must be stripped into position later on, and substantially reduces the cost of halftone reproduction. It also eliminates the need for photostats since the print itself is used for position.

Other advantages are that silhouetting, line surprints and reversals, benday panels, etc., can all be incorporated to make up a camera-ready mechanical. All parties concerned with the final appearance of the job can see it in finished form before any printing plates have been made. If production deadlines require the same ad in several locations, extra prints can be supplied quickly and economically. Additional handwork, if required, is easily accomplished with "china white" or black opaque. The flexibility of screened prints is also increased by the ease with which they may be cut and pasted together. If one halftone image is to be placed on top of another it is advisable to sand, or

"feather," the edges of the top print so that no shadows will be cast when it goes before the camera. An additional precaution is to blacken the edges of the top print.

The quality of a screened print can be judged by its overall appearance, which should be slightly lighter than anticipated in the printed reproduction. Examination with a glass should reveal hard black dots in the light areas and clean white dots in the shadows. If these are weak or veiled over they will not reproduce well.

Screen ruling is determined by the final printing process. Newspaper ads, screen printing, and flexography call for rulings between 55 and 85 lines per inch; offset lithography can go as fine as 120.

Properly used, screen prints offer flexibility in design and speed and economy in production, and yield excellent-quality photomechanical reproductions.

LINE CONVERSIONS
Joel A. Levirne, JOEL A. LEVIRNE/GRAPHIC IMAGES, LTD.

Line conversions are created by changing black-and-white continuous-tone prints, color prints, or transparencies into line form suitable for printing. The conventional halftone screen consisting of a regular array

Figure 8.9: Mezzotint.

Figure 8.11: Linear screen.

Figure 8.10: Concentric circle.

of dots is replaced by any one of a variety of special-effect screens that yield tone effects through varying thicknesses of lines or other patterns, rather than dot size. In addition, there are techniques which use masks to convert the graininess of the original photograph into tone areas or to condense the continuous tones of the photograph into only two or three tones.

The screens used in line conversions produce unusual, striking effects suggestive of the scratch-board method used in the past, when highly skilled master engravers spent days etching lines to create their printing plates. Nowadays process cameras, contact frames, enlargers, and textured screens are used to simulate these artistic effects.

A variety of textured screens is available, including mezzotint, linear, etching, linen, wood grain, and charcoal screens (see figures 8.9 through 8.14). The mezzo is a stippled, patterned texture that creates a line reproduction from all types of original copy. It has full value range from high contrast down through the middle tones. The linear screen has ruled parallel lines that can be made to run horizontally, vertically, or diagonally. It holds most of the original tones. The coarseness of the lines will vary, depending upon the type of paper being used and the reproduction method. Variations of this screen are the concentric circle, creating a bull's-eye effect, and the wavy line screen, which gives a contour feeling. The etching screen produces a random scratch line pattern that closely resembles an old-

Figure 8.12: Linen screen.

Figure 8.13: Etching screen.

Figure 8.14: Charcoal screen.

time engraving. The linen screen, as the name implies, is derived from the weave texture of linen material. It is also sometimes called a canvas screen. Wood grain screens simulate the grain patterns of various kinds of wood. A charcoal screen is one which closely resembles the embossed texture of an artist's charcoal paper. Other new patterns are constantly being devised; there is in fact no practical limit to the number of effects which may be obtained.

Not all line conversions are done by screening processes. One technique makes use of a basic line shot. A high-contrast negative of the original photograph is shot in a process camera, so that all the gray tones of the original are lost and only the details in the black areas are picked up. Another technique is the *tone-line* (fig. 8.15) in which a mask is used to pick up the texture of the grain of the original photograph; in this way, the image is broken up into tone areas. The tone-line works best from a sharp, unretouched photograph because retouching destroys the natural grain structure. A second masking technique is *posterization* (fig. 8.16) in which the various gray tones of a continuous-tone photograph are condensed into two or three values, which are then screened for reproduction purposes.

In recent years, there has been further development of two-, three-, and four-color conversions utilizing all the screen and masking processes described above (see figures 8.17 through 8.20). One style is the *duotone*, in which one plate is used for the detail and the other

Figure 8.15: Tone-line.

Figure 8.16: Posterization.

Figure 8.17: Three-color posterization.

Figure 8.18: Solarization.

Figure 8.19: Two-color conversion using combination of tone-line and posterization.

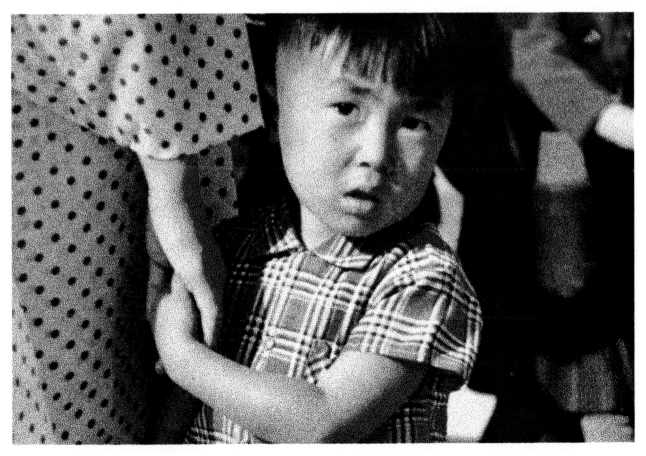

Figure 8.20: Four-color mezzotint.

for the color. In posterization, the gray values may be separated and reproduced as colors. A variation of posterization is *solarization,* in which some or all of the dark and light values are reversed to create a negative-positive image. The four-color conversion is the newest and most advanced of the color processes. Full-color separations are made from color prints or transparencies using special-effect screens.

Line conversions can convert a routine piece of copy into an exciting piece of graphics with high visual impact. An added advantage is that line conversions will reproduce well in the printing process, and on poor grades of paper such as newsprint they far surpass the conventional halftone in clarity.

While it is true that a poor original, unfit for conventional reproduction, can sometimes be salvaged through the skillful use of these methods, it is always better to begin with a good original. Some think that a high-contrast photograph is required, but that is not the case. An original with a full tonal range is preferable, as it offers more possibilities for control and manipulation. Limited originals limit the results.

DIFFUSION TRANSFER PROCESS

Conventional black-and-white photography consists of exposing a photosensitive layer, usually coated on a transparent film substrate, and developing the latent image to a negative. The negative is then exposed to a photosensitive paper, which is developed to yield a positive image following a procedure essentially identical to the making of a negative. It had been known by photographic scientists for many years that a positive and negative image could be produced together, and for all practical purposes simultaneously, by using a principle known as *diffusion transfer reversal.*

The general principle of conventional photography is that upon exposure to light certain salts of silver can be reduced to metallic silver through a chemical process known as development. The grains of silver metal are of such a size and distribution that they appear black, rather than shiny, as if coated on a mirror. The silver salts which have not been exposed to light are dissolved away so that an image is formed which records the amount of light that struck the film at any point in terms of blackness. Such an image is, of course, *negative* to the original scene. Repeating the process will form an image *positive* to the original scene, and the sequence of photographic steps usually involves a change in polarity, that is, positive to negative, negative to positive, and so on.

If, however, the unexposed silver salts could be made black we would have a positive image directly. In diffusion transfer, if the exposed emulsion is developed with a developer which contains a silver halide solvent, the unexposed crystals can be made to migrate to a suitably prepared support held in intimate contact with the original. The support need not be coated with a light-sensitive material requiring re-exposure but must contain substances which are capable of converting the transferred silver halides to a visible image.

The number of crystals transferred at any point is inversely proportional to the amount of light they received. When blackened by chemical reaction with substances present in the support, the resulting image is positive with respect to the original scene. The image is also laterally right-reading since the exposed negative and the material to which the image is transferred are placed in face-to-face contact.

The transfer can be carried out in one step, or, if for some reason it is more advantageous, a two-step procedure can be employed.

KODAK PMT MATERIALS

This article was adapted from publication Q-201, "Kodak PMT Products Offer Timesaving Production Options," with permission of Eastman Kodak Company.

Kodak PMT materials, used in the diffusion transfer process, are designed to produce high-quality positive or negative images on paper, film, or plates. They can eliminate many conventional procedures in the production of mechanicals and plates.

HOW PMT MATERIALS WORK

A light-sensitive "donor" material is exposed to the original copy just like a piece of film. It is then removed from the camera or contact frame and placed emulsion-to-emulsion with a sheet of "receiver" material. The two sheets are fed into the processor simultaneously, where they are first separated and then squeegeed together by roller pressure. A chemical reaction takes place when intimate contact is made between the two materials in the presence of a processing solution, and a positive image is formed on the receiver. Upon exiting from the processor, the two PMT materials are still in contact, and after a short wait—30 seconds or so—the sheets are separated by hand. The donor with its negative image is discarded. If the positive image on the receiver will be used immediately, it needs no further treatment. A 15-second rinse in tempered water to remove the residual chemicals will extend its useful life. (This basic process is varied with PMT Reversal Materials, which produce a negative from a positive or a positive from a negative.)

Using conventional methods, each step—exposure, development, fixing, washing, and drying—must be done twice, once for the film and again for the paper. With PMT Materials only one exposure is made and the processing is shortened to a single step.

AVAILABLE MATERIALS

Kodak makes four donor papers, five receiver materials, and two processing solutions—an activator and a developer. The receiver materials include a paper plate, a metal plate, transparent film, and two kinds of paper. The developer is required for reversals. All other materials are processed in the activator. However, one of the receiver materials, PMT Receiver Paper Type 2 AD, can be processed in either the activator or the developer, so it is not necessary to change chemicals for an occasional reversal.

The exposing, light-sensitive donor papers are:
• *Negative Paper*, for use in a process camera when size changes are needed. It can be used to expose line work, including prescreened and printed halftones. Continuous-tone prints can be screened directly by using a PMT Gray Contact Screen. The image can be transferred to either paper or transparent film.
• *Reflex Paper*, for same-size line reproduction in a contact frame to make reflex or contact exposures. In reflex printing, the original is placed face up in a frame with the donor material emulsion side down on top of it. The image can be transferred to paper, film, or litho paper plates.
• *Litho Negative Paper*, for use in a process camera to transfer line and halftone paste-ups to either paper or metal litho plates.
• *Reversal Paper*, for use in a camera to produce right-reading reversal prints. The image may be transferred only to paper.

APPLICATIONS

While PMT materials have many uses in photomechanical reproduction, their versatility makes them particularly well suited for the production of offset newspapers, technical manuals, and yearbooks, where paste-up methods are widely used. Finished copy or proofs of excellent quality can be prepared quickly, accurately, and quite simply. PMT materials can reduce production steps, save time, minimize errors, and generally improve overall production efficiency.

The number of steps normally used for the preparation of plate-ready negatives and flats can be reduced by using Kodak PMT materials to produce a plate-ready composite negative. The diffusion transfer process saves the time normally needed for exposing and processing film negatives, as well as the time required to convert film negatives to reflection copy for use in the paste-up composition. Screened prints are easy to produce, and using them for paste-up eliminates line and screen film negatives and stripping in the flat.

The transparent film receiving material is useful for overhead projection slides, intermediates for diazo proofs, and positive transparencies for screen process printing. Metal and paper plates are available in the small press and duplicator sizes, and permit copy to go directly from camera to plate.

Original copy can be printed, typewritten, or drawn in pencil or ink on transparent, translucent, or opaque stock. The prepared surface of Kodak PMT Receiver Paper accepts pencil or ink for crop marks or margin notes. It will also stand reasonable amounts of erasure. Large areas can be removed from most receiver materials with PMT Deletion Fluid.

Image quality on Kodak PMT materials is noteworthy. Images are dense black with sharp edges; whites are bright and contrast well with the images. Dot quality on screened paper prints is excellent and lends itself well to subsequent reproduction.

POLAROID IN THE GRAPHIC ARTS
William Field, FREE-LANCE GRAPHIC DESIGNER

By far the most ingenious, and by now the most common, use of diffusion transfer is to be found in the Polaroid system developed by Dr. Edwin Land. Once regarded as a novelty that would only have acceptance in the field of amateur photography, the usefulness of "instant" prints has spread widely to such areas as medical and scientific research, industrial and engineering applications, and commercial photography. The continuing technological development undertaken by the Polaroid Corporation, both in increasing its product line and improving the imaging quality of the system, promises an expanding field of applications, including many of interest to those in the graphic arts.

Today there are 24 camera-imaging emulsions which develop instantly to give the professional user his choice of black-and-white positive, negative, or transparency, in high contrast or continuous tone, with a variety of film speeds.

These materials, combined with versatile camera systems manufactured by Polaroid and other concerns, allow the graphic arts professional—art director, paste-up personnel, production assistant, or printer—to complete a wide variety of photographic tasks without down time or outside services. But time and cost efficiency are not the only reasons for using the Polaroid system. Quality is another. Polaroid photographs regularly hang in art galleries and museums around the world.

Perhaps the finest argument for this system, however, could be made on the point of creativity. Instant-developing films allow the user to work uninterrupted from inception to completion of an idea. The confidence of being able to see results instantly, at each step of the process, permits the user absolute control over the final image.

ADVERTISING AND PRINTING PRODUCTION

Of particular interest to photographers, art directors, and printers is Polaroid Type 808 8" x 10" Polacolor 2 Land film. With Type 808 film, full-color, high-resolution prints are available in just 75 seconds—ready for the retoucher or for the printer. Polaroid 8" x 10" color prints make excellent originals for graphic arts reproduction. And what the photographer sees in the finished print, he can expect to get, with careful printing, when the image is published, since the density range of a Polacolor print is closely matched to the capabilities of ink on paper. Matching color is also much easier with a reflective print than with a transparency. With a reflective print, there are no problems in viewing with different light sources. When everyone involved in the reproduction—the photographer, client, art director, and printer—is comparing a Polacolor print to a proof or press sheet under the same light conditions, differences in interpretation are considerably reduced.

Type 808 film also makes an excellent copy medium, in conjunction with a vertical copy camera. With a Polaroid full-color instant stat, designers can quickly copy a transparency or print to make a client presentation, experiment with design ideas, or proof a job showing all copy and photographs in position before going to press. With an in-house color stat capability, production is speeded up and costly mistakes reduced.

For photocopying applications a camera system must be rigidly supported, have controllable lighting, and use flat-field copying lenses. The Polaroid MP-4 Camera is designed to meet this need. The camera is mounted on a vertical stand, with lights attached to the base that can be adjusted for uniform or directional lighting as required.

This equipment readily lends itself to type size changes and corrections or alterations. Individual characters or words may be photographed on Polaroid Type 51 high-contrast film from existing repros, sample books, or press-on adhesive characters. Finished line copy, ready to be cut and pasted into the mechanical, is available in 15 seconds. The size limitation of the 4" x 5" format is not insurmountable since larger copy can be photographed in overlapping sections and fitted together during the paste-up. When a negative image is required for reverse type, Polaroid Type 55 or Type 665 Film may be used. The negative which is produced along with the regular positive print may be rephotographed on high-contrast positive material, producing a reverse stat for paste-up purposes.

Continuous-tone prints serve as high-quality photostats for layouts, comps, or mechanicals. Again, the availability of a high-quality, continuous-tone negative with Type 55 material is useful if additional prints or great enlargements are called for. An accessory kit for the MP-4 can produce halftone prints in screen rulings from 65 to 120 lines per inch. Contrast control is achieved in basically the same manner as conventional screening with supplementary flashing exposures. Screened prints made in this manner are available instantly for approval and can be pasted up with the type for the final mechanical. Halftone reproductions can also be made directly from halftone originals since the acuteness of the system permits the dot structure to be recorded accurately.

Many art departments and printers have found the capability of instant recording useful merely to keep track of layouts and other incoming material. Original artwork out on loan can be recorded along with pertinent information on the back of the print.

Diazo and similar materials requiring a positive transparency can be accommodated with Type 46L for continuous-tone originals, and Type 146L for line work.

Murals, posters, and other large, short-run graphics can be produced with either Type 55 or Type 665 P/N film. The resulting negative is able to take great degrees of enlargement without loss of image quality, because of the extremely fine grain and high resolution characteristic of this type of material.

PHOTOGRAPHY AND ART

For general-purpose photography the MP-4 camera may be removed from the stand and used as a view camera. It will accept all of the film types produced by Polaroid, which is an important consideration since some types are available in only one format.

Where greater portability is needed there are a number of Polaroid Land pack cameras featuring automatic exposure timing, superimposed-image range finders, and accessories for portraiture, close-ups, and other special requirements. The 600 SE camera provides professionals with a rangefinder camera with manual controls, interchangeable lenses, and a versatile pack film format for black-and-white or color film.

Where maximum versatility is essential a number of cameras will accept Polaroid Land pack film backs, permitting the camera to be converted to instant photography. The Hasselblad 500C, Rolleiflex SL-66, Mamiya RB-67 and Universal, Graphic XL, and the Horseman are among the smaller cameras accepting Polaroid backs. Nearly all of the 4" x 5" view and press cameras are adaptable.

Using Polaroid images in the studio and on location for pre-shooting approval is a widespread practice. Lighting, composition, and other elements that require considered judgment by a number of people can be communicated easily without the need for all to be present. The quicker release of models, bays, and merchandise resulting from the faster approvals more than justify such an approach.

Polaroid films can be used in many creative ways by the artist. Posterization, tone-line separation, silhouettes, pseudo-solarization, and a wide variety of other graphic effects can be obtained quickly and with maximum control over each step by a creative artist using Polaroid materials.

AGFA-GEVAERT MATERIALS

Agfa-Gevaert manufactures a variety of diffusion transfer materials. These include materials for producing paper prints, film, and metal plates, as well as a panchromatic material used for color separation.

PAPER AND FILM

Agfa-Gevaert manufactures three negative materials used for making paper prints or film copies: CPN, a high-contrast material for exposing line or halftone copy or for making halftones from continuous-tone copy; CPTN, for exposing continuous-tone copy; and CPRV, a high-contrast reversal material for line and halftone work.

These materials are processed to produce paper or film positives or, from the reversal materials, right-reading reversals. A developer is used for reversals; the other materials are processed in an activator.

METAL PLATES

Materials are also available for making aluminum plates for offset printing. Two negative materials are manufactured: camera-speed CRRO and contact-speed CRSO. After exposure, the negative material is processed together with the plate in a diffusion transfer processor with a special developer. The plate is then treated with fixer and lacquer; the lacquer adheres to the image areas.

TRANSFERLITH

Agfa-Gevaert makes a panchromatic diffusion transfer material called Transferlith, which is suitable for direct-screen color separation (see page 356). The panchromatic negative film is exposed to a full-color original, using the same silver masks as in conventional direct-screen color separation. The material may be integrated into an existing optical/exposing system or may be used in conjunction with Agfa-Gevaert's TCS 850 system. This system consists of a unit performing the dual function of camera and enlarger, a register punch system, and programmable exposure control. The exposed material is processed in contact with the positive receiver material in a Transferlith processor to produce a screened positive separation film. The processor is designed to insure absolute register of the separations.

Transferlith materials require significantly shorter exposure times than conventional direct-screen materials. In addition, the film is sensitized so that the exposures for all the separations are of nearly uniform length.

The complete processing cycle (dry-to-dry) takes less than two minutes. The processor costs a fraction of the price of the usual lith processor, and the processing chemistry is far less critical with regard to oxidation and exhaustion. Time and temperature controls are built into the processor. The critical replenishment system inherent in automatic lith processing is not required.

The halftone dots on the separations are very well formed, with extremely sharp edges. The material responds to the supplemental flash and bump exposures needed for controlling tone reproduction. The adjacency effect, or bromide drag, which has plagued the conventional lith processor, is eliminated.

PREPARING COPY FOR ELECTRONIC COLOR SCANNERS

Edward R. Novota, GRAPHIC ARTS CONSULTANT

The belief commonly held in the computer industry that "you get out only what you put in" is not absolutely true in the field of electronic color separation. Today's scanners have unique features which permit the user to vary the separation output and to introduce special effects. Carefully engineered adjustment controls allow the operator great flexibility:

• Gray balance and gradation can be altered to meet the specific ink/paper/press requirements.

• Color-correction masking can be changed to fit particular conditions.

• Undercolor removal can be altered in both amount and the range of tones over which it extends.

• Edge definition can be varied in either direction to increase detail or subdue minor imperfections.

• Type and panels can be photocomposed into the subject.

• Enlarging and reducing features are available, yielding scans to final size.

• Halftone dots can be generated directly by electronic means rather than through an intervening screen, providing superior rendition of fine detail.

• Special circuits are available to create effects not otherwise obtainable through conventional separation techniques, such as (1) a neutral gate for removing unwanted color in gray areas and introducing increased amounts of black in the same areas, and (2) the selective enhancement of highlights.

With flexible features such as these, it might be assumed that anything is possible with any kind of copy. Certainly, much can be done; but, by the same token, it should always be remembered that the ultimate quality of the output reproduction actually does depend a great deal upon the quality of the input material.

PREPARATION OF TRANSPARENT COPY

It is well known that transparencies vary in both highlight and shadow densities. Because of this, it is advantageous to mount transparencies on the scanner in related groups so that compatible ones fall in the line of scan (see figure 8.21). This method permits *split scanning*, or separate setup adjustments for each group aligned in the scanning path. If transparencies are already stripped in final page position, it is still possible to balance the different highlight values by adding neutral density filters to the lighter transparencies, as shown in the illustration.

In grouping or positioning to page composition, it would be well to strive for a minimum highlight density of about 0.40 to 0.45, rather than lower densities which tend to give the impression of brightness, the reason being that important highlight differences or information in the original transparency is better retained when placed above the flat part of the toe of the duplicate emulsion characteristic curve. Brightness in the scanned

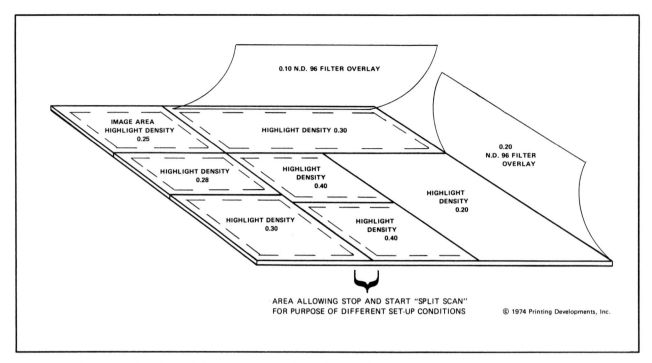

Figure 8.21: Transparencies of mixed densities assembled for split scanning.

separations can be accomplished by programming the highlight setup properly.

Improvements in highlight and color balance of a group, as well as enlargement and final positioning, often justify the use of duplicate transparencies. Further color correction can be made through dye retouching of the duplicates, a practice not always permitted on a "one of a kind" original transparency.

The stripping of duplicate transparencies into final page assembly is an established art and falls into three basic categories, as illustrated in figure 8.22. In addition, transparencies may be assembled using photographic techniques.

Tape

Transparencies can be held in position by thin, clear, pressure-sensitive tape. Tape is always attached to the base of the transparency. If attached to the emulsion side, there is the danger of scanning out of focus since the tape prevents intimate contact with the surface of the scanning drum.

Abutment

Where no space is possible between transparencies to allow for the tape, they may be cut and the edges "melted in" with acetone or another solvent that welds together the acetate base. Good results can be obtained even when the edges are not straight cuts but intricate configurations such as the inset of one transparency within another.

Cut line edges of melt-ins are noticeable but in many cases unobjectionable.

Emulsion stripping

The layers of color emulsion are removed together from the acetate support, cut to shape, and reassembled on a new support with a protective membrane covering the entire assembly. If emulsion stripping is carefully done, the edges are invisible and will not be picked up by the scanner.

Photocomposition

Direct photocomposition on one sheet of duplicate film is also possible. Each element is sized and positioned at the time the duplicate is being made. The result is a single piece of film without cut edges, which requires less extreme care in handling.

PREPARATION OF REFLECTION COPY

Most scanners will accept reflection copy provided it is sufficiently flexible to be wrapped around the scanning drum. Copy mounted on stiff illustrator's board must be converted to transparency form for scanning. Photographic color prints can be cut and pasted into position on a flexible support, or color negatives can be photocomposed onto a single sheet of print paper using the same technique as described for photocomposed duplicate transparencies.

PHOTOCOMPOSITION IN THE SCANNER

As in any photocomposition technique, the position of type or panel inserts within the subject must be known. Instructions for the scanner are provided in the form of a *command mask* based on the pin register system of the particular scanner being used. These masks, also referred to as *burn-outs* or *opaquers*, record the areas in the original subject which are to be replaced by a tint or solid, or dropped out altogether.

300

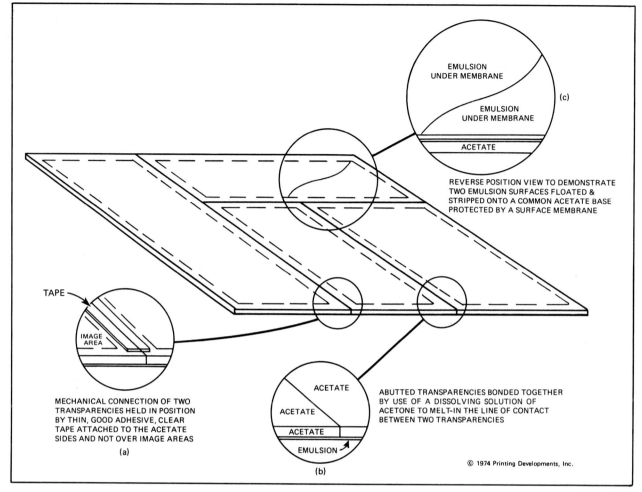

Figure 8.22: Three basic methods for position stripping of duplicate transparencies.

COPY REQUIREMENTS FOR SCANNING

Because of the extreme fidelity obtainable in scanners, the surface condition of transparencies is a matter of importance. Scratches, abrasions, imbedded dirt, and fingerprints can only degrade the final image quality.

Original transparencies are not always photographed under optimum conditions. The illumination may be insufficient, or, as in sport scenes, the subject may be in motion, necessitating high shutter speeds. "Forcing" the image in the subsequent processing steps may yield undesirable color shifts. High-speed emulsions designed for situations with low lighting levels gain their speed through the use of larger silver halide grains. As a result, graininess is much more apparent than with the lower speed color films. This can be reduced somewhat in reproduction by decreasing the scanner resolution.

Emulsion layers within a color film are balanced for an optimum shutter speed, and wide departures from the recommended speed result in reciprocity failure, characterized by hue changes, especially in the shadow areas. A useful way to restore color balance is through duplicate transparencies; if complete correction is not possible in the duplicate, further correction can be introduced by scanner adjustment.

Careful preparation of copy prior to scanning is an important factor in obtaining the highest reproduction quality, as well as in effecting substantial economies. Electronic scanning systems are continually being improved. Some innovative systems already feature halftone dot generation, digital sizing, electronic photocomposition, and automatic highlight programming. Now under development is a more comprehensive method of programming the color scanner by using a coded insert card which would select the proper mask percentages, undercolor reduction, black curve characteristics, and other factors relating to the requirements of a given reproduction process. As new systems are presented to the industry, additional thought will have to be given to copy preparation if we wish to use them to their maximum advantage.

LIMITING FACTORS IN PICTORIAL REPRODUCTION

Robert Loekle, COLOR REPRODUCTION CONSULTANT

Since so much of the printing process is concerned with the reproduction of pictorial images, it may be helpful to review some of the limitations that are inherent in current printing technology. Generally speaking, these are of minor concern: the main causes of disappointing results are more likely to be found in careless handling of the process than in its inherent limitations. Nevertheless, there are occasions when even the best materials and the most impeccable craftsmanship yield results that are not up to expectations. By understanding the causes, the graphic designer can frequently circumvent the problem; and those responsible for production can reduce the contumely with the printer which seems to be a frequent and unfortunate by-product.

It is not possible to construct a hard and fast list of "do's and don't's" for guidance, nor is it desirable to set arbitrary bounds to the inventiveness of the artist; but it is desirable to draw his attention to those areas in which the reproduction process itself counsels that creativity ought to be tempered by caution.

BLACK-AND-WHITE PHOTOGRAPHY

A common example occurs in the reproduction of a simple black-and-white photograph, the conventional "8 x 10 glossy." Sophisticated purchasers of printing who are accustomed to dealing with a volume of color reproductions are often dismayed by the poor quality of an apparently simple black-and-white job. The accuracy of the reproduction seems to fall below the high standards they have been accustomed to in color.

In black-and-white reproduction, accuracy is established largely by the representation of brightness differences. The problems of hue and saturation, two extra dimensions provided by color, are nonexistent. If at each point in the reproduction the darkness of a tone were the same as the corresponding point in the original, then the two would be indistinguishable from each other.

Such a situation is easy to conceive, and could be achieved in practice were it not for one obstacle: the deepest black that can be obtained by ink printing on paper is not so deep as the blackest area of an "8 x 10 glossy." This can easily be verified by punching a hole in the area of a print where the ink is printing solid and holding it over the deepest black of a photograph. It is easy to perceive several steps of difference between the blacks.

This poses an interesting problem. If we follow the principle of matching tone for tone, by the time we arrive at a point in the original whose darkness is equal to the solid printed ink we have come to the end of the reproducible tone scale, as it is impossible to exceed 100% coverage of the paper. All tones in the original darker than the solid ink would be indistinguishable from each other, the effect being that no detail or shape

in the shadow areas could be discerned.

The problem can be visualized by treating the tone differences quite literally as steps, as illustrated in the diagram in figure 8.23. The broken line represents the ideal tone-for-tone match, the darkness of each tone in the reproduction being the same as its corresponding step in the original. The real situation is represented by the solid line.

One way to overcome this, since obviously the total obliteration of shadow detail is an intolerable situation, is to reduce the height of each step by a proportional amount and so preserve some of the differences in the shadows (fig. 8.24). This would work quite well were it not for another disturbing fact: the eye is quite sensitive to small differences in the highlights and middletones. Reproductions treated in this manner lack modelling and highlight sparkle. Flesh tones, which are rendered in black and white as middletones, seem chalky and washed out.

The most satisfactory compromise for a wide variety of work seems to follow the highlights and middletones quite carefully and put all the compensation in the shadow steps (fig. 8.25). For some types of originals, however, such a treatment may be inappropriate. A low-key picture is almost wholly dependent upon good separation of the shadow tones, and figure 8.24 might be expected to give a preferred reproduction in these circumstances. A high-key picture, on the other hand, such as a bridal dress of satin and lace, demands good separation of the highlight tones if the lustrousness of the satin and fine detail of the lace are to be rendered satisfactorily. In such a case, figure 8.23 might be preferred for tone reproduction.

The considerations that go into the choice of the most appropriate tone reproduction are the province of the graphic arts photographer, who has at his disposal a wide variety of techniques for adjusting the distribution of tone differences. These techniques can also be applied to improve the reproduction of poor copy. The important thing to remember is that when the tone scale of the original greatly exceeds that obtainable in the reproduction process, some compromise must be made. If tones are to be reproduced accurately at one end, then they must be squeezed together at the other.

There is a solution, however, which avoids this compromise through a technique of double printing. After the sheet is printed in the normal fashion it is run through the press again and receives a second black image from a plate which carries only those tones in the original that exceed the blackness of a single solid ink film. The use of two ink films run in succession yields a maximum black very close to that found in a photograph (see figure 8.26). When the steps of the second impression are positioned on the first, the differences are restored and the entire tone scale of the original can be reproduced.

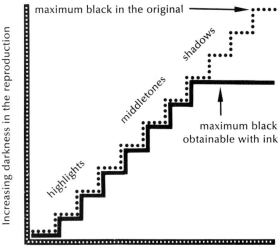

Figure 8.23: Tone scale of reproduction compared with that of original photograph.

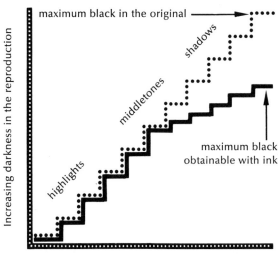

Figure 8.25: Compression in the shadow steps only.

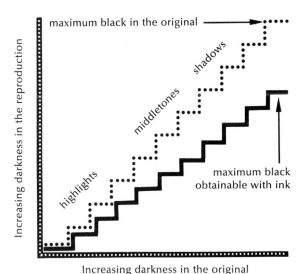

Figure 8.24: Compression of the reproducible tone scale by reducing the height of each step.

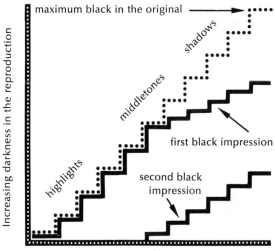

Figure 8.26: Use of two-black printing to lengthen tone scale of reproduction.

No diagram can adequately convey the appearance of a reproduction treated in this manner. The depth and modelling in the shadows and the overall impression of richness is in startling contrast to the compromise we have come to accept as normal in black-and-white reproduction. Considering the availability of two-color presses which can yield the final result in one printing, it is surprising that the technique is not more widely used. The costs for preparation of the second plate and a slight increase in ink consumption are easily justified by the gains in reproduction quality.

COLOR SATURATION AND TINT PURITY

The same effect occurs in color reproduction, but to a lesser extent since the four inks used in process-color printing combine to form a black considerably darker than one ink alone. Modelling in the shadows can be conveyed by differences in color as well as darkness, which further relieves the problem.

An analagous effect occurs when highly saturated colors in an original exceed the maximum of the reproduction process. This is often the case when the original is a color transparency, and the problem is further compounded by the different modes of viewing for transparency and printed reproduction. A common example can be found in brilliant reds, which often seem washed out in the reproduction. If the modelling is dependent upon subtle differences in saturation, the reproduction will appear flat and lack drawing. This may have to be restored by painstaking and expensive handwork on the magenta and yellow plates, which make up the color, or the modelling may have to be introduced artificially in the black plate. Occasionally neither of these solutions will prove to be entirely satisfactory.

Again the possible use of an additional plate suggests itself as a means of extending the range of the reproduction process. This is often referred to by the printing trade as a *touch,* or *patch,* plate.

Since the saturation of color is in large part a function of the strength to which the inks are printed, a simple solution might seem at first to be found by merely running more ink. For the transparent inks used in process work, however, there is an optimum ink-film thickness. Once this point is reached, more ink contributes little to increased color saturation but only degrades the purity of the ink color, as though a small amount of black had been mixed with it.

Problems associated with excessive inking also occur in drying. The worst consequence is *blocking,* where the printed sheets cannot be separated, and are actually glued together by the ink. Just as serious, however, is the increased chance of setoff (transfer of ink to the back of the next sheet) and smudging.

Halftone work is particularly sensitive to excessively heavy ink films, as the areas of the dots tend to grow. Growth is first noticeable in the shadow areas where the small, open spaces fill in most quickly.

There are minimum limits, as well, to the amount of ink which can be run. A certain amount is required to insure uniform transfer to the paper. In lithography, the presence of water in the dampening solution adds further complications. Thin ink films tend to pick up this moisture, which becomes emulsified in the ink, and colors printed with an ink and water emulsion lack brilliance and gloss.

For all these reasons, the conventional wisdom of "making the job on press" by tinkering with the ink flow ought to be reexamined. The adjustments on the press are intended to provide the means for achieving an optimum ink-film thickness uniformly across the plate. When they are used to force or hold back certain areas to achieve results that are not in the plates to begin with, one should be aware that he is wandering in a mine field of unforeseen consequences.

Another limitation peculiar to halftone color reproduction processes occurs in the highlight end of the tone scale. A true subtractive system (as described in Section 2, *Color*) implies that at each point in the reproduction the light-absorbing colorants, whether dyes or pigments, are superimposed. Although halftone processes are often referred to as subtractive systems, it is clear that this is only so where the dot areas are large and there is considerable overlap. Lighter tones are represented by decreasing the area of the dots, and in the highlights they often lie side by side with only minor fractions of overprinting.

This is more than a theoretical shortcoming. It has serious practical consequences for the reproduction of clean, pastel colors. The effective mixture produced by small areas of pigment printing side by side is noticeably different from that of continuous layers of the same pigments, and appears gray and dirty by comparison. The effect is least noticeable in most gravure printing, which for practical purposes can be considered a continuous-tone process inasmuch as the main variable used to establish tone differences is ink volume rather than area.

In general pictorial work the phenomenon may pass unnoticed. Illustrations, however, that have critical requirements for the reproduction of clean lavenders, pinks, and turquoises will have to be compromised. Little can be done about it short of printing a match color. The use of a different set of process inks may be helpful, although the extent of the difference if any worthwhile improvement is to be gained is of such an order that it has limited usefulness if there is a wide gamut of other colors to be reproduced. The colors of the primaries that predominately form the color to be matched must be shifted in the direction of the desired hue.

When the designer can foresee the problem and can exercise some options, he can diminish the graying effect by increasing the fineness of the screen ruling, decreasing the surface gloss of the paper, or decreasing the strength to which the inks are run.

AVOIDING PROBLEMS IN REPRODUCTION

There is an adage in the trade that "the copy you like best is best for reproduction." This is a reflection of the current state of the art in printing technology, in which the main aim has been to develop materials and methods directed towards improved accuracy in reproduction. The need for excessive contrast and grotesque retouching of highlights in photographic prints to allow for the "graying down" associated with the printing process is now more likely to create problems for the printer than provide any positive benefits. Similarly, the once prevalent practice of underexposing color transparencies to allow for a loss of color saturation in printing is in general disuse. With contemporary technology, a transparency exposed in such a manner will yield a print which appears too dark unless special compensations are introduced during color separation.

This is not in conflict with the previous discussion, which concerns theoretical limitations admittedly of minor importance unless some special combination of circumstances thrusts them to the forefront. In general, considerations for the printing process will be subordinate to those of design and aesthetics.

So long as the printing process contained large and characteristic errors in pictorial reproduction, it seemed a practical and commonsense precaution to provide a corresponding exaggeration in the original. Such was the rationale behind the glossy print. The presence of gloss in itself provided a longer tonal range, and since the printer was bound to lose some, then the more he had at the start the more likely it seemed he would wind up with an acceptable range in the reproduction. The validity of this approach may be argued; it most certainly created a situation in which the difference between original and reproduction was maximized.

A contemporary practice is to make the original photographic print on a matte or luster surface. This compresses the tonal range into one that can be more closely reproduced by the printing process. If the necessary compression is introduced at the first stage of copy preparation, rather than in printing, the artist can make a better judgment as to how specific details will appear in the reproduction. This provides a situation in which differences between original and reproduction are minimized, and certainly one that eases the communication among printer, artist, and client.

304

Range and contrast are two different qualities we assign to tone reproduction. Because they are often used interchangeably in common speech, the lack of precision can introduce some confusion. By *range* we mean the brightness difference between the lightest and darkest tone in the picture. By *contrast* we mean the relative brightness differences among the intermediate tones. Referring to the "step" diagrams (figures 8.23 through 8.26) may clarify this further. The range is the height of the top step; the contrast is the steepness of the ascent.

Contrast in black-and-white photography is controlled in the chemistry of the process. Film emulsion type, the conditions of development, and the choice of graded contrast papers are the main variables. The apparent contrast of a photograph is also influenced by the lighting, a theatrically lighted scene seeming much more contrasty than a mist-shrouded landscape, for example. The art of photography depends largely upon how successfully these variables are manipulated.

In color photography, the contrast gradient of the film is built in at the time of manufacture. Artificially lighted scenes, interiors, and studio photographs depend upon careful placement of the illuminating sources for a pleasing rendition of tone contrasts. This is particularly so since the camera tends to exaggerate the contrast. For color work in particular, flatter illumi-nation results in photographs that more closely compare with our visual memory of the scene.

The problem of nonreproducible colors seems to be less than was once thought when the original is a colored photograph. Much can be attributed to errors in the color-separation techniques and the available choices of process inks, which have since been overcome. Because of the different modes of viewing transparencies and printed reproductions, substantial errors can be introduced if attention is not paid to compatible sources of illumination. The American National Standards Institute has provided guidelines for the choice of transmission and reflection sources. Holding a transparency up to the window while simultaneously viewing the print under a desk lamp will make intelligent commentary about reproduction accuracy a meaningless exercise. The problem is less severe when comparing a reflection original with a printed reproduction since ordinarily both are viewed with a common source of illumination. (Viewing conditions are discussed in greater detail in "The Measurement and Specification of Color," page 21.)

Nonreproducible colors frequently occur when the original is a painting. Artists are not restricted to the pigments of a printing process or the dyes of color photography. Greater tint purity can be obtained when the choice of colorants it not confined to three pri-

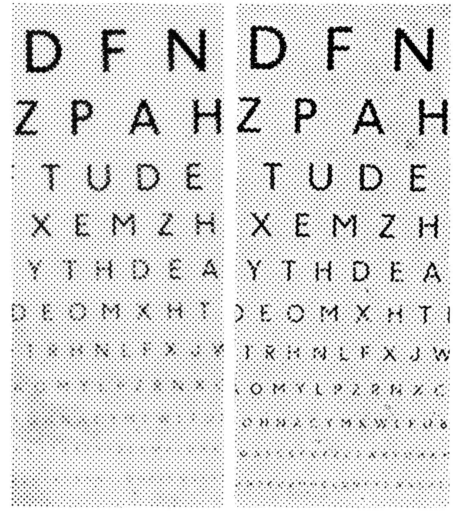

Figure 8.27: Type photographed through halftone screens. The small charts at the top are reproduced by means of a conventional glass screen (left) and a contact screen (right). The lower charts are photomicrographs of parts of the upper charts and show that the contact screen reproduces more fine detail because fine lines are less broken into dots. *From* Reproduction of Colour, *2nd Edition, 1967, published by Fountain Press.*

maries most suitable for subtractive color-reproduction methods.

The use of fluorescent or Day-Glo pigments for special effects can often lead to trouble. These have considerably higher purity than is obtainable with conventional pigments. The result is that two colors which appear quite distinct in the original are insufficiently discriminated in the reproduction. Special care must be exercised by the artist, or the "accent" colors obtained by fluorescence will be lost unless similar pigments are used in the printing.

IMAGE QUALITY

Up to this point the discussion has been confined to the reproduction of tones, either by black ink alone or the combinations of colored inks. Accurate reproduction of tones and colors is essential for good pictorial representation. However, there is another judgment we also make that is quite independent of tone and color. This has to do with *image quality*, mostly in the sense of sharpness conveyed by the print. This is especially true, of course, when the original is a photograph and we anticipate the crispness and fine rendering of textures that is associated with photography. In a halftone process, the geometrically straight edges of a line in the original must be represented as a series of dots that have more or less definite shapes of their own. The more these dots tend to remain true to the shape imposed by the screen, the more ragged the line edge representation. This is particularly true of the crossline glass screen, as can be verified by examining the dot structure in a halftone of printed type as in figure 8.27. Advantage is often taken of this effect by using the glass screen in cosmetic ads, where the lack of resolution tends to obscure minor surface irregularities in the model's skin.

However, for most purposes, the glass screen's lack of sharpness is considered a disadvantage, and the contact screen, which has virtually replaced it, is characterized by a considerably sharper image. An examination of the dot structure under low magnification will reveal that the edges of the individual dots are distorted and conform more closely to a geometrically straight edge. Most recent improvements in this area are found in the electronic scanners which make a screened positive (or negative) directly from the original. Several manufacturers offer models which bypass the conventional halftone screen techniques altogether and directly generate a dot which varies in edge configuration as well as area. These are quite capable of reproducing thin lines in the original as straight thin lines in the film. The effect on reproduction is quite startling and at first seems unnatural, so accustomed have we become to the loss of image sharpness characteristic of traditional halftone reproduction. Still another improvement can be found in the continuous-tone or screenless method of lithography, in which the halftone screen is omitted and the image exposed directly on a specially prepared litho plate from continuous-tone negatives. The surface roughness, or grain, of the plate acts as a random screen pattern equivalent to extremely fine ruling. The random pattern also eliminates the problem of superimposed screen image interference patterns known as *moiré*.

The sense of sharpness is also conveyed by the contrast gradient at the very edge of a line image. A practical means of controlling this is to bind a slightly diffuse or "out-of-focus" mask with the original. This has the effect of reducing contrast uniformly in broad areas but selectively in the fine detail, which it does not resolve. The result when the combination is exposed at

the next step is a relative increase in contrast in the fine details, which increases the apparent sharpness. In conventional color separation this is referred to as *unsharp masking* (referring to the characteristics of the mask rather than the effect it produces). A similar principle is to be found in some electronic scanners, which scan ahead and at the recognition of fine detail send back a signal to provide for a local increase in contrast at line edges.

The sharpness of the printed image is not a function of the sharpness of the film image alone. The characteristics of the ink, paper, and printing transfer pressures all influence final image sharpness. It is not possible, of course, to improve image sharpness over that of the plate during printing, but incorrect adjustments on press can easily degrade the sharpness that exists in the plate image.

In general, the smoother the paper, the sharper the image will appear. Uncoated papers, which tend to act as blotters for the ink, degrade image sharpness, as can be readily conceived. Excessive printing pressures and heavy ink flow or *flooding* also contribute to unsharp printed images.

Slight misregister between succeeding impressions in multicolor printing impairs the image quality. The paper must be not only smooth but dimensionally stable so that it does not stretch or warp under the forces exerted in printing. Oddly enough, the sharper the plate image is, the more critical this becomes. A fuzzy image misregistered is far less likely to be objectionable than an exceedingly sharp one.

From the designer's or artist's standpoint the message ought to be clear: graphic design is not complete when the client accepts artwork for reproduction. The responsibility extends to the final printed piece. Contemporary printing technology has some inherent limitations. They are minor, but nevertheless they exist and can sometimes be critical. Any options open to the designer should be exercised in favor of working with the materials and the process rather than against them.

PICTURE RESEARCH: AN INTRODUCTION

Ann Novotny, RESEARCH REPORTS & PICTURES

This introductory essay was adapted, with the permission of the publisher, from Picture Sources 3: Collections of Prints and Photographs in the U.S. and Canada, *edited by Ann Novotny and Rosemary Eakins (New York: Special Libraries Association, 1975), a joint project of Picture Division, SLA, and American Society of Picture Professionals.*

Professional picture researchers are employed today by book and magazine publishers, newspapers, film

and television producers, educational filmstrip companies, designers, and advertising agencies. Many of these professionals work in the publishing industry—a result of the dramatic change caused by the development of the modern picture book and by the fact that authors are no longer expected to supply all illustrations at their own expense, as was once the case. Many picture researchers are full-time staff members, but some work as free-lance consultants supplying visual materials to a cross section of the picture users mentioned above. The great majority are members of the 13-year-old American Society of Picture Professionals, with headquarters in New York and branches in Boston, Chicago, and Washington.

WHAT DOES A PICTURE RESEARCHER DO?

The work of a picture researcher entails far more than leafing through files of prints and photographs. The first task usually is to read the manuscript, film script, or outline, and to prepare a list (as specific as possible) of images to be sought. Preferably the researcher will make up his or her own list, rather than work from an inflexible one prepared by the editor, producer, or designer of the project. As well as the list of required pictures, the researcher needs a corresponding list of the photo agencies, libraries, museums, and other sources to be visited or contacted by letter or telephone.

The way in which these lists of possible pictures and their sources are drawn up depends to a great extent on the budget and the time available for the project. A minimum amount of time and money is required for any given project; an experienced researcher learns how to estimate these, and will in many cases be given the task of drawing up a preliminary budget and timetable. The picture researcher always has the responsibility of advising an employer or client if time or money restrictions make a project impossible.

If the budget is very limited, a project can often be accomplished successfully by granting the picture researcher an extra amount of time in which to contact those government departments, far-flung historical societies, and foreign sources (such as the Bibliothèque Nationale in Paris, for example) that respond slowly to mail inquiries and orders but permit publication of their uncopyrighted pictures for only a minimal print fee (often $2.50 or less). When time is at a premium, a project can be rushed to completion by alloting a large budget to pay for long-distance telephone calls, "rush" charges in the darkroom, and the reproduction rights fees charged by commercial picture suppliers who will provide instant service.

These rights fees vary widely, according to whether a picture is in color or black and white, and in what format and for what purpose it is to be reproduced—whether it is to be shown in a film, for example, or in a textbook and, if in a book, whether it will cover one quarter or a full page; whether it is purchased for the standard "one-time North American" editorial rights or for world distribution in many foreign language editions. One guide to the sliding scale of commercial fees charged by contemporary photographers is the 95-page *Professional Business Practices in Photography* (1979), published by the American Society of Magazine Photographers (60 East 42nd Street, New York, N.Y. 10017). Fees for historical pictures or for reproductions of art are usually less than those for contemporary photographs.

The research time needed for a project can vary almost as much as the budget for rights, depending in part on the subject matter. For example, pictures to illustrate abstract concepts ("culture shock," "alienation of the individual," "conspicuous consumption in the American economy") are much more difficult to

select than those of famous people, historical events, or works of art. One elusive picture may take many hours to track down, or it may fall into a researcher's hands almost by good luck.

As pictures are located and selected, a researcher must deal with the business of what is often called *permissions*. Does the supplier of the picture insist on any particular wording in the credit line? May the picture be cropped? Does this particular museum insist on approving color page proofs before publication? Is an old engraving or photograph in the public domain and available for free use, or is it still protected by copyright? If a photograph of a living person is to be used for an advertisement or book jacket, has the photographer obtained a signed release from the model? Is there any chance that a photographed person will object to the way in which his or her picture is used and possibly sue for libel or invasion of privacy? Experience is the best teacher in some of these areas, and many publishers retain lawyers who can advise a researcher or editor in doubt. Some guidelines can be found in *Photography and the Law* by George Chernoff and Hershel Sabin (New York, Amphoto, 1971); Howard L. Walls' *The Copyright Handbook for Fine and Applied Arts* (New York, Watson-Guptill, 1963); and *Photography: What's the Law?* by Robert M. Cavallo and Stuart Kahan (New York, Crown, 1976).

A picture researcher's responsibilities include the physical care of pictures, particularly when these are on loan (the fee paid to a commercial supplier is usually only for the right to use the print or photograph, which must be returned after use). Pictures must be counted carefully when they are received and returned, protected from such damage as bent corners or thumb prints, and returned to their source as soon as possible, together with a clear accounting of their use. Suppliers who send out a choice of pictures are always grateful to have the "preliminary rejects" returned as soon as the first selections have been made. Some suppliers charge holding fees if pictures are held for longer than two or three weeks. A picture researcher should be responsible for ensuring that borrowed materials are returned on time, or that the supplier is notified of the reason for delay.

These typical tasks of picture research are familiar to most users of pictures and to the librarians, curators, photographers, and agents who supply them. But only in recent years (and partially as a result of the work of the American Society of Picture Professionals) has the position of picture researcher been clearly defined and understood by many employers. A few companies use the term *picture editor* or even *art editor* as synonyms of *picture researcher*, but in some publishing houses the terms are applied to clearly different positions. Whatever the actual name given to the position, picture researchers always act as "editors" in one basic sense—by selecting and rejecting pictures from the large assortment which only they, not the project director, have seen.

WHAT SHOULD A PICTURE RESEARCHER KNOW?

Publishers and other users of pictures demand an almost limitless range of subject matter. The broader the picture researcher's general knowledge, therefore, the better he or she can serve an employer or client. Clearly, a picture researcher needs a good background in the liberal arts. Especially important is familiarity with political, cultural, and scientific history, because research for almost anything but an up-to-date news feature or sociology text means dealing with historical materials.

Good visual taste, or an eye for pictures, is difficult to define but is essential in this profession. Another necessity is an accurate memory for visual images (the ability to pair a photo in hand with one seen several years previously, in order to form a striking comparison on the page, for example). Imagination plays a vital part in helping a researcher visualize fresh uses for pictures remembered from the past.

Imaginatively choosing precisely the right picture depends partly on the researcher's understanding of the function the picture is to fill in its particular context. A picture on a record cover or book jacket is chosen primarily *to sell*, to attract a browser's attention and interest at first sight; it must be eye-catching. In a textbook or manual, an illustration may be used *to inform*, to supplement the text by clarifying factual descriptions or instructions; it should be clear, above all other considerations. Aesthetic standards, always important, come to the fore when illustrations are used in their simplest function, *to decorate*, to give pleasure to the viewer. In countless contemporary books, magazines, posters, films, and exhibitions, pictures are chosen *to persuade* (to act, as William Ivins wrote, as "tools in the struggles of opinion"), to convince the viewer of the dangers of pollution, the reality of starvation, the desirability of a political candidate, or the attractions of travel; the researcher must choose pictures that have the desired emotional impact. Some of the obvious and subtle ways in which photographs can be selected to carry emotional messages are described in Wilson Hicks' classic on photojournalism, *Words and Pictures* (New York, Arno Press, 1973), and in parts of *Photographic Communication* (New York, Hastings House, 1972), an anthology edited by R. Smith Schuneman.

When working on such large-scale projects as a picture book on American social history, for example, a researcher must choose from vast quantities of material. Common sense, therefore, must be added to taste, memory, and imagination as a necessary attribute for anyone embarking on picture research as a career, for the biggest problem is often in deciding what should be stressed and what avenues are not worth pursuing.

The choice of pictures may sometimes be so wide that it seems almost overwhelming. When illustrating a nineteenth-century subject, for example, a researcher can choose wood engravings from newspapers, reproductions of paintings, lithographed cartoons, daguerreotype portraits or other original photographs made from glass-plate negatives. The wide range of visual materials available for the four centuries before photography came into general use is indicated in *Sources of Illustration 1500–1900*, by Hilary and Mary Evans (New York, Hastings House, 1972). Another summary issued by the same publisher is *A History of Visual Communication* by Josef Muller-Brockmann. Among the immense number of images available to the modern researcher are reproductions of paintings, drawings, and other original art, including sculpture, pottery, mosaics, murals, stained glass windows, architectural details, tapestries and other needlework, and even cave art and graffiti. Not to be overlooked are the millions of images available in advertisements, postcards, cartoons, comic strips, calendars, posters, greeting and trade cards, maps, manuscripts, postage stamps, wallpaper, engineering and architectural plans, even stock certificates and currency. These items tend to be housed in separate collections in museums or libraries, and sometimes they offer illustrations that are more original than those in standard "picture" collections.

Different printmaking techniques should be familiar to a picture researcher, who has to know enough about a print to judge if it will be effective when reproduced. Prints can be made from wood, metal, stone, or silk screens. The nature of these materials and the way in which they are worked (cut away in relief with a chisel-like tool, engraved with a sharply pointed burin, etched away with acid, coated with grease and ink, or inked through a stencil) give each type of print a distinctive character. A fifteenth-century woodcut with thick lines may be reduced to very small size without loss of detail, but it will look unattractively crude if enlarged too much. The fine lines and stipples of an eighteenth-century steel engraving, however, can be considerably enlarged. Crayon lithographs originally printed in color may look fuzzy and muddy when reproduced as black-and-white illustrations, unless special care is taken.

Woodcuts, engravings, etchings, lithographs, and silk-screen prints of various kinds are well described in *Sources of Illustration*, mentioned above, and in many other books on the graphic arts, including Gabor Peterdi's *Printmaking: Methods Old and New* (rev. ed., New York, Macmillan, 1971); Gottfried Lindemann's *Prints and Drawings: A Pictorial History* (New York, Praeger, 1970); John Petrina's *Art Works: How Produced, How Reproduced* (Freeport, N.Y., Books For Libraries, 1970); and *The Complete Printmaker* by John Ross and Clare Romano (New York, Free Press, 1972). One of the best simple introductions, available in paperback, is *How Prints Look* (Boston, Beacon Press, 1964) by William M. Ivins, Jr., former curator of prints at the Metropolitan Museum of Art and author of other useful books, including *Prints and Visual Communication* (New York, Da Capo Press, 1969). Another brief, good guide from the Metropolitan Museum is *Guide to the Collections: Prints*, edited by A. Hyatt Mayer (New York, 1964). *A Guide to the Collecting and Care of Original Prints*, by Carl Zigrosser and Christa M. Gaehde, sponsored by the Print Council of America (New York, Crown, 1969), contains a useful glossary of terms related to printmaking.

Photographs—the pictures now most in demand by publishers and other users—are available in almost as many formats as the artworks described above. They range from nineteenth-century ambrotypes and tintypes, through movie stills, to X rays, multiple-flash stroboscopic photographs, and composite views of earth as seen from satellites hundreds of miles away.

Whatever the medium of the pictures being researched, beware of the simple expedient of copying them from the pages of books or periodicals! This approach is full of technical and legal pitfalls.

A woodcut, etching, or engraving can, if care is taken, be reproduced from the pages of an old book or periodical with little loss in quality. But photographs, printed by the halftone process (broken down through a fine screen into tiny dots to obtain gradations of tone), can seldom be well reproduced from the printed page. In any case, most photographs published in the twentieth century will be illegal to reproduce because they are still protected by copyright; permission must be obtained and, frequently, a reproduction rights fee paid.

Only if a picture is in the public domain and not copyrighted can it simply be reproduced without permission. Government-sponsored art and photography, for example, is generally free of restrictions; but pictures published in books or magazines are covered by that publication's copyright and require permission. The copyright law has recently been revised (see "Copyrights, Patents, Trademarks, and Trade Secrets," page 599), but a safe rule of thumb is to assume that no illustration may be copied without permission unless the publication it is in dates from 1921 or earlier. Exceptions to this rule are the books of old illustrations and designs recently issued by Dover Publications, carrying a specific statement that a certain number of images may be reproduced or copied without permission.

Illustrations published in the earlier years of the twentieth century were often photographed or engraved specifically for the book or periodical in which they appeared; credit lines naming an outside source rarely occur. In these cases, the picture researcher's first approach must be to the publisher—who may no longer be in business. A great deal of detective work may be required before the researcher can discover whether the original artwork, photographic prints, or negatives still exist, and where they may be found. Clearly, the original, authentic version of any picture is always the researcher's goal. When this cannot be reached, and when there is no copyright problem involved in copying a picture from a publication, the picture researcher has to exercise judgment to decide whether the published illustration is sharp enough for reproduction.

The desirability of finding a picture in its original form is obvious: with each intervening process, the picture loses some of its original quality. For example, an old engraving made from a drawn copy of a painting or tapestry should never be used if the museum now housing the original artwork will instead provide a good modern photograph of the object itself. A *Harper's Weekly* wood engraving of a Civil War scene will have less impact than the Mathew Brady photograph from which it was copied. A World War I photograph published as a halftone, and copied from the printed page, would be an extremely poor substitute for a modern photograph made from the original negative, or one made from a copy negative derived from an original, unscreened photographic print.

Today readers expect illustrations to be as accurate and carefully researched as written material. We have come a long way from the early years of book illustration, when one woodcut of a city or of a crowned man could be published many times as a symbolic illustra-

tion of different places or kings. The ability to distinguish between authentic period pictures and later re-creations is an important part of the picture researcher's skill. By today's standards, it may be better to leave a historical event unillustrated rather than publish an anachronistic picture purporting to be of the original event (Victorian paintings of the landing of the Pilgrim Fathers, for example).

Contemporary pictures of every historical subject do not exist, of course, much as picture researchers would wish it. And when contemporary illustrations do exist, they are not always reliable as sources of information. There are said to be no authentic portraits of Shakespeare's contemporary, Christopher Marlowe; and no one will ever be quite sure what the interior of the Parthenon originally looked like. A picture researcher can never state positively that a specific picture does not exist, but can assume on the basis of knowledge and experience that its existence is unlikely. A basic knowledge of the history of photography, as well as of art history, is essential for a professional picture researcher, who cannot afford to waste time groping in the wrong direction. A professional must know, before looking, which events and people may be impossible to document through photographs, for example, and which will have to be illustrated by prints or other types of pictures.

The technical limitations of photography in the years immediately after its invention in 1839 restricted early photographers to making static portraits, architectural views, scenic landscapes and still lifes. Nineteenth-century photographic plates had to be exposed for too long a time to catch any movement. The Crimean War and the U.S. Civil War mark only the beginning of documentary photography, and picture researchers must be ready for unrealistic editors (they exist) who demand "real action shots" of either of these conflicts. Until the 1880's, news photographs continued to be translated into wood engravings for the purpose of publication. Not until the halftone printing process was invented could actual photographs appear in the pages of newspapers and magazines.

Commercial photo services, such as the pioneering Bain News Service, appeared in New York soon after the turn of the century. They supplied newspapers and magazines with current photographs of celebrities and politicians, presidential activities, political upheavals around the world, inventions, and sports events. Photography began to be used as a journalist's tool for social protest. Cameramen such as Jacob Riis and Lewis Hine recorded the desperate poverty of immigrants, the hard lives of coal miners and steel-mill workers, the degradation of child labor. Today's wire services and modern photojournalists follow the lead of these pioneering photographers.

The number of books on the history of photography increases every year. The three most useful general histories are Beaumont Newhall's *The History of Photography from 1839 to the Present Day* (New York, Museum of Modern Art, 1964); *The History of Photography 1685–1914: From the Camera Obscura to the Beginning of the Modern Era* (New York, McGraw-Hill, 1969), by Helmut and Alison Gernsheim; and Peter Pollack's *The Picture History of Photography from the Earliest Beginnings to the Present Day* (New

York, Harry N. Abrams, 1969). Also of interest are Michael Braive's *The Photograph: A Social History* (New York, McGraw-Hill, 1966), and Robert Taft's *Photography and the American Scene: A Social History 1839–1889* (New York, Dover, 1964), originally published in 1938. There are other books on special types of photographs (daguerreotypes, stereographs), on distinct subjects (photographs of war, landscapes), on photojournalism, and on the art of photography. Among the best recent books are the 18 volumes in the Life Library of Photography issued by Time-Life Books (New York, 1971, 1972): specifically recommended for picture researchers are the four volumes *Great Photographers; Documentary Photography; Photojournalism;* and *The Great Themes.*

HOW TO FIND THE RIGHT SOURCE

Faced with a challenging problem in picture searching, the more homework a researcher can do, the more time he or she can save when looking through actual files of prints and photographs out in the field. How can a researcher learn in advance about the possible pictures available on any given subject, and where they are located?

The usefulness of the *Picture Sources 3* directory, published in 1975 by the Special Libraries Association, is obvious (it has a particularly helpful subject index, through which you can find pictures of anything from Abolitionists and Abu Simbel to Zinc and Zuni Indians; it also has geographical and alphabetical indexes of sources). Another SLA publication, a bibliography compiled by Renata V. Shaw (*Picture Searching: Techniques and Tools,* 1973), lists nearly 500 reference books useful to picture researchers. Professional picture researchers use these two books to supplement their own general knowledge and experience and to lead them to illustrated publications as well as to specific collections of visual material.

A useful guide to collections is Lee Ash's *Subject Collections* (New York, R. R. Bowker, 1967), a guide to university, public, and special libraries holding special collections of books (and pictures) on specific subjects. Some collections of photographs and prints (mainly commercial) are listed in the annual *Literary Market Place, Writer's Market,* and *Photography Market Place* directories issued by R. R. Bowker of New York. The membership list of the American Society of Magazine Photographers offers a geographic list of members, with a one-line summary of each person's specialities. In New York City, the *Manhattan Yellow Pages* includes listings for "Photographers," "Photographers' Agencies," "Photographs, Stock," "Picture Libraries," and "Press Photo Service." (The telephone directory should not be underestimated as a simple research tool. Particularly in New York City and Washington, D.C., a researcher who needs pictures of a foreign country or of a specific subject can often find a government information office, trade association, or small museum simply by turning to the key word in the white pages of the phone book.)

A more recommended method of research is to visit the library and consult a professional directory, encyclopedia, or other reference book. *Picture Sources 3* contains a broad cross section of picture collections in American and Canadian libraries, museums, universities, business companies, trade associations, professional societies, government departments, historical societies, chambers of commerce, and newspapers, but it does not include all such collections (some sources, acknowledging that they did hold collections of pictures, specifically asked not to be listed in *Picture Sources 3* for fear that they would be overwhelmed by the demand for their materials).

The subject index to the three-volume *Encyclopedia of Associations* (Detroit, Gale Research Co.) enables a researcher to locate trade associations and societies in all fields. If photographs of an industrial process or manufactured product are needed, a researcher may contact the public relations departments of large companies listed by industry in *Thomas' Register of Manufacturers.* Newspapers across the United States will often provide photographs of local personalities and news events for a moderate fee. These papers can be located geographically in N. W. Ayer's *Directory of Newspapers.* Other collections of pictures can be traced through the many directories of general and special museums, libraries, research centers, historical societies, religious and health organizations, foundations, government agencies, and so forth. For example, the *Museums Directory of the United States and Canada,* issued by the American Association of Museums, covers the entire range of museums—art, history, science, and special museums, as well as art centers and associations, historic houses and societies, aquariums, arboretums, botanical gardens, herbariums, planetariums, zoos, preservation projects, wildlife refuges, historic sites, and government-sponsored parks. This directory and others are described in a variety of general aids to library research, such as Constance Winchell's *Guide to Reference Books; The Reader's Adviser,* published by R. R. Bowker; Frances Neel Cheney's *Fundamental Reference Sources; The Research Handbook: A Guide to Reference Sources* by Adrian A. Paradis; *How and Where To Look It Up,* by Robert Murphy; and Robert B. Downs' *How To Do Library Research.*

Instead of looking for a specialized institution that may (or may not) be a source of pictures on a required subject, another approach is first to find the picture itself, by searching through illustrated books and periodicals. Find a published picture that you like (or one close to what is wanted), and look at the credit line to learn the name of the photographer, agency, or institution that supplied the picture to the publisher. You can then approach the cited source directly.

Periodical articles in all fields are indexed by subject (with a note on whether or not they are illustrated) in the invaluable *Reader's Guide to Periodical Literature* and its nineteenth-century forerunners. Some well-illustrated periodicals issue their own indexes (*American Heritage, Horizon, National Geographic, The New York Times,* for example). *Ulrich's Periodicals Directory* will lead a researcher to many small, highly specialized publications, whose editors may offer advice even if they are not able to provide pictures. Subject indexes to magazine articles in special fields are issued regularly: these include serial indexes for the fields of art, biography, business, education, social sciences and humanities, and applied science and technology.

Recently published illustrated books on any subject can be located through the subject index to *Books in Print* (issued annually by R. R. Bowker), older books through a library card catalog or published bibliography. Illustrated encyclopedias and dictionaries offer a good starting point for a picture researcher who wants to browse through a wide range of subjects, scanning credit lines. Picture sources are carefully acknowledged in the *Britannica, Collier's,* the *Americana,* and *Compton's;* and some of the encyclopedias for younger readers, such as the *World Book,* rely heavily on illustrations. Especially valuable are large reference works in a special field—such as the 15-volume *Encyclopedia of World Art* (New York, McGraw-Hill, 1959–1968) or the 6-volume *Picture Source Book for Social History* (London, Allen & Unwin, 1961) and the picture histories on subjects such as the performing arts, American labor, or the settlement of the American West.

In recent years, the practice of printing a credit line under or beside each illustration (or on a separate page at the front or back of the publication) has been observed with increasing punctiliousness. Clear, accurate credit lines benefit the picture researcher above all. In turn, the researcher has an obligation to make sure that a credit line is given for the new use, in legible typeface, and as accurately as possible. This is not an optional courtesy. Many government departments and travel offices, for example, which once gave away photos for free use with no restrictions, now insist on a compulsory credit line with specified wording. Some commercial photo stock houses double their reproduction-rights fee if their photo appears without a credit line, even if this omission happens through carelessness alone. Even when a credit line is not an explicit condition of use, a picture researcher today has a professional obligation to make sure that no picture is used without a proper acknowledgement to its source. This applies if the picture's use is free (usually indicated by the phrase *courtesy of*) or if the reproduction rights are purchased. Credit lines for illustrations should be given the same attention as acknowledgments for passages of text quoted from other books. Note also that it is not honest to change a picture by severely cropping it, tinting it, or using it as part of a photomontage without pointing out these changes to the reader in the credit line or caption; these practices are, moreover, sometimes explicitly forbidden by the supplier of the picture.

VISITING OR CONTACTING THE SOURCE

Once the best source for a needed picture has been identified, doing research in the files is not always as simple as it might sound. The organization of picture files is not consistent and is not even restricted to two or three major systems of filing (as is the case with books). Almost every picture collection organizes its prints and photographs and other visual materials in a unique system that best suits the retrieval needs of its own users. A picture researcher who visits the Museum of Modern Art or the International Museum of Photography at George Eastman House with a list of required subjects in nineteenth-century social history, for example, will find many photographs from that century but may be dismayed to learn that they are indexed primarily by name of photographer. Motion-picture stills in some collections may be filed only by the title of the film, not by subject or even by actor. Photographs in NASA's audiovisual branch are arranged by space-flight number. At the National Archives, historical materials are filed according to the government department or program to which they originally belonged. In all collections, color transparencies of various sizes will be stored away from black-and-white photographs, and there may well be separate filing areas for large posters and maps, valuable original engravings or drawings, cartoons, daguerreotypes, or stereographs.

In some collections, each individual picture is cataloged and indexed. In others (for example, at newspapers and wire services where time is at a premium), photographs are tossed by the hundred into folders or large boxes designating only the most obvious subject content.

One convenient aid to cataloging (where a catalog exists at all) is the use of cards that include a postage-stamp-size image of the indexed picture. These modern cards, unfortunately, are used in relatively few picture collections because of their expense. Another recent development is the use of microfilm or of microfiche cards to reproduce series of photographs; this miniaturization saves time for the researcher, saves space for the librarian, and saves some wear and tear on original materials. Image retrieval by computer is still in its earliest stages, although many picture collections in the United States are presently investigating the possibilities of automation.

Picture researchers need to understand the many differences in the organization and day-to-day operations of commercial sources, on one hand, and government departments, public libraries, historical societies, and private collections, on the other. Commercial picture agencies (whether they provide contemporary photographs or historical pictures) exist to make a profit by offering better and faster service than their competitors; they serve researchers as quickly and as well as possible, in return for a fee, and have no other functions. Government, noncommercial, and private collections are not in any position to offer immediate service, even when speed is important to the researcher. Frequently their function is primarily archival, and their pictures are organized for study purposes. Because they derive little or no financial profit from having their pictures published, they are not usually willing to fill long, varied request lists received by mail or telephone. These noncommercial sources seldom keep duplicate photographic prints on file, so researchers may be forced to wait for weeks while pictures are copied, captioned, and mailed. Even the largest government agencies, with immense collections of visual materials, may have no more than two or three reference librarians serving the public. This shortage of staff prevents most noncommercial sources from offering service in depth to individual researchers and from making editorial selections for out-of-town users.

Modern copying machines, which reproduce prints and photographs well enough for identification, have simplified long-distance communication between the picture researcher and the librarian or supplier. Whenever a researcher mails a request accompanied by a photocopy, the supplier's searching time is shortened and mistakes can be avoided. Experienced picture researchers always include a photocopy with their requests when they have a specific image in mind.

Even when a picture researcher is not certain that a particular picture actually exists, the request made to the possible source should be as specific as possible. As one commercial agency specializing in historical material pleads: "When you need a bespectacled country doctor on a white horse, please don't simply specify 'medicine.'"

CONCLUSION

Original research, even when it involves out-of-town travel to institutions housing the visual materials needed, is always worthwhile. The easier course of scanning publications and imitating the choices of an earlier picture researcher is never as effective as original research, largely because it leads to overuse of the same few illustrations. Culling information about picture sources from previously published books can offer a researcher interesting leads to follow, but it should never be used as a substitute for making fresh discoveries in untapped picture files.

The wish to save money is often the simple rationale for reusing previously published pictures. Photographic prints made from existing negatives are usually cheaper than pictures which have to be copied for the first time. And publishers who simply order pictures which they have seen published in books with detailed credit lines are able to save the cost of many hours of research and possibly of travel. Picture researchers should make every effort, however, to convince publishers and other users that there are benefits, in terms of prestige and sales, in bringing fresh material to an audience of increasing sophistication.

GRAPHIC ARTS PHOTOGRAPHY

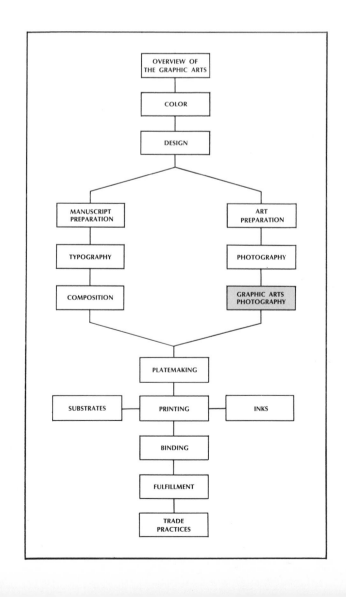

9

INTRODUCTION TO GRAPHIC ARTS PHOTOGRAPHY
Michael H. Bruno, GRAPHIC ARTS CONSULTANT

Graphic arts photography is the process by which original graphic images are transformed into film positives or negatives for use in making the majority of modern-day printing plates. Compared to other forms of photography that are more familiar to the layman, graphic arts photography is highly specialized, using special equipment and techniques. Most graphic arts photography is done in printing plants and by specialty firms serving the graphic arts trade. However, reproduction departments of large organizations that are handling more of their own printing are doing an increasing amount of graphic arts photography, although usually the simpler forms.

Graphic arts photography employs cameras, enlargers, and contact printing frames to expose film. Each of these is used at certain stages for specific situations. The principles of these three exposure systems, illustrated in figure 9.1, differ from each other essentially in the way light is passed from the light source to the film to be exposed. In the camera, light moves from the source to the copy being photographed and then through the lens system to the film. In an enlarger, the light passes through a film transparency (opaque copy cannot be used), through the lens, and to the film. In contact printing, the light passes from the source directly through a film negative or positive which is in tight contact with the film; no lens is used.

Of these three methods, the camera and enlarger are true photography techniques, using lens systems to enlarge or reduce images and focus them on the film. The contact technique is limited to producing same-size images.

BASIC PHOTOGRAPHIC PROCEDURE

Cameras and enlargers work on the same fundamental principles, but the camera is by far the prevalent photographic device used in graphic arts because it is the most flexible. Therefore, this discussion of procedures will be based on camera methods, with the understanding that enlarger techniques are similar.

The graphic arts camera, like other cameras, has a flat surface to hold the film and a lens to focus light rays onto the film. But it also has a third element, a copyboard with lights mounted to illuminate it. The original images to be photographed are mounted on this copyboard. Both the lens housing and the copyboard can be moved along a track on which the camera parts are mounted, which permits enlarging and reducing of original images.

Original images, commonly called *camera copy,* can be of many kinds. They can consist of type matter or illustrations. Illustrative material may be photographs, line drawings, sketches, watercolors, paintings, or a combination of these. These illustrations can be black-

on-white or in full color. Full-color illustrations can be either *reflection copy,* including opaque artwork and photographic prints, which are viewed by light reflected from them; or *transmission copy,* such as photographic transparencies, which are viewed by light transmitted through them.

All copy, even that supplied as finished mechanicals, should be checked thoroughly before production begins for clarity and sharpness, cleanliness, and freedom from blemishes and other defects. It is a well-known axiom that the end result of the photographic process cannot be any better than the original material, and more troubles probably originate with the copy than anywhere else. If new copy cannot be obtained to correct faults, then the faulty copy should be retouched by an artist to correct it.

The basic photographic process that is used in graphic arts is similar in principle to other types of photography. Copy to be photographed is placed on the copyboard of the camera, illuminated by high-intensity lights, and focused to the correct size on a ground glass in the back of the camera. Some process cameras have automatic focusing devices. Most have scales and slide rules that are used to indicate the position of the copyboard and lens planes for each magnification ratio and each lens.

The minimum distance between copy and film is four times the focal length of the lens, which is the position at same-size reproduction. At same-size, the distance between lens and copy is twice the focal length of the lens, as is the distance between the lens and the film. When making enlargements, the distance between lens and copy decreases and the distance between lens and film, or the *bellows extension,* increases; but the total distance is always greater than that at same-size. When making reductions, the distance between lens and copy increases while the bellows extension decreases. There are formulas for calculating these distances, but the scales and tables that are provided with the cameras eliminate the necessity for making the calculations. Focusing can also be done visually on the ground glass of the camera, but this method takes much longer. Usually the ground glass is used to check the size and sharpness of the image to make sure the scales have been set correctly.

After the image has been focused, the film is placed on the vacuum back of the camera, which is then put in place of the ground glass; the aperture is set on the lens; and the exposure is made through a solenoid-operated shutter which may be triggered manually using a stop watch or automatically by a timer, a light integrating meter, or one of the other devices described in "Exposure Controls" (page 331). After development, fixing, washing, and drying, the result is a negative which is reverse-reading on the emulsion side.

316

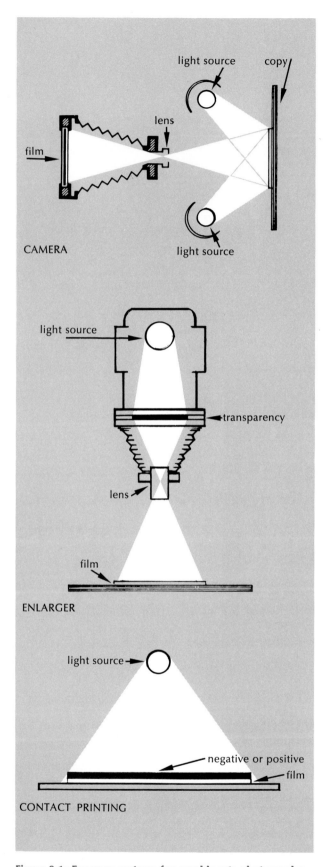

CAMERA

ENLARGER

CONTACT PRINTING

Figure 9.1: Exposure systems for graphic arts photography.

CONTACT PRINTING

Contact printing is a much simpler method of exposing photographic materials, compared to either camera or enlarger methods, but it is limited to making reverse or duplicate images in the same size as the original. Opaque copy cannot be used; only images such as photographic negatives and transparencies that are capable of transmitting light through them can be used as originals.

Contact positives are made by placing a negative on top of a sheet of unexposed film in a vacuum frame (page 323). Tight contact is maintained between the two pieces of film by exhausting the air from the space between the backing of the frame and its cover, a sheet of flawless plate glass. When the films are placed emulsion-to-emulsion, the image on the newly created positive will be straight-reading. If the positive must be reverse-reading, as required for *deep-etch* and some *bimetal* platemaking methods in lithography, the negative is placed with the emulsion side away from the unexposed film.

A point-source light is used for the exposure, which is timed accurately with a timing mechanism. The film development is controlled with targets such as the GATF Sensitivity Guide, the star target, and the dot gain scale. (See "What to Look For in the Proof," page 367, and "Quality Control Methods," page 439.)

LINE AND CONTINUOUS-TONE COPY

The basic photographic process just described is fully capable of translating some copy for graphic arts purposes, but additional techniques are required for other copy. The kind of copy that can be processed as described is known as *line* copy; the kind that requires other treatment is called *continuous-tone* copy.

Line copy includes any image which is made up of only two tones: a light tone and a dark tone. The lines of demarcation between the two tones are sharp; there is no blending or blurring of one tone into the other. Type, pen-and-ink drawings, and the like are typical line copy.

Continuous-tone copy includes all images which contain gradations or shadings between the dark and the light areas. Typically the various tones fade into one another gradually, as in photographs, watercolor illustrations, wash drawings, and paintings.

The problem which most printing processes present in reproducing these two types of material is their inability to apply ink to paper in a range of subtle gradations—ink must be either printed at full intensity or not printed at all. This causes no problem in reproducing line copy, but it requires that a special technique called the *halftone* process be used for continuous-tone material.

THE HALFTONE PROCESS

A halftone illustration actually is an optical illusion. It is printed as line material in such a way that it fools the human eye into seeing the tonal gradations that were in the original camera copy. A halftone is simply a pattern of dots, usually too small for the eye to see individually without the aid of a magnifying glass. A

Figure 9.2: Halftone illustration and enlarged portion showing halftone dots. *Photograph by Robert Goldman.*

halftone illustration has the same number of dots to the square inch throughout its area, but the dots vary in size, thus covering more or less of the lighter-colored paper in their assigned areas. The various ratios of light paper to dark areas in different parts of the illustration blend to create overall impressions to the eye of different shades, in effect simulating the original continuous tones of the copy. (See figure 9.2.)

This is all possible because of the poor resolving power of the eye. For example, at a distance of one-half mile two basketballs merge into one object, and at 200 yards two baseballs merge into one. Carrying this down to a reading distance of 10 to 12 inches, two points separated by 1/250 inch merge into one point.

Translating this into halftone images, a halftone with 125 dots to the linear inch (125-line screen) is just about at the edge of resolution for the normal eye.

Halftone photography is the procedure by which continuous-tone copy is converted into film negatives made up of halftone dots. The dots are created by placing a *halftone screen* in front of the film so that the light from the copy must pass through the screen. The screen converts the light reflected from the image into dots, each proportional in size to the amount of light reflected from its specific area on the copy. Light areas of the copy reflect more light through the screen to the film, resulting in larger black dots on the processed negative. Darker areas of the copy reflect

318

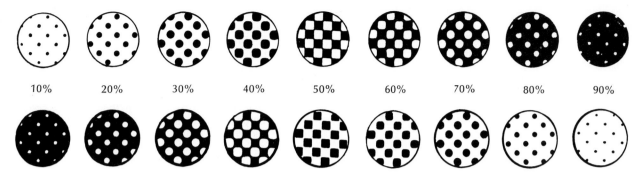

| 10% | 20% | 30% | 40% | 50% | 60% | 70% | 80% | 90% |

Figure 9.3: Diagram of halftone dots. The dots in the upper row are positive; those in the lower row are negative. *Courtesy of Graphic Arts Technical Foundation.*

less light, producing smaller black dots and larger clear areas on the negative.

Halftone screens can be either *glass screens,* which consist of crossed rules of straight lines, or *contact screens,* which have vignetted dots on a film base (see "Halftone Photography," page 342). They range in rulings from 65 lines to 300 or more lines to the inch depending on the printing process and the product. Newspapers printed by letterpress generally use 65-line to 85-line halftones. Newspapers printed

by offset lithography use 85-line to 100-line screens. Magazines and commercial printing by letterpress and lithography use 120-line to 150-line screens. Lithography is capable of printing much finer screen rulings than letterpress, and screens as fine as 300-line are sometimes used for color work. Gravure screens are different, and screen rulings are usually 150-line to 175-line, with some special screens as high as 300-line for line work.

The size of a halftone dot is expressed as a per-

Figure 9.4: Types of halftones: silhouette (left) and vignette.

centage, which represents the percentage of the dot matrix occupied by the dot. A 100% (*shadow*) dot is solid black, occupying the whole dot matrix. A 50% (*middletone*) dot occupies half the area of the matrix. A 10% (*highlight*) dot occupies one-tenth of the area. (See figure 9.3.)

There are a number of techniques for varying a conventional halftone to add interest to an illustration. Occasionally the highlight dots are deliberately dropped out of an illustration to heighten the appearance of white areas, such as a ribbon of light reflecting off a silver object. When this is done, the reproduction is known as a *dropout halftone*. Other types of special halftones with distinctive features can be created by altering the basic halftone camera techniques. Two of these are illustrated in figure 9.4.

COLOR REPRODUCTION

A large proportion of graphic arts production involves the reproduction of color subjects, such as drawings, paintings, photographs, or transparencies. Until the theory of three-color vision was adapted to color reproduction about 1900, as many as 15 or 20 separate printings were used to reproduce paintings and other color subjects. Most color reproduction now is done in the three subtractive primary colors—yellow, magenta, and cyan—with black and sometimes an additional color, such as pink to enhance flesh tones.

The original subject is photographed through light filters corresponding to the additive primaries of light—red, green, and blue—to produce three separation films, the one photographed through the red filter becoming the cyan printer, the one through the green filter becoming the magenta printer, and the one through the blue filter producing the yellow printer. (See "Color and Light," page 14, and "Color Reproduction," page 346.) Because of deficiencies in the printing inks,

corrections must be made in the separation films and a fourth printing with black ink must be introduced to make the grays neutral. The corrections can be done by hand in a process called *dot etching*, they can be made photographically using masks, or they can be prepared electronically using elaborate and expensive electronic scanners.

One facet of halftone printing that applies specifically to color reproduction is the use of *screen angles*. In process-color printing, the dots of different colors must print in a fixed pattern on the sheet. To eliminate objectionable patterns, known as *moiré*, the screened images for the four colors are printed at specified angles to one another (see page 347).

NEW TRENDS

Because of their speed, accuracy, and reproducibility, scanners have been used increasingly, not only for color separation and correction but also for computerized image-processing prepress systems in which complete page makeups and full signature layouts are made without the use of intermediate film. Systems are being developed which will go directly from the original copy to the final printing plate without the use of cameras or film. Another innovation in graphic arts equipment is the laser camera, such as the AM International-ECRM Autokon 8400. With the laser camera, text, line art, and single-color halftone illustrations in 65-line, 85-line, or 100-line can be made in negative or positive and straight-reading or reverse-reading form, and images can be tilted or distorted controllably. Also being developed are nonsilver films which can be exposed by lasers and do not require processing. These new trends can conceivably change the whole concept of photography and convert it to an all-electronic computer-assisted system not requiring the use of conventional cameras, intermediate films, or processing.

PHOTOGRAPHIC EQUIPMENT

Michael H. Bruno, GRAPHIC ARTS CONSULTANT

The equipment used in graphic arts photography is highly specialized. It consists of cameras, lenses, screens, exposure controls, pin register systems, lights, filters, and vacuum frames. Most of these subjects are covered in this article; others (automatic exposure controls, pin register systems, and light sources) are discussed in separate articles.

CAMERAS

Graphic arts photography is done on large cameras with suspension systems to eliminate the effects of

vibration on the images because long exposures are used, in comparison with amateur or commercial photography. Like an ordinary camera, a process camera consists of a lens, shutter, bellows, and film back. In addition it has a copy holder, which can hold transparencies or reflection copy; a screen holder, if a glass screen is used; high-intensity lights to illuminate the subject to be photographed; and a suspension frame which ties all the units together and eliminates the effects of vibration.

Cameras can be either horizontal or vertical. In horizontal cameras, the copy-lens-film axis is a horizontal

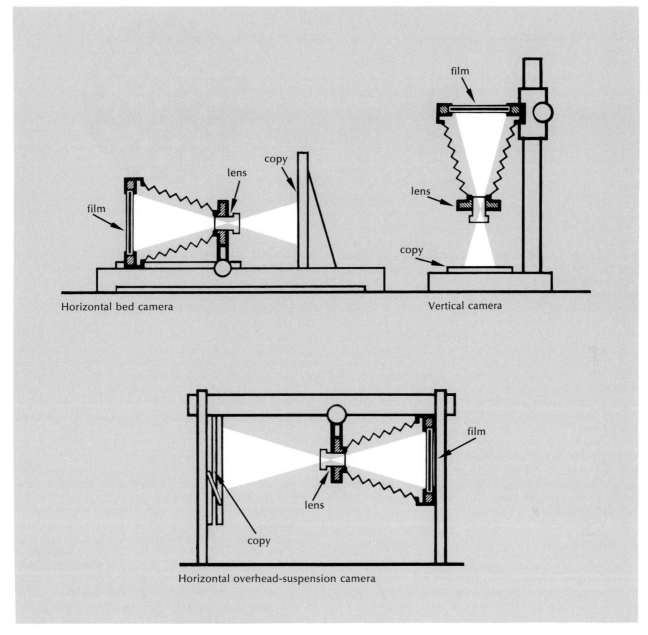

film

copy

lens

Horizontal bed camera

film

lens

copy

Vertical camera

copy

lens

film

Horizontal overhead-suspension camera

Figure 9.5: Types of graphic arts cameras.

line; in vertical cameras, this line is vertical, with the film usually at the top of the camera and the copy at the bottom. Horizontal cameras may have *bed* or *overhead suspension*; both types are shown in figure 9.5. Vertical types take less space.

Cameras can be either *gallery* or *darkroom* types. Gallery types, which are located in the camera room, must have light-tight backs and use special light-tight film holders like commercial cameras. Darkroom cameras are by far more practical and popular. In this type, the copyboard, lens, and bellows are in the camera room, while the camera back is usually built into the darkroom wall and therefore does not have to be light-tight. Enlargers are also used, especially for direct-screen color separations (see page 356). Many of

these enlargers are equipped with elaborate exposure controls (see page 331) that compute the proper exposure for each separation negative.

LENSES

Lenses for process work are highly specialized and must be built to very rigid specifications. They must be color corrected, or *apochromatic*. They should be coated to reduce flare and are usually of symmetrical design to eliminate distortion in the images. (See figure 9.6.) Because of the requirements for high resolution and minimum aberrations, process lenses have fairly small maximum apertures—from $f/8$ to $f/11$. In comparison, 35mm cameras have lenses with apertures of

321

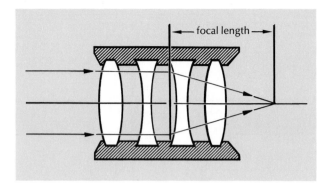

Figure 9.6: Construction of a thick lens.

Figure 9.7: Enlarged photograph of a crossline screen. *Courtesy of Graphic Arts Technical Foundation.*

f/1.4, f/2, f/2.8, and so forth. (The smaller the number, the larger the lens opening: an aperture of f/1.4 lets in twice as much light as f/2; f/8 lets in twice as much light as f/11.) Focal lengths range from 8 inches for wide-angle lenses for a 20-inch camera to as long as 48 inches for a 40-inch camera; 35mm cameras have lenses with focal lengths of 50mm, or about 2 inches. Some cameras use prisms for reversing the image laterally, as is required for photoengraving. There are special anamorphic lenses which can distort images in one dimension without affecting the other dimension.

Camera flare results in images with less contrast, especially in the shadow areas, and fine line fill-in or high fog in background areas. It is due to internal reflection in the lens and stray light in the camera system. Coated lens elements eliminate the flare from the lens. To eliminate stray light within the camera, the camera room should be painted a flat dull black or dark gray; a gray background should be used on the copyboard, and all shiny or reflecting surfaces should be eliminated from the camera. Kodak and GATF have both published tests for camera flare.

HALFTONE SCREENS

Halftone screens are used to convert continuous-tone images to halftones, in which the image is broken up into small image elements each having the same density and spacing but varying in area. (See "Introduction to Graphic Arts Photography," page 316.) The spacing of the elements, or *dots*, as they are known, is of the order of 65 to 300 lines per inch—designated as 65 l.–300 l.

There are two types of halftone screens in use: *glass crossline screens* and *contact screens*. The invention of the modern halftone process using a glass crossline screen is generally credited to Frederick E. Ives of Philadelphia who developed the method in 1886 and Max Levy who perfected a way of making the screen in 1891. Others had made halftones previously but Ives and Levy were the first to make them successfully and consistently. The glass crossline screen consists of two sheets of glass, each ruled with parallel lines which are approximately equal in width to the spaces between them, cemented together so that the lines are at right angles to each other (fig. 9.7.) The number of lines per inch is termed the *screen ruling*. Newspapers printed by letterpress commonly use screens with

rulings of 65 to 85 lines per inch, while those printed by offset lithography employ screens with rulings from 85 to 100 lines per inch. For many magazines and much commercial printing by both letterpress and offset lithography, screen rulings today are between 120 and 150 lines per inch. A 133-line halftone is just beyond the resolving power of the eye at normal reading distance, which is about 125 lines per inch. Screens with finer rulings are generally used for printing on coated papers and for special effects.

Contact screens are now more widely used than crossline screens. The contact screen is on film base and is made from a glass screen. It consists of vignetted dot elements with variable density across each dot, all with equal spacing corresponding to the ruling of the glass screen from which it is made (fig. 9.8). There are gray screens, in which the dots consist of the silver images developed in the screen after exposure, development, and fixing. There are also dyed screens, usually magenta, in which dye-coupling development is used and the silver in the dots is replaced by magenta dye. In addition to the conventional square dot screens, there are special screens such as the *chain dot* screen which has elliptical dots and the *Respi* screen in which the highlight dots have double the spacing of the middletone and shadow dots. (See figure 9.9.)

As a general rule, the finer the screen ruling the sharper the rendition of detail in the reproduction

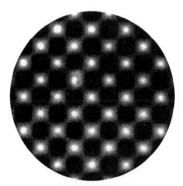

Figure 9.8: Enlarged photograph of a contact screen. *Courtesy of Graphics Arts Technical Foundation.*

322

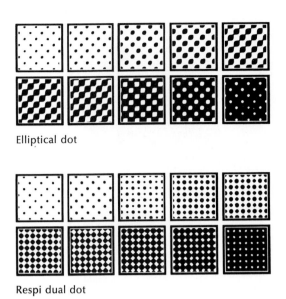

Elliptical dot

Respi dual dot

Figure 9.9: Halftone dot shapes. *Courtesy of Graphic Arts Technical Foundation.*

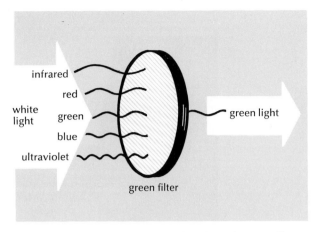

Figure 9.10: Diagram of light passing through green filter.

Usually there is little advantage, however, in using a screen finer than 150 lines per inch for a black-and-white or single-color reproduction, because there is a minimum dot size that can be printed in the light tones or *highlights* of the reproduction and, with finer screens, the step from the white of the paper to the first printed dot is too great and tone reproduction in the highlight areas suffers. This can be avoided, however, by using a Respi screen, which drops out the intermediate dots in the highlights, so a 200-line screen produces highlights equivalent to a 100-line screen while the rest of the picture is similar to a 200-line screen. In color reproduction, the finer the screen the purer the colors because more of the image is covered with ink and the graying effect created by the white paper is reduced.

FILTERS

Filters are thin sheets of dyed gelatin or colored glass which are placed in front of the lens on the camera or in the filter slot in the lens mounting and which transmit light of certain colors while absorbing light of other colors. There are some specially coated glass filters known as dichroic filters that are used for special purposes. A filter never changes the color of the light. It allows a part of some colors in the light to pass through and stops the other colors. A green filter appears green when it is held in the path of white light because it transmits green light to the eye and absorbs the red and blue light. This is illustrated in figure 9.10. All filters absorb some of the light which strikes them, so that the exposures must be longer than when no filter is used.

Because filters have some thickness, they can distort the image if the thickness is not the same throughout. In cases where split exposures are used, as in color separation and masking, if the filters are not exactly the same thickness there can be some displacement and/or distortion of the image. A special type of filter manufactured by Kodak, the Wratten Photomechanical Filter, is specially selected with very close color and thickness tolerances.

There are two basic uses of filters in photography. First, filters are used to emphasize or de-emphasize tonal areas in making black-and-white pictures. A yellow filter may be used, for example, to emphasize clouds in a sky or a green filter to drop out green areas in a reproduction. Secondly, red, green, and blue filters are used in making color separations for color reproduction. Special filters are used for masks and for making the black printer. (See "Color Reproduction," page 346.)

Each of the two uses of filters requires a different method of calculating the correct exposure. The first is based on *filter factors*; the second is based on *filter ratios*.

The filter factor is a number such as *2* or *4* which indicates the number of times the exposure without a filter must be increased when the filter is used. This information is usually contained in the instructions which come with the film.

The filter ratio is used for color-separation photography. The correct exposure for the red-filter negative is first determined by trial or by the use of an exposure index. When this has been determined, the correct exposure for the other filters is calculated directly by multiplying the red-filter exposure by the appropriate filter ratio for each of the other filters as stated on the film instruction sheet. For color-separation work, filter ratios are expressed for negatives developed to the same contrast. If different contrasts are desired, as for direct-screen exposures, the filter factors are modified to compensate for the differences in contrast.

Filter factors and filter ratios are dependent on illumination and the color temperature of the light, so light integrators are almost an absolute necessity in controlling exposures.

VACUUM FRAMES

Vacuum frames are used in photography for contact printing and in platemaking for exposing film assem-

Figure 9.11: Vacuum frame holding a flat. *Courtesy of Eastman Kodak Company.*

blies, or flats, to printing plates. A vacuum printing frame usually consists of two wooden or metal frames, one of which holds a corrugated or channeled rubber blanket and the other a sheet of flawless plate glass (fig. 9.11). Often a special "water white" glass is used which transmits more ultraviolet light than ordinary glass. In the smaller sizes the two frames are generally hinged together on one side. The rubber blanket is connected to a vacuum pump by a flexible rubber hose. In photography, flat perforated metal slabs similar to the vacuum back of a camera are sometimes used; vacuum is established between the exposing surfaces by placing a sheet of transparent plastic over the frame and exhausting the air between the plastic and the perforated metal slab.

When an ordinary printing frame is open, the blanket frame is horizontal and the glass is raised up out of the way. The light-sensitive surface is laid on the blanket, coated side up. When films are used they are usually backed by heavy cardboard or metal plates so the ribbed blanket does not pull the film away from the negative or positive. The negative or positive to be exposed is laid on the sensitive surface with the two emulsion sides facing each other. The glass frame is lowered and the two frames are locked together. The vacuum pump is turned on. Air is exhausted from between the blanket and the glass until a vacuum of about 25 inches is recorded on the vacuum gauge (30

inches of vacuum is considered a perfect vacuum at sea level). This is no guarantee that the vacuum between the sensitive surface and the film is at this level, as air can leak between the blanket gasket and the glass if the gasket is not in good condition and if parts of the film or masking paper protrude beyond the gasket. The frame should be checked periodically for such leaks. After proper vacuum has been achieved, the exposing light is turned on to produce the proper exposure. In photography, a timer is usually used for the exposure. In platemaking, usually because of the longer exposures, a light integrating meter is used to control the exposure.

Generally in contact printing and in plate exposure as exact an image as possible is desired; therefore, a point source of light is used at a reasonable distance so that the exposure is fairly even over the surface of the film. In special cases where spread or sharpened images (usually called "fats" and "skinnies") and unsharp masks are required, broad light sources, film separators, and sometimes even rotating frames are used to get the desired effect. Because undercutting of the image (fig. 9.12) is possible if contact between the exposing surfaces is not good, it is recommended that either the exposing light be shielded so that it only covers the exposure area, or that the walls around the vacuum frame be painted a matte black so no light will reflect from the walls and undercut the image.

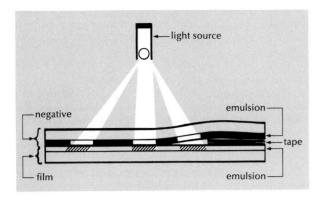

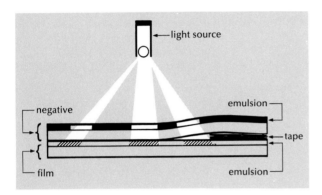

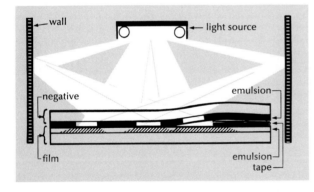

Figure 9.12: Undercutting in film exposure. Undercutting occurs when light rays creep in slightly beneath the edge of the image on the negative emulsion and create a wider image on the unexposed film. Undercutting is caused by light traveling through the negative to the film emulsion at an oblique or non-perpendicular angle. To minimize undercutting, a point-source light should be used and the emulsion on the negative should be in direct and as perfect contact as possible with the emulsion on the unexposed film. These conditions are shown correctly at the left and center in the top diagram. The right side of this diagram shows improper use of stripping tape, which is positioned too close to the negative image area, lifting it out of contact with the film. The middle diagram shows incorrect positioning of film and negative emulsions as well as improper use of tape; the negative is positioned with the emulsion up, out of contact with the film. The bottom diagram illustrates undercutting from a broad light source with light rays reflecting from wall surfaces; undercutting here is especially serious when contact is reduced by poor stripping, thick tape, poor contact, and so on.

SAFELIGHTS

The function of a safelight (fig. 9.13) is to illuminate the darkroom by transmitting a maximum of the visible light to which the photographic material is least sensitive. With color-blind films, an orange or red safelight can be used. Orthochromatic films can be used with a red safelight. A ruby bulb should never be used because many of them transmit some green light to which orthochromatic films are sensitive. With panchromatic materials, which are sensitive to all colors of light, it is best not to use any safelight at all. A good photographer should know his darkroom so well that he can get around it in total darkness. Darkrooms should be as light-tight as possible and should be painted white or a very light green so that, when safelights can be used, as much illumination as possible is obtained without fogging the film.

Any photographic material will fog if left long enough under safelight illumination. This is not necessarily because the safelight transmits any light it should not, but because even blue-sensitive or color-blind materials have some sensitivity to green, yellow, and red light. This sensitivity is not sufficient to be useful in photography, but is enough to cause fog with prolonged exposure to a safelight, especially after the normal exposure is made in the camera. This is particularly true in halftone exposures. The size of a halftone dot is determined by the amount of exposure it receives, and the slight additional exposure from the safelight may be sufficient to enlarge the dot and cause fog in the areas between the dots.

A good test for the effect of safelight exposure on halftones is to expose an even halftone tint of about 25% to 30% on a film in total darkness. The film is placed on a bench and a portion of it masked off with an opaque object like a coin. The safelight is turned on for several minutes and the film is developed. The effect, if any, of the safelight exposure will be shown by an enlarged pattern in the unprotected areas.

Figure 9.13: Darkroom illuminated by a safelight. *Courtesy of Eastman Kodak Company.*

AUTOKON 8400 LASER CAMERA

The Autokon 8400 laser camera is an electronic optical system produced by AM International-ECRM. It reproduces many kinds of copy: continuous-tone and screened photographs, original and screened artwork, typographic material, and combinations of these. In this system, laser light beams scan the original and record its features on treated reproduction paper or film, which must be processed. In some cases the Autokon enhances the quality of the original in much the same way as an electronic scanner using unsharp masking. It cannot reproduce colors but can render color originals in black, white, and gray tones.

The Autokon's capabilities are:

• It can produce line copy and control its quality.

• It can produce 65-, 85-, and 100-line screened halftone copies and can control and vary tone reproduction, sharpness, and overall quality.

• It can control and vary the size and shape of line or halftone copy by overall magnification or reduction and by anamorphic (one direction or unequal) magnification or reduction.

• It can enhance the sharpness and quality of many types of pictures for publication or display.

• It can produce any kind of copy in one or more of four modes: positive, reverse (negative correct image), negative (negative mirror image), and flop (positive mirror image).

The user can choose and adjust each of these effects by controls on a main control panel.

The Autokon camera has found considerable use in newspapers and has been introduced into in-plant shops. When the camera has 150-line capability, it will find considerable application in magazine, book, and commercial printing.

PHOTOGRAPHIC FILMS

The following information on films has been adapted from the Kodak publication "Photographic Materials for the Graphic Arts" and is used with permission of the Eastman Kodak Company.

Generally speaking, photographic films are made up of several layers of extremely thin, carefully coated materials. The essential layers are illustrated in figure 9.14. The photographic films used in the graphic arts are similar to those used in other types of photography, with the exception that there are a number of special types of *emulsions* used in preparing the films.

EMULSION

Most photographic emulsions are suspensions of silver salts (usually a mixture of halides such as chlorides, bromides, and iodides) in gelatin by themselves or blended with other polymers. Special sensitizers and dyes are added to control the speed and color sensitivity of the emulsions, and emulsions must be ripened and washed before coating. Making the emulsion is a very involved and intricate operation in which not only the composition and purity of the ingredients is important, but also the time, temperature, and other atmospheric conditions. It is no wonder that the actual ingredients and operations are kept secret, and it is miraculous that emulsion lots duplicate each other as well as they do. A number of different emulsions are made for special uses. For gravure and indirect color-separation work where continuous-tone emulsions are used, the emulsions are usually the same as those for ordinary photography. For line, halftone, and direct-screen color-separation photography, special high-contrast emulsions are needed.

BASE

Film base is the transparent material which serves as the support for the various layers shown in the illustration. For many years, films for the graphic arts have been coated on what is known as *safety base*, which consists of either cellulose triacetate or cellulose acetate-butyrate. Polyester plastic, such as Estar, offers the best available dimensional stability in a flexible film support. This tough, uniform base is almost completely unaffected by changes in humidity, which cause most register troubles.

ANTIHALATION AND NONCURLING FEATURES

Light penetrating all the way through an emulsion may be reflected from the back of the base so that it strikes the emulsion again, causing *halation*, or spreading of light causing a blurred image. This effect is

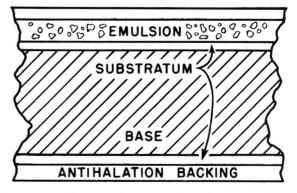

Figure 9.14: Diagram of cross section of a piece of film, showing essential layers.

particularly noticeable in areas of the negative representing excessively bright areas in the original copy. With graphic arts films, a light-absorbing material is incorporated into the backing layer, which then serves the double purpose of preventing both halation and curling of the film. The light-absorbing material is always bleached out, but the backing is not removed during processing.

COLOR SENSITIVITY OF FILMS

The photographic properties of a film determine the type of image obtained after exposure and processing. The kind of film used is selected for the type of image to be reproduced. Specifying such properties as color sensitivity, speed, and contrast usually narrows the choice of material to a few possibilities. The first consideration in the choice of a photographic film is usually the color sensitivity needed. In most cases, this is primarily a choice between the materials for use in black-and-white reproduction and those for color reproduction. The former have sensitivity to a few colors of light, while many of the latter are sensitive to all colors. The color sensitivity of each film is indicated by the "wedge spectrogram" shown on most of the data sheets accompanying the films. In these diagrams, the height of the clear area indicates the relative sensitivity of the film to the various colors. Figure 9.15 shows wedge spectrograms representing three types of film sensitizing, and, for comparison, a wedge spectrogram representing the sensitivity of the human eye.

Blue-sensitive photographic materials record high negative densities for blue areas of the original and, in the final reproduction, render blues very light, and reds, yellows, and greens very dark. They are useful in such specialized work as copying black-and-white photographs; preparing positives for the gravure process; making positive masks, pre-masks, and principal masks for two-stage masking used in color reproduction; and making duplicate or contact halftones. Generally speaking, blue-sensitive emulsions are photographically slow, but they do have the advantage of a high tolerance to safelight illumination.

Orthochromatic films are not sensitive to red light and, therefore, render reds as very dark when reproduced. These materials are normally faster than blue-sensitive materials because they are sensitive to a wider

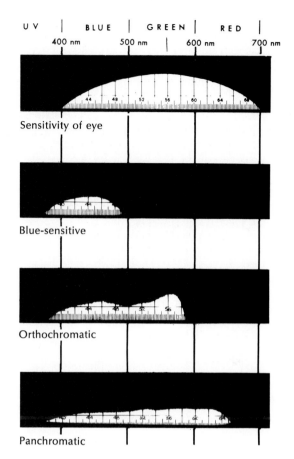

Figure 9.15: Wedge spectrograms representing three types of film sensitizing and, for comparison, the sensitivity of the human eye.

range of colors. Most graphic arts line and halftone films used on the camera fall in this category.

Panchromatic films are sensitive to all visible colors, as well as to ultraviolet light. They therefore give excellent monochromatic rendering of colored copy. In the graphic arts, panchromatic films are used in color reproduction for both transparency masking and camera-back masking and for making the color-separation negatives. Because of their wide sensitivity, these films must be handled in total darkness.

AUTOMATIC FILM PROCESSORS IN THE GRAPHIC ARTS
Ronald C. Gibson, LOGETRONICS, INC.

The essence of any efficient manufacturing process is control. In the graphic arts, the successful translation of the graphic designer's concepts into finished printing depends on the control of several manufacturing processes.

Photography is the first step in the photomechanical reproduction process and is the foundation on which subsequent steps depend. While no single process is more important than another, it is axiomatic that "it's got to be in the negative."

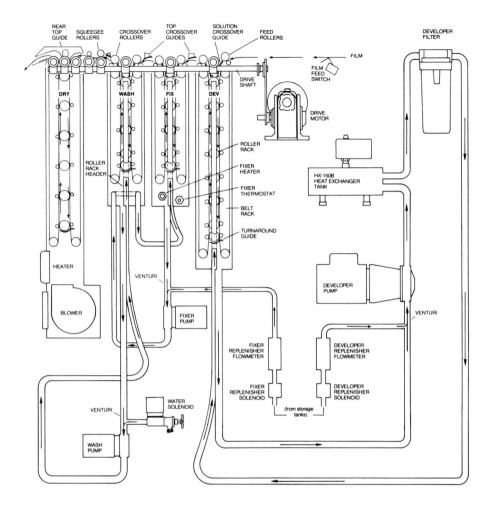

Figure 9.16: Diagram of Log-
Eflo LD-24AR film processor.

Before he had automatic processing equipment, the photographer had to process his film (develop, fix, wash, and dry it) in a ritual that requires experience, good judgment, and a fair amount of physical dexterity. To make his task harder, he had to do this either under darkroom safelight conditions, or, in the case of high-speed panchromatic film, in total darkness.

While engaged in processing film, the photographer could not get on with the real business of his highly skilled craft—the manipulation of his camera, the exposure of film, the creation of images. The photographer's efforts at the darkroom sink were concentrated on performing an essentially mechanical task, the achievement of a uniform, controlled process—just the kind of task best performed by machines.

The automatic graphic arts film processor is the tool which has enabled the prep department to deliver quality negatives consistently and with lower material and labor costs. A working definition of *automatic film processor* might be: a machine which accepts sheet or roll photographic material fed into it by an operator or automatic roll camera, and processes it through development, fixing, washing, and drying. The machine transports the material "dry-to-dry" without film hangers or other attachments to the film, and finally deposits it in a receiving tray. Figure 9.16 is a functional diagram of the LogEflo LD-24AR processor.

FILM PROCESSING

Film processing is a function of four interdependent parameters: *time, temperature, chemical activity* of processing solutions, and *agitation*—the movement of processing solutions over the film (emulsion) surface. A processor must control these parameters precisely, and it must transport material consistently through a series of processing stages at a controlled rate of speed.

Time

Transport speed determines the time that the film spends at each stage. The processor must have provision for transport speed adjustment because the time of development—the most critical stage—must be adjusted to suit the particular requirements of the film, chemistry, and the remaining control parameters.

Temperature

The processor must control the temperature of the processing solutions, particularly the developer, to within close tolerances. Variations in developer temperature of as little as 0.5°F can produce a visible difference in a camera halftone. Temperature control systems in general function on a principle whereby the solutions are alternately heated, usually by an electric heating element, and cooled, either by cool tap water

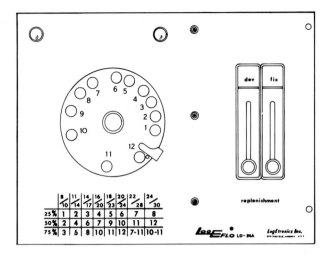

Figure 9.17: Dial replenishment system.

or by a refrigeration system, under the control of a sensitive thermostat.

Chemical activity

Maintenance of stable chemical activity in the processing solutions is accomplished by the addition of chemicals known as *replenishers*. The need for re-

plenishment is a function not only of the area of material processed, but also the amount of developed silver in the image.

The chemical manufacturer formulates his products to optimize the image quality of the film and to simplify the operational and monitoring techniques required of the processor operator to maintain stable chemical activity. From the processor design point of view, provision must be made to introduce the appropriate amounts of replenishing solutions. Processors employ several types of systems for replenishment.

The dial replenishment system illustrated in figure 9.17 is essentially an operator-controlled system. It consists of a dial-operated timer and a chart from which the operator selects a number on the basis of film size and percentage of exposure. The operator dials a number as each piece of film is fed into the processor. Replenishing solutions are introduced into the system for as long as the timer runs, at rates determined by the adjustable flow meters.

Replenishment systems which scan the processed film, measure the amount of density (developed silver) on the film, and replenish accordingly, are also available. One of these is used in the LogElasor II and is illustrated in figure 9.18. In this system, the film passes between a light head and a sensor head. As developed silver in the film reduces the amount of light received by the sensor, the integrator system samples the

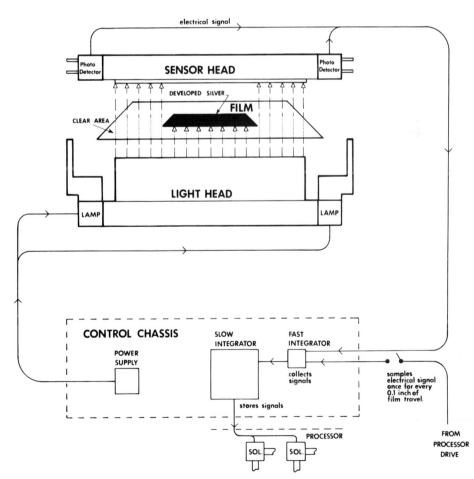

Figure 9.18: Diagram of Log-Elasor II automatic replenishment system.

changing signal level every 0.1 inch of film travel and stores the signal in the slow integrator. When a certain signal level is reached, replenishment occurs automatically.

Replenishment for processed film is not, however, the whole story. Lith developer is subject to chemical decomposition and oxidation by oxygen in the atmosphere. These effects are time-dependent and occur whether film is processed or not. When a large quantity of film is being processed and large volumes of replenisher are being added, the time-dependent decay factor is proportionately small and is effectively counteracted by conventional replenishment.

During periods of low-volume use or standby operation, however, the time-dependent deterioration becomes a significant problem. Replenisher of the conventional two-part type is formulated to combine with film-development by-products to reconstitute a balanced working developer in the processing tank. Without the by-products contributed by the film, however, two-part replenisher added to compensate for time-dependent decay has an unwanted, unbalancing effect. Diagnostic and technical skill on the part of the operator is then required to control the system.

To solve the time-dependent decay problem, several developer systems have been formulated with a three-part replenisher. The third solution, variously called *equalizer* or *oxidation replenisher*, is added either when the rate of use of replenisher for film falls below a predetermined level, or at timed intervals regardless of how much film is processed.

Automated devices which mix developer concentrates with water and add the equalizer on the required schedule have proven to be an effective and accurate means of delivering the replenisher to the developer tank. Especially important is the fact that the chemical elements of the replenisher which slowly oxidize the developing agent are kept separate until the moment they are mixed in the developer tank. In effect, fresh replenisher is mixed each time the system goes through a replenishment cycle.

Agitation

Agitation results from the effects of the mechanical elements transporting the film, and from the flow of the solutions as they are recirculated within the system. Processor designers place particular emphasis on achieving uniform agitation over the entire emulsion surface of the film.

HISTORY OF PROCESSORS

Today the automatic film processor is the indispensable tool of the modern graphic arts photographic and phototypesetting department. Several processor manufacturers produce a wide variety of models designed for special and multipurpose applications, but it was only in the late 1950's that the pioneers in graphic arts film processing tackled what was then, and is still today, the most challenging task—the machine processing of high contrast lith film, and, most difficult of all, of original halftones.

Early processors were· modifications of photostat or X-ray film processing machines. In 1957, the Haloid-

Xerox Lithoflo processor was introduced, the first designed specifically for graphic arts film. It employed the roller/belt film transport principle and would accept leaderless sheets of cut film up to 20 inches wide. The Lithoflo had three wet tanks with a water jacket around the developer tank for temperature control—optional at extra cost! No provision was made for recirculation or agitation of the developer. Film exited into a wash tray for conventional air drying.

By 1964, this machine, now known as the LogEflo processor, had built-in systems to control temperature, chemistry, and developing time more accurately than had been achieved up to that time.

Despite widespread skepticism, these machines were surprisingly successful even though the chemicals then available, designed for tray use, were unstable, and films were not pre-hardened to withstand the effects of mechanical transport. But these early successes were clearly recognized as the harbingers of a mechanical revolution in the darkroom. Stable chemistries were designed that were capable of remaining in good condition for several months with replenishment. Films having physical and chemical characteristics ideally suited to mechanical processing in replenishable chemistries were also developed.

The final element which required attention from the film and chemistry manufacturers was the development of a monitoring technique by which the processor operator could measure the activity of the processing solutions, especially the developer. Today, most monitoring systems consist of processing a *control strip* under consistent time and temperature conditions. A control strip is a piece of film, pre-exposed by the film manufacturer with a graduated series of exposures. After processing, specific target densities on the strips are measured with a densitometer, and the result is compared with standard values. Density shifts correlate with changes in developer activity and become the basis for adjustment of the replenishing system.

Reliance on automatic film processors as a means of increasing production and reducing materials waste has paralleled the growth of the printing industry in general, and lithography and photocomposition in particular. From the early concept of an all-purpose machine, the trend, more recently, has been to design machines for specialized applications. These include machines to process the output of photocomposition equipment, wide machines for contact work and reprographic films, and continuous-tone processors for color-separation work. Among more recent developments are shallow-tank machines, which operate at higher solution temperatures and are known as "rapid access" processors because of their short dry-to-dry times, about 90 seconds.

Despite our "working definition," strictly speaking there is no such thing as a truly automatic film processor. As with even the most "space-age" automated systems, the machine must be programmed. Optimum processing conditions must be established and· the machine's controls appropriately adjusted. Once properly programmed, however, the film processor is a tool which frees the photographer to concentrate on what he does best and which multiplies the effectiveness of his efforts.

EXPOSURE CONTROLS

Leo Lehrer, LEO LEHRER ASSOCIATES; PRES., GRAPHIC ARTS AND SCIENCES CO.

In order to control the photographic process, it is essential that all phases of exposure and film processing be controlled to a very close tolerance. If the photographer controls his exposure to plus or minus one-half of one percent and does not control his processor to the same degree, his accuracy will be based on the weakest link in the chain.

Because of electrical power shortages which cause brownouts throughout the United States and the rest of the world, the camera, contact room, and plate room have run into severe make-over problems which have increased operation and material costs considerably. This electric power reduction affects the exposures on sensitized material in two ways: first, by reducing the volume of light, and second, by a shift in color temperature of the light. All sensitized materials used in the graphic arts have a narrow color sensitivity band and respond only to that portion of light to which the products are sensitive.

LIGHT INTEGRATORS

Both of these problems can be overcome by the use of a light integrator (fig. 9.19) with a phototube sensitive to the ultraviolet, blue, green and red bands (3000 to 7000 angstrom units). With a phototube that has this sensitivity, one can match the filter to the sensitivity of the material being used. This compensates for color shifts and volume of light, thus delivering consistent exposures, reducing make-overs and material costs, and resulting in a general upgrading of quality.

In the case of offset plates, which are only sensitive to UV light from 3000 to 4000 angstroms, the light limiting filter transmitting only this portion of light could be used. Therefore, the phototube would only see the portion of light that the plate is sensitive to. A light integrator is needed because UV light is beyond the visible spectrum and it would be almost impossible to detect light changes visually. In fact, if one looked through the black light filter, everything would appear a deep purple-black.

Light integrators for exposure control in the contact room can also match the sensitivity of the photo material being used. In recent years contact film has increased in popularity, since it can be handled in yellow light, making the handling of contact flats easier. Contact films are just blue-sensitive or color-blind. The use of a blue filter similar to the 47 B in the phototube would not only monitor voltage reductions or increases, but also compensate for color temperature changes, which influence the exposure to a great extent. This could also be applied to direct or indirect color separations. With the use of the proper filters on the phototube, the complete exposure system could be monitored.

EXPOSURE COMPUTERS

There are several exposure computers on the market today for use on the camera, the point light source, and enlargers. The mathematical functions on all these computers are the same; the approaches are different. There are three basic approaches.

One exposure system relies on an independent densitometer. The operator independently takes the density readings, marks them on a *control sheet* or on the back of the copy, and then manually dials these densities directly into the exposure computer. The phototube on this computer monitors light fluctuation and the density dial shifts the exposure on the new copy density and copy range.

The second type of exposure computer has its own densitometer built into the reflection, transmission, or photometer system (fig. 9.20). It is an integral part of the exposure-control system. The operator merely puts

Figure 9.19: EMPCO SM-1 Luxometer mini light integrator with phototube. This integrator with solid-state construction has digital timing dials and is used on plate frames, point light source, and camera. It measures constant volume of light to be delivered to the sensitized material.

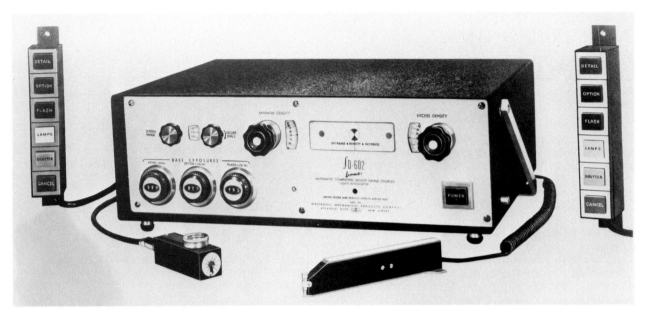

Figure 9.20: EMPCO SD-602 Luxometer exposure-control system. This system reads and feeds light and copy information to an analog computer. It handles three base exposures and screen range. Reflection probe, transmission density accessory, or photometer head may be plugged in.

the densitometer probe on the highlight of the copy, presses a button, and nulls the needle; and automatically the highlight density information is fed to the computer. The operator repeats this procedure in the maximum density area. During the exposure, information from the phototube and density information is assimilated into the computer section of the exposure-control system.

Several of the exposure-control systems supply extra memory banks so more screens, separations, or masking operations can be programmed. One system, which feeds directly into the console, also has an LED (light emitting diode), which displays actual exposure or actual density and shows the progress of the exposures. It also has a system for automatic programming, while holding 19 preprogrammed exposure systems. For flat copy or reflection copy, a reflection probe is used. For transmission copy, such as transparencies, negative or positive separations, or masks, a transmission unit is used, and for reading densities on an enlarger easel, a photometer is used.

A third system, manufactured by Graphic Technology, is a portable battery-operated unit that combines a densitometer with an exposure computer. It converts log E densities to log E time, displaying the exposure information on a ½-inch LCD (liquid crystal display). By going directly to exposure time, it eliminates a step in the process and the expense of a separate computer and densitometer. The unit is compatible with all existing cameras on the market and can be moved from one camera to another. Because it does not require any electrical hookup, it works independently of the camera's electrical system, which uses its own timers.

To use the system, the operator puts a probe on the highlight of the photograph, reads the correct exposure, and then repeats the same operation in the shadow of the photograph. The system can be programmed for halftones, duotones, posterization, line conversions, and positive or negative screens. It can also be used for color-separation exposures.

CONTROLLING DEVELOPER ACTIVITY

Another problem as important as control of exposure is control of development. Even with automatic film processors, constant developer activity must be maintained carefully. Systems used to monitor or measure developer activity are described in "Automatic Film Processors in the Graphic Arts," page 327.

PRINCIPLES OF PIN REGISTER

Harold Sigler, PRINTING TECHNIQUES INTERNATIONAL, INC.

The following article has been adapted from a paper given at an annual meeting of the Technical Association of the Graphic Arts and is used with the permission of TAGA.

For color and close-fitting work, register is **very** important. In the past, positives were used extensively, and most registering of image elements was done visually, using tape to hold the elements together. Now with the development of pin register systems these are used almost exclusively for registering.

REGISTER THEORY

All registration techniques in the graphic arts can be reduced to a common base: the methods of locating a plane in space. These are illustrated in figure 9.21.

Elementary solid geometry theorems state that a plane can be located in space by either two intersecting lines or three non-collinear points. The cases are really identical since two intersecting lines can be drawn through the three points.

The principle of redundancy illustrated on the right of figure 9.21 is an undesirable condition. The analogy shown is a three-legged stool and an ordinary chair with one short leg. The problem is to find a stable location for the seat in both cases.

In the case of the stool, even if each leg is not quite equal to the other, the stool seat becomes firmly set in space once the three legs are set upon the ground. This occurs even if the ground is uneven. Dairy farmers have known this for years.

The chair is quite another matter. Since there is one short leg, there are two different positions the seat can occupy if the legs are set on a level surface. If all the legs were unequal, there would be four possible positions that the seat can occupy in space. Clearly the fourth leg of the chair is causing a problem because it is redundant.

The consequences of a redundant system are obvious. Unless extreme care is exercised to control dimensions, mechanical instability results. A corollary of this is: to design a mechanical system with maximum stability, a minimum of redundant features must be employed.

EDGE REGISTER

Edge register is usually employed for rigid bodies such as glass plates or for situations in which other locational methods would require damaging the body, as in paper feeds for presses.

The two geometric theorems previously discussed adequately cover edge register. Either the two lines or the three points are located on the plane (such as the feed board of the press). The body to be registered is placed upon that plane and forced against the lines or points to produce an accurate location in space.

In practice the two lines are straight edges of bars. The bars are usually set at right angles to each other in their plane for maximum accuracy. They should be almost as long as the edge of the body they are to locate.

Three points are also generally arranged so that two lines drawn through them will create a right angle. Ideally they should be placed as far apart as possible.

The preceding makes three assumptions about the bodies to be registered:

1. Their control edges are at perfect right angles to each other.

2. Their two control edges are perfectly straight.

3. The bodies are rigid and will not buckle under a force parallel to the control plane.

These three assumptions are never completely true, and therefore it has become necessary to consider another method of registration when more accuracy is required and especially for flexible materials. For this we employ the principle of redundancy.

BODY OR PIN REGISTER

For the purpose of this discussion, we shall assume that we have already established a plane in which the registration should take place. All we wish to do is to locate a flat sheet on this plane. This is a common situation in contact printing or on a camera back.

The illustration in figure 9.22 indicates that the flat sheet has three degrees of freedom as shown by the arrows. There are two degrees of freedom by translation both in the x and y directions and one degree of freedom in the rotational direction. Once we have removed all the degrees of freedom, the sheet will be firmly located in the reference plane.

Suppose we punch a round hole in the sheet and

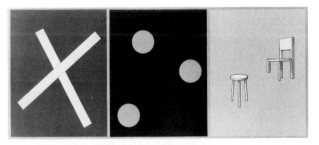

Figure 9.21: Register theory: the location of a plane in space. From left, two intersecting lines, three non-collinear points, principle of redundancy.

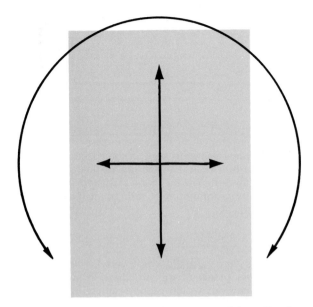

Figure 9.22: Body register for flexible materials. A flat sheet has three degrees of freedom, as indicated by arrows.

place it over a round tight-fitting pin. The sheet can now only rotate about the pin as shown in figure 9.23, thus removing two degrees of freedom. A second round hole (indicated by the dotted line) would result in redundancy and would require extreme accuracy to ensure that the center-to-center distance of the pins and the holes is exactly equal.

The correct solution, rather than using a second round hole, is to punch a slotted hole in the sheet, preferably with the slot pointing towards the round

Figure 9.23: Redundant system created by use of two round pins. The first pin (top) removes two degrees of freedom, allowing only rotational freedom (indicated by arrow). A second round pin (represented by dotted line) would also remove two degrees of freedom, resulting in a redundant system.

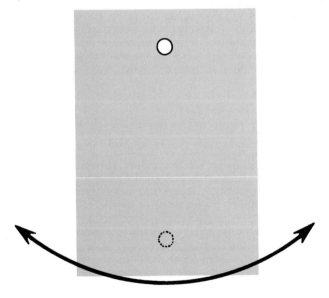

hole. A round pin inserted in the slot will remove only one degree of freedom. That would be the translational degree of freedom at right angles to the slot. This is a perfect, non-redundant system.

In actual practice, the contact pressure at the point where the round pin touches both edges of the slot may cause local buckling. It is preferable to increase the bearing surface by putting flats on the contact surfaces of the pin. Only a slight amount of redundancy is introduced, necessitating proper alignment of the direction of the slotted hole.

Unstable materials

Even polyester base materials show some size changes due to film processing, temperature changes, and humidity changes. The saving feature is that generally all sheets in a group to be registered have undergone the same ambient history and have either shrunk or expanded by approximately the same amount.

Example A in figure 9.24 shows the case covered in the preceding discussion. Note that if a 0.006-inch change occurred between the two holes, the error would be distributed proportionally between them.

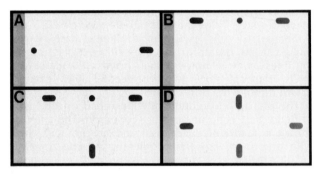

Figure 9.24: Hole configurations used in pin register.

This situation is generally used in camera-back and enlarger easels. For larger sheets of material, example B is preferable even at the expense of some redundancy since here the same 0.006 inch change will be split in two directions from the center resulting in only a 0.003 inch error to be distributed in two directions from center. Example C is usually used in stripping situations. The lower slotted hole is needed on large sheets to prevent buckling or "tail whip" when working in this area of the sheet. The most accurate and least redundant situation for unstable materials is shown in example D where four slotted holes point towards the center of the sheet. However, this configuration is usually not practical for the graphic arts and is generally only used for mapmaking or printed circuit applications.

Punches

A punch is required to produce holes in the same location from sheet to sheet. Figure 9.25 shows the punches used to produce the hole patterns shown in figure 9.24. Note that these punches have movable heads in addition to the fixed hole punches. The movable heads have the capability of being accurately repositioned to within 0.001 inch, if their spacing has

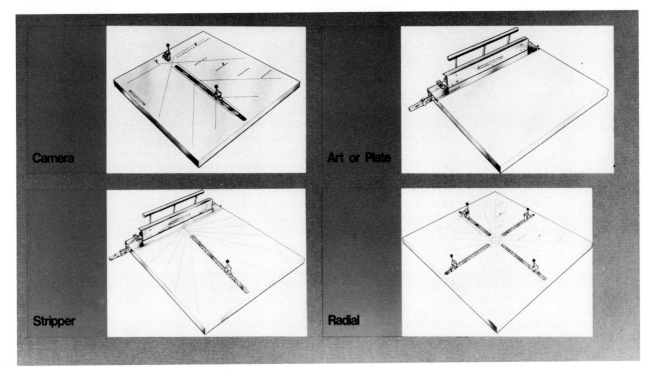

Figure 9.25: Types of general-purpose punches.

to be changed. The punches also feature centering devices which work as edge guides to approximately locate the hole pattern with respect to the sheet edge.

Pins

The types of pins available in one system are shown in figure 9.26. The round pin only fits round holes. The universal pin is a round pin which has been ground flat on two sides to match the width of a slotted hole. This latter pin will fit both round and slotted holes. It will also connect a round hole with a slotted hole for certain platemaking operations. The round pin prevents a sheet punched as in figure 9.24A from being rotated in its own plane 180° since it will not fit a slotted hole.

Figure 9.27 shows that these two types of pins are each available in a number of different heights depending upon the desired use. The longest are used for artwork, medium sizes for stripping, and shorter sizes for vacuum frame work.

Tabs

A tab is an externally attached hole. This device is used when a punch is not available. Sheets are matched to external pins on a stripping table after being regis-

Figure 9.26 (above): Types of pins. The round pin fits round holes only; the universal pin fits both round and slotted holes.

Figure 9.27 (right): Berkey-Ascor register pin sizes. Top row, regular 1/4" diameter round pins; bottom row, 1/4" diameter pins with 3/16" flats. Sizes range from super long to extra short.

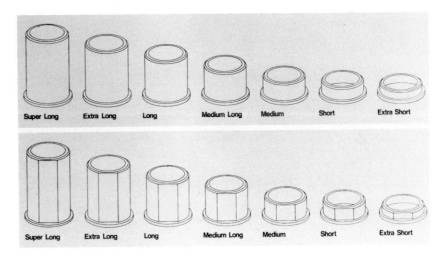

335

Figure 9.28: Berkey-Ascor register tabs. From left to right: regular ¼" round, ³/₁₆" x ⅜" horizontal slotted, ³/₁₆" x ⅜" vertical slotted. These are available in both plain and pressure-sensitive types.

tered visually. The resulting combination will pin register each sheet for subsequent operations. Figure 9.28 shows three different styles of tabs, each available in two types, for various situations.

Hole strengtheners

Another device quite often employed is the hole strengthener shown in figure 9.29. As its name implies, it is applied to reinforce a previously punched hole in a sheet that is to be used many times. The illustration shows two other applications: mounting a register pin to a smooth surface, and accurately locating an oversize hole to an existing register pin. The hand twist cutter shown can be used instead of a razor blade to create this slightly oversized hole.

AREAS OF USE FOR PIN REGISTER SYSTEMS

To be properly used, pin register systems should coordinate the various areas of a printing plant. This way the work performed in one area will automatically fit into the process being used in the subsequent area.

Copy preparation

Copy should be punched with a configuration shown in figure 9.24B. All overlays should be punched on the same unit before they are prepared. The overlay should be connected to the copy with pins and then the artist can make his dropout masks, mechanical color separations, etc. This procedure is much more accurate and faster than using tape hinges.

Camera

The copyboard of the camera should have pins mounted on it to match the hole spacing on the punched copy. Copy and/or overlays can be rapidly interchanged over the pins. The overlays are not as prone to mechanical damage as taped overlays since they are completely removed from the copyboard, not folded back.

The camera back should also have pins, but because there is an optical transfer the pin arrangement on the camera back does not have to match the system used on the copyboard. The ideal arrangement for camera back is shown in figure 9.24A. If only line shots are being made, the pins can be mounted on the camera back as in figure 9.29. If a contact screen is used, the pins must be retractable to prevent damage to the screen.

The camera film should be prepunched and placed on the pins prior to exposure. The resulting films are then automatically registered to each other for matching color plates or for surprints.

Stripping

Flats should be punched with a hole configuration shown in figure 9.24C. For simple black-and-white jobs, the film is located on the flat and a window is cut out. (See "Image Assembly," page 369.)

For color work or surprinting on one plate, the holes in the film are also used. Register pins are placed into the first-down film holes. When a matching flat is laid on top over the outer register pins in the flat, a hand twist cutter is used to cut holes in the flat around the

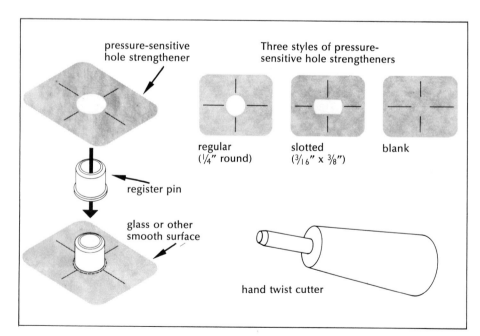

Figure 9.29: Hole strengtheners. In addition to reinforcing previously punched holes, strengtheners may be used for semipermanent mounting of register pins and for accurate fitting of a hole to an existing register pin.

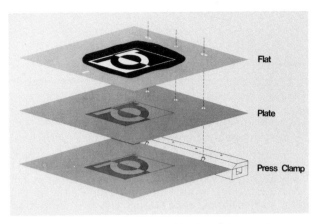

Figure 9.30: Departmental coordination. Pin register coordinates flat with plate and plate with press.

register pins in the film. The matching film is then laid onto these pins and taped to the flat. The films are now in register with respect to all the pinholes. The process is repeated for all matching films, so that all elements are registered and ready for platemaking.

Platemaking

Plates are generally punched with three round holes. These holes have the same center-to-center distances as the three in-line holes on the flat.

Figure 9.30 shows that the three round holes on the plate are aligned with the three in-line holes of the flat, using universal pins, for exposing the plate in the vacuum frame. The "tail hole" is not used because the flat will not buckle in the vacuum frame.

Press

As a final step two round pins are inserted in the press clamp to pick up the outer two holes on the plate. A removable pin or "register peg" is sometimes used when vertical clearance on the press is a problem.

This article has shown one typical system of completely coordinating an entire printing plant. Other systems are also available where special copy or production considerations dictate a different arrangement of holes.

SPECIAL-PURPOSE PUNCHES

While the preceding discussion has been centered on integrated systems of pin register, there are certain types of punches that can be considered to be out of the main flow of operations. Two of these are illustrated in figure 9.31.

The color-register punch is essentially the same as the camera punch shown in figure 9.25. The addition of the deep throat and the relocating pin plate allows an operator to take ganged separations or masks and repunch them in pin register. The relocating pin plate has the additional function of accurately controlling the center-to-center distance of the repunched holes.

The step-and-repeat punch will punch holes at any incremental distance controllable to 0.001 inch. Usually these holes are made in a strip of heavy-gauge Mylar. The Mylar is then pinned to a stepping template. Short register pins are inserted through the holes in the Mylar strip. These pins are used to position a masking sheet containing the desired master image. The image can then be stepped over a plate attached to the same stepping template. Any possible combination of steps or work-and-turns can be created.

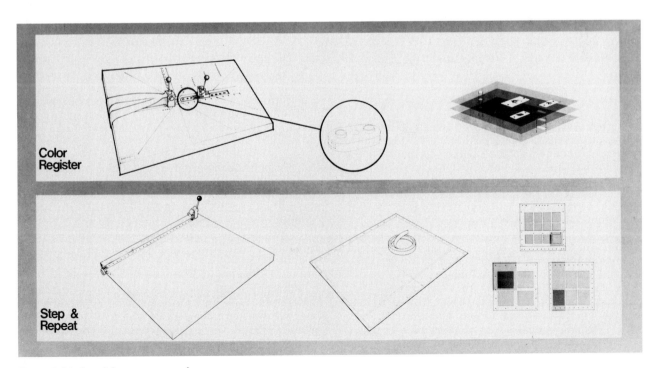

Figure 9.31: Special-purpose punches.

LIGHTS FOR PHOTOGRAPHY AND PLATEMAKING

Max Michalski, BERKEY TECHNICAL CO.

This article has been adapted from "What Every Printer Should Know About Graphic Arts Light Sources," published by Berkey Technical, a division of Berkey Photo, Inc.

Light did not become important in the graphic arts until the camera and photosensitive coatings and films came into use in the last century. Carbide gas lamps were used as the first light sources, but these were soon supplanted by carbon arc lamps, which remained the standard for the industry for many decades. Carbon arcs are still used, but in the last two decades major strides have been made in developing new and better kinds of light sources for graphic arts use. Today there are six major types of light sources in use, each offering its own special advantages.

GRAPHIC ARTS LIGHTING SYSTEMS

Before discussing specific kinds of light sources, however, an understanding of the basic kinds of lighting systems used in graphic arts is needed. A light source is only one part of the complete system—it generates the light. Other parts of the system include reflectors and other devices which concentrate light rays to greatly increase the efficiency with which the light is used. Graphic arts lighting systems are of four types:

• *Reflector systems,* in which the light source is placed within a reflector to bounce the light rays back in the direction of the object to be lit.

• *Diffusion systems,* in which the light is passed through a sheet of translucent material to scatter the light rays evenly across the sheet and remove excess glare at the center spot where the light source is located.

• *Condenser systems,* in which the light source is housed in a reflector that also has glass lenses called condensers mounted in the opening from which the light emanates to concentrate the light rays even more.

• *Special systems,* which are variations on the three basic schemes, such as a reflector housing with a long thin slit as its opening to provide exposure of thin lines along photosensitive materials.

Figure 9.32 shows examples of these types of lighting systems. These lighting systems are used in three major types of applications: camera lighting, enlarger lighting, and lighting for contact printing.

In camera lighting, the light travels from the lighting system to the copy to be photographed, and then through the camera lens to the film beyond. Most camera lighting is done with reflection systems where the light is projected onto the copy and then reflected back through the camera lens. However, color transparencies must be lit from the rear with the light shining through the transparency and then to the lens. For this, diffusion systems are used, usually a "light box" arrangement in which the light source is enclosed in a box with one side made of the translucent material.

Enlarger devices house the light source in a special unit, and the light travels through the film image and lens to reach the material being exposed. Most enlarger lighting systems are condenser types, but sometimes a diffusion system is used.

Contact printing is used in both the photographic darkroom and the platemaking room in printing plants. It consists of laying the film image directly on the material to be exposed, and then shining a light source on the sandwich. No enlarging or reductions are possible with contact printing. Reflector-type systems or a bare light source itself is used for contact printing. Generally the light source should be a *point-source* type—that is, all light should emanate from a single point, not a long tube or other type of bulb—to prevent undercutting of the image.

Other types of applications also use these various kinds of lighting systems. For example, transparency viewers used in offices for looking at color transparencies are usually a light-box style diffusion system, and the special slit-type lighting system is used in blueprint and diazo exposure machines to expose the material as it passes beneath the slit. Rotogravure cylinders also are exposed by means of slit-light systems.

EVALUATION OF LIGHT SOURCES

In evaluating light sources, a number of factors should be considered, including intensity, spectral energy distribution or color temperature, constancy of light output, evenness of illumination, efficiency, ease of operation and maintenance, and economy.

Intensity

Intensity is usually given in total lumen output. However, comparisons of light sources based on lumen output alone are not valid, since factors like color temperature and light fixture design determine the effectiveness of the light source and hence the exposure time. The best comparison is made by making performance tests on an equal and controlled basis.

Spectral energy distribution or color temperature

Each light source has a specific color temperature at which it is effective for a particular application because at that color temperature the light source gives off the optimum spectral energy distribution and level for that use. Some light sources can be used for many applications; however, this usually requires a compromise, and the performance in many of the appli-

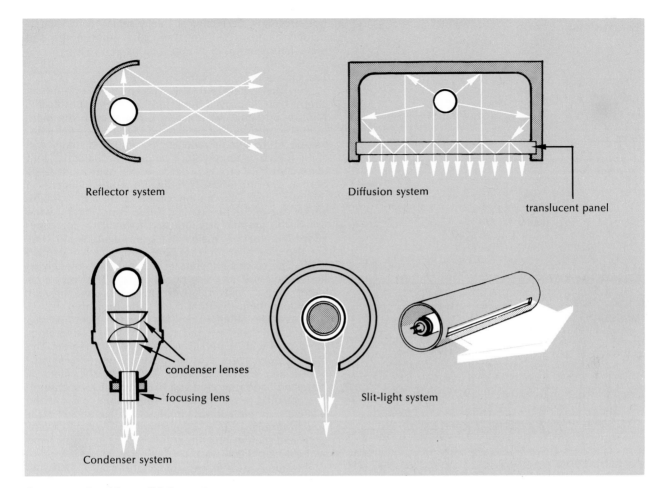

Reflector system

Diffusion system

translucent panel

condenser lenses

focusing lens

Condenser system

Slit-light system

Figure 9.32: Graphic arts lighting systems.

cations is marginal. Graphs of the spectral energy distribution of various graphic arts light sources are shown in figure 9.33.

Constancy of light output

Variation of light output with input voltage, color temperature change, lamp age, and other factors shoud be considered. Power-supply design and control circuitry are important in the performance of the light. If not properly designed, they allow kelvin temperature change and intensity change during exposures, resulting in inferior quality, particularly in color separation.

Evenness of illumination

Reflector and fixture design are important for maximum evenness of distribution of illumination across the copyboard, vacuum frame, or transparency stage.

Efficiency

The efficiency of the light source and the reflector design are of utmost importance in producing an efficiently performing light unit. Power-supply design with a good power factor resulting in low power consumption also contributes to the overall efficiency of the system.

Ease and economy of operation

Equipment should be reliable and easy to operate, clean, and service. The cost of operation includes power consumption, lamp life (lamp replacement), and maintenance costs; and these factors should be considered.

CHARACTERISTICS OF MAJOR LIGHT SOURCES

There are a number of light sources in use, including carbon arcs, tungsten and quartz-halogen lamps, pulsed xenon lamps, mercury lamps, fluorescent and cold cathode lamps, and metal halide lamps.

Carbon arcs

Carbon arcs were used for every application in the graphic arts. They have high efficiency (40 to 55 lumens per watt) and a high color temperature which can be varied by the inclusion of metal additives in the carbon core. However, carbon arcs cause many problems, such as unstable light output and color temperature, high maintenance cost (cleaning of fixtures and replacement of carbons), and the creation of fumes and dust in an area that must be as dust-free as possible. Other drawbacks are the necessity for a venting system and the potential fire hazard because of the open flame. Car-

339

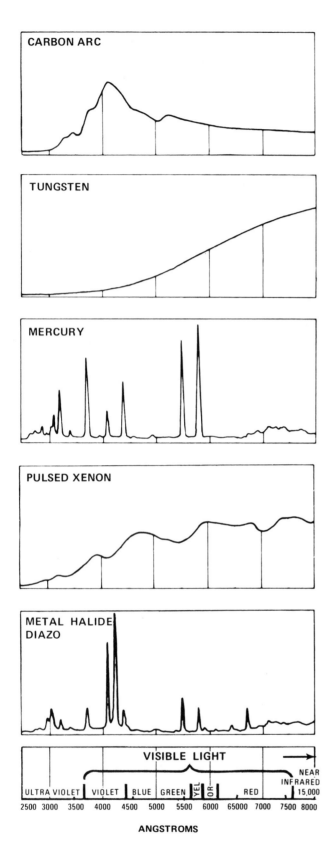

CARBON ARC

TUNGSTEN

MERCURY

PULSED XENON

METAL HALIDE
DIAZO

VISIBLE LIGHT

NEAR
INFRARED
15,000

ULTRA VIOLET | VIOLET | BLUE | GREEN | YEL | OR | RED

2500 3000 3500 4000 4500 5000 5500 6000 65000 7000 7500 8000

ANGSTROMS

Figure 9.33: Spectral energy distribution of various graphic arts light sources.

340

bon arcs have been almost totally replaced by quartz-halogen lamps, PXA lamps, mercury vapor lamps, and metal halide lamps in all applications.

Tungsten and quartz-halogen lamps

The quartz-halogen (also known as *quartz-iodine*) lamp is an improved tungsten or, more specifically, photoflood lamp. An inherent problem with the high-intensity tungsten lamps is rapid blackening of the envelope which greatly reduces the lamps' efficiency and shifts the color temperature output. The halogen lamp eliminates this problem because the quartz envelope permits the inclusion of iodine or other halogens to minimize the evaporation of the tungsten filament, which causes the blackening. These lamps have a wide use in the graphic arts industry, particularly for copy-board illumination, mainly black-and-white work. They are also used over small vacuum frames for film contact work. The color temperature of 2,800 to 3,400 kelvins limits their use in color photography. The low ultra-violet output, plus relatively low intensity, virtually eliminates their application for plate exposure.

Most of the radiation emitted is in the green, yellow, orange, red, and infrared range, and the lamp finds more uses with materials sensitive in that region. The main disadvantages are the great amount of heat produced and the short lamp life when the lamp is "boosted" and operated at a higher color temperature. The advantages are the lower initial lamp cost and the relatively simple control circuitry. The lamps are available in tubular form in a large variety of voltages, wattages, and dimensions, from the smallest 100-watt lamp to the largest 2,000-watt.

The luminous efficiency ranges from 20 lumens per watt for the low-color-temperature, long-life lamps and up to 32 lumens per watt for the lamps rated at 3,400 kelvins and 25-hour life.

Pulsed xenon (PXA) lamps

The pulsed xenon lamp was a joint G.E. and Berkey-Ascor development and was announced in 1958. The development was the outcome of the photographic electronic flash technique applied to repetitive flashing. The lamp is made of quartz tubing filled with low pressure xenon. It is flashed 120 times per second by means of capacitors which alternately charge and discharge electrical current through it. Although pulsed, the frequency is such that the light appears continuous. This produces a very efficient light source of 25 to 33 lumens per watt, depending on the lamp type used. One of the great advantages of the xenon lamp is its high color temperature (5,600 kelvins), instant start and stop, and constant color temperature.

The cost of the lamp is higher than the quartz-halogen lamp, but the lamp life is longer and ranges from 300 to 1,000 hours. The lamp is produced in tubular and helical form. The tubular lamps are used for copyboard lights and boxlights. The helical lamps are used for printing lamps and condenser enlarger light sources. The tubular lamps are made in 300-watt, 750-watt, 1,500-watt, and 3,000-watt types; the helical lamps range from 1,500-watt to 8,000-watt.

The spectral output of the xenon lamp is 5,600 kelvins—very close to standard daylight. This characteristic makes it ideal for color camera work. For printing applications, the lamp has had great success in spite of the relatively low blue and ultraviolet output. The advantages of cleanliness, instant stop and start, and reduction of maintenance time outweigh the disadvantages of heat and the longer exposures necessary with some materials.

Mercury lamps

This type of lamp contains mercury in a quartz envelope. When the current passes through the lamp, the mercury is vaporized and ionized, producing bluish-green light. The lamp requires about 2 to 5 minutes warm-up time before reaching full output. The lamp has a discontinuous or line spectrum, and its energy is concentrated in the blue-violet and ultraviolet regions. This precludes its use for color-separation work, but makes it highly efficient in exposing blue-sensitive emulsions, printing plates, and diazo materials. The lamps operate at a medium- to high-pressure range, and the cost of the lamps is about the same as the PXA lamps. Power supplies are of the self-regulating type and are quite economical in use and price. However, because of the warm-up time and the danger of the erythemal radiation, the lamps are used almost exclusively for diazo and blueprint applications where the light source is burning continuously and is contained in an enclosure. Another difficulty is that once the lamp is extinguished, the lamp has to cool down before it can be restarted. The lamp life is in the range of 1,000 to 2,000 hours, and its luminous efficiency is quite high—about 35 to 55 lumens per watt. The mercury lamps are available in linear and helical configurations of various wattages and are available from several large domestic and foreign lamp manufacturers.

Fluorescent and cold cathode lamps

Fluorescent and cold cathode lamps are actually mercury-vapor lamps with a coating of phosphors to reconvert the ultraviolet energy to visible light with high efficiency. Spectral output is dependent on the selection of the phosphors and can be varied to suit the application.

Another advantage of this type of lamp is low infrared output, which permits their use very close to the film or other materials which can be damaged by heat. White output lamps are used for enlarger and contact printing and some copyboard illumination. The lamps are available in various shapes and sizes. However, the light output per square inch is low, and it is impossible to obtain the kind of small, high-intensity light source that is required for most of the copyboard illumination and platemaking applications.

Metal halide lamps

This latest light source provides much shorter exposure times at lower power ratings when compared with the conventional light sources used up to now for platemaking, proofing, and other applications. Basically it is a mercury lamp with metal halide additives, and it provides greater output in the spectral range needed for these uses. It is a well-known fact that photosensitive materials have maximum spectral sensitivity in various regions of the ultraviolet, visible, and infrared

portions of the spectrum. This characteristic makes it desirable to adjust the energy output of the light source to match the maximum sensitivity of the material used.

The first practical application of the new metal halide lamp for graphic arts industry usage was the Ascor Addalux graphic arts light pioneered by Berkey Technical in cooperation with Sylvania Electric Products, Inc. The Addalux was introduced to the industry in November, 1967, and it has been used in all types of applications, including platemaking, proofing, photofabrication, screen printing, gravure, and many others, where it has replaced carbon arcs, pulsed xenon lamps, mercury lamps, and other light sources.

The problems of warm-up time and waiting time for cooling before restarting have been eliminated by operating the unit at standby condition so that the lamp is idling at a reduced power level. The light unit is equipped with a shutter which opens for the exposure; at the same time, the lamp is boosted to full power. This system provides a rapid start-and-stop control which is comparable to on-and-off control of other light sources.

The lamp operates at relatively low pressure and has an average lamp life at full power in excess of 500 hours. Its improved actinic efficiency permits operation at lower power, thereby reducing heat buildup on the vacuum frame. For all practical purposes, the metal halide lamp has 4 times more actinic output than the PXA lamp, 2 times more than the mercury lamp, and 2½ to 3 times more than the carbon arc, when compared on equal wattage bases.

Improved resolution and sharper line definition are obtainable with the metal halide light because of the more monochromatic light output of the lamp and improved reflector design.

Presently there are two types of metal halide lamps available—the diazo type, which output peaks at 4,170 Å, and the mercury lamp, which peaks at 3,650 Å. The lamps are interchangeable and can be used in the same equipment without modifications. The lamps require special power-supply ballast design, ignition circuit, and cooling for successful and practical operation.

In order to obtain maximum lamp life and safe operation, the lamp should be operated at its recommended loading. Some manufacturers design equipment to operate lamps well above the specified safe rating. This should be an important consideration when selecting and specifying lighting equipment.

CONCLUSION

The future of graphic arts lighting looks very promising. New, more efficient light sources are being developed and technology limits are being expanded with continuing research and development.

The trend is to develop more powerful light sources that are more closely matched to the sensitivity response of emulsions and coatings of various materials as used in the graphic arts industry. This will also result in development of specialized lighting equipment for use in complete systems as progress toward total automation is accelerated.

HALFTONE PHOTOGRAPHY
Michael H. Bruno, GRAPHIC ARTS CONSULTANT

Halftones can be made by a number of techniques, all of which vary with the type of screen used. The first type of screen used in halftone photography was the glass crossline screen, developed by F. E. Ives in 1886. In the 1940's, with the advent of high-quality plastics, however, plastic contact screens were developed which provide generally sharper and better results and are simpler to use. A third method of making halftones is the use of prescreened films and prints—materials which have screen patterns already built into them prior to photography.

GLASS-SCREEN PHOTOGRAPHY

Glass-screen halftones are made in a graphic arts camera equipped with a glass crossline screen mounted just in front of the camera back which holds the film. The light reflected from the copy passes through the lens and then through the screen to reach the film. The openings between the crossed lines in the screen act like tiny pinholes and produce patterns on the film which result in the exposure of dots. These dots are proportional in size to the amounts of light reflected from the corresponding areas of the copy. (See figure 9.34.)

Several theories have been developed over the years to explain the phenomenon of dot formation in dif-

ferent sizes on the film, but none has been proven conclusively. All of these theories arrive at the same result, however, and those results have been adequate to permit development of several systems of glass-screen photography, complete with special aperture controls for the camera.

Glass-screen photography is a complicated process which demands precision equipment, exceptional skills, and considerable care. The setting of the screen a certain distance in front of the film—called the *screen distance*—is especially critical and affects halftone contrast as well as dot shape and quality. The screen distance varies with the screen ruling and with the lens aperture and bellows extension of the camera. This distance is very small, less than one-fourth inch for a 133-line screen.

Once the camera is set up, photographing the copy usually involves several exposures, not just one. A halftone image can be obtained with a single exposure, but it will be inferior to a multiple-exposure product. There are three major multi-exposure systems: the one-stop, the two-stop, and the three-stop. The basic one-stop system actually uses two exposures, and two different *f*/stops for lens settings. One exposure is the normal recording of the picture on the film and is known as the *detail* exposure. The second exposure, known as the *flash*, is made with a much smaller lens opening by

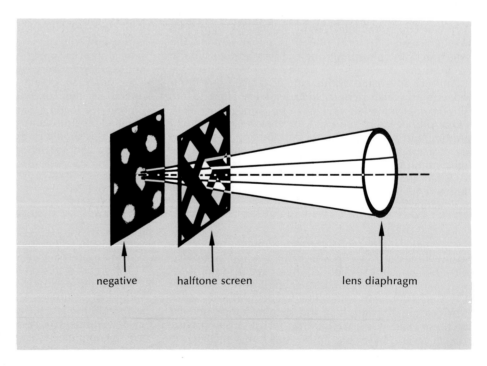

negative · halftone screen · lens diaphragm

Figure 9.34: Principle of halftone dot formation.

342

shining a small tungsten lamp into the lens or by photographing a well-lighted blank white sheet. The purpose of the flash exposure is to compensate for the inability of the main exposure to record the entire range of densities in the copy by ensuring that tiny highlight dots are formed in the shadow areas. This is accomplished without seriously affecting other tones.

The two-stop and three-stop systems build from the one-stop. In the three-stop system, two exposures are added to the first main exposure; the flash exposure is retained in addition. The three exposures can thus be used to record the shadow, middle, and highlight tones under conditions most suited to each. The two-stop method is used as a shortcut on copy without wide tonal ranges, which does not require three exposures to capture all of the tones. Exposures are determined in these systems mostly through trial and error for the particular equipment being used, and there are great differences of opinion among professionals as to which variations of these methods are best under what conditions.

Because of the complexity of the glass-screen systems of halftone photography, these have been almost entirely replaced with the contact-screen method in the United States and Canada.

CONTACT-SCREEN PHOTOGRAPHY

Halftone photography with a contact screen is much simpler than glass-screen techniques and requires much less skill. With this method, the screen is placed in direct contact with the film and pressed firmly in place during exposure. Because of this, contact-screen halftones can be made in a vacuum frame and on the bed of an enlarger as well as in a camera. In fact, it is this method that is used in making direct-screen halftones in the direct-screen color process (page 356). Some systems have even been developed for making contact-screen halftones on electronic color scanners and directly on printing plates.

A contact screen is different from a glass screen in that the contact-screen dots are vignetted while the glass-screen openings are crisply outlined clear squares between the lines. A vignetted dot has its greatest density at the center, and the density decreases from the center to the edge of the dot. Thus when film is exposed, varying amounts of light will be allowed through the openings between the dots on the screen; the stronger the light coming through the screen, the larger the dot that will be formed on the film. (See figure 9.35.)

In contact-screen halftones, the contrast of the reproduction can be varied within limits by means of multiple exposures as in glass-screen halftones, but generally fewer exposures are needed—one to three rather than two to four. One main exposure to record the copy is supplemented by a flash exposure to produce pinpoint dots in the shadows, and—when needed—by a third *no-screen, highlight,* or *bump* exposure to boost contrast and detail recorded in the highlight areas. The no-screen exposure is made by removing the screen during a short part of the exposure to the copy.

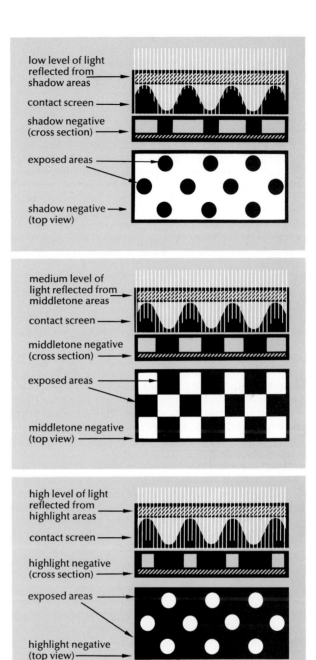

Figure 9.35: Principle of contact-screen photography.

With dyed screens, additional control over contrast is possible when different colored filters are used during part of the exposure. A yellow filter used with a magenta screen, for example, increases the contrast of the magenta-screen dot elements and thus decreases the contrast of the final reproduction. A magenta filter with a magenta screen has just the opposite effect. With these filters and dyed screens, a small difference in light will produce a large difference in dot size.

PRESCREENED FILM

The simplest way of producing halftones is with pre-screened film such as Kodak Autoscreen Ortho Film. When this is used properly in an ordinary camera, a 133-line halftone negative is produced directly without the use of a screen. Two exposures are necessary: (1) a detail exposure to the copy, and (2) a flash exposure with a flash lamp all over the film. The detail exposure produces dots of different sizes according to the amount of light reflected from the copy. The flash exposure insures that the inertia of the film is overcome and a dot is produced all over so that there will be adequate detail in the shadows. This is essentially the same purpose of the flash exposure in glass-screen and contact-screen photography. Autoscreen film requires less exposure and is capable of higher resolution, especially of type images, than glass or contact screens.

SCREENED PRINTS

There are two methods for producing screened prints directly in the camera. One is to use Kodak PMT Negative Paper with a contact screen. PMT is Kodak's new photomechanical transfer material that uses the diffusion transfer method for producing the image. It has many applications besides making screened prints. After exposure in the camera, the PMT Negative Paper is placed in contact with a Kodak PMT Receiver Paper and processed in a special diffusion transfer processor. The product is a screen print in the screen ruling of the contact screen used.

Another method is to use the Polaroid MP-4 Copy Camera System. This system comes with a selection of four screens, a special aperture control, and a high contrast print film which produces 4" x 5" screened prints in 15 seconds. This system also uses diffusion transfer to produce a positive correct-reading halftone in the screen ruling of the screen selected.

Screened prints are useful for pasting up with other copy to make a complete mechanical layout that can be photographed as a line shot in the camera, eliminating the need for stripping in the halftone negatives. This technique is used for printing newspapers, house organs, school annuals, and other types of work for which the quality requirements are not critical. (See "Screened Prints," page 291.)

DUOTONES

A duotone is a two-impression halftone image made from the same continuous-tone, black-and-white original, with each image recording different tonal ranges of the original. The main purpose of a duotone is to extend the tonal range of the reproduction so it comes closer to that obtained by a photograph. The tonal range in a photograph is often from a density of 0 to about 2.0 on a densitometer. Since densitometry is based on logarithms, this density difference is equivalent to a range of tones that vary in reflectance from about 100 to 1. Most combinations of printing inks and papers seldom produce density ranges higher than from 0 to 1.5 or 1.6, and producing this high a density usually requires very glossy surfaces like Kromekote or

Lusterkote and ink film thicknesses that have a great tendency to set off as they enter the delivery of the press. This range of tones from 0 to 1.5 or 1.6 is only equivalent to a range of reflectances of about 30 to 40 to 1. The addition of a second impression increases the shadow density so that the range of tones become equivalent to those in a photograph. Duotones are used mainly in letterpress and lithography. They are not needed in conventional gravure, as single-color prints have a tonal range equivalent to and exceeding photographic images without the danger of setoff because solvent inks are used and they are dried immediately after printing.

The most popular duotone at present is one that uses two black images to extend the tonal range of the reproduction to produce an image that simulates a conventional gravure print of an original. Duotones are also used to produce special effects by printing one of the halftones, usually the long-range one, in a lighter color that blends with the subject, such as blue for sky or seascapes, brown or green for landscapes, orange or tan for skin tones, etc.

The techniques for making duotones vary considerably. The most common technique uses two halftones of the same screen ruling with the key (darker or primary) halftone at a screen angle of 45° and the long-range or lighter one at a screen angle of 15° or 75° (30° from the key halftone). The key halftone has a full range of tones except that the shadow dots are more open than usual (about 80%–85%). The long-range or lighter halftone is made with no dot in the shadows and about a 25% dot in the highlight areas.

There are many variations of this technique. The two-black technique uses a full-range negative and short-range one which prints from about the 40% tone down to the shadow. Some duotones are shot with different screen rulings, using a 150-line halftone for the key and a 200- or 300-line halftone for the secondary one. The latest technique uses a halftone screen for the key halftone and a random-element screen for the secondary one. Screen angles are not critical in either of these last techniques, as moiré (page 347) is not a serious problem.

TONE REPRODUCTION IN HALFTONE WORK

Tone reproduction and contrast are two important conditions that determine the quality of the reproduction. If a stepped gray scale (as in figure 9.36) is considered, good tone reproduction in halftone photography is achieved when the darkest area of the subject (shadow) prints as a solid on the press sheet and the lightest area (highlight) as a white, with no evidence of a screen in either tone (fig. 9.37, scale 2). The intermediate tones of the gray scale should have varying sizes of dots from about a 2%–5% dot area in the highlight end to about an 80%–95% dot area in the shadows, with a checkerboard pattern in the 50% middletone area. The minimum printable dot sizes depend on the condition of printing and whether the printing is on smooth or rough paper, coated paper giving the widest range of dot sizes when printed properly.

High contrast exists when two or three steps in the

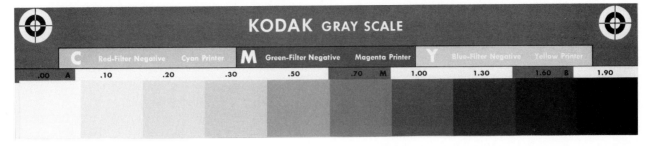

Figure 9.36: Kodak gray scale.

shadow end print solid and/or several steps in the highlight end print white, with a corresponding increase in density difference between the other steps of the scale (fig. 9.37, scale 1). In glass-screen photography, contrast can be deliberately increased by making the highlight part of the exposure in a multiple-stop system with a large lens aperture, or by using a larger lens aperture in the one-stop system. In contact-screen photography, contrast can be increased by using a no-screen exposure; by turning the screen over and shooting with the back of the screen in contact with the film emulsion; and, with magenta screens, by making part of the exposure through a magenta filter like the Wratten No. 33.

When the deepest blacks contain 80%–90% dot area and/or the highlights contain 10%–20% dot area, with reduced density differences in the rest of the scale, the reproduction has *low contrast* (fig. 9.37, scale 3). When a crossline screen is used, contrast can be reduced by using smaller apertures throughout the exposure or by increasing the flash exposure to a white sheet over the copy or to a flash lamp which exposes a screen pattern all over the film independent of the image. With a contact screen, contrast is also reduced by flashing, but with an overall exposure of the film through the screen using yellow light. Contrast can be lowered even further with magenta screens by making part of the exposure through a yellow filter like the Wratten No. 12. With Autoscreen film, PMT, and the Polaroid system, contrast can also be affected by changing the exposures.

Scale 1 — no flash

Scale 2 — 17 seconds

Scale 3 — 24 seconds

Figure 9.37: Halftone reproductions of original gray scale.

COLOR REPRODUCTION

Michael H. Bruno, GRAPHIC ARTS CONSULTANT

Color reproduction is based on the theory of three-color vision. According to this theory (as described in "Color and Light," page 14), white light, which contains all the wavelengths of light, consists of three primary colors—blue, green, and red. These are broad bands of color, each covering about 100 nanometers of the visible spectrum. The eye contains three different types of receptors in the cones of the retina, each sensitive to one of the primary colors of light. When the eye views a scene, the receptors in the cones are activated by the colors in the scene to which they are sensitive and send impulses to the brain. The brain recreates the scene from the impulses it receives.

COLOR SEPARATION

The process of color separation in color reproduction is similar to the way the eye sees color, in that color filters are used to separate the scene or subject to be reproduced into three records, each representing one primary color of light. The three colors—blue, green, and red—are called *additive primaries* because three lights of these colors add together to produce white light. In color-separation photography, the subject is photographed using a continuous-spectrum light source like a pulsed xenon arc and three filters, each corresponding in color and light transmission to one of the additive primaries.

When the subject is photographed with the red filter over the lens, the negative produced is the red separation negative, which is a recording of all the red light reflected from or, in the case of a transparency, transmitted through the subject. When a positive is made from this negative, the image in this positive corresponds to the areas in the subject which do not contain red—that is, which contain the other two colors of light, blue and green. In effect, the negative has subtracted the red light from the subject, and the positive is a recording of the two remaining colors, which are blue and green. This combination of colors is called *cyan*, and this positive is called the *cyan printer*.

In the same way, photography through the green filter produces the green separation negative which records the green in the subject. The positive made from this negative is a recording of the red and blue, which combined are called *magenta*, and this positive is called the *magenta printer*.

Similarly, photography through the blue filter produces the blue separation negative which records the blue in the subject. The positive made from this negative is a recording of the red and green, which produce the sensation of *yellow*, and this positive is called the *yellow printer*.

These three colors—*yellow, magenta*, and *cyan*—are called the *subtractive primaries*. They are the colors which are left after one additive primary is subtracted from white light. These are the colors that are used for the printing inks in process-color reproduction. Each process color thus transmits two additive primaries of light and absorbs the third. Process-color inks must be transparent so that they transmit light of their characteristic colors to the paper or other substrate, which in turn reflects the colors back through the ink to the viewer. Cyan transmits blue and green light and absorbs red; magenta transmits red and blue and absorbs green; yellow transmits red and green and absorbs blue.

When the positive made from the blue separation negative printed in yellow ink is combined with the positive from the green separation negative printed in magenta ink and the positive from the red separation negative printed in cyan ink, the result should be a faithful reproduction of the original. Actually it is not. All the colors except yellow and red are dirtied and muddied; there is too much yellow in the reds and greens and too much red in the blues and purples. This is not because the theory is at fault but because the pigments used in the inks for color reproduction are not ideal.

The theory of color reproduction is illustrated in figure 9.38, pages 348–349.

IDEAL VERSUS ACTUAL PIGMENTS

As described in "Color and Light," page 14, the yellow pigments used for color reproduction are quite good in spectral characteristics, but not so with the magentas and cyans. The ideal yellow pigments when illuminated with white light should transmit all the green and red light and absorb all the blue light. The yellows that are used absorb most of the blue light, transmit practically all of the red light, and absorb a small amount of the green light, so that they are very slightly orange.

The ideal magenta should transmit all the blue and red light and absorb all the green light when illuminated with white light. Actual magentas transmit a small amount of green light and absorb some red light and appreciable blue light, so they are slightly gray (green transmission) and behave as though they have considerable yellow in them (blue absorption). They are too red.

The ideal cyan, when illuminated with white light, should transmit all the blue and green light and absorb all the red light. Actual cyans transmit some red light and absorb considerable blue and green light. They are reddish (red transmission), quite gray or dirty (blue absorption), and behave as though they have considerable yellow (blue absorption) and magenta (green absorption) in them.

346

These inaccuracies can be shown by making densitometer readings of the inks, using filters corresponding to the additive primaries or the filters used for color separations. Optical density as measured on a densitometer is a means of expressing *light absorption*, or the amount of light absorbed by a color. The color analysis of a set of process inks is expressed in a *color matrix*. An ideal set of inks with ideal pigments and light-absorption characteristics would have a color matrix of densitometer readings as follows: (The numbers in parentheses after the colors of the filters correspond to the Wratten numbers of the filters used in the densitometer to make the readings.)

Printed inks	Red filter (25)	Green filter (58)	Blue filter (47)
Yellow	0.00	0.00	1.60
Magenta	0.00	1.60	0.00
Cyan	1.60	0.00	0.00

Densitometer readings made from an actual typical set of balanced process inks, however, would produce a matrix like the following:

Printed inks	Red filter (25)	Green filter (58)	Blue filter (47)
Yellow	0.01	0.06	0.95
Magenta	0.10	1.15	0.46
Cyan	1.20	0.50	0.20

COLOR CORRECTION

The figures that appear in the spaces of the second matrix where there are readings of 0.00 in the first matrix are measures of the color errors in the inks. The blue absorption in the magenta and cyan inks corresponds to the amount of unwanted yellow these inks contain. The green absorption of the cyan ink is unwanted magenta in the cyan ink. To compensate for the effect of these errors on the final reproduction, corrections must be made in the color separation negatives or positives. The yellow printer is reduced in those areas where it prints with magenta and cyan ink, and the magenta printer is reduced where it prints with cyan. Masks are used to reduce these printers in the necessary areas (see "Manual and Photographic Color Correction," page 353), and formulas based on the color matrix of the inks determine the amount of reduction necessary.

Note that in the second matrix the ratios of blue to green absorption of the magenta and cyan inks are the same—0.40 in each case ($0.46:1.15 = 0.20:0.50 = 0.40$). This is what is known as a set of *balanced inks,* which means that the blue absorption errors of the magenta and cyan inks can be corrected with a single mask made from the magenta printer applied to the yellow printer. This mask removes the correct amount of yellow where magenta and cyan print.

In the correction process, the amount of yellow printing with the magenta and cyan printers must be reduced in proportion to the ratio of the blue absorption to green absorption of both the magenta and cyan inks. The amount of magenta printing with the cyan printer must be reduced in proportion to the ratio of green to red absorption of the cyan ink. In addition to these fundamental corrections, other adjustments may have to be made in the separation films to compensate for other special factors in the specific job. The color, ink absorption, and gloss of the paper can also affect the hue, grayness, and saturation of the inks and must also be considered during the correction phase.

BLACK PRINTER

Even after these corrections are made, a reproduction made from the three corrected printers printed with the proper inks is still not satisfactory. The grays and deep shadows are brownish instead of neutral because of the poor blue transmission of the magenta ink and especially the low blue and green transmission of the cyan ink. To overcome this, a fourth printer, the black printer, is used to make the grays and deep shadows neutral. The use of the black printer along with the three process-color printers is the basis of four-color reproduction (see figure 9.38).

The black printer can be a skeleton black or a full black depending on the process used or type of printing done. Most offset lithography has been done with a skeleton black. Most letterpress, especially high-speed magazine printing, is done with a relatively full black, and the other colors are proportionally reduced in these areas so that the inks transfer or *trap* properly on the high speed presses. This operation of reducing the colors and printing a full black in the shadow areas is called *undercolor removal*. This technique is also being used in lithography to reduce the use of colored inks, which are more expensive than black ink. (See "Effects of Undercolor Removal on Printing Quality," page 355.)

SCREEN ANGLES

In four-color process printing from halftones, there is a problem with patterns from screen images that are superimposed. The patterns are called *moiré* and are caused by the angles between the screens. (See figure 9.39.) A minimum pattern is formed when the axes of the screens are separated by 30°. Since halftone screens consist of line rulings at 90° to each other, there is room for only three 30° angles before they repeat. In four-color printing, two of the colors must be printed either at the same angle or separated by an angle other than 30°. As a rule, because yellow is a

Figure 9.39: Moiré patterns. *Courtesy of Graphic Arts Technical Association.*

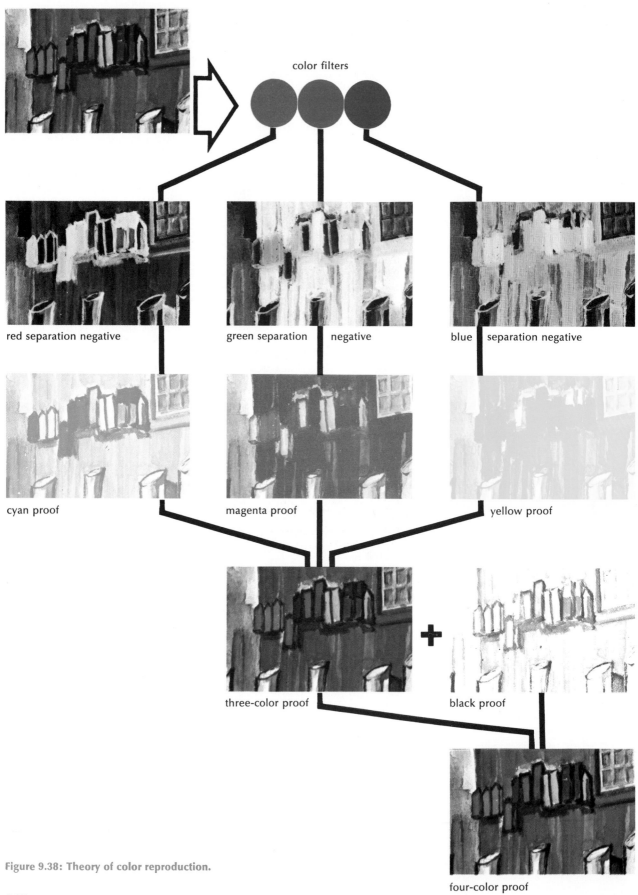

color filters

red separation negative

green separation   negative

blue   separation negative

cyan proof

magenta proof

yellow proof

three-color proof

black proof

four-color proof

Figure 9.38: Theory of color reproduction.

Illustration by Lou Palisano

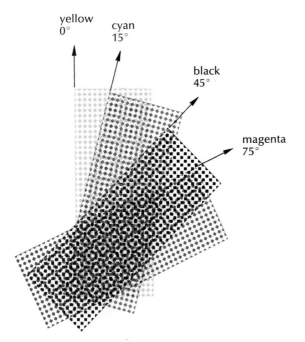

yellow
0°

cyan
15°

black
45°

magenta
75°

Figure 9.40: A common set of screen angles used in color reproduction.

light color, it is printed at an angle of 15° from two other colors, usually cyan and magenta. A common set of screen angles are yellow 0°, cyan 15°, black 45°, and magenta 75° (see figure 9.40). These angles can cause moiré patterns in greens and reds; if the patterns are serious, the angles are changed. The further two colors are apart, the less pronounced is the moiré pattern. Also, the angles themselves are very critical. Errors as small as 0.1° can cause objectionable moiré patterns in grays or areas where three and four colors print together. It is possible that the screens themselves can have errors of this order between the two systems of straight lines when they are made— that is, they may not be at exactly 90°. In addition, slight misregister between colors, local distortion of the paper in printing, and improper transfer of ink, called poor *trapping*, can cause moiré patterns.

INK TRAPPING

Proper trapping is the condition in printing in which the same amount of ink transfers to a previously inked area of the paper as to an unprinted area. Poor trapping results when less ink transfers to the inked area than to blank paper. This is a serious problem in printing on high-speed multicolor presses on which ink must transfer to wet ink films. It is much more serious in letterpress than lithography, as thicker ink films are printed in letterpress. If the inks are not formulated to trap properly, the result is poor trapping or *under-trapping*, which shows up as weak overprint colors (red, green, and blue) and accentuated moiré patterns. This is a main reason why undercolor removal is used in letterpress and lithographic printing.

Gravure often shows effects of *over-trapping*, as the inks are dried between printings and there is more hold-out of ink printed over previously printed ink than on plain paper. The previously printed and dried ink seals the surface of the paper so its absorption is reduced and the ink lays more on the surface, giving it greater brilliance and gloss, referred to as *hold-out*. The overprint colors are purer since absorption into the paper desaturates the colors and makes yellows appear weaker, magentas redder, and cyans and blues dirtier.

SOME NEW AND OLD TRENDS IN COLOR REPRODUCTION
Frank Preucil, GRAPHIC ARTS CONSULTANT

The following article has been reprinted with permission of Graphic Arts Monthly.

In the 1920's and 1930's color separations of fine art calendar pictures sometimes took as long as a week's time for color-correction retouching of each color, working by hand on collodion ground-glass positives. The predecessors of today's modern dot etcher were lithographic artists who mostly had learned their trade by hand drawing on stone. At that time, color retouchers preferred weak photo-images over which they strengthened and almost completely redrew the picture, because it was easier to add than reduce color strength. Probably the present generation of dot etchers and photographers could hardly believe that all this inefficiency preceded them. One photographer could easily keep six to ten artists busy.

As late as 1949, printed reference confirmed this deplorable state of the art. The *Printing and Promotion Handbook* of that year stated: "Process color is basically photomechanical, but handwork is inevitable; in fact, the handwork necessary in improving a photomechanical set of plates to the point where they can give an exact reproduction of the original is often greater than the handwork needed to make freehand fake process color images."

HAND CORRECTION

During this period a trend developed away from continuous-tone ground-glass positives to halftone film positives. Handwork went from pencil, eraser, and air brush to staging lacquer and brushes wet with cyanide or Farmer's reducer. In the early 1940's, forty hours of dot etching per four-color set was considered not unreasonable. In the 1960's, Al Clair of Eastman Kodak Company was able to say that if you spent more than an hour, or at most two, something was basically wrong with your photographic steps. This gives us the real clue as to why dot etching time has so drastically diminished in the past ten years, and why some work is accepted with no handwork. The masks, separations, and halftones now being made are more scientifically correct.

The final stages of the long trend from all handwork to no handwork in printed color reproduction have progressed more successfully because of vast improvement in understanding and control of the photographic images. The first masking patent was granted in 1899, but these ideas were not seriously applied until after 1934 when Kodak published Alexander Murray's studies in a booklet, "The Modern Masking Method of Correct Color Reproduction," which discussed using a densitometer for control. However, densitometers then were principally laboratory instruments and were practically nonexistent in the average printing plant.

The first Lithographic Technical Foundation color survey of 1958 showed that the great majority of process inks were so far out of color balance that mask systems could not do a complete job of picture correction. The second survey five years later showed improvement in use of process colors, but at that time it was estimated that at least half the dot etching time was really tone-value correction and gray-balance adjustment due to improper tone curves, lens flare, etc.

Even prominent companies could be found making all four color-separation negatives of a set with exactly the same tone-gradation curve, ignoring gray balance and a compatible black printer. Millions of hours of dot etching time must have been wasted in straightening out tone and color errors built into this seemingly logical photography.

The Kodak AMB three-point aim system has been a major factor in recent years in cutting down such unnecessary handwork. These curve-shaped masks and separations control tone values and gray balance beyond just compression and color correction. These were the uncontrolled factors previously made even worse in many two-end-point controlled masks and separations.

Machine processor development, which has replaced tray development, makes masks and separation negatives even more precisely balanced.

The last major needs for dot etching have been largely controlled. About 80 percent of present dot etching time is estimated to be by customer request to improve less than perfectly lighted or processed transparencies, or for close product match. Occasionally, even a perfectly matched color may look wrong because of an adjacent or surrounding color brought into more influence by reduction in size. Dot etching may then create a wrong color that looks right.

Originally, all color copy for reproduction was reflected art, and large copyboard process cameras were necessary. When transparencies entered the field, they were large and professionally made, customarily 8″ x 10″, 5″ x 7″, or at least 4″ x 5″ in size. The trend in recent years has been to smaller and smaller sizes, first 2¼″ x 2¼″ and now many 35mm taken even by amateurs. These lower quality transparencies are one of the factors keeping more dot etching alive.

CAMERA WORK

Because most modern color copy is now in the form of small transparencies, separating groups by contact is now a popular way. Another trend has been away from process cameras to vertical enlargers. With their short-focus lenses, they handle a much greater range of size change for both color separating and screening. In addition, their condenser light sources provide the brighter light needed for enlarging. Without these light sources, an enlarged blue-filter exposure was sometimes as long as 25 minutes. Unfortunately, the condenser lenses cast sharp shadow images of dust, scratches, and dirt. The modern solution to this problem is for enlargers to be equipped with diffuse light, and the trend in power brightness has gone from 500 to 12,000 watts.

In recent years, the enlarger trend has been to the addition of more and more complex computer-style consoles which accept density numbers and programs and determine and control exposures. The Rayne Colormaster goes even beyond this, adding automation to change filters and screens.

The actual technique of extra color correction has entered into a new phase in recent years with a trend going away from traditional wet chemical dot etching to so-called "dry etching." Stencil windows are cut in Rubylith or Amberlith coated film, and additional contact exposures of relatively long duration are made back and forth from positive to negative to positive. This results in smaller or larger halftone dots. Some of the smaller, newer color companies that have never employed a regular dot etcher use these techniques.

While the original AMB density number specifications have helpfully served as the "Bible" of most photographers to produce standardized tone, color, and gray corrections, the original numbers have been modified to compensate for unusual subjects. Dot etching time may be saved by raising the M point if there is expected press dot gain or if the printing will be on uncoated paper. Also, the A–B range of the separation negatives is reduced when they are developed with the MP system. This gives better screening without strong yellow filters.

The new AMB two-, three-, and four-mask systems have given excellent picture quality from good originals. Highlight contrast, middletone strength, and gray balance are well controlled, and these three factors are more important to picture quality than the absolute accuracy of individual colors. These masks also give good color correction for the better inks printing on the better papers; however, with average and poorer inks and papers, they render some colors under- or over-corrected. This, of course, accounts for some of the residual dot etching today when more exact color is wanted.

COLOR SCANNERS

The need for electronic color scanners was first conceived in the 1940's to bypass the then serious hand-correction bottleneck. The first Crosfield and Interchemical scanners were, in fact, purely color-correction devices working from camera-separation input.

The first color-separation scanners could not fully correct some of the poorer ink imbalances of the time. More recent generations of scanners, however, can fully correct process inks of higher hue error and can also restore over-correction of purer colors needing less mask effect. Positive and negative correction signals are now more complexly mixed so that the theoretically required photographic six-mask system that nobody ever used is now a reality in scanners. The trend to completely capable and versatile color correction and control has approached its ultimate goal in present scanners.

The trend to more scanner use has been faster in Europe and Japan than in the United States, although this situation is changing. In 1978 it was estimated that over 2,000 scanners were in use world wide, almost half of them in Japan, and that about 50 percent of all separations were made on scanners.

While scanners have had more versatility and a wider range of control of color and tone correction than photography, their adoption was slowed up by their high cost and their inability to outproduce one photographer with a large contact separation frame. The newer scanners, however, have upped their speed two to three times and now, remarkably, are about 50 times faster than the first ones.

Some trends in photographic color separation have probably been reactions to improvements in scanners. The first scanners made photographers take masking more seriously. Faster scanners led some photographers to larger contact frames. Today, the direct-screening capability of scanners may have something to do with the new interest in photographic direct screening.

A scanner that direct-screens can outproduce an indirect photosystem. At first this capability of scanners was not taken seriously by photographers because the scanner could only operate same-size, and the photographer still retained the screening step with size changes. The first enlarging scanners then came in, but with their small input of only 35mm or 2¼ " x 2¼ " sizes, one-up direct screening was still no threat. The current enlarging scanners can take page-size original transparencies or grouped dupes, and enlarge, reduce, and direct-screen them. Of course, the camera can also do this, but the scanner is again one step ahead of photoseparations in being able to direct-screen to half-

tone positives, bypassing the negative stage completely and saving four pieces of film.

It should be realized that the photographic direct screening process so popular in recent years is not a new idea. It is simply a reversion to the early days of process color. In the first 30 years of photoengraved process color, probably 99 percent of all separations were direct-screened. Working directly with only one lens-camera step gives a clearer, sharper final image than indirect systems.

In lithography, indirect separation was used with ground-glass continuous-tone positives to give maximum control of color and tone correction. Then when masking was introduced, less hand correction was needed, and positives were screened to permit dot etching to imitate the photoengravers' fine-etching techniques. Now, with still better masking control and very little need for dot etching, much work can be acceptable with direct screens.

A very advanced trend in catalog printing is the assembly of a number of smaller pictures at final size into page layouts for scanning. This has been successful with scanning of rotogravure positives. Lithographers are now doing more and more of this, using changed-size duplicates.

Two things have been making this more practical. The duplicate color transparencies are now of closer quality to their originals, and they are now easier and more economical to obtain. The new color duplicating films no longer need the extra photographic step of a mask for tone compression, and the printer does not have to buy a complete service or develop them himself. There are now a number of color processing labs in many cities, and it can be most convenient to size and expose the film and get one-day-service developing. More same-size direct screening results.

UNDERCOLOR REMOVAL

The old trend to undercolor removal has actually reversed, and much offset work is now printed without it—even on four-color web presses. Skeleton black plates instead are the general rule.

Letterpress magazines still specify undercolor removal, although the full need of it has diminished with the use of the newer quick-setting inks. The thicker ink films of printed letterpress are more prone to smudge or block with heavy coverage than the thinner transferred lithographic inks.

Today, in large volume plants, undercolor removal can be more of an economic consideration than a practical necessity. It has been calculated that it costs five times as much to create a black area with the three process color solids than to print the area in black alone. When the yearly ink bill runs over a million dollars, this can be significant.

MANUAL AND PHOTOGRAPHIC COLOR CORRECTION

Michael H. Bruno, GRAPHIC ARTS CONSULTANT

Color correction of the separations made for process-color printing is required to compensate for spectral errors in the three process-color inks. It is rare that a printer is asked to produce a four-color reproduction directly from the separations without alteration. Either the separations must be adjusted to yield a result as close as possible to the original copy, or they are deliberately altered to create a special color effect not present in the original.

There are three primary techniques used for color correction: manual correction, known as *dot etching* or *fine etching*; photographic correction, known as *masking*; and electronic correction, known as *scanning*. The first two techniques are done as separate steps in the color reproduction process, but the electronic method is performed as part of the total electronic color-separation process at the same time the separations are being made. The manual and photographic techniques are discussed here; electronic correction is discussed in "Principles of Electronic Color Scanning," page 358.

DOT ETCHING

Manual correction methods are the oldest of the three techniques, and today have been greatly supplanted by the other two. However, some dot etching is still required for manipulations which the other techniques cannot handle and is used to supplement them. A basic understanding of the manual methods will illustrate the specific approach used in all systems to change color values.

The basic idea of all color correction is to change the sizes of the halftone dots so they will print more or less of their particular color on the paper. In manual dot etching, these corrections are usually made on the halftone positives produced from the original color separation negatives. These positives are deliberately made as *full-density* films—with the dots as dark as possible and somewhat larger in diameter than they will be in the finished product—so that the dot etcher can selectively reduce the size of the dots by means of chemical reducers. It is far easier to reduce dot sizes than to enlarge them by manual methods.

Etching can be done in two ways. Areas not to be corrected may be protected by application of a staging lacquer, and the film then dipped into a tray of reducing solution; or reducer may be applied in small areas by means of a brush. The dot etcher usually uses a color chart or guide of some sort which aids him in getting the correct dot size for the tone desired.

Hand correction also can be done on metal halftone engravings used for letterpress printing by staging the areas not to be etched with an acid-resistant lacquer and then etching away with an appropriate acid some of the metal on the dots in the unstaged areas. Gravure cylinders also can be corrected manually by etching the cells locally after the basic image has been etched into the cylinder.

Dot etching generally is a highly skilled craft. The etching of printing plates, however, as opposed to work done on film, is especially delicate and is called *fine etching* or *re-etching*. The craftsmen who do it must have considerable experience and skill, and are among the highest paid in the industry.

PHOTOGRAPHIC MASKING

Unlike manual color correction, photographic masking attacks the problem of color adjustment prior to halftone screening, in the continuous-tone-separation stage of the reproduction process. A mask is simply another piece of film exposed to the image to be reproduced, but with density values different from those of the separation films. Both negative and positive masking techniques can be used; negatives masks are made from the original copy, while positive masks are made from the separation negatives. There are a variety of masking systems in use today, but one of the simpler ones, the *positive* or *indirect* method, illustrates the basic principles of masking most clearly.

The problem that must be solved is that the process inks are not pure—each appears to be contaminated by the others. To compensate for these inaccuracies, two masks are used in making the final magenta- and yellow-printer images. The masks reduce the strength of the magenta and yellow printers in areas where they print with the other inks that contain significant amounts of magenta and yellow, respectively (see "Color Reproduction," page 346).

In the indirect method, the masks are low-density positives made from the green and red separation negatives. The mask from the green separation negative is made to a density range corresponding to the ratio of blue to green density absorption of the magenta ink. (In the example on page 347, a positive

354

mask with a density range of 40% of the blue separation is made.) The mask is placed over the blue separation negative before the yellow halftone printer is made. If the inks were balanced, the ratio of blue to green absorption in the cyan ink would be equal to the ratio for the magenta ink. The mask would then remove yellow from the yellow printer in proportion to the amount of excess yellow in the magenta and cyan inks, thereby keeping the areas where the magenta ink prints with yellow ink bluer and the areas where the cyan ink prints with yellow ink cleaner.

A similar mask is made from the red separation negative in a density range equal to the ratio of green to red absorption of the cyan ink and applied to the green separation negative before the magenta halftone printer is made. This mask removes the magenta from where the cyan prints with it in proportion to the amount of excess magenta in the cyan ink.

No color correction mask is used on the cyan printer. A weak mask is often made from the black printer and put on the red-filter negative before making the cyan halftone positive. This is necessary to increase the saturation of the cyan ink printing in solids. There are a number of ways of making the black printer, depending on what effects are desired and how much undercolor removal is used.

Indirect masking has largely been replaced today by simpler and more comprehensive systems which accomplish the same result by putting a correction mask on a transparency, as in direct screening; by putting a mask on the back of a camera (camera-back masking), for flat originals; or by electronic scanning.

EFFECTS OF UNDERCOLOR REMOVAL ON PRINTING QUALITY

William A. Rocap, Jr., PRINTING GROUP, MEREDITH CORPORATION

The following article has been reprinted with permission of Printing Management.

For a number of years, the use of undercolor removal to produce a density of tone suitable for good-quality four-color wet printing has been advocated by only some printers. However, printers interested in lowering polluting emissions, reducing ink costs, and increasing print quality should investigate undercolor removal.

A recent recommended standard specification for advertising reproduction material for magazine web offset printing by the American Association of Advertising Agencies and the Magazine Publishers Association states that "density of tone for four-color wet printing should not exceed 260% (unless otherwise specified by the publisher) and no more than one solid should be used." Conventional color-separation methods are naturally adapted to three-color process; addition of a fourth color (black) creates problems. If the black is to be more than a skeleton image (which it should be), the amount of the other colors must be decreased whenever black is to be printed, to make room for the black. This is known as *undercolor removal* (*UCR*).

PRODUCTION METHODS

There are various methods of accomplishing *UCR*; however, it is usually done photographically. A positive mask is made from the black-printer negative, and this UCR mask is combined with each of the three other separation negatives when making positives.

A second method, when reproducing color transparencies, is to use the black-printer negative itself as a UCR mask and combine it with the transparency during part of the exposure when the other color-separation negatives are made. This undercolor-removal negative is used in addition to the normal color-correcting masks. It should be fully exposed and of rather high contrast.

A third method of attaining an excellent black printer, good undercolor removal, and proper gray balance in the other three colors is through the use of an electronic scanner.

Through experimentation, it has been found that by combining all factors—ink, plate, blanket, press, and film—a black may be produced by printing a 55% dot of yellow, 50% of magenta, 65% of cyan, and 75% of black. This amount of cyan imbalance produces a good three-color neutral under the black.

PURPOSE OF UCR

Undercolor removal serves four purposes: it permits more black to be printed, so that the balance of the printing process becomes less critical; it lowers ink costs; it reduces air pollution, as less heat is needed to dry the thinner ink film; and it results in improved color saturation in those subjects in which the saturated colors are reproducible but the blacks are too dense to be reproduced in three colors.

Color saturation

The reason for this improvement in color saturation is that when undercolor removal is not used, the three color printers have to be reduced in contrast to cover the full density range of the original. This lowers saturation. An undercolor-removal mask will have the effect of lowering the density range without affecting the saturated colors, and will thus permit the contrast of the subsequent steps to be increased with improved color saturation.

Ink consumption

While the nature of the press form has a great effect on ink consumption, an average coverage should be considered. Take, for example, a form with all four-color subjects, a 23½″ x 38″ sheet, perfecting, running at 30,000 impressions per hour. Under these conditions, 200 pounds of ink per hour (all colors and black) would be run with no undercolor removal. With full undercolor removal, 141 pounds of ink per hour would be used. The savings in ink, with full undercolor removal, would be 59 pounds per hour; with 50% UCR, 29.5 pounds per hour; and with 25% UCR, 14.8 pounds per hour.

Assuming a fairly large amount of black printing—50% of the area affected by UCR—the dollar saving would be appreciable. With a light form—about 25% of the area affected—the saving would be about half.

Pollution control

Undercolor removal also reduces solvent emissions. The usual heat-set ink formula contains about 40% solvent, which must be heated to put it into the form of vapor and remove it from the printed sheet.

Under the conditions described, the web offset blanket-to-blanket perfecting press with a conventional high-velocity dryer will put out 80 pounds of solvent per hour with no undercolor removal. With 25% of the area covered, with UCR, output will be 74 pounds per hour; with 50% coverage, 68.3 pounds per hour.

To a printer trying to meet local, state, and federal regulations, and trying, through the use of low-emission inks, to reach a minimum level, this reduction in emissions due to the use of less ink could be of considerable importance. Another factor is that, with an appreciable decrease in the ink solvent to be driven off, oven heat could be decreased to effect a saving on gas consumption.

DIRECT-SCREEN COLOR SEPARATION
Harold Sigler, PRINTING TECHNIQUES INTERNATIONAL, INC.

Traditionally, color separations have been produced by the indirect process. This involves making masks, then making continuous-tone separations from the masked separations, and finally screening the continuous-tone separations. The technique requires considerable expertise in every step of the process, is quite time-consuming, and completely ties up the photographic apparatus in use until the job is complete.

Direct-screen color separation was developed in the early sixties by Kodak as a contact separation method for transparencies. In this process, the separation step and the halftone-preparation step were combined into one operation. Its only requirement was a somewhat more powerful light source than is normally used for contact work. Since these light sources were readily available, the process enjoyed some limited success. In this contact method, the separations produced are the same size as the original transparencies. The contact method was not fully utilized because only same-size separations could be produced. The advent of improved color duplicating films and dichroic filter enlarger systems in the early seventies reactivated the use of contact direct-screen separations, for sound economic reasons.

In 1966, Berkey Technical introduced a new enlarger system that was capable of utilizing the Kodak contact direct-screen method in a projection mode. The key to the enlarger method was an extremely powerful

pulsed xenon light source along with an automated system of exposure control. This enabled an operator to produce halftone color separations even faster than with the contact method, with the additional benefit of being able to change size. Since then, other enlarger manufacturers have produced similar equipment.

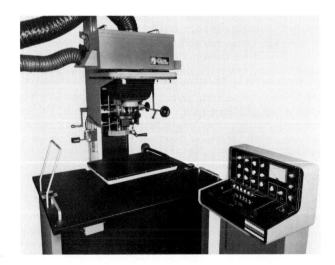

Figure 9.41: Enlarger.

Figure 9.42: Kodak three-point transparency guide.

In order for reflection copy to be used in the enlarger direct-screen system, it had to be converted into transparency copy by rephotographing it onto color transparency film. However, in the early seventies faster separation film was developed, as well as more powerful process camera lights. It is now possible, using either or both of these items, to produce direct-screen color separations in process cameras using reasonable exposure times.

ADVANTAGES OF DIRECT SCREENING

As opposed to the conventional indirect process, direct screening offers many significant economic advantages.

• Masking is done on a continuous-tone panchromatic masking film or on a dye image film for both processes. For transparency work, the masks are generally prepared by contact. The current trend is toward the use of silver masking films because of the ease of developing them in the newly available automatic dry-to-dry film processors. Even though the masks are continuous-tone they can be successfully processed in lith-type chemistry because of their short tonal range. The direct-screen process requires a maximum of two silver masks, while the indirect process usually requires a minimum of four silver masks.

• The direct-screen process eliminates the step of continuous-tone separations and thus saves four more sheets of film, along with the additional time for exposing and developing.

• Exposing of direct-screen separations on enlargers is controlled by metering and programming systems and is rapid and predictable with few make-overs. It is somewhat inconvenient to set exposure times for contact and process-camera direct-screen separations because of the difficulty of metering the image just prior to exposure. In all cases, direct-screen separations are exposed on panchromatic lith film.

• Training of operators in the direct-screen process usually takes only two to three days because of the simplicity of the operation.

• Quality control of separations in the direct-screen process is simplified because only two steps with predictable aim points are employed.

• Since the direct-screen process requires fewer steps, the final reproduction is generally sharper.

• The direct-screen process results in considerable savings in operating time and in materials used.

CAPABILITIES AND LIMITATIONS

The direct-screen process can obviously do the best job in reproducing a good color original "as is." However, by adjusting mask exposure time, either highlight or shadow detail can be emphasized to correct deficient color originals. Color casts are easily corrected by adjusting the relative exposure times of the separations. Finally, the halftone separations themselves can be dot-etched by conventional techniques if local color correction is required.

In cases where the amount of local color correction required is more extensive than can be achieved by dot etching, then the indirect separation method must be employed. Further local work can be done on the continuous-tone separations.

When halftones of many sizes are required from the same original, as in calendar work, and the color original cannot be retained by the color separation house, it is sometimes more practical to resort to the continuous-tone separation method. Then a halftone of any size can be produced at a later date from the continuous-tone separations.

PROCEDURE

Direct-screen separations done in the contact frame, process camera, and enlarger follow the same basic operations. Since the enlarger (as illustrated in figure 9.41) is the most common way of preparing direct-screen color separations, the following discussion will relate directly to that equipment.

Making the masks

A piece of exposed and developed film is prepared by punching register holes (see "Principles of Pin Register," page 333), cutting out a window to accept the transparency, and cutting out another window to accept a control strip. The transparency and the control strip are taped into their respective windows. The control strip contains, among other things, three dye density patches labeled A, M, and B. These represent the typical highlight, middletone, and shadow densities, respectively, of a normal color transparency. (See figure 9.42.)

In total darkness, masking film is punched on the same punch used for the transparency. The masking film is placed with the emulsion side up on pins in a vacuum frame; the transparency is placed over the same pins also emulsion up. The frame is closed and vacuum applied. The exposure takes place from a point-source light through a red filter. This is repeated through a green filter on a second sheet of panchromatic film. In certain newspaper work with lower quality requirements only one mask is made using an orange filter. After exposure, the mask film is placed in a film processor.

Note that the contact is not emulsion-to-emulsion, so that a slightly diffuse or unsharp mask is produced. This simplifies register and produces a sharper-appearing final result because of edge contrast effects.

For enlargements over 12x the mask is sometimes

made by projection onto the enlarger easel to the finished separation size by camera-back masking techniques. This has the advantage of insuring perfect register and reducing the silver grain effect from the mask.

The A, M, and B patches of the developed masks are measured on a transmission densitometer. *Mask range* and *mask number* are calculated from these measurements and compared with previously established plant standards. The mask range is a measure of mask development time, while mask number is a measure of the mask exposure time.

Making the separations

The film carrier of the transparency holder has pins set at the same spacing as the holes punched in the mask film and the transparency film. The transparency and the mask are placed over these pins with the emulsion side either up or down, depending upon the orientation needed in the final separations (right- or wrong-reading negatives). Since the mask was exposed over common pins with the transparency, register at this point is automatic. The transparency holder is inserted into the enlarger and locked into place with another register device which ensures that the transparency is always in the same spot in the optical path. The enlarger is then set to size and focused.

Overall exposure for highlight and shadow is set by a metering device measuring the projected image of the transparency. If overall hue corrections are desired, the individual separation exposure times are adjusted by on-easel measurements taken by the exposure probe or by previously taken off-easel measurements made with a color densitometer. Thus all exposure times are preprogrammed before exposing the set of separations.

Prepunched panchromatic lith film is placed on the enlarger easel on retractable pins. Vacuum is applied to hold the film, and the pins are retracted. A contact screen is laid over the film, and vacuum is applied to hold the contact screen down. An exposure is made through the transparency, the mask, a color-separation filter, and the contact screen onto the film. This is followed by or done along with a flash exposure going through the contact screen only.

The same procedure is used for all four separations. However, the separation filter and contact-screen angle are changed for each color. A *bump* or no-screen ex-

posure is usually added to the cyan separation to control the middletone characteristics. The mask is changed for certain separations, depending upon the panchromatic lith film characteristics.

The separation procedure outlined in this section usually takes ten minutes. All four separation films are placed in an automatic film processor (page 327). The product is a set of four halftone negative separations that are in register with each other.

IMPORTANT EQUIPMENT FEATURES

Regardless of which method of direct-screen separation is used, probably the most important item is a proper light source. It has to be quite powerful to go through the assembly of films, filters, and contact screen, and produce reasonable exposure times. Furthermore, the light should have a continuous visible spectrum with a relatively high blue content because of the characteristics of the separation film. Except for contact work, the use of a pulsed xenon light source is mandatory. (See "Lights for Photography and Platemaking," page 338.)

Since all operations are done on panchromatic film, no safelight is used. Pin register should be used wherever possible to facilitate the work. For camera and enlarger work, retractable pins are mandatory, and automatically retractable pins are preferred. One type of solenoid-operated pin interlocked with the vacuum pump is especially desirable. The contact screens used in all cases are gray, negative, and preferably have elliptical dots.

FUTURE OF DIRECT SCREENING

The direct-screen separation method offers an economical method of producing high-quality color separations at relatively high production rates. Improvements in films and masking methods have significantly raised the quality level. The equipment developed for this process is largely automated, making operator decisions and training much simpler. All these factors combined have induced many new and smaller shops to go into color separation work, which may have been impractical with other methods. The new smaller scanners, such as the Crosfield 510, Hell Chromagraph 299, Linoscan 3040, and those by Dainippon Screen, are bound to affect this trend.

PRINCIPLES OF ELECTRONIC COLOR SCANNING

Michael H. Bruno, GRAPHIC ARTS CONSULTANT

Electronic scanning of original color copy can be used to replace most of the steps in preparing process-color halftone films including separation, overall correction, undercolor removal, and halftone screening.

Scanners in use today vary in complexity, in how many functions they can perform, and in the methods they use to accomplish their final results. However, they all use the same basic principles of operation.

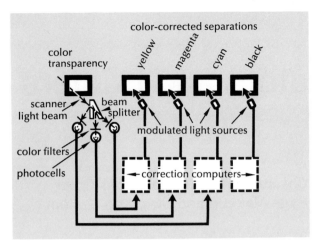

Figure 9.43: Diagram of an electronic color scanner.

A complete color scanner consists of three major sections: the color-scanning mechanism, an electronic computation unit, and a film-scanning unit. As shown in figure 9.43, the copy scanner converts colored light from the copy into electronic signals, the electronic computation unit modifies these signals, and the film scanner produces the final film separations. Figure 9.44 shows a typical machine in use today.

In a full-color scanner that produces all separations in one operation, the original copy is passed under a *scanning head* containing a photosensitive receiver. A beam of light is precisely focused to illuminate one spot on the copy and then to pass into the receiver. As the copy moves past the light beam, the light trans-

mitted to the receiver varies in amount and color composition. In the receiver, the light beam is passed through a filter system to separate out the desired basic colors—red, blue, and green—and these are then focused in turn on three photocells which convert light energy into electrical energy. The resulting electrical currents are proportional to the basic color values in the original copy.

The electrical signals are fed into the electronic computation unit, which contains four analog computers. Three computers receive the signals from the photocells and modify them appropriately for generating the three color-separation films. The fourth computer is fed signals generated from the other three, representing values which should be in the black printer of the four-color set. The fourth computer then produces the information from which the black printer is exposed.

The computers permit the machine operator to make a number of adjustments in the electrical signals and thus in the final separations. By setting various dials on the console of the machine, he can alter the color values in the separations. This enables him to perform the same corrections done by masking in the photographic correction system, as well as adjusting for undercolor removal, tonal range, and inks and papers to be used in the job.

Since these electronic corrections are made at the same time as the separations are produced—not as separate steps as in camera procedures—corrections must be predicted and the machine controls set beforehand. This is done through the use of mathematical curves developed for use with the scanner. The curves relate various instrument readings made from the copy to the various control settings required on the scanner.

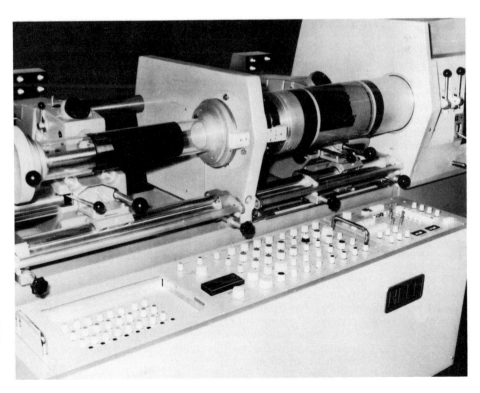

Figure 9.44: Electronic color scanner. *Courtesy of HCM Corporation.*

The latest innovation in scanner design is the use of digital computers for color correction, as in the Crosfield Magnascan 550. In this system, special programs are used for the corrections and for other functions normally performed in the computer. With the digital computers, the scanner has greater versatility, simplicity, and speed of operation than with an analog computer.

As with photographic masking, most scanners now in use cannot introduce local color changes or corrections such as changing the color of the background, a garment, or other article. These usually must be made by hand retouching on individual separations, by dot etching on the halftone positives, or by fine etching on letterpress plates or gravure cylinders. On a few of the newest scanners, however, such local changes can be accomplished through use of masks or digitizing tablets, which alter the exposures appropriately during scanning to produce a color different from that on the copy.

After processing by the computers, the four electrical signals are sent to the film-scanning unit where separation films are exposed. On a scanner producing all separations in one operation, four sheets of film are mounted on four exposing drums beneath four scanning heads. Each head contains a light source controlled by one of the electrical signals from the computers. As the light is varied in intensity, the appropriate image is recorded on the film.

Scanners in use today vary in the features and capabilities they offer the user. Most color scanners use drums for holding the copy to be scanned and the film to be exposed. Machines with a single drum have one section for copy and another section for film. Machines with multiple drums for copy and film permit the drums to be interlocked so that they rotate in precise synchronization from a single drive mechanism, thus maintaining the copy and film in perfect register. In either case, copy for drum scanners must be either color transparencies or flexible color prints which can be wrapped around the drums.

Rigid flat copy can be scanned only on a machine with a flat bed. Either the bed must move back and forth beneath the scanning head, or the head must move across the copy. The film exposure unit must also be designed to synchronize with this system. One widely used flat-bed scanner was the Vario-Klischograph, a machine which engraved letterpress printing plates instead of exposing film as it scanned. The trend today, however, is to the drum-type machines, for which flat copy is first photographed to produce a transparency.

Scanners also differ in the number of separation films they produce in one operation. The type of machine just described produces four at once. Other machines produce one or two scanned separation films at a time; the copy must be put through multiple scanning cycles to get a complete set of films. Machines that produce only one separation at a time normally offer other advantages not possible on a machine producing all separations at once, such as extreme ranges of enlargement or reduction.

A third major difference among various machines is the amount of control provided to the operator to manipulate the final result. Color scanners started out as devices to correct separation negatives. Since then they have become separation producers and halftone screening devices as well. Some scanners use contact halftone screens mounted over the copy so that halftones are produced directly. Others compute mathematically the precise size of each dot instead of relying on optical systems and screens. With computed dot sizes, such devices as lasers can be used to expose the film with great precision.

For many years, it was popular to consider scanning as incapable of producing a four-color illustration that would look very nearly like the same illustration produced by other separation and correction methods. However, electronic dot generation, such as by laser, has changed the situation. As long ago as 1974, at the Print 74 graphic arts exhibition, the Du Pont company exhibited a color transparency which had been reproduced by all of the major color separation methods: indirect, direct screening, scanner, scanner with contact screen, and scanner with laser screening. All of the reproductions looked almost exactly alike, except the one produced by laser screening. This one was definitely sharper, showing finer detail.

WHERE ARE COLOR SCANNERS GOING?

Frank Preucil, GRAPHIC ARTS CONSULTANT

The following article originally appeared in Modern Lithography *and is used with permission. It has been modified and updated.*

Scanners today bear little resemblance to those of their first generation, and we may expect that those of the not-too-distant future will surely look and perform still differently. To put present and future scanners into proper perspective, we must realize that they have always reacted and will continue to react to contemporary needs and competitive methods. The first operational graphic arts scanners were born in a much different era of color reproduction efficiency than today, and had much simpler goals. Color copy originals for printed reproduction were almost totally large, flat reflection copy, such as oil paintings, watercolors, pastels, and occasionally some photographic carbro or dye-transfer prints; and the first scanners were made simply to correct color-separation negatives.

EARLY SCANNERS

While the early scanners took three to four hours to color-correct a four-color set, they were accomplishing this step at least ten times faster than typical hand re-etching, which they were more scientifically replacing. Today, scanning is in an entirely different ball park, having to compete with masking systems for color correction where commercially acceptable photographic images can be produced with either no hand correction or only an hour or two of handwork. Of course, the modern scanner now does color correction with much more control; it also includes the separation and halftoning steps and eliminates the need for extra film and the time costs of masking and halftoning.

As more and more original color copy for printing came to be color transparencies, scanners became color-separation as well as color-correction devices. Printing Developments, Inc. (PDI) was the first in the field, followed by Fairchild, to speed up the output by a factor of four by exposing four colors at once. These drum- or cylinder-type scanners got rid of the lost time due to backward motion and have steadily increased their output efficiency through higher and higher rotational speeds. Simply spinning the cylinders faster, however, was not the answer to delivering more acceptable scans; the frequency response of the circuitry also had to be increased. The on-off exposure time of a scan spot today is as short as two millionths of a second or less.

The early scanners had over one hundred radio-type filament-burning vacuum tubes, and many resistors and condensers. The electrical power input was normally kept on 24 hours a day because of the significant signal drift from warm-up temperature change. Today, transistors, diodes, and printed circuit boards have revolutionized the internal design.

EVOLUTIONARY DEVELOPMENTS

While scanners have always competed with photographic methods of separation and color correction,

Can You Identify These Logos?

ON THE **8** th FLOOR

engravings for letterpress
Master Eagle Photoengraving Corp.

ON THE **7** th FLOOR

color separations for offset
Craftsman Color Lithographers Inc.

ON THE **6** th FLOOR

phototypography
The Type Group Inc.

ON THE **5** th FLOOR

positives for gravure
Intaglio Service Co. of New York City

he Master Eagle Family of Companies

40 West 25th Street. New York. N.Y. 10010 • (212) 924-8277

All Under One Roof

scanners also compete now with other scanners in efficiency and performance. The first widespread use of scanning in the United States was with the PDI studio scanners which made all four color-corrected separations at once. Less complex, lower cost in-plant scanners were developed whose output was only one color at a time but whose speed was greater. The scan time has been progressively reduced so that what once took an hour now takes about three minutes. Over 2,000 in-plant scanners are now in use worldwide.

When most professional color transparencies for reproduction were 8″ x 10″, 5″ x 7″, or 4″ x 5″, all continuous-tone scanners made same-size separations with the adjustment to final printed size made in a process camera in the screening step. With the improvement in fineness of grain and detail in modern color films, the trend has been to smaller-size originals, and many 35mm and 2¼″ x 2¼″ transparencies are now being furnished for printed reproduction. The most-used 500-line scanning gave good 3x screening enlargement, normally sufficient for 4″ x 5″ or larger originals. For 35mm transparencies, 1,000-line scanning was needed, but the image lost detail if screened larger than 6x. Better results were achieved with 2,000-line scanning, but what is really needed from small originals is a larger-size output image. A next generation of scanners provided this enlargement capability, first mechanically, and then, still better, electronically by storing digital signals in magnetic memory and playing them back faster or slower to give output size change. The Crosfield Magnascan was the first in this digital field, soon followed by Hell's (HCM) DC300.

An important advance in scanner design has been the increase in output spot brightness, permitting full exposure through contact halftone screens to high-contrast lith-type films. In addition, the development of electronic dot generation has made possible halftone imaging using lasers. Direct screening has become popular because the images are a little clearer and production costs lower. It has become more practical because process inks are better, and, with good masking, little or no hand correction is needed for average commercial reproduction. Scanners with direct screening have two advantages over photography. The fine image detail can be clearer because there are no intervening mask images; and scanning can go directly to positives if plates are to be made from them, eliminating four more pieces of film.

PRESENT AND FUTURE TRENDS

The question raised by the title of this article is "Where are scanners going?" So far we have set the perspective by describing where they have been and how far they have come. The question "Where are they going?" can be reasonably well answered by looking at the trends developing today.

The large scanners such as the Crosfield 550 and the Hell DC 300 have become very sophisticated and too expensive for use by the average medium-sized plant. Therefore, there has been a trend toward smaller and less expensive scanners for use by the large number of these plants. The cost of the smaller scanners is between one-third and one-half that of the large scanners, but they still have much of the larger scanners' sophistication. The Crosfield Magnascan 510, the Hell Chromagraph DC 299, the Linoscan 3040, and the small Dainippon Screen scanners are examples of this new breed of electronic scanner. All can perform most of the color correction functions of the large scanners, and most can enlarge and reduce and produce direct-screen halftone separations using contact screens.

PDI, which produced the first commercial electronic scanner, has introduced a modular scanner system in which input and output can be separated so that the scanning of originals can be done in one location while halftone separations are produced in another. This scanner also has a unique digital curve corrector for producing any desired tone reproduction.

The most dramatic of the new developments has been the use of scanners in completely electronic computerized image-processing prepress systems, in which complete page makeups of color subjects can be made without any intermediate photographic operations. The most advanced of these systems is the Sci-Tex Response 300, which accomplishes electronically the traditional functions of color separation and correction, area color modifications, screening, contacting, stripping (including page assembly), and proofing, producing as its output fully assembled film flats ready for platemaking. Hell has a similar system under development, known as the Chromacom, and Crosfield's Magnascan 570 can accomplish many of the same functions. A number of other systems are under development. It can be predicted with reasonable certainty that scanners and computers will usurp many of the traditional operations in the makeup of printing units and their assembly into plate or signature layouts.

COLOR PROOFING
Michael H. Bruno, GRAPHIC ARTS CONSULTANT

Color proofing is used to determine what the final printed job will look like, insofar as possible, before it is committed to reproduction on press. Color proofs are used to make sure that all image elements are in proper position and in the correct colors; but most important, they provide the customer with an opportunity to see that the reproduction looks like his original, or that changes he directed to be made actually came out as he wanted.

Two major forms of color proofs are in use today—press proofs and prepress proofs. Prepress proofs are desirable as a means of cutting the high cost of producing color proofs, which traditionally have been prepared on special presses or even on actual production presses on occasion. Prepress proofs have found widespread use only for certain purposes, however, and press proofs still remain an essential part of the color checking procedure.

PRESS PROOFS

Press proofs, when made and used properly, are fair matches to what will be produced on the production press, but they are expensive. Most printers and customers, however, have always felt that press proofs are the best way to match the results that will come off the production press.

Traditionally such proofs have been made on a flat-bed proof press, printing each color in succession after the previous color has dried. In recent years, production-type presses have been installed by color lithographers for making proofs; most have been single- or two-color machines, but some printers have installed four-color presses for proofing use.

The use of expensive multicolor production-type equipment is an attempt to overcome a basic problem in matching proofs and production results: that of dry versus wet printing. On large multicolor production presses, which print the complete image in one pass through the press, inks are laid down in succession before the first-down inks have dried. When they do dry, they tend to produce different results than if they had been dried before the next color was printed, as normally happens on proof presses. This problem remains even when the printer uses one- and two-color production presses to proof jobs with more colors. In the last few years, specially designed four-color proof presses have appeared as a further effort to solve this problem.

When dry proofing must be used for jobs that will be produced by wet-printing presses, many techniques are used to try to match what happens on the production press. So many techniques are required because each press has its own distinguishing characteristics and prints differently from other presses. One basic technique used on flat-bed proofing presses and single-color presses is to reduce the inks more than normally would be needed to get the proper color strength in the reproduction. Using these inks and excessive pressure in printing, the printer hopes to simulate the dot spread which occurs on multicolor presses. Another technique is to use a soft, conventional lithographic blanket which, with over-pressure, causes much more dot spread and image distortion than a compressible blanket.

Quality printers also use a variety of test devices on their proofs to enable them to spot improper printing conditions. Such devices include color bars, star targets, and dot gain scales. (See "What to Look for in the Proof," page 367, and "Quality Control Methods for the Graphic Arts," page 439.)

PREPRESS PROOFS

With the increasing use of photographic systems in the composition and preparatory stages of production, as well as the great growth of multicolor printing, printers have made many attempts to replace press proofs with systems that could reproduce the final press image without the high cost and variability of press proofs. These systems have been known generally as *prepress* proofing systems and are made photomechanically or photographically.

The simplest and oldest kind of prepress proof is the *blueprint,* also called a *blueline, brownline, silverprint,* or other name which usually denotes the color of the proof image. Blueprints, the least expensive of all prepress proofs, are made from paper impregnated with iron-salt compounds. Brown prints are made from paper sensitized with silver nitrate. Multicolor images can be indicated on these proofs by exposing each color film to the proof sheet for a different length of time; when developed, the different color images appear lighter or darker than their companions. Such prints can indicate the presence of all image elements and their positions, but they cannot show the final colors which will be printed. As such, they are used for single-color and simple two-color or three-color line work where color is established separately by color swatches.

In recent years many attempts have been made to develop prepress proofing systems which can reproduce the image in full color as it would be printed on a four-color-process production press. Most of these have fallen into disuse, however, because they could not reproduce a color image close enough to the final printed image. Less than a dozen such systems are still in regular use, mainly as in-plant controls or guides to photographers, dot etchers, and artists. Only in a few cases are these proofs accepted in place of press proofs, and then there is usually a long-standing relationship between the printer and customer with an understanding by the customer that the final print may not look quite as sharp as the proof and that the color balance may also vary slightly.

These prepress color proofing systems are of two types. In one, the colors are laid down one at a time on a base sheet. In the other, each color is recorded on a separate sheet of clear material, after which the sheets are laid over one another in register. Prepress color proofing systems in use today are described below.

Watercote

The oldest prepress color proofing system in continuous use is *Watercote*, manufactured by Direct Reproduction Corporation. It has limited application because of the length of time needed to produce proofs, but it is available in the largest sizes of any prepress material. The base consists of a white plastic sheet which is coated in a whirler with a sensitizer pigmented to match one of the process colors. It is then dried, exposed to the appropriate negative, and developed. After drying, the plastic is recoated with a pigmented sensitizer for a second color, dried, exposed to the next negative in register, and developed. This process is continued until the print is completed. It takes about 40 minutes to produce a proof, and colored sensitizers can be mixed to achieve almost any color desired. The process was developed originally for mapmaking, but its application has spread to other areas of the industry.

Kwik-Proof

Direct Reproduction Corporation has another preproofing system that they call *Kwik-Proof*. It is based on the use of wipe-on coatings and is much faster than Watercote. The faster method and the lower cost of this material are desirable features, but the saturation of the color is poor so that, while it can be used to check register, position, fit, editing, and so forth, it cannot be used to check color. The most recent development in Kwik-Proof is a double-sided material which has shown particular appeal for publication printers. It is apparently the only system on the market that can produce a multicolor proof that can be folded into a dummy of a magazine or booklet. It does not have color fidelity, but it has all the other features an editor is interested in. The fact that the material cost for a four-color proof on both sides is much lower than the cost of the separate proofs of other systems is especially appealing, particularly when accurate proofs are not required.

Viewfoils (Osachrome)

This system, manufactured by GAF Corporation, consists of plastic foils coated with diazo compounds which, on exposure to positives and development in an ammonia chamber, produce dye images corresponding to the ink colors. The problems with these foils are (1) the background is not completely transparent, so that the white appears gray; (2) the colors of the dyes do not match the ink pigment colors exactly; and (3) there is some variability in the results. The use of separate foils makes it possible to see what individual colors look like, and progressive proofs can be made by combining two and three foils in the printing sequence; but the final colors are desaturated somewhat because the whites are actually gray due to the number of layers of foil.

Color-Key

This system offered by the 3M Company also uses overlay plastic foils. These are coated with diazo-sensitized emulsions which are colored with actual ink pigments corresponding closely to the ink pigments commonly used in printing. For printing proofs, they are exposed to photographic negatives and positives, but they also can be exposed to a wide range of other image-carrying media such as translucent paper, sketches on vellum, and so on.

Color-Key is available in both negative- and positive-acting emulsions, and can handle images as fine as a 300-line halftone screen. Negative-acting Color-Key film is matched to the most popular colors of the Pantone color matching system (see page 509), plus variations of process colors and opaque colors. One set of process colors has been specifically designed to match closely the 4A/MPA colors specified for magazine advertising printing (see page 442).

Color-Key is one of the most widely used prepress proofing systems.

Transfer-Key

Another 3M product, Transfer-Key is also widely used. This proofing system lays all of the colors down on a single base sheet, using the same chemistry and equipment as 3M's Color-Key process. The use of the single sheet of base material minimizes discoloration of the image which often results with overlay methods, and also provides a single proof sheet which is easier for the customer to work with.

Gravure-Key

Gravure-Key is another 3M product similar in principle to Color-Key and Transfer-Key but specially formulated to be compatible with gravure ink standards. Color-Key and Transfer-Key are matched to lithographic inks which are quite different in consistency from gravure inks. Gravure-Key proofs are made in the same way as Color-Key proofs.

Cromalin

Cromalin, developed by DuPont, is the most widely accepted of the prepress proofing systems. It is primarily a process for making one-piece paper proofs but can also be used to make transparent overlays. The process uses dry color toners which can be custom blended to simulate the hue and density of most printing inks. The system consists of Cromalin photopolymer film; a table-top laminator to attach the film to the proof stock, usually Kromekote or similar paper; a UV exposing unit; a toning console; and toners. Proofs are made in three steps: (1) the Cromalin film is laminated to the proof sheet; (2) the laminated stock is exposed in contact with the first halftone positive; (3) the exposed stock is placed on the toning console, the protective cover sheet is peeled off, and the color toner is applied in a prescribed manner with a special applicator. After the excess toner is wiped off, the three steps are repeated for each of the other films to produce the final proof. A process is available for making proofs from negatives. A special Cromalin gravure proofing system has also been developed and is used extensively for preproofs for gravure.

Enco PAPS

This positive-acting presensitized proofing system is an overlay method developed by Azoplate Corporation. It features emulsion-to-emulsion exposures which permit little chance for dot spread, provided that sufficient vacuum contact is used and the exposure is not too long. Film comes in the four process colors—black, yellow, magenta and cyan—which are balanced, as are process inks.

The process also features one-step development, and no bleaching is required to clear the background.

Enco NAPS

The Enco NAPS system is similar to the Enco PAPS system except that its proofs are made from negatives rather than positives. It also has the advantage of emulsion-to-emulsion exposures, and it is available in the following transparent colors: magenta, yellow, cyan, black, red, green, blue, brown, and orange.

Gevaproof

The Gevaproof system works from halftone negatives to produce single-sheet proofs that simulate proofs printed on paper. The base material (Gevaproof S) is a dimensionally stable polyester film coated on both sides with a smooth white opaque layer, giving it the appearance of good-quality paper. Light-sensitive colored emulsions are held on temporary base sheets while exposed, after which the emulsions are transferred to the primary base sheet. The images are developed in two solutions, an ethyl alcohol/water bath and an activator bath.

Pigments used in Gevaproof materials are the same as those used in printing inks. Proofs can be made for lithography and letterpress.

WHAT TO LOOK FOR IN THE PROOF

Robert Loekle, COLOR REPRODUCTION CONSULTANT

After color copy is sent to the printer, a proof is submitted for approval. This proof serves two purposes. First, and most obvious, it is a general evaluation of the accuracy of the reproduction. Unless there are specific instructions to the contrary, the printer will strive for an accurate reproduction of the original, and the buyer will be expected to comment upon areas where, in his opinion, there are departures.

The lack of sharp focus, poor register, dirt spots, or other evidence of faulty technique can be pointed out and communicated to the printer in easily understood terms. Color differences, however, may present more of a problem since they are less easily defined and the descriptive language is less precise.

The second function of a proof is to provide an accurate simulation of the job as it will finally appear, even though the conditions of final printing are different from those of proving. The importance of this should not be underestimated. A proof is quite useless if it cannot be simulated under production conditions. This is often overlooked; and, since it is of overriding importance, the criteria for acceptance will be dealt with first.

INTERPRETING THE COLOR BARS

At the tail end of the sheet will be the color bars, their size and format varying with the sophistication of the particular supplier. Solid bars of the single color inks are a minimum requirement. If these bars are not uniformly inked across the sheet, or if the color and strength of the inks do not match those printed under production conditions, there is bound to be difficulty when the job is finally printed.

Specifications are sometimes given for the single color inks, particularly for the strength they are to be run. This is useful but incomplete for process-color reproduction where most colors are obtained by some combination or overprinting of the inks. Red, green, and blue patches, consisting of the overprint combinations of each pair of primaries, ought, therefore, to be included in the color bars. In multicolor presswork, the ability of an ink to be deposited uniformly and in the same amount on a previously printed wet ink film as upon unprinted paper is referred to as *trapping*. If the magenta *traps* well to the yellow, a vivid red will result. If it traps poorly, the overprint will be orange even though the magenta alone is printed to the proper strength.

When the proof is printed in the sequence yellow-magenta-cyan, look for poor trapping of magenta to yellow and of cyan to yellow. This can be detected easily with instrumentation; however, in lieu of a densitometer you may use red and green filters to view the overprint patches. Through the green filter, if the magenta appears darker where printed singly than where it overprints yellow, you can suspect poor trapping. Similarly, the cyan-yellow or green overprint should not be perceptibly lighter than the cyan alone when viewed through the red filter.

Tone patches on the color bar will be useful if you have a densitometer. Otherwise use the GATF *Star*

Target, a pattern of pie-shaped wedges, and the GATF *Dot Gain Scale*, a series of numbers printed on a background of different screen rulings. (These are illustrated in "Quality Control Methods for the Graphic Arts," page 439, figures 11.29 and 11.30.)

The center of the star target will be filled with a dark spot if the dots have been "squashed" during printing. If there is a "slur" in the printing, the center will be egg-shaped. A "figure-eight" pattern will be apparent if the dots have been elongated, or enlarged in only one direction due to a condition referred to as "doubling." The precise cause is the printer's concern; the effect is yours. It means that the proof has exaggerated the tones actually appearing on the printing plate. If the colors in the proof are satisfactory, you may expect a lack of color in the final print *unless the same causes are exactly duplicated*. This is seldom the case, and few press adjustments are available to overcome this.

On the dot gain scale, one of the numbers when viewed from a moderate distance will be indistinguishable from the background. The higher this number is, the greater the dot gain involved in the reproduction. There is no absolute value for good and bad, but careful observation and experience will enable you to detect abnormalities.

PICTURE QUALITY

After you have checked the proof for printing quality you may proceed to picture quality. This encompasses many areas of taste and judgment which are beyond our scope if they are artistic rather than technical in nature. Technical shortcomings, particularly if they can be ascribed to the sources outlined above, can be easily communicated to the printer. A fairly precise language exists for this, and it is merely a matter of your understanding the fundamentals of the printing process and developing the ability to use the technical terms involved.

However, not all errors in color reproduction are accounted for by poor printing quality. The sources are complex, and need not be detailed here. Of more importance than the source is how you are to communicate the desired effect to the printer. Generally this reduces itself to the description of small color differences. Recognition of color errors arises from a set of artistic values which may not be shared with others. Effective communication with the printer is not dependent upon the elegance with which you attempt to impose your artistic values upon him, but upon the simplicity and precision you bring to the description of small color differences. These are the only areas in which his technical skills can be of help.

When the color differences are obvious or a reference color is available, the simple notation "see copy" is sufficient. In many cases this is not possible and you will have to make clear to the printer the amount and direction of the required change. In this connection it is useful to remember that the principles of psychophysics assign only three attributes to colors. All descriptive modifiers can be expressed as changes in the magnitude or direction of one or more of these attributes. If this is kept firmly in mind, the ambiguity of the commonly used descriptive terms can be eliminated.

Hue refers to the common name by which the broad families of colors are distinguished, such as red, yellow, purple, and so on.

Saturation refers to the concentration of the color. We might, for example, imagine a flask containing some water-soluble colored dye. As part of the solution is removed and replaced with water the color becomes progressively weaker, or less saturated. Thus, purple becomes lavender, red becomes pink, and orange becomes a "flesh-tone" as saturation decreases.

Darkness can be thought of as the black content of a color. It is this characteristic which is referred to by the use of such descriptive modifiers as "prussian" blue and "forest" green.

The names of the attributes are arbitrary but the concepts they convey are not. The Munsell color system uses, for example, the words *chroma* and *value* in place of saturation and darkness.

Words which cannot be clearly identified as a synonym for one of these attributes are misleading and dangerous for the purpose of color notation.

As an example, suppose there is a notation to make a certain color "lighter." Under a given set of circumstances, this can be construed as decreasing the darkness of the color by lessening the black component. Another observer might interpret the comment as a call for a less saturated or paler color. To still another observer it may imply a change of hue, such as going from lime green to chartreuse. Each observer will have grounds for justification unless the word "lighter" can be assigned unequivocally to one of the distinct attributes of color.

There is a relationship between the abstract ideas of hue, saturation, and darkness and the concrete manipulation of the primary colorants. In colors made up of three primaries there is always one which prints in the least amount. This primary controls the darkness of the color. Changes in the amount do not affect the hue of the color, provided it does not exceed either of the other two.

The hue is determined by the proportion to each other of the two major primaries. Imagine, for example, a certain color which we shall call "red." It can vary from warm to cold, from orange to rose, as the proportions of its two major components, magenta and yellow, are changed. The addition of cyan has no effect on "warmth" or "coolness" but only contributes to the darkness of the color. In this sense it is indistinguishable from the addition of black; and, in fact, black may be substituted for cyan without altering the effect.

Changes in saturation are accomplished by changing the two major components "together" so that their original proportions remain the same. Obviously, the addition of white, whether by the use of a transparent extender in "flat" color work, or the increase in area of unprinted paper in process color work, will reduce the saturation.

SUMMARY

The printer has three basic primaries which can be adjusted to produce color changes. The correct amounts can seldom be specified directly, but must be communicated in descriptive terms. The terms used must be consistent with a set of color mixing principles and must direct the changes in an unambiguous manner. Communication between printer and client is successful only when descriptive terms have the same meaning for both parties, and confusion can be resolved if the terms used can finally be reduced to changes in the direction and magnitude of the three attributes of color perception. These have separate rather than overlapping identities and are related directly to the remedial techniques available in photomechanical processes.

IMAGE ASSEMBLY
Michael H. Bruno, GRAPHIC ARTS CONSULTANT

Once individual films of various kinds—type matter, line shots, halftones, color separations—have been completed for a job, a series of assembly operations are required to position them for exposure of printing plates. The films must be inspected and *opaqued*, or spot-coated with opaque paint, to block out pinholes and other defects. Then they must be checked for size, fit, and register, and assembled into pages. Finally, the pages or sub-units must be combined into a *flat* or final assembly the size of the printing plate to be made from it. All of these operations fall within the province of *image assembly*, or *stripping*, as it is more commonly called.

Stripping for photomechanical platemaking directly parallels the traditional letterpress operations of page makeup on galleys and of form imposition on the stone. The stripper works with pieces of film instead of metal type, slugs, rules, cuts, and furniture. The complete flat corresponds to the locked-up form in the chase. Photomechanical plates are made from the finished flat; letterpress plates are made from the locked-up form, or the form is placed directly on press for printing from the type.

The quality of initial workmanship is perhaps more critical in stripping than in letterpress operations, however, because a complete press-size plate is made from the flat, whereas only single-page plates or no plates at all are made for letterpress. Unlike letterpress, the image elements on a photomechanical plate are fixed in location relative to each other once they are exposed to the plate and cannot be shifted later for color register, backing, or other alignment. In letterpress, the form can be unlocked and elements shifted, and individual page-size plates can be shifted on press.

The essential quality controlled by the stripping process is accuracy of position on the printed sheet. The skills used in copy preparation and graphic arts photography largely determine the quality of printed detail that will be reproduced. Skills in image assembly determine the quality of register and location of printed elements.

MANUAL STRIPPING OF PAGES AND FLATS
The fundamental assembly process in stripping is very simple in principle. Each piece of film is positioned carefully to a guideline of some kind on a master carrier sheet and taped in place with small pieces of adhesive tape. (See figure 9.45.) Almost anyone can learn enough in a few minutes to strip up a small single-color job consisting of a couple of pieces of film for a small-size plate to be printed as a single sheet. However, the assembly process quickly becomes exceedingly complex, requiring highly skilled craftsmen, as more images must be assembled in precise register for multicolor printing and binding into multiple-page products.

Figure 9.45: Stripper assembling film at a light table. *Courtesy of R. R. Donnelley & Sons Company.*

369

As noted earlier, stripping can be divided into two basic kinds: assembly of pages or other sub-units, and assembly of the final plate-size flat. Page stripping is concerned with the positioning of many different kinds of elements into pages—text matter, illustrations, runningheads, page numbers, and the like. If multicolor images are involved, the stripper prepares separate overlay sheets for each color. He first assembles the sheet with the key elements in place and then lays each color sheet over the key sheet, registering the other color films precisely to the key images. Registration of the color images to one another, and on the flat later, is maintained by use of a pin register system (see page 333).

While pages can be made up by stripping together individual film images, the wages paid skilled strippers are far higher than the cost of having mechanical artists assemble elements into *paste-ups* or *mechanicals* (see page 259) prior to photography. Most page assemblies, therefore, should come to the stripping stage as single-piece negatives or positives photographed from paste-ups or mechanicals. These can be made for multicolor jobs as well as for single-color projects by preparing overlays of color images keyed to the master image. Register marks and other position-control devices should be included on such camera copy. Usually such mechanicals include separate sheets for line and halftone copy (although not always), and photographs are scaled and shot separately. Thus, in many instances, when the films from this copy reach the stripping department, all the strippers have to do is place the halftones in position on the master line films.

It is also possible to do certain kinds of manipulation of illustrations at the assembly stage. For example, a photograph might be more effective if the background were eliminated and the central object silhouetted on the white paper. If the photograph does not already have the background removed prior to photography, the stripper can simply paint it out in the opaquing operation.

The second kind of stripping, that of assembling the flats for platemaking, requires additional knowledge of how the job will be printed and bound. When laying out a flat for stripping, the stripper must allow for all the subsequent operations—for positioning the flat on the press plate, for locating the plate on the press, for determining color register between printings of the sheet, and for all finishing work such as folding, cutting, binding, and trimming.

It is extremely important for the stripper to have a knowledge of the principles of *imposition*—the placing of pages on the press sheet so that the job can be run economically on press and then be cut and folded after printing to form the desired booklet, flyer, brochure, or other finished product. The considerations which must be taken into account when determining an imposition and its related margins and allowances on the flat can become extremely complex. (See "Imposition," page 519.)

In stripping for negative-working photomechanical plates, the flat is made by taping film negatives into position on a sheet of colored masking paper called *goldenrod*, or on a special orange plastic sheet if color or close register is involved. To locate the films properly on the flat, a diagram of the imposition plan

Figure 9.46: Step-and-repeat machine. *Courtesy of Rutho-Graphics Division, Sun Chemical Corporation.*

Figure 9.47: Automatic image assembly machine. *Courtesy of Royal Zenith Corporation.*

is drawn on the masking sheet prior to taping down the films. When all films are in place, the stripper turns the flat over and cuts windows in the paper or plastic masking sheet wherever images on the films are to be exposed to the plate.

If film positives are required for the platemaking process, a contact film may be made of the negative flat; or individual film positives of the various pages or sub-units can be laid out in position on a transparent sheet of acetate or Mylar. (Mylar is the most dimensionally stable type of base sheet and therefore best for close register work.) Positive flats are required for deep-etch platemaking. Also, they have been widely used for color work because it is easier to register color images in positive form. Modern pin-register systems, however, have made it easier to work with color negatives, and much more color work is now being stripped in negative form.

STEP-AND-REPEAT

When a large printing of a relatively small label or package is required, substantial press time is saved by combining many duplicate images on one plate for a large press, in order to produce many images with each press revolution. Plates of this kind can be made by producing the proper number of duplicate negatives or positives and stripping them up on a large flat, but it is usually done by a technique known as *step-and-repeat*. In this process, one master negative or positive is exposed a number of times on the plate. Some plates are made from just one negative or positive. More common are combination plates, for which multiple exposures of a number of films are made. The master film or films are mounted in a special carrier frame called a *chase*, which in turn is mounted on a step-and-repeat machine. The plate is mounted on the bed of the machine, and the carrier frame can be positioned very precisely at any desired point over the bed through use of micrometer controls. The exact positions for the duplicate images on the plate are com-

puted and the carrier frame is moved to one position after the other, with an exposure being made at each position. Figure 9.46 shows one type of step-and-repeat machine.

Some step-and-repeat machines have devices that automatically advance the chase horizontally and vertically to new positions, or move the chase in one direction and the plate in the other. These machines are controlled by programmed punched tapes or decks of punched cards. Some are also equipped with special programmed film cassettes that automatically remove a film that has been exposed to the plate and insert a new film for the next exposure. One has a semiautomatic feature in which the cassette is eliminated and the next film is put into place by the operator. In these film-replacement systems, pin register is used instead of a fixed image carrier.

AUTOMATED STRIPPING

The film cassette step-and-repeat machines which change films are actually a form of automated stripping. They replace the handwork done by the stripper in laying down pages on a flat. In book and publication work, where many pages of the same size must be positioned to the same imposition specifications, such systems offer great economies. One machine commonly used in book production is shown in figure 9.47.

A more recent development in the area of automated stripping has been the photographing of multiple-page units on a single piece of film, which is then inserted in a plate exposure device for automatic positioning of the entire unit at one time. One system known as the Photo-Imposer employs page images mounted four-up on a fan-folded continuous web of paper similar to a continuous business form. The paste-ups are assembled under control of a computer-generated digital display program. The four-up paste-ups are photographed automatically at full size on 24-inch roll film, which is then inspected and opaqued. Halftones are inserted and the film roll is cut into four-up units for imposition and platemaking without conventional stripping or layouts.

In addition to systems that work with finished-size pages, a number of systems have been developed which employ microfilm images during the assembly and exposure of press forms. The micro-images offer advantages over same-size images in cost of film and storage space required. However, these advantages may be offset in some cases by the convenience of working at same-size. Because these microstripping systems also involve other operations in addition to stripping, they are discussed separately in the following article.

MICROFILM-TO-PLATE SYSTEMS

Richard D. Murray, INSTITUTE FOR GRAPHIC COMMUNICATION

Critical paper shortages, increasing document storage costs, and the availability of improved hardware have prompted many printers and publishers to reevaluate the role of microfilm in their future. Those in graphic arts management, who had clearly rejected the idea of using microfilm, are now concluding that microforms can supplement paper, and that both media are here to stay. Commercial printers are now seriously evaluating new techniques for printing-plate production directly from microfilm.

Figure 9.48 diagrammatically shows the work flow of a conventional platemaking system. A full-size (1:1) film is prepared from original hardcopy supplied by the customer or produced by a typesetter, or the typesetter may prepare his copy directly on film. The full-size film is *stripped* or *imposed* into a *flat* along with other films. The printing plate is then produced by placing the light-sensitive plate material in contact with the film flat and exposing the two to a suitable light source.

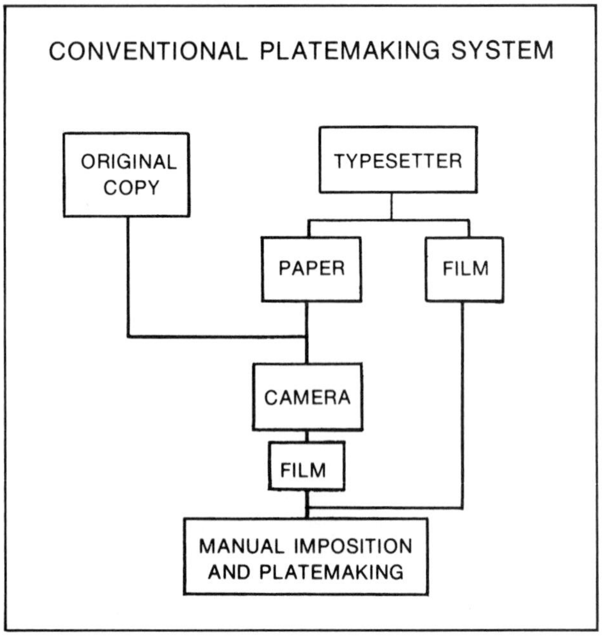

Figure 9.49 shows a common imposition. The fact that pages are not in order, that neither plate contains all consecutive pages, and that pages are not oriented in one direction have a profound effect on the concept and design of the projection platemaking systems. (See also "Imposition," page 519.)

OLDER PROJECTION SYSTEMS

Projection platemaking or printing systems have been commercially available for some time. They are characterized by relatively small sheet size, plates or

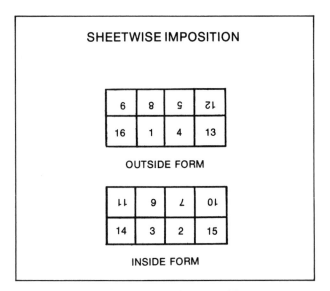

Figure 9.49: A common sheet-wise imposition.

Figure 9.48: Diagrammatic representation of work flow of a conventional platemaking system.

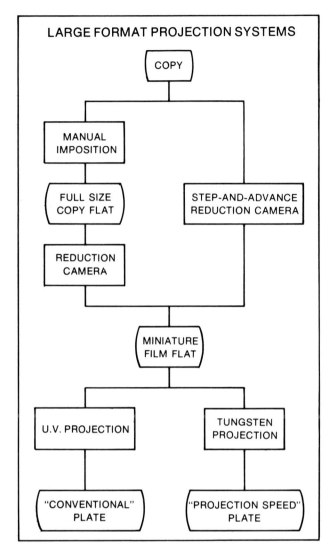

LARGE FORMAT PROJECTION SYSTEMS

Figure 9.50: Large-format projection systems. Diagram shows work flow for projection methods for making printing plates from microfiche or film chips. Tungsten light is used with projection speed plates and ultraviolet radiation with conventional plates.

NEWER PROJECTION SYSTEMS

Projection platemaking systems can be classified into two types: large-format projection systems (see figure 9.50) and step-and-advance projection systems (see figure 9.51). Both can be subdivided according to whether the projection is done using ultraviolet light for *conventional plates* or visible (tungsten) light for *projection speed plates*.

Areas of application

There are two main driving forces for development of projection platemaking systems. First is an upsurge in the quantity of computer-generated dynamic documents which must be reproduced rapidly with moderately good quality and in the form of many-paged documents. An increasing amount of material is generated in microfilm by COM (computer output onto microfilm) and is not available as full-size copy for input to the printing process. Second, there is a need for cost reduction in both commercial and in-plant printing shops. For many users, both of these factors are reinforced by improvements and pending developments in large-size, production-speed lithographic plates.

Figure 9.52 diagrammatically shows that these forces are causing expansion of the *reprographic* or *utility* printing area and the *graphic arts* printing area into each other's domain. The overlap area (where the requirements of graphic arts and utility printing are identical), as well as the areas adjacent to the overlap, are suitable candidates for the newer projection platemaking systems. These areas are among the fastest growing in the printing industry today.

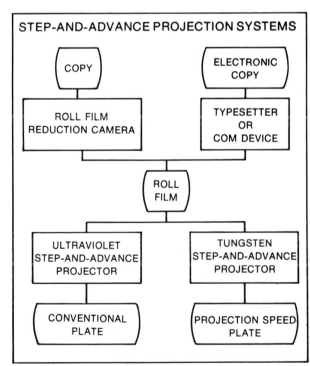

STEP-AND-ADVANCE PROJECTION SYSTEMS

Figure 9.51: Step-and-advance projection systems. Diagram shows work flow for projection technique for producing printing plates from roll films.

processes with high sensitivity in the visible spectrum (*projection speed plates*), and relatively short production runs. These early systems fall into the following classifications:

• Direct copy to plate
• Microfilm to plate on a single page-per-plate basis
• Microfilm *blowback* to printed sheet (e.g., xerographic microfilm printers)
• Copy to printed sheet (e.g., electrostatic copiers or hybrid machines which produce plates and provide offset copies, all in a single unit)

The older systems, listed above, are well known and will not be detailed in this discussion. The newer microfilm-to-plate techniques, reviewed below, are characterized by large sheet sizes and are related to conventional printing operations rather than reprographic systems.

Time and other economic factors will prevent the newer projection systems from finding use in utility printing; that is, rapid reproduction of material with a low copy count in small sheet sizes. Likewise, quality considerations will preclude the use of these systems, at least for the time being, for those graphic arts applications which require very close register, very high resolution, and combinations of tonal and line copy.

Projection platemaking has many potential uses. They include production of phone directories, maintenance manuals, parts lists, supply catalogs, computer program listings, library lists, law enforcement listings, illustrated parts catalogs, instruction manuals, price lists, inventories, business forms, stock market reports, charts and graphs, maps, credit card listings, real estate listings, and trade books.

Cost factors

Three principal cost-reduction factors for projection platemaking systems should be considered. First is reduced *film costs*. Since film is priced roughly on an area basis, reduction from full-size to smaller sizes is economically desirable. The approximate savings in film for reduction from 8″ x 10″ to smaller film sizes are as follows:

Film size	Area reduction ratio	Percent savings
8″ x 10″	1.00	0
105mm	0.32	67
70mm	0.12	88
35mm	0.03	97
16mm	0.006	99+

For printing systems which already use COM-generated microfilm, there is, of course, no saving due to the reduction of size. However, there is a saving due to the ability to directly use the output of the COM device in the printing process.

A second area in which costs may be reduced is in *labor costs for imposition*. Depending on work load and labor rates, this factor may be at least as significant as the reduced film costs.

Third, costs for *flat storage and retrieval* are lowered. In some graphic arts applications, the cost of storage, retrieval and remake of flats is very significant.

Plate cost can also be a critical factor in choosing a platemaking system. Paper projection plates compete price-wise with diazo and wipe-on plates, but they are not capable of long runs. Projection plates seem to be unsuitable for long runs at the present time.

Problem areas

Projection platemaking represents a significant departure from conventional platemaking systems, especially for graphic arts printing. It cannot be introduced without some consideration of the effect it will have on the entire system and possible compromises which may have to be made. The major technical problems include:

Image quality requirements. The definition of image quality, the setting of quality criteria for each printed

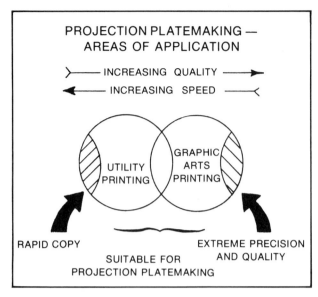

Figure 9.52: Projection platemaking: areas of application. Diagram shows that except when extremes of speed and quality are required (shaded areas), projection platemaking is suitable for both high-quality graphic arts printing and high-speed moderate-quality utility printing markets. To some extent these markets have merged (overlap area).

product, and the relation of these requirements to projection system design have not received adequate study. Projection systems will, in general, not give the image quality and product flexibility obtainable from manual contact platemaking systems. While the projection quality can be quite high (often higher than required by the job), the lack of suitable objective criteria can lead to some reluctance to accept less than the "absolute best" in image quality.

Surburn methods. In roll film systems, where projection is done on a page-per-frame basis, surburn for printers' marks and additions of some unchanging data can extend platemaking time excessively. Surburns can be accomplished on the microfilm by multiple exposure, on the projection platemaker by multiple exposure, or as a conventional contact exposure with an unchanging full-size flat after projection from film. Selection of the right method depends on a detailed evaluation of the particular printing requirement.

Exposure time. For ultraviolet roll film systems especially, exposure time can be very long because of the low light-sensitivity of the plate. Work load must be carefully analyzed to arrive at the maximum exposure time per frame allowable. To shorten the exposure time, high ultraviolet light intensities must be used. Heat generation in the microfilm, due to absorption of light, must be carefully considered.

SUMMARY

Microprojection platemaking systems use microfilm for input and, in a single step, produce plates ready for use on the printing press. They can be divided into two categories: sequential (also known as step-and-advance or step-and-repeat) for exposing one-up or two-up images, and signature-composed (large format). The main feature of the signature-composed projection platemakers, the automation of the imposition step, should lead to dramatic cost savings.

Acceptance of microfilm-to-plate systems should grow during the next few years. These platemaking systems offer considerable economic benefits for a wide range of printing requirements. Some of the systems, particularly those using tungsten light, are enjoying commercial use. Ultraviolet projection systems may offer advantages in terms of allowing use of conventional plates.

Benefits of projection plate systems include faster platemaking capability and less expensive lay-up of camera-ready copy compared to stripping film-negative flats. The need for opaquing is reduced. Small film is easier to file and requires less storage space than full-sized negatives. The equipment is more compact, and labor and material costs are lower.

Book printers, in-plant printers, and commercial printers are using projection platemaking systems to good advantage. Successful use of projection platemaking in individual cases will depend on how well it is implemented as part of the entire printing process.

PLATEMAKING 10

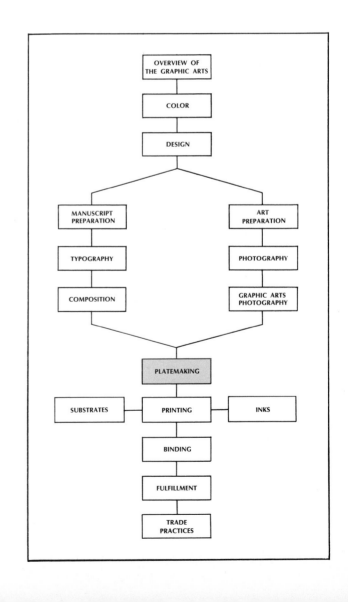

OVERVIEW OF
THE GRAPHIC ARTS

COLOR

DESIGN

MANUSCRIPT
PREPARATION

ART
PREPARATION

TYPOGRAPHY

PHOTOGRAPHY

COMPOSITION

GRAPHIC ARTS
PHOTOGRAPHY

PLATEMAKING

SUBSTRATES

PRINTING

INKS

BINDING

FULFILLMENT

TRADE
PRACTICES

FUNDAMENTALS OF PLATEMAKING
Michael H. Bruno, GRAPHIC ARTS CONSULTANT

Each printing process uses a *plate*, or some form of *image carrier*, which transfers the ink image to the paper or other substrate during printing. To do this, every printing plate in some way or another must be selective in picking up ink in the areas to be printed and rejecting ink in the non-printing areas. *Relief* plates, used in letterpress printing, do this by having a raised surface on which ink is applied, while non-printing areas are depressed below the level that the inking rollers on the press can reach. *Intaglio* plates or cylinders, used in gravure, are the reverse of letterpress; they have tiny depressions or wells that are filled with ink to be transferred to the paper, while the non-printing areas are scraped clean of ink before the plate contacts the paper. *Planographic* plates, used in offset lithography, have image and non-image areas on the same plane but separate the ink and non-printing areas by means of physicochemical principles; the image areas are ink receptive, while the non-image areas are water receptive so that they reject ink. *Screen* or *stencil* image carriers have porous image areas through which the ink is forced; the ink is blocked in the non-image areas. (Figure 10.1 illustrates these four types of image carriers.)

There are several methods used to produce printing plates. Hand cutting or hand carving is the oldest method, dating back before the invention of movable type. Full-page images were carved on a single block, which formed a relief plate for letterpress printing. Although this kind of carving is no longer used for commercial production, hand cutting of stencils for screen printing is still done, and many steel dies for engraved printing are still produced by hand engraving. Lithography first started with the use of hand-drawn images on stone; this technique is still used by some artists to produce lithographs in limited signed editions.

For hundreds of years following the invention of movable type, the type itself was used as the primary printing surface. The metal type was cast as raised characters and constituted a relief or letterpress surface. In the late 1800's, with the development of mass-market magazines and metropolitan daily newspapers, a need for longer lasting *duplicate plates* came into being. These duplicate plates had to be relatively inexpensive so that multiple sets could be made easily from the master image. In the last 50 years, there has been a broad movement to *photomechanical* platemaking for all printing processes.

THE PHOTOMECHANICAL PROCESS

Regardless of the printing process for which they are intended, all photomechanical plates are made by exposing a light-sensitized plate surface through a film positive or negative and then processing the plate to separate printing and non-printing areas in some man-

ner. When a plate is exposed, the coating areas struck by light are, in most cases, hardened so that they are insoluble in solutions used for developing the plates. There are some coatings, however, that are rendered soluble when light-exposed, and are impervious to developer solutions in the areas that are unexposed. In all cases, the soluble coating is washed away. The insoluble coating may serve as the ink-carrying vehicle

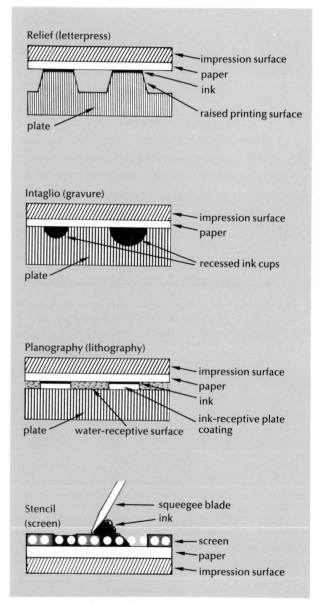

Figure 10.1: Basic principles of the four major printing processes.

378

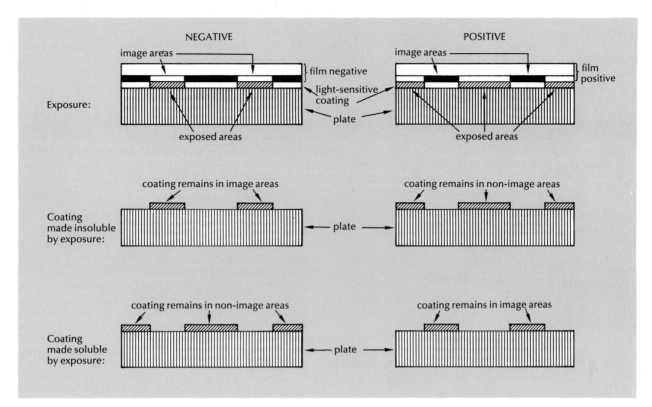

NEGATIVE

image areas

film negative

light-sensitive coating

Exposure:

plate

exposed areas

POSITIVE

image areas

film positive

exposed areas

coating remains in image areas

Coating made insoluble by exposure:

plate

coating remains in non-image areas

coating remains in non-image areas

Coating made soluble by exposure:

plate

coating remains in image areas

Figure 10.2: Negative-working and positive-working materials. Negative-working platemaking systems start by exposing the light-sensitive plate coating through a film negative; depending on the kind of coating used on the plate, the coating remains in either image areas or non-printing areas after development. Positive-working systems start with exposure through a film positive; here, too, the coating may remain in either image or non-image areas. Some plates thus coated are ready for use on the press; others require further processing, such as etching.

during printing, as in all letterpress plates and lithographic surface plates. These plates are made from negatives. In plates made from positives, the insoluble coating serves as a protective barrier—a *stencil* or *resist*—during an etching step that divides the plate surface into printing and non-printing areas. Plates using this principle are used for lithography, gravure, and screen printing. (The principles of negative- and positive-working plates are illustrated in figure 10.2.) Most plates are developed by manual techniques, but in recent years there has been a trend toward the use of automatic processors.

LIGHT-SENSITIVE COATINGS

The most important types of coatings in use are *bichromated colloids, diazos,* and *photopolymers.* There is a relief plate using a silver halide coating, but, in general, silver halide and electrostatic coatings are used for sensitizing special-purpose plates used especially in duplicating. A new type of electrostatic coating has the resolution and light sensitivity for use in lithography (see "Special Plates" page 395).

Bichromated colloid coatings

Until 1950, practically all the coatings used for photomechanical plates were bichromated colloids. Some are still in use. The bichromate is usually ammonium bichromate, but potassium bichromate is also used in special processes such as collotype. The colloids in use are shellac, glue, albumin, and polyvinyl alcohol (PVA) for photoengraving; albumin, casein, alpha protein, PVA, and gum arabic for lithography; and gelatin for gravure, screen printing, and collotype. The bichromated coatings are usually applied to the metal plates in a machine called a *whirler*, which spreads the coating over the plate as it rotates.

While bichromated colloids have been in use for a long time, they require considerable skill and judgment since their light sensitivity is affected by a number of factors. These include temperature, relative humidity, pH, and coating thickness—which itself is affected by the surface roughness or *grain* of the plate, relative humidity, rate of application of coating, coating temperature and viscosity. Because of the difficulty in controlling these factors, considerable research has been aimed at reducing the need for bichromated coatings by expanding the usefulness of presensitized and precoated plates for all processes. Water pollution by heavy metals such as chromium has also been a problem, and some communities are outlawing the use of bichromated colloids.

Diazo coatings

The use of diazo coatings for presensitizing metal lithographic plates was introduced about 1950. Diazo coatings are also used for lithographic wipe-on plates, in which case the coating is applied by the platemaker

379

with a sponge, or on a simple roller-coater instead of a whirler. The coatings are applied to relatively smooth or very fine grained plates that are pretreated or electrically anodized to prevent contamination of the coating by the metal. The common plate pretreatment, which also renders the metal water receptive, is usually a silicate, but other types of pretreatments can be used. Anodized aluminum surfaces are more effective in plate processing and are longer lasting on press than silicate-treated aluminum surfaces.

Diazo coatings are thin and thus vulnerable to abrasive wear during press runs. For this reason lithographic surface plates, on which a hardened diazo coating constitutes the image areas, are not suitable for runs much in excess of 75,000 impressions. There are, however, some prelacquered diazo plates which have better resistance to abrasion, and these are used for runs in excess of 100,000.

Most diazo plates are coated for processing with negatives, but positive-process coatings are also used. One type of diazo is used to sensitize other colloids used for coating some positive-process plates. Diazo coatings are also used to presensitize deep-etch and bimetal plates.

The main advantage of diazo coatings is that under normal conditions of use they are not affected appreciably by temperature and relative humidity, and therefore have a storage life of about six months to a year. Exposure to temperatures above 125°F can permanently damage plates and cause them to *scum,* or take ink in non-printing areas. Refrigeration extends the storage life of most photosensitive materials.

Diazo-coated plates can be processed in automatic processing machines that speed up platemaking and produce more consistent results than manual platemaking. Automatic plate-processing machines are available for every platemaking process. One unit designed for wipe-on diazo plates even incorporates exposure of the plate. Another for photopolymer plates incorporates coating as well as exposure. Automatic processors are used extensively, especially for making plates for newspapers printed by web offset.

Photopolymer coatings

Terminology in platemaking has become quite confusing since the introduction of many new photosensitive systems which are all being referred to as *photopolymer* plates. Leonard and Traskos, in a paper presented before the Society of Photographic Scientists and Engineers in October, 1972, suggested the following names for the different photoreactions: *photopolymerization, photocrosslinking, photorearrangement,* and *photodegradation.* It is difficult to apply these terms properly to the commercial products in use without a careful study of the patent literature to identify the products with particular methods. In this section some products that should be identified differently will be called photopolymers because of a lack of complete information describing the product.

In general, organic soluble coatings, such as Kodak Photo Resist (KPR), which contains cinnamic acid esters and is used for all three major printing processes and for printed circuits, are of the photocrosslinking type. Many of the other polymer coatings used in letterpress and lithography contain photopolymers.

Some new lithographic plates made from positives are of the photorearrangement and photodegradable types.

The main advantages of photopolymer plates are their abrasion resistance, which gives them good wear characteristics in printing, and their insensitivity to changes in temperature and relative humidity, which gives them long shelf life in storage before use. Some have good solvent resistance and are useful in processes such as flexography that employ solvent inks. Run life of photopolymer lithographic plates has been extended to as high as 1 million impressions by baking the plates after processing in an oven at about 500° F (250° C) for 4½ to 5 minutes.

EXPOSURE OF PHOTOMECHANICAL PLATES

The most common method of exposing photomechanical plates is contact printing. Certain types of short-run duplicating plates are designed for exposure by enlargement projection from miniature images such as microforms. Such projection systems hold much promise for certain fields, such as book production, but major limitations on their ability to reproduce all kinds of subjects on heavier duty plates have so far prevented widespread use in the printing industry.

Photomechanical plates are exposed in either a vacuum frame or a step-and-repeat machine. Both types of equipment hold a film negative or positive in tight contact with the sensitized plate through use of vacuum while the exposure is made. In a contact frame, the film is registered to the plate manually. In a step-and-repeat machine, the master film image is positioned manually or by pin register in a special carrier called a *chase,* which is then mounted on a precision indexing mechanism on the machine. The chase is positioned for the first exposure, and then moved or *stepped* to the next exposure position. Step-and-repeat machines are thus used to expose multiple images precisely on a plate from a single master film image. Step-and-repeat machines are available in which the steps are programmed on punched tape or cards, and films are stacked so that exposures are made automatically after the first exposure.

A light source rich in ultraviolet rays makes the exposure. Pulsed xenon lamps or metal halide lamps are used. Two types of metal halide lamps are made with peak emissions corresponding to the peak absorption bands of the plate coatings used. Diazo coatings show their maximum absorption at about 410 nm, while most photopolymer plates have their maximum absorption at about 360 nm. Pulsed xenon has a relatively continuous spectrum so it can be used for either type of plate, but exposures are longer.

For further discussion of contact printing, microfilm-to-plate systems, vacuum frames, step-and-repeat machines, and lights for platemaking, see Section 9, *Graphic Arts Photography.*

The newest photomechanical method for exposing images on printing plates is with lasers. EOCOM Corporation's Laserite system uses lasers to expose an image on the coating of a lithographic plate; the plate then requires conventional processing. Another laser platemaking system is the LogEScan, in which lasers are used to transfer the image-area coating onto an uncoated metal plate. (See page 397.)

LETTERPRESS PLATEMAKING
Michael H. Bruno, GRAPHIC ARTS CONSULTANT

Two basic types of plates are used in letterpress printing—*original plates* and *duplicate plates*. Original plates are made by photomechanical means from art or photographs which have been converted to line or halftone negatives. They can be either photoengraved metal plates or photopolymer plates. Duplicate plates are made from molds formed from original plates. Original plates can be used either directly for printing—in which case they are called *direct plates*—or for making duplicate-plate molds. In general practice, photoengraved metal original plates are used for direct printing only in shorter-run situations, and duplicate plates are made for long-run production. (Wraparound metal and photopolymer plates are used for long runs as well.) Most original and duplicate letterpress plates are made in small pieces or in individual-page sizes for assembly in a form or on the printing cylinder of the press.

ORIGINAL PLATES

Original plates today can be made from various metals by acid etching processes, or from various plastics, which are *photopolymers*. In the United States, various kinds of original metal plates are usually

called *photoengravings*, or simply *engravings*; in England, they are called *blocks*, because engravings for letterpress printing were originally mounted on blocks of wood to make them type-high. There are three general types of engravings: line, halftone, and combination. (Line and halftone etching processes are illustrated in figure 10.3.) Original plates are made from negatives; the negatives must be straight-reading on the emulsion side, as the image on the plate must be reverse-reading for direct printing on the paper.

Another kind of original letterpress plate used in certain applications is the so-called *wraparound plate*. A wraparound letterpress plate is actually an original plate made by the same general photomechanical means by which engravings are produced. Unlike other letterpress plates, however, it is made to the full size of the press cylinder and mounted in one piece that wraps around the cylinder; other letterpress plates are made in smaller units and mounted on only a portion of the press cylinder.

In this respect, wraparound letterpress plates are similar to lithographic plates, which are all wraparound in principle, and to sheet-fed gravure plates, which are used in place of removable press cylinders.

In letterpress, wraparound plates are used in letterset

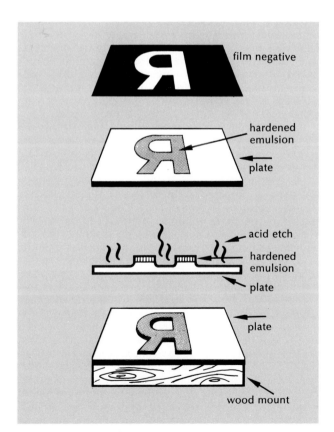

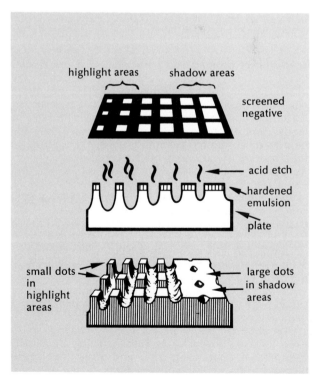

Figure 10.3: Photoengraving process. Line engraving is shown at left; halftone engraving, below.

381

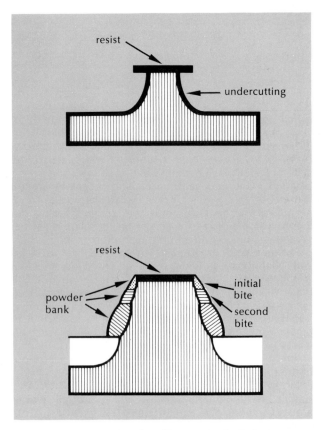

Figure 10.4: Conventional etching method of photoengraving. Plate must be etched in a series of "bites" to prevent undercutting. If plate is etched in one bite as shown at top, acid will eat metal away horizontally as well as vertically, cutting under the resist and reducing size of image area from that desired. When plate is etched in several bites as shown at bottom, sides of image area projection are coated with powder after each bite to protect them from undercutting during subsequent bites.

or dry offset printing and on wraparound presses for direct printing. The major advantage is that all of the image elements are fixed on a single plate in the proper position for printing, reducing the time for setup, or *makeready*, as it is called. The plates are plastic or metal, from 0.017" to 0.030" in thickness, so they can be bent to fit into the cylinder clamps and conform to the curvature of the cylinder during printing.

Photoengravings

Photoengravings are made on zinc, magnesium, or copper of about 16 gauge (0.065") in thickness. In the United States, zinc and magnesium are generally used for line engravings, and copper is used for halftones. In Europe, zinc is used for both types of engravings.

Photoengravings are made by etching away areas of the plate which should not print, leaving only printing areas at the full height. During etching, the printing surfaces are protected from the etching chemicals by a hardened photosensitive coating.

Conventional photoengraving. The coating sensitizers used in conventional photoengraving are usually bichromated shellac for zinc and magnesium, and bichromated glue for copper. Some plates are pre-

coated with Kodak Photo Resist, a special acid-resistant coating. After the plate has been coated, exposed, and processed, the metal in the non-printing areas is removed by chemical etching and by mechanical routing in the large areas. Nitric acid is used to etch zinc and magnesium, and ferric chloride solutions are used for copper. Depth of etching can vary in 133-line halftone engravings from 0.0014" in the shadows to 0.0029" in the highlights, and on line engravings from 0.020" for a high-finish paper to 0.040" for flexographic printing on rough papers such as the liner for corrugated board. (Conventional etching is illustrated in figure 10.4.)

The main problem in conventional etching is to maintain the correct dot and line width while achieving the proper etch depth, since chemical etching occurs sideways as well as downwards during successive etching steps, or *bites*. Until recently, the control of sidewise etching, or *undercutting*, of halftone dots was implemented by *scale compression* in the negative. In scale compression, much larger dots are left in the highlights on the negative than are necessary to reproduce the original, thus compensating for the undercutting that reduces the size of the highlight dots during etching. However, it is difficult to control middletone and shadow dots this way. *Four-way powdering* has been used to prevent undercutting of these images. By this method, a reddish powder called *dragon's blood*, or another acid-resistant material, is brushed onto the plate after each etching step to cover the sides of the etched areas. The plate is then baked in an oven so that the powder fuses onto the sides of the etched image elements, protecting them from attack during subsequent applications of etch. This procedure may have to be repeated a number of times until the correct printing depth is reached. Four-way powdering is a time-consuming operation that requires considerable skill and judgment. In addition, because of the unevenness of etching, considerable hand correction in the form of *fine etching* is needed. This is not only time-consuming but very expensive.

Conventional etching techniques were used for all photoengravings until the development of *powderless etching*. Now the older photoengraving methods are practically obsolete.

Powderless etching. In this photoengraving method, the plate is prepared as in the conventional process, but the negative is normal, not requiring scale compression. The same coatings can be used as in conventional etching. A special etching machine is used, and the etching bath consists of an emulsion of nitric acid, oils, and a wetting agent. During processing, as the etch breaks up the protective coating on the plate, the wetting agent and oil form a *banking agent* that continuously adheres to the sides of the etched image elements and resists lateral or sidewise etching. (Powderless etching is illustrated figure 10.5.) The first system was developed for magnesium and was adapted for use on zinc, and a modification of it has also been developed for use on aluminum. A mechanically similar system has been developed for copper. The ingredients of the etching baths are quite different for different metals, but the principles of operation are similar. These systems can be used for wraparound plates as

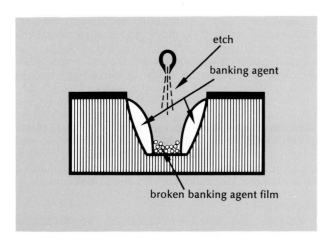

Figure 10.5: Powderless etching method of photoengraving. Plate is etched in one "bite," and chemicals in the etch solution coat sides of the etched area to protect them from undercutting.

well as original plates. A modification of the copper system is also used for etching gravure cylinders.

Photopolymer plates

Photopolymer plates (fig. 10.6) are precoated and can be used as original (direct) and wraparound plates or as molds for duplicate plates. A number of these are in use or in development. Among the most important and most promising photopolymer relief plates are the following:

Dycril. Dycril photopolymer plates were introduced commercially by Du Pont in 1959 to provide the printing industry with a more versatile and rapid means for preparing relief printing plates. Dycril plates have since attained worldwide application in flat, rotary, and wraparound letterpress printing and in letterset printing. They also serve as patterns for preparing stereotypes, electrotypes, and rubber printing plates.

Dycril plates are supplied in a wide range of thicknesses, sizes, and structures. They consist of a layer of light-sensitive plastic that is bonded to a metal or film support. When the Dycril plate is exposed to ultraviolet radiation through a line or halftone negative, the exposed areas are polymerized and hardened. The unexposed surrounding areas are then washed away with an alkaline water spray. A relief printing design remains that is correctly structured and firmly adhered to its supporting metal or film base.

Dycril plates can be prepared flat or curved to fit most types of presses. They are simple to finish and mount. They offer increased productivity since they reduce makeready time on the press and provide good ink transfer because of their uniform thickness and resiliency. When used for letterset printing on offset presses, they produce long runs at high speeds with less stock waste during start-up.

Nyloprint. Nyloprint printing plates, manufactured by BASF, are photopolymer plates consisting of a photosensitive layer securely bonded to a backing material which may be aluminum for flat-bed plates, steel for wraparound plates, or distortion-resistant foil for special applications. The photosensitive polymer

layer is based on nylon, a polyamide noted for its strength and wear resistance.

Nyloprint plates have a characteristic built-in makeready; thus makeready time is considerably shorter than for conventional plates. Total processing time for Nyloprint plates is less than 30 minutes, according to plate type, and processing is easy and accurate. Nyloprint also offers high printing quality, simple storage, absolute stability, and identical tonal values in multiple plates made from the same negative.

Nyloprint plates may be used in every letterpress and letterset printing application for a wide variety of printed matter. They can also be used for molding. Nyloprint correction foils are available for minor changes of completed plates. Steel-base Nyloprint plates mounted on magnetic cylinders are the most extensively used system for magazine and other long-run letterpress printing.

Letterflex. The Letterflex plate, made and marketed by W. R. Grace & Co., is used by a number of newspapers as well as by the book industry. The primary use in book printing has been on the Cameron Belt Press, which prints and binds books in one operation (see "Book Production Systems," page 431).

Letterflex plates consist of a liquid photosensitive prepolymer, which is coated in a special machine onto a polyester sheet and exposed to a negative. Exposure converts the liquid polymer to a solid in the printing areas. Non-printing areas remain liquid and are removed in the processing step. The plates are flexible and can be bent easily around press cylinders. Moreover, they can be repeatedly flexed without damage, which is the property that permits their use on the Cameron machine.

Dynaflex. The Dynaflex plate is used mainly for newspapers. The plate consists of a dry prepolymer photosensitized coating which must be kept under refrigeration until exposure. During exposure in contact with a negative, the image areas are polymerized and hardened, and the non-image areas are removed by development in water.

NAPP. The NAPP plate is a denatured polyvinyl alcohol bonded to steel or aluminum and was de-

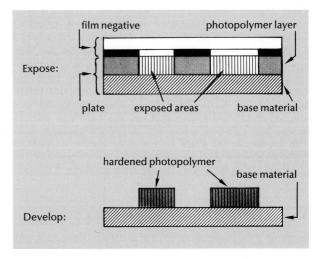

Figure 10.6: Photopolymer process. After exposure, unexposed polymer is dissolved away through washing or etching.

veloped by the Nippon Paint Co., Ltd. (Osaka, Japan). It is manufactured and marketed in the United States through a joint venture of Nippon Paint and Lee Enterprises, Inc. (Davenport, Iowa). The plates come from the manufacturer presensitized and ready for exposure. After a plate is placed with a negative in an exposure frame and exposed, it is washed in plain water to remove the unexposed non-printing areas. The process is very quick, and the plates are said to be inexpensive enough to compete with stereotypes. Halftone screens up to 150 lines have been printed successfully with these plates, although letterpress newspaper work typically uses much coarser screens.

While currently offered only as a letterpress plate, the NAPP materials and processing system are readily applicable to lithographic and gravure plates; a water-developed lithographic plate has been made.

Merigraph. The Merigraph plate is a liquid unsaturated polyester photopolymer like the Letterflex plate and is made in a similar manner by coating just before exposure. It was developed as the APR plate in Japan and is manufactured in the United States by Hercules, Inc. (Wilmington, Delaware). It is used also as a flexographic plate and has produced good 133-line halftones on the Cameron Belt Press.

Other Japanese plates. A number of other Japanese photopolymer relief plates have been developed, such as the Sonne KPM 2000, Toplon, Tevista, and Torelief plates. None of these plates have found use in the U.S. One new Japanese plate, called Printight, is a nylon-based photopolymer plate that is developed in water. It is manufactured by the Toyobo Co., a prominent Japanese textile manufacturer. The plate is on a polyester base and can produce good-quality halftones up to 150-line. When generally available, it could provide the means for producing high-quality halftones on the Belt Press. It will also be useful in eliminating water pollution, which is a problem with some of the other photopolymer relief plates.

Kodak Relief Plate (KRP)

The Kodak Relief Plate is used mainly as a wraparound plate for letterset printing in packaging. It consists of four layers which are, from top to bottom: a silver halide photographic emulsion; a white pigmented layer; a relatively thick layer of cellulose acetate modified so that it is soluble in an alkaline solution; and a sheet of lacquered steel as the substrate. After exposure to a negative, the plate is placed in a special developer which hardens, or *tans*, the emulsion in the image areas, making it resistant to the action of the etch. The plate is then processed in a special machine which removes the cellulose acetate in the non-printing areas with a special alkaline bath. The Kodak Relief Plate is not very abrasion resistant and therefore not recommended for direct printing, but it is capable of long runs for letterset printing.

DUPLICATE PLATES

Duplicate plates are made by casting or otherwise forming moldable material in a mold. They fall into four basic classifications depending on materials and/or molding techniques used. These classifications are: *stereotypes, electrotypes,* and *plastic* and *rubber* plates.

Duplicate plates are desirable for several reasons. First, certain types of duplicate plates, such as electrotypes, can be made with much harder surfaces than original plates, affording longer life on press. Also, duplicate plates can be made in curved form to fit press cylinders whereas original plates sometimes cannot. In addition, the making of duplicate plates for use on press enables the original plates and molds to be protected from damage during printing; if press plates are damaged, replacements can be made quickly. And finally, multiple sets of plates can be made for printing on more than one press, thus shortening the elapsed time required for producing very long print runs.

Stereotypes

Virtually the sole application of stereotypes is letterpress newspaper printing, and with the introduction of photopolymer plates, this use is diminishing rapidly. For production of a stereotype, a special papier-mâché mold, or *mat*, is made from an original plate, and the printing plate is cast by pouring molten metal into the mat. For long runs, the plate can be plated with nickel, chromium or iron. Once the mat is made, duplicate plates can be made in less than a minute and at very reasonable cost.

Several plastic molded plates have been developed to replace stereotypes, but none have been completely successful for newspapers because they are more expensive than stereotypes. The *Asahi Shimbun*, a Japanese newspaper with a national circulation of over 6 million, has developed the Asahi Rollflex system, in which ordinary stereo mats are made with special coatings and polypropylene is used as the molding material. These plates have many advantages, but the increasing cost of polypropylene, a petrochemical, has made them too expensive for use. The *Los Angeles Times* has also developed a polypropylene duplicate plate; the *Times* has made the process cost-effective by recycling the used plates.

Electrotypes

Electrotypes are used for high-quality letterpress, commercial, book, and magazine printing. The first step in the production of an electrotype is making an impression of the original engraving in hot plastic. This mold is plated with silver to make it conductive and then is plated electrolytically with a thin shell of copper or nickel. The shell is removed from the mold and is backed with molten metal. The face of the electrotype shell can be nickel, iron, or chromium plated for long runs of up to several million impressions. However, photopolymer plates are replacing electrotypes.

Plastic and rubber plates

Plastic and rubber plates are made from molds similar to those used for electrotypes. They have the advantages of being lightweight and low in cost.

Plastic plates are used for some types of commercial printing and are molded from thermoplastic vinyl resins. They are in short supply because of the shortage of oil from which vinyl resins are derived and because of regulations on the toxicity of the vinyl monomer used in resin manufacture.

Rubber plates are molded from either natural or synthetic rubber or combinations of them, depending on the solvents in the inks used for printing. Rubber plates are used in flexography for printing such materials as wrapping paper, bags, envelopes, corrugated boxes, and milk cartons, where the resilience of the rubber is of help in printing on the relatively rough surfaces. They are also used on special central-impression presses for printing extensible printing films for flexible packaging. Paperback books, too, are printed from rubber plates, but generally by letterpress, as oil-base inks are used instead of the solvent inks used in flexography.

FLEXOGRAPHIC PLATES

Most flexographic plates are rubber plates made from plastic molds that are cast from photoengravings (see figure 10.7). In recent years there has been considerable development of special plates to improve the quality of flexographic printing. The first of these was the Corning Glass plate (now known as Graphinetics glass plate), which consists of photosensitive glass that produces a mold directly from a negative. Rubber plates molded in this system are very uniform in thickness and in printing characteristics. The first 150-line flexographic full-color printing was done from these plates.

Photopolymer direct printing plates, which do not require an original plate or mold, have also been developed for flexography. At present, four plates are produced especially for flexography: the Uniroyal plate, Du Pont Cyrel, W. R. Grace Letterflex, and the Hercules Merigraph plate. All of these plates show improvements in quality and performance over conventional rubber molded plates.

Conventional plates have also been improved with the use of compressible sticky-back tape and a waffle-back compressible pattern on the backs of the plates. The improvements in flexographic plates are so dramatic that flexography is entering many fields of printing other than packaging.

TRENDS IN LETTERPRESS PLATES

Letterpress is declining in use, and by 1985 its main use will be in large daily newspapers, label and packaging printing, and business forms. Its use in

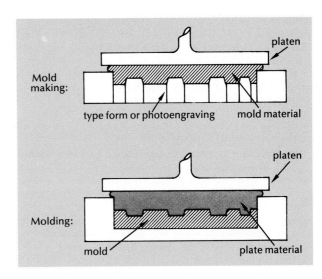

Figure 10.7: Molded plastic or rubber plate process. Mold of relief type and engravings is first made, then used as a master to make duplicate plates.

magazines and other publications will diminish. Newspapers will use mainly low-cost plates. In other uses, the most popular plate system appears to be steel-base Nyloprint plates on magnetic cylinders.

The plates used for newspaper printing cover a wide gamut. According to information from the American Newspaper Publishers Association Research Institute (ANPA-RI), 495 newspapers were printed by letterpress in the United States in 1978. Of these, 169 or 34.1% were printed with NAPP plates, 84 (17%) used Letterflex plates, 82 (16.6%) were printed by Di-Litho (lithographic plates on a letterpress press), 56 (11.3%) used Merigraph plates, 54 (10.9%) still used stereotype plates, 33 (6.7%) used Dynaflex plates, 8 (1.6%) used magnesium plates, 6 (1.2%) used Dycril plates, 2 (0.4%) were printed on a flat-bed press, and 1 (0.2%) used injection-molded plastic plates. Also of interest is the information that 1,724 of the 1,778 daily newspapers printed in 1978, or 97% of all U.S. dailies, used plates made with films prepared by phototypesetting methods.

GRAVURE PLATE AND CYLINDER MAKING
Michael H. Bruno, GRAPHIC ARTS CONSULTANT

Modern gravure printing is done principally on web presses from intaglio images etched in copper-plated cylinders, and is generally referred to as *rotogravure*. Some sheet-fed gravure printing is done, principally in Europe, but it accounts for a very small portion of all gravure printing.

Gravure printing cylinders can vary from 3 inches in diameter by 1 inch wide for printing special labels to about 3 feet in diameter by 18 feet wide for printing floor coverings. Magazine presses range from 6 to over 8 feet wide. Gravure presses for packaging are usually narrower and seldom exceed 60 inches in width. On sheet-fed presses the printing element is a thin copper plate wrapped around the cylinder. Preparation of the printing surface is essentially the same for both cylinders and plates.

There are three different types of systems used for gravure: *conventional, direct-transfer* or *variable-area,* and *variable-area–variable-depth.*

CONVENTIONAL GRAVURE

Platemaking for the *conventional gravure* process (fig. 10.8) utilizes either bichromate-sensitized carbon tissue or special photographic transfer film as a light-sensitive coating and plate etching resist. The carbon tissue consists of pigmented gelatin coated on a paper substrate and is sensitized with a bichromate solution immediately before use. The photographic resist is a special photographic emulsion coated on film.

The platemaking process is the same for both the carbon tissue and the film. The resist is given two exposures, one through a continuous-tone positive and the other through a screen consisting of transparent lines and opaque dots, with 150 or 175 lines to the inch. The ratio of line to dot width on these screens is usually 1 to 3. During exposure to the continuous-tone positive, the bichromated gelatin is hardened in proportion to the amount of light received, which is inversely proportional to the optical density of the positive. In the highlight areas, for example, more light passes through, and the gelatin becomes harder than in the shadow areas. During the other exposure, the transparent lines of the gravure screen allow the maximum amount of light to pass through, producing hardened lines on the gelatin.

The exposed carbon tissue or transfer film is moistened and squeezed into contact with the clean copper surface of a copper-plated cylinder or a copper plate. Warm water is applied, and the paper of the carbon tissue or the backing of the film is peeled off. The gelatin thus transferred to the copper surface is further developed (washed) with warm water to produce a gelatin relief resist. The more exposure the gelatin has had, the more gelatin remains on the copper, and the more protected from etching will be the corresponding areas of the plate or cylinder.

Etching is done with ferric chloride solutions of different strengths. These solutions etch the copper to different depths, depending on the thickness of the gelatin resist in the different tone areas. Solutions of different strengths are generally used to control etching time and depth. The final etched cylinder consists of wells which are all the same size but vary in depth. The highlights are very shallow and the shadows are quite deep. The areas corresponding to the screen lines remain unetched and provide "lands" to support the doctor blade during printing. A representation of the final plate surface is shown in figure 10.9.

For longer runs, the etched cylinder or plate is chromium plated to resist wear. These cylinders are not capable of very long runs, even with chromium plating, because of doctor-blade wear on the highlight dots, which are very shallow. Conventional gravure is used mainly for high-quality, single-color reproductions in expensive books and magazines, many of which are done on sheet-fed gravure presses.

386

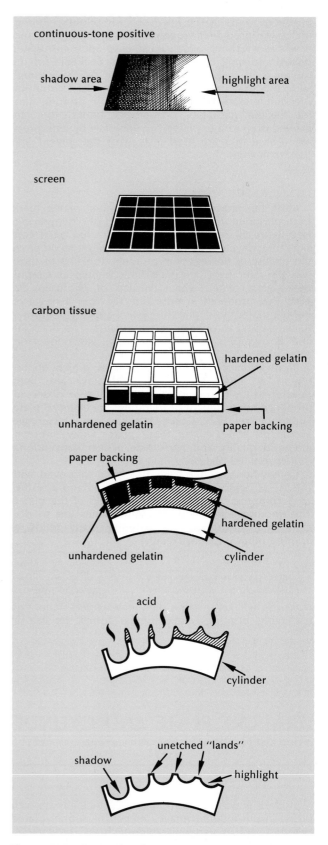

Figure 10.8: Conventional gravure cylinder making using carbon tissue. Image is transferred directly to cylinder surface and etched into it.

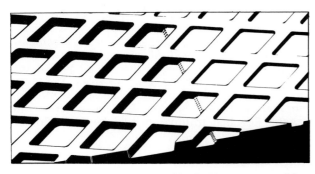

Figure 10.9: Conventional (variable-depth) gravure etching. *Courtesy of Graphic Arts Technical Foundation.*

Figure 10.11: Variable-area-variable-depth gravure etching. *Courtesy of Graphic Arts Technical Foundation.*

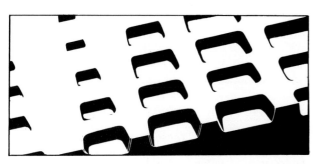

Figure 10.10: Direct-transfer (variable-area) gravure etching. *Courtesy of Graphic Arts Technical Foundation.*

DIRECT-TRANSFER GRAVURE

In the *direct-transfer* or *variable-area* process (fig. 10.10), a special halftone positive is used; the dots in the shadows are all the same size, as in conventional gravure, but in the other tone areas the dot sizes vary, as in letterpress and lithography. The halftone positive is contact printed directly onto a copper cylinder which was previously sensitized with a photopolymer, usually of the Kodak Photo Resist type. This kind of gravure is usually called direct-transfer because the image is produced directly on the cylinder without having to be transferred from some other medium. After being etched, the printing surface consists of disconnected ink cells of varying size but approximately the same depth. These cylinders have a limited tone scale and are used mainly for packaging, where run length and consistency are more important than tone scale.

VARIABLE-AREA–VARIABLE-DEPTH GRAVURE

The principal gravure process for multicolor printing in the United States—especially catalog, magazine, and newspaper supplement printing—is *variable-area–variable-depth* gravure (fig. 10.11). This method consists of making both a special halftone positive, as in direct-transfer gravure, and a continuous-tone positive, as in conventional gravure, for each color. The two positives are contact printed successively, in register, onto a sheet of carbon tissue or transfer film, and the gelatin is transferred to the copper cylinder as in the conventional process. In publication printing, the re-

sists are usually transferred in page sizes or double-page spreads. Development and etching are essentially the same as for conventional cylinders. The printing surface thus consists of disconnected ink cells of varying size and depth corresponding to the tones desired. The tone scale is between that of conventional and direct-transfer gravure. These cylinders are capable of very long runs because the highlight dots are smaller and deeper than in conventional gravure, and therefore do not wear as readily from abrasion of the doctor blade. Chromium plating also contributes to long plate life, and when the chromium wears due to friction of the doctor blade, the cylinder can be replated.

OTHER METHODS

One serious problem with gravure cylinder making has been the difficulty of reproducing identical cylinders from the same originals. The difficulty exists because of the effect that differences in materials, etching solutions, impurities in the copper, environmental conditions, and other factors have on bichromated colloids and silver halide chemistry. This problem has been the main reason why prepress proofing has not been successful in gravure, and also why costs of cylinder making are so high. Other methods have been developed to try to control the reproducibility of etching and the tone production of gravure cylinders. These have included controlled etching, powderless etching similar to that used for copper photoengraving plates, and electromechanical engraving. Controlled etching has shown some success, but electromechanical engraving so far has demonstrated the most promise.

The Hell Helio-Klischograph is an example of an electromechanical engraving system. It scans the copy with a photoelectric pickup which produces signals that actuate an electromechanically driven diamond stylus. This stylus cuts pyramid-shaped cells into the surface of the copper cylinder at the rate of 4,000 cells per second. (A 150-line halftone has 22,500 dots per square inch.) Multiple scanning heads and diamond stylus engraving heads are used so that large cylinders can be made in less than an hour.

Another electromechanical engraver similar to the Helio-Klischograph has been produced by the Ohio Electronic Engraving Co., in Dayton, Ohio. Research is also being done with electron beam etching, which can reach speeds up to 10 times those of electro-mechanical engravers.

As in lithographic platemaking (see page 397), the use of lasers is growing. Crosfield has developed a Lasergravure System, in which lasers are used to engrave plastic-coated gravure cylinders. The lasers can be driven from the digital data output of the Magnascan 570 page-composition system (see page 364).

Still another novel means of producing gravure cylinders is by use of positives made for lithographic printing. A double exposure is made of the screen positive onto carbon tissue; one exposure is diffused to simulate continuous tone in order to accomplish variations in depth as well as dot size. Two such processes are in use. One is the TH process, developed by Toppan Printing Co. in Japan. The other process was developed by Jean Chevalier, a printing consultant in Paris, who described the system at the Gravure Research Institute Annual Research Conference in 1977.

SCREENS FOR SCREEN PRINTING
Michael H. Bruno, GRAPHIC ARTS CONSULTANT

Image carriers for screen printing are screens made of finely woven fabrics to which stencils of various kinds are adhered. The stencils allow ink to pass through the threads of the screen fabric in the image areas and block passage in the non-image areas. To make a complete screen, the fabric holding the stencil is pulled tightly over a wooden or metal frame and secured. The fabric and frame form a shallow rectangular container, as shown in figure 10.12, which will hold a quantity of printing ink. On press, the ink is pressed through the fabric by a squeegee, which is drawn across the screen pushing the ink before it.

SCREEN FABRICS

Screens for screen printing were originally made of silk; hence the old name, *silk screen*, for the printing process. Today, however, other types of fabrics are used more often than silk. These include wire mesh, made of a metal such as stainless steel, and numerous synthetics such as nylon and polyester. In addition, there are variations within each type of screen. Screens made of the same material can vary in thread diameter, space between threads, and type of thread (multifilament or monofilament). A particular fabric must be selected on the basis of wearability, dimensional stability, printability of fine detail, ability to adhere to the particular stencil material used, and compatibility with the kind of ink to be printed.

TYPES OF STENCILS

The stencil image is formed on the screen by filling in the spaces between the threads in the non-printing areas with a substance that prevents the ink from passing through the fabric. This can be accomplished by a number of methods: hand-cut film, photographic film, direct coating, direct-indirect photostencil, and wet-direct photostencil.

Hand-cut film

A hand-cut film stencil is made by first cutting the image areas from the film and then adhering it to the screen. The film is manufactured on a base sheet that supports it during cutting, which is done manually with a sharp stencil knife. After the image areas have been removed, the cut film, still attached to the backing sheet, is laid against the screen fabric, and both are swabbed with adhering liquid. After drying, the backing sheet is removed.

Photographic film

Two types of photographic films are available for making screen stencils—presensitized and unsensitized. Presensitized films are ready for exposure to the image-bearing film positive when they are taken from the

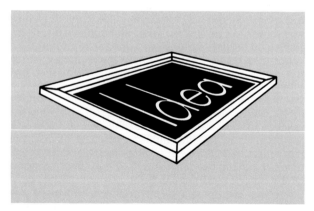

Figure 10.12: Screen for screen printing. *Courtesy of Graphic Arts Technical Foundation.*

388

package; unsensitized films must first be put through a sensitizing step by coating them with a photosensitizing solution.

Presensitized films are exposed in a vacuum frame to a film positive of the image, so that the non-printing areas are exposed. Then the film is developed in a solution which makes the unexposed image areas soluble in water. These areas are washed or etched away by running water over the film. The film emulsion is adhered to the printing screen fabric and the backing sheet removed. This process is illustrated in figure 10.13.

Unsensitized films are processed in a similar manner, except that they must first be sensitized. In addition, the developing step is eliminated because the type of sensitizer coating used is already soluble in water if it has not been exposed.

Most films must be exposed in vacuum frames with very intense lighting. However, one presensitized film made by Du Pont, which has an emulsion that is much more light sensitive than most, can be exposed in a standard graphic arts camera or by projection in an enlarger, as well as in a vacuum frame.

Direct coating

Screen fabrics also can be coated directly by pouring a liquid, light-sensitive emulsion onto the screen and letting it dry prior to exposure. Usually, two or three coatings are applied and smoothed out carefully to achieve a stencil that will wear well on press. The coated screen fabric is then exposed in a vacuum frame to the film positive, and the image areas are washed out of the fabric under a water spray. The screen is then dried and mounted on a frame.

Direct/indirect photostencil

The direct/indirect photostencil process is actually a combination of the photographic film and the direct coating methods. An unsensitized base film is laminated to the screen and sensitized by the direct application of the light-sensitive emulsion. The product is a very durable, thick stencil providing high print quality.

Wet-direct photostencil

A relatively new process, the wet-direct method eliminates the need for a vacuum frame, as the film positive is held in place by a wet photopolymer emulsion. The emulsion, which does not contain

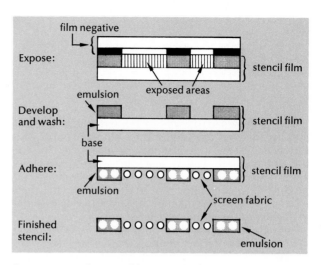

Figure 10.13: Photographic method of making screen printing stencil. Developed emulsion of special stencil film is transferred and adhered directly to screen fabric.

water, hardens when exposed to ultraviolet light, resulting in a predictable stencil thickness and very good image resolution. The stencil will not be affected by solvent- or water-based inks throughout extremely long print runs.

REMOVING STENCILS

Most types of screens can be reclaimed for use by removing the adhered stencil. This is done by applying various types of solutions, depending on the kind of stencil material and screen fabric used, to dissolve the stencil.

ROTARY SCREENS

The latest method of screen printing uses rotary screens. For this process, a tubular plate is made by electrolytically plating a steel cylinder and then sliding the plating off. A photomechanical coating is applied to this newly formed cylinder. It is then exposed through a positive and a screen, and the image areas are etched out to form pores in the cylinder. On rotary screen presses, the ink is pumped into the inside of the cylinder, where the squeegee is located.

LITHOGRAPHIC PLATEMAKING

Andrew J. Alagna, LITHOGRAPHIC PLATEMAKER

The widespread growth of lithography in the last two decades has spawned the development of a wide variety of plates and platemaking processes for this printing method. Today, one can select lithographic plates that are suited to specific job requirements and production economies. An understanding of these types of plates and how they are processed is essential in making proper plate selections.

Lithographic plates differ from other types of image carriers in that during printing their image and non-image areas perform different physicochemical functions which control where the plate accepts ink and where it rejects it. Platemaking for this method is fundamentally a matter of forming image areas that have an affinity for ink (are *oleophilic*) and non-image areas that are water receptive (or *hydrophilic*).

Most lithographic plates in use today fall into three major categories based on how their printing and non-printing areas are formed. *Surface* plates consist of a naturally water-receptive base metal that is covered with a light-sensitive coating. After exposure to a photographic negative or positive, the coating is removed from the non-printing areas but remains in an ink-receptive state in the image areas. *Deep-etch* plates also have a hydrophilic base metal, but these plates are processed by creating an oxide on the plate surface in the image areas and then applying an image-bearing coating that adheres to the oxide but not to the base metal. This process also countersinks the image slightly into the plate. *Bimetal* plates use an ink-receptive metal plated onto a different, water-receptive metal, or vice versa. Photomechanical and etching methods are used so that each metal surface ultimately forms the appropriate image or non-image areas. *Trimetal* plates are often considered a category of bimetal plates since they also have two metal layers that form image and non-image areas; but these are plated onto a third base metal which serves as a substrate.

Platemaking processes for all types of lithographic plates are identified by their use of photographic positives or negatives. Coatings used for positive and negative processes differ in the way they react when exposed to light. When a plate is exposed through a positive, the non-image areas of the plate are light-exposed; when a negative is used, the image areas are exposed. Surface plates may be coated for either the positive or negative process, while deep-etch plates use positives only. One of the two principal types of bimetal plates may be processed with either positives or negatives, and the other type uses only positives. Plate development after exposure varies depending on the type of plate used. These procedures are discussed later in this article.

Many platemaking shops are better equipped to process either positive-working or negative-working plates, rather than being equally geared for both. Strong claims have been made for the merits of each process. Some platemakers, for example, feel that an important feature of the positive process is that it generally lends itself to better dot etching and so offers a higher degree of tone control, which is especially sought in process-color printing. For this reason, some people prefer positive-working plates, especially the more durable deep-etch and bimetal plates, for high-quality, process-color jobs. The same positives that are used to make the press plate can be used for proofing.

Positive-process plates can also reproduce tonal values without halftone photography. Considerable work has been done on this process, and runs up to 300,000 impressions have been made by screenless lithography on web offset plates (see page 396).

There is also the question of what type of *grain* a plate should have for a given job. Graining is the process of creating one of several types of roughened surfaces on an otherwise smooth plate. Graining is performed so that the chemicals used in plate processing, and the fountain solutions used on press, can adhere to the plate surface more readily. This adhesion directly affects both the ease of handling of the plate on press and the plate's press life. The smoother the grain, the better the dot-to-dot reproduction, but the shorter the press life of the plate. The cost of plates increases for grains that are capable of longer runs.

Plate grains are classified by the graining process used and the type of surface created. Both of these factors play an important role in determining plate usefulness. Graining is done with metal or marble balls, wire or bristle brushes, and sandblast techniques, as well as by chemical methods. The types of surfaces created are called smooth, directional, nondirectional, and electrolytic. The nondirectional type is an industry favorite because it lends itself well to both plate processing and presswork. Any of the different types of grains may be electrically anodized by the manufacturer. This process creates a very hard surface that is receptive to plate and press chemistry and that is capable of an extended press life.

SURFACE PLATES

Surface plates have an aluminum base metal and a light-sensitive coating which is removed from the non-image areas after exposure through either a negative or a positive. Processing is less complicated than for the other types of lithographic image carriers. Figure 10.14 illustrates surface plate processing.

Surface plates have commonly been used for short and medium runs of up to 100,000 impressions. Among the variety of surface plates that are described in this article, however, are newer photopolymer types that have expanded the press-run range to over 250,000 impressions or, with a baking process, to over 1 million impressions. Surface plates are sold either in the

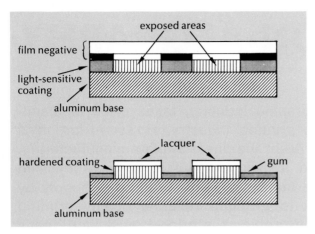

Figure 10.14: Surface plate. Exposure step (top) and finished plate which results (bottom).

wipe-on variety that must be coated by the platemaker or in a *presensitized* form that is supplied ready for exposure and development. Wipe-on plates, which are the least expensive lithographic plates, cannot usually be stored any longer than one day after being coated for processing. Presensitized plates, on the other hand, may be stored before processing for six months under proper conditions, and in some cases up to a year. Thus far, the variety of presensitized plates outnumbers that of the wipe-on type.

Presensitized plates

Presensitized plates in use today are coated for both the negative and positive processes. The coating used for the negative process is hardened in the image areas by exposure to light. The hardened coating, or *stencil,* bonds with the plate surface and protects it from the developer solution used to dissolve the unexposed coating in the non-image areas. In the positive process, when the non-image areas are exposed to light, the coating in these areas becomes soluble. A developer solution dissolves the non-image area coating, and the image area coating forms the stencil.

Additive and subtractive plates. Development of presensitized plates after exposure to light depends on whether the plate is of the *additive* or *subtractive* type. Development of additive plates utilizes a developer solution that contains a lacquer and a desensitizer. As the solution dissolves the non-image area coating, the lacquer adheres to the stencil, making it ink receptive, and the desensitizer prevents the base metal in the non-printing areas from becoming sensitive to ink. Often, gum arabic is applied to form a protective barrier that prevents contamination of the non-image areas before the plate is put on press. Subtractive, or *prelacquered,* plates are supplied by the manufacturer with a lacquer impregnated in the plate coating. The lacquer offers superior abrasion resistance and ink receptivity in the developed stencil. Plate development is simply a matter of dissolving, or subtracting, the non-image area coating and then desensitizing the aluminum plate surface. Subtractive plates are capable of runs in excess of 100,000 impressions, and in some cases, over 200,000 impressions.

Photopolymer plates. Photopolymer plates, one of the newer developments in surface plates, have a base of aluminum but use photopolymer rather than diazo coatings. They have the best abrasion resistance of all surface plates and are capable of runs of over 250,000 impressions. When baked at 500° F (250° C) for 4½ to 5 minutes, they produce runs on web presses of up to 100,000. Long press life makes these plates a serious contender for the deep-etch plate market. Photopolymer plates may be processed in less than half the time required for deep-etch plates.

Photopolymer plates are processed like subtractive plates. There are both positive and negative plates. Photopolymer plates are preferred for use on web offset presses, and they dominate the long-run publication market.

Two-sided plates. Presensitized two-sided plates are coated by the manufacturer on both sides, thus enabling the press department to print two jobs or two colors with the same plate. The same image may also be developed on both sides of the plate so that plate wear or malfunction does not result in lengthy downtime if a second plate is needed. Two-sided plates are often used to speed up short-run book and commercial work.

Paper-base plates. Presensitized paper-base plates are used for short runs. They are very economical both in terms of plate cost and processing time.

Wipe-on plates

Wipe-on plates require more skill and judgment in processing than presensitized plates, but they offer the platemaker more control over the variables that affect plate development. The platemaker can apply the diazo coating in a thickness that is best suited to environmental conditions, to plate processing equipment standards, and to the type of work the plate will reproduce. Wipe-on plates are used predominantly for the negative process, although positive-working coatings are also in use. Plate development is the same as with additive presensitized plates. Photopolymer coatings are not now available for wipe-on plates, but research is being done in this area.

DEEP-ETCH PLATES

Deep-etch plates have been the main lithographic production plate in many plants, especially those doing quality color printing. The ruggedness of their image areas makes deep-etch plates more dependable as well as longer and cleaner running than surface plates. Until the introduction of photopolymer coatings, deep-etch plates were used exclusively for long runs of up to 400,-000 impressions. Deep-etch plates are made only from photographic positives. Processing these plates requires considerable experience, but in the hands of a skilled craftsman their tonal values are relatively easy to control. This factor, together with their dependability, has made these plates preferred for high-quality, process-color jobs in excess of 100,000 impressions.

Deep-etch plates have an aluminum base metal and a light-sensitive coating. There are several types of presensitized deep-etch plates, but these are used less commonly than the whirler-coated type. Image areas are frequently copperized for longer press life. An

 # HOWSON-ALGRAPHY
INCORPORATED

Howson-Algraphy, a leader in the lithographic industry, takes pride in manufacturing quality products to serve the printing industry. Howson-Algraphy's Positive and Negative working plates represent the finest in plate manufacturing. Howson-Algraphy's plate processors add a new concept in plate processing technology. Howson-Algraphy completes the cycle of one source of supply by manufacturing the chemicals necessary to produce reliable, quality printing plates. Howson-Algraphy understands the problems a printer must face, that's why we manufacture printing plates that keep all plate systems GO.

A LEADER IN THE LITHOGRAPHIC PLATEMAKING INDUSTRY

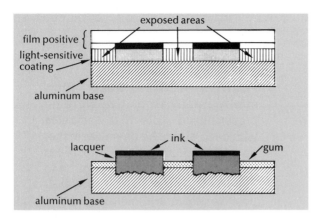

Figure 10.15: Deep-etch plate. Exposure step (top) and finished plate which results (bottom).

anodized aluminum plate is also used, mostly in Europe, but it cannot be copperized.

The platemaking process for deep-etch plates (see figure 10.15) is an involved one that requires considerable judgment on the part of the platemaker. The first step in deep-etch platemaking is the application of a counter-etch solution that cleans the plate surface and prepares it for the complete process. Next, the light-sensitive coating is applied and allowed to dry. When the plate is exposed through a positive, the non-image areas are hardened. (Note that this differs from the coating reaction of positive-working surface plates, in which the non-image area coating is rendered soluble by exposure to light.) A developer solution is used to dissolve the unhardened coating in the image areas, and then an etching solution is applied to the plate to create a clean surface in the image areas; the non-printing areas are protected by the stencil. Then the developer and etching solutions are washed off the plate with alcohol. If the plate is to be copperized for longer press life, a cuprous chloride solution is applied, which chemically deposits copper on the image areas, and the plate is once again cleaned with alcohol. A lacquer is then applied to make the image areas more ink receptive and resistant to press abrasion. An ink is applied to further protect the image areas and to provide the platemaker with a visual image so that the plate can be checked for errors. The stencil remaining in the non-image areas is removed down to the bare aluminum surface, and a desensitizing solution is applied to coat the non-printing areas with a gum deposit which is hydrophilic. The plate receives a final gum to protect it from humidity prior to presswork.

A number of suppliers have introduced "quick" deep-etch plates with significantly simplified development procedures. These plates are developed and etched in one step and then copperized. No intermediary alcohol washes are necessary, and lacquering and inking are done in one step. The platemaking time and cost are cut almost in half.

BIMETAL PLATES

Bimetal plates are similar to copperized deep-etch plates since they utilize the fact that certain metals, such as copper and brass, are naturally ink receptive,

while others, such as chromium, aluminum, and stainless steel, have a natural affinity for water. Bimetal plates are composed of two electroplated metal layers, one of which will ultimately form the non-printing areas, while the other becomes the ink-carrying vehicle. These plates are almost indestructible and are capable of runs of over a million impressions. They are also usually the cleanest running and easiest to handle on press. If the plate malfunctions during a press run, a single corrective treatment usually restores the image and non-image to their proper receptivities. With other types of lithographic plates, treatments used to restore the function of a plate are more critical; unless skillfully done, the corrective treatment may have a short-lived effect, and second plates may have to be made ready in order to avoid excessive downtime for continued plate treatment.

Bimetal plates are available for both negative and positive processes. Positive-process bimetal plates are commonly used for high-quality, process-color reproduction. Two basic types of bimetal plates are manufactured: one is copper-surfaced; the other is the chromium-surfaced trimetal type. These are illustrated in figures 10.16 and 10.17.

Copper-surfaced plates

Copper-surfaced plates have an underlying base metal layer of either aluminum or stainless steel. These plates are supplied either presensitized or for in-plant coating. They are usually exposed with negatives, although some are used with positive-process coatings. After a copper-surfaced plate is exposed, a hardened photomechanical stencil protects the copper image areas. An etching solution removes the copper surface from the non-printing areas, leaving the base aluminum or stainless steel exposed. The copper image areas are then chemically sensitized to be made oleophilic.

Chromium-surfaced plates

Chromium-surfaced plates have an underlying metal layer of either copper or brass which forms the image areas. These plates are processed with positives only and are thus developed in the same manner as deep-etch plates. A photomechanical stencil formed in the non-printing areas protects them from the action of an etching solution used to remove the chromium in

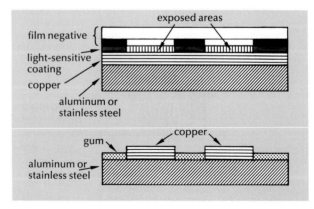

Figure 10.16: Bimetal plate. Exposure step (top) and finished plate (bottom).

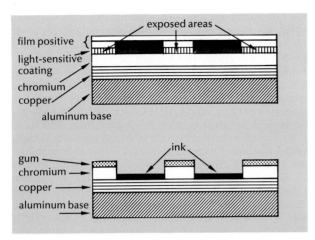

Figure 10.17: Trimetal plate. Exposure step (top) and finished plate (bottom).

the image areas. The chromium-surfaced plate is popularly sold in the so-called *trimetal* or *multimetal* form; that is, with the chromium and copper layers plated onto a third layer of aluminum, zinc, steel, or black iron. This third layer acts as a substrate or base material and has nothing to do with the formation of printing and non-printing areas.

WHY LITHOGRAPHY AND WHICH PLATE

Although the development of lithography was at one time held in check by early, highly fallible plates, now the plates are among its chief advantages. For example, images can be readily added or deleted from all types of lithographic plates without the extensive and intricate hand tooling required on letterpress plates and gravure cylinders. Plates are also less expensive than for other printing methods, and automatic processors are available for every type of lithographic plate, resulting in fast development of consistently high quality image carriers.

The improvement of surface plates has helped make the process of choosing a plate for medium runs less of a compromise between the quality guaranteed in expensive long-run plates and the economy and simplicity of surface plates. This has been largely the result of developments in photopolymer coatings, which have extended the dependable press life of surface plates and which have a seemingly infinite variety of applications.

In addition to the more obvious criteria used in selecting a lithographic plate, such as length of run, type of work to be reproduced, and quality demands, there are several other production factors that a plate must accommodate. Plates must be suited to the equipment and capabilities of the platemaking and press departments where they will be processed and used. Also, such factors as temperature and relative humidity in the platemaking and press rooms, and plate storage conditions, have a bearing on plate selection. An important question is whether the skills are on hand to maintain quality standards with a surface plate that will be pushed to the limit of its press life. Under certain circumstances, a more expensive, longer running plate that is easier to handle on press may be the better choice. A plate must be chosen to withstand the splitting force, or tack, of the ink that will be used, as well as the packing pressure of the press cylinders required for the job.

SPECIAL PLATES
Michael H. Bruno, GRAPHIC ARTS CONSULTANT

In recent years, a number of unconventional types of printing plates have been developed, most for lithographic-type processes. Some have resulted in great growth for their related printing processes, and others promise further growth of new printing techniques in the future if the plates can be perfected. The primary distinction between the lithographic plates discussed in this article and those described in the previous article is a basic departure from conventional lithographic platemaking principles either to simplify platemaking or alter the printing method.

DRIOGRAPHIC PLATES

One of the most interesting and potentially most important printing plates is the *driographic plate*, an aluminum planographic plate with diazo and silicone rubber coatings. After processing, the diazo and silicone rubber are removed from the image areas but remain in the non-image areas. Because silicone rubber has a low surface energy and does not wet by ink, no fountain solution is needed for printing. The process, however, requires a special printing ink because, under the pressure of printing, ordinary lithographic ink spreads over the silicone rubber causing plate scum, or *toning*, as it is called. The special ink has lower surface energy and higher cohesive forces which also result in higher separation forces, or *tack*. This can cause severe troubles with picking of the paper surface, especially on newsprint. The ink works well for several hours on press until the rollers heat up and the ink breaks down, causing toning.

395

If and when this problem is solved, driography could be the most important innovation in printing in the past half-century. It does away with all the disadvantages of lithography caused by the need for the ink/water balance, but retains the advantages of low plate costs, ease of makeready, high speeds, and good quality in printing. Driography also has the ease of printing and consequent low waste features of letterpress, but does not have the letterpress drawbacks of slow makeready and differential pressures. Coatings for driography now exist for negative- or positive-process development as well as for exposure by glow or corona discharge.

Many companies are working on solving the problems of driography. One answer is in the formulation of new inks, but the solution could also be as simple as water cooling the ink rollers on the press. Several runs of over 100,000 impressions have been made with driographic plates on presses with water-cooled ink vibrator rollers.

SCREENLESS LITHOGRAPHY

Some diazo coatings can reproduce a long tone scale, and plates sensitized with these coatings are used with continuous-tone negatives or positives for screenless lithography (no halftone screen is used). The process, however, is dependent upon critical production factors and is not used often. The tone scale of the positive or negative must be correlated to the reproducible tone scale of the plate; and this is dependent on the coarseness of the plate grain and the coating thickness. Both of these factors are difficult to control. Work is now being done with presensitized positive coatings on anodized aluminum which have produced runs in excess of 300,000 impressions.

DIFFUSION TRANSFER PLATES

Diffusion transfer is a photographic process (used in Polaroid film) in which part of the silver in the exposed emulsion is transferred to another surface in contact with it, producing a visible or printable image. A number of plates using this principle have been developed and used for reprography.

The latest development in diffusion transfer is the Kodak PMT (Photomechanical Transfer) family of materials, which are used in both reprography and traditional lithographic printing. The PMT family includes PMT Negative Paper for making exposures in a camera, PMT Reflex Paper for making exposures by contact, PMT Receiver Materials, and the PMT Metal Litho Plate. The receiver materials and the plate have a special coating which receives the image from the exposed Negative or Reflex Paper. A special processor and solution are used. The Kodak PMT Metal Litho Plate is capable of runs up to 25,000. It is of special interest in conjunction with the microstripping methods used with microfilm-to-plate systems (see page 372), since it can be exposed on projectors using conventional lenses. There is also a Kodak PMT Paper Litho Plate, which is used for run lengths of about 2,000.

Diffusion transfer plates and other products are also produced by Agfa-Gevaert. (See "Diffusion Transfer Process," page 296.)

(see page 372)

THE 3M PYROFAX SYSTEM

The 3M Pyrofax plate was developed primarily for the newspaper market but can be used in any lithographic application. The system consists of two units: an Imager and a Heat Fuser. Camera copy in the form of a pasted-up page layout of type and halftones is optically projected onto a 3M photosensitive Transfilm. Exposures take from 10 to 15 seconds, and enlargements and reductions can be made from 115% to 85%. The film is electrostatic, becoming differentially conductive upon exposure to light. After exposure, the film is passed through a dry imaging station where dry toner is applied to the image. Then the toned film is brought into contact with a coated rubber base, Transmat, which accepts the toned image. The next step is to insert an ordinary uncoated, unsensitized lithographic metal plate into the fuser unit. The imaged Transmat is pinned onto a blanket cylinder. Transmat and plate are rolled into contact, and the image is transferred to the plate and fused. The Transmat is peeled from the plate for reuse and the plate is gummed for printing. The first plate takes about three minutes to make, and with both units working in tandem, plates can be produced every 70 seconds. Runs of 100,000 impressions are usual for these plates, and costs can be lower than for conventionally produced plates.

ELECTROPHOTOGRAPHIC PLATES

For duplicating, or reprography, and for several newspaper printing systems, plates made by electrophotographic means are used. The most popular is the Xerox method, which uses a selenium plate or drum. Another method uses the Electrofax principle, in which zinc oxide dispersed in a binder or in an organic photoconductor is coated on paper or metal. The Electrofax method is used for newspapers.

In both methods, the plate or drum is charged with a corona discharge and then exposed in a camera to produce the printing image. Toner is applied to the exposed plate, and, in the case of selenium, the image is transferred to a paper or metal printing plate. In the Electrofax method, there is no transfer of the toned image. In both cases, the toner on the image is fixed by heat or solvent vapor, and the non-image areas are treated with a special solution to make them water receptive. There are a number of copier/duplicators on the market that use this type of plate.

PLATES FOR REPROGRAPHY

In addition to electrophotographic plates, several other types of plates are used in reprography.

Direct image plates can be prepared by typing, drawing, or lettering directly onto a paper master. Special ribbons, pencils, and inks are used. Although inexpensive and easy to make, these plates are limited in quality and used only for short runs.

There are two types of silver emulsion plates used for reprography. One is the 3M Camera Plate System in which the plate is made directly in the camera, processed, and mounted on the press. It is capable of runs up to 1,000 impressions. (A new version of this plate claims runs up to 10,000.) The other is based on the Kodak Verilith plate, which consists of two photographic emulsions and a coating containing developer coated on a paper base. Exposure and development produce ink-receptive image areas and water-receptive non-image areas. The plate has a rather sensitive ink/water balance, but it is used in the Itek Platemaker and the A. B. Dick Photomat systems, and has produced runs in excess of 10,000 impressions. (This plate has also been used in AM International's Photo-Direct system, which is no longer being produced.)

LASER PLATEMAKING

Lasers have significant potential for use in making lithographic plates. The Laserite system of EOCOM Corporation (Irvine, Calif.) uses lasers to expose images on printing plates. The process begins with a paste-up of the original material to be reproduced rather than the stripped-up flat of negatives or positives used in a conventional system. The paste-up is scanned by a helium/neon (He/Ne) laser, which sends electrical signals to a modulator. The modulator in turn actuates an argon laser that does the actual exposing of the coating on the plate. The plate is then processed in a conventional manner. The main problem is in matching the sensitivity of the plate coating to the emission band of the laser. A number of plate coating manufacturers are working on such systems, and several are in use.

Another laser platemaking system is the LogEScan, made by LogEtronics (Springfield, Va.). It gets around the need for special plate coatings by using a YAG infrared laser and a special Lasermask—a polyester film with a carbon black coating. The Lasermask is placed in contact with an uncoated litho plate. A paste-up is scanned with a He/Ne laser, and the impulses are sent to the YAG laser. As the YAG laser impinges on the Lasermask, it heats the coating in the image areas, transferring that part of the coating to the metal plate. A litho plate is produced on the metal and a negative on the Lasermask simultaneously. An advantage of the system is that no processing is needed for the negative, which can serve as a back-up or for making duplicate plates.

Laser platemaking is attractive because plates can be made directly from the output of computerized composition systems. Such systems now produce type on film, but the technology exists to use the digital signals in the computer to drive a laser directly and produce plates without going through the film stage. This has been done with a Laserite system, and eventually the paste-up may be eliminated completely.

KC PLATES

The newest lithographic plate is an electrophotographic plate known as KC-Crystalplate, made by Coulter Systems Corp. (Bedford, Mass.). The KC plates are faster than other electrophotographic plates, with a speed similar to lith films, so they can be exposed by projection. Because they are panchromatic, they can be used with low-cost, high-reliability He/Ne lasers. They could, therefore, be the answer to problems in projection and laser platemaking when they become generally available.

The KC plate consists of cadmium sulfide crystals sputtered onto a metal base. In processing, the plate is charged with a corona discharge and exposed by projection, contact, or lasers. It is then toned with a liquid toner, fused, and converted so that the cadmium sulfide in the non-image areas is water receptive. On the press it is handled like any litho plate and it is capable of runs in excess of 100,000.

PRINTING

11

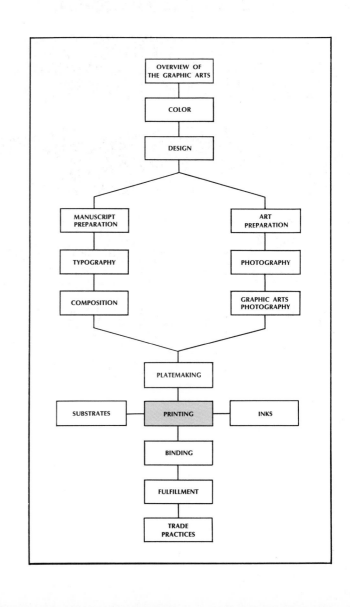

OVERVIEW OF
THE GRAPHIC ARTS

COLOR

DESIGN

MANUSCRIPT
PREPARATION

ART
PREPARATION

TYPOGRAPHY

PHOTOGRAPHY

COMPOSITION

GRAPHIC ARTS
PHOTOGRAPHY

PLATEMAKING

SUBSTRATES PRINTING INKS

BINDING

FULFILLMENT

TRADE
PRACTICES

Lip Service.

At Pearl-Pressman-Liberty
"Lip Service" is a very, very
important part of our company.

Our business is Graphics . . . both Printing and
Typography; we depend heavily on the telephone.
When you call PPL, or our typographic division,
Graphic Arts Composition for an estimate, for advice or
your job progress, you can count on quick, courteous
answers and appropriate information.

This is one of many versatile services offered by
us. In Philadelphia dial 925-4900 or from New York
925-5162 and a helpful PPL rep will tell you of our
many other services, and with no "lip."

PEARL-PRESSMAN-LIBERTY, INC./PRINTERS
5th and Poplar Streets • Philadelphia, Pennsylvania 19123
Telephone: (215) 925-4900/(212) 925-5162

INTRODUCTION TO PRINTING

Michael H. Bruno, GRAPHIC ARTS CONSULTANT

Printing processes may be classified into two types: conventional and unconventional. The conventional printing processes produce numerous reproductions of an original subject by means of a printing press, which holds an inked image carrier and applies the pressure necessary to transfer the image to a substrate such as paper, paperboard, metal, plastic, cloth, or glass. The unconventional printing processes include photography and noncontact processes like electrophotography, thermal imaging, and jet printing, which do not use conventional image carriers or presses. The main difference between the two types is that in the conventional processes a single plate or image can produce a number of reproductions on a press, while in the unconventional processes a new image must be generated for each reproduction, even if the identical subject is being reproduced.

This article introduces the basic features of the conventional printing processes, which account for most of the printing done today. Some unconventional processes are described in separate articles in this section.

CONVENTIONAL PRINTING PROCESSES

The major printing processes are generally considered to be letterpress, offset lithography, gravure, and screen printing. There are a number of minor processes, including collotype (or photogelatin), steel-die engraving, thermography, and others. In all conventional printing processes, as described and illustrated in "Fundamentals of Platemaking" (page 378), the image carrier must consist of two basic areas: the image areas, which hold the ink that will produce the image, and the non-image areas, which remain uninked. The printing processes may be classified according to the way in which the image and non-image areas are distinguished from one another.

In relief printing, the image area is raised and the non-image area is below the raised surface so that it does not contact the substrate in printing. Common examples of this type of printing are *letterpress* and *flexography*. The *typewriter* is also an example of relief printing. Letterpress covers the gamut of printing from short-run job printing such as letterheads, billheads, envelopes, announcements, invitations, and small advertising brochures to general printing, advertising, books, catalogs, magazines, newspapers, and packaging. Flexography, a form of rotary web letterpress using flexible rubber plates, can also print a wide range of products; it is often used to print on foil, cellophane, plastic films, corrugated board, cartons, and bags, and to print shorter runs by heat transfer printing.

In intaglio printing, namely *gravure* and *steel-die engraving*, the image consists of tiny indentations, or wells, in a plate or cylinder, which hold the ink. In gravure, the non-image areas are scraped clean with a metal doctor blade, which contacts the smooth outer surface of the plate or cylinder. In the case of steel-die engraving, a wiper paper is used. When the substrate and plate are pressed together, the ink is drawn out of the wells. The most common type of gravure is *rotogravure*, commonly used for printing newspaper supplements, magazines, and mail-order catalogs. Gravure is also used for printing foils and films for packaging and for such specialties as floor tiles, linoleum, textiles, and plastics. It is also the most common process used for heat transfer printing. Steel-die engraving is used for printing name cards, letterheads, invitations and announcements, and greeting cards.

In planographic printing, the printing and non-printing areas are essentially on the same plane but differ in their receptivity to ink and water, the printing areas accepting the ink and the non-printing areas accepting the water. *Lithography* is the most common process using this principle. *Collotype* is another example. Common examples of lithography are general commercial printing, letterheads, business forms, advertising, greeting cards, art reproductions, posters, books, catalogs, labels, packaging, folding boxes, decalcomanias, coupons, trading stamps, newspapers, shopping news, encyclopedias, and magazines.

In stencil or porous printing, a metal, silk, or nylon screen or fibrous material is used. The non-printing areas of the screen are blocked so that the ink only goes through the porous areas, which represent the image. *Screen printing* is the best example of this type of printing. It is used for banners, posters, decalcomanias, displays, catalog covers, wallpaper, textiles, and heat transfer printing. The *mimeograph* is another example of porous printing.

PRINTING PRESSES

Printing presses vary in size, construction, and operation, depending upon many variables, such as the type of product being printed, the number of products (or *run length*), and the kind of image carrier used. However, printing presses must perform a basic set of operations in order to accomplish the crucial step of transforming an image on a single image carrier into a large number of consumable products for a mass audience. Printing presses must provide the following operations: mounting of the image carrier on the press; storage of ink and paper in quantities sufficient to maintain presswork; feeding and conveying of paper or other substrate through the press; application of ink to the image carrier; regulation of pressure to transfer the image to the substrate; and temporary storage of material after printing. (See "Basic Press Operations," page 404.)

There are three basic types of presses, which differ in how they hold the image carrier and how they bring it in contact with the paper. They are *platen, flat-bed*

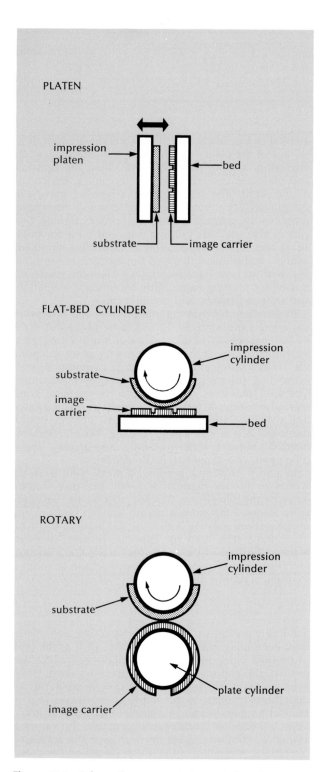

PLATEN

impression platen

bed

substrate

image carrier

FLAT-BED CYLINDER

impression cylinder

substrate

image carrier

bed

ROTARY

impression cylinder

substrate

image carrier

plate cylinder

Figure 11.1: Schematic representations of the three basic impression methods: platen, flat-bed cylinder, and rotary. In a platen press, the bed holds the metal type or the printing plate and the platen holds the paper and applies the needed transfer pressure. The flat-bed cylinder press also has a bed which holds the image carrier, but the paper moves around an impression cylinder, which applies the transfer pressure. A rotary press has two cylinders: an impression cylinder, as on a flat-bed press, and a plate cylinder, which holds the image carrier.

cylinder, and *rotary* presses (see figures 11.1 through 11.4). Regardless of printing process, every press uses one of these principles. The platen press, used in letterpress printing, has a bed that holds the image carrier (metal type or a plate) and a smooth platen that holds the paper. In a flat-bed press, the image carrier is on a flat bed, which may be either horizontal or vertical, and the paper is fed over a cylinder, which applies the transfer pressure. Flat-bed presses are used chiefly for letterpress and screen printing and for proofing. In a rotary press, the paper is fed over one cylinder and the printing plate is mounted on another cylinder. The heavier plates used in letterpress must be curved so that they fit the contour of the cylinder. Lithography uses relatively thin wraparound plates, which fit into clamps on the cylinder.

Figure 11.2: Platen press for letterpress printing. *Courtesy of Heidelberg Eastern, Inc.*

Figure 11.3: Flat-bed cylinder press for letterpress printing. *Courtesy of Heidelberg Eastern, Inc.*

402

Figure 11.4: Rotary press for letterpress printing. *Courtesy of Heidelberg Eastern, Inc.*

During printing, the ink may be transferred from the plate directly to the paper, a process known as *direct printing,* or it may be transferred to an intermediate cylinder covered with a rubber blanket and from there to the paper, in *offset printing.* Letterpress, gravure, and screen printing are all methods using mostly direct printing, but letterpress and gravure can also be printed by the offset method. Lithography, on the other hand, is almost exclusively done by offset printing, so much so that when the term *offset* is used it usually refers to the lithographic process. The main advantage of the offset method is that the rubber blanket can transfer the ink to rough surfaces so that higher quality printing can be done on them.

Presses may also be classified, according to the form in which the paper is fed into and through the press, as *sheet-fed* and *web-fed* (see figures 11.5 and 11.6). On a sheet-fed press, sheets of paper are fed into the press one at a time, the impression is made, and each sheet is removed or delivered into a pile. On a web-fed press, the paper is fed from a roll, and printing is continuous as the paper passes over the impression cylinder in contact with the inked plate or blanket on the rotating cylinder. All of the major printing processes can use presses of both sheet-fed and web-fed design.

Printing presses may be *single-color* or *multicolor,* according to the number of printing units they contain. Newspaper and book work, for example, generally require only black ink to convey textual and pictorial matter and so necessitate only a single printing unit. Commercial printing, on the other hand, frequently calls for an accent color in addition to black, and process-color reproduction requires four different colors. Additional printing units are incorporated so that all the required colors can be printed in one pass of the paper through the press. Single-color presses, of course, may be used to the same end by successively changing the plate, washing up the press, inserting different ink in the fountain, and refeeding the already

printed sheets; however, the costs of repeated handling make this economical for only very short runs.

Single-color perfecting presses may contain more than one printing unit if they are required to print both sides of the sheet. This can be accomplished by "turning" the paper for successive impressions or by using a *blanket-to-blanket* press, which prints both sides of the sheet in one pass.

Printing presses also vary in size, commonly ranging between an image area of 8½" x 11", suitable for quick-copy reprography, to 60" x 80" for packaging, book printing, and broadsheet poster work. Sheet-fed presses cover the entire range in graded intervals that accommodate standard sheet sizes. Web-fed presses for commercial printing are more restricted, with the

Figure 11.5: Single-color sheet-fed lithographic press. *Courtesy of Graphic Systems Group, Rockwell International.*

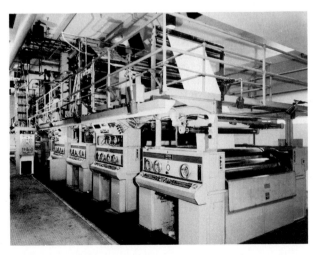

Figure 11.6: Multicolor web-fed lithographic press typically used for newspaper printing. *Courtesy of Graphic Systems Group, Rockwell International.*

403

cylinder circumference *(cutoff length* or *repeat length)* suited to page sizes of publications.

These differences among printing presses are largely independent of the process or printing method used. Presses for letterpress, gravure, and lithography may all use direct or offset transfer, may be either flat-bed or rotary, accept paper in either sheets or in a roll, may be single or multicolor, and are manufactured in a wide variety of sizes. There are at least no theoretical constraints. In practice, however, for economic or engineering reasons, one size, configuration, or design becomes closely associated with a particular process.

BASIC PRESS OPERATIONS

Robert Loekle, COLOR REPRODUCTION CONSULTANT

Although the construction of printing presses varies according to the type of printing process used and the nature of the product to be printed, all printing presses must perform a basic set of operations to transfer an inked image to paper or another substrate. Presses must:

• Provide a method of securely mounting the image carrier on the press.

• Store the ink and printing stock in quantities sufficient to maintain continuity throughout the run.

• Feed the paper or other substrate to the press and continually convey it through the cycle in correct position to delivery.

• Apply a uniform thickness of ink to the image carrier (and in lithography apply dampening solution).

• Transfer the ink from the image carrier to the substrate and regulate the pressure required for impression.

• Remove the printed material immediately after printing and provide temporary storage.

MOUNTING THE IMAGE CARRIER

Presses must provide a method for precise placement of the image carrier. Adjustments for final positioning in the front-to-back and side-to-side directions are accomplished by slight movements of the image carrier or the substrate or both. Correcting images with rotational error *(cocked* images) is difficult.

In gravure, the image is an integral part of the printing cylinder, engraved in the copper surface which has been electrochemically deposited on a massive steel core. The cylinder rides in a set of fixed bearings and the entire unit is removed at the completion of the job.

Lithography and letterpress both employ printing cylinders that are an integral part of the press. The image is carried on a separate metal, paper, or plastic plate clamped firmly to the cylinder.

STORING INK AND PAPER

Ink for the large presses used in newspaper or web-fed commercial printing is often stored at a considerable distance from the press and pumped to the press automatically on demand. Similarly, paper rolls may be fed directly from a central storage area. In sheet-fed work, however, the required quantity of paper is brought to the floor in skidded packages which are unwrapped and fed to the press in small lifts. The ink fountain is replenished manually to maintain a more or less constant volume during the run.

FEEDING AND CONVEYING PAPER

All processes are adaptable to feeding the substrate from either stacked sheets or a roll. For long runs such as newspapers and magazines, the roll- or web-fed principle has always been preferred for the higher speeds obtainable and the supplemental folding and trimming attachments.

Lithography was late in converting to the web-fed principle, as the complexities of the process hampered a straightforward approach. In the last 25 years, however, web-fed lithography has achieved remarkable growth and competes favorably with the other processes in the long-run market. Just as important, perhaps, is the fact that it has overwhelmed the large-size sheet-fed lithographic presses, which were built with cylinders up to 78 inches across. As the break-even point in length of run continues to be forced down, we may expect more and more commercial printing to be done on web-fed presses.

In sheet-fed presses the paper is removed from the feed pile one sheet at a time by vacuum rubber suckers and guided down a feed board so that one side is properly aligned. As the sheet leaves the feed board, it is grasped firmly by metal clamps, or *grippers,* which are attached to an endless chain and convey the sheet in a fixed position through the printing cycle until it is released at the delivery end. There the printed sheets are again formed into piles, which are removed by the press operator at regular intervals throughout the run.

On web-fed presses the paper is unwound from a reel and drawn through the press by the friction of the various rollers. Side-to-side movements can be made while the web is in motion, and the web tension is continually monitored and adjusted during printing to insure front-to-back registration. Only simple finishing operations, such as scoring and perforating, can be carried out on sheet-fed presses; on roll-fed presses the web can be carried directly into a series of bindery operations without the need for intermediate handling.

In either sheet-fed or web-fed presses, the paper must be conveyed in precise position and with minimum stress to insure the registration of multiple images. It is also necessary that the image be placed properly relative to the gripper edge and one of the sides, since the same edges will be used to guide the paper through bindery equipment (see "Imposition," page 519).

INKING THE IMAGE CARRIER

Differences among the processes in the manner of distributing ink to the image carrier and taking an impression arise directly from the way in which the image has been formed. The method of differentiating the image and non-image areas of the image carrier largely determines the requirements to be met in printing press design.

Relief and planographic processes require a fairly stiff or viscous ink to be applied to the image. Thus letterpress and lithography both use a train of rollers to conduct the ink from the fountain to the image surface. A large number of rollers is required to provide uniform distribution of ink over the entire image. Basically the train consists of four types of rollers which are varied in number, diameter, and surface properties (rubber, steel, plastic, etc.) according to specific engineering requirements.

The *ductor roller* conducts ink from the ink fountain to the roller train. Control of the amount of ink fed is through intermittent contact.

Distributor rollers maintain a uniform ink-film thickness to replace the amount transferred to the paper at each printing cycle.

Vibrators, or *oscillating rollers,* besides rotating in the roller train, have a small amount of lateral movement so that the ink is distributed evenly across the rollers, and thus across the image, as well as from top to bottom. The need for lateral movement is self-evident when one considers that the form itself varies in the amount of image area to be printed across the sheet and will therefore accept ink unequally from the uniform supply with which it is provided.

Form rollers are the final rollers, which transfer ink to the image.

Lithography has the additional requirement that the plate be dampened prior to inking to prevent ink from adhering to the non-image areas. Each printing unit contains its own separate fountain for the dampening solution, or *etch,* which is conveyed to the plate by a separate roller system.

The presence of moisture in the inking system is one of the most bothersome aspects of lithography. The conditions for good lithographic printing are referred to as a correct *ink/water balance* and are a critical factor in the engineering and design of lithographic presses, as well as calling for additional skills on the part of the pressman. At best, lithography is probably unable to achieve the uniformity of inking over the sheet and throughout the run obtained by letterpress and gravure; however, the extent of the variation encountered in practice seldom is objectionable for commercial use.

The simplest inking system is that of gravure, where the image carrier is partially immersed in a bath of ink, with the excess wiped off by a doctor blade just prior to printing. Evenness of distribution over the image and throughout the run is assured by this method, which eliminates the need for a complex train of ink distribution rollers. To some extent the simplicity of inking with low viscosity fluids is offset at a further stage of the printing cycle when the solvents in the ink must be driven off in order for drying to take place. Large drying ovens, chill rollers for cooling, and mechanisms for solvent recovery account for a large part of gravure press engineering.

TRANSFERRING THE IMAGE

In the three processes under discussion, transfer of the inked image to the substrate requires an impression force. Variations in the manner of applying pressure is again derived from the fundamental structure of the image carrier.

In gravure, the web is fed directly between the inked cylinder and an impression roller. Sufficient force must be applied to press the paper in firm contact with the wells containing ink so that maximum absorption takes place. The impression roller is rubber or a similar material and is backed by one or more steel rollers which provide adjustable pressures, moving the impression rollers closer to the printing cylinder to increase the pressure. In this way, large forces can be exerted without causing damage to the relatively weak walls of the cells etched below the surface of the copper cylinder.

Lithography employs the offset principle. The image is first transferred to a rubber surface, and thence to the substrate. Offset printing from a rubber surface offers many advantages and has been adapted to letterpress, where the process is known as *letterset.* However, in lithography it is not an alternative but an essential part of press design. At the speeds encountered in rotary presses, few papers would be able to withstand the moisture if they came directly in contact with the lithographic plate. Moreover, the image on a lithographic plate is chemical rather than physical and would soon be destroyed by abrasion and trace impurities in the paper.

The printing unit of a lithographic press thus contains three cylinders of equal circumference, referred to as *plate cylinder, blanket cylinder,* and *impression cylinder.* The plate is mounted on the plate cylinder, the ends being tucked inside a small gap where they are firmly secured and have provisions for adjusting the tension. The blanket cylinder is similiar in appearance and function and carries the renewable rubber surface or *blanket.* Both plate and blanket cylinders use paper packing to change their diameters and thus the pressure with which they come in contact. The paper is carried between the blanket and impression cylinder, pressure on the latter being adjustable by movement in the bearings.

In sheet-fed lithography, the plate and blanket cylinders are adjusted with packing, while the impression cylinder is adjusted by moving it either forward or backward.

A more usual configuration for multicolor web lithographic presses is *blanket to blanket,* in which the web is passed between two blanket cylinders. This system obviates the need for impression cylinders because the blanket cylinders themselves provide the transfer pressure. Such units are *perfecting*, or capable of printing both sides of the web simultaneously. The upper and lower units are independent and may print different colors.

In another arrangement, an oversize impression cylinder is shared by two plate/blanket units. This is known as a *common impression cylinder* design. It is advantageous in sheet-fed printing since the sheet is held between impressions, thus aiding close registration of succeeding images. Letterpress also uses the common impression cylinder principle, with as many as six satellite plate stations.

Letterpress accepts direct impression from a relief image. The paper passes between two essentially rigid surfaces, which should be smooth and flat and in perfect contact at all points. Because there is no rubber impression surface that can conform to an uneven configuration, the use of packing is critical. It is used to build up any low spots on the relief surface, as well as for regulating overall transfer pressure. In flat-bed presses, in which elements of different heights may be locked together, packing is used to make the elements a uniform height.

STORING PRINTED MATERIAL

After printing, some facility for immediate and temporary storage of the printed material is required.

Sheet-fed presses have delivery units which jog and stack the outcoming sheets. The amount of ink printed and the ink drying characteristics are the two main constraints on the height of the pile which can be accumulated. Racking or removing the sheets at more

frequent intervals prevents the transfer of wet ink to the sheet above, a condition referred to as *setoff*, particularly troublesome in sheet-fed printing. Delivery units are constructed so that removal of the printed material can be performed without the need for completely stopping the printing operation.

More possibilities are available when the paper arrives at delivery in a continuous web. The simplest means of storage is perhaps a rewind device; however, the usefulness of a roll of printed material is restricted to special applications. Storage and handling are simplified when paper is delivered in piles. The web can be readily converted to sheets by means of a sheeting device attached to the press.

By far the greatest number of web-fed presses, however, make use of in-line finishing and binding operations, which make intermediate storage and handling of the printed material unnecessary. Web-fed presses with in-line provisions for cutting and folding produce a steady stream of folded signatures, which are removed and bundled as they come from the delivery.

LETTERPRESS PRINTING

Michael H. Bruno, GRAPHIC ARTS CONSULTANT

Taking an impression from a raised inked surface was the forerunner of all the processes which today we refer to as "printing." The principle is currently embodied in that process known as letterpress, and although some of the equipment and techniques are considered obsolete by modern standards, they can still be found in use in job shops and private presses.

Letterpress is distinguished by the wide variety of printing machinery developed for special purposes. The three main categories of printing presses are *platen, flat-bed cylinder,* and *rotary* presses.

PLATEN PRESSES

Until the early nineteenth century, all letterpress printing was done on hand-operated platen presses of

a classic design that had remained practically unchanged for 350 years; it was only under the pressure of mechanization that cylinder and rotary letterpress appeared. In its conversion to machine operation, the platen press itself was radically redesigned, although its principle of operation has remained basically the same.

As illustrated in figure 11.7, two flat surfaces, the bed and the platen, make up this type of machine. The bed carries the image, which may be hand-set or cast metal type, or photoengraved plates, mounted together and locked into position. The platen provides a smooth surface on which the paper is held. The paper is pressed against the inked image to complete the transfer.

On the later presses like the Kluge, Gordon, and

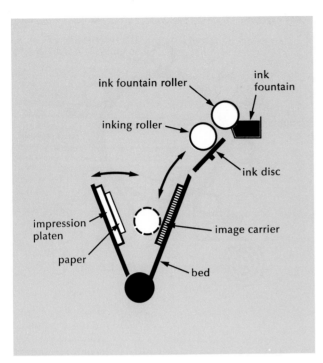

Figure 11.7: Schematic drawing of letterpress platen press.

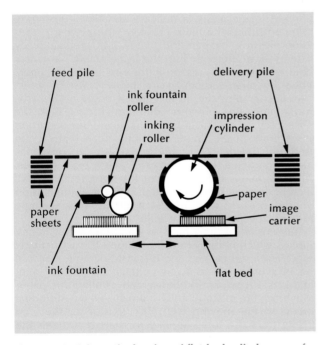

Figure 11.8: Schematic drawing of flat-bed cylinder press for letterpress.

Heidelberg presses, the beds are vertical rather than horizontal, the plates are inked by inking rollers, and the impression is "pulled" on sheets fed manually or automatically over the platen. The printing area of modern platen presses goes up to about 18" x 24".

Platen presses are still used for many jobs such as letterheads, billheads, forms, posters, announcements, imprinting, embossing, steel-rule die cutting, and hot leaf stamping (see "Finishing Processes," page 551). They are the basic tool of the traditional job shop.

FLAT-BED CYLINDER PRESSES

Flat-bed cylinder presses are made with either vertical or horizontal beds. Presses may be one-color or two-color. On *perfecting* presses both sides are printed in one pass, the sheet being turned over between impressions. Figure 11.8 is a schematic drawing of a flat-bed cylinder press.

Horizontal presses can handle a wide range of sheet sizes, from about 17" x 22" (the same size handled by small platen presses) up to very large sheets such as 42" x 56". Type and plates are locked up on the bed as in a platen press, but the sheets are fed automatically over a cylinder, which also provides the necessary transfer pressure. The presses are slow, and much of the work formerly done on them has been diverted to rotary letterpress or lithography. Many are still used for steel-rule die cutting, and some are used for proofing. Manufacture of horizontal flat-bed presses was discontinued in the United States in 1962, although some are still being made in Europe.

Vertical flat-bed presses are still popular for general job and commercial printing, imprinting, and other areas where their versatility proves useful. Vertical flat-beds are faster than the horizontal presses, producing 5,000 impressions per hour. The maximum sheet size is 14" x 20".

ROTARY PRESSES

The greatest amount of letterpress printing—which includes long-run commercial, packaging, newspaper, book, and magazine printing—is performed on rotary presses. All rotary presses require curved plates for mounting, such as stereotypes, electrotypes, and molded plastic or rubber plates. Wraparound plates may also be used. (See "Letterpress Platemaking," page 381.)

Sheet-fed rotary presses were made in sizes up to 54½" x 77" with rated speeds as high as 6,000 iph (impressions per hour). Although manufacture of such large sizes has been discontinued, there are still a number in use.

Web-fed rotary presses for periodical and book printing are either *unit* type or *common impression cylinder* (CIC). A unit press has a separate, complete printing unit for each color. This system offers an advantage in multicolor printing: it allows more time between successive impressions, which improves the trapping of wet inks. The common impression cylinder or *satellite* type consists of one large cylinder around which the separate printing units are placed. This system offers the advantage of better register since the sheet is held firmly to the single, large impression cylinder between colors. Figure 11.9 shows schematic drawings of a unit-design rotary press and a rotary CIC press.

For printing on coated papers, rotary presses are equipped with dryers. They are usually of the high-velocity hot air type, although open flame and steam

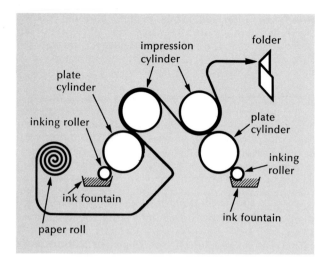

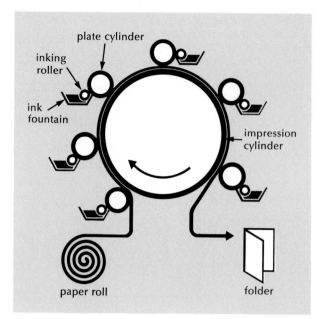

Figure 11.9: Configuration of two types of rotary letterpress printing presses. Above, unit-design perfecting rotary press. Right, rotary letterpress typically used for magazine printing, employing common impression cylinder.

dryers are still found. The effectiveness of a dryer depends on the use of heat-set inks, which require chill rollers to cool and set the resins after they have been softened by the heat of the dryer.

For printing letterpress newspapers, web-fed presses are built in couples which print both sides in succession, generally eight pages on a side with a four-page width to the web. Recently introduced are the six-page-wide presses which measure 90 inches across. Drying apparatus is not used on newspaper work, because the ink soaks into the highly absorptive paper. The degree of drying is considered sufficient for the purpose, although the ink tends to smear and dirty the hands of the reader.

FLEXOGRAPHIC PRESSES

Although not strictly considered letterpress, flexography uses rotary web-fed relief presses. Flexographic presses have found special use in printing packaging materials, both paper and flexible film. Flexography uses rubber or photopolymer plates and water-based or solvent-based inks with a simple, two-roller inking system.

The presses are of three types: (1) *stack* type, in which the printing units are placed vertically, the complete press usually consisting of two such stacks; (2) *central impression cylinder*, corresponding to the common impression cylinder letterpress used in magazine printing; and (3) *in-line*, corresponding to the unit-type magazine press. These presses are discussed in "Flexographic Printing," page 418.

CONSIDERATIONS IN RELIEF PRINTING

One of the serious problems in printing from a plate with a relief image is the pressure variation caused by differences in the areas of the image elements. Uniform pressure applied over the total expanse of the cylinder or bed will be distributed unevenly according to the area above the plate base which is in actual contact with the paper. Thus small highlight dots, fine lines, type serifs, and so on, can exert high unit pressures which can puncture or emboss the paper surface. Adjusting the pressure needed for ink transfer to the different image areas, a delicate and time-consuming task, constitutes the main problem of *makeready*. Precision electros, wraparound plates, and premakeready systems have helped, but the appreciable time still required is the main reason letterpress has been superseded by other processes for many types of work.

In flexography the rubber plate flows or distorts, overcoming the pressure differentials, so that the makeready is not so critical. However, the distortion sets a limit on the fineness of the screen that can be used and the degree of register which can be maintained, particularly on unit and stack type presses. With reasonable care, rulings of 150 lines per inch have been printed on flexible films using central impression cylinder presses with precision plates, reverse-angle doctor blades, and ceramic anilox rollers.

The *tension* of the web is an important factor in any process which employs a roll of paper. It is particularly important in letterpress and offset lithography because the inks used are tacky in comparison to the more fluid inks of gravure and flexography. Pulling the paper away from the inked plate or blanket sets up additional forces on the moving web. The tension in the web arising from the force applied to draw it through the press also varies with the nature of the paper. Applying even a relatively small force to paper causes it to change dimensions, and the changes may not be constant for a given paper, or even within a single roll. The erratic behavior of paper under stress results in inconsistencies in the final product such as variations in unit-to-unit register, side lay, cutoff, and folding accuracy. In extreme cases the result is a web break. Tension control is achieved by either a *dancer roll* to provide constant torque, or a device that controls the flow rate of the web by varying the speed.

ADVANTAGES AND LIMITATIONS

The advantages and limitations of letterpress are summarized below.

Advantages
· The process is simple in conception; the image and non-image areas are physically separated on different planes.
· Printing can be performed directly from metal type.
· Presses are available in a wide variety and are easily adaptable to special purposes.
· Thickness of the ink film applied utilizes the mass-tone of inks; gold and other metallics print well; high ink gloss is obtainable.
· Uniformity of color throughout the run is excellent.

Limitations
· High cost of photoengravings.
· Direct transfer requires smooth printing surfaces to avoid mottle.
· Pressure differentials, the consequence of relief images, must be adjusted by careful makeready.
· In multicolor work special effort is required to insure good trapping of wet inks.

LITHOGRAPHIC PRINTING

Michael H. Bruno, GRAPHIC ARTS CONSULTANT

Lithography is a planographic printing process: the image areas are neither raised nor depressed, as in letterpress and gravure, respectively, but are on essentially the same plane on the surface of the printing plate as the non-image areas. The two areas are differentiated chemically: the image areas are made grease-receptive and water-repellent, and the non-image areas are made water-receptive and grease-repellent. On press, both a water-based dampening solution and greasy ink are applied. The dampening solution wets the water-receptive non-image areas of the plate and prevents the ink from adhering to them. The image areas accept the ink.

DEVELOPMENT

In the 100 years following Senefelder's invention of lithography about 1800, lithographic printing was confined to direct printing on flat-bed presses to accommodate the heavy lithographic stones on which the images were hand drawn or hand transferred. To make use of a rotary press the lithographic image had to be carried on a metal plate which could be wrapped around a cylinder.

Techniques for the preparation of metal lithographic plates were introduced about 1900. The original image was drawn on stone in the customary manner and rolled up with a specially prepared "transfer" ink. An impression was pulled on a damp, gelatin-coated or starch-coated paper. This paper was placed in contact with a thin sheet of zinc to which the greasy image was transferred by pressure. The non-image areas were desensitized by gum arabic and acid and the image areas strengthened by successive "rubbing up" with special ink until a suitable printing image was obtained.

Another revolutionary change occurred in 1906, the year in which Ira Rubel and A. S. Harris simultaneously but independently invented the rotary offset lithographic press. Previously the image had been transferred from the plate to the paper directly. On an offset press the plate image is first transferred to a smooth rubber surface called the *blanket* and then offset to the paper. Some relief (letterset) and even gravure (offset gravure) printing uses this principle, particularly for printing packaging materials, but lithography uses it almost exclusively, and the terms *offset* and *lithography* generally are used interchangeably.

The offset principle gives five important advantages to lithography and to some extent to letterpress and gravure when it is used for those processes:
· The rubber printing surface conforms to the irregularities in the paper surface. Less printing pressure is needed so that halftones of good print quality can be obtained on rough-surfaced papers.
· The paper does not contact the metal printing plate. This reduces the abrasive wear and increases the running life of the plates.
· Printing speeds are increased. Over 15,000 impressions per hour are possible on sheet-fed presses and over 40,000 per hour on web-fed presses.
· The image on an offset plate is straight reading instead of appearing in reverse. This facilitates both the preparation of the plates and the correction of errors.
· Less ink is required to obtain equal coverage. Use of less ink improves trapping, speeds up ink drying, and reduces smudging or setoff in the delivery pile.

PRESS DESIGN

The basic printing unit for lithographic presses consists of three cylinders of equal circumference: the *plate*, *blanket*, and *impression* cylinders. Since the lithographic principle requires the plate to be dampened as well as inked, there are two fountains, one for ink and one for the dampening solution. Two trains of rollers independently provide a uniform distribution of ink and moisture to the plate. The plate and blanket cylinders are of fixed circumference and position. To provide sufficient pressure for transferring the inked image to the blanket, and to accommodate plates and

409

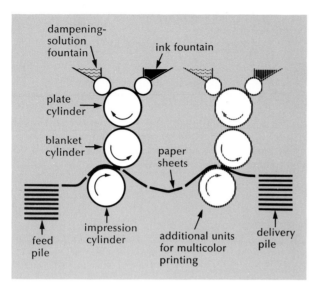

Figure 11.10: Schematic of unit-design lithographic press.

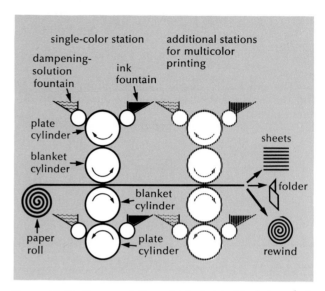

Figure 11.12: Representation of blanket-to-blanket perfecting lithographic press.

blankets of different thickness, the cylinders are *undercut*. The difference between the thickness of the plate and the undercut is made up by inserting thin sheets of paper or plastic packing under the plate until the required circumference for the cylinder is obtained. The impression cylinder is adjustable; it can be moved closer to or away from the blanket cylinder to obtain the necessary transfer pressure and to accommodate papers of different caliper.

There are three basic press configurations: *unit* design, *common impression cylinder* design, and *blanket-to-blanket* design. In unit design, illustrated in figure 11.10, a self-contained unit made up of a plate cylinder, a blanket cylinder, and an impression cylinder forms a printing station. Several of these stations may be joined in sequence for multicolor printing. In a common impression cylinder press, two or more sets of plate and blanket cylinders share a single impression cylinder, as diagrammed in figure 11.11. Thus two or

more colors may be printed at the same station. The blanket-to-blanket press, illustrated in figure 11.12, has no impression cylinder. Two plate/blanket units form a station. The paper passes between the two blanket cylinders, which not only print both sides of the paper simultaneously but are adjusted to provide the necessary transfer pressures.

Lithographic presses may be sheet-fed or web-fed.

Sheet-fed offset lithographic presses

Sheet-fed offset presses handle sheet sizes from 17" x 22" to 55" x 78" and range from single-color to six-color. Multicolor presses may be of unit design or common impression cylinder (CIC) design. A common CIC configuration is a four- or six-color press combining two or three two-color units with one feeder and delivery. Perfecting sheet-fed presses print both sides of the paper in one pass through the press. Some use the blanket-to-blanket design; other perfecting presses are designed to turn the sheet over between impressions. Duplicating presses are smaller and are mostly single color.

Web-fed offset lithographic presses

Most web-fed offset presses are of blanket-to-blanket design. They may have as many as 12 units (consisting of a plate cylinder and a blanket cylinder) feeding into two folders. A popular size for magazine printing takes rolls 38" wide with cutoffs of 22¾" to 25½" depending on the page size. When webs are much wider than 38" on blanket-to-blanket presses, there may be register problems due to *fanout*, particularly serious in process-color work. Fanout, the effect of moisture and mechanical roll-out, which tend to stretch the web sideways as it goes through the press, causes the image of the first colors being printed to be wider than the images of succeeding colors. Blanket-to-blanket presses up to 72" wide are used for book and directory printing, but not for critical color work.

Common impression cylinder presses in widths up to 76" are used for process-color reproduction since

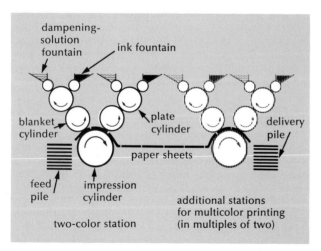

Figure 11.11: Representation of common impression cylinder lithographic press.

410

they hold the sheet firmly between impressions and give it little chance to stretch. On these presses one side of the paper is printed at a time. Some web offset newspaper presses have combinations of blanket-to-blanket units for single-color pages and common impression units for color printing.

CONSIDERATIONS IN PRINTING

In the lithographic printing cycle, the dampening solution is applied to the plate before it is inked. Although very little moisture is required to accomplish proper dampening, there must be a continuous film over the non-image areas of the plate to prevent the transfer of ink. The film of moisture applied to the image areas is discontinuous and does not seriously interfere with the transfer of ink.

However, if an excess of fountain solution is used, or if it is incorrectly formulated, or if its pH value is too low, the proper transfer of ink to the image areas of the plate will be hampered. Insufficient amounts will permit ink to adhere to the non-image areas, resulting in *dry-ups,* irregular blotches in the background, and the filling in of halftone shadow areas. Excessive amounts will be carried back into the ink train where the speed and pressures of the rollers quickly cause formation of a water-in-oil emulsion. Lithographic inks are designed to hold some moisture in suspension, which evaporates as the inks dry on the printed sheet. Once the critical limit is passed, the moisture forms small beads or splotches in the printed solids ("snow-flaky solids") or in extreme cases appears as water droplets on the rollers and in the ink fountain.

Adjusting the amounts of ink and dampening solution, or *ink/water balance,* is a critical factor in the operation of lithographic presses. Although much effort has gone into the development of improved dampening systems, most of which use direct drives and alcohol, there are still problems with ink/water balance. For this reason lithography generates more waste paper than either letterpress or gravure. There are compensatory advantages, of course, but on long runs letterpress and gravure can be more reasonable in cost.

Web tension is a more serious problem in offset lithography than in letterpress. Since tackier inks are used, more pull is needed to draw the paper through the press; with the lightweight papers used in magazine printing serious web breaks may occur. Devices which control web tension and improved infeeds such as flying pasters with accumulators, which permit the rolls to be pasted in a stopped position, have helped reduce the incidence of web breaks. Nevertheless, rolls of paper which are baggy or tight-edged or over one-quarter inch out or round may present problems.

DRIOGRAPHY

Driography is a recently developed process which uses the lithographic principle of surface chemistry to separate the image and non-image areas but does not require dampening (see "Special Plates," page 395). This process has great potential for overcoming the

main disadvantage of lithography while maintaining its other advantages. Driographic printing is done on standard lithographic presses, but the dampening system is not used.

ADVANTAGES AND LIMITATIONS

The advantages and limitations of offset lithography are summarized below.

Advantages

• Preparatory and plate costs are substantially lower.
• The offset principle permits quality halftones to be printed on rough surface papers.
• Both sheet-fed and web-fed presses are available in a variety of sizes and can be adapted to special purposes.

Limitations

• Purer and stronger papers are required to resist the moisture and the picking tendency of higher tack inks.
• The critical ink/water balance induces color variation in long runs and increases makeready waste.
• The very thin ink films used reduce the gloss of the dried ink and cause problems of coverage with gold and other metallic inks.
• Because multicolor printing is wet on wet, trapping problems frequently are encountered, but less than in letterpress.
• In the impression nip (the point where the paper and the blanket come in contact), the paper may fan out, resulting in poor register and sometimes producing wrinkles.
• The rubber blanket tends to distort in the nip, resulting in slur, doubling, and spreading in halftones.

GRAVURE PRINTING

Michael H. Bruno, GRAPHIC ARTS CONSULTANT

Intaglio processes make use of the principle that the slightest scratch or indentation upon a polished metal surface is capable of holding ink. When the surface is flooded with ink and the excess is wiped away, paper applied with sufficient pressure will withdraw the ink remaining in the depression. Mechanically it is a simpler task to pull clean, sharp impressions from fine lines sunk below the surface than from relatively coarse lines which stand above the surface. When the image is drawn by hand, it is also obvious that the fineness of line, and therefore the ability to render detail, can be realized more effectively by scribing the surface rather than gouging out the unwanted areas.

By the early part of the seventeenth century, engravings and etchings on metal had replaced woodcuts for book illustration in serious works and fine editions, establishing the supremacy of intaglio printing in pictorial reproduction which persists to the present day. The reproduction of text remained the province of relief printing, which was better suited to movable type. It was not until the early part of the twentieth century that photomechanical techniques broke down the barriers confining intaglio (as well as lithography) to pictorial reproduction.

Contemporary gravure uses a photographic image to define the printing and non-printing areas. Large solid areas must consist of a number of small cells since there is a limit to the area of a depression which will hold ink. The photographic image is therefore exposed through a screen which imposes a uniform pattern of cells. Depending upon the technique used, the cells provide tone modulation by varying their depth, their area, or both.

Gravure printing can be divided into sheet-fed gravure and web-fed or *rotogravure*. The latter makes up by far the largest share of the market; it is used extensively for publication printing and packaging applications. In sheet-fed gravure the image carrier is a metal plate, flexible enough to be wrapped around a plate cylinder. In web-fed gravure the image is prepared directly on the surface of a copper-clad, steel-core cylinder, combining the functions of image carrier and carrier support in an integral unit.

The costs of preparing the image carrier, whether plate or cylinder, are high. On the other hand, they wear extremely well and can yield a high number of impressions with little or no degradation of the image. A consideration in the decision to use gravure, therefore, is whether or not the length of run offsets the higher preparatory costs.

SHEET-FED GRAVURE PRESSES

Sheet-fed gravure is devoted almost entirely to pictorial reproduction, where its quality can hardly be approached by other printing processes. When the appearance of sheet-fed gravure is an overriding consideration, runs of only a few thousand sheets may be printed; ordinarily, run length is in the tens of thousands rather than hundreds of thousands. It is used occasionally for proofing of intermediate results prior to making cylinders for rotogravure, and for package printing in small or experimental quantities.

The printing unit consists of a plate cylinder and an impression cylinder of the same diameter with a gripper mechanism to hold the sheet during impression. After mounting the plate on the plate cylinder the gap is covered with a protective shield to keep out the

412

fluid ink, which is flooded on the plate with a fountain roller.

On multicolor presses, drying between units is necessary to insure good trapping; after the last impression a volume of air is supplied to the printed surface before stacking. The drying equipment is considerably less complex than in rotogravure, and adjustments may easily be made to the heaters or fans while the job is in progress.

In single-color jobs, plates may contain multiples of the same image; in full-color work they seldom do, since it is difficult to obtain exact duplication of the image with conventional etching techniques which rely upon considerable handwork. Four-color work is seldom printed sheetwise as the preparation of two sets of plates is an expense to be avoided when possible.

Press varnishing on gravure presses is almost the equal of that done on independent equipment. Gravure ranks well ahead of letterpress and lithography in this respect.

ROTOGRAVURE PRESSES

The intaglio process calls for special considerations in press design. The ink must necessarily be of low viscosity in order to enter the cells and be wiped clear of the surface by the light pressure of a doctor blade. Therefore, no elaborate train of inking rollers is required, for the cylinder rotates in a bath of ink which provides uniform ink distribution. Transfer pressure is provided by a rubber-covered impression roll and a bare steel backup roll which do not require a circumference equal to that of the cylinder. Figure 11.13 is a schematic design of a rotogravure press.

Inks of such low viscosity require a large volume of air at high temperature to drive off the heavy concentration of solvents. Inks cannot be overprinted wet but must be thoroughly dried between impressions. A large part of gravure presses is devoted to drying ovens

or tunnels, chillers, exhaust units for capturing the solvents, and ancillary equipment which enables a large part of the captured solvents to be recovered and reused or incinerated.

The need for thorough drying between impressions also raises special problems when both sides of the web are to be printed. Unlike blanket-to-blanket web offset which can print both sides simultaneously, the rotogravure web must be completely printed on one side before it can be printed on the reverse.

There are several ways to overcome this apparent handicap. The web may be printed on one side, rewound, and turned over for printing on the other. Alternatively, the number of printing stations may be doubled, with turning bars between the stations that print top and bottom, or the web itself may be *double-ended*. Double-ending means that the width of the press must be at least twice that of the web being printed. After one side is printed the web is turned by angle bars and perfected on the same press, both sides of the web running next to one another as if they were two different webs. The cylinders for printing the two sides are different; the two sets print side by side, each printing a different side of the web.

Publication presses

One of the main uses of rotogravure lies in the field of magazine publication. High printing speeds, the ability to produce high-quality four-color illustrations on less expensive papers, variable cutoff lengths, and the flexibility of the folding equipment all tend to give rotogravure a competitive edge in the publication of mass-circulation magazines.

Presses for printing the inside signatures of magazines consist of as many as ten separate printing stations, four for color and one for monochrome text and illustration for each side of the web. Such a press is illustrated in figure 11.14. On a full-width web of 54 inches, three different kinds of signatures can be pro-

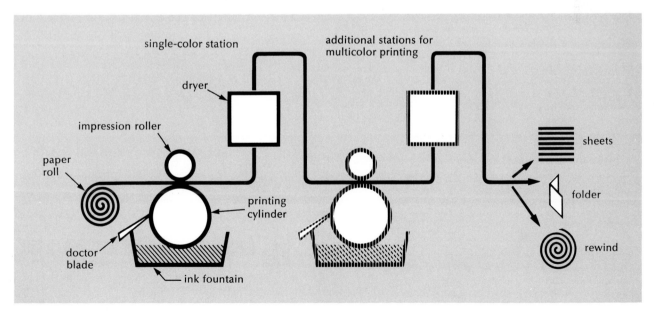

Figure 11.13: Schematic of rotogravure press.

413

American Book-Stratford Press, Inc.

COMPLETE BOOK MANUFACTURING
WEB FACILITIES

Levey #65-2, Two Colors, 42¾″ Cut Off, 65″ Web Width

Hantscho #35-4, Four Colors, 42¾″ Cut Off, 35″ Web Width

Hantscho #36-4, Four Colors, 22¾″ Cut Off, 36″ Web Width

Hantscho #36-2, Two Colors, 22¾″ Cut Off, 36″ Web Width

Hantscho #49-4, Four Colors, 27³/₃₂″ Cut Off, 49″ Web Width

Harris Cottrell #405-4, Four Colors, 38¾″ Cut Off, 40½″ Web Width

Strachen Henshaw #405-2, Two Colors, 38¾″ Cut Off, 40½″ Web Width

American Book-Stratford Press, Inc.
95 Mayhill St., Saddle Brook, N. J. 07662
COMPLETE BOOK MANUFACTURER AND COLOR PRINTER
☐ Design   ☐ Composition   ☐ Platemaking   ☐ Brightype
☐ Letterpress   ☐ Sheet-Fed and Web Offset Printing
☐ Edition and Perfect Binding — Hard and Soft Cover Books
☐ Fulfillment   ☐ Packaging   ☐ Shipping   ☐ Warehousing

201-843-4200

414

duced at the folder: one signature of 32 pages, two
signatures of 16 pages each, or four signatures of 8
pages each. This equipment handles large-format magazines with trimmed page size of approximately 11" x
13". Monthly magazines of up to 200 pages with circu-
lations of over one million copies are run routinely on
this type of equipment.

An infinite variety of page dimensions is possible, of
course, by varying the width of the printing area on the
cylinder and by changing to a cylinder of larger or
smaller circumference. One of the main advantages in
rotogravure is that each press accommodates cylinders
of varying circumference.

In a ten-station press with ribbon folders, leading
the web through the press is a complicated task. As
much as 500 feet of leader may be required, depending
on the number of stations used, the number of turning
and angle bars required, and the arrangement of the
folded signatures. Register adjustments can be made in
two directions, lengthwise and radially. The cylinder
can be advanced or retarded in small increments by
electrical controls. Rotation, or cocking obviously is not
possible.

Packaging presses

Printing, cutting, and creasing of folding paper boxes
in one continuous in-line operation is another main
use of rotogravure. Since such items are usually printed
on one side only, the number of printing stations is
fewer than required for publication presses.

Packaging often requires more than the basic process
colors. Match colors, metallics, and varnishing require
separate stations. Laminating stations in which foil is
applied to the board before printing provide additional
flexibility in meeting the requirements of packaging.

In the other branches of printing, image quality is
probably the greatest concern of production personnel.
In the manufacture of folding paper boxes, however,
it plays a somewhat secondary role. That is not to say

that it is unimportant, but gravure cylinders provide
the requisite quality and are relatively trouble-free in
operation. The prime concern is the cutting and creasing of cartons with precision so that they can be assembled into a final product. The machinery which
folds the carton at the time the product is packaged
cannot accept cartons with dimensional variations, and
close tolerances are the working rule.

Other uses

Gravure is used extensively in the printing of textile
patterns because the continuous printing surface provides the "repeat" needed to form a continuous pattern. Heat transfer printing using special subliming
dyes is used to print images on paper, which are later
transferred to polyester textiles by heat and pressure.
Wallboards, plastics, floor coverings, and similar materials calling for a wood grain or other continuous
pattern are also adaptable to gravure printing.

ELECTROSTATIC ASSIST

A serious problem in gravure printing has been the
necessity for very smooth papers. Otherwise there are
"skips" in the printing. The introduction of trailing-
blade-coated papers about 1957 was a big boon to
gravure, but it did not help in printing on newsprint or
rough boards. The development of the *electrostatic
assist* by the Gravure Research Institute has helped to
solve the problem of skips and raise the general level
of quality of gravure printing on all paper and paperboard stocks. The ink pigment in the wells of the
cylinder develops an electrostatic charge. When an
opposite charge is applied under the substrate during
printing, the ink is lifted from the wells so that it
transfers to the paper. The shape of the meniscus of
the ink in the wells is changed so that it contacts
the low spots in the paper even though these spots are
not in direct contact with the cylinder.

415

ADVANTAGES AND LIMITATIONS

The advantages and limitations of gravure printing are summarized below.

Advantages
- Inks of low viscosity cause fewer problems with web tension.
- Between-station drying insures excellent trapping.
- In the variable-depth gravure processes, variations in ink-film thickness provide good color reproduction and high tint purity; brighter colors can be obtained with cheaper pigments.
- Variable cutoff lengths are easy to obtain; the continuous printing surface meets a number of special needs.
- High uniformity of color can be obtained throughout the run.

Limitations
- Printing with split fountains not possible.
- Direct transfer calls for smooth papers to avoid highlight skips.
- Cylinders are expensive to prepare; there is no way to obtain proofs short of printing the full-size cylinder.
- Volatile solvents require extensive equipment for recovery and are fire and explosion hazards.

SCREEN PRINTING
Timothy B. McSweeney, SCREEN PRINTING ASSOCIATION INTERNATIONAL

The term *screen printing* is derived from the use of a porous screen made of finely woven fabric or metal mesh. Adhered is a stencil which blocks the openings in the screen in the areas which are not to be printed. During printing, the substrate is placed under the screen; ink is applied to the screen and forced through the fine mesh openings in the areas not protected by the stencil, producing the image on the substrate.

BASIC ELEMENTS
The three basic elements of screen printing are the screen, the squeegee, and the ink. Each of these interrelated elements is a determinant of quality.

The printing screen
The screen is the heart of the system, and the point at which quality must begin. It consists of the fabric, a stencil, and a frame.

As reflected in the earlier term *silk screen*, silk was the fabric used for many years. With the introduction of synthetic fabrics such as nylon and polyester, the industry has overcome the problems associated with the use of silk. Indeed, fabric problems have been virtually eliminated, since today's synthetics can do almost anything the printer calls upon them to do. The latest developments in screen materials include metalized polyester and stainless-steel wire mesh, both of which allow greater ink flow and stencil stability.

A second component of the printing screen is the stencil, the pattern which determines what areas of the screen will transmit ink and what areas will not. Today the hand-cut stencil, which was once the staple of the industry, has been replaced in many applications by photomechanically prepared stencils. (Production of stencils is discussed in "Screens for Screen Printing," page 388.) The introduction of the photomechanical screen has made the process capable of rendering extremely fine detail, so that type as small as medium-weight eight-point can be printed. The limiting factor in resolution is now more often than not the substrate rather than the screen stencil. Glass or hard plastics will take an exceedingly fine, detailed image, whereas the fabric of a T-shirt will not.

The introduction of the photomechanical screen has made possible four-color process printing. Process-color work now can be printed on virtually any substrate. This fact makes it possible to use photographic color transparencies and full-color artwork as original copy.

The third component is the screen frame, made of wood, aluminum, or steel. The frame supports the stencil fabric and allows for the proper degree of fabric tension. The relative tautness of the screen is a major determinant of accurate color registration. Insufficient tension may also result in smearing or uneven ink deposit, and will eventually cause excessive wear on the screen.

The squeegee
The squeegee is the blade drawn across the screen to force the ink through the mesh. This simple tool varies in the material of which it is made, the form and size of the blade edge, the blade angle in relation to the fabric, and the pressure and speed with which it is drawn across the screen. These factors are adjusted according to the job being printed. Their control is an essential ingredient of screen printing quality.

Irregularities such as warp and nicked edges have been greatly reduced by the introduction of synthetic materials in place of rubber. Although rubber is relatively easy to draw across the screen, it is unstable and tends to round or warp quickly, making it suitable for short runs on certain coarse or porous substrates, such as canvas or cotton. The new materials, such as polyurethane, make possible runs of 25,000 or more with no variation in image quality due to the squeegee.

The ink

The characteristic which most distinguishes screen printing from the other printing processes is the extreme thickness of the ink film which can be applied. This accounts for some of the unusual effects obtainable in screen printing. When the brilliance of a color is dependent upon opacity, screen printing yields results that can hardly be approximated by the other processes. It is particularly useful when metallic or fluorescent inks are run or when highly colored substrates are used.

The extreme simplicity of the manner in which the ink is applied also extends the range of usable dyes and pigments; few restrictions are imposed by the process. (Lithography, by contrast, must exclude all pigment classes which tend to bleed in water since the presence of moisture is an integral part of the printing process.) By printing an adhesive compound and then dusting with cotton, silk, or rayon flock, the finished design can be made to appear like felt or suede leather.

The thickness of the ink, however, increases the time for drying. Sheets must be racked separately until dry or passed through a heated tunnel or dryer before they can be piled. New types of inks permit thinner films and better drying characteristics yet retain the vivid colors associated with the process. Ultraviolet inks requiring special curing equipment are coming into extensive use.

SCREEN PRINTING PRESSES

Until recently screen or stencil printing was a hand-operated process. The methods and materials are simple, and the results achieved by a skilled operator are satisfactory from the standpoint of both quality and economy. However, hand operation limits the process to fairly short runs. It is only with the introduction of power-operated presses that screen printing has become a viable commercial process.

Both single-color and multicolor presses are widely used in commercial screen printing. Because of the diversity of work done, however, multicolor printing is often achieved by multiple runs on single-color presses. Additionally, single-color presses are often constructed in oversize proportions, as required for highway signs, or in special configurations, as required for the application of images to glass bottles for subsequent fusing.

Screen printing presses are of three types: flat-bed, cylinder (both essentially types of "flat-screen" presses),

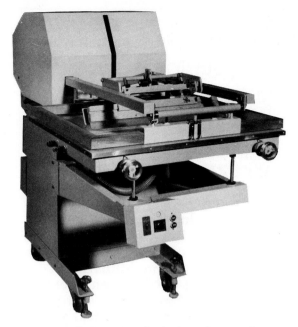

Figure 11.16: Single-station flat-bed semiautomatic screen printing press. *Courtesy of Medalist/M & M Research & Printing Aids.*

and rotary screen. Flat-screen presses (see figures 11.15 and 11.16) require an intermittent or reciprocating motion as each screen is printed. The printing cycle has three steps:

1. The screen is moved into position in preparation for actual printing.

2. The squeegee is pressed across the screen, forcing the ink through the open mesh areas.

3. The screen is lifted as the substrate advances to the next position. (In multicolor work, butts and overlaps require close register, which limits the running speed.)

The rotary-screen press (fig. 11.17) uses screens made of thin metal formed into continuous, seam-free, open-ended cylinders. The cylinders are capped at each end so that they may be fitted into rolling blocks at the side of the press. The squeegee is a round steel bar which rides freely inside the cylinder. Squeegee pressure is adjusted by magnets placed under the bed of the machine. A constant level of ink is maintained inside the cylinder by pumping fresh ink through the open end.

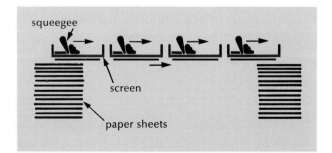

Figure 11.15: Schematic drawing of a flat-screen type press. Screens lift after each application, as substrate advances.

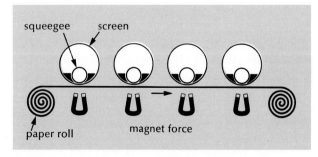

Figure 11.17: Rotary-screen printing press. Magnet force is applied to control the squeegee pressure.

Monochrome and color halftone work can be done from any form of original, such as renderings or photographs. In the preparation of process-color separations for screen printing, certain characteristics, such as halftone dot density and tonal reproduction range, are different from those required for lithography. Often special substrates must be taken into account when color separations are made.

There is a direct relationship between halftone line count and the number of openings in the screen fabric, or *mesh count*. As a general rule, the lower the mesh count (implying larger openings between threads), the lower the halftone line count that may be reproduced. Some fine-mesh screens of 450 mesh counts per inch may accurately print up to 150-line halftones.

USES

Screen printing has distinct advantages for short runs because of the simplicity of the equipment and the process. For longer runs this advantage may be outweighed by the greater speed of other printing processes. However, for most of its applications screen printing represents the only feasible process. Its present markets are quite secure, and it continues to capture new areas of application.

The first major surge of growth came in the field of advertising and sales promotion; the brilliant colors are ideal for posters, point-of-purchase displays, and so on. The use of screen printing for this type of advertising has grown at an annual rate of 25 percent in recent years, compared to a rate of 17 percent for the screen printing industry as a whole.

The exceptional degree of fade resistance of the inks has steadily expanded the market for the screen printer in all forms of printing designed to stay outdoors—everything from bumper strips to highway billboards. The exceptional adhesion of the inks makes them a natural for use on highway traffic signs.

In the field of container decoration, modern printing equipment makes it possible to decorate the formed container directly, a technique used extensively on glass bottles.

The great versatility of screen printing is demonstrated by the variety of products which are screen printed and of surfaces which can be decorated, including paper, fabric, leather, wood, glass, plastic, and metal, all of which may be rigid or flexible, flat or formed.

Rotary-screen presses are continuous-running and fast. They are used extensively for textiles, wallpaper, and other products which require unbroken patterns.

COPY PREPARATION

Most screens are prepared from original art by photomechanical methods. Same-size film positives are the ideal way to present artwork, although most screen printers have facilities for preparing positives from reflective art or transparencies. If the art requires substantial enlargement, as a large poster may, it may be necessary to do some additional handwork on the line art in order to maintain crisp, hard-edged lines.

FLEXOGRAPHIC PRINTING

G. H. Anthony, GRAPHIC ARTS CONSULTANT

Flexography is a web-fed rotary printing process combining features of letterpress and rotogravure in its use of relief plates and low-viscosity, fast-drying inks. Its relatively inexpensive rubber plates, simple printing techniques, and two-roller ink distribution system are other features which provide for quick makeready and cleanup and easy change from job to job. Flexography is consequently among the least expensive of the printing processes, yet it is capable of high-speed, good-quality printing on many substrates.

DEVELOPMENT

Flexography's predecessor, the "aniline" printing process, named for the dyes used in its inks, appeared about the same time as rotogravure (1880), but because of mechanical and ink problems it remained a cheap marking process rather than a printing process until the appearance of cellophane in 1930. It was the only process capable of printing on cellophane economically in small and medium quantities. From that time on, applications expanded to other substrates such as polyethylene, polypropylene, polymer-coated cellophane, cellulose acetate, and other plastic films; glassine, tissue, paper, and paperboard; and foils and laminates. The name *flexographic printing* was formally adopted in 1952, and the Flexographic Technical Association was chartered in 1958.

Early aniline printing had many problems. Press speeds of 100 to 150 feet per minute were typical, and the transparent-dye printing inks were unsatisfactory for printing on transparent substrates. Pigmented alcohol-shellac inks, water-based inks, and the anilox roller for metering them were developed in the thirties and forties to overcome these shortcomings. The nitrocellulose inks followed and were, in turn, succeeded in 1955 by the polyamide resin inks employing a co-solvent mixture of alcohol and a hydrocarbon.

In the last two decades, press speeds have increased to 2,000 feet per minute. This increase was made possible by heavier printing presses, web scanners, automatic viscosity controls, unwind and rewind roll tension controls, push-button running register adjustments, flying splicers, improved ink drying tunnels and between-station dryers, edge guides, pneumatic and hydraulic impression controls, and many other improvements used on other types of web presses.

CURRENT USE

Flexographic printing quality has improved to a point where it challenges that of some of the other major printing processes. No longer a cheap "rubber stamp" process, it is capable of good-quality printing in line, tint, halftone, duotone, and the three- and four-color processes, usually using screens with rulings from 100- to 133-line. It still retains the advantages of minimal press downtime for job changes, off-press plate mounting, makeready, and proofing, which were the original sources of low cost so attractive to industry. Products printed by flexography now include bags, labels, corrugated board, box coverings, gift wraps, paper cups and containers, candy wrappers, wallpaper, decalcomanias, textiles and many other products in the area of converting printing.

Since flexographic printing quality has become competitive with that of the other major printing processes, types of copy and copy preparation for line, tint, halftone, and color process work for flexography are similar to that for letterpress and offset. Except for allowing for plate shrinkage and stretch, no special copy techniques are required for flexography. All treatment is determined by the copy itself and the substrate on which it is to be printed.

In purchasing printing, buyers are coming to realize that the comparatively low cost of flexographic printing is due to its efficiency and not to low printing quality. Unfortunately, too many printing buyers still are wedded to the concept that the higher the halftone line count and the more colors used, the higher the printing quality will be. While it is true that the higher the numerical designation of halftone line count the closer the printed image will come to the original continuous-tone copy, there is one important qualification which is too often overlooked. Dots finer than those in a 125-line halftone are beyond the resolving power of the eye (see "Introduction to Graphic Arts Photography," page 316.) It makes sense to use the lowest halftone value consistent with acceptable quality on specific substrates. A 133-line screen is impractical on natural kraft paper, newsprint, corrugated board, and other such rough surfaces; a costly coated paper stock is wasted in printing a 60-line halftone; and a 150-line halftone printed by four-color process is inappropriate on a billboard normally viewed at several hundred yards. Such misuse represents squandered effort, time, and money.

PRESSES

There are three basic types of flexographic printing presses, depending upon the roller and cylinder arrangement.

The *stack type* press has individual color stations (also called units or decks) arranged vertically, usually in two stacks on both sides of the main press frame. Each station has its own impression cylinder and is driven through gear trains supported by the press frame. Such presses usually have from two to eight stations, with six being the most common.

The primary advantages of the stack press are the accessibility of the color stations, facilitating change-over, wash-up, and makeready; the ability to modify color stations so that both sides of a web may be printed in one pass through the press; the adaptability to in-line printing with other equipment such as bag and corrugated board machinery; and the ability to apply coatings of various types. The stack press is used extensively in milk carton production in conjunction with unwind, rewind, sheeter or cutter, and creaser.

Stack presses may be used to print almost every type of substrate but will not hold register closer than plus or minus .031 inch on extensible or thin webs.

The *central* (or *common*) *impression cylinder* press, or *CIC* press, has all color stations around a single impression cylinder mounted in the main press frame. The web contacts the central cylinder as it enters the press and remains "locked" to it until the web leaves the press at the last press station, preventing register shift from color to color. The CIC presses may have from two to eight stations, with six being the most common.

The central cylinder is normally a double-walled, cast iron or rolled steel cylinder. Temperature-con-

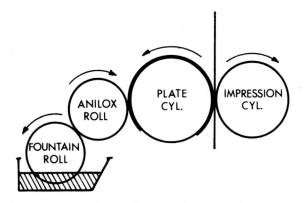

Figure 11.18: Stack-type flexographic press using standard two-roller system.

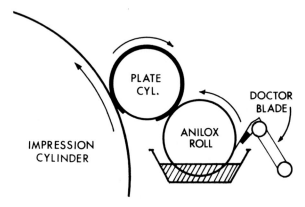

Figure 11.19: Central impression cylinder flexographic press with reverse-angle doctor blade.

The *in-line* press consists of separate color stations in a horizontal line. As in the other types of press, all stations are driven by a common line shaft. These presses can print large web widths with designs that are not critical with respect to register; they can hold register on narrow web presses when color stations are close to each other, as in small label presses. In-line presses are commonly used for bags, corrugated board, folding boxes, and similar products.

Rotogravure stations may be incorporated in any of the flexographic presses to extend versatility in printing on different substrates.

Some variations in press configuration are diagrammed in figures 11.18 through 11.20. Figure 11.18 shows the standard two-roller system used in a stack press. There is a rubber *fountain roller* in the ink pan and an *anilox roller*, similar to an engraved gravure cylinder, for transferring the ink to the rubber plate on the plate cylinder. (The latest development in ink rollers is the ceramic roller, which is much tougher and lasts longer than conventional metal anilox rollers.) Figure 11.19 shows the reverse-angle doctor blade used without a fountain roller on a central impression cylinder press. This blade makes it possible to improve ink flow control. Figure 11.20 shows the doctor blade with a fountain roller on both sides of a CIC press. The arrows on all three illustrations indicate the direction of rotation of the rollers and cylinders. These and other roller and cylinder configurations, such as those used in roller coating and offset gravure, may all be used on all three types of presses—stack type, central impression cylinder, and in-line. It is these simple arrangements of comparatively inexpensive rollers and cylinders which provide the quick change for varying repeat sizes that helps make flexography an economically sound process.

NEW DEVELOPMENTS

The future of flexography seems unlimited. Broader use of flexography in both industrial and commercial printing is encouraged by its low cost and efficiency and by continuous new developments.

One of the major advantages of flexography is the use of printing plates made of rubber or other types of elastomeric materials, from .125" to .312" in thickness,

trolled water circulates within the cylinder for expansion control. It may have a total included runout (TIR) of .0005" and may run from 30" to 83" in diameter, with a 60" diameter most common.

This type of press is becoming the mainstay of converters due to its ability to hold good register, even with complicated close-register designs, on all substrates, including lightweight papers and flexible films.

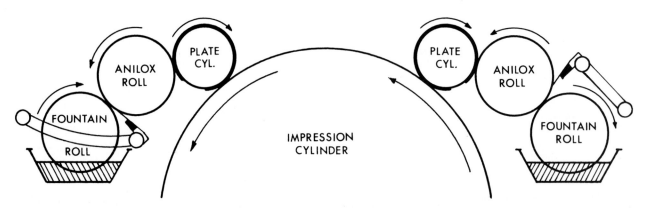

Figure 11.20: Central impression cylinder flexographic press with reverse-angle doctor blade and fountain roller.

which facilitate makeready. New compressible plates, compressible plate backings, and magnetic plate backings further reduce makeready and printing press downtime, simplify plate mounting, make higher printing quality easier to achieve, and contribute significantly to further cost reduction. Recently developed photopolymer plates, which are original plates rather than duplicate plates made from photoengravings, also reduce time-consuming manual multiple-plate mounting each time a job is rerun. In the future, thinner printing plates with relief as low as .015" will find greater use as their potential for greater accuracy and higher printing quality are realized.

Heat transfer printing, through which images printed flexographically on paper are transferred thermally to textiles, extends flexography to textile decoration (see page 429). More importantly, the efficient flexographic ink distribution system and flexible printing plates are invading the newspaper printing industry for use with conventional paste-bodied inks. This, in turn, makes available to flexographers the press-stable letterpress and lithographic inks, including polymer inks, which dry almost instantly with no vapor emissions upon exposure to UV or electron beams. The advantages of higher ink viscosities and thinner ink films for producing higher quality flexographic printing will be more widely recognized as the reverse-angle doctor blade and the new inks become more widely used. The UV inks are particularly important in fostering the use of higher viscosities. With improving technology, flexography will continue to expand into new markets.

SPECIAL PRINTING PROCESSES

Besides the major printing processes, there are many processes which have more specialized or limited use. These processes, some of which are discussed in the articles that follow, may be classified into several groups:

• "Screenless" processes for reproducing continuous-tone illustrations. *Screenless lithography* is one printing process that can reproduce continuous-tone images without the use of a halftone screen (see "Special Plates," page 395.) Another is *collotype*, which is used mainly for fine art reproductions.

• Noncontact processes. A common type of noncontact printing is *electrostatic* printing (see "Reprography," page 429). Another printing method, *ink jet printing*, forms images on the surface of the paper by directing charged ink droplets through an electrical field.

• Variations of traditional printing processes. The offset principle, usually associated with lithography, may be applied to both gravure and letterpress. Offset letterpress, usually called *letterset* or *dry offset*, is used in packaging, metal decorating, and publication, commercial, and specialty printing. Standard offset presses can be modified to take the relief plates used. *Offset gravure* is used in packaging and is being considered for use in publication printing. Flexographic presses can be converted for offset gravure by using gravure cylinders in place of the anilox rollers and mounting a continuous rubber surface on the plate cylinder. Another "variation" process, *driography* is based on the lithographic principle of chemical separation of image and non-image areas, but it uses a special driographic ink and does not require a dampening system (see "Special Plates," page 395).

• Specialized printing. Special printing techniques are needed for specialty applications. For example, *steel-die engraving* is used for producing embossed printing for stationery, announcements, and similar items. *Thermography* simulates engraving and has similar uses. (It should not be confused with the reprographic process also called thermography. See page 430.) Although *decals* are printed by traditional processes, they require special assembly techniques. *Heat transfer printing* is used to transfer printed images onto textiles.

COLLOTYPE
Ernest Wuchner, ARTHUR JAFFE HELIOCHROME COMPANY

Collotype, or photogelatin printing, is a screenless printing process capable of yielding almost photographic quality in printing. Unlike most printing processes, it reproduces continuous-tone images without the necessity for converting them to halftone. Because it produces no dot effect, it is among the purest forms of printing, achieving rich velvet tones and fine gradations. Collotype is used predominantly for fine art reproductions of importance and lasting value. It is also used for the reproduction of pencil and crayon sketches, greeting cards, catalog illustrations, displays, and posters.

The printing procedure may start with original artwork or a color transparency. The art is photographed to produce color-separated continuous-tone negatives. Retouching is done for color correction.

Next, an aluminum plate is coated with bichromated gelatin, a light-sensitive coating. Heat is applied to the plate to cause reticulation, or the formation of a random pattern of fine lines in the gelatin equivalent to a screen ruling on the order of 300 to 500 lines per inch. The plate is then exposed to a continuous-tone negative with a density range of about 1.2. The gelatin hardens in proportion to the amount of light received: the dark areas of the negative stop most of the light, so the gelatin is least hardened in those areas; in lighter areas of the negative, more light passes through and the gelatin becomes harder. The surface of the gelatin on the final plate is hardened in proportion to the tones in the continuous-tone negative.

The plate is then washed clear of bichromate and dried. Before use, it is soaked in a glycerine and water solution. The unhardened gelatin absorbs the solution; the harder areas take up less moisture, and the hardest areas almost none. As the gelatin takes up the solution, it swells in proportion to the amount of moisture absorbed. The glycerine acts as a humectant; that is, it helps retain the moisture content of the plate.

The final plate is both oleophilic (ink-receptive) and hydrophilic (water-receptive) in varying proportions in all areas of the plate. When the plate is inked, the areas which absorbed least moisture are most ink-receptive and the areas which absorbed more moisture are less ink-receptive; the highlight areas, which contain most moisture, are ink-repellent. The amount of ink that adheres to any area of the plate depends upon the moisture content of that area.

Collotype is generally considered to be a planographic printing process because, like lithography, it makes use of the principle that ink and water repel each other. It also is related to intaglio because of the graduated swelling of the moist gelatin surface and because the ink-film thickness varies in proportion to the tones of the original.

The press-ready plate is strapped onto the press cylinder, inked by a system of inking rollers, and pressed into direct contact with the paper. No dampening system is needed because the gelatin retains its own moisture. However, the humidity in the pressroom must be carefully controlled to keep the plate moist. It must be gradually increased as each impression removes some moisture from the gelatin. After about

1,000 impressions, the plate is usually sponged with glycerine solution to restore moisture to the gelatin, at which time the relative humidity of the pressroom must be reduced, and the cycle starts again.

Collotype has a number of limitations. Most presses are hand fed, and therefore speed of printing is slow, rarely exceeding 200 copies per hour. Because of abrasion of the gelatin surface against the paper, plate life is usually limited to about 5,000 impressions. Not all paper stock is suitable for gelatin printing. Paper must be pure and as lint-free as possible. Proper consistency of ink and correct temperature and humidity during printing have an important role; any deviations can greatly influence the result. Collotype is decreasing in use, mainly because of the cost and the lack of skilled craftsmen to carry it out. However, the slow-running presses and limited daily output make it possible to keep a constant watch for quality.

INK JET PRINTING
J. James Stone, A. B. DICK COMPANY

New printing techniques recently developed "write" on recording surfaces by propelling small droplets of ink across a short air gap. Only the ink strikes the surface, forming a mark. No pressure is needed between the printer and the recording surface to transfer ink images. These noncontact systems, called *ink jet* printers, promise to expand printing opportunities in the future and provide distinct advantages over present printing techniques.

Several types of ink jet printers have been developed. In all of them, the ink droplets flow toward the printing surface through a small orifice, the information needed to specify the position of the droplets being provided by a computer-based system. Printers differ in how the ink accelerates toward the surface, in how droplets form, and in how the flight of the droplets is controlled electronically.

EARLY INK JET PRINTER

An early form of ink jet printing, the Inktronic printer, as developed by Teletype Corporation, accelerated the ink stream toward the paper surface by means of a high-voltage accelerating field. The high voltage "pulled" the dielectric ink from a small orifice, causing it to neck down and form into a tiny stream of uniform charged droplets. These passed through·an aperture in the high-voltage plate and then through a pair of "x" and "y" deflection plates. By appropriate signals on these plates, the droplets could be deflected so as to form characters on the paper.

An Inktronic terminal printer was developed using 40 nozzles to produce 80 alphanumeric characters per line. This equipment is no longer manufactured.

THE SWEET PROCESS

The printer in most commercial usage at the present time uses a pressurized source of ink to form a thin, high-velocity stream of ink as diagrammed in figure 11.21. In this system, as developed by R. Sweet of Stanford University, a piezoelectric crystal mechanically vibrates the nozzle assembly, breaking the ink stream into droplets at a frequency equal to that of the signal supplied to the crystal. As the droplets form, each receives an electrical charge from the voltage placed on the charging tunnel at the time each droplet breaks away from the fluid stream. This charge stays with the drop for the remainder of its flight toward the printing medium.

If the droplet receives a zero charge, it moves along a straight line and enters the return orifice. It then returns to the ink return tank, from which it recirculates to the orifice. If, on the other hand, the droplet receives a charge, the high-voltage field between the deflection plates causes it to be deflected upward and over the top of the return orifice. As a result, it strikes the printing medium at a point dependent upon the amount of charge. Thus, over a short vertical distance the print position can be controlled electrically. By mechanically moving this writing assembly across the surface of the printing medium, or moving the medium

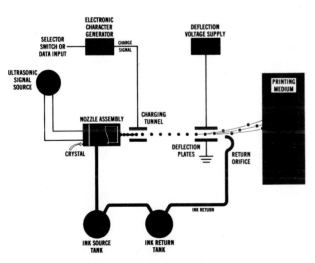

Figure 11.21: A. B. Dick's Videojet printing process.

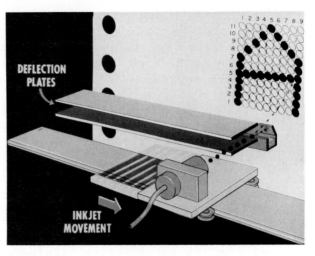

Figure 11.22: Letter printing by ink jet.

past a stationary writing assembly, printed images can be formed.

Alphanumeric characters, by this technique, are formed as shown in figure 11.22. The dot matrix indicates the positions of individual ink spots formed by scanning the vertical positions shown, as the writing assembly moves across the medium in a horizontal direction. If the charge on a single drop is suppressed by making the charging voltage zero while it forms, then that drop enters the return orifice instead of forming the spot in the matrix normally occupied by it. The droplets that are not wanted are left out; the remaining droplets form the desired character or symbol.

A. B. Dick Company uses the Sweet process for printer systems. Characters in a 5 x 7 dot matrix can be printed at up to 1,375 characters per second per nozzle assembly on a large variety of printing surfaces. Up to 15 such nozzles have been attached directly to web offset presses to print variable information on business forms. The information on the item may be electronically controlled and derived from a computer, a counter, or another source. It is possible to print direct mail addresses on Internal Revenue forms, for example, permitting the output to be mailed right after assembly, without subsequent addressing operations. The equipment is also used to address newspapers at press speed or to address publications on-line with binding machines. (See "Fulfillment of Mass Mailings," page 576.)

Such ink jet printers can deposit an image lightly on other types of surface, too. Corrugated cardboard, pills, capsules, curved can bottoms, butter, fruit, and fabric can be as easily printed upon as plain paper. The required mechanical motion can be that already moving the component or part from one location to another. For example, A. B. Dick's single- and dual-headed printers now batch and date-code food and beverage containers directly on the conveyor line as they are filled at full speed.

Systems producing smaller drops and more drops per character can produce output as shown in figure 11.23. IBM, with its 6640 ink jet printers, produces typewriter-like quality at up to 92 characters per second using a

This copy is an example of the present state of the art
in the A. B. Dick Company program to achieve ink jet print quality
closely approximating the electric typewriter.

It was produced on an experimental test setup in the IPO Advanced
Research Department in which a 9600 line printer was modified with
a special nozzle system and other changes.

The typeface simulates the IBM Courier font. Each character
was analyzed on an enlarged matrix design and programmed into a
minicomputer which served as the character generator.

There are many potential applications for this new capability
of the ink jet printing, including the general field of plateless
printing.

Figure 11.23: Example of high-resolution ink jet printing.

24 x 40 matrix to form them. This system is used extensively in word processing installations.

Sharp and Hitachi, in Japan, are marketing ink jet equipment under a license from A. B. Dick Company. Sharp has developed communications terminal equipment, while Hitachi has developed industrial marking printers.

Recognition Equipment Company uses a single jet in OCR equipment to print information in fluorescent bar codes on the reverse side of documents. Subsequent document processing can be done by less complex, more reliable readers.

OTHER SYSTEMS

Mead Digital Systems has developed a similar ink jet printing system incorporating up to 100 jets per inch along a single straight line across a moving paper web. Unwanted ink droplets are deflected into an ink return system while uncharged droplets are permitted to proceed to the printing surface. As a result, each nozzle prints, in an electrically controlled manner, a single vertical line of spots. Printers with speeds up to 700 feet per minute have been offered, and rates as high as 2,400 feet per minute should be possible.

Another system, developed by H. Hertz, projects a stream of tiny droplets at the paper surface. An aperture in the path of uncharged droplets permits them to strike the paper surface and mark it. If a charging ring in the region of drop formation charges the droplets, then, as a result of mutual electrostatic repulsion, the stream disperses into a mist and is blocked by the aperture plate. Mechanical motion of the printing head scans the surface to be printed and produces the desired image.

Bell and Howell uses up to eight of the Hertz nozzles to produce up to eight lines of alphanumeric information for direct addressing. Each head is mounted onto a galvanometer movement and oscillated in a direction perpendicular to the paper motion by an amount equal to the character height. A sharp edge replaces the aperture along the oscillating scan. As the nozzle oscillates, electrical control signals turn the writing stream on or off so as to form desired characters. Such systems produce up to 275 characters per second per address line. Dennison uses an oscillating head in a similar manner to produce tags.

Finally, another ink jet printer system generates an ink droplet only when needed for printing. For this system an electrical impulse applied to the piezoelectric crystal in the nozzle "squeezes" the ink and causes a droplet to be propelled toward the paper surface. Each time a droplet is required, an electrical pulse produces one.

Siemens and Silonics have both developed and are marketing terminal printers of this type. Both systems print characters on a 5 x 7 dot matrix using seven impulse nozzles vertically arranged along the height of the characters to be printed. As the print-head assembly, containing the nozzles, moves across the paper, individual nozzles are pulsed to produce the required dots. These printers can produce up to 300 characters per second.

FUTURE DEVELOPMENT

Future ink jet printers will probably be developed to permit higher speed operation, full-color printing, gray scale capability, higher resolution, and higher quality. The results will include quiet typewriters for the office; facsimile machines for business and home; revolutionary lightweight, high-performance printing presses; office copiers and duplicators; and new and different industrial marking and coding procedures. Ink jet printers have reached commercial usage only recently, but the prospects for the future seem unlimited.

LETTERSET

Letterset printing, also known as *dry offset* or *indirect letterpress*, is a relief printing process which uses a letterpress plate on an offset press. In other words, the blanket cylinder receives the image from a relief plate and offsets it onto the paper. The plate is usually a photopolymer wraparound, thinner and in lower relief than an ordinary wraparound letterpress plate, in order to fit a standard offset press. Since no water is needed, the dampening rollers are disengaged or the entire dampening unit is removed from the press.

Indeed, the elimination of water from the process is letterset's chief advantage. The whole problem of ink/water balance is avoided, wastage is decreased, chemical costs are cut, high-gloss inks can be used, inks set more quickly, color can more easily be kept constant throughout the run, and substrates affected by water can be printed. All this is added to the traditional advantages of offset printing: good impressions on a variety of papers, high speed, ease of makeready, long plate life, low ink consumption, and use of right-reading images.

Problems with the plate, however, have kept letterset from being widely used. Offset plates are normally less than .012″ thick; conventional wraparound relief plates vary in thickness from .020″ to .040″. Offset presses were modified to accept the thicker plates, but the results were not always satisfactory. The development of photopolymer relief plates, which were thin enough to be used on standard offset presses, solved this problem (see "Letterpress Platemaking," page 381), but other problems remained. For example, since photopolymer letterset plates are in very low relief (.003″), care must be taken in locking up the plate and adjusting the clearance between plate and blanket to avoid printing on image areas. For the same reason care must be taken in platemaking: the edges of the characters must be as sharp and perpendicular as possible and the characters firmly bonded to the plate base. A hard blanket must be used, which is more difficult to adjust properly.

Letterset has been found to be a practicable process given experience and high standards of workmanship. Quality equipment is available, and plates are being manufactured at low cost. Dry offset inks have been formulated which, because they need be only half as tacky as offset ink, permit long runs at high speed with no plate or blanket wash-up and no lint buildup or image deterioration. At least two newspapers are printed letterset, proving that long, reliable, and economical runs are feasible.

STEEL-DIE ENGRAVING

Harvey Langlois, LEHMAN BROTHERS

Imprinting from an intaglio engraved line is one of the oldest forms of graphic art. This method of printing, by which the image or text is engraved in reverse into the surface of a metal die or plate, produces a finished stamping that is sharply defined and of high quality. It is commonly used for such products as stationery, business cards, announcements, and invitations.

ENGRAVING THE DIES

Although the process is known as *steel-die engraving* or *die stamping*, the image carrier may be either a steel die or a copper plate. The same basic process is used for both. Sometimes the plate is engraved directly; more often, the plate is coated with a protective resist which is removed in the image areas, allowing an etching solution to etch those areas away. Nitric acid is used for etching steel dies, and iron chloride is used for etching copper plates.

Engraving may be done manually, mechanically, or photomechanically. Some dies, such as those for monograms, are cut by hand by an engraver using tools called *burins* or *gravers*. Various engraving machines are also used which trace type and other images from masters onto the die or plate. Photomechanical methods of distinguishing between the image and non-image areas are used as well (see "Fundamentals of Platemaking," page 378). When engraving is done photomechanically, methods similar to those for photoengraving of relief plates are used (see "Letterpress Platemaking," page 381). Powderless etching, the method most widely used for relief photoengraving, may be used for copper plates but not for steel dies.

PRINTING

Presses for steel-die engraving, also known as *die-stamping* or *steel-die embossing* presses, are available in a number of sizes, taking dies from 2½″ x 4″ up to 8″ x 12″. The paper size handled usually includes standard 8½″ x 11″ sheets and may go up to sizes such as 15″ x 17″.

In printing, the etched areas of the plate are filled with ink, and the surface is wiped clean. The paper is forced against the plate, and a *counter* applies pressure in the etched areas, as in embossing (see "Finishing Processes," page 551). The ink is drawn from the etched areas; at the same time, the paper is forced into the depression and smoothed elsewhere. The result is the embossed printing characteristic of business cards, letterheads, and similar products.

The cost of such printing is commensurate with the high quality. The price of a specific job can be determined only after the engraver has seen what is to be reproduced. Many factors are involved, such as color, register, and area of paper to be stamped. The cost of corrections or changes is also high, but it depends again on what has to be done to the die.

COPY PREPARATION

Copy for steel-die engraving must be line art, in either positive or negative form; tonal gradations are not printed by this method, so photographs and other continuous-tone art are not acceptable copy. Copy may be furnished camera-ready by the customer or may be prepared for the camera by the engraver's art department. Any line art can be etched into a plate. The engraver also has a variety of typefaces available.

Proper preparation of copy is very important because changes are difficult and costly to make after the plate is engraved. The buyer of engraving can request a sketch or series of sketches in color to get an idea of the finished product before the engraving is made.

USES

Besides letterheads, business cards, and social stationery, including wedding invitations, monograms, and announcements, engraving also lends itself effectively to advertising and printing on manufactured materials. Much engraving is done for the watch industry. Satin linings for watch cases have been engraved in two or more colors and on occasion stamped with a logo or trademark in gold leaf. Pieces for window or counter display have been engraved on heavy board; the depth and clarity of color has great eye appeal. Engraved bank notes, stock certificates, and diplomas are common examples of the quality and workmanship of engraving.

Steel-die engraving can render very fine detail. Because of the thickness of the ink deposit, it can produce colors with great depth. In conjunction with blind embossing or hot leaf stamping, it can make a letterhead, a greeting card, or an advertisement into an effective, attention-getting piece. Blind embossing is used for such copy as logos and trademarks. Hot leaf stamping is used in conjunction with engraving for the same purposes as blind embossing and also for background effect and outline. (These processes are described in "Finishing Processes," page 551.)

Choice of paper is strictly a matter of taste; most papers adapt to engraving very well. The better papers with rag content are often used to complement the detail and quality of the image. Wedding announcements, invitations, and similar pieces are usually run on special stocks made for these purposes.

THERMOGRAPHY

Thermography is a modification of letterpress printing long used to imitate the engraved or embossed printing produced by the far more costly process of steel-die engraving, described above. A standard relief printing press is used, supplemented by special in-line equipment. The image is printed from ordinary raised type or relief plates using a special slow-drying ink. The sheet is then dusted with a resinous powder which adheres to the tacky ink. After a suction device has removed the powder from uninked areas, the sheet passes through a heater which fuses and dries the ink and resin. The resin swells slightly as it is heated, so the final result is a raised and slightly glossy printed image.

If colored, gilt, or silvered printing is desired, pigment, bronze, or aluminum powders can be added to the resin powder.

Thermography is most often used for printing stationery, invitations, and calling cards. However, offset lithographic presses can also be adapted to thermog-

raphy, and in this form the process is widely used for decorating paper, especially for greeting cards.

(This should not be confused with the reprographic process also called thermography. See page 430.)

DECALCOMANIA PRINTING
Warren R. Erickson, THE MEYERCORD CO.

Decalcomanias, commonly known as decals, are designs printed on specially prepared paper which may be transferred onto a variety of surfaces. Decals are designed to be permanent, durable markings, unlike printed labels or stickers, with which they are often confused.

TYPES OF DECALS

Decals may be press-built or premade. Premade decals are made of high tensile strength film, either polyester or elastomeric, attached to a release coated carrier sheet with a pressure-sensitive adhesive. The plastic film is peeled from the carrier sheet and pressed onto the surface to be marked. No water or solvent is used. Film for premade transfers is generally purchased in sheet or roll form by a converter, who then adds graphics, using an ink or color system compatible with the particular film.

In constructing a typical press-built transfer, layers of ink are applied to a special decalcomania paper, which acts as the temporary carrier. To prevent absorption of inks by the paper, one side has been coated, usually with dextrin. When the decal is moistened for application to an object, the dextrin dissolves slightly, releasing the printed film so that the paper base can be removed. As it dries, the dextrin acts as an adhesive. For those surfaces to which the dextrin will not adhere, cements or solvents are normally used. A solvent may be wiped on both the face of the decal and the surface to which it is to be transferred, or the decal may be dipped in solvent before transfer. In these cases the solvent softens both the printed film and the surface so that when they dry they will be permanently bonded together.

Press-built decals are also processed on wax-coated and polyethylene-coated stock, in which case application involves a solvent or a pressure-sensitive or heat-activated adhesive system.

Press-built decals may be printed on the carrier sheet face up (that is, with the image right-reading on the printed film), in which case they are applied to an opaque surface by sliding the carrier sheet out from under the printed film. They may also be printed face down by reversing the image and the order of application of colors, in which case application involves peeling off the carrier sheet, leaving the printed image right-reading on the surface. This variety of decal requires either another coating of adhesive on top of the printed film or the use of a solvent in application. There are also decals manufactured to be applied to the inside of plate glass doors or windows, with the appropriate adhesives built in. It is also possible to print the same transfer dually face up and face down with

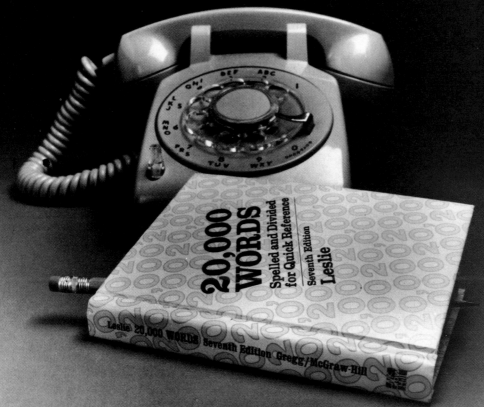

the same design on both sides (or with two different ones) so that it can be read on both sides of the glass.

Whether the decal is applied to a transparent or an opaque surface, it is customary to print the design in opaque white ink first and then overprint in the desired colors. This prevents the color of the object to which the decal is finally applied from showing through and changing the decal's own color.

PRINTING METHODS

Decals may be printed by a number of printing processes, but most commonly screen process or offset lithography is used.

Screen process

Screen printing permits a relatively heavy deposit of ink, particularly when solid colors are printed rather than halftones. The attendant advantages of weatherability, fade resistance, and opacity particularly recommend screen-printed decals for use out-of-doors. When halftones are used, good pictorial reproduction may be obtained, even in billboard-size dimensions. This technique is effective when used in truck fleet decoration.

Screen-printed decals are also commonly manufactured for indoor uses. Nameplate decals are used for product identification, caution messages, and operating instructions. Identifying, instructional, and decorative transfers are specially formulated for wood, metal, glass, leather, rubber, vinyl, plastic, fabric, and fiberglass substrates, as well as the human body.

Point-of-sale signs mount either to opaque surfaces such as gasoline pumps in service stations or to the inside of plate glass; often transfers are printed dually so that a design may be seen on one side of the glass and a courtesy message on the other.

Other special features that can be built into screen-printed decals include high abrasion resistance for surfaces subjected to extreme conditions of scratching and abrasive wear, and high temperature resistance for surfaces that normally heat up during use, such as engine manifolds, fuel lines, electronic equipment, and heat-producing appliances. Another complete line is made up of decals with ceramic properties for application to glassware, china, and porcelain. These properties permit firing of the decorated product following application, in which the decal becomes an integral part of the product rather than a mere surface decoration. Coupled with high-speed automatic application, ceramic decals permit economical, permanent high-color decoration of tile, fine dinnerware, glassware and decorative glass containers, and porcelain-clad aluminum and steel cookware.

Offset lithography

Offset lithography, with its lighter deposit of ink, is used in decal printing in cases where permanence and durability are of less importance or where four-color process designs are required. It is used, for example, for decorative decals intended for product enhancement, such as florals, scroll work, and juvenile designs of furniture and toys. The process is also ideal for pictorials used in point-of-sale, and for decals marketed to the consumer and designed for use by him in hobbies, crafts, and other forms of home decoration; in short, anything with an indoor end use.

Many governmental units make use of decals for revenue indicia in the collection of taxes on commodities such as cigarettes and liquor. Some of these are offset printed in sheet form, usually for smaller volume municipality users; but most states purchase tax stamps which have been roll printed on web rotogravure equipment and have them mechanically applied at wholesale distributor locations. To guard against counterfeiting, secret markings are designed into these decals, and tight security measures are enforced to prevent theft during the printing, inspection, and shipment of this material.

DESIGN AND PRODUCTION

The creation of a decal involves elements of design, quality construction, and appropriateness to the purpose for which it is intended. A reputable decal house should offer both a creative art facility and the capacity for faithful reproduction of the client's art and should be able to make recommendations based on knowledge of the products and established research and quality control. In color printing, for example, choosing a color from the manufacturer's standard line, which has been lab-researched and on-the-job tested, is less likely to create problems of mismatch or fading due to prolonged exposure.

Production art varies from one decal type to another. Block lettering and other basically simple large-area designs, characteristic of truck decals and courtesy valance panels, are often stencil-cut by hand from finished pencil sketches. Most small decals require finished black-and-white art on which the copy is typeset, although often spaced by hand. A sharp cut of any logo which can be photographically enlarged or reduced is commonly used to minimize art costs. Since the colors must overlap to simplify register, colors are printed from lightest to darkest and trapping is indicated on the copy. A $1/32''$ color overlap is usually the minimum. Full-color art is separated by conventional means and usually printed by offset lithography.

Quantity buying in standard press-run multiples most often results in unit economies. Because of costly plate work, litho runs usually start at 10,000 sheets; they are never under 5,000. Nameplates, small window signs, and similar screen-printed designs are usually ganged on combination sheet runs in multiple quantities of 2,500. On the other hand, 250 or 500 sheets may represent a very reasonable run for larger truck fleet and heavy equipment markings.

CONCLUSION

Decals are an excellent graphic medium that spells economy, convenience, and accurate image portrayal for the broadest possible spectrum of end uses. At a reasonable cost—based on number of reproductions, square inch area, and color multiples—all of the printing operations are performed in one plant. Later the decals may be transferred onto a wide variety of surfaces at one or more work sites at times convenient to the end user in order to form products which can advertise, identify, instruct, and decorate.

HEAT TRANSFER PRINTING
G. H. Anthony, GRAPHIC ARTS CONSULTANT

Heat transfer printing is a process for transferring an image printed on paper to another material through the use of special sublimable dyes, heat, and pressure.

Almost any image, in almost any color, whether in line, tint, or halftone, that can be printed on paper may be transferred to a suitable substrate through heat transfer printing. However, time-honored tradition related to printing different color combinations with a single set of printing plates places certain limits upon image design in the textile yard goods field.

Suitable papers for heat transfer printing range from coated supercalendered stocks to kraft papers.

Proper inks contain dyes which sublime at temperatures between 350° and 425° F (180° and 220° C). They should have adequate resistance to light, washing, moisture, smudging, and ruboff.

Materials best suited to receive the final image from the paper are those with a molecular structure which permits acceptance or ingestion of the heated ink vapors or gases and which allows the ink to cool and condense back to the dye colors of the image transferred. The most widely used materials at present are synthetic-fiber textiles of the polyester type. The heat transfer process has the potential of replacing much of conventional textile dyeing. New applications, such as counter tops, polyester-coated ceramic tiles, and coated metals, are being found; almost any material which can be coated or impregnated with a suitable synthetic resin having the necessary characteristics, such as the proper melting point and molecular structure, is a possibility for heat transfer printing.

At the present time, rotogravure and flexography account for most of the estimated 200 million meters of textile yard goods printed by heat transfer printing. However, this process is still in its infancy and has many possibilities for expansion.

REPROGRAPHY
Wayne M. Gilgore, NEW VENTURE TECHNOLOGIES

The business world runs on paperwork. How fast it works depends on the flow of paperwork. Reprography —the copying and duplicating of text matter and pictures—plays an important role in the generation and processing of that paperwork.

INFORMATION EXPLOSION

In today's business, it is estimated that paperwork is multiplying at a rate of 15 percent each year. Over 15 trillion pieces of paper are being circulated or stored in U.S. business offices alone, and each minute of each working day a million new pages are added. With the popularity of the word processor, the proliferation of even more reports each day can be expected in the next decade. The copier/duplicator, facsimile transmission, and computer-generated data are causing an "information explosion."

INDUSTRY AREAS

Businesses, both large and small, are now processing a vast amount of all their duplicating and printing needs in their own facilities. In some cases, they have decentralized the reprographic activities with copying equipment strategically located throughout the facilities. In other cases, centralized in-plant paper-based communications departments have been economically justified. There are almost 70,000 in-house shops in the United States that specialize in this type of work. In addition, there are many *quick-copy centers* located in most major cities.

The reprographic industry also encompasses part of the commercial printing market. The commercial printer is not in competition with the quick-copy center or the in-plant shop. Commercial printing prefers to take on longer-run, more labor-intensive and complex jobs, leaving the simpler ones to the quick-copy and in-plant printers. Some specialized work such as business forms, cards, and invitations are sent out to mail-order houses where they can be run on automated equipment that can do the job at lower cost than the average printer.

PERSONNEL

The people who run reprographic equipment range from the office employee to the reprographics specialist. Reprographics curricula are included in vocational schools, high schools, and business schools in courses such as office machines, business machines, office practices, occupational training, and secretarial procedures. The manufacturers of most equipment also offer school and on-site training to key operators.

While almost all office employees are required to operate one or more kinds of reprographic equipment, only a small number are employed in that capacity on a full-time basis because of the simplicity of the reprographic machines. "Key operators" are office employees who are designated to be on-site caretakers for copiers.

429

Their job usually includes simple tasks such as loading paper, adding toner, clearing paper jams, and doing general housekeeping around a copier. In addition, they can instruct others in the proper use of the equipment and when necessary call a factory-trained service person to come to the location and repair the copier.

Operators of offset duplicators usually have additional responsibilities and need knowledge of reproduction quality. Much of their job involves platemaking, press makeready, machine cleaning, maintenance, and lubrication. In addition, they should be knowledgeable in associated areas such as word processing equipment, graphic arts camera work, layout and graphic design, binding, techniques, and systems of paper handling and distribution.

PAST AND FUTURE

Reprographics as an industry is relatively new. Most copiers that are used today were first introduced in the early 1960's. Quick-copy centers have been in existence for only about 15 years. Word processors, minicomputers, phototypesetters, and micrographic devices first got off the ground in the early 1970's. The copier/duplicator and high-speed facsimile were introduced in the mid-1970's. The leading manufacturers used the latest technological advances to mass-produce reasonably priced equipment to automate the generating, duplicating, and disseminating of paperwork.

In the early history of the office reprographic industry, one trend stands out: hardware was made smaller, less expensive, and thus more accessible to the end user. Once restricted to situations requiring a room full of equipment, the reprographic process is now so compact that it can be used to make copies on the corner of a desk, send photographs and data directly from a facsimile unit to a police car, or transmit news photos to the wire service from a telephone booth. Reprographic-system interconnects may some day make it possible to work right out of your home and avoid the commute to the office.

COPIERS AND DUPLICATORS

The equipment used in reprography includes various types of copiers and duplicators, including plain-paper and coated-paper copiers, offset duplicators, and stencil and spirit duplicators.

Plain-paper (Xerographic) copiers

Practically all plain-paper copiers today are based on the *transfer electrophotographic process* (as is *Xerography*), in which light reflected from the original copy alters a charge pattern on an electrophotographic surface. The surface can be a drum or belt of photoconductive material, such as selenium or cadmium sulfide. The image is developed by applying an oppositely charged toner, which is then transferred to a sheet of plain paper.

Coated-paper copiers

The *Electrofax* process is similar to transfer electrophotography, except that it uses paper coated with zinc oxide. This paper records the charge pattern and be-

comes the final copy. The charge pattern is made and developed as in the transfer electrophotographic process, but the image does not have to be transferred to another surface. For this reason, the process is simpler and less expensive, but the copy-paper cost is higher. Mailing costs are also higher because the paper is heavy. In addition, it is easily scratched and tends to slide down in vertical files.

The *Electrographic* copier is based on the transfer of charge from an electrophotographic surface onto a dielectric paper. The paper is developed and used as the finished copy. Electrographic paper costs about the same as the Electrofax zinc-oxide-coated paper, but it handles better.

The low-volume convenience copying processes include *thermographic, diazo, diffusion transfer, burn-off,* and *carbon-paper* methods. In thermography, heat is used to transfer the images to a heat-sensitive paper which darkens in the image areas. (This process should not be confused with the printing process, also called thermography, described in "Special Printing Processes," page 421.) The other methods involve the use of papers that respond to light, sparks, or pressure. Many of these methods were popular before the introduction of electrophotographic copiers. Now they are not used to any appreciable extent.

Offset duplicators

The offset process used for reprography is the same as conventional offset lithography except that the equipment is smaller, less sturdy, and simpler to operate. Very low cost master plates can be made on a paper, plastic, or metal substrate. They may be prepared by a variety of methods: writing or typing; electrophotography; Electrofax; photographic means; diffusion transfer; and photomechanical methods, including presensitized and wipe-on processes, as in traditional lithography. The master plate, when printed on the offset duplicator, produces plain-paper copies which set the quality and price standards for the reprographics industry.

Stencil and spirit duplicators

Stencil and spirit duplicators are old processes that generally have been displaced by copiers and offset duplicators.

The stencil, screen, or "mimeograph" process uses a master with porous area corresponding to the image areas. The master can be prepared by typing, writing, thermography, or spark discharge. It is mounted on an ink-filled porous cylinder which releases ink through the openings in the stencil when it is pressed against plain paper.

The spirit, dye transfer, or "ditto" process uses a master with a special dye image. When the master is brought into contact with an alcohol-moistened paper, some of the dye is released to produce a copy. Masters are made with special carbon papers or crayons containing resins colored with soluble dyes. A master can print two or more colors simultaneously from one plate, but it is limited to comparatively few copies per master. Another drawback is the lack of a good black. Most copies are produced in blue since this color dye is the longest running.

HIGH-SPEED REPROGRAPHIC EQUIPMENT

For runs over 10, the high-speed electrophotographic copier and the offset copier/duplicator are by far the work horses of the quick-copy and in-plant printers.

High-speed electrophotographic copiers

The high-speed copiers such as the Xerox 9200 and 9400 and the Kodak Ektaprint 100 and 150 are in principle complete reproduction centers. They convert an original to a copy by electrophotography. The high-speed copier is more economical than the offset duplicator for reproducing fewer than 100 copies. Since it does not use a master plate, it can reproduce the first copy in a shorter time and at lower cost.

These sophisticated copiers can automatically feed up to 50 originals, reproduce same size or reduce, print one or both sides, and change paper stock. Another feature is a 50-bin sorter. Copy quality is not as good as in offset lithography, but most readers would not know the difference unless shown samples side by side.

Offset copier/duplicators

The copier/duplicator combines a copier with an offset duplicator. A master plate is made in an Electro-fax-type copier on paper coated with zinc oxide. The master is charged, exposed, and developed with an oleophilic (ink-receptive) toner. The plate is then treated with a chemical to make the zinc oxide hydrophilic (water-receptive). Next the plate is transported automatically to the offset duplicator, which prints multiple copies in the same manner as a standard offset lithographic press, using the principle of the separation of oil and water. The rest of the press functions as a paper transport to separate the sheets and register them for printing. Usually the sheets are delivered into an automatic stacker or sorter after printing.

EQUIPMENT FEATURES

Reprographic equipment can be classified by its features, which meet the needs of almost every reproduction task. The purchaser should consider his own specific requirements and the various features available before buying a machine. Considerations include the following:

First copy time	User interface
Copies per minute	Clearing paper jams
Plain or special paper	Loading supplies
Copies per month required	Document handling
Price of equipment	Paper cassette size
Cost per copy	Work area
Cost of service contract	Power requirement
Copy quality	Environmental effects
Wet or dry process	Safety
Roll or sheet fed	Two-sided copying
Heat or pressure fusing	Same size or reduction
Development system	Maximum paper and copy
Automatic document	size
handling	Platen or sheet scanner
Sorting	Paper transport

ELECTRONIC PRINTING

The word-processing connection to reprographics is growing. "Smart" typewriters can automatically feed in paper and reproduce standard letters with variable names and addresses. The copier has been linked to the text composer to be used as a reprographic center. Facsimile equipment has also been used for copying and sending information to local and remote locations via telephone data links.

Copiers such as the Xerox 9700, the IBM 3800 and 6670, and the Wang Image Printer have been linked up with computers, so that business forms and other copy with variable information can be created and reproduced with ease. Copiers have also been used to reduce information storage requirements: one type of copier produces microfilm copy from information stored in the computer; another system stores the originals in microfilm form and enlarges them for the final copy. Computer-controlled laser light makes it possible to expose offset duplicator printing plates or a copier drum with reconstructed text and pictures. These new technologies, combined with improved communications links such as facsimile transmission, videotape, and holographic recording, are being developed to augment the tools of the reprographic industry.

BOOK PRODUCTION SYSTEMS

One of the most significant and radical developments in printing press design in modern times is the web press that can print a complete book in a single pass. In such systems the printed web is slit, folded, cut, and collated into complete books as it emerges from the printing units; thus the need for folding and gathering in the bindery is eliminated. If binding equipment is hooked directly by conveyor to the press delivery, a complete in-line system is formed for the manufacture of books from raw paper stock to finished books. One such system, designed to produce books with mechanical bindings, is described in "Looseleaf and Mechanical Binding," page 546. The Cameron Book Production System and the Wood Book-O-Matic, used for producing bound hardcover and paperback books, are described here.

THE CAMERON BELT PRESS

Charles Aaron, CAMERON-WALDRON DIV., MIDLAND-ROSS CORP.

The Cameron Book Production System, more commonly known as the "Cameron Belt Press," has made a considerable impact on the book publishing industry. Since its introduction at the Kingsport Press, in Kingsport, Tennessee, in 1968, it has proven itself equal to the task set for it: the production of books at a substantially reduced unit cost in quantities from 2,500 to 25,000 copies.

The books are of high quality, printed in single-color letterpress, with second spot color available, and many contain halftones in addition to type and line work. Multi-page inserts may be added at either the front or back of the book. The papers used range from 32-pound newsprint to 80-pound book paper, with bulks from 325 to 595 pages per inch. The presses are offered in widths of 26", 38", 44", 62", and 70".

The Cameron Belt Press derives its name from its use of two printing belts on which flexible plates are mounted. Each plate is page size and attached to the belt with double-sided sticky-back. The plates are shallow-relief photopolymer and are arranged on the belts in the imposition required at the delivery end of the press for collating. Thus all the pages of the book are printed in one pass on a moving web of paper which is then slit, folded, and cut into a stream of two- or four-page signatures continuously being collated into books (the operations of the press are diagrammed in figure 11.24). The collated signatures are then delivered to an in-line bindery where they are adhesive bound, backed, trimmed, delivered into a counter-stacker, and finally packed in shipping cartons.

DETAILS OF OPERATION

The printing belts are made from lengths of .010" polyester film, joined to form a loop. As shown in figure 11.26, they are wrapped around a series of idler rollers and tensioned by a take-up roller. This arrangement will accommodate belt loops varying in length from 60" to 756". Along both edges of the belt are holes punched in precise 1/4" increments. These are engaged by sprockets at both ends of the plate cylinder, which synchronize the speed of the plates and the paper web.

The plates mounted on the belt pass around a plate cylinder and are inked by a precision letterpress inking system. The paper is fed from an automatic paster and passes around an impression cylinder mounted directly above the plate cylinder. Only .002" to .003" printing impression is required, which greatly extends the plate life.

After being printed on one side, the web goes through a dryer, over chill rolls, and around a turning bar to the other side of the machine. Here another turning bar completes the web reversal, and the second printing unit and belt stand print the back side. Back-to-back registration is controlled by an electric eye.

Emerging from the second dryer, the web is slit into ribbons one or two pages wide. Two-page ribbons are perforated in the middle to insure accurate folding. The slit ribbons pass around individual angle bars and former folders. The folded ribbons are married one above the other in page alignment and fed to a rotary cutoff cylinder, which cuts them into packets of two- or four-page signatures. Accuracy of cutoff is also controlled by an electric eye.

The packets are delivered in a lapped stream to vertically descending forks or fingers, with each successive pair of forks receiving a completely collated book as it descends.

Cutoff length can be changed quickly between jobs by replacing a single change gear. Replacing another change gear quickly accommodates books with different numbers of pages. Books range in untrimmed heights from 7" to 12" in 1/4" increments. Selection of belt length determines the number of pages, and on a 38" web the number can vary from approximately 48 to 1,440 depending on page size. The maximum compressed book thickness is 2".

Collated books are delivered from the Cameron press to the adhesive binder by a specially designed transfer device which can also divert books to a shingling belt if and when the binder stops for short periods.

After leaving the transfer device, books are turned vertically, spine down, in a conveyor and jogged to bring all four- and two-page signatures down to the spine. The jogged books are then delivered into the clamps of the binder and pass through a backbone preparation station, as shown in figure 11.24. Here, whenever possible, book spines are roughed but not trimmed, in order to keep the inherent strength and lay-flat characteristics of a book made of four-page

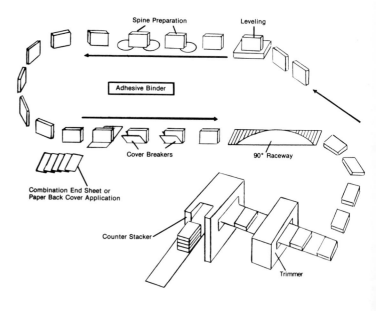

Figure 11.24: Schematic representation of the Cameron Book Production System (opposite and above).

signatures. The books continue around in the clamps to the other side of the binder, where an application of one-shot melt is made to the spine just prior to attaching a paperback cover, fed from a cover feeder.

When producing books for subsequent edition binding, one-shot roundable hot melt can be applied to the spine, which is then covered with a precombined end sheet in place of a paperback cover. End sheets can also be added from hopper feeders ahead of the binder clamps and capped by stretch cloth after a cold-emulsion application is made just beyond the spine roughers.

After covering, the books are delivered to a three-knife trimmer. Trim taken on books is normally ⅛" top and bottom and ⅛" on the front. Therefore, paper savings on trim waste are quite substantial. This paper saving is in addition to the large saving realized on the press, which utilizes a letterpress printing system and is not subject to the high waste rates that occur with the web offset process.

Trimmed books are then delivered into a counter-stacker where they can be either cartoned as finished paperbacks, or skidded, if they have been prepared for edition binding in a hard-covering line.

ADVANTAGES OF THE SYSTEM

The Cameron Belt Press is a web press with an effective plate cylinder diameter varying from about 19 inches to 20 feet. This offers the publisher the page size flexibility of a sheet-fed press, while retaining the economic and production advantages of a web-fed press.

Only one makeready is required per job, as opposed to the multiple changeovers required in conventional multisignature printing. On job changes involving a series of books with identical page sizes and the same number of pages, the changeover can be accomplished in the time it takes to change belts—15 or 20 minutes. Average makeready time, however, is an hour.

Since signature collection and gathering ahead of the adhesive bindery is eliminated, very important labor savings are possible. The total labor requirement for the Cameron Belt Press is much less than that required for the production of an equal number of books by the conventional short-run methods using sheet-fed offset presses, folders, and binders and requiring the handling of work in process.

The economies of the Cameron Book Production System—including small labor complements and fast makereadies, minimum running waste and trim waste, no handling of work in process, and no signature waste from mismatch of quantities or from loss in storage—have made it possible for many publishers to minimize risk and inventory costs by placing initial orders for 3,000 to 5,000 books. Reorders of larger quantities can be met quickly to respond to market demand. Reprint orders are especially attractive since the plates stored in position on the belts can be used without additional or repetitive preparatory steps. The plates are paid for in the initial run and can be used up to 500,000 impressions without incurring additional costs. The reprint volume in Cameron systems is about 40 percent of total output.

Although the Cameron system is most economical in short-run production, many first-run printings of 50,000

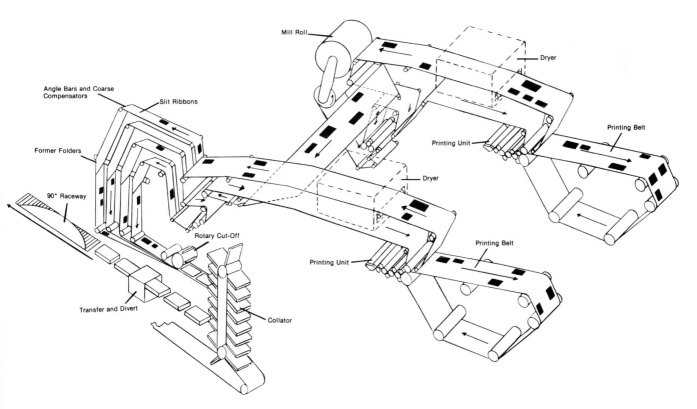

to 150,000 and even 750,000 books have been made. Delivery is quick because there is no delay while signatures are being accumulated for collating and binding, and it is easier to schedule and control production. These advantages of the Belt Press have appealed to publishers anxious to bring a particular title to market as rapidly as possible.

NEW DEVELOPMENTS

The use of the Cameron Book Production System is growing as new developments are introduced. New entries to the market are the narrow 26″ press for small books and the 70″ press for high-speed production of mass-produced paperbacks in run lengths averaging 100,000. The 70″ press slits the paper web into eight ribbons of double-page width and feeds them in two streams of four ribbons each for two horizontal interleaving formers; then they are married and fed into the standard rotary cutoff and collator. The new interleaving formers allow the production of more rigid signatures on lightweight paper such as newsprint, telephone directory paper, and Bible stock, making the press suitable for printing products using these papers. In addition, illustration quality has been improved with the introduction of new flexible photopolymer plates capable of producing good-quality 133-line and 150-line halftones. Another development is a second-color flexographic printing unit mounted directly above the standard printing unit for spot color use.

A newly developed festooned belt stand (see figure 11.25) permits drastic reduction in the overall space required for the belt stands and makes quick changes possible. After completion of a printing job, the stands already in printing position can be removed sideways and standby belt stands can be brought rapidly into printing position on tracks.

The Cameron Book Production System will grow as further refinements are introduced. Larger presses have allowed the system to move into the long-run market in the area of shelf-sized paperbacks and may permit the production of telephone books in the future. Magazines could be printed if a method were found for positioning preprinted inserts in exact page location. The Belt Press has already made a valuable contribution to book publishing, and it is expected to expand to meet the demands of the future.

THE WOOD BOOK-O-MATIC
Howard Aber, WOOD INDUSTRIES

The Wood Book-O-Matic is a complete in-line system for the manufacture of books, magazines, or any product which requires printing in sequence, collating, and binding.

Books and magazines ranging in size from 4¼″ x 7″ to 8½″ x 11″, single-color or multicolor, can be printed on the Wood Book-O-Matic. The quality of printing, whether line, type, or halftone, is dependent upon the printing process and plate system used. If a single-color printing system is used, multicolor signatures, cards, or single pages can be inserted.

Normally an adhesive binder with trimmer and stacker is coupled in-line to the press to produce finished softcover books or bound and trimmed book blocks, with end sheets, ready for hard covering. If adhesive binding is not desired, the books can be sewn or stitched.

Stated simply, raw paper stock is transformed into finished bound books in one continuous in-line operation in less than two minutes at rates up to 24,000 books per hour (see figure 11.26).

The predominant printing method used with the Book-O-Matic is offset lithography. The perfecting offset printing unit for the Book-O-Matic has plate and blanket cylinders that are 114″ in circumference by 54″ in width. This offset system is unique in that, by using the fixed 114″-circumference printing cylinder and a variable-size cutoff, it can produce books in all popular sizes. The following chart, for a two-web press, indi-

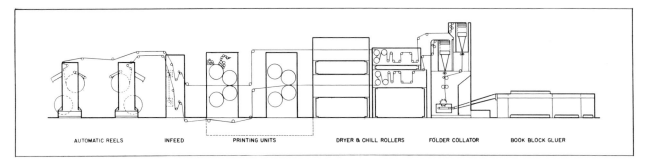

Figure 11.26: Schematic representation of the Wood Book-O-Matic system.

AUTOMATIC REELS   INFEED   PRINTING UNITS   DRYER & CHILL ROLLERS   FOLDER COLLATOR   BOOK BLOCK GLUER

cates the plate arrangement for the various sizes of books which can be produced by this system in a single run. Higher page counts may be obtained by using multiple runs or a three-web configuration.

Trim size (inches)	Cylinder circum-ference (inches)	Pages around	Maxi-mum pages across	Cutoff length (inches)	Maxi-mum pages per run
8½ x 11	114	10	6	11.40	240
7 x 10	114	11	7	10.36	308
6¼ x 9¼	114	12	8	9.50	384
5¼ x 8¼	114	13	10	8.77	520
4¼ x 7	114	15	12	7.60	720

All pages of the book to be produced are plated for a single press run. For example, in printing a 520-page 5¼″ x 8¼″ book, each of the four cylinders is plated 13 around (13 × 8.77″ = 114″) by 10 across (5⁷⁄₁₆″ × 10 = 54″ web) for a total of 130 (13 × 10) pages per cylinder, or 260 pages per web, to produce 520 pages for the two webs. Different page counts are obtained by varying the number of pages across the cylinder. Production of offset books produced in this manner can exceed 8,000 books per hour.

The basic system is available with any one of four different printing methods: flexography, letterpress, offset, and gravure. The printing method is determined by the requirements of the product. Because the reel stand and infeed, as well as the collator, remain the same for all processes, the type and number of printing units placed between the infeed and collator can be determined as necessary. If softcover newsstand-type novels were being produced, the most advantageous printing method would be flexography because it is economical and gives the print quality required. For high-quality books, either single-color or multicolor, the printing system most likely chosen would be offset or gravure. For the short-run book market, requiring high-quality printing and low-cost plates, the offset system would be used.

Regardless of the printing method used, the print repeat on the web is an entire book rather than a single signature. The in-line procedure used to convert the completely printed web into book form is described, below (see figure 11.27).

The web is slit into up to six ribbons, usually two pages wide, which are directed over adjustable turning bars and adjustable compensator rollers. The ribbons,

aligned one on top of the other, pass over a single former folder. This is the only folding operation in the entire process.

Once folded, the ribbons are cut to page length via rotary cutoff cylinders. If the full six ribbons are utilized, there are six ribbons folded one inside the other. When these folded ribbons are cut to page length there are six 4-page signatures folded one inside the other, or a 24-page signature.

The signatures printed in sequence to provide a complete book are placed on a slow-speed shingling

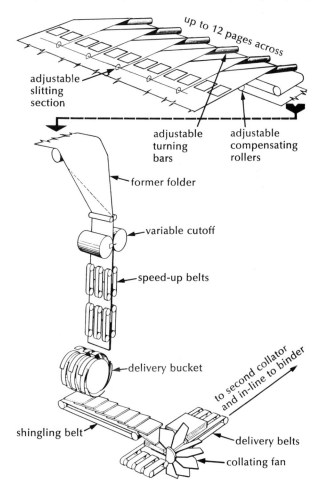

Figure 11.27: Folder-collator section of the Book-O-Matic.

435

Arcata Book Group
An Arcata Operating Group

Fairfield Graphics
Halliday Lithograph
Kingsport Press

SALES OFFICES

New York, New York
212-489-6891

Stamford, Connecticut
203-329-2622

North Quincy, Massachusetts
617-328-3700

Annapolis, Maryland
301-269-0588

Mountainside, New Jersey
201-233-4148

Kingsport, Tennessee
615-246-7341

Chicago, Illinois
312-332-0377

Arlington Heights, Illinois
312-640-8644

Bala Cynwyd, Pennsylvania
215-878-2070

Dallas, Texas
214-942-6168

Los Gatos, California
408-358-2761

Van Nuys, California
213-785-3183

Columbus, Ohio
614-262-3484

Brentwood, Tennessee
615-373-3110

Composition Sales
Kingsport, Tennessee
615-246-7341

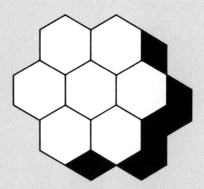

The full spectrum of services for publishers

ART SERVICES
COMPUTER-ASSISTED
  PHOTOCOMPOSITION
COLOR SEPARATION
OFFSET
SHEETFED AND WEBFED
  SINGLE-COLOR
  MULTI-COLOR
BELT PRESS
DELUXE LEATHER BINDING
SMYTH SEWN
SIDE WIRE
SIDE SEWN
ADHESIVE
SADDLE-WIRE
SPIRAL
WIRE-O
CERLOX
LOOSE LEAF
WAREHOUSING
SHIPPING
ORDER FULFILLMENT

436

belt by a separating wheel. The shingled signatures, still in page order sequence, as provided by the printing cylinders, are now separated into individual books by a collating wheel and delivered to the binding operation. (An alternative to coupling a binder in-line to the press is to have a book-block gluing device after the folder-collator. In this case, the sequential signatures from the press are bound together with a strip of adhesive to form a block, which is fed to an adhesive binder out of line.)

The transfer section between the press and binder, in addition to transferring books between the two major units, has an escapement mechanism to divert books onto a shingling belt so that the press can continue to run during momentary binder downtimes. Also located in the transfer is an inserting section to provide placement of one or more inserts between any two signatures of a book.

In addition to versatility of book size and printing method, the Wood Book-O-Matic offers great versatility in binding of books. Normally books produced on the Wood Book-O-Matic are adhesive bound, but since the books are in signature form they can be sewn. If the sewn book is the exception to the rule, the collated books can be stacked at the divert section and then fed into a sewing line. If the books are always sewn they can be conveyed directly into a sewing line. When adhesive bound, the fully collated books, with inserts, are delivered from the transfer section into a commercial adhesive binder, where the backbone is roughened, adhesive is applied, and the cover or end sheets are attached to the book.

The book, now bound and covered, is transported to an in-line trimmer and stacker and, if desired, to a stain booth and packing unit to complete the process from raw paper stock to finished packaged book.

IDENTIFICATION OF COMMON PRINTING FAULTS

Robert Loekle, COLOR REPRODUCTION CONSULTANT

Compared to other imaging processes, which make use of complex physical and chemical reactions, printing seems straightforward and deceptively simple. An ink film of uniform thickness is applied to a carrier, usually a plate, and transferred under pressure to a substrate, usually paper. However, the characteristics of the basic materials (ink and paper) vary considerably. Much of this variation stems from the requirements of different end uses; the remaining variation comes from the different methods employed and the difficulties inherent in each.

Mechanical transfer is performed by a press which positions the image carrier and substrate, provides a supply of ink, and applies contact pressure to insure transfer; it repeats the cycle with great precision at high frequency. One need only observe the mass of such machines, their mechanical intricacy, and the speeds at which they operate to realize that they constitute a kinetic system of great complexity. A simple model is incapable of explaining contemporary printing processes.

For a single-color sheet-fed offset press the Graphic Arts Technical Foundation has identified over 60 *inputs;* that is, identifiable characteristics of the materials, method, and machine which are roughly "fixed" at the beginning of a printing job or not easily changed once a run commences. Also included as inputs are the controls and adjustments available to the press operator, such as the rate of ink feed, pressure settings, and press speed.

At the delivery end of the press there are over 40 *outputs,* attributes of the printed sheet by which to evaluate printing quality.

The foundation's list of input and output variables is by no means exhaustive. It includes those variables most frequently encountered but leaves out many in areas where knowledge is still incomplete, or where agreement is lacking as to whether or not a cause-and-effect relationship exists. The list for a single-color sheet-fed press excludes, of course, additional variables found in more complex systems such as multicolor web-fed printing presses.

Given the large number of input and output variables and the few, relatively coarse adjustments the press operator can make, it is not surprising that the printing process does not always achieve the expected level of quality. Causes traceable to input variables are technical in nature and of primary concern to the printer. They are dealt with in other sections of this manual, and intensive discussions are available in the technical literature. Some of the more common printing faults are listed below, limited to the effects *as they appear on the printed sheet.* Only the most probable and immediate causes are given, to enhance communication between buyer and printer through increased understanding of the process.

GENERAL FAULTS IN INK TRANSFER

Basically the printing plate consists of two clearly defined areas: the image area, from which we expect to transfer a smooth, continuous layer of ink, conforming closely to the image outline; and the non-image area, from which no ink should print. Uneven transfer over areas large enough to be seen at normal viewing distances produces a mottled or streaked appearance.

437

Ink transfer can be uneven on a *micro* scale, that is, visible only under low magnification, such as the irregular ink films characteristic of poor trapping and water/ink emulsification. Also on the micro scale are distortions of the image edge, such as slurring and filling in halftone areas. That these failures can be positively identified only under magnification does not mean that they are unimportant and can be ignored. They contribute to more complex problems, such as poor tone reproduction, lack of image sharpness and smoothness, and other print quality factors which are readily sensed, although perhaps not so obvious as ink hickies and other localized imperfections.

Faults in ink transfer, which appear either on the micro level or by normal viewing, include the following.

Ink film mottle: Blotches approximately ⅛″ to ⅜″ in diameter in what should be a smooth, solid area. Usually such mottling is caused by insufficient transfer pressures or by running too thin an ink film.

Gloss mottle: Differences in surface gloss, similar in appearance to ink film mottle. Papers with "wild" formations or nonuniform absorption accept the ink vehicle at different rates, resulting in areas of higher and lower gloss on the dried film. Gloss mottle is characteristic of hard papers such as card and tag stock.

Blanket low spots: Areas of low ink density on the printed sheet. They show that the blanket is too low to provide enough transfer pressure. Fairly sharp edges to the blotch indicate a smashed area in the blanket. Larger, cloudy patterns may be due to uneven blanket thickness or packing.

Gear marks: Alternate light and dark bands parallel to the gripper edge of the sheet. These marks may be aggravated by excessive transfer pressures. Most often mechanical adjustment of the press is required for complete elimination.

Streaks: Light or dark stripes in the printed sheet, either parallel or at right angles to the gripper edge. In lithography, streaks can be induced by excessive water feed, improperly adjusted dampeners, and loose blankets.

Ghost images: Light or dark images corresponding to other printed areas in the around-the-cylinder direction. These images are often called "starvation" patterns, referring to the inability of the ink distribution system to replace a full charge of ink in an area with abrupt and heavy takeoff. Most ghosting can be minimized by adjusting the ink in order to improve its flow characteristics.

Snowflaky solids: Small white spots or pinholes in the solid ink film. Again lack of impression results in incomplete transfer of ink to paper. Snowflakes also can arise from too thin an ink film or from water which becomes emulsified in the ink. Running ink too thin hastens the uptake of water in lithographic inks to the point of snowflaking, although all inks need some moisture for proper printing.

Hickies: Small dark spots surrounded by a circle which does not accept ink. Hickies are caused by small ink-receptive particles that stick to the blanket; as they are above the blanket surface, no ink is transferred at their immediate edge.

Spots: Non-printing spots in an otherwise solid ink film. Both hickies and spots occur at random over the sheet; they are distinguished from pinholes in that

once they start to print they continue to appear in the same place. Spots are caused by particles of water-receptive material, such as paper fiber, lint, and coating, which adhere to the blanket and repel the ink.

Tinting: A light tint printing in all non-image areas. Tinting is caused by an oil-in-water emulsion, formed when pigment particles migrate to the dampening solution. If wiped off the plate, the tint immediately reappears. Some pigments are prone to "bleeding" in water, and the fault can be corrected by changing to another ink. Tinting can be induced in many inks by chemical properties of the paper surface, in which case changing paper may be necessary.

Scumming: Blotches of ink appearing in the background or between the halftone dots. The plate loses its desensitization or ability to repel ink. Scumming is difficult to clean out with plain water but will usually respond to an etching or plate-cleaning solution, although it may gradually reappear as the run continues.

Dry-ups: Desensitization due to the lack of dampening. Dry-ups usually start at the edges of the sheets, increasing rapidly toward the center. Increased water feed or decreased ink feed is usually sufficient to restore the balance.

Poor trapping: Incomplete transfer of ink to a previously printed wet ink film, causing loss of color saturation in overprint solids. Trapping is affected by the relative tack or resistance to splitting of the ink films; to assure transfer, the ink being applied should split more readily than the wet film to which it is being applied. A decreasing tack sequence is usually called for in multicolor printing. The fault may still persist because in the dynamic situation on press the velocity of separation, ink viscosity, film thickness, area being separated, and presence of water emulsification give tack values different from those obtained under laboratory testing conditions.

FAULTS PECULIAR TO HALFTONES

All of the above faults are found in halftone areas as well as solids. However, some additional faults are either unique to halftones or most troublesome when halftones are being printed.

Doubling: A light, ghost dot alongside the proper dot, particularly in the highlights. Doubling increases the highlight tones and gives muddy reproductions. In multicolor work the blanket picks up a faint impression from the preceding sheet and fails to transfer it in exact register to the next one being printed. Doubling appears at random and usually can be corrected only by extensive mechanical adjustments to the press.

Slur: A "tail" or directional filling in of open areas between the shadow dots. Slur reduces shadow contrast. It is caused by the ink acting as a lubricant in the heavy areas, permitting the sheet to slip in the impression nip.

Fill-in: A nondirectional filling in between shadow dots, similar in appearance to slur. Running an excessive amount of ink is the usual cause.

Moiré: Dark blotches appearing at regular intervals in a symmetrical checkerboard pattern. They are formed by the angling of the halftones and appear most frequently in medium values of near neutral colors. There is no adjustment during printing to overcome them short of rescreening and making new plates.

Haloes: Also called *bromide drag;* wisps of lighter or darker areas which tail out from places showing an abrupt change of value or contrast. Haloes are distinguished from press ghosting by their smaller size and the fact that they are found on the printing plate. They are peculiar to halftones processed by mechanical devices with strong directional agitation. There is no press remedy.

FAULTS IN INK DRYING

The remaining printing faults are perhaps the most difficult since they stem from problems in the ink drying mechanism and therefore usually are not detectable until the job has been printed.

Setoff: Transfer of wet ink from the surface of the printed sheet to the back of the one above it in the delivery pile. Setoff can be controlled in most cases by increasing the amount of offset spray used, decreasing the height of the delivery pile, and taking care to run without excessive ink. Setting and drying times of the inks should be matched to the paper characteristics, particularly if the coverage is heavy.

Chalking: Rubbing of ink off the paper even though it is dry to the touch and does not set off in the pile. Chalking occurs mainly on coated papers. It is the result of too rapid absorption of the ink vehicle, leaving unbound pigments at the surface.

Crystallization: The inability of ink coating or varnish to trap to a previously printed and dried ink film. It is not related to crystal formation in chemistry but is the result of waxy or other ink-repelling substances migrating to the surface during drying.

QUALITY CONTROL METHODS FOR THE GRAPHIC ARTS

Robert Loekle, COLOR REPRODUCTION CONSULTANT

Quality in printing is measured by how well a printer meets customer specifications. Quality control is a set of methods for assuring quality at minimum cost to the customer.

Unfortunately, printers and buyers alike tend to equate "quality" with appearance alone, so that four-color process printing garners the accolades for "quality printing" while simple black-and-white work may be dismissed as routine. Such a narrow interpretation misses the point; it is a major reason why quality control methods have had such slow acceptance in the graphic arts.

Four-color process printing differs from black-and-white line work only in the number of quality characteristics which must be specified, the greater difficulty of meeting them by available processes, and the buyer's difficulty in giving them objective definition. The same quality control principles apply to all manufactured products.

QUALITY CHARACTERISTICS

The first step in establishing a control system is to isolate those characteristics by which the customer will judge the quality of the printed product. Book work, for example, might be judged by the uniformity of the type in line thickness, and the evenness of the inking from signature to signature. In process work, not only the evenness but the level of the inking is critical. In addition, *dot gain* (increase in dot size) in halftone areas influences quality. In multicolor wet printing the ability of a wet ink film to *trap,* or overprint a previously inked area, will determine the gamut of hues that can be reproduced.

For every printing job there are a number of such characteristics. Experienced buyers and printers are aware of them intuitively; nevertheless, it is often helpful at some time to put them down on paper. Such a checklist can be valuable in communicating job requirements between buyer and printer, and in setting priorities when not all characteristics can be met with equal ease.

PRINTING STANDARDS

Each characteristic ought to have some standard against which it can be judged. Prior experience can furnish many such standards. Informed buyers and printers are also aware that the printing process contains a number of variables, so that it is unreasonable to expect that the standards will always be met exactly under all conditions. Some tolerances must be permitted, but they must be stated with clarity. It is not enough to say "run it 'normal,' plus or minus a 'little.'" The standard and the tolerance must be spelled out in such a way that reasonable people cannot disagree on interpretation.

Standards may be evaluated by visual checks, in which case samples should be provided, along with samples that show the limits of acceptability. Many characteristics lend themselves to instrumental measurement, which, of course, is generally to be preferred. The use of instruments, however, is not a substitute for common sense. Often they yield numerical values which correlate poorly with the quality characteristic in question or give a degree of precision which is unnecessary. At such times, the expense of instrumentation and the time involved in making measurements may not be justified. Each case will have to be decided upon its merits.

439

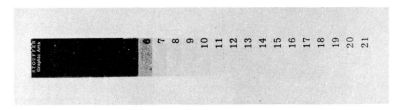

Figure 11.28: The GATF Sensitivity Guide image as it appears on a negative-working plate. *Figure 11.28 through 11.34 courtesy of Graphic Arts Technical Foundation.*

Figure 11.29: GATF Star Target (from left to right): cleanly printed without dot distortion; nondirectional enlargement of dots, as from overpacking; dot doubling; slurring.

Figure 11.30: GATF Dot Gain Scale and Slur Gauge. Printed images of the dot gain scale show the different effects of ordinary dot gain and slur in actual size. The top scale shows dot gain without slur, and the bottom scale shows dot gain caused by slur.

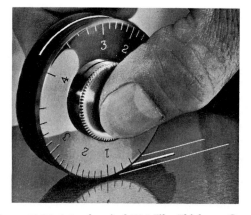

Figure 11.31: Interchemical Wet Film Thickness Gauge.

Figure 11.32: Baldwin Packing Gauge.

Figure 11.33: A pH meter.

Figure 11.34: E. J. Cady DWL Bench Micrometer.

440

SIMPLE DEVICES FOR QUALITY CONTROL

Since no two pieces of copy are exactly alike, inspection of the work itself does not provide the best method of controlling quality. An objective device, which can be carried from job to job, is preferable. Besides judging proofs and printing under the same or similar light sources (see "The Measurement and Specification of Color," page 21), the most familiar, and probably earliest, use of a control device is the gray scale used in photography. This is a scale of selected neutrals which may be found in the original copy to be reproduced. By controlling the values, or densities, at certain key points in the scale, the photographer is able to make judgments about reproduction that would be awkward or impossible to make by relying on measurements made from the original copy. (The gray scale is illustrated in "Halftone Photography," page 342.)

The concept of representing a complex image by a simple device from which objective judgments can be made is central to controlling image quality. The principle has been extended by several devices:

A *neutral step wedge* consisting of various transmission densities accompanies photographic halftones which are to be contacted. The density of a certain step in the contact is representative of the amount of dot sharpening.

A *continuous-tone gray scale* photographed along with line work represents changes occurring in line width, according to the position of the totally blackened step.

The density, after processing, of a series of carefully controlled exposures on a film strip represents changes in the level of developer activity in the processing machine.

A *transmission step wedge* (usually referred to as a *Stouffer scale* or *GATF Sensitivity Guide* by platemakers) is exposed along with the flats in making the plates. The position of the last solid step indicates the amount of exposure that the plate emulsion has received. A sufficient amount of exposure is required to harden the plate and insure a long plate life. However, excessive amounts of exposure will change the size of halftone dots. (See figure 11.28.)

A *star target* printed along with the job represents a small section of image edge, such as type or a halftone dot. Changes in the edge shape due to slur, doubling, or "squash" are greatly magnified and can be detected readily. Due to the target's symmetrical design, such changes can be differentiated and assigned to the correct cause. (See figure 11.29.)

A *slur gauge* provides high visibility for slur in either with-machine or across-machine direction. A *dot gain scale* provides a rapid method of estimating relative changes in dot area. (See figure 11.30.)

Color bars represent the density of the solid colors from which all others are obtained. (See "What to Look For in the Proof," page 367.)

SIMPLE MEASURING TOOLS

The devices given above reveal changes in image quality. Although they often point to the general source of such changes, these devices may be insufficient to pinpoint them. For example, both excessive inking and excessive pressures may cause slurring. To distinguish between these causes, printers require some method for measuring ink-film thickness and pressures. The measuring tools available include the following.

The *wet film thickness gauge* (fig. 11.31) can be applied to the steel roller nearest the form rollers to determine the amount of ink fed into the ink train.

A *packing gauge* (fig. 11.32) is used to measure the height of the blanket above the bearers, which is, of course, related to the transfer pressure.

The influence of fountain solution acidity on ink drying time is another well-known phenomenon. A small, portable *pH meter* (fig. 11.33) is a valuable tool for determining the acidity of the dampening solution.

A *bench micrometer* (fig. 11.34) is preferable to the regular machinist's micrometer for measurement of blanket thickness. Not only is uniform pressure applied, but the blanket can be measured at any point on its surface.

SIMPLE MATERIAL TESTS

There are occasions when neither devices nor tools are sufficient. The color bars, for example, may indicate insufficient density even though measurements for ink film thickness, transfer pressure, and so on, fall within the ranges required for good printing. The next step may be to investigate the transparency of the inks and their tinctorial strength. In such a case the printer should devise a test, under carefully controlled conditions, by which the characteristics of inks that perform well can be compared with those giving trouble.

Unless a great many tests are routinely performed absolute values will be of less use than the relative values derived from comparison tests. It is often misleading to quote absolute values unless special precautions are taken in establishing test methods. Usually questions can be answered in terms of "more" or "less," and experience shows how much more or less makes a real difference.

Many important quality characteristics of the materials used in the graphic arts can be determined from a few simple tests. Thus, the tack and viscosity of ink can tell the printer a great deal about its performance even though many of its other properties are not defined. Such information is available from the ink supplier. Likewise, the ink absorptivity of paper is important to hold-out, drying time, and image quality. The *K&N test* provides a simple method of comparing the absorptivity of different papers. When the results are combined with paper gloss measurements, as suggested by the Graphic Arts Technical Foundation, they yield a single value called Paper Surface Efficiency (see "The Influence of Paper on Color Printing," page 481). This value is probably the best single guide to the printing quality of coated papers.

STATISTICAL METHODS OF CONTROL

For many printers the devices, tools, and tests, of which only a brief account has been given, yield a quality product on a predictable basis. Indeed, many printers feel, probably with ample justification, that they are able to satisfy their customers' needs with considerably less than has been outlined.

But there is another aspect to quality control. In today's competitive market, it is no longer enough to fulfill the customer's present needs. New needs will arise tomorrow: needs for greater economy, for speedier delivery times, for better service, and for more reliability. To prove a job over and over, or to print it twice to make it right, is a luxury which can be afforded no longer. Regardless of the appearance of the final job, or how satisfied the customer may be, such a method is wasteful of resources and labor and inconsistent with the concept of quality.

For printers who feel the rise in costs and the increasing pressure of competition, there must be a continuing effort to optimize the process. For them the methods already given may still be insufficient to their needs. A much more careful study of their process is then in order, and a more sophisticated approach to quality problems must be undertaken.

The much broader field of industrial quality control is approached through the scientific discipline of applied statistics. The more variables a process has, the more useful a statistical approach becomes, since statistics is that branch of science that deals with the nature of variation.

As printers become more deeply involved in efforts to control quality, they are likely to observe that many of the "qualities" which have long been considered subjective, and gave rise to the "art" in "graphic arts," can be given more objective definition. Increasingly, they tend to rely on instruments and measurements to obtain control. Since measurements yield numbers, and numbers form a data base, they soon possess a large field of data which is an accurate history of each process.

A statistical approach provides a method whereby a printer can distill from a mass of data the key information which can be applied to developing improvements in a process. The main concern is no longer to eliminate variation but to distinguish the variation one can do something about from that over which one has little control.

Like any endeavor, statistical analysis can be pursued at different levels of complexity. The most powerful tools of statistical analysis are beyond some printers' reach at present since the resources of a small firm are insufficient. However, evidence is accumulating that even simple statistical tools are capable of providing a rational framework for decision making.

MAGAZINE ADVERTISING REPRODUCTION STANDARDS

Frank E. Church, GRAPHIC ARTS CONSULTANT

Many attempts have been made to establish standards for the printing industry, but none have been completely successful. Standards have been agreed on by certain segments of the industry, especially for comparing proofs to originals, for comparing printed sheets to proofs, and for standardizing inks on proofs of prints that will appear in a number of magazines. The American National Standards Institute (ANSI) has a number of committees working on industry standards. Other industry organizations, such as the Magazine Publishers Association (MPA), the American Association of Advertising Agencies (AAAA or 4A's), and the American Business Press (ABP), have combined committees to develop standards for magazine advertising reproduction. There are no regulatory agencies established to enforce standards. The ones adopted are suggested standards, and their adoption, use, and "policing" depends upon relations between buyer and producer.

Magazine publishers have a peculiar problem. They are responsible for producing thousands, or millions, of well-printed advertising reproductions—yet they do not have manufacturing control of the supplied proofs they are obliged to match on their printers' production presses, especially as to amount of ink, which directly affects color balance and the printed result.

Current practice (which is not likely to change) is for advertising agencies to buy the engravings and films,

plus proofs, from numerous photoplatemakers whose disciplines in manufacturing and proofing can, and do, vary from shop to shop. The printer must use this prime material when he makes multiple units of press plates for his presses.

When two or more (most generally four) advertisements are imposed side by side on the press, each receives the same amount of ink as the ink travels in-line from the inking fountain to the plates. Only when the materials prepared in different shops have been manufactured in compliance with recommended standards does the printer have the opportunity of producing acceptable matches to the proofs supplied.

This problem, which caused an inordinate amount of confusion and recriminations during the transition period of progressing from two-and-two "dry" printing to four-color "wet" printing some years ago, was tackled in 1948 by the two industry organizations most directly concerned. The American Association of Advertising Agencies and the Magazine Publishers Association appointed representatives to form the AAAA/MPA Joint Committee on Magazine Advertising Reproduction. This committee published its first report that year titled: "Improving the Physical Presentations of Advertising in Magazines."

In 1968, the work of the AAAA/MPA Committee, which is still active, was supplemented by the formation of a Graphic Arts Technical Foundation advisory committee on letterpress proofing. GATF provided the umbrella for a group of 20-plus representatives from eight industry organizations: AAAA, MPA, American Platemakers Association (APA), Platemakers Educational and Research Institute (PERI), National Association of Printing Ink Manufacturers (NAPIM), Printing Industries of America (PIA), Gravure Technical Association (GTA), and GATF itself. Both committees have worked effectively in promulgating and publishing recommended standard manufacturing procedures so that letterpress materials and proofs produced by one shop will be similar to those produced by other shops. The standards have been revised and updated when necessary.

PERI and APA have recently merged, forming the International Association of Photoplatemakers (IAP), 552 West 167th St., South Holland, Ill. 60473. This organization now acts as a coordinator for a standards committee made up of representatives of the various associations involved in recommending, reviewing, and revising standard manufacturing procedures.

Standards currently in use include the following.

LETTERPRESS

AAAA/MPA Joint Committee *Recommended Standard Specifications for Advertising Reproduction Material in Magazine Letterpress Wet Printing*, Report No. 5, June 1967. Specifications are updated and appear in each quarterly edition of Standard Rate and Data Service's *Print Media Production Data*—latest revision, June 1974. Copies of these specifications are also available from the IAP (formerly PERI) under the title, *Recommended Standards for Advertising Material for Letterpress Publications.*

AAAA/MPA Standard Body Proofing for Letterpress Reproduction, July 1971. This paper is marketed only by Consolidated Papers, Inc., Chicago, Ill., as "Standard AAAA/MPA Proofing Paper."

Standard Proofing Inks. These are manufactured by Printing Ink Division, Borden Chemical Co., Cincinnati, Ohio, and are sold through their branches. Ink of the same manufacturer is sold as standard proofing ink by other members of NAPIM.

Standard Letterpress Color Bars. The IAP is responsible for issuing the standard color bars, illustrating both the design and correct ink amounts. They are printed on standard proofing stock, using standard inks, and are available from the IAP.

Production Operating Communications Standards, The Technical Association of the Pulp and Paper Industry's CA Report No. 13, October 1967. The report specifies a standard roll numbering system and standard roll cards and illustrates mechanical paper defects with a numbered glossary.

OFFSET

AAAA/MPA/ABP *Recommended Standards for Advertising Material for Web Offset Publications,* November 1975, now referred to as *Specifications Web Offset Publications* (SWOP Standards); second revision, July 1978. These standards are constantly reviewed; a third revision is now in progress. Specifications are printed in each quarterly edition of Standard Rate and Data Service's *Print Media Production Data* and are also available from the IAP.

Standard Offset Color References. These are printed and selected by the IAP and specify standards for hue and amount of ink to be used when preparing proofs for magazine color reproduction. The reference color bars are printed on standard proofing stock using standard proofing inks and the GATF color bar design; they are available from the IAP.

DENSITOMETRY

The introduction of the reflection densitometer has made it possible to improve upon visual appraisals of ink amounts by providing numerical comparisons. Recommended reading on this advance is as follows:

Platemakers Educational and Research Institute Technical Bulletin No. 22, *Use of Reflection Densitometry in Four-Color Proofing* (available from the IAP).

Graphic Arts Technical Foundation Research Progress Reports Nos. 90 and 91, August 1972: *Graphic Arts Applications of Reflection Densitometry* and *Using the Reflection Densitometer for Ink Film Control.*

STANDARD LIGHTING

The American National Standards Institute (ANSI) has established standard viewing conditions for the graphic arts. The following bulletins are available: ANSI PH2.31–1969, *Direct Viewing of Photographic Color Transparencies;* ANSI PH2.32–1972, *Viewing Conditions for the Appraisal of Color Quality and Color Uniformity in the Graphic Arts;* and ANSI PH2.45–1979, *Projection Viewing Conditions for Comparing Small Transparencies with Reproductions.*

GRAVURE

Over the past 20 years, the Gravure Technical Association has established standards in the following areas: photographic processes, screen rulings, positive density requirements, viewing guides, proofing stocks, reproduction curves, standardization of tools for implementation, calibration for transmission and reflection densitometers, certified three-step positive color bars, gravure inks standard color charts, and standard methods and procedures.

SUBSTRATES 12

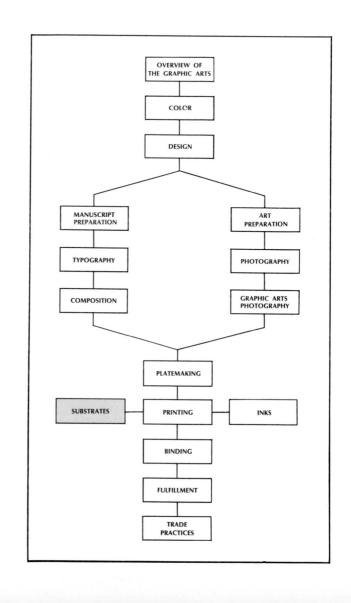

PAPER NAMES AND CLASSIFICATIONS
Paul D. Doebler, PUBLISHING MANAGEMENT CONSULTANT

As in most classification systems that have grown up over several centuries, the categories into which kinds of paper may be grouped are not clear-cut. The terminology is based on many factors involved in the ways paper is made and used. These factors, however, are essentially of three types:
· Properties built into the paper itself, such as type of printing surface or fiber content
· Printing processes with which the paper is designed to work
· End uses for which the paper is intended
Various types of paper can have a great many different properties, the most important of which are discussed in other articles in this section. It would be impossible to include all the properties of any given paper in its name, but when a property is of overriding importance in describing the paper's essential nature, it will usually be indicated in the name of the sheet.

CLASSIFYING BY PHYSICAL PROPERTY
The most important kind of physical property that a sheet can normally have is its printing surface characteristics, and probably the most widely encountered designation in this area is the distinction between *coated* and *uncoated* sheets. Coated papers generally provide superior printing surfaces for reproduction of halftones and full-color process. Within the coated paper category, however, there are several kinds of coatings, including *cast, glossy, dull, matte,* and *machine.* Among uncoated papers, too, there are a number of different surface finishes, including *antique, eggshell, vellum, English,* and *supercalendered.* (See "Knowing Paper Finishes," page 461.) These specific terms are often used in paper names to place them in their proper surface classifications.

Other properties, such as *bulk, grain direction, brightness,* and *opacity,* can be used to classify papers. (See "Fundamental Physical Properties of Paper," page 471, and "Appearance Analysis in the Graphic Arts," page 477.) However, these terms are seldom used in naming papers, and the buyer desiring an exceptional degree of one of these characteristics—such as high bulking or opacity—normally must inquire specifically about these properties.

Another major classification scheme employing physical properties is based on the fiber content of the paper. Although all paper is composed of cellulose fiber, these fibers come from a variety of wood pulp grades as well as from cotton. The major classifications of paper based on the wood pulp used are *groundwood* and so-called *free* sheets, which are made of chemical pulp. Groundwood papers, which are not processed as fully as chemical pulp sheets, contain small undigested chips of wood which tend to mar the surface; free sheets, on the other hand, are free of such chips. Papers made of cotton fiber generally are more expensive than those made of wood fiber, and are limited mostly to use in writing papers such as bonds and ledger stocks. Although most paper names do not indicate what kind of wood pulp is used in them, many bond papers are identified by the amount of cotton used (often stated as *rag content*). On occasion, bond paper names may also indicate the type of chemical wood pulp used in manufacture, such as *sulfate* or *sulfite.*

CLASSIFYING BY PRINTING PROCESS
The second major method of classifying papers—by printing process to which they are suited—also is not used universally. However, a process designation is usually stated when the paper is specially compounded for that process, or when its predominant characteristics make it particularly suitable for the process.

The most important printing process classification is that of *lithographic* or *offset* papers, which must be resistant to chemical reactions and wetting actions of the fountain solutions used in this printing method. *Gravure* papers generally are so named only because they are especially suited for use in that process, not because they are specifically compounded for it. Both of these papers can also be printed by letterpress. So-called *letterpress* papers are best suited to that process, but often they can be printed by other processes as well under certain conditions. Letterpress and gravure papers are simpler to manufacture than offset papers, which require special chemical additives in addition to the basic ingredients.

CLASSIFYING BY END USE
The most extensive classification system for various kinds of paper is based on end uses which will be made of the stock. There are literally hundreds of designations based loosely on end-use considerations that are currently employed to describe specific types of papers, such as *laminated, metallic, onionskin, Bible, rag bond, label, gummed, heat-seal, poster,* and *parchment,* to name just a few. (A more complete list of specific kinds of paper, including classification names based on physical properties and printing processes as well as on end-use, may be found in "Papers in Common Use," page 453.)

Almost all of these hundreds of specific paper types, however, fall within a broad end-use classification scheme which has developed in the paper industry over many years, a classification system which also includes a standard method of specifying the sheet size and weight of paper when purchased from a paper supplier. For printing and writing papers, there are nine categories in this classification system, each of which has been assigned its own basic sheet size. Paper actually is available in a great many sheet sizes, but in each of the nine categories one particular size has been designated as the basic size to provide a standard reference point from which to compute various basis weights of paper.

Basic size and basis weight

The concepts of *basic size* and *basis weight* are fundamental to all paper calculations. Paper is sold by weight, and prices are tied to this system. Also, the universal method of describing papers of various weights—such as a 50-pound book paper or a 20-pound bond—is derived from this system. The definitions of basic size and basis weight are as follows:

• Basic size is the sheet size used to compute the basis weight of a ream (500 sheets) of a given paper.

• Basis weight of a given paper is the weight of a ream (500 sheets) of that paper in the basic size. (This does not mean that the paper is available only in that size; it simply means that the paper under consideration would weigh that if cut to that size, and it is used as a standard for computing costs.)

Thus, if a paper is identified as 50-pound book paper, it means that one ream (500 sheets) of that paper cut to 25" x 38" (the basic size for book paper) weighs 50 pounds. The 50-pound weight is called the basis weight and is a fixed characteristic of the sheet, defining it just as other properties do. From the basis weight (and the knowledge that it is based on a certain number of sheets in a basic size), the weights of other quantities of the paper in other sizes can be determined. (See "Paper Tables and Formulas," page 449.)

Basic-size categories

The nine primary categories and their basic sizes have been derived from the end uses to which papers in these categories are most often put. Normally, standard-size products in each category make most efficient use of the basic-size sheet. For example, more books use a 6" x 9" page size than any other size. Eight 6" x 9" pages can be printed on one side of a 25" x 38" sheet and eight on the back side, forming a 16-page signature which is most often ideal for processing in the bindery. The 25" x 38" size allows the proper margins around each page for bleeds and trimming in the bindery. Thus the 25" x 38" sheet size has become the standard, or basic size, from which book paper calculations are made. The same is true for bond papers—the 8½" x 11" stationery size cuts perfectly from the basic size of 17" x 22"—and for all other types of stock as well.

Each of the nine basic-size categories traditionally has been given a name according to the primary end use most commonly associated with it. In most cases, these names have remained unchanged for many years, but in the case of book paper (as noted in the chart at right) the changes in printing technologies and the rise of new classes of papers have caused some new terms to come into use.

The nine major basic-size categories, their most common basis weights, and their primary end uses are as follows:

Basic size category	Common basis weights (in pounds)	End uses
17" x 22" Bond	13, 16, 20, 24, 28, 32, 36, 40	Bonds, ledgers, thin papers. All papers in this class are also called business papers or writing papers.
19" x 24" Blotting	100, 120, 140	Blotting papers.
20" x 26" Cover	25, 35, 40, 50, 60, 65, 80, 90, 100	Cover papers. Frequently discussed in terms of the caliper or thickness of two sheets measured together.
22" x 28" Blanks	140 to 915 (usually designated by thickness, not weight)	Blanks. A heavier stock used primarily for displays, usually measured in terms of caliper or thickness. Most common calipers range from 15 to 48 points (thousandths of an inch).
22½" x 28½" Printing bristol	67, 94, 100, 120	Printing bristols, postcards.
24" x 36" Newsprint	32 (for newsprint)	Newsprint is the original name for this basic size. However, many other types of paper which have no relation to newsprint now use this same basic size. These include wrapping papers, tissues, waxed papers, tag stock.
25" x 38" Book	30, 40, 50, 60, 70, 80, 90, 100, 120	Book paper is the original name for this category. In recent decades, a variety of subdivisions and new names have been added. These include offset, text, letterpress, gravure, publication, uncoated book, coated book, coated offset, uncoated offset.
25" x 40" Paperboard	(Designated by thickness, not weight)	Paperboard. Usually described in terms of caliper, and ranges from 14 to 24 points.
25½" x 30½" Index bristol	90, 110, 140, 170	Index cards, file cards, etc.

PAPER STOCK FOR WEB PRINTING

Paper supplied in rolls for web printing is classified within this same system of kinds of paper, basic sizes, and basis weights. A 50-pound stock of a given type is the same paper whether supplied in rolls or in sheets, and weights of paper in rolls can be computed from the standard basic-size and basis-weight data.

In web printing, one aspect of paper measurement is different from sheet measurements, however—that of roll or web width and cutoff length. These dimensions correspond to the sheet-size dimensions in sheet stock. These paper dimensions once depended on the individual press used, because roll paper often was made to fit a specific machine. Later, with the growth of web offset in many printing plants, standard press models were installed widely, and a predominant group of "standard" web widths appeared in the 35- to 38-inch range, with "standard" cutoff dimensions grouped around 22½ to 23 inches. More recently, a family of larger web presses spurred a group of standard web sizes with widths in the 50- to 65-inch range and cutoff lengths of 39 to 41 inches. The newest group of presses are smaller ones taking web widths in the range of 22½ to 31 inches, with a cutoff of around 19 inches.

PAPER TABLES AND FORMULAS

The calculations involved in planning the use and purchase of paper are fundamental to all areas of the graphic arts. Many reference tables, formulas, explanations, and time-saving slide and dial scales are offered by paper suppliers and other dealers to aid the designer and production planner. For a high degree of precision in decision-making and planning, specific data on the particular paper or papers being considered must be obtained. However, in many cases average data is adequate to answer the questions at hand, and the following tables and formulas will cover the majority of graphic arts needs. These tables include data on the types of paper most used in general commercial printing and publishing.

BASIS WEIGHTS AND BASIC SIZES

The *basic size* for a given type of paper is the standard on which the paper's weight description, or *basis weight,* is computed. (See "Paper Names and Classifications," page 447.) For example, all bond papers have the basic size of 17" x 22", even though the sheets used in a specific job may actually have a size that is different. The basic size is used to calculate the basis weight, and the basis weight designation—20-pound, for instance—remains the same regardless of the actual size to which the sheets are cut. The basis weight of the paper is determined by weighing 500 sheets of the stock cut to the basic size—thus, 500 sheets of a 20-pound bond cut to 17" x 22" will weigh 20 pounds.

WEIGHT PER THOUSAND SHEETS

Traditionally, paper prices have been quoted on the basis of 500 sheets (one ream), but a growing practice today is to quote on the basis of 1,000 sheets (IM or double-ream). In keeping with this newer practice, tables 12.1A through 12.1F give the weight per 1,000 sheets in the most common sizes and weights of various types of paper.

The basis weight and basic size of a paper can be used to compute the weight of a given number of sheets in any other size. The basic formula for this computation is as follows:

$$\text{Total weight} = \frac{\text{weight of 1,000 sheets} \times \text{number of sheets}}{1,000}$$

The formula for finding the weight of 1,000 sheets is:

$$\text{Weight per 1,000 sheets} = \frac{\text{area of actual sheet}}{\text{area of basic size}} \times \text{basis weight} \times 2$$

Tables 12.1A through 12.1F provide the answers to the calculations in the formula for weight per 1,000 sheets for the most commonly used sizes and weights of various types of paper. To find the actual weight of 1,000 sheets of a given stock, refer to the appropriate table, locate the desired sheet size in the left-hand column (the basic size is in boldface), and find the weight for 1,000 sheets in the appropriate basis weight column.

TABLE 12.1A: WEIGHT PER 1,000 SHEETS—BOOK
Basic size 25" x 38" (book, offset, text, letterpress, gravure, publication, coated and uncoated)

Size in inches	Weight in pounds — Basis weights											
	30	35	40	45	50	60	70	80	90	100	120	150
17½ x 22½	25	29	33	37	41	50	58	66	75	83	99	124
19 x 25	30	35	40	45	50	60	70	80	90	100	120	150
20 x 26	33	38	44	49	55	66	77	88	99	109	131	164
22½ x 29	41	48	55	62	69	82	96	110	124	137	165	206
22½ x 35	50	58	66	75	83	99	116	133	149	166	199	249
23 x 29	42	49	56	63	70	84	98	112	126	140	169	211
23 x 35	51	59	68	76	85	102	119	136	153	169	203	254
24 x 36	55	64	73	82	91	109	127	146	164	182	218	273
25 x 38	**60**	**70**	**80**	**90**	**100**	**120**	**140**	**160**	**180**	**200**	**240**	**300**
26 x 40	66	77	88	99	109	131	153	175	197	219	263	328
28 x 42	74	87	99	111	124	149	173	198	223	248	297	371
28 x 44	78	91	104	117	130	156	182	207	233	259	311	389
30½ x 41	79	92	105	118	132	158	184	211	237	263	316	395
32 x 44	89	104	119	133	148	178	207	237	267	296	356	445
33 x 44	92	107	122	138	153	183	214	245	275	306	367	459
35 x 45	99	116	133	149	166	199	232	265	298	332	398	497
35 x 46	102	119	136	153	169	203	237	271	305	339	407	508
36 x 48	109	127	146	164	182	218	255	291	327	364	437	546
38 x 50	120	140	160	180	200	240	280	320	360	400	480	600
38 x 52	125	146	166	187	208	250	291	333	374	416	499	624
41 x 54	140	163	186	210	233	280	326	373	419	466	559	699
41 x 61	158	184	211	237	263	316	369	421	474	527	632	790
42 x 58	154	179	205	231	256	308	359	410	462	513	615	769
44 x 64	178	207	237	267	296	356	415	474	534	593	711	889
44 x 66	183	214	245	275	306	367	428	489	550	611	734	917
46 x 69	200	234	267	301	334	401	468	535	601	668	802	1002
46½ x 67½	198	231	264	297	330	396	463	529	593	661	793	991
52 x 76	250	291	333	374	416	499	582	666	749	832	998	1248

TABLE 12.1B: WEIGHT PER 1,000 SHEETS—BOND
Basic size 17" x 22"
(bond, ledger, thin, business, writing)

Size in inches	Weight in pounds							
	Basis weights							
	13	16	20	24	28	32	36	40
16 x 21	23	29	36	43	50	57	65	72
16 x 42	47	58	72	86	101	115	130	144
17 x 22	**26**	**32**	**40**	**48**	**56**	**64**	**72**	**80**
17 x 26	31	38	47	57	66	76	85	95
17½ x 22½	27	34	42	51	59	67	76	84
17 x 28	33	41	51	61	71	81	92	102
18 x 23	29	36	44	53	62	71	80	89
18 x 46	58	71	89	106	124	142	160	177
19 x 24	32	39	49	59	68	78	88	98
19 x 28	37	46	57	68	80	91	102	114
19 x 48	63	78	98	117	137	156	176	195
20 x 28	39	48	60	72	84	96	108	120
21 x 32	47	58	72	86	101	115	130	144
22 x 25½	39	48	60	72	84	96	108	120
22 x 34	52	64	80	96	112	128	144	160
22½ x 22½	35	43	54	65	76	87	97	108
22½ x 28½	45	55	69	82	96	110	123	137
22½ x 34½	54	66	83	100	116	133	149	166
22½ x 35	55	67	84	101	118	135	152	168
23 x 36	58	71	89	106	124	142	159	177
24 x 38	63	78	98	117	137	156	176	195
24½ x 24½	42	51	64	77	90	103	116	128
24½ x 28½	49	60	75	90	105	120	135	150
24½ x 29	50	61	76	91	106	122	137	152
24½ x 38½	66	81	101	121	141	161	182	202
24½ x 39	66	82	102	122	143	164	184	204
25½ x 44	78	96	120	144	168	192	216	240
26 x 34	61	76	94	113	132	151	170	189
28 x 34	66	82	102	122	143	163	184	204
28 x 38	74	91	114	136	159	182	205	228
34 x 44	104	128	160	192	224	256	288	320
35 x 45	109	135	168	202	236	270	303	337

Cut sizes:

	Basis weights							
	13	16	20	24	28	32	36	40
8½ x 11	6.5	8.0	10.0	12.0	14.0	16.0	18.0	20.0
8½ x 13	7.7	9.4	11.8	14.2	16.5	18.9	21.3	23.6
8½ x 14	8.3	10.2	12.7	15.3	17.8	20.4	22.9	25.5
11 x 17	13.0	16.0	20.0	24.0	28.0	32.0	36.0	40.0

TABLE 12.1C: WEIGHT PER 1,000 SHEETS—INDEX BRISTOL
Basic size 25½" x 30½" (index bristol)

Size in inches	Weight in pounds				
	Basis weights				
	90	120	140	170	220
20½ x 24¾	117	157	183	222	287
22½ x 28½	148	198	231	280	363
22½ x 35	182	243	284	344	446
25½ x 30½	**180**	**240**	**280**	**340**	**440**
28½ x 45	297	356	462	561	726

TABLE 12.1D: WEIGHT PER 1,000 SHEETS—COVER
Basic size 20" x 26" (cover)

Size in inches	Weight in pounds						
	Basis weights						
	50	60	65	80	90	100	130
20 x 26	**100**	**120**	**130**	**160**	**180**	**200**	**260**
22½ x 28½	123	148	160	197	222	247	321
23 x 29	128	154	167	205	231	257	333
23 x 35	155	186	201	248	279	310	403
26 x 40	200	240	260	320	360	400	520
35 x 46	310	372	403	495	557	619	805

TABLE 12.1E: WEIGHT PER 1,000 SHEETS—PRINTING BRISTOL
Basic size 22½" x 28½" (printing bristol, folding bristol, postcard)

Size in inches	Weight in pounds								
	Basis weights								
	67	80	90	94	100	110	120	140	160
22½ x 28½	**134**	**160**	**180**	**188**	**200**	**220**	**240**	**280**	**320**
22½ x 35	165	196	221	231	246	270	295	344	393
23 x 35	168	201	226	236	251	276	301	352	402
26 x 40	217	259	292	305	324	357	389	454	519
28½ x 45	268	320	360	376	400	440	480	560	640

TABLE 12.1F: WEIGHT PER 1,000 SHEETS—NEWSPRINT
Basic size 24" x 36" (newsprint, wrapping, tissue, waxed, tag)

Size in inches	Weight in pounds													
	Basis weights													
	30	32	40	50	60	70	80	90	100	125	150	175	200	250	300
22½ x 28½	45	48	59	74	89	104	119	134	148	186	223	260	297	371	445
24 x 36	**60**	**64**	**80**	**100**	**120**	**140**	**160**	**180**	**200**	**250**	**300**	**350**	**400**	**500**	**600**
28½ x 45	89	95	119	148	178	208	238	267	297	371	445	520	594	742	891

TABLE 12.2: EQUIVALENT WEIGHTS

Basis weight	Equivalent weights (500 sheets)			
Book 25 x 38	*Bond* 17 x 22	*Cover* 20 x 26	*Bristol* 22½ x 28½	*Index* 25½ x 30½
30	12	16	20	25
40	16	22	27	33
45	18	25	30	37
50	20	27	34	41
55	22	30	37	45
60	24	33	41	49
65	26	36	44	53
70	28	38	47	57
75	30	41	51	61
80	31	44	54	65
90	35	49	61	74
100	39	55	68	82
120	47	66	81	98
Bond 17 x 22	*Book* 25 x 38	*Cover* 20 x 26	*Bristol* 22½ x 28½	*Index* 25½ x 30½
13	33	18	22	27
16	41	22	27	33
20	51	28	34	42
24	61	33	41	50
28	71	39	48	58
32	81	44	55	67
36	91	50	62	75
40	102	56	69	83
44	112	61	75	91
Cover 20 x 26	*Book* 25 x 38	*Bond* 17 x 22	*Bristol* 22½ x 28½	*Index* 25½ x 30½
25	46	18	31	37
35	64	25	43	52
40	73	29	49	60
50	91	36	62	75
55	100	40	68	82
60	110	43	74	90
65	119	47	80	97
80	146	58	99	120
90	164	65	111	135
100	183	72	123	150
Printing bristol 22½ x 28½	*Book* 25 x 38	*Bond* 17 x 22	*Cover* 20 x 26	*Index* 25½ x 30½
88	130	51	71	107
100	148	58	81	121
120	178	70	97	146
140	207	82	113	170
160	237	93	130	194
180	267	105	146	218
Index bristol 25½ x 30½	*Book* 25 x 38	*Bond* 17 x 22	*Cover* 20 x 26	*Bristol* 22½ x 28½
90	110	43	60	74
110	134	53	74	91
140	171	67	94	115
170	207	82	114	140
220	269	106	147	181

EQUIVALENT WEIGHTS

Table 12.2 shows standard basis weights and indicates what those weights would be when translated into another basic size classification. For example, 500 sheets of 24-pound bond paper, if supplied in sheets measuring 25" x 38" (the basic size for book paper), would weigh 61 pounds. The 24-pound bond paper is, therefore, almost equivalent in weight to 60-pound book paper, and in certain cases might be used as a substitute. Consulting this table will show that, in the same way, a 50-pound book paper is equivalent in actual weight to a 20-pound bond, a 27-pound cover, a 34-pound printing bristol, and a 41-pound index bristol.

CALIPER AND BULKING

The caliper, or thickness, of a sheet of paper is measured in thousandths of an inch, often called *points*. Table 12.3 gives representative calipers for various types of paper. These values are averages, not

TABLE 12.3: AVERAGE CALIPER VALUES

Type of paper	Basis weight	Calipers in thousandths of an inch			
		Coated paper	Smooth finish	Vellum finish	Antique finish
Book (25 x 38)	40	.0019	.0025	.0031	.0034
	45	.0021	.0028	.0035	.0037
	50	.0023	.0031	.0038	.0041
	60	.0028	.0038	.0046	.0050
	70	.0034	.0044	.0054	.0058
	80	.0040	.0050	.0059	.0065
	90	.0046	.0057	.0065	.0074
	100	.0052	.0063	.0071	.0082
	120	.0060	.0076	.0082	.0100
	150	.0072	.0095	.0106	.0123
Bond (17 x 22)	13		.0021	.0025	.0027
	16		.0026	.0031	.0033
	20		.0032	.0039	.0042
	24		.0038	.0047	.0050
Cover (20 x 26)	50	.0044	.0058	.0070	.0075
	60	.0056	.0070	.0084	.0090
	65	.0060	.0076	.0092	.0097
	70	.0064	.0082	.0099	.0105
	80	.0072	.0093	.0113	.0120
	90	.0082	.0105	.0127	.0135
	100	.0092	.0116	.0140	.0150
	110	.0102	.0127	.0155	.0164
	120	.0112	.0139	.0169	.0177
	130	.0122	.0150	.0184	.0190
Index bristol (25½ x 30½)	90		.0080	.0084	
	110		.0096	.0104	
	140		.0132	.0140	
	170		.0144	.0160	
Printing bristol (22½ x 28½)	90	.0055	.0069	.0084	.0090
	100	.0061	.0076	.0093	.0100
	120	.0073	.0092	.0111	.0120
	140	.0085	.0107	.0130	.0140
	160	.0097	.0122	.0148	.0160
	180	.0110	.0137	.0167	.0180
	200	.0122	.0153	.0185	.0200
	220	.0134	.0167	.0204	.0220

specific thicknesses of specific brands of paper, and they should be used accordingly. Where high accuracy is important, specific values for the paper involved should be obtained from suppliers.

These caliper values can be used to determine the thickness, or *bulk,* of a book, an important factor in the planning of a cover which must wrap around the backbone of the book. The formula for determining bulk is as follows:

$$\text{Bulk (in inches)} = \frac{\text{number of pages} \times \text{caliper}}{2}$$

The above formula applies if the pages of the book are to be printed on both sides of the sheet or leaf. If the pages are to be printed only on one side of the paper, there is no need to divide by two.

ROLL WEIGHT AND YARDAGE

For computing the weight and linear yardage of paper in rolls, an average factor is used for each of various types of paper. The basic formula for calculating roll weight is as follows:

$$\text{Roll weight} = \text{roll diameter}^2 \times \text{roll width} \times \text{factor}$$

The following average factors apply in the above formula for all weights of paper in the respective classes:

Newsprint	.016
Antique finish	.018
Bond	.021
Uncoated offset	.022
Machine finish, English finish	.027
Supercalendered, coated one side	.030
Coated two sides	.034

The number of linear yards of paper in a roll is derived from the following formula, once the roll weight has been calculated:

$$\text{Linear yards} = \frac{\text{roll weight} \times 500 \times 24}{\text{roll width} \times \text{basis weight}}$$

PAPERS IN COMMON USE

Most of the terms in this alphabetical listing of common kinds of paper have been taken from the Paper Handbook, *a Boise Cascade publication, with permission of Boise Cascade. Others are from Walden's* Paper Catalog, *published by Walden-Mott Corp.*

Absorbent paper. Paper capable of absorbing water and excess ink. These are mainly blotting and duplicating papers but also include photographic blottings, filter papers, matrix paper, towelling, and cellulose wadding.

Anti-tarnish paper. A lightweight kraft or tissue wrapping paper with neutral pH and low sulfur content.

Artists' board. See *illustration board.*

Artists' paper. Superior drawing paper made with a close weave.

Backlining paper. Extremely durable paper, cut into strips and glued to the backbone of a hardcover book.

Bank note paper. Thin, tough paper used for bank notes and made mostly from cotton fibers.

Barrier material. A term that includes packaging papers and boards with greaseproof, waterproof, vaporproof, and bloodproof properties, among other protective qualities.

Base stock. Refers to paper that will subsequently be coated, laminated, or finished in other ways.

Bible paper. Referred to as such because of its use in Bibles, and characterized by its opacity, light weight, and low bulk, with a basis weight generally ranging from 14 to 30 pounds. This paper has diverse commercial uses. (Also called *India paper* or *Oxford India paper.*)

Binder's board. One of the highest quality paperboards, used in the construction of a case-made book cover.

Blanks. Members of the paperboard family, consisting of boards ranging in thickness from 15 points to 56 points and manufactured in a number of plies. Blanks come coated and uncoated; the latter are referred to as *plain mill blanks.*

Blueprint paper. A sheet whose prime quality must be its freedom from chemicals that would affect the sensitizing processes it must undergo. It is used primarily by printers, engineers, and architects. Other unique qualities of this specialty paper are its well-formed, even surface and its uniform wet-strength and absorbency.

Bond paper. A term originally used to describe paper characterized by durability and high strength, which was used for legal documents, stock certificates, and government bonds. Today, the word still indicates strength, rigidity, and good absorptive and erasing qualities but refers primarily to a wide variety of papers used by stationers, forms printers, and in-plant operations.

Book paper. A general term that encompasses a wide group of papers used predominantly in the commercial, book, and publication segment of the printing industry. Book papers are regarded as traditional printing papers and generally possess the properties essential to good printing.

Box board. Low-cost board used in the manufacture of heavy cartons and boxes.

Box paper. Either plain or coated paper, usually colored and embossed.

Braille paper. A sheet made suitable for the raised-dot production process utilized in manufacturing reading material for the blind, characterized by its smooth, level surface and high strength.

Bristols. The family of papers characterized by extreme hardness, foldability, strength, and overall ruggedness, due to considerable fiber refinement during the papermaking process. The group includes printing bristol, index bristol, and wedding bristol.

Bulking book paper. A sheet intentionally manufactured to provide maximum bulk for a given number of pages.

Business papers. Papers commonly used in business applications such as correspondence, bookkeeping, and records.

Carbonizing paper. Lightweight base stock manufactured with the proper finish on one or both sides of the sheet for later conversion into carbon paper.

Carbonless duplicating paper. A sheet capable of generating its own internal image as the result of pressure on its surface, in effect combining the functions of plain paper and carbon paper. A chemical is built into cells and blended with the pulp fibers of a paper, which comes off the paper machine as a finished product, with the ink-forming cells evenly spaced throughout both sides of the sheet. Under pressure the cells are ruptured, releasing the chemical to react and form a bluish-purple image through the depth of the paper. In effect, carbonless duplicating paper provides the user with carbon copies without carbon paper.

Cast coated paper. Paper with an extremely glossy finish achieved by passing a machine-coated paper under pressure against a highly polished, usually steam-heated drum. Next to plastic-laminated paper or board, cast coated papers have the highest gloss of all coated papers.

Chart paper. Smooth-surfaced paper made for chart and map printing, usually by offset lithography.

Chipboard. A paperboard manufactured from mixed waste papers to a low density and used whenever durability or appearance are not important factors.

Coated paper. Any sheet whose surface has been covered with a coating of adhesive and mineral pigment. Among the many coateds are book and cover papers, bristols, tags, and various paperboards.

Converting paper. An extremely general term that embraces all paper made to be converted into a paper product with characteristics and appearance very distinct from the original sheet. Examples are paper produced to be converted into envelopes, and kraft paper made to end up as gummed tape.

Corrugated board. Paperboard that has passed through a corrugating machine and that is used primarily as protective and cushioning material in packaging and shipping. The types include single-faced and double-faced corrugated and corrugated container board.

Cotton-content paper. See *rag-content paper.*

Cover paper. A large category of papers so named because they primarily serve the function of covering and protecting other printed materials.

Crayon paper. A heavy paper on board, used for crayons or watercolor. It is either white or tinted, with a glazed surface on one side and rough-finished on the other.

Crepe paper. Paper given a crimped surface by crowding it against a doctor blade during the papermaking process. The result is a pliable, extremely stretchable sheet.

D.T. cover paper. An abbreviation for "double thick" cover paper, referring to two thicknesses of cover paper bonded to produce an extra-stiff sheet. The more common weights are 100-pound (resulting from two 50-pound sheets) and 130-pound (two 65-pound sheets).

Decal paper. Paper manufactured specially to accept the decalcomania printing process of transferring images onto a permanent surface from a temporary base. This coated paper is characterized by good absorbency and wet-strength, plus a smooth surface. One side of the stock is usually coated with adhesive. Simplex decals are single-sheet products; duplex decals consist of high-grade tissue laminated to a heavy stock.

Decorative paper. Members of the package-printing family of papers, manufactured in a large assortment of weights, coatings, finishes, and colors for a number of end uses, primarily decorative.

De-inked paper. Stock from which previously printed ink has been removed through a combination of mechanical and chemical processes so that the stock can be reused.

Detail paper. Thin, good-quality, hard-sized paper that is semi-translucent. (Also called *layout paper.*)

Document manila. A low-grade, heavy board manufactured from both mechanical and sulfite pulps. To some, the term also denotes paper sizes in excess of 24 by 36 inches.

Double-faced board. Two laminated thicknesses of paperboard.

Drawing paper. Good-quality, dull-finished paper sufficiently stable to take erasures.

Duplex paper or board. A paper or paperboard that differs in colors, finish, or texture on its two sides. The difference is achieved either on the paper machine, during finishing, or by pasting together two papers or boards. Duplex paper is used widely for attention-getting appeal in advertising and direct mail.

Duplicating paper. An extremely broad category of papers, including papers used in fluid and stencil duplicating, the diazo process, electrostatic copying, and even the smaller offset presses. Each group of papers fills a specific need and possesses properties uniquely suited to the duplicating process it serves.

Enamel paper. A coated paper with a high-gloss finish, suitable for kiss impressions.

End paper. Strong, fine-quality paper, either plain or coated, and sometimes colored or marbled, used at both ends of a book. (Also called *end sheets.*)

Envelope paper. A large collection of papers which generally measure up to the demands of writing and envelope converting.

Film coated paper. See *pigmented paper.*

Fine papers. A term encompassing grades generally used for writing and book printing, including bond, ledger, cover, and book papers.

Flock paper. A specialty paper with suede-like flocking adhered to its surface.

Fluorescent paper. Paper containing fluorescent dye. This type of paper can be either colored or white. In white papers, the dyes are selected to appear "whiter than white."

Foils. Members of the package-printing family of papers, consisting of thin metals ranging in caliper from 0.00023 to 0.006 inch. Foil can be laminated with paper or paperboard to form labels, box-wraps, etc.

Free sheet. Wood pulp which has been treated and cleansed of impurities. Also, a sheet containing no groundwood.

Greaseproof paper. Wrapping paper made from chemical wood, with good water and grease resistance.

Groundwood paper. A category of papers that contain a substantial amount of groundwood fiber. These represent more than 25 percent of all paper manufactured in the U.S. Combinations of groundwood and chemical pulps have resulted in many useful printing, packaging, and converting grades, characterized by their economy and useful qualities such as high opacity, resiliency, and bulk. The most common type of groundwood paper is *newsprint.*

Gummed paper. A category that broadly includes all papers that bear an adhesive on one side of the sheet. The type of adhesive might be of a re-moistening variety, thermo-adhesive or heat-seal, or pressure-sensitive. Papers used for this purpose should be extremely hard-sized to prevent penetration of the adhesive material.

Handmade paper. Paper made by hand, usually as separate sheets with a deckle-edge finish. (Also called *mold-made paper.*)

Heat-seal paper. Those grades coated with thermoplastic adhesives utilizing synthetic resin bases that require heat rather than moisture for reactivation of the adhesive. Heat-seal papers play an important role in present-day packaging.

Illustration board. Hard-sized paper mounted on board, designed mainly for ink and watercolor uses without warping. (Also called *artists' board.*)

Impressed watermark paper. Paper with an imitation watermark made by a stereo placed on a press or smoothing roll.

Imitation handmade paper. Embossed machine-made paper, finished with special felt rollers to simulate handmade paper.

Index bristol. A type of bristol produced on the Fourdrinier machine for end uses such as booklet covers, postcards, business forms, menus—in general, whenever ruggedness, rigidity, and erasability are prime requisites. (See also *bristol.*)

India paper. Lightweight paper most commonly referred to in this country as Bible paper, but still called India paper or Oxford India, the name given to it in England where it was originally developed. (See also *Bible paper.*)

Japan paper. A specially finished, handmade Japanese paper, characterized by a mottled surface and long fiber formation.

Jute paper. A long-fibered, extremely durable, highly foldable sheet manufactured from a combination of jute plant and kraft pulps. Wrapping papers, some tags, and pattern papers are examples of jute paper.

Kraft paper. Another name for unbleached sulfate pulp, from the German *kraft,* meaning *strength.* The brown pulp is used to produce container board, wrapping and bag papers, etc., and is used in combination with other fibers such as jute.

Laminated paper. Paper joined by adhesives to other papers or boards or other materials such as aluminum foil.

Layout paper. See *detail paper.*

Ledger paper. Classified as a business paper along with bond, onionskin, tabulating board, safety papers, punch-card stock, mimeo and duplicating papers, among others. A strong sheet, ledger paper has properties akin to bond and is used for accounting and the maintenance of records.

Lithographic paper. See *offset paper.*

MICR paper. Stands for magnetic ink character recognition paper, paper that is suitable for the acceptance of this exacting magnetic ink. This paper must have high strength to withstand repeated handling and folding. Its surface must be suited to the acceptance of writing ink as well as imprinted magnetic ink and must be free of all metallic and magnetizable particles. Levelness, good stiffness, and a propensity for flatness despite continual handling are additional important properties.

Manifold paper. A lightweight sheet usually varying in basis weight from 7 to 9 pounds (17" x 22"/500) and used as carbon-copy paper, airmail stationery, special catalogs, etc. Desirable manifold properties are strength and high opacity.

Manila paper. Strong, durable, buff-colored paper, often used for strong envelopes and file folders.

Metallic paper. Foil-like paper made by several methods, among them the coating of paper with a lacquer or unpigmented adhesive followed by pigmenting or dusting of the wet surface with aluminum or bronze powder.

Mill board. Heavy board, usually used for bookbinding and box making.

Mimeograph paper. A group of grades that falls in the business paper category and is used primarily on mimeograph duplicators. It is a relatively impermanent sheet, but one that nevertheless provides satisfactory surface smoothness, opacity, and absorbency.

Mold-made paper. See *handmade paper.*

Mounting board. A laminated board, finished with good-quality paper on one or both surfaces and used for mounting photographs and prints.

Newsprint. The most-used but lowest-cost paper available for printing, and the standard stock for newspapers.

OCR bond. Paper made to function on high-speed computers and optical character recognition (OCR) equipment.

Offset packing paper. Paper stocked in calipers from 0.001 to 0.015 inches, used in offset makeready under blankets and plates to assure even printing pressure.

Offset paper. Paper produced primarily for use on offset presses, generally possessing characteristics vital to the printing process such as dimensional stability, cleanliness, pick resistance, etc. (Also called *lithographic paper*.)

Onionskin. A lightweight paper used primarily for copies in office correspondence and classified in the business papers category.

Opaque paper. Brilliant white paper with a high degree of opacity.

Outdoor poster board. A weatherproof board used for outdoor advertising signs and displays.

Papeterie. Paper manufactured from either chemical pulp or rag fibers or a combination thereof, usually both internally and externally sized, with characteristics of high opacity, good foldability, bright color, and uniform finish. The sheet is used for stationery, greeting cards, announcements, etc. Papeterie is made in white, ivory, and pastel colors predominantly and features numerous finishes.

Parchment. Historically, a sheet made from the skins of goats and other animals. Present day imitation parchment (also called *vegetable parchment*) is manufactured to resemble animal parchment by producing an unsized base stock, bathing it in sulfuric acid to gelatinize the fibers, and subsequently washing with water and an acid-neutralizing bath to produce a tightly bonded sheet with parchment qualities, such as extreme hardness of surface, high wet-strength, grease resistance, etc.

Pattern paper. Markedly stiff, strong paper of varying heavy thicknesses, made for repeated usage.

Pigmented paper. Paper with a light coating, usually applied at the size press of a paper machine, to improve the uniformity, smoothness, and printability of an ostensibly uncoated sheet. (Also called *film coated paper*.)

Plastic-laminated paper. Paper that is laminated with plastic and is used mainly for covers.

Postcard paper. A paper manufactured for the production of postcards. Postcard stock comes uncoated, coated-one-side, and even cast-coated-one-side.

Pressboard. Heavy-duty board characterized by its stiffness and denseness.

Pyroxylin paper. A stock manufactured with a sulfite base which is lacquered for special pearly, bright, iridescent, and metallic effects.

Rag-content paper. High-quality paper containing rag or cotton fibers, the content varying from 25 to 100 percent. It is so named because it was originally made from rags. (Also called *cotton-content paper*.)

Railroad bond. A heavy-duty board ranging in caliper from .018 to .024 inch, manufactured on a cylinder machine for display and sign purposes.

Register paper. The name given to a type of bond paper manufactured primarily for multi-form use.

Reinforced paper. A duplex paper sandwiching a strengthening material, with all elements bonded by asphalt or latex.

Release paper. Extremely smooth paper, glazed on one side and usually treated with silicones for use in conjunction with tacky materials.

Reproduction paper. Very good quality, coated-one-side paper, suitable for fine-screen and color printing and also used for reproduction proofs.

Safety paper. Paper used primarily for bank checks and other negotiable and legal documents. Safety paper is designed and specially treated to prevent the erasure or alteration of any writing or printing on its surface.

Stencil board. A board of high strength, rigidity, and finish, usually ink-resistant, manufactured for the making of cut-out marking stencils.

Tag board. Extremely heavy and durable paper, usually made from a combination of kraft and jute pulps.

Text paper. High-quality book papers, manufactured in a wide variety of designer finishes and colors. Many mills feature matching cover grades for selective advertising and direct mail items.

Tissue paper. A term encompassing papers of extreme lightness and transparency, such as grades used for napkins and bathroom tissue.

Translucent paper. Paper primarily manufactured as master copies for blueprint and ozalid reproduction methods.

Tympan paper. A makeready packing paper manufactured in calipers ranging from .003 to .015 inch. Extremely uniform, the sheet also possesses high tensile strength, and when treated is totally resistant to oil, ink, and chemicals. Because of these and other exacting requirements, tympan paper is made expressly for printing makeready use.

Vegetable parchment. Tough cellulose made to imitate an animal parchment. (See also *parchment*.)

Velvet paper. Paper sprayed or coated with a flocking powder to resemble velvet. (Also *flock paper*.)

Watercolor paper. Uncoated paper, often handmade, suitable for watercolor use.

Writing paper. A general term applied to papers used for writing purposes.

Xerographic paper. Photocopying paper specially suited for printing by the electrostatic process.

HOW PAPER IS MADE

The information for this article and the accompanying "papermaking chart" (fig. 12.1) have been supplied by Boise Cascade.

The basic component of paper is cellulose fiber, which is generally obtained from wood. In parts of the world where wood is not readily available, other fiber sources of varying cellulose content, such as jute, bamboo, hemp, straw, or rope, may be used. An important fiber source, used either by itself or in combination with other fibers, is cotton, which makes for a strong paper such as rag bond or onionskin. Many other materials besides fibers are used in the papermaking process: millions of gallons of clean water, many thousands of tons of chemicals like sulfur and chlorine, and minerals such as clay.

Because of raw material shortages during the last decade, much of the fiber for paper and paperboard manufacturing has been obtained from the previously wasted wood chips from sawmills and plywood mills and through the recycling of various grades of waste paper. However, the primary source throughout the world continues to be wood in the form of logs, in sizes and species that cannot be used effectively for other wood products.

The first step in the papermaking process is the arrival of the logs, waste, or chips, by rail, water, and truck at the paper mill. Logs are stored in the water or mill yard to await removal of the bark either by high-powered jets of water or by a large revolving barker drum. Chips are stored in piles in the mill yard.

PRODUCING PULP

Depending upon the requirements and capabilities of the paper mill, the wood will be made into pulp by either mechanical or chemical means. In mechanical or *groundwood* pulp, the two main ingredients of wood, cellulose fibers and lignin, are both present. In the chemical pulps, *sulfite* and *sulfate*, only the fiber is present, for the lignin, which tends to discolor and weaken the pulp, is removed. Mechanical and chemical pulp can be produced in either a bleached or unbleached condition.

Groundwood pulp

Groundwood pulp is produced by (1) grinding barked and cleaned logs against a grindstone or pulpstone to reduce them to a mass of short fibers, or (2) passing chips of a desired species through a refining operation. The second method usually produces a stronger paper. Groundwood papers produced by both methods are economical, because all of the wood is used in the process, and they have good absorbency, bulk, opacity, and compressibility, although they lack brightness and strength. Newsprint is an example.

Chemical pulp

Sulfite and sulfate pulp are produced chemically, by cooking the wood in acid or alkaline liquors to remove the lignin, resins, gums, and other components so that the pulp is made up only of cellulose fibers for greater permanence and strength. The logs for chemical pulping are first passed through the rapidly revolving knives of the chipper and cut into chips one-half to one inch long. These chips are passed through flat, vibrating screens to remove unusable sawdust, slivers, and larger wood chunks, yielding chips suitable for pulping.

Sulfite pulp is produced by cooking chips of softwood coniferous trees like spruce, pine, and hemlock in a sodium, magnesium, ammonia, or calcium acid sulfite liquor. Bond papers were originally all made from this pulp because of its strength and essentially bright color in an unbleached state. However, technological advances in the sulfate (kraft) bleaching process have somewhat changed this.

Sulfate (or kraft) pulp is produced in a cooking liquor of sodium hydrosulfide and caustic soda from a wide range of woods, including the more plentiful hardwoods. Unbleached kraft is used for wrapping papers and container board in which strength, and not color, is a primary consideration. Bleached sulfate, depending on the degree of bleaching, can be used in such products as milk carton board, bristols, and bond.

The chips are cooked in these liquors under steam pressure in huge steel digesters from two to ten hours to obtain pulp, a mass of separated cellulose fibers.

BLEACHING AND WASHING

Next the pulp is refined in a series of washing and screening processes, which are very important in producing a strong, clean sheet of paper. In the thickener most of the water is removed from the pulp, leaving it thick and firm. A revolving wire cylinder picks up the watery pulp on one side. Vacuum draws the water through the fine mesh into the inside, and the damp pulp is scraped off the cylinder on the other side.

Most pulp is bleached to change its natural tan color, and this is done in a series of large towers (bleaching cells). Giant screws thoroughly mix the chlorine bleaching agents with the pulp and constantly agitate the whole mixture. After each bleaching stage, a washer rinses out most of the excess impurities.

After being bleached, the pulp passes through centri-cleaners, which are shaped like long, skinny cones. As the watery pulp whirls around centrifugally, tiny impurities are discharged out the bottom of each cone. Clean pulp is forced through the center of each cone and out the top.

In the final washing, all the remaining impurities are removed. The washer is a revolving wire mesh cylinder with a vacuum on the inside. The pulp is picked up on

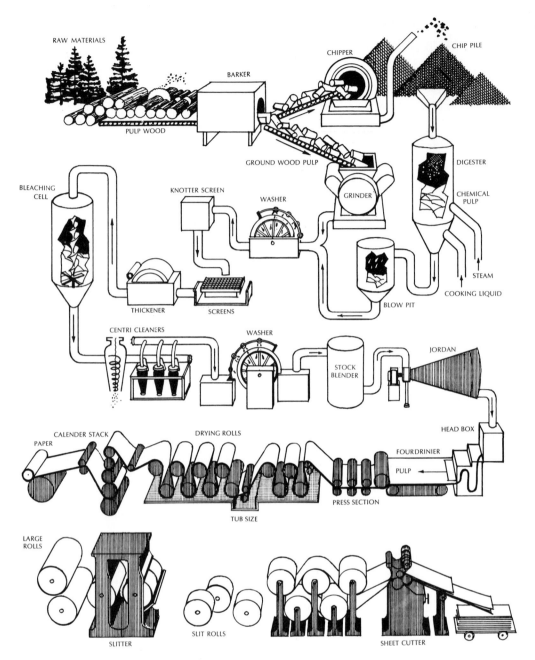

Figure 12.1: Papermaking chart. *Courtesy of Boise Cascade.*

one side, and streams of water spray on it from all angles. The bleach rinses through the screen, and the clean pulp is deposited on the other side.

REFINING AND SIZING

For certain stronger, harder papers, the pulp fibers have to be made shorter and frayed to help them interlock with one another. This is achieved by high-speed cutting and brushing in a conical Jordan or other refining machine.

Depending upon the kinds of paper characteristics desired to make the paper suitable for its end use, additional materials are mixed into the pulp. *Rosin size* is added to make the paper more resistant to water, ink, or weather. The three sizing groups into which the industry classifies papers (and examples of each) are: (1) *waterleaf* or unsized (blotting paper), (2) *slack-sized* or weakly sized (newsprint), and (3) *hard-sized* or strongly sized (bond paper). Fillers, which fill the spaces between fibers, include clays, which add smoothness, opacity, and ink receptivity to the final sheet, and

458

titanium dioxide, which adds brightness and opacity. Colored dyes and pigments are added to produce colored papers.

FORMING PULP INTO SHEETS

The Fourdrinier machine was developed in England by Henry and Sealy Fourdrinier in the early nineteenth century, and although it has been highly improved since then, the process remains essentially the same.

The pulp, which is about 99 percent water, is pumped through the headbox onto the *wet end* and spread evenly over the fine wire mesh moving belt. The screen vibrates from side to side as the water is drained and sucked through, and the fibers interlock to form one continuous sheet. In general, the lighter the stock to be produced, the greater the speed of the belt. However, the production rate of the paper machine is directly related to the drying capacity.

As the sheet moves off the wire belt, at a point when it is still wet enough to be compressed, it passes under the *dandy roll* which improves its formation. The dandy roll, a light wire mesh cylinder, may have lettering or a design on its surface for watermarking and for producing laid or wove markings.

When the newly formed sheet leaves the screen it is pressed between heavy rotary presses to squeeze out more water and to help level and compact its surface. Then it passes into the *dry end,* and runs over the steam-heated, cast-iron drying rolls, 4 to 6 feet in diameter. When the moisture content is down to approximately 4 to 5 percent, the sheet may be tub-sized by coating it with a surface sizing. Papers which need strength, body, and better printing qualities are given this treatment.

CALENDERING

Certain grades of paper need a higher finish than others. To achieve this, the continuous web is run between the polished steel rolls of the vertical calender stack on the end of the paper machine. The number of rolls, or nips, used in the stack varies according to the grade of paper being made. The more rolls used, the higher the finish. As soon as it comes off the calender stack, the paper is wound onto a reel. Then it is usually rewound and slit to form rolls of the proper width and diameter.

Supercalendering, an auxiliary calendering process which takes place off the machine and after the paper has been wound, gives an even higher finish. The supercalender rolls, stacked vertically, consist of alternating rolls of steel and cotton or of steel and paper. Supercalendering is used for coated as well as uncoated papers. (For information about coated papers, see "How Paper Is Coated," which follows, and "Knowing Paper Finishes," page 461.)

PACKAGING AND SHIPPING

More and more printing and paper converting equipment is designed to use a continuous web of paper from a roll. Most paper is shipped in rolls to be used on high-speed printing presses or to be manufactured into various paper products, such as envelopes, cartons, or grocery and merchandise bags.

If a customer wants sheets, a cutter in the finishing room accurately trims webs of paper into sheets as they unroll. Counters check the number of sheets as they pile up. Trimmers then cut them to the exact size called for in the customer's order, and they are packaged and shipped.

HOW PAPER IS COATED
Kenneth B. Latimer, GRAPHIC ARTS CONSULTANT

Coated papers are in great demand today because they provide a higher quality printing surface than the fibrous surface of uncoated papers. Perhaps the largest use of coated papers is for publications, particularly weekly and monthly magazines with high-quality, four-color printing of both advertising and editorial matter. In addition, advertising brochures, annual reports, playing cards, menus, and many other items use coated papers to achieve high-quality printing. Many types of food-containing cartons, particularly for frozen foods, are coated and printed in four colors.

COATING INGREDIENTS

Coatings are composed essentially of a pigment and a binder. The pigment is used to produce a smooth, non-fibrous surface; the binder is used to hold the pigment to the paper.

Pigments

Pigments are usually composed of clay; but frequently mixes composed of titanium, calcium carbonate, talc, satin white, or barytes in varying proportions or with a clay foundation are used. Today, clay producers offer a wide variety of products designed to provide an optimum printing surface with controlled smoothness, gloss, and ink hold-out properties.

Binders

The binder, or adhesive, which holds the pigment to the paper, must resist the tackiness or pull of the ink and, in the case of offset printing, must resist the

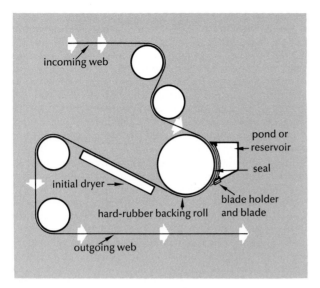

Figure 12.2: Pond-type trailing blade coater.

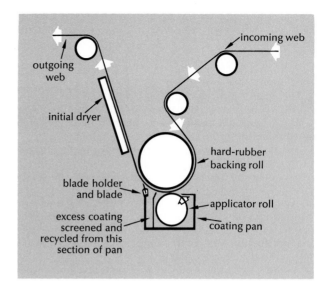

Figure 12.3: Inverted-blade trailing blade coater.

softening and washing effect of water used in the offset process. Perhaps the most widely used binder is cornstarch in various grades, highly modified to control viscosity and operating characteristics. The classic binder used to be casein, but price considerations have reduced its use. Soya bean protein is widely used in the carton industry. Latex (styrene-butadiene) is increasingly used in the offset field because of the smoothness and water resistance of the coating produced. Polyvinyl alcohol is increasing in use in gravure printing where resistance to tack or pick is less of a problem than in letterpress or offset.

COATING METHODS

There are a number of methods of coating paper, but today three systems are the most widely used. All three can be used on the paper machine or as separate off-machine operations.

Trailing blade coater

The trailing blade coater is probably the most widely used method of applying coating. A large-diameter, smooth, hard-rubber backing roll supports the moving web or sheet as it comes in contact with the trailing blade. Modern off-machine trailing blade coaters attain speeds of over 3,500 feet per minute.

In the *pond* type (fig. 12.2), a pond or reservoir of coating is held in contact with the moving sheet. The lower or trailing edge of the pond is formed by a flexible steel blade which regulates the descending flow of coating to the moving sheet. The pressure of the blade against the backing roll can be adjusted to control the amount of coating released.

In the *inverted blade* type (fig. 12.3), the applicator roll below the backing roll covers the moving sheet with an excess of coating. The blade, which is held in an adjustable holder, smooths the coating onto the sheet and returns the excess to the coating pan below.

In a refined version, known as a jet fountain applica-

tor, the coating is extruded onto the sheet, removed by a doctor blade, and refiltered before being reapplied. In twin-blade jet fountain coaters, opposing jet fountains and opposing blades permit coating both sides of the paper at the same time. Another version uses the jet fountain applicator on one side and a multiroll differential-speed coater on the other side, simultaneously coating both sides of the paper.

Air knife coater

The air knife coater (fig. 12.4) is used on paperboard, paper, and films. An excess of coating is applied to the incoming web by an applicator roll or other device. As the web subsequently passes around the backing roll, a carefully controlled air jet or "knife" of air removes the excess and leaves a coating covering the substrate at the desired weight. Control of the angle, thickness, and pressure of the air jet is crucial.

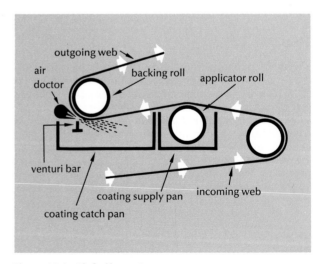

Figure 12.4: Air knife coater.

460

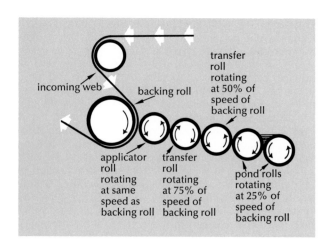

Figure 12.5: Roll coater.

Roll coater

The roll coater (fig. 12.5) has been developed to a high level of efficiency and quality in the publication field. It has been extensively used as an on-machine method. The roll coater is frequently followed by trailing blade coaters when a double coating is desired.

Essentially, the roll coating process may be thought of as a method of "printing" the coating on the sheet. Coaters consist of a series or train of rolls which transfer the coating from a pond to the sheet. Roll speeds increase from roll to roll through the train up to the last roll, the applicator roll, which usually runs slightly above web speed. The speed of each roll, as well as the pressure between rolls, can be controlled in order to achieve even distribution of the coating and control of the coat weight.

There are many variations of roll coaters. Train rolls may be all rubber or alternately rubber and chrome-plated steel. Roll speeds and pressures between rolls can also vary. Both sides may be coated at the same time by running the web between two backing rolls, which become applicators, each of which is fed with a train of rolls.

ADDITIONAL PROCESSING

After coating, the paper is usually supercalendered to produce the desired smoothness and gloss for the end use. (See "How Paper Is Made," page 457.)

Cast coating is an additional coating process which gives the paper an extremely glossy finish for specialty uses. The paper is passed under pressure against a polished, usually steam-heated drum. These papers are not supercalendered.

KNOWING PAPER FINISHES
Thomas E. Hess, THE BECKETT PAPER COMPANY

Whatever the ultimate objective of a printed piece, a proper selection of paper can help produce a better job. The finish of the paper—its smoothness or texture—must be carefully considered. Coordinating the selection of paper with design, illustration, and type in the initial planning will increase the overall effectiveness of the end product.

Selecting the right paper for the job is not an easy task. There are so many colors, textures, brand names, and other practical considerations that it is sometimes hard to know where to begin. Paper can help convey a mood; it can be subtle or exciting, official or informal, glamorous or strictly utilitarian. Questions concerning availability, cost, and printability are important considerations. Finding the right surface, the right texture, or the right color can be a critical and time-consuming job.

UNCOATED AND COATED PAPERS

Basically there are two types of paper surfaces: *uncoated* and *coated*. Both uncoated and coated papers are used extensively for book, publication, and commercial printing. One has a thin film of coating sealing its surface while the other does not. Within these two categories are a myriad of different finishes.

Uncoated papers

Uncoated papers provide a wide range of papers—book papers, offset papers, opaque papers, and text and cover papers. Text and cover papers are of special interest and, if properly selected, can add distinction to a printed piece. Text papers provide texture, bulk, and increased opacity. They are available in a wide range of colors and in a multitude of finishes from the very rough surface of felt-marked paper to very smooth English or machine finish. Cover papers provide strength and protection as well as prestige to a printed piece. Their special characteristics provide an excellent background for die cutting, blind embossing, and other mechanical operations. Excellent printed results are possible on uncoated papers by letterpress, offset, or screen printing.

Coated papers

Coating is applied to the paper to level out the hills and valleys on the surface. There are many coating formulations in use by paper manufacturers and several methods of applying the coating to the surface of the paper. (See "How Paper Is Coated," page 459.) Whether the coating is applied by the roller, blade, or air-knife method, the objective is a smooth and level surface. The coated surface may be further polished in several ways to produce various finishes. Although most coated papers are available in white only, there are a few manufacturers who offer coated papers in colors.

Coated papers are desirable when very fine screens are used for halftone reproduction. In general, the finer the halftones to be printed, the smoother the paper should be. As the size of the halftone dot becomes extremely fine, as in a 150-line screen, it is necessary that the paper be as smooth as possible so that the dot can reproduce as sharply as possible.

Coated papers are at their best when used for four-color reproduction by offset. They are widely used in books, publications, catalogs, and other advertising and product information materials.

IDENTIFYING PAPER FINISHES

Because there are so many terms used to identify paper finishes in both uncoated and coated papers, it is a good idea to look at samples of different types of finishes to become more familiar with them.

Finishes for uncoated papers

Listed below are some of the terms most frequently used to describe the classes of uncoated finishes available. Antique, eggshell, vellum, machine, and English finishes are the common types of finishes applied on the paper machine.

Antique, eggshell, vellum. These terms are often used interchangeably to refer to uncoated papers with a rough textured surface. Each of these finishes is lightly polished but preserves its bulk and distinctive surface texture. All three are soft to the feel and reflect little light. Because they reduce glare, they are easier to read and make a good choice for printed materials with heavy type coverage. Their relative bulkiness provides them with a feeling of richness and quality. Antique is the roughest, followed by eggshell, which has a pitted texture, and vellum, which is the smoothest of the three.

Machine and English. Machine finish (MF) and English finish (EF) differ from the antique finishes in that they are smoother and more highly polished, having passed through additional "nips" in the calendering operation. English is generally smoother than machine finish. Although both provide a smoother surface for halftone reproduction than the other finishes, they are more often used for line art reproduction. Many text and cover grades are offered in these finishes. Today, both are often referred to as "smooth finish."

In addition to this standard range of finishes, a number of special finishes are available. These include supercalendered, felt, laid, and embossed finishes.

Supercalendered finish. This is a very shiny, smooth finish which is obtained by passing the paper through the alternating steel and cotton or steel and paper supercalendering rolls. This operation smooths and levels the paper, giving an excellent printing surface for letterpress halftones.

Felt finishes. This type of finish is obtained on the paper machine with marking felts which transfer their designs to the paper when it is partly dried. The designs imitate old handmade paper surfaces.

Laid finish. This special finish features a pattern of fine vertical and horizontal lines. These are put onto the paper by wires on a special roller, the dandy roll, on the paper machine. A laid finish gives a very distinctive and readily identifiable finish to the paper. It is used often for stationery, invitations, prestige brochures, and other printed communications where an impression of quality is desired.

Embossed finishes. Embossed finishes are applied to the paper after it comes off the paper machine. A wide variety of embossing patterns are available which can create any number of interesting effects. Embossing of the paper surface is accomplished by passing the paper between two rollers, one of which stamps (or *embosses*) the pattern onto one side of the sheet. This process is then repeated for the other side. Paper manufacturers offer a variety of embossed finish papers with such descriptive names as Coral, Satin Shell, Linen, Spanish Grain, Emboweave, Stucco, Leather, and Pinseal. The wide selection of embossing finishes can be used to enhance printed materials such as product sheets, magazine inserts, brochures, menus, posters, and folders.

Finishes for coated papers

Coated papers are available in a variety of different finishes. These papers vary according to gloss (shininess) and special characteristics of manufacture. The term *enamel* is sometimes used to denote heavier grades of coated paper. Listed below are descriptions of the most popular coated paper finishes and their applications.

Glossy coated. High gloss is achieved by passing the paper through the alternate steel and paper rollers of the supercalender under pressure. Glossy coated papers are principally used for magazines, advertising pieces, and sales brochures, where four-color reproduction is widely used. The high gloss surface is excellent for exact reproduction of fine-screen halftones. The major disadvantage of these papers is that they are less readable because of harsh glare in the type areas.

Dull coated. These papers are passed through a special supercalendering machine which imparts a low level of gloss to the surface, making it possible to achieve excellent fine-screen halftones while at the same time providing a readable surface for typed areas. Dull coated papers are widely used for annual reports.

Matte coated. These papers are fully coated but are not supercalendered. The matte coating and lower polish produce a finish resembling that of uncoated papers but without their bulking characteristics or texture. The matte coated surface is fully sealed, making possible fine-screen halftone reproduction and full-color reproduction by offset. Like dull coated papers, they have the advantage of reducing glare, and thus are ideal for folders, brochures, and booklets with large amounts of type matter.

Embossed coated. Like uncoated papers, coated papers can be embossed after being made and are available in many patterns. Usually, coated papers are more lightly embossed than uncoated text and cover papers, but they offer the same three-dimensional effect for use in booklets, brochures, annual reports, and other types of publications.

Cast coated. These papers have a highly polished surface with mirror-like reflectance and provide the highest gloss of the coated papers. Cast coated papers are widely used for annual report covers and for the reproduction of extremely fine-screen halftones.

Coated-one-side. Papers coated on one side are widely used for labels. One side is left uncoated to provide a more compatible surface for application of glues and adhesives.

Duplex papers

These interesting and colorful papers greatly expand the specifier's selection opportunities. A *duplex* is produced by pasting two sheets of paper into a single sheet, thus permitting the use of two different colors or finishes simultaneously. An endless variety of unusual combinations can be produced—blue on one side, white on the other; antique finish on one side, embossed on the other; and so on. Duplex papers are used in combination with other papers in folders, booklets, and brochures or may be used by themselves as invitations or announcements.

CHOOSING A PAPER FINISH

The vast array of finishes available can make the selection of paper a complex and time-consuming job. Many variables—the kind of printed piece to be produced, its purpose, and the special requirements it must meet—are involved in the wise selection of paper. For the specifier who is not fully conversant with the paper field, consulting a paper merchant can be very helpful in planning a job. The paper merchant can save the specifier hours of searching because he normally represents a number of paper mills and is knowledgeable about a wide selection of printing papers, many of which are stocked in his own warehouse. Since many paper mills maintain extensive printed sample libraries for customers, he can also provide printed samples of papers he recommends for the job at hand.

USING COLORED PAPER

Michael P. Corey, CHAMPION PAPERS

Colored paper is a powerful design element. When used properly and with good taste, it can enhance a printed message and increase its impact. Used indiscriminately, colored paper reduces overall effectiveness and in many instances may actually be counter-productive. Color communicates by evoking complex sets of conscious thoughts and unconscious emotions, in many instances quite powerful. The challenge to the paper user and the designer is to make sure that color is used to elicit a positive response, and the challenge to the printer is to successfully produce the desired effect by using the proper materials and methods. As we shall see, both of the challenges are difficult ones.

THE ROLE OF COLOR

Color is used in our everyday lives for two main reasons—function and aesthetics. The same holds true for paper. In business papers, for instance, a standard color sequence of blue, pink, canary, and white assists in coding and collating business records. Other papers for fine printing applications are chosen strictly for their visual properties, similar to their use in the fashion industry. Color availability in paper, in fact, tends to parallel color trends in fashion, but with a year or two time lag due to manufacturing and inventory considerations. Many paper colors are offered, using the same merchandising principles found in the fabric industry. Interest is usually added to traditional neutral lines by mixing in bold, trendy colors for the primary purpose of attracting attention. Year after year, however, the neutral colors enjoy the widest acceptance.

Different schools of thought exist concerning the role of colored papers in design. One idea is to create harmony by matching colors for a particular booklet or brochure in both text and cover weights. Another stresses the use of complementary colors, a bold attention-getting one for the cover and a softer one for enhancing readability in the body of the piece. Still another opinion calls for a compromise, recommending the use of duplex cover papers which feature an eye-stopping color on one side of the sheet and a subdued color on the other side that matches a corresponding text paper. Most paper mills adhere to one of the above philosophies, and their lines of paper reflect it.

SELECTING A COLORED PAPER

Thousands of different colored papers are manufactured by mills and sold through distributors. It should be remembered when planning a job around a particular colored paper that more time should be allowed for delivery. The cost of inventorying large quantities of colored papers in all of the standard sizes is in many instances prohibitive. Therefore, most distributors maintain minimal stock on most colors they carry, relying upon the mills' master rolls as a backup. If a large quantity of a particular color is needed, the mill might be able to supply it if sufficient stock is on hand. Otherwise, the paper would have to come out of a manufacturing run. For a mill producing hundreds of colors, the delivery time might be considerable. Colors are generally run in cycles at large mills; some colors may be run only once or twice a year. Some small mills have the ability to accept relatively small orders for a particular color and be in a position to deliver them within a few weeks. The critical consideration is to plan ahead.

There are many ways of selecting a particular colored paper for a specific job. Here is a suggested chronology of paper specification events that may help prevent problems:

• Select a colored paper at the conceptualization stage of a project. Paper affects all other design and printing variables, such as artwork, typeface, ink colors, and plates.

• Search for the color by considering all the types of colored papers available, including text, cover, business, envelope, label, and giftwrap papers. Sometimes specialty papers offer interesting effects when used imaginatively as fly-sheets, for text applications, or laminated to board stocks for covers.

• Do a thumbnail sketch of the project to see if the visual idea works with the color chosen.

• Have a full-size comprehensive dummy made to obtain a more accurate preview of the end-product's look and feel.

• Ask for printed samples on the particular color to see how it accepts inks.

• Review color-on-color paper and ink guides to select the best inks for the job. Acetate sheets preprinted with colors positioned over a colored stock are helpful, but keep in mind that ink printed on paper will have a different character due to such factors as ink hold-out and the physics of color.

• If possible, plan on proofing the job. A few extra dollars spent at the beginning of a job may mean better results because proofing allows for color modifications.

A word of caution is in order. Colors vary in their degree of permanence. Some of the brightest colors are fluorescent and will age rather quickly; others, when exposed to direct sunlight, will fade dramatically. Find out as much as you can about a particular stock, and evaluate it in terms of your end-use requirements.

PRINTING ON COLORED PAPER

Printing color-on-color designs is one of the most demanding jobs a printer can process. To facilitate his job, make sure that he is given a large enough swatch of ink to match. Tell him whether you want to print the particular color on a colored paper and let the printed color vary as it is bound to do, or if the swatch you are giving him is the printed color you actually want to see. In the second case, he will mix his inks to achieve the desired result.

Remember to provide your printer with swatches of ink on the type of stock you plan to use. For instance, don't provide your printer with a swatch of color on coated paper if the job is going to be printed on uncoated paper, or vice versa. Also, if you are providing him with an ink formula based on a printed color on a white paper, be aware that the ink color will change when printed on a colored paper.

Some papers require the use of special inks due to their surface characteristics. Appearances are frequently misleading. Two papers that look alike might in fact have quite different printing surfaces; on one the ink might tend to sit on the surface and take longer to dry than on the other. Ink suppliers can be most helpful in providing guidance about specific inks for specific substrates, such as foils and plastics, and cast-coated, blade-coated, and uncoated papers.

Printing processes also vary in their ability to execute particular designs on colored paper. A designer may want to print a bright white graphic element on a bold, glossy colored paper: one impression of white by offset lithography probably will yield a gray, while one impression by screen printing will yield the desired result. Know the capabilities of your printing processes.

CREATIVE APPLICATIONS

Colored paper is a canvas. Used creatively, it can yield powerful results. Maximum benefits can be derived by the designer and printer working closely together. Imaginative alternatives might include: using four-color process, when appropriate, to duplicate the feel of a textile or painting; using three-color process utilizing the paper as the fourth color; die cutting a design into an unprinted sheet to show a printed message underneath; embossing a pattern to simulate a texture; silver stamping, bronzing, or varnishing a design instead of using an ink. The alternatives are endless. Caution must be taken, however. Without good taste and moderation, the power of colored paper might be diluted. Used with intelligence, the results might be multiplied a thousandfold.

BIG. FAST. COMPETITIVE. THE RIS TEAM.

There's an attitude at Ris that starts at the top. And affects everyone on the team. It's that we're the best in the industry. Because we're big. We're fast. And we're competitive. Over one hundred major mills serve as sources. We've got eleven distribution points from Maine to Virginia. And Ris prices are competitive with the best in the industry. We don't actually do a lot of hard selling. Because we spend most of our time doing a lot of hard servicing. Call big, fast, competitive Ris. In paper distribution the Ris Team is the first team.

RIS DELIVERS

Albany · Allentown · Baltimore · Boston · Concord · New Haven · New York · Philadelphia · Providence · Richmond · Rocky Hill · Washington

USING LIGHTWEIGHT PAPER

Ralph W. Mirkin, ALLIED PAPER INCORPORATED

From the time of the printing of the Gutenberg Bible, ways were sought to produce the approximately 1,500 pages in a portable yet readable volume. Lightweight paper was first developed, and used extensively, for this purpose. It was also used for such publications as dictionaries and encyclopedias to reduce their bulk. In recent years, because of increased demand and improved technology, the market has expanded considerably. Lightweight papers are no longer limited to "Bible" papers but include a wide variety of printing papers which are now available in numerous grades, weights, and finishes. A review of Bible paper requirements, however, should serve as a useful introduction to lightweights.

BIBLE PAPER

Bible papers must be light and thin. In order to publish a portable book of 1,500 pages, most Bibles are printed on paper that bulks in a range from 1,000 to nearly 2,000 pages per inch. The weight of this paper falls roughly in the 17- to 30-pound range (25" x 38"/500). Until the 1960's nearly all Bibles were printed by sheet-fed letterpress at slow production speeds on printing equipment that had to be adjusted specifically for running lightweight paper; binding equipment as well had to be operated at slow speeds to accommodate this paper.

Reducing basis weight normally results in reducing certain desirable paper characteristics, such as strength and opacity. Paper mills compensated for this strength reduction in Bible papers by using high-quality pulps with great fiber strength. For many years Bibles were printed on thin, strong paper called *India paper*. India paper was made from fibers of flax or hemp, or from cotton rags (before synthetic fibers were mixed with cotton). Very little Bible paper is now made from flax, hemp, or cotton; wood pulps of very high quality are used. To improve opacity, fillers are used to reduce the translucency of the wood fibers. There is a limit to the amount of filler which can be used since the paper can retain only a small percentage of filler materials (which do not mesh with the pulp fibers) and because too great a filler concentration would reduce paper strength and stiffness. The limit on filler concentration imposes a limit on opacity. In Bibles a slightly reduced opacity is not detrimental since the type of one page backs up the type of another. Copy with halftones, solids, and large white spaces, however, cannot be printed acceptably on 20-pound paper without careful layout preparation.

DEVELOPMENTS IN LIGHTWEIGHTS

The need for lightweight papers increased during the late 1950's when postage rates began to escalate. With each increase in first class mail came a comparable increase in bulk rates, magazine rates, and book rates. As the postal rates increased, many people involved in the production of catalogs, books, and advertising mailings called for a reduction in basis weights of the paper used. In addition, increased page counts of books, directories, and indexes encouraged the use of lightweight papers.

Faced with changing needs, the technology of the 1960's turned toward paper that had changed very little since the early 1900's. Lightweight letterpress paper was manufactured with a surface sized for offset, but unfortunately the high-speed offset presses could not handle the paper originally developed to run on slow letterpress equipment. At this time, however, mills that had been manufacturing Bible paper began to develop various grades of lightweight paper suitable for the high-speed offset process as well as for the slower letterpress method.

Lightweight printing paper has gone through several improvement stages, including the addition of effective sizing materials, better fillers for increased opacity, and improved wood pulps, to provide for the printing characteristics necessary in a paper to be used for a wide range of applications.

As a group, lightweight printing papers fall within the 17- to 40-pound weight range. Bible papers are in the 17- to 30-pound range; but a great quantity of lightweight printing paper falls in the 30- to 40-pound category. This category, for which there is a large market today, includes paper used for such publications as handbooks, textbooks, anthologies, dictionaries, catalogs, and indexes.

It should be noted that, in addition to printing papers, a variety of lightweight bond, manifold, onionskin, and writing papers are available. These other types of lightweight papers should not be confused with the lightweight printing papers discussed here.

CONSIDERATIONS IN USING LIGHTWEIGHTS

With the increasing need to use lightweights to offset high postage, shipping, and storage costs and to provide a more portable product, more production people will turn toward papers totally unfamiliar to them. There are still certain drawbacks that must be considered in any decision to use lightweights.

Layout

Although opacity has been improved, lightweights require careful layout preparation of type, halftones, and solids to overcome problems of show-through that may detract from the printed message. Backing halftones with screens and type with type, and avoiding white space with type or line drawings on the reverse side, should be considered in lightweight preparation.

Printing

Some care must be taken in the handling of lightweight papers, and the printer must be prepared to make the adjustments necessary to overcome minor paper defects. Paper should be conditioned properly, according to conditioning formulas which are adapted for various weather conditions; and skids, rolls, and cartons should be covered after they are opened. Feeding adjustments should be made to compensate for reduced paper weight. Air blasts and vacuum should be reduced, and feed rollers should be adjusted to prevent overdriving the paper on the feed board. For offset printing, ink tack should be reduced and impression pressure should be increased to produce the best printed results. Reducing the flow of fountain water will help to prevent curling. For best letterpress results, a "kiss" impression is necessary since the reduced bulk of lightweight paper provides very little paper to absorb a heavy impression. Static electricity which may be present in both heavy and lightweight papers will hinder smooth press performance as the basis weight is reduced. Such auxiliary equipment as mechanical static eliminators and sprays usually help to provide an even pile of delivered paper. On web presses, web tension should be maintained uniformly across the web, and oven dryer temperatures should be kept as low as possible.

Binding

In the bindery, proper care must be taken with folding equipment to prevent erratic feeding and wrinkling. One of the great advantages of lightweight paper is its ability to be folded into 32-, 48-, and 64-page signatures. Air should be released by perforating properly to help prevent gusset-forming wrinkles.

Manufacture

The responsibility for producing a high-quality printed piece on lightweight paper requires care and craftsmanship not only on the part of the printer and binder, but also on the part of the papermaker. Press performance is affected greatly by defects in lightweight paper, such as curl, baggy rolls, and wavy edges. The papermaker must make lightweight papers with uniformity across the web and throughout the run to prevent an uneven caliper profile, moisture imbalance, weight variation, and opacity variation.

Cost

In planning the total budget for a printed piece, all costs should be considered to help in the selection of a particular grade of paper from among several alternatives. Included in these considerations should be not only the price of paper, printing, and binding, but also the various distribution costs involved in getting the printed piece into the hands of the ultimate consumer. Very often the additional cost of using lightweight paper will be more than offset by the reduced cost of postage and other distribution charges. For example, if 50-pound offset is used for a small catalog with a total weight of 10,000 pounds for all catalogs shipped, a substitution of 35-pound paper would reduce the total weight of the catalogs to 7,000 pounds, a reduction of 30% in weight. This reduction could save over $1,000 in postage for the same number of catalogs. This kind of cost analysis will help determine the best choice of basis weight for a particular piece.

LOOKING AHEAD

At one time the standard uses for lightweight printing paper included Bibles, dictionaries, encyclopedias, insurance rate books, and pharmaceutical inserts. Today with the improvements in high-speed printing presses and in lightweight paper manufacturing techniques, we find that the uses for "Bible" paper have extended into diverse fields such as textbooks, directories, direct mail, and industrial catalogs. The information explosion continues, and in the future more uses will develop as the costs of shipping, mailing, and storage increase. The technology is now available to produce adequate lightweight substitutes for many heavier papers, and printers are learning to overcome the minor drawbacks inherent in running lightweight grades.

TWIN-WIRE PAPER MACHINES
Kenneth B. Latimer, GRAPHIC ARTS CONSULTANT

As a result of considerable research and development over the past 25 years aimed at improving the quality of printing papers, a number of new papermaking machines known as "twin-wire" machines are now in operation.

Since the early nineteenth century, the Fourdrinier paper machine has been the device for producing practically all newsprint, book paper, and magazine paper. The process has been vastly improved over the years, but the principle has changed very little. Paper stock, which consists of about 99 percent water, is delivered to a moving endless wire screen, and is dewatered downwards. Because of the uni-directional removal of water on the wire, the top and bottom surfaces of the

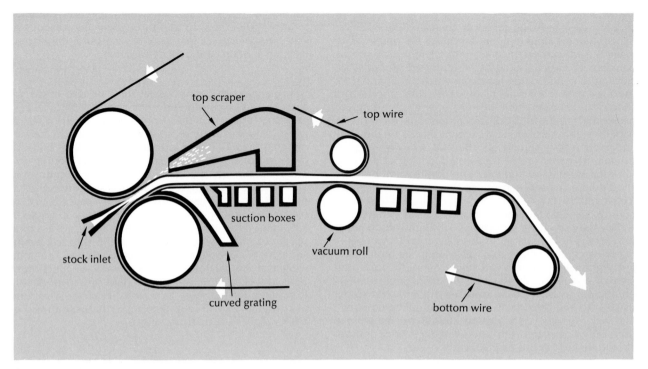

Figure 12.6: Time Inc. twin-wire machine.

sheet differ in printing quality. The wire side retains a wire mark which can be covered only by a rather heavy layer of coating.

In the publication paper field, the increasing use of four-color printing particularly emphasized the shortcomings of the base sheet produced on the Fourdrinier machine. Some kinds of four-color pictures simply could not be printed on the wire side with a satisfactory result. In addition, show-through of images from one side to the other was a serious problem. It was caused by differences in ink receptivity on the two sides and by lack of opacity in the sheet.

These printing problems were becoming more evident at the same time that postal rates were starting to climb. The significant rise in postal costs in the late 1950's added impetus to the development of lightweight publication paper. Twin-wire machines offered, in addition, the possibility of a high degree of uniformity in terms of strength, formation, opacity, porosity, and print quality. They also had great potential for web speeds in the 3,000 to 4,000 feet per minute range and for greatly increased tonnage with little or no increase in labor.

It is interesting to note that between 1955 and 1959 four separate groups in North America began research and development of twin-wire machines. All four groups developed commercial machines and obtained patents on various aspects of the machinery.

The original stimulus for research of twin-wire machines was the success of the "Inverformer," a machine with multiple wires (a long base wire and four separate top wires) developed in England by the St. Anns Board Mill in the mid-1950's for the production of multi-ply board. The research in twin-wire machines, however,

was directed to the manufacture of newsprint, directory, and lightweight coated publication papers.

Since wire mark is a problem, one might question the desirability of producing paper with two wire sides. However, the product generally shows a much reduced wire mark since the water is removed through both sides instead of all one way as in the Fourdrinier.

Figures 12.6 through 12.11 are schematics of the configurations of six twin-wire machines discussed below. Each schematic shows the configuration of the wet end, the section of the paper machine where the wires are situated.

THE TIME INC. PILOT MACHINE

As a major publisher of coated paper magazines, Time Inc. was vitally concerned with both printing quality and postal costs. In 1955 they began a major research effort aimed at reducing publication paper weight from the 45-pound to the 30- to 32-pound level. The program was twofold: (1) to develop lightweight, high-opacity coatings with superior print quality, and (2) to develop a lightweight, high-opacity, high-groundwood-content base sheet. The base sheet research soon led to a pilot plant devoted to the study of twin-wire machines. A prototype pilot machine was operating by 1959. Many configurations were investigated, and countless modifications and paper runs were made. By 1965 a 264-inch machine was ordered, and in 1967 it went into operation in St. Francisville, Louisiana.

In the Time Inc. machine (fig. 12.6), a jet of paper stock is forced between the two wires which converge and run over a curved slotted surface, below which is a compartmented vacuum box for water removal. Water is also expressed upward by the force of the jet and by centrifugal force. Almost half of the water in the stock goes upward via the top scraper. Additional suction boxes remove more water. The vacuum roll holds the sheet on the bottom wire at the point where the top wire pulls away for the return run.

THE BELOIT BEL-BAIE FORMER

Beloit Corporation, a major manufacturer of paper machinery, developed twin-wire machines in several versions. Their research and development work was almost simultaneous with the Time Inc. work, and their first machine in Niagara, Wisconsin, was almost an upside down version of the Time Inc. machine, although it was developed independently.

Beloit developed at least two versions of their Bel-Baie former. The early design used a solid shoe, rather than a slotted forming area, in a configuration somewhat like the Time Inc. device.

The later Bel-Baie design (fig. 12.7) uses a vertical forming system in which the paper stock is sent upward between the two wires. An integral part of this system is the stock inlet called the Beloit Converflo headbox. The paper stock is delivered upward by the headbox be-

tween the two wires which converge over the curved retention shoe. Water is removed by the angled doctors in the shoe. Water also drains through the No. 1 wire and is collected and removed by another doctor. The retention shoe is followed by a vacuum box and a suction couch roll which removes water and holds the sheet on the No. 2 wire.

THE BLACK CLAWSON VERTI-FORMA

The Black Clawson Company developed the Verti-Forma paper machine in the same time period that others were being developed (1956–1966). Like the other companies, Black Clawson undertook the research and development with a clear understanding of the need for better and lighter weight papers.

The Verti-Forma concept was basically different from other efforts. In this machine (fig. 12.8), the paper stock is directed vertically downward between two wires. A series of doctors alternately remove water from each side. The doctors are followed by a vacuum holding box which causes the sheet to follow the wire on that side, and removes more water. The suction couch roll removes water and continues to keep the sheet on that wire.

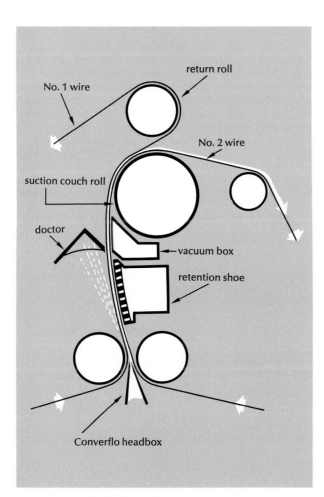

Figure 12.7: Beloit Bel-Baie former.

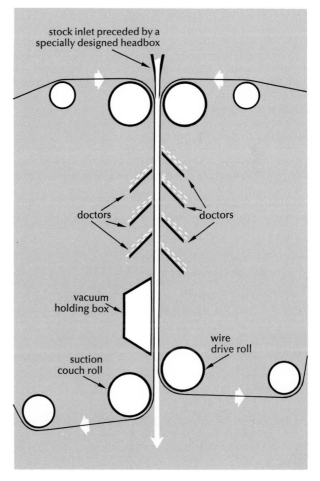

Figure 12.8: Black Clawson Verti-Forma.

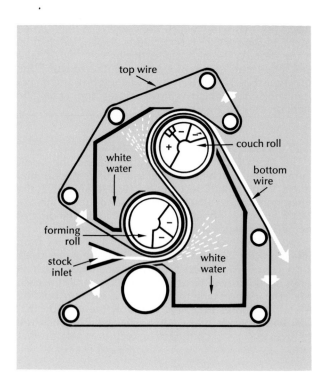

Figure 12.9: Dominion Engineering Papriformer.

the roll and is also expelled through the bottom wire by centrifugal force. After leaving the forming roll, both wires wrap the couch roll which has a positive pressure compartment followed by two vacuum compartments. Thus water is drained in both directions a second time. The white water save-all pans inside the wire runs collect the water thrown out of the two rolls.

NEW EUROPEAN DESIGNS

The Voith Duoformer. This machine, in operation in Sweden, was designed by the J. M. Voith Company of Germany. The Duoformer appears to combine some of the features of the Time Inc. machine—a stock jet at an upward angle and initial forming on a vacuum forming box—with a compartmented vacuum roll like the Papriformer's.

In the Duoformer (fig. 12.10), water is removed into the forming roll and is also thrown out centrifugally. This is followed by a doctor, then a vacuum box, and finally a suction couch with three compartments.

The Sym-former. The Valmet Company in Finland has developed this machine (fig. 12.11). A short Fourdrinier composed of foils gives initial formation. This is followed by a top wire section and a curved shoe under the lower wire which causes drainage through the top wire. Finally, there are vacuum boxes under the bottom wire.

THE DOMINION ENGINEERING PAPRIFORMER

The fourth system was developed by the Pulp and Paper Research Institute of Canada with financial support from Dominion Engineering Works. The commercial machine, called the "Papriformer," is built by Dominion Engineering.

This machine (fig. 12.9) is quite different from those described earlier. All the water is removed by rotating components and the wires do not slide over any stationary members. The paper stock is delivered between the two wires which then both wrap around a large-diameter, wire-covered forming roll. Water is drawn into the roll by the two vacuum compartments within

THE FUTURE OF TWIN-WIRE MACHINES

Many of the twin-wire machines had wire-life problems when they first came into use. However, improvements in materials for stationary surfaces have greatly extended wire life. Aluminum oxide and synthetics such as polypropylene are used extensively. Use of plastic wires has also helped.

In addition to their capability for producing publication papers, all of the twin-wire machines have shown considerable advantages in making a sheet for offset newsprint. They produce a sheet which shows little or no fuzzing or picking on either side, since both sides are wire sides. Wire mark is very much reduced compared to the normal Fourdrinier wire mark. All of the

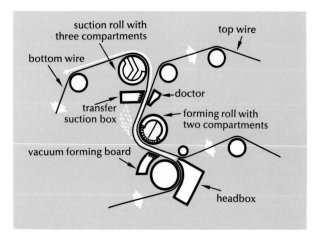

Figure 12.10: Duoformer.

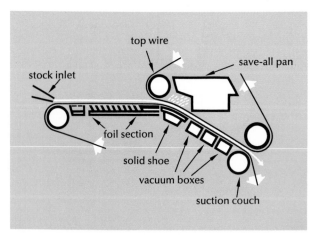

Figure 12.11: Sym-former.

commercial machines appear to be capable of making very satisfactory newsprint at high speeds; and a number of paper mill executives have expressed the opinion that all new newsprint machines will be twin-wire.

The future for twin-wire machines appears to be very bright. A number of each of the makes are in operation in North America, Europe, and Japan, at least one for the production of paperboard. It is likely that, in the years to come, a wide variety of papers will be made on twin-wire machines.

FUNDAMENTAL PHYSICAL PROPERTIES OF PAPER
Walter L. Strong and Philip C. Evanoff, MEAD PAPER

A great many factors influence the physical characteristics of paper, and as a general rule these factors and characteristics are closely interrelated. It is normally impossible to change any one characteristic of a sheet of paper without, at the same time, changing others.

It is beyond the scope of this discussion to examine all of the possible characteristics of paper and their interrelationships. However, among all of these characteristics there are a few basic ones which interact to determine the majority of the others. These can be discussed here in detail, and they should be thoroughly understood by everyone dealing with paper. (For purposes of this discussion, the term "property" will be used to refer to these fundamental traits, while the term "characteristic" will be used to denote secondary or resulting traits of paper.)

These fundamental properties of paper are: *grain direction, moisture sensitivity, formation, basis weight,* and *caliper.* They are discussed under the headings that follow. Some of the most important secondary characteristics of paper are defined in the accompanying list (page 472).

GRAIN DIRECTION

Grain in a sheet of paper is the tendency of the paper fibers to align in one direction and not in others. The *grain direction* of any given sheet, therefore, is the axis along which most of the fibers are aligned in parallel.

Grain is created on the Fourdrinier machine. As wet pulp is moved rapidly along the Fourdrinier wire, with the water draining out of it, the fibers tend to orient themselves parallel to the direction in which the wire is carrying them. As the paper is wound into rolls at the end of the machine, therefore, the grain direction, or direction in which most of the fibers are parallel to each other, runs around the roll. In web printing operations, the grain of the paper will thus always run the length of the web.

In sheet stock, however, the grain can follow either the long dimension of the sheet or the short dimen-

sion. This is accomplished in the finishing department of the mill when the rolls are cut down into sheets of different sizes. If the longer dimension of the sheet is laid out across the roll to be cut, then a sheet with grain running the short way will result. If the sheet is laid out with the long dimension running parallel to the paper web, a sheet with grain running the long way will be created.

Sheet stock, therefore, must always be specified "grain long" or "grain short" when grain direction is important in a job. Care must be exercised here, however. If a job requires sheets 19" x 25" in size with grain long, they may be purchased in the 25" x 38" size and cut in half by the printer. However, the paper must be purchased grain short in the larger size in order to get grain long in the smaller size.

Practically all other physical characteristics of paper are affected by grain direction, particularly stiffness, fold quality, fold strength, tensile strength, stretch, tear strength, and dimensional stability. Grain direction is especially important in relation to the paper's direction of travel through printing and binding equipment. As discussed below, paper may be more dimensionally stable in one direction; on a press, this can be important in holding color register. In binding, paper will fold better if the fold is made parallel to the grain instead of across the grain.

MOISTURE SENSITIVITY

The basic raw material in paper is cellulose fiber. Cellulose is a hygroscopic material—this means that it will exchange moisture with its environment until an equilibrium is attained. Therefore, moisture content of paper will change with changes in relative humidity of the air surrounding it.

Dimensional change

When cellulose fibers change in moisture content, they change in size, swelling with moisture gain and shrinking with moisture loss. The change in size of fibers due to moisture change is greater across the width of fibers than along their length. When the

IMPORTANT CHARACTERISTICS OF PAPER

Many specific physical characteristics of paper result from the fundamental properties discussed in the accompanying article. Among the most important of these secondary characteristics are the following:

Absorptivity: The ability of paper to take up liquids or vapors with which it is in contact.

Bulk: A measure of the thickness of a pile of a specified number of sheets under a specified pressure.

Bursting strength: A measure of the force required to rupture a given area of paper surface.

Curl: Distortion or non-flatness where corners or edges of sheet paper tend to roll up. Curl may be parallel to paper grain, perpendicular to paper grain, or diagonal to paper grain, and may be toward either the felt or wire side.

Density: The value obtained by dividing basis weight by caliper (in thousandths of an inch). Paper that is more compact and tightly formed will have a higher density value.

Dimensional stability: The ability of paper to maintain constant size in response to stresses applied or to changes in temperature and humidity.

Folding quality: The appearance of the fold in a sheet of paper. Specifically, the quality of a fold is determined by the degree of visual cracking that occurs along the outside curvature of the fold line.

Folding strength (endurance): The number of folds that a specimen will withstand before failure under specified conditions in a specified instrument. In the usual test, a specimen is subjected repeatedly to double folds through a wide angle while under tension. Folding strength is required in papers which must be folded, unfolded, and refolded many times—for example, maps, papers bound into saddle-stitched booklets, etc.

Hygroexpansivity: The change in dimension of paper that results when the moisture content changes due to change in the ambient relative humidity. Hygroexpansivity is commonly expressed as a percentage and is usually several times higher across the grain than parallel to the grain (machine direction).

Internal bond: The strength or force with which fibers are bonded to each other within a sheet of paper.

Porosity: Permeability of paper to air flow from one side of the sheet to the other under controlled conditions. The two important control conditions are area of sample and pressure of air.

Stiffness: The ability of paper to resist deformation under stress. All other things being equal, the stiffness of paper varies as the cube of the thickness.

Stretch: (1) The ability of paper to elongate under tension. The elongation is expressed as a percentage of original length when stressed at a stated load. (2) The elongation corresponding to the point of rupture in a tensile-strength measurement. It is usually expressed as a percentage of the original length. *Note:* paper is partially elastic and will return to its original length when relieved of load, providing the force exerted has not stretched the paper beyond its elastic limit.

Surface strength: A measure of the ability of the paper surface to withstand stress, principally the forces of ink splitting and separation during the printing operation.

Surface texture (finish): The texture or finish of a paper surface denotes the condition or appearance of its surface. Textures of papers range from high, smooth, hard finishes to rough, toothy, low finishes. They may also be decorated by embossing in a wide variety of ways.

Tearing strength: A measure of the tearing resistance of paper or the force required to tear a specimen under standardized conditions.

Tensile strength: The force in pounds required to break a specified strip of paper under specified conditions of loading.

---

fibers are bound together in the form of a sheet of paper the changes in fiber size are transmitted to the sheet as a whole, and it changes in size.

If the distribution and orientation of fibers in the sheet were completely random, the dimensional change that resulted in the sheet due to moisture change would be equal in both directions. If the fibers were all "lined up" in one direction, the size change that occurred in the sheet would be minimal in the direction of fiber alignment, and almost all the dimensional change would occur in a direction across this alignment of fibers.

In actual practice neither of these conditions exists. Due to the method of manufacture, there is a definite tendency for fibers to line up in one direction, but not all fibers do this. As a result, both dimensions of a sheet of paper will change with changing moisture content, but there will always be more change in the across-the-grain direction than in the grain direction.

Although dimensional change in paper is probably the most important effect of moisture change, other characteristics are also affected.

Fiber bonding and flexibility

Fiber bonds relax as moisture content increases, and at lower moisture levels fiber bonds become stronger. As a result of this effect, increase in moisture content will cause a decrease in: hardness and rattle (desirable in bond papers), bursting strength, tensile strength, and surface strength. The opposite is observed when moisture content decreases.

In addition, increasing moisture will produce greater flexibility and pliability in fibers. The combined results of increasing moisture content on fiber bonds and flexibility will bring about improvements in folding quality, folding strength, and tearing strength. However, the fiber flexibility that is produced by increasing moisture content will cause stiffness to decrease. The softening of the fiber and the fiber bond relaxation that accompany increasing moisture content will provide an increase in compressibility of the paper. This will improve print quality for letterpress and gravure but will have little or no effect on offset print quality. The opposite effects will be observed in situations where moisture content is decreased.

Curl

Curl is also caused by changing moisture content but follows no general pattern. Due to the effects of changing moisture content (and corresponding changes in fiber bonding, flexibility, and sheet size), the stresses present in paper may become unbalanced, and curl will develop. Some few types of paper stay relatively flat over the whole humidity range, but the great majority will show some curl at 30% RH (relative humidity) or lower. A sheet that is flat at 50% RH may stay flat or curl at one or both of the extremes, but a sheet that exhibits curl at 50% RH will usually not improve at either extreme.

Static electricity

Static electricity is always generated when a non-conductor like paper is moved. It becomes troublesome when it cannot leak away because of low humidity in the paper or of the air immediately surrounding the paper. As the moisture content of paper increases, the paper becomes more conductive, allowing the static charges to leak away. When the RH of the paper and air is 35% or higher, static normally is not a problem.

FORMATION

Formation is the property of paper which relates to the uniformity of distribution of the fibers in the sheet structure. Formation is normally evaluated by the visual appearance of the paper when viewed by transmitting light through the sheet from the rear—the look-through appearance. A good formation will show uniform distribution of fibers, while poor formation will show the fibers in clumps. This property is fundamental, not only because of its influence on the appearance of the sheet but because it will affect the level and uniformity of many other properties and characteristics.

Poor formation is commonly associated with high-strength papers containing high percentages of long fiber, with inefficient drainage conditions on the wet end of the paper machine, and with high paper-machine speeds. As formation becomes poorer, or more "wild," the following properties and characteristics will be increasingly affected:

- Optical characteristics (gloss, opacity, etc.) will be less uniform.
- Surface levelness will be decreased.
- Caliper, basis weight, density, and most strength characteristics will become more variable.
- Printing quality will be lowered by all processes. Most commonly, halftones printed by letterpress and gravure will become broken, and solids printed by offset will be mottled.

BASIS WEIGHT

The basis weight of paper in the United States is the weight (in pounds) of 500 sheets of paper cut to a given standard size (in inches) for that grade. The standard or basic size is not the same for all grades, but varies according to trade practices. (See "Paper Names and Classifications," page 447.) The mixture of papermaking materials delivered to the paper-machine wire is the major factor determining basis weight of paper being produced. For example, a mixture which is 98% water and 2% fiber, filler, etc., will produce a sheet with twice the basis weight as the same materials diluted so that the composition is 99% water and 1% fiber, filler, etc.

Basis weight influences many optical characteristics of paper and most physical characteristics. As basis weight varies within a given grade of paper, either caliper or density (or both) will vary, and all characteristics affected by caliper and density will also be influenced. These characteristics include stiffness, strength, stretch, tear, dimensional stability, etc.

CALIPER

Caliper is the average thickness of a single sheet as determined by measuring the thickness of a number of single sheets and averaging the results. Caliper is generally expressed in thousandths of an inch, also known as *points* or *mils*.

Caliper is determined primarily by the amount of machine calendering accomplished on the paper machine. Although all pressure operations that occur on the paper machine have their influence, the machine calendering operation is the most significant. As the amount of calendering increases, the sheet becomes thinner (lower in caliper) and more dense, and the surface smoothness increases. The increased density also affects certain optical characteristics—in particular, it lowers opacity. When basis weight is held constant within a given grade, caliper and surface smoothness are inversely related—the higher the caliper, the rougher the paper surface; the lower the caliper, the smoother the paper. The most significant characteristics affected by caliper, other than surface smoothness, are stiffness and bulk.

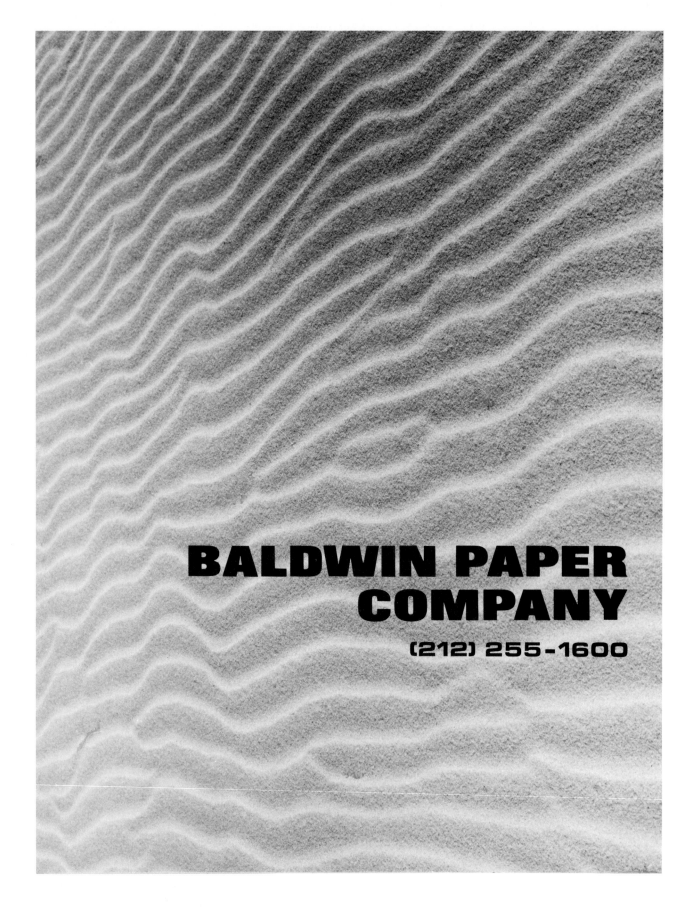

BALDWIN PAPER COMPANY

(212) 255-1600

PRINTABILITY AND RUNNABILITY

This article has been adapted with permission of Mead Paper, Dayton, Ohio, from one of their series of Graphic Arts Bulletins.

Paper has many physical characteristics which govern its performance in printing, but these all can be grouped under just two main use classifications which indicate the basic effect they have on quality of the printed job. These use factors are *runnability* and *printability*.

Runnability, essentially, is the ability of the paper to run easily through a printing press or other paper-handling or converting machines such as bindery equipment. Printability is the capability of the paper to produce with good fidelity the kind of printed image sought, when printed with the appropriate inks under proper conditions.

RUNNABILITY CHARACTERISTICS

Runnability characteristics, which apply to both sheets and rolls of paper, include the following:

Flatness: Freedom from buckles, puckers, waves, and curl.

Cleanliness: Freedom from loose material from all sources—trimmer and cutter dust, slitter dust, other foreign material resting on or clinging to the surface.

Stiffness: Rigidity of the sheet, a property which tends to make the sheet easier to run through the press and which sometimes assists materially in blanket release in offset printing.

Surface strength: Ability of surface materials on a sheet of paper to withstand the pull exerted on it by inks, offset blankets, and other tacky or sticky materials with which the paper comes in contact during printing. Lightly bound surface materials have lower surface strengths and are more likely to be pulled off the sheet by tacky substances.

Water resistance: Ability of a sheet to withstand the softening effects of water. In an uncoated sheet, individual fibers or fiber clumps may be softened so they can be pulled off the sheet by inks or blankets. In coated paper, an overall "milking" or whitening effect may occur.

Non-reactivity with fountain etch: Paper printed by lithography should be free of materials that may change the chemical composition of the fountain etch used in lithography. Such changes can cause the etch to lose its ability to maintain a sharp demarcation between printing and non-printing areas on the plate. Active alkalies or certain dispersing agents have been known to cause scumming or tinting (the printing of ink in non-printing areas), although most reasons for these troubles reside elsewhere than in the paper.

Moisture content (percentage of relative humidity): Variations in moisture content cause variations in paper dimensions; higher moisture levels cause paper fibers to expand. Moisture content must be held constant during multicolor close-register printing to ensure proper register of colors.

Paper surface/ink relationship: Effect of paper on drying rate, chalking or smudging, and hold-out of gloss inks or varnish. (These characteristics generally are considered under runnability although they also affect printability.)

Mechanical perfection: Freedom from holes, wrinkles, torn edges, scraps, turned-over corners, stuck spots, and the like. In addition, roll stock should be evenly and tightly wound with even edges and a minimum of splices.

PRINTABILITY CHARACTERISTICS

Printability factors include the following:

Smoothness: Evenness of the surface contour of the paper, in which minute pinpoint irregularities in depth are spaced from $\frac{1}{100}$ to $\frac{1}{200}$ inch apart. As a rule, these pinpoint differences cannot be seen with the naked eye, but are readily visible with an eight-power lens and a low-angle light beam shining across the surface of the paper. In printing, as smoothness diminishes, printed solids usually deteriorate first, followed by halftones. Type is generally affected very little or not at all.

Levelness: Evenness of surface contour where irregularities extend across $\frac{1}{8}$ to $\frac{1}{4}$ inch or more. Lack of levelness is usually due to poor formation and clumping of the fibers, and is almost always more of a problem with heavier basis weights and long fiber content. As a rule, it may be seen readily with the naked eye when viewed from a low angle, and is usually most noticeable in coated cover stocks and bristols. As levelness diminishes, halftones—especially light ones—become uneven and mealy; solids may show mottle; type is not affected to any great degree.

Cushion: Compressibility or resiliency of paper. Theoretically, a paper with a high degree of cushion should make up for irregularities in plate and press motion as well as in its own structure. In practice, there is no workable way to measure cushion under dynamic operating conditions. Static measuring methods have, on occasion, shown some correlation with the quality of printed results. However, in specific instances where sheets have been criticized as deficient in cushion and showed excessive embossing, it was found that the simplest and most effective cure was to make the paper smoother, thus automatically reducing the need for impression on the press.

Coverage: Degree to which the fibers are covered up and concealed by the coating. This goes back to the original reason for coating paper—the fine-grained coated surface will print with more ink hold-out and provide greater brilliance, contrast, and detail than the fibrous uncoated surface. All other things being equal, the better the coverage the more these desirable characteristics will be present in the job.

Ink receptivity: Ability of paper surface to absorb ink. While this term is commonly used in reference to printability, it has been shown repeatedly that receptivity has negligible influence on the quality of reproduction as such. On the other hand, it is of considerable importance in its effect on drying rate, on tendency to offset onto adjacent sheets, and on scuffing and chalking of the dried ink film. These are actually conditions of runnability rather than printability, but because of industry custom, ink receptivity is described here under printability.

COATED VS. UNCOATED PAPERS

Various paper surfaces, which range from uncoated fibers to fully coated surfaces with no fibers showing, have different printability capabilities. Each kind of surface tends to perform quite consistently compared to other surfaces, regardless of the printing process used. For example, the fully coated surface will produce much more "snap" and brilliance in the appearance of illustrations and is capable of much more ink hold-out. The superior gloss and ink hold-out of coated sheets over uncoated papers will in many cases give a more pleasing, more striking appearance to the finished job due to surface characteristics alone. The use of gloss inks has increased tremendously in recent years, and coated papers have also been used more because they complement these inks.

There are, however, large differences among different coated papers in terms of these characteristics. Coated papers can be divided into three groups on the basis of optical characteristics of the surface.

Glossy coated papers include all sheets having a gloss reading between 50 and 75. Glossy coateds will increase to some degree the snap and brilliance of images printed by offset lithography and gravure; they will almost always produce much better results with letterpress.

Dull coated papers have a gloss range from 20 to 50, and the snap and brilliance of images on these sheets are somewhat less than those printed on glossy papers. However, these papers reproduce detail in approximately the same degree of excellence in all three of the major printing processes.

Matte coated papers include those with a gloss range from 7 to 20. These normally produce a printed result somewhere between dull coated and uncoated papers, and print fine detail very well in lithography. Detail in letterpress and gravure, however, is not comparable to that produced by the lithographic process. In addition, matte coated papers are more likely than other coateds to show mottle.

PAPER PERFORMANCE WITH VARIOUS PROCESSES

In getting the best results with a particular printing process, certain paper characteristics are much more critical than others. Which characteristics are most important will vary markedly from process to process.

Letterpress

The most important characteristics in letterpress are smoothness, levelness, cushion, coverage, and ink receptivity. Of these, smoothness is easily the most important. Essentially, all of these apply to both sheet-fed and web-fed heat-set letterpress, and all are printability characteristics rather than runnability factors.

In addition, in web printing, the paper must not blister in ink-drying ovens, either by being run at too low a moisture content or by having too porous a surface which loses too much moisture in drying. Further, to be resistant to strength degradation caused by the heat, the paper usually needs a fairly high content of alkaline long fiber.

Offset lithography

The most important factors in sheet-fed lithographic printing are surface strength, water resistance, non-reactivity to fountain etch, moisture content, ink receptivity and stiffness. As opposed to letterpress, these are almost entirely concerned with runnability rather than printability. Due to the resiliency of the offset blanket, offset printing is relatively insensitive to differences in smoothness, although they do have some effect.

Runnability requirements throughout the entire quality range of offset papers are reasonably constant. Since these are the characteristics that are of prime importance, differences between the top and bottom of the basic quality scale are confined to superficial characteristics such as color, brightness, opacity, and the like; and problems encountered in the manufacture of a top-grade offset sheet are substantially the same as those found in a low-grade sheet.

The above comments apply essentially to sheet-fed offset. During the first few years of the move toward web offset, it was found that at least one-third or more of the web printers were able to use standard letterpress papers with fairly good results. The balance required a sheet about halfway between letterpress and sheet-fed offset insofar as surface strength and water resistance are concerned. However, as web offset quality has reached very high levels and runs have become longer, there is evidence to indicate that the web offset sheet in some cases should be even higher in water resistance and resistance to whitening than that for sheet-fed offset.

Gravure

In gravure printing, there is more difference between sheet-fed and web-fed operations than in the other processes. Web or rotogravure is essentially a very high speed, long-run production process while sheet-fed gravure is a deluxe, top-quality process for fine reproductions in limited quantities.

The rotogravure printer generally uses vast amounts of either supercalendered or machine-coated stock, with surface smoothness and mechanical condition of the rolls the main concerns. Cushion theoretically is of importance, but this is supported only by indirect evidence. Surface wettability, or the ability to rapidly accept the highly liquid gravure ink, has been found to be significant on rare occasions.

Screen printing

In screen printing, the requirements for both printability and runnability are much less severe than in other processes. Requirements that do exist are basically runnability factors. Sheets must be mechanically good—that is, free of curl, buckle, wrinkles, ridges, welts or other imperfections which would prevent the screen from coming into full contact with the paper.

Higher bulk sheets are more rigid and thus more resistant to the warping effect of the thick ink films used. Also, paper should be resistant to shrinkage, curl, or warping that can be caused in drying ovens, particularly in multicolor printing.

APPEARANCE ANALYSIS IN THE GRAPHIC ARTS
Richard S. Hunter, HUNTER ASSOCIATES LABORATORY, INC.

In most areas of graphic arts, the physical appearance of the printed piece is a controlling consideration in determining adequacy of the final product for its intended end use. Printers and paper manufacturers for many years have been trying to gain better control of the factors that influence appearance. Through application of scientific techniques, many of these factors have gradually been identified and measured, permitting everyone in the production chain—from technicians in the paper industry to printing buyers and designers—to manipulate them precisely to achieve pre-specified results.

Only in recent years, however, has this work progressed far enough to permit us to combine various individual techniques into an integrated approach to controlling the overall appearance of printed products. This movement to incorporate the various individual measures of appearance into a unified system of control has become known as *appearance analysis*. Appearance analysis offers the paper and printing industries several advantages over prior control methods:

· Appearance measurement techniques assign specific numbers to appearance factors and thus facilitate communication among those working with the materials.

· Standardized conditions of observation provide permanent records that can be completely understood at later dates.

· Specific observing conditions can be chosen deliberately to match and test the most critical aspects of the product.

· Data from appearance measurements can be used to compute and derive much more accurate formulations for products than are possible without statistical data.

Responsibility for the various attributes of appearance in the finished job is divided between paper manufacturers and printers according to which attributes each controls. Those appearance attributes inherent in the paper itself fall under the control of the paper manufacturer, while those which depend on how inks are applied to the paper are the responsibility of the printer.

These appearance attributes, whether of paper or printing, divide into two basic classes: *chromatic* (having to do with color) and *geometric* (having to do with the geometric distribution of light). For example, brightness falls into the first category; uniformity belongs to the second classification. The chromatic attributes are by far the more important commercially, but it is still necessary to account for the geometric characteristics of light distribution if total appearance is to be measured and controlled.

Involving as it does a potentially infinite variety in both spectral and geometric distributions—to say nothing of varieties in shape, markings, and the like—total appearance is very complex. To measure all of the almost infinite combinations of these elements is an impossibility. However, it is feasible to measure, with instruments under controlled conditions, most of the specific attributes which are important for each specific type of paper or printing. If the controlled conditions are chosen properly, they will provide measurements that will relate well to other conditions commonly found in the commercial world where the printed product will be viewed. Information on the identification and measurement of color is contained in the article "The Measurement and Specification of Color" on page 21.

APPEARANCE ANALYSIS IN MANUFACTURING
During the paper manufacturing process, five major optical properties of paper must be controlled to achieve desired appearance. These are: *color, brightness, opacity, gloss,* and *surface uniformity*. They are controlled initially by the amount and kind of bleaching done on the pulp and by the addition of various pigments, dyes, resins, clays, and starches to the mixture. After the paper is formed on the machine, calendering and coatings may be used to further alter these characteristics.

The bleaching process removes impurities (chiefly lignin) which absorb blue light, improving the blue reflectance of the paper. Increasing the blue reflectance raises the brightness quality. Blue reflectance is mea-

| Type of paper | Major uses | Important properties | Raw materials | | | Manufacturing process | Important appearance attributes | |
			Types of pulp	Stock additives	Separate coating		Raw materials	Finished product
Fine papers	Bond, ledger, and writing; for use in office and home	Suitable for writing; permanent, strong, attractive in appearance	Bleached. Sometimes cotton or rags added	Sizing (resin); dye and/or white pigment		Fourdrinier machine	Blue reflectance (brightness) of pulp	Color, opacity
Printing & book papers — Uncoated	For printing type and line copy, but not halftones	Prints well; has good opacity at minimum cost	Bleached. Sometimes bleached groundwood added	Sizing and usually dye and/or pigment		Fourdrinier machine	Blue reflectance of pulp	Color, opacity
Printing & book papers — Coated	For magazines and all printing where good halftones are required	Smooth printable surface, good opacity and color at minimum cost	Bleached; sometimes bleached groundwood added	Dye	White clay and possibly TiO$_2$ in starch coating	Fourdrinier machine; coated on or off machine; frequently super-calendered	Blue reflectance of pulp and clay	Color, gloss, opacity
Newsprint	Used mainly for newspapers	Low cost, prints well	Groundwood, mostly unbleached	Dye		Fourdrinier machine	Blue reflectance of pulp	Color
White boxboard	For cartons, printed packages, posters, etc.	Whiteness, rigidity, printability	Reclaimed newspaper inside, white pulp outside	White clay usually added with white pulp	Sometimes clay and starch coating added	Cylinder machine forms paper in layers	Blue reflectance of white pulp	Color of white surface, gloss (in some cases)
Kraft and shipping	For wrapping paper, bags, and shipping cartons	Good strength	Unbleached		Sometimes white-pulp surface is added	Fourdrinier (corrugated paper is made on separate machine)		
Tissue	For household and packing uses	Creped and soft	Bleached	Dye, resin		Fourdrinier with creping attachment	Blue reflectance of pulp	Color
Specialty	Waxed, glassine, gift wrap, etc. Used for food and other special purposes	Vary with type	Bleached	Dye, white clay, and/or sizing	Wax, oil, plastic, or other coating as required	Fourdrinier with additional machines for coating	Blue reflectance of pulp	Color. Sometimes transparency and gloss of food packaging papers

sured regularly during paper manufacture to assess the whiteness potential of the pulp as well as its purity and permanence characteristics.

Other appearance characteristics which are important, however, are not usually measured as consistently as brightness is during manufacture. Table 12.4 lists eight major types of paper, their important properties, the raw materials from which they are made, the manufacturing processes employed, and the important appearance attributes that are measured. The table shows that the color of the finished product is very important for seven of the eight grades—only in brown kraft packaging paper is it unimportant. The other seven types of paper are most frequently made in

478

white shades, but tints and sometimes even saturated colors are produced.

In practice, blue reflectance (or brightness) is widely used during manufacture as a partial measure of the coloring in white grades. However, the brightness measurement is only one dimension involved in color, and color in white papers should be measured in all three of its dimensions—hue (shade) and chroma (saturation) as well as brightness. Color in white papers can become very important when two different stocks are used in the same magazine, book, or other job. And it may be crucially important in high-quality color reproduction where the coloring of the sheet interacts with the colored ink laid on it.

Table 12.5 lists the major optical properties of paper, the related appearance and optical performance attributes, the corresponding optical processes responsible, and the structure and ingredients involved. In general, it can be said that brightness, color, and opacity are important for all white papers. In cases in which very good printing quality is needed, particularly for halftones in color, high gloss and good surface uniformity are also required.

Most appearance measurements in paper mills today are made with laboratory instruments. However, higher costs and the resulting need for tighter control in the manufacturing process has fostered the increasing use of on-machine instruments to monitor appearance characteristics of pulp and paper as it is being made. These instruments, when coupled with process control computers, make possible closed-loop automation systems (that is, those with on-line computer control) for controlling appearance characteristics within preset tolerances much finer than can be achieved manually.

Data processing techniques also are making it possible for readings taken in the laboratory on one kind of instrument to be matched against and compared to different data obtained from on-machine instruments

which record in a different manner. The technology for obtaining data on appearance characteristics and converting it into meaningful quantities has been advancing rapidly. It now seems possible to simulate electronically the kind of extremely sophisticated detector-computer combination that exists between the human eye and brain. We can already electronically read color difference, whiteness, yellowness, tomato color, and citrus color directly from light-sensing instruments having built-in analog computers. Instruments of the near future can be expected to provide direct readings of brightness, texture, and print sharpness, and also probably provide direct readouts of corrections to be made in product formulas to achieve desired results.

APPEARANCE ANALYSIS IN PRINTING

There are three basic optical problems to be controlled in the printing process:

- Matching colors of inks to the paper to be used
- Applying inks at the proper rates during the press run
- Obtaining adequate ink hold-out to create the required gloss on the dried ink

Inks are essentially paints designed for application at high speeds in very thin films. Like other paints, inks are bound together with either oxidizable oils or resins that harden from polymerization and/or evaporation. High-speed printing requires inks that harden very rapidly.

Although the different printing processes and styles of presses have an influence on the printing appearance factors, they do not significantly alter the basic problems or methods of controlling them. Similar techniques are used throughout the printing processes.

The first step in controlling the three printing factors of appearance is to measure the inks themselves before

TABLE 12.5: MAJOR OPTICAL PROPERTIES OF PAPER

Optical property	Related appearance attributes	Optical performance attributes	Optical processes	Structure and ingredients
Color	Color: lightness and (a) hue and saturation, or (b) redness-greenness, yellowness-blueness	Color is important primarily for appearance	Absorption of light is responsible for color. Color results from greater absorption at some wavelengths than at others	Dyes on fibers and colored pigments in coatings and between fibers provide the absorption responsible for color
Brightness (blue-light reflectance)	Whiteness is partially, but not wholly, dependent on brightness	Brightness is primarily a measure of freedom from brownish (blue-light absorbing) contaminants	Scattering of light increases brightness. Absorption of blue light decreases brightness	Fiber and pigment scatter light. Dyes and impurities absorb blue light
Opacity	Opacity is ability to obscure underlying copy	Opacity is essential for printing papers that are easy to read	Scattering and absorption prevent passage through sheet of all but small fraction of incident light	Fiber and pigment scatter light. Dyes and impurities absorb light. All contribute to opacity
Gloss	Shininess (glossiness)	Printing quality is partially related to gloss	Specular (surface) reflection	Paper surface and its smoothness
Uniformity	Formation; printing quality	Printing quality tends to be related to formation and surface uniformity	Uniformity of scattering and surface reflectance from point to point	Fiber and pigment uniformity of distribution

TABLE 12.6: APPLICATIONS OF APPEARANCE MEASUREMENT IN PRINTING

Aspect measured	Purpose of measurement	Measurement techniques	Ink film or print	Books, magazines, pamphlets	Labels, posters	Office & business letters & forms	Cardboard & cartons	Bags & wrappers	Standard test methods
Color	Conformity of specimen color to numerical color specification	Product specimen compared to standard and numerical specification	•	•	•	•	•	•	TAPPI T524 TAPPI T527
	Conformity of specimen color to match color of standard. Magnitude of color change with time	Product specimen compared to standard to measure color difference	•	•	•	•	•	•	ASTM D2244
Tristimulus reflectance	Measure brightness of paper and paperboard	Blue reflectance of product specimen compared to standard and numerical specification		•	•	•	•		ASTM E313
	Measure whiteness to assess appearance desirability & clearness	Product specimen compared to standard and numerical specification		•	•	•	•		ASTM E313
	Determine opacity to test ability to obscure background	Contrast ratio method; product specimen compared to standard and numerical specification			•		•	•	ASTM D589 TAPPI T425
Density	Reflection density of ink film. Used to measure changes in ink-film thickness by changes in density	Reflectance with colored filters, each transmitting spectral region of maximum absorption of one ink	•	•	•		•	•	ANSI PH2.17-1958 (R1976)
Gloss	Determine gloss of book paper. Determine gloss of ink film on paper and magnitude of change with time	Product specimen compared to standard	•	•	•	•			ASTM D1223 TAPPI T480
	Determine gloss of waxed and plastic coated paper	Product specimen compared to standard					•	•	ASTM D1834 TAPPI T653

printing. Corrections are easy to make at this stage. Inks are measured at this point for numerical identity with the chosen colors, for color difference to determine whether various samples are within the tolerances established, and for specular gloss. (See Table 12.6.)

At the start of a press run, color difference measurements are taken to indicate whether the ink lay-down is appropriate to produce the desired color. Even though the inks may be formulated within the standards set for them, final color on the printed sheet can still vary widely with the thickness of the ink film and its combination with the sheet.

To monitor variations after the press run is under way, color density readings are taken periodically to guide the adjustment of the ink fountains. (See Table 12.6.) With the higher speed presses in common use today, precise measurement and quantitative control data obtained during the press run are more important than controlling overall initial appearance. As in paper mills, on-press color density measurement and closed-loop color-control systems for presses are being developed and used to provide this control under computer guidance.

THE INFLUENCE OF PAPER ON COLOR PRINTING

This article has been adapted from Bulletin No. 6 of the "How Will It Print" series published by the S. D. Warren Company, a division of Scott Paper Company, Boston, Massachusetts.

It is obvious to anyone looking at a piece of color printing on white paper that the colored inks used create the basic colored image. What is not so obvious, however, is the crucial role played by the so-called "white" paper on which these inks are printed.

HOW PAPER AFFECTS PRINTED APPEARANCE

Every sheet of white paper actually has overtones of color and physical surface characteristics which affect the final colors seen by the viewer. The sheet of paper influences the appearance of the image printed on it in two ways: (1) The hue and brightness of the paper influence the color quality of a transparent process print; and (2) the mechanical characteristics of the paper surface—its smoothness or roughness, absorptivity or lack of it—affect the appearance of solids and halftones, color or black and white. These characteristics, unless balanced carefully to the ink, will produce color shades different from those intended.

Influence of hue and brightness

The color of any object, as perceived by the human eye, is wholly dependent on the quantity and quality of the light which illuminates it. The most immediate source of illumination for a transparent ink film is the sheet of paper on which it is printed. This is reflected illumination.

A sheet of paper has the property of absorbing some wavelengths and reflecting others. If it reflects all wavelengths equally, which means that it does not alter the quality of the light, it is a neutral or *balanced* white sheet of paper.

If it absorbs more of some wavelengths than others, it appears tinted. It is an *unbalanced* white paper. For example, if it absorbs more green and red wavelengths than it does blue wavelengths, it will be tinted blue, because, to look at it another way, it reflects more blue than other wavelengths.

If it absorbs all the wavelengths of white light (reflecting none) it will be black paper. A neutral gray sheet of paper is simply one that absorbs a good part of the quantity (without altering the quality) of light that strikes it. You might say that a neutral gray paper is a balanced white paper at low brightness. Just as natural colors become duller and less brilliant during the onset of darkness, so ink colors become duller and less brilliant as the brightness of a sheet of paper decreases. The unprinted area of a sheet of paper is the brightest portion of the overall printed page. The printed areas are less bright than the non-printed areas because they have absorbed some of the light. If a printer starts with a paper of low brightness the print will be correspondingly low in brightness. The unprinted areas of a tinted paper add their characteristic color to the light reflected from the print to the eye, so that additional distortion is incurred.

A yellow ink film which requires proper amounts of red, green, and blue light to provide accurate reproduction will not receive proper amounts when printed on a tinted (unbalanced white) sheet of paper. Therefore, the most accurate color reproduction is obtained on papers that reflect the light that strikes them without changing its quality.

In general, the most brilliant color reproductions are obtained on papers with high, balanced reflectance.

Influence of mechanical characteristics

The configuration of the paper surface also influences the appearance of the ink printed on it.

A rough fibrous surface is composed of a multitude of non-uniform reflecting surfaces. When light strikes them, they scatter it randomly and, accordingly, adulterate the print with white light. A black solid or halftone, for example, is grayed because of this addition of uncontrolled and unwanted white light. A colored solid or halftone is not only grayed (loses purity or saturation) but also tends to change its hue.

Smooth coated surfaces with fibers buried under layers of pigment minimize bothersome light interference by allowing uniform directional reflection of light.

As a rough surface contributes to color degradation, so does an excessively absorbent—or "open"—surface. An open surface may absorb both ink vehicle and pigment, or it may absorb gloss-giving vehicle but leave dull pigment particles on the surface.

A surface with good ink hold-out—a "tight" surface —retains both vehicle and pigment on the surface with the pigment "buried" in the glossy vehicle. Only enough vehicle penetrates the surface to provide good bond of ink to paper. Ink gloss contributes to purity of printed ink color. Paper gloss contributes to ink gloss.

Accurate glossy color results may be obtained on some dull coated and embossed coated papers. Even though the papers are not glossy, their surfaces are so refined that—even over the surfaces of the relatively large hills and valleys of embossed finishes—a gloss layer of ink may be supported. Sufficient vehicle is supported as a smooth film to maintain the color purity of the pigments immersed in it.

PROVIDING AN IDEAL PRINTING BACKGROUND

The paper manufacturer should provide the printer with a reasonably bright paper as color-balanced as possible—paper that reflects all colors of the spectrum equally so that transparent process inks have the proper quality of light in sufficient quantity to work in the most efficient manner.

RUN-ABILITY

It's what Permalin® has more of

Permalin non-woven cover material has many fine qualities. But the one book manufacturers like best is its "run-ability." Because Permalin has an uncoated surface and exceptional uniformity, it runs like a dream in pressroom and bindery. You get crisp, clean impressions at top speed... more print production per hour. And Permalin combines high Mullen, tensile and tear strengths with flexibility... enabling it to breeze through any hard- or soft-cover binding operation without a hitch.

Permalin is available in regular weight (white and colors) for casebound books... in three heavier weights for paperbacks. Why not give it a try.

PERMALIN PRODUCTS CORP.
Port Washington, NY 11050 • 516 883-6500

Chicago: 312 852-5808 • Tennessee: 615 357-4892

Further, the surfaces should be uniformly smooth and level with good ink hold-out. In this regard, glossy coated surfaces are generally best; however, some dull coated and embossed coated surfaces are notable exceptions.

The biggest problem, though, lies not in the papermaker's ignorance of what he should do, but in what he can do, and do consistently.

His ability to satisfy needed surface and shade requirements depends on knowledge, available materials, skills, and the potentials of his equipment. He is also aided or hindered by the means he has to measure and control the qualities he seeks.

Simply stated, without proper controls and measurements, the papermaker cannot know whether his product is up to snuff or not. Simple visual inspection and many standard measuring devices are not sophisticated or sensitive enough to measure slight but important departures from the color and surface standards the papermaker must meet.

Measuring paper brightness

In the matter of paper brightness, for example, the papermaker's measuring device has historically been the brightness meter. Increasing awareness of the importance of balanced paper brightness led to the realization that most brightness meters reflected an incomplete picture of a paper's color and brightness. Generally, these meters take a reading in the blue end of the spectrum, which means they indicate a particular paper's ability to reflect light in only that one small segment of the spectrum but do not indicate a paper's reflective characteristics in other portions of the spectrum. A bright bluish-white paper measured by standard brightness meters would produce high brightness readings, yet because it is bluish, its brightness would be low in the green and red areas of the spectrum. How low, however, would not be indicated, nor how detrimental this lower brightness might be to accurate color printing.

Therefore, it was realized that a measuring device capable of recording brightness at all points of the spectrum was needed to determine the true color and brightness of a paper. Such an instrument is the recording spectrophotometer, which reads reflectance across the breadth of the spectrum and records the information as a curve on graph paper. The spectrophotometer provides an accurate picture of a paper's color and brightness characteristics. It reflects the success or failure of the adjustments made in paper furnish or coatings to obtain balanced color and balanced, high brightness in the papermaker's product.

Measuring gloss and absorptivity

The mechanical characteristics of paper surfaces are measured in many ways to predict their printing potential, and most high-quality printing paper mills use a variety of devices to control the quality of their products.

In addition, the Graphic Arts Technical Foundation has developed a system designed to measure a paper's potential for color printing. They state, in essence, that the least ink-absorptive surfaces with the highest gloss reproduce color most accurately.

The paper characteristics of surface gloss and ink ab-

sorptivity are easily measured; the former by standard gloss meters and the latter by densitometer readings of special test ink stains. GATF developed a formula utilizing numerical readings of these two characteristics to indicate the color printing potential of paper surfaces. They call the solution of their equation "Paper Surface Efficiency," which is expressed as a percent. Color-balanced papers with a high P.S.E. percentage have a balanced combination of gloss and ink hold-out properties and thus reduce the number of provings necessary for a given job. Printed color can be more accurately predicted with high P.S.E. papers—thus providing the printer with economies he might not otherwise realize.

Paper Surface Efficiency is another means by which the printer may check the quality of the product he receives and is another "double-check" the papermaker may employ to affirm that the quality of the product he delivers is what it should be. But it is a method that—as with other testing procedures—one must apply knowledgeably.

Paper Surface Efficiency is an excellent tool, but it is recognized that it, too, does have its limitations and exceptions. Therefore, it is a valuable measure of a paper's color printing potential but not the only measure. For example, P.S.E. provides no indication of how a given paper will physically meet the stresses placed upon it by modern, high-speed, multicolor printing equipment—nor for that matter, how it might behave in subsequent operations, such as folding and binding. A paper with a perfect P.S.E. rating—100%—would be a problem. With inks normally used, it would cause severe offsetting in the delivery pile and great difficulty with ink trapping on multicolor presses. Quick-setting inks would not function; they could neither set nor dry.

It is within the coated paper category that P.S.E. encounters exceptions. Cast coated papers, for example, defy conventional gloss measurements and are relatively ink absorbent; but proper ink formulation allows them to produce superior gloss results. Some dull coated papers—obviously low in gloss measurement—possess refined surfaces that provide high ink hold-out. Some embossed coated papers have "micro" smoothness but cannot be measured for gloss because of "macro" roughness. They have the hills and valleys of the embossing pattern, yet a very smooth, refined surface on those hills and valleys.

Both of these types of paper are exceptions to P.S.E. because they have the potential for reproducing accurate colors at normal viewing distances. These exceptions could be overcome if the gloss of the printed ink film were measured instead of the gloss of the paper.

Among glossy coated papers there are some surprises, too. The castor oil base of the stain used for P.S.E. absorptivity readings is not similar to the ink vehicles in common use. Quick-setting inks used on certain coated papers will produce a higher gloss with fast-draining paper surfaces—those which would be very absorptive to the stain. Furthermore, gloss readings and visual gloss do not always coincide, so it is possible for an exception to arise from this discrepancy.

SUMMARY

In practical fact these measurements provide confirmation that papers vary widely and that no paper of commercial manufacture provides perfect color balance or 100% P.S.E. Furthermore, those papers which come closest to the best color balance at very high brightness are uncoated papers and therefore possess the surface character and ink handling qualities that lower P.S.E.

What present techniques of testing and control do provide, however, is the opportunity to offer—or select—papers with the highest combination of color balance and surface efficiency.

It is not always necessary or desirable to have papers with high color balance and P.S.E. Where these characteristics are especially important is in re-runs; that is, in repeat printings of the same subject. In these cases, it has been found that if the P.S.E. of the re-run paper is more than 5% different from the first run paper, the difference in the hue of the reds and magentas and saturation of greens, blues, and cyans will be noticeable and in critical cases can cause rejection.

RECYCLED PAPER

William R. Thompson, BERGSTROM PAPER COMPANY

Recycling is not a new idea, but it has assumed a new importance as a result of the constantly increasing amount of solid waste generated by industry, business, and the general public. New York City alone produces 1,100 to 1,200 tons of solid waste per hour.

Recycling is simply the reuse of materials which have been outworn or discarded in their original manufactured form. Recycling is the reclaiming and reprocessing of previously wasted raw materials to remake them into useful products.

Perhaps more than any other material, paper is recyclable. Recycled paper is defined by the federal government as follows: "The paper stock shall contain not less than 10 percent, by weight, of fibers reclaimed from solid waste or waste collected as a result of a manufacturing process, but shall not include those materials generated from and reused within a plant as part of the papermaking process." This definition is presently being changed. The Environmental Protection Agency, in cooperation with a study by Franklin Associates, is looking into a new definition which would deal primarily with the description of waste materials, rather than with percentages. Furthermore, they may break down waste materials into Type I and Type II. In any case, a new definition is being formulated, and recycling is of continued interest at the government level.

There are 47 grades of waste paper defined by the Paper Stock Institute. Of the 47 defined grades, Bergstrom, for example, uses 21. These are frequently referred to as "high grades," a term used in the trade for waste that can be recycled into fine printing papers. "Low grades" can be recycled into folding cartons, building board, and roofing materials. Old newspapers can be recycled into new newsprint.

The key to successful resale of waste paper by the end user is the proper sorting into appropriate grades and the removal of contaminants. In turn, the waste paper dealer continues the grading process. Upon arrival at the mill, waste paper is again sorted.

There is little difference in cost between recycled papers and virgin fiber papers. Bergstrom has been in the business for over 75 years, competing for the most part with mills using virgin pulps. In comparing costs of papers, one must compare similar grades, whether they be publishing, commercial, or converting papers.

INCENTIVES FOR RECYCLING

Reduction of the amount of solid waste is an essential component in the perservation of the environment. With the involvement of paper manufacturers and the government, and as production capabilities improve and further uses for reclaimed papers are developed, a much higher percentage of the great quantity of solid waste will be processed. In 1978, the United States consumed 69.5 million tons of paper and paperboard. In the same year, 16.7 million tons was collected for recycling. Of that, 14.8 million tons, or 21.3% of the fiber consumed, was used to make paper and paperboard. With the proper legislation, it is possible to reclaim much more. During World War II, under conservation controls, almost twice that percentage was reclaimed. A recent piece of legislation aimed at encouraging recycling is an added investment tax credit for recycling, passed in 1978. In addition, the Department of Energy is mandated to set recycling targets for several industries, including the paper industry; however, it has not been clearly demonstrated that setting such targets is an effective way to increase recycling or that successful targets can be set.

A multi-funded study is under way by the Institute of Paper Chemistry into the elimination of contaminants, such as hot melts, tar, asphalt, and pressure-sensitive materials, which comprise the major contaminant problems in virtually all sectors of the recycling industry. The Recycling Committee of the American Paper Institute is also involved in this study. It is expected to be ongoing and to contribute substantially by pointing the way to increasing the amount of waste material available for recycling.

There is also some discussion in the industry, encouraged by the Environmental Protection Agency, concerning waste paper future markets. The EPA feels that developing scrap future markets could encourage collection of waste paper through the mechanism of commodity contracts.

POLLUTION MANAGEMENT

The de-inking process involved in recyling is often cited as a pollution problem. In terms of pollution, however, de-inking is no different from making virgin pulp from trees. Both types of pulping (de-inking and wood pulping) generate waste, although the waste generated by each process is different and must be disposed of in a different manner. Both processes have stringent standards, making them an extremely costly part of paper manufacture.

The de-inking mill must dispose of the materials (clays, inks, binders, coatings, etc.) which have been removed from the cleansed, recycled waste paper fiber. In the case of Bergstrom, these materials are carried by the pulp mill waste effluent to the company's water management center where they are separated. The China clay recovered is used as land fill and the cleansed water is returned to the stream.

Similarly, as a result of the cooking and cleansing of the virgin fiber in wood pulping, several contaminants are carried off in the pulp mill effluent. These, too, are usually treated in some form of pollution abatement system. Emissions of various chemical compounds into the atmosphere comprise a major pollution control problem in conventional wood pulping, and virgin pulp mills are spending millions of dollars in order to meet today's standards.

In some cases, recycled paper can be produced without the de-inking process. This of course eliminates many of the waste disposal and pollution problems. Until 1971, all of Bergstrom's waste papers went through a de-inking process. Now certain grades are not de-inked; the entire content of the reclaimed paper is put into the papermaking system. As a result, the amount of solid waste has been reduced by almost 80 percent. In other words, Bergstrom normally has a solid waste of 20 to 25 percent from the waste paper bales it receives. This waste is reduced to 4 to 5 percent on these 100 percent recycled grades.

SPECIFICATIONS AND END USES

When discussing recycled papers, some significant points are often raised about quality, grades produced, specifications, and end uses.

The recycling of waste paper has been in existence at least since the year 1800, when Matthias Koops was issued the first known patent on de-inking by the Crown of England. Since that time, the de-inking process has been vastly improved. Those mills that use waste paper as a primary fiber in paper manufacture have become virtual experts in the manufacture of printing and writing grades.

Recycled printing papers can be used for all types of printing, including offset, letterpress, rotogravure, electrostatic printing, all forms of office printing, commercial printing, publishing, and converting. Recycled papers can be printed sheet-fed, web-fed, and in one, two, and four colors. No special precautions have to be taken when using recycled papers, whether they are 25 or 100 percent recycled. They perform as well as, and in some instances better than, virgin fiber sheets. They are generally more opaque, are affected less by atmospheric changes, and print as well as other types of comparable grade. Basis weights range from 28-pound (25" x 38") to 220-pound (25" x 38"), from Bible to board grades, in high whites to deep colors, plain finishes to embossed papers.

A very large number of printers, including in-plant, book publishing, and commercial, have been using recycled papers for many years and were not aware of it. It was only 20 years ago, for instance, that Bergstrom Paper Company started advertising that its products were manufactured from recycled de-inked waste paper, a process that has been in use since 1904.

FUTURE OF RECYCLED PAPERS

To forecast the future for recycling, it is important to examine the availability of fiber and the waste management necessary to cope with solid waste now and as it grows.

The amount of waste available will grow each year as the production of paper and paperboard grows. In 1999, according to a Franklin Associates report, paper and paperboard demand is expected to be 107 million tons and waste paper recovery 28.5 million tons. The report also estimates that in 1999 municipal solid waste generation will be about 214.3 million tons. We must ask ourselves: Where will we put that waste? Obviously, recycling will be necessary. As more waste is generated, better systems of sorting will develop, and the waste management industry, which showed marked growth in the 1970's, will continue to grow.

Recycling is coming of age, and a more concentrated effort must be made in this direction in the future because of the very serious solid waste disposal problem as well as the burden put on the forest resource industry. Not all trees are used for producing pulp. There is great competition for the wood from trees; it has many uses, only one of which is as pulp wood. Recycling works well the second, third, and fourth time around. This type of resource recovery has proven itself successful in the past and has a bright future.

PRINTING ON FOILS AND FILMS
Thomas J. Cavallaro, MEAD PAPER

Printing on non-paper materials such as foils and plastic films has grown steadily and substantially in recent years, finding uses in an ever-widening array of products. The major applications for foil and plastic films continue to be found in the packaging field, but important uses also have been made in advertising and sales promotion displays and many specialty products such as maps, looseleaf binders, labels, greeting cards, and the like.

PRINTING PROCESSES

Most of these films can be printed by all of the four main printing processes—letterpress, lithography, gravure, and screen printing. Printed foils and plastics can be produced by any printer; however, these materials require special techniques which the printer must be willing to live with. In actual practice, those printers who have made the effort to acquire the special knowledge required have become a group of specialized converters who operate quite apart from the rest of the printing industry. The offset lithographer, especially, must adjust to special conditions such as slower running speeds, smaller printed loads for handling, extensive humidity and temperature controls for the plant, and most important, to the use of special inks in the proper sequence.

Standard letterpress printing finds some use on tags and other flat-sheet work, but it is not as well suited to printing on plastics as its fast-growing offspring, flexography. This process uses a raised-image plate, but it is made of flexible rubber which conforms to plastic surfaces much more readily. Inks for flexography offer fast drying, freedom from blocking or smudging, high gloss, good adhesion, low odor, and water resistance. They also resist extreme temperatures well, and they can be easily overprinted with varnishes and lacquers for protection. Production speeds are high, up to 1,200 feet per minute on some presses.

Dry offset—a hybrid combination of a raised letterpress plate (although one with much less relief depth than a standard letterpress plate) and the offset principle used in lithographic presses—is also used for some plastic printing of containers such as tubes and other cylindrical shapes. Varnishing can also be done along with four-color printing, all at speeds of 20,000 or more pieces per hour.

Lithography is used mainly to print flat sheets of material—usually polyethylene, plastic-coated board, polyvinyl chloride, and acetate. Most work is sheet-fed, but some web printing is done on such products as milk cartons. Die-cutting operations sometimes are performed in-line with the printing of these materials.

Gravure has found wide use in printing on foils and plastics, including items ranging from packages to shower curtains and other decorative household materials. Gravure inks are very similar to flexographic inks, although they permit somewhat greater freedom in the use of different solvents. An important difference between flexography and gravure is the latter's greater ability to handle finer halftone screens. However, gravure plates cost far more than flexographic plates, and the process is economical only when quantities of several hundred thousand or more are to be produced.

Screen printing is one of the most versatile means of printing foils and plastic films, but its slow printing speeds limit it to shorter runs. Also, there is a limit, because of the screen mesh, as to how fine the screen of a halftone can be in this process. Outside of these two limitations, however, the process offers virtually unlimited versatility in the kinds of inks and materials that can be handled, and screen printing presses are available for printing on a broad range of unusually shaped objects such as bottles and other containers.

Often these printed materials are laminated to other sheets of plastic to protect the image and/or to strengthen the finished sheet. In the packaging field, most printing for later lamination is done by flexography or gravure; but in other parts of the graphic arts, lithographic printing is also laminated afterward.

TYPES OF SUBSTRATES

The great demand for plastics and foils for many applications has led to the manufacture of many substrates that look and feel similar to one another but have different chemical compositions and properties. Choice of printing process is dependent on a consideration of all the important properties of these materials (especially their handling characteristics), as well as those of special surface coatings, inks, or other chemical treatments that may be required. In turn, selection of an acceptable substrate for a particular use depends on such variables as the quality of printing obtainable on it, wear characteristics, any special procedures involved, and overall cost. In other words, there are no handy basic rules of thumb in this field to simplify this selection process; each project must be handled on its own merits.

The major plastic films used in graphic arts products include cellophane, cellulose acetate, fluorohalocarbon, ionomer, nylon, polypropylene, polyethylene, pliofilm, polybutylene, polycarbonate, polyester, polystyrene, polyurethane, polyvinyl alcohol, and vinyl. The best printing results can be obtained on cellophane and acetate, but most of the rest of these materials will produce good printed results if handled properly. Materials which yield only fair to good results under the best conditions include ionomer, pliofilm, polybutylene, polyester, low- and medium-density polyethylene, polypropylene, polyurethane, and polyvinyl alcohol. Some of these materials need special surface treatments to make them ink-receptive; these are fluorohalocarbon, ionomer, polybutylene, polyethylene, and polypropylene. Others require special inks; these are pliofilm, polystyrene, polyurethane, polyvinyl alcohol, and vinyl.

Foils can be made from a number of metals, but aluminum is by far the dominant material used because of its light weight and low cost. It also can be colored easily. Aluminum foils can be printed directly with certain inks, but the foil must be absolutely free of oils, a condition which is very difficult to maintain during handling and processing. Therefore, virtually all aluminum foil is surface-treated prior to printing with a thin alcohol-shellac mixture. The alcohol evaporates almost instantly upon application, leaving a microscopic layer of shellac on the foil surface to accept the ink. This coating can be applied on a regular printing press, or pre-treated foil can be purchased from the supplier.

Various coating techniques are being used to make films and foils ink-receptive in those cases where they are not naturally so. The particular type of coating used depends on the specific kinds of inks and substrates that must be matched. In addition, these coatings often must have additional features when they are used in conjunction with other materials. For example, printed films used in packaging perfumes or liquor must be alcohol-resistant, rub-resistant, and scuff-resistant, and any coatings must also have these characteristics. Printers and coaters of these films and foils must establish laboratory testing facilities to conduct peel and wrinkle tests.

INK SYSTEMS

Each of these substrates requires special attention regarding the ink system used, even though special inks may not be required. Proper ink formulation of whatever inks are used is imperative. All plastic films and foils are smooth and non-porous. Since they are usually printed in rolls and rewound, they require inks which must dry without absorption almost instantly with little heat to prevent curling, cracking, melting, or other damage. Typical ink-drying methods for plastics are oxidation, polymerization, evaporation, or a combination of these. Proper ink drying is very important in preventing *blocking* (causing smearing and smudging of the image) which may occur if the ink retains the solvent.

PRESS CONDITIONS

It is particularly important to control web temperatures and tension on the press. Plastics generally are susceptible to stretching or other distortions when heated or pulled. Improper heat and tension conditions on press can cause misregister in the printing units or distortion of the final image in the drying units. In practice, it is very difficult to predict in advance of actual production exactly what settings should be used. Therefore, the printer must carefully check every incoming shipment of material for chemical and physical condition when received, and then make further tests at the start of each production run.

A critical factor in the printing of these materials is the number of colors desired. True process color, for example, requires the use of process cyan, magenta, and yellow on a white surface. If the job is to be printed on clear film or foil, a layer of white may have to be printed first as a base. Other colors, too, may require special consideration. A deep black, for example, may not be obtained if printed over a very opaque yellow, which in turn is needed to provide adequate coverage on a clear film.

Another area requiring special care is that of matching proofs of halftones on paper. The printing characteristics of the proof paper will be very different from the characteristics of films and foils, and what may work well on the paper will not necessarily work on the film. Choices of screen values, especially, may have to be different, and here, too, a special layer of white may have to be printed first as a suitable base for even a single-color halftone.

Artwork also must be suitable for reproduction on films and foils. Sharp, contrasty transparencies may be used, but better results usually can be obtained from an artist's opaque drawing than from a transparency.

CONCLUSION

If one fact should be impressed on those working with these materials, it is that a far wider range of variations is encountered compared to paper and board, resulting in the need for careful communication all the way through the production process.

The natural makeup of papers and boards and the coatings and inks used on them make these substances inherently more predictable than films and foils. The ingredients and processes used to make foils and films and their inks allow much wider variations in the end results. Many other characteristics important to printed quality (such as opacity, gloss, color, and the like) also vary much more widely in films and foils than they do in paper. The only way to overcome such problems is to have complete communication between all parties involved in the production of the job.

PRINTING ON COVER MATERIALS
Fred Klinger, PRESIDENT, LEHIGH PRESS LITHOGRAPHERS

Over the past 35 years, the variety of materials used for covers of books, pamphlets, looseleaf binders, record albums, and the like has grown rapidly with the introduction of many kinds of plastics and other synthetic materials. Virtually all of these new materials have required the development of new ink chemistries and special handling processes at the printing press to ensure adherence of the ink to the substrate. While most printers have equipment that can be used to print these materials, the special conditions of manufacture have given rise to a small group of companies which specialize in the printing of such materials.

All of the major printing processes—letterpress, lithography, gravure, and screen printing—can be used to print at least some, and often all, of these materials in multiple colors, including four-color process. Artwork and plates can be made by the conventional means, requiring no special or unusual techniques.

The printer must always be consulted, however, when spotting or other damage. Within each basic family of the required special inks and handling techniques are used. The nature and composition of many plastics are not readily evident from their outward appearance. If the printer is not informed as to the precise material being used, he may not realize that some special ink or procedure is required. When this happens, the entire job usually is a complete loss, as the ink may not stick to the substrate at all.

PRELIMINARY CONSIDERATIONS

Choosing which cover material to use is a matter of balancing quality of the printing, wear characteristics, and cost. Cover materials come in a wide quality range, from clay-coated papers to solid plastic sheets which will not tear or wrinkle and are impervious to most spotting or other damage. Within each basic family of materials there are often various grades or quality levels.

One source of help in selecting the appropriate kind and grade of material for a given job is the specialist printer familiar with the entire field of cover production. Another is a set of quality specifications used in the book industry to define the quality levels that must be built into school textbooks. These specifications, adopted by the National Association of State Textbook Administrators (NASTA) with the advice of the book industry, are quite specific and involve the use of numerous scientific tests to establish the standards. These tests include measurement of abrasion resistance, tear strength, scuff resistance of ink, and the like. Copies of these specifications are available for a nominal fee from the Book Manufacturers' Institute, Stamford, Connecticut. Of all the tests involved, the Taber abrasion test is probably the most important in most situations and should be performed on all jobs.

Cover materials usually come to the printer in sheets ranging in size from 18" to 22" to 44" x 66" or in rolls to be sheeted by the printer. Some cover materials can be printed on one side only, while others can be printed on both sides. Some are made of one kind of material throughout, such as a solid plastic sheet, but most are combinations of materials, such as a coating of plastic or starch over a substrate of paper or cloth.

STANDARD CLASSIFICATIONS

The NASTA specifications classify all cover materials into four major groups according to the ways different substrates are combined with printing surfaces. These are: cloth-based, paper-based coated, paper-based reinforced, and all synthetic. A distinction is made also between "woven" materials (essentially the cloth category) and "nonwovens" (all others).

Each of the four categories includes a number of different surface materials. *Cloth-based* materials, for example, are either starch-filled, or coated or impregnated with pyroxylin or acrylic. Raw or unsurfaced cloth by itself is used only in very special cases for unusual bookbindings and is not generally suited to printing. It is usually foil-stamped or embossed if it is decorated at all.

Paper-based (or kraft-based) materials can be coated with many kinds of plastics, but pyroxylin and vinyl are the most used. In addition, acrylic compounds have been added to clays used for some coated papers in recent years, and these have taken over a large part of the market for pyroxylin materials.

Reinforced paper-based materials are also made primarily with pyroxylin or vinyl and are handled identically in manufacture to the materials coated with these plastics.

All-synthetic materials are the newest category and also the one in which the newest developments have occurred. Vinyl was one of the first plastics used by itself for covers, but recently it has been joined by several varieties of polyolefins in the form of both thin "plastic papers" and heavy sheets from which hardcover cases are stamped in one operation. The one-piece hardcover case for conventional books is still experimental but can be expected to make a place for itself in the bookbinding market. To date, the rigid or semirigid plastic cover has been used primarily for looseleaf binders, while the lighter weight materials have been used for book and pamphlet covers and for a variety of specialty applications.

PRINTING CONSIDERATIONS

Clay and pyroxylin surfaces have been in use for many years for covers, and their printing has now become a well-developed technique, presenting no significant problems for the printer skilled in the technology. Acrylics, although newer, also have been reduced to a routine production process at about the same level of difficulty as pyroxylin printing. For each of these surfaces, universal inks, which will work with all of the specific surfaces of a given type, are now available.

Starch surfaces, too, have been in use for as long as any other material, but they are not easily printed by lithography or screen printing. Starch-filled cloth generally is foil-stamped for decoration.

The newer plastics have presented significant problems in recent years because of their newness. Although they are being brought under better control now, vinyls and polyolefins still are not as easy to handle as the older materials. While these surfaces can take ink quite adequately today, the inks do not dry readily and this requires special techniques, extra care, and slower speeds in handling the printed sheets. Ink on nonporous plastics must dry completely by oxidation, not by absorption into the sheet as happens in printing on paper. There is hope that new drying methods, such as ultraviolet curing, will help solve this problem.

Another problem is the flexibility and limpness of vinyl, which permits it to stretch out of shape as it is pulled through the press. Cylinder pressures must be set very carefully, especially when printing over embossing, if image distortion is to be avoided. Vinyl is especially suited to screen printing because cylinder-type presses are not used for short runs. Also, the heavier lays of ink possible with this process improve the abrasion resistance of the completed job.

One of the synthetic materials, Tyvek, requires its own special inks. This is a relatively moderate-cost material used widely on elementary and high school textbooks, which employ lithographic printing extensively for decoration. Tyvek has very good printability (with the proper expertise) by this process.

All inks for printing on nonporous surfaces must have special qualities, including extra resistance to bleeding, fading, or color change. Although these inks are also made to be more resistant than others to abrasion, it is still necessary to apply a separate liquid top coating over the printed image for protection. In addition, therefore, the inks must be bleed-proof. Some book publishers are also laminating printed covers with a polyester film for protective coating. Some printers, at the publisher's request, can emboss the cover after film lamination to more closely match the "feel" and esthetics of cloth. The trend toward film-laminated covers is very prevalent today.

With the cost of traditional cover materials rising, new kinds of materials are being sought. One, for example, which is being tried is a simulated cloth for bookbinding which is made by printing a cloth pattern on a paper base or a reinforced paper base by gravure and then embossing it to get the texture of woven cloth. This material can be printed by screen process; thus far the use of other printing methods is limited.

INKS   13

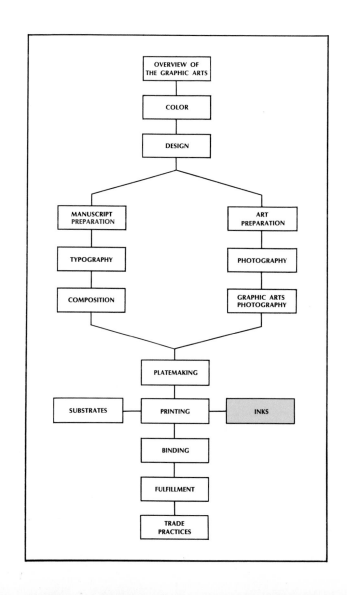

INTRODUCTION TO PRINTING INKS

Gary G. Winters, INMONT CORPORATION

It has been estimated that well over a million new ink formulations are created each year in the United States to meet specific customer needs. The length of the list of raw materials from which inks are created is equally amazing. There is certainly no other industry in the graphic arts which is called upon to tailor high-performance products, literally daily, to conform to so great a variety of end-use and processing requirements.

In the last 40 years, printing ink technology has at least kept pace with the printing revolution, and today inks are available that can print and dry faster than presses and ancillary equipment can run. In fact, the newest presses still are not taxing the drying speeds of available inks. It is possible, with present ink technology, to produce inks for web-fed lithographic presses that will run at 3,000 feet per minute.

Printers and printing buyers, who exert a great deal of influence on printing ink formulation, may find that a knowledge of what inks are and what they can do will help insure satisfaction with the printed result.

THE PROPERTIES OF INKS

The key properties of inks, aside from their color properties, are *viscosity*, *yield value*, *tack*, and *drying mechanism*.

Viscosity and yield value

Viscosity and yield value together determine the *body* or consistency of an ink, but it is important to separate these two properties.

Viscosity is defined as the relative resistance to continual shear (or flow). Sheet-fed inks are high in viscosity (that is, they are fairly heavy or thick), and flexographic and gravure inks are low; most other types of ink fall in between.

Yield value (thixotropy) is the relative resistance to initial shear. Thixotropic inks are those which have initial body, but soften when agitated or worked. Inks of high yield value are called "short" inks and have the consistency of butter or mayonnaise. Those with low yield value are said to be "long," having flow properties like honey.

Many factors affect choice of viscosity and yield value. For example, lithographic and letterpress inks for coated paper need heavy body (high viscosity and yield value) to give gloss, print sharpness, hold-out, and other desirable characteristics, while inks for newsprint need thinner body to permit penetration into the stock. Gravure inks need quite low viscosity and yield value so the ink can flow out of the cells of the plate or cylinder.

Tack

Tack is defined as the relative force required to split the ink film between two surfaces. It is a measure, therefore, of the internal or cohesive strength of the ink film. Tack selection is based on a balance between high tack to give sharp printing and low tack to produce good solids or to prevent linting (pulling of fibers from the surface of the paper by the ink), picking (lifting of paper coating by the ink), or tearing of the paper. Lithographic inks must retain tack even when mixed with fountain solution. In multicolor printing, the tack of the first-down ink must be higher than that of the second-down ink at the moment of impression, or the second-down will not lay down properly (*trap*) onto the first film. In letterpress and lithography, it is common to "tack-grade" inks for color sequence (from tackiest to least tacky) to optimize trapping. In flexography and gravure, this is not necessary, since each color is dry before the next is applied.

Drying mechanism

The *drying* mechanism is the process by which a printing ink changes from a wet film to a dry film. All of the common drying methods are discussed later.

Primarily because of the differences in the drying mechanisms involved, the composition of inks varies widely from one printing process to the next. Not until the introduction of ultraviolet curing inks has it been possible to use a single drying mechanism for lithography, letterpress, flexography, gravure, and screen printing.

THE COMPOSITION OF INKS

The list of basic types of ingredients that make up printing inks is deceptively short.

Element	Basic purpose
Colorant	To provide the visible image.
Vehicle	To bind the colorant to the substrate, and to serve as the carrier on the press.
Solvent	To keep the vehicle in liquid form until the ink is to be dried.
Additives	To impart a wide variety of special properties.

Within this simple framework, there are innumerable variations and combinations which can go into the composition of a particular type of ink.

Ink colorants

The colorant is the portion of the ink that is responsible for the placement of a visible image on a substrate. In colored inks, it imparts the properties of color (shade or hue), color intensity (strength or saturation), and cleanliness (lightness or absence of black). (See "The Measurement and Specification of Color," page 21.) Advances in the development of pigments have made possible a color explosion in the graphic arts. Hundreds of colors are available for use on all kinds of packaging and reading material.

Pigments are selected with great care, for they impart a number of other properties to inks besides color, including *opacity* and *transparency, rheology* (viscosity), *fade resistance* (lightfastness), *heat resistance, chemical resistance,* and *water resistance.* Pigments partially determine whether an ink is suitable for lithography (water resistance), soap wrappers (chemical resistance), four-color process printing (transparency), bread wrappers (opacity), or outdoor signs (fade resistance).

Ink colorants can be divided into five categories: *blacks, organic color pigments, inorganic color pigments, whites,* and *dyes.*

Black pigments. These are basically carbon black (soot), manufactured by burning or cracking gas or oil. Several types of blacks are available, with unique properties resulting from each. Ink formulations often contain several types of black pigments to obtain desired properties. Alkali blue pigments or similar toners are often added to blacks to darken their original gray or brownish shades.

Organic color pigments. These are the pigments most commonly used in inks. They are generally very complex in chemical structure and low in specific gravity compared to inorganic colors. The most popular ones used in commercial and publication printing are described below.

Diarylide Yellow: Highly transparent, very strong; the most popular pigment for process yellow in all printing methods.

Rhodamine Red: Used for highest quality process red in lithographic and letterpress inks because of its shade and its cleanliness.

Lithol Rubine Red: Less expensive than Rhodamine Red; a medium-clean pigment for lithographic process color.

Phloxine Red: Clean process red widely used in heat-set letterpress and publication gravure; bleeds in water, so it is not widely used in lithographic inks.

Red Lake C: A "warm" red widely used in lithographic inks because of its bright shade and low cost.

Phthalocyanine Blue: High-quality pigment; the most popular blue pigment for process-color work in all printing methods.

Peacock Blue: High-quality pigment used primarily for process work for publication gravure; not used in lithography because of bleeding.

Victoria Blue: Popular because of shade, known as "royal blue."

Alkali Blue: Because of dark top-tone and high color strength, widely used to "tone" blacks. It comes in a variety of reddish blue shades.

Inorganic color pigments. These are generally used in packaging applications because of their resistance properties. They are mostly compounds of metals and are therefore heavy materials. The most popular ones are described below.

Chrome Yellow: A class of lead compounds, produced in a number of shades, from greenish to lemon, with lightfastness and solvent resistance; used in heat-set letterpress, but to a declining degree.

Chrome and Molybdate Oranges: Lead compounds similar in structure to Chrome Yellow.

Cadmium-Mercury Reds: A wide range of red shades with excellent lightfastness and solvent resistance.

Iron Blue: A transparent iron compound available in a number of different shades, including Prussian, milori, and bronze.

Silver: A powdered aluminum used to produce a silver-colored ink.

Gold: Powders made from various copper alloys which yield numerous metallic gold shades, available in many grades and finenesses.

White pigments. There are two basic types of white pigments: transparent and opaque. The popular transparent whites are alumina hydrate, magnesium carbonate, and calcium carbonate. They are used to "extend" colored transparent pigments for making tint colors. The two primary opaque whites are titanium dioxide and zinc sulfide. Opaque whites are used as primary pigments themselves, or to extend colored opaque pigments to increase opacity or lighten the color.

Dyes. All of the colorants discussed above are pigments, which means that they are insoluble in either the vehicle or the solvent used in the ink. Dyes, on the other hand, are soluble in the ink vehicle. Inks containing dyes are characterized by high gloss and cleanliness and brilliance of color. However, the fact that dyes are soluble in the vehicle does place definite limitations on their use, particularly in lithographic and letterpress inks, where their main use is as toners for blacks. Dyes are primarily found in flexographic inks.

Ink vehicles

The vehicle is the fluid portion of the ink which serves as a carrier for the pigment. It is the single most important component affecting press performance. Although the primary task of the vehicle is to bind the colorant to the substrate, its job is much more complex than that. The ink's tack and flow characteristics are largely determined by the type of vehicle it contains; it is also the vehicle that determines the drying method of the ink.

The composition of vehicles varies greatly from one kind to another, but they usually contain some combination of oils, resins, and solvents. The printing process to be used and the drying system required determine the type of vehicle needed. Ink vehicles extend all the way from simple mineral oils (in news inks) to complex oligomers which polymerize in the presence of free radicals (in ultraviolet curing inks) to form new materials with unique properties. (The various types of vehicles are described in greater detail in the section on drying mechanisms later in this article.)

Ink solvents

Technically, the ink solvent—provided the ink contains one—is part of the vehicle, but it is isolated here for the purpose of discussion. A solvent is primarily used to provide a means of drying. It is also needed to solubilize the hard resins in the vehicle to provide flow to the vehicle system.

In a solvent-containing ink, the vehicle is soluble in the solvent, but it reverts to a hard, dry film—its normal state—when the solvent evaporates. Until the development of ultraviolet curing inks, in which no solvent is needed, evaporation of the solvent was the only reasonably practical way to attain "instant drying" in such processes as flexography, gravure, heat-set lithography, and heat-set letterpress.

There is quite a bit of variation in the chemical nature and boiling point of ink solvents. The solvent systems used in the inks should be compatible with the rollers, blankets, and/or plates used in the particular printing process. A substance such as toluene, for example, would soften and swell a natural rubber plate, so a synthetic rubber plate would have to be used with this type of solvent system. In some printing processes, the solvent is force-evaporated by heat; in others, heat may or may not be used.

In heat-set lithography and letterpress, the ink solvent is usually an aliphatic petroleum fraction with a boiling point in the range of 435°–535°F. Typical solvent contents of lithographic and letterpress heat-set inks are 35%–45% and 45%–50%, respectively. Drying is achieved by heating the paper to 280°–320°F.

In gravure, the solvents are petroleum fractions such as toluene and lactol spirits (in publication work) and esters and ketones (in packaging). These are more volatile than the lithographic and letterpress solvents, and the paper is heated to about 140°F to flash them off. Solvent content is about 85%.

In flexography, the solvents used are volatile enough so that heat is often not even required. Typical solvents are alcohols (ethanol, propanol), ketones (methyl ethyl ketone), and esters (ethyl acetate). Flexographic inks contain 70% solvent.

Ecological regulations on ink solvent emissions for flexography and gravure are now fairly well finalized, with ultimate compliance scheduled for the early to late 1980's, depending upon the individual abatement approaches used. Earlier regulations permitted use of "exempt" solvents, considered at the time to be not photochemically reactive. However, it has since been determined that even these solvents contribute to smog in the presence of ozone and other atmospheric oxidants. For practical purposes, all ink solvents for flexography and gravure—except, of course, water—are classed as photochemically reactive and will be subject to abatement regulations. The primary approaches to abatement are (1) adoption of water-based inks and (2) solvent recovery or incineration for solvent-based inks. Final regulations for heat-set lithography and letterpress have not been promulgated, but some degree of control or abatement will be required. The future availability and cost of energy will be key factors in the role incineration plays in solvent abatement. In the meantime, the so-called nuisance regulations on smoke and odor continue in effect. (See "New Ink Technologies," page 512.)

Ink additives

Inks almost always contain one or more additives designed to impart special properties, either during printing or in the final product. Additives—such as driers, waxes, gums, lubricants, and starches—may be used to obtain the following properties and effects:

Gloss
Flatness (absence of gloss)
Hardness
Fast drying
Fast setting
Rapid penetration
Sharp printing
Rub and scratch resistance
Water tolerance
Lubricity
Thixotropy (resistance to initial flow)
Adhesion (attachment of ink to substrate)
Imprintability (the ability of one layer of ink to adhere to a layer which is already dry)
Magnetic response (for detection by electronic devices)
Viscosity adjustment
pH adjustment
Tack adjustment
Reduced strike-through (reduction of penetration of the vehicle through the paper so that the ink will not be visible on the reverse side)
Freedom from setoff (no transfer of ink from one sheet to the back of another)
Non-misting (prevention of ink's "flying" off the press rollers in a mist or spray)
Foam resistance (suppression of tendency of inks to foam upon agitation)
Non-skinning (prevention of drying in the can, which results in the formation of a skin or crust)

HOW INKS ARE CLASSIFIED

The types of inks, and their uses, are so many that it is difficult to classify them in any one single way. Among the ways to categorize them are by:

Drying mechanism (oxidation, solvent evaporation, etc.)
Printing process (lithography, gravure, etc.)
Type of plate surface (planographic, raised, etc.)
Substrate (paper, foil, etc.)
End use (newspapers, books, etc.)
Special properties (metallic, magnetic, etc.)
Paper feed (sheet, web)

Many of these are interrelated. For example, multicolored printing on a foil web (substrate) requires an "instant dry" ink (drying mechanism), which calls for flexography or gravure (printing process) or ultraviolet inks.

Classifying by drying mechanism

Classifying by drying mechanism is one of the best ways to see how ink compositions and printing processes relate. In many cases, the type of printing process dictates the drying mechanism. For example, heat-set printing requires inks with a significant portion of an evaporative solvent. In almost all cases, inks are applied wet (except for some cold-set inks) and must attain a dry state before further processing or use. The primary drying methods are listed and described in table 13.1.

Classifying by printing process

Inks may also be broadly classified by the printing processes for which they may be used. For a given process, however, ink properties may vary considerably, depending upon the drying method, the substrate, and other variables. For example, web offset inks for coated paper may be quite different from those for newsprint, even though the same printing press is used. This should be taken into account in using the

Drying method	Typical ingredients and mechanisms	Printing process
1. Oxidation	Inks with vehicles containing "drying oil," such as linseed, china wood, castor, or soybean oil (often modified with synthetic resin to form alkyds for faster and harder drying), dry through the initial step of oxidation (absorption of oxygen from the air) followed by polymerization (a linking of small molecular units to form a few large units). This type of drying is preceded by a *setting* step during which a small amount of solvent which has been added is absorbed rapidly by the paper, causing a quick increase in viscosity. This process, known as the paper-ink reaction, results in a "quick-setting" feature. Infrared emitters are being used on a limited basis to accelerate this quick setting. The heat from the units speeds up the absorption of solvent into the paper surface. Infrared emitters do not increase the oxidation rate itself, since the heat level (120° F) is too low.	Sheet-fed lithography Sheet-fed letterpress Steel die engraving Collotype Screen printing
2. Solvent evaporation	Resin, dissolved in the solvent, returns to a hard state upon forced (using heat) or normal evaporation of the solvent. Typical resin-solvent combinations are outlined below, along with the percent of solvent in each total ink formulation.	Heat-set lithography Heat-set letterpress Flexography Gravure Screen printing

Process	Resin	Solvent type	%
Heat-set lithography	Rosin ester	Hydrocarbon	40
Heat-set letterpress	Hydrocarbon	Hydrocarbon	45
Flexography	Nitrocellulose	Alcohol	70
Gravure	Gum rosin	Toluene	85
Screen printing	Drying oil	Toluene	20

	Some heat-set inks are now available which dry at paper-surface temperatures of 220°–260° F, versus the typical range of 280°–320° F. These "low-temperature-drying" inks reduce the energy required for heat-set solvent evaporation. They do not involve a new drying mechanism, so they are merely a subgroup under the solvent evaporation type. They differ in that the particular combinations of resins and solvents employed can tolerate more solvent retention in the dried film. Since less solvent needs to be evaporated, less energy is required.	
3. Penetration	A solventless vehicle of non-drying oil such as petroleum or rosin oil dries simply by soaking into an absorbent substrate, such as newsprint. Because there is little or no binder, the ink can be rubbed off fairly easily.	Letterpress Lithography
4. Ultraviolet curing	This method requires a reactive vehicle (epoxidized drying-oil-modified acrylates) and a light-sensitive catalyst (photosensitizer). Upon exposure to ultraviolet light, the light-sensitive catalyst stimulates the reactive vehicle to undergo a rapid increase in molecular size (polymerization), resulting in a cured, hard film.	Lithography Letterpress Flexography Gravure
5. Thermal curing	Inks that dry by this method contain a mixture of chemically reactive materials (alkyd-amines) which polymerize in the presence of heat. An acid catalyst and the application of heat in the temperature range of 300°–350°F are sufficient to produce a cured, hard film.	Heat-set lithography Heat-set letterpress
6. Cold-set	Waxes and resins, which are solid at room temperature, are melted before printing; on contact with the paper, they cool and solidify. In the case of electrostatic inks, melting may take place after the application of dry powder resin to the image area, followed by re-solidification on cooling.	Letterpress Electrostatic printing Transfer
7. Moisture-set	Water-insoluble resins are dissolved in glycol, which is hygroscopic (that is, it readily takes up and retains moisture). After printing, moisture is introduced and is absorbed by the glycol. Since the resin is water-insoluble, it precipitates out, taking the pigment with it.	Letterpress

following chart, which gives the basic properties needed in inks used for each of the major printing processes.

Process	Ink requirements
1. Sheet-fed	
(a) Letterpress	Moderately heavy body and tack.
(b) Lithography	Somewhat heavier body and tack; resistance to water; higher color strength (to compensate for thinner film of ink than in letterpress).
2. Heat-set web	
(a) Letterpress	Lower body and tack and more flow than sheet-fed counterpart.
(b) Lithography	Lower body and tack and more flow than sheet-fed counterpart; high resistance to water emulsification.
3. Non-heat-set web	
(a) Letterpress	Low tack; good flow.
(b) Lithography	Somewhat heavier body and tack and higher color strength than for letterpress; resistance to water.
4. Flexography	Relatively fluid, with fast-evaporating solvent.
5. Gravure	Quite fluid, to permit transfer from cells; free of grit, to prevent wear.
6. Screen printing	Short and buttery, for easy squeegee use; controlled solvent volatility to prevent clogged screens.

Matching ink to substrate

One of the most important factors in the selection of inks is the type of surfaces upon which they will be printed. This is particularly true in the packaging field, although even commercial and publication printing utilize a wide, and increasing, variety of stocks.

The substrate, the printing process, and the ink must be compatible to insure the desired result. If any one of the three is not a match, problems are likely to result. Some of the pitfalls of improper matching of inks to substrates are exhibited in the form of:

Poor trapping
Strike-through
Setoff
Unsharp halftone dots
Linting
Picking
Poor adhesion
Poor gloss
Skipped printing (unprinted areas due to surface roughness of paper, stiffness of ink, etc.)

Blistering (heat-related bubbling of paper coating from entrapped moisture during the ink-drying process)
Yellowing (heat-related discoloring of stock during ink-drying process)
Puckering (distortion of paper due to the water in the fountain solution)

Note that these are not always the result of poor ink-and-substrate matching. For example, blistering and yellowing can be the result of simply heating the paper web to a higher temperature than is necessary to dry the ink.

The following is a summary of popular substrates matched against the key ink properties needed and printing processes normally used. Note that other printing processes may be used, but special considerations are usually required. For example, sheet-fed lithography can be used to print foil and some plastics, but drying time is long, and special handling is required to prevent setoff.

Substrate	Ink requirements	Printing processes
Coated paper	Gloss, sharp printing, rub resistance	All
Uncoated paper	Sharp printing, low tack	All
Newsprint	Good absorptivity, low tack	Web letterpress, web offset, gravure
Boxboard	Hard film, rub & fade resistance, low tack	Sheet-fed lithography, gravure
Corrugated	Fast drying, good flow	Sheet-fed letterpress, flexography
Kraft	Fast drying, good flow	Flexography, letterpress
Plastics	Fast drying, adhesion	Flexography, gravure
Foil	Fast drying, adhesion	Flexography, gravure

THE RIGHT INK FOR THE JOB

It is obvious that many different factors must be taken into account in selecting an ink. National surveys indicate that inks comprise an average of only five percent of the total cost of printing—but they are absolutely critical to the final result.

The printer and the printing buyer must communicate to the inkmaker the exact requirements of each job, for two important reasons: to confirm that the expected results are attainable, and to insure that the proper materials and workmanship are used to achieve the desired results. Foresight and good communications will help the ink manufacturer to furnish the right product for the job.

INKS IN COMMON USE
Theodore Lustig, SUN CHEMICAL CORPORATION

Classification of all the various inks available today into neat categories is very difficult because there are many parameters by which inks may be classified. It is customary, however, to use descriptive terms to identify various ink types, and a brief discussion of the various classifications into which an ink may fall should be helpful here.

One way to classify inks is by printing process; and most inks can be described as lithographic, letterpress, gravure, flexographic, or screen printing inks. Inks can be further divided within each process by the type of press they are designed for, such as sheet-fed or web offset inks, rotary letterpress inks, and the like.

Another way of classifying inks is by method of drying, such as heat-set, thermal curing, or ultraviolet. Still another descriptive system often used is by end product; and we have newspaper inks, magazine and catalog inks, and so forth.

Often physical properties are used to describe inks, such as scratch resistance, translucency, opacity, light-fastness, slip or non-slip, to name a few.

A distinction is often made between common inks and so-called "specialty" inks, but the dividing line is so ill-defined that it is virtually impossible to use the specialty concept in a specific classification scheme. In general, however, the specialty label is applied to inks with unusual characteristics, such as indelibility, alkali or soap resistance, water resistance, acid resistance, and freedom from poisonous substances. These inks may have special ingredients such as metallic powders, magnetic ingredients for electronic machine detection, or perfume for giving attractive smells to advertising pieces. Most of these special properties are useful in specific situations or industries, such as food packaging where inks must not contaminate the food inside the package, or in banking where magnetically printed checks are read electronically.

The descriptive terms listed here are limited to the more common kinds of inks used widely in the industry, plus some of the more publicized inks with additional special properties. It should be noted that the categories as listed are by no means exclusive. More than one classification scheme is often used to define a given ink, such as heat-set lithographic inks, and inks may be formulated to contain varied combinations of properties needed for specific printing processes or end uses. Two inks may have a number of characteristics in common and differ in other aspects. For example, one formulation of a high-gloss, ultra-violet-reactive metallic ink may be required for the offset printing of a beverage can and another for the letterpress printing of an annual report cover.

The list is presented in alphabetical order to simplify its use as a reference.

Abrasion-resistant inks: Inks containing certain additives which give them the ability to withstand the effects of repeated rubbing or scuffing. Abrasion resistance in inks is of particular importance in such products as folding cartons, book covers, and high-quality brochures and magazines. (Also called *rub-resistant* and *scuff-resistant inks.*)

Aluminum inks: Metallic inks whose principal pigment is aluminum powder. Often referred to as "silver inks," they are used when a silver color is desired. The metallic effect is enhanced by use on high-finish coated stock.

Bronze inks: Metallic inks whose color source is bronze powder, which consists of fine flakes of any of various alloys of copper and zinc. Depending upon the proportions of copper and zinc in the alloy, a color range from gold through bronze to copper can be achieved. These inks may tend to tarnish. They require good quality paper for maximum impact. (Also called *gold inks* or *gold bronze inks.*)

Can-decorating inks: See *metal-decorating inks.*

Cold-set inks: Solid, predominantly black inks which require melting and application on a press with heated rollers. Solidification occurs when the ink cools on contact with the unheated paper. This type of ink is used mainly in the production of carbon paper. In general, the process is used for full coverage of a page or for large black areas.

Comic inks: Special formulations of standard four-color process inks used on newsprint for the printing of comic supplements and advertising inserts. These inks may have less color strength than standard four-color process inks because the quality of the end product is not critical. (See also *news inks.*)

Cover inks: See *opaque inks.*

Day-Glo inks: See *fluorescent inks.*

Doubletone inks: A type of ink containing a soluble toner which bleeds out to produce the effect of a second color. Thus, a single impression can give the effect of a duotone or two-color printing.

Dull inks: See *matte inks.*

Electrostatic inks: Not inks in the truest sense. They are actually toners composed of a very fine powder which is attracted to paper by means of an electrostatic charge. This is the technique used in the most popular dry office copying machines.

Flexographic inks: Quick-drying, low-viscosity, solvent-type inks, containing both dyes and pigments, which are used with rubber plates for printing by flexography. Flexographic inks are similar to gravure inks and can print on a wide range of substrates. Their primary application is for packaging printing, especially on polyolefin films and cellophane, as well as on paper, board, and corrugated cartons.

Fluorescent inks: Highly brilliant inks which appear to glow. Available in a limited range of colors, these inks are translucent and work best on a white background. They are easily contaminated by conventional inks, losing much of their distinctive reflective quality. In some instances, two impressions are required in printing. Some of these inks have such good spectral qualities that they are used for process printing on uncoated paper. The best known trade name for these inks is *Day-Glo*.

Fugitive colors: Inks containing non-permanent pigments or dyes, which change or lose color quickly when exposed to light, moisture, heat, or other adverse environmental conditions.

Gloss inks: See *high-gloss inks*.

Gold inks: The common name for gold-colored bronze inks, whose pigments consist of metallic powder composed of an alloy of copper and zinc. (See also *bronze inks*.)

Gravure inks: Quick-drying, solvent-based inks, which usually dry by evaporation of the solvent. They must be fluid enough to fill the wells of the engraved cylinder or plate used in gravure printing but must have enough body so that they will not spread out of the wells and will be drawn out by the substrate. The binder and solvent system must be such that there is good adhesion to the substrate. Gravure inks must contain no hard particles that could scratch the surface of the plate or cylinder.

Grease-proof inks: Inks that resist the action of fats, oils, and greases, used principally for printing packaging for food and lubricants.

Halftone inks: The name applied to the inks used to reproduce photographs or other images which have been screened to reduce their black and gray areas to dot patterns so that the tonal gradations in the images can be reproduced by the printing process. These are finely dispersed inks with high tinctorial (color) strength, formulated to print and retain fine detail without fill-in.

Heat-reactive inks: See *thermal curing inks*.

Heat-set inks: Quick-drying inks containing solvents which evaporate upon application of heat, usually from gas-fired, high-velocity, hot-air dryers at the delivery end of the press, leaving the dried ink with good gloss after chilling. Once dried, heat-set inks are in a thermoplastic state—that is, they can be re-softened with the application of heat. They are used for both offset and letterpress printing.

Heavy-bodied inks: Inks with high viscosity or stiff consistency, which find best use where rather heavy lay-down of ink is required. Such inks are often short and buttery and have poor flow characteristics.

High-gloss inks: Inks that provide a high gloss or luster, even on dull coated stock, because of gloss varnish content and minimum penetration of the paper. These inks can be overprinted on conventional or matte-finish inks of the same color—black on black, for example—for an unusual effect. (Also called *gloss inks* or *glossy inks*.)

Imitation gold inks: Gold-colored metallic inks formulated with colored pigments for hues and aluminum paste for their metallic sheen instead of with bronze powder. (See also *bronze inks*.)

Indelible inks: A special formulation used principally on textiles where the desire is for permanency and resistance to repeated laundering.

Invisible inks: See *sympathetic inks*.

Job inks: Heavy-bodied inks formulated for general-purpose, low-cost printing to meet the needs of smaller sheet-fed presses. Associated with the letterpress process, this is a versatile type of ink that readily adapts to a variety of printing projects.

Letterpress inks: Inks which are used to print from raised surfaces as in the letterpress process. Tack and viscosity are generally moderate but vary depending upon the type of paper and press for which the inks are intended. Drying methods include oxidation, evaporation, penetration, precipitation, and polymerization.

Lithographic inks: Inks used in the offset lithographic printing process. They are formulated to resist excessive emulsification by the water-based fountain solution used in offset printing. These inks are highly stable with generally higher tack, body, and color strength than letterpress inks and must be suited to the type of paper and press used.

Magnetic inks: Specialty inks containing iron oxide powders which permit them to be magnetized after printing so that the printed portion can be read by various electronic devices. Their principal use is on checks and similar documents where identification is required in high-speed data processing equipment.

Matte inks: Inks that dry with a non-gloss or dull finish. They can be used to produce special contrast effects in conjunction with conventional or gloss inks and are often used in lithography to simulate gravure printing, which is usually dull. (Also called *dull inks*.)

Metal-decorating inks: A specific formulation for use in printing at high speeds on cylindrical beverage cans, either aluminum or steel, and on flat metal sheets of all types. The printing on cans is done on special can-decorating equipment by the dry offset printing process, with up to four colors and a varnish applied at speeds of up to 800 cans per minute. Ultraviolet instant-drying inks are now being introduced for this use.

Metallic inks: The class of inks containing any of various types of metallic powders suspended in a vehicle, usually a varnish, to produce a metallic effect. (See also *bronze inks* and *aluminum inks*.)

Moisture-set inks: Inks used for letterpress and formulated with a vehicle containing water-insoluble resins in a solvent, usually a glycol, that attracts moisture. When the solvent has drawn sufficient moisture from either the paper, the surrounding atmosphere, or a moisture source on the press, the water-insoluble binder precipitates out, causing the ink to set. Moisture-set inks are relatively odorless, a characteristic which makes them suitable for food packaging printing. (Also called *precipitation inks* and *steam-set inks*.)

News inks: A formulation for letterpress of black or colored pigments, usually in a mineral-oil vehicle, for use on newsprint paper. Conventional news inks dry by absorption, but newer formulas may employ heat-set or emulsion systems.

Opaque inks: Heavy-bodied inks with a high concentration of pigment, used where high hiding power is desired to completely cover the substrate or any previous printing without any show-through. (Also called *cover inks*.)

Perfumed inks: An innovation in novelty inks in which a highly concentrated perfume or other distinctive scent is dispersed in a conventional ink. The principal use is in advertising. One type of perfumed ink releases its odor only when rubbed or scratched.

Permanent inks: Inks highly resistant to fading under continued exposure to light or heat.

Precipitation inks: See *moisture-set inks*.

Process inks: Inks of three specific colors—yellow, magenta, and cyan—which are used in modern four-color printing with a black ink to reproduce color illustrations. The inks must have the proper characteristics for printing by the particular process and with the particular paper and press to be used. (Further information about process inks and process-color printing may be found in Section 2, *Color*, and Section 9, *Graphic Arts Photography*.)

Quick-setting inks: Inks which dry or set quickly, by filtration, coagulation, selective absorption, or a combination thereof. The formula generally contains a resin-oil vehicle which separates, due to borderline solubility, upon application to the substrate; the oil solvent is absorbed and the resin remains on the surface as a dry film. These inks are used most effectively in sheet-fed printing on certain high-gloss coated papers and paperboards.

R.O.P. inks: R.O.P. stands for *run of press*, a vague term adopted many years ago by newspapers. It refers to the standard colors made available for advertisers running color ads to eliminate the need to match special ink colors that the advertisers might demand. Ad colors are limited to those colors that can be produced using this limited range of inks, either alone, in blends of two or more, or mixed with white.

Rub-resistant inks: See *abrasion-resistant inks*.

Safety inks: A type of specialty ink that changes color or bleeds if water or ink eradicator is applied to the printed surface, or if an erasure is attempted. These inks are used principally on checks and similar documents to facilitate detection of illegal alterations.

Screen printing inks: Inks used in screen printing, which have good body and low flow, or are short and buttery, so as to facilitate the forcing of the inks through the mesh screen and to give a clearly printed image. These quick-drying inks contain volatile solvents which must be carefully controlled to avoid clogging of the screen due to too-rapid evaporation.

Scuff-resistant inks: See *abrasion-resistant inks*.

Silver inks: The name commonly used for silver-colored metallic inks whose pigments consist primarily of aluminum powder. (See also *aluminum inks*.)

Steam-set inks: See *moisture-set inks*.

Sympathetic inks: A type of novelty ink with limited application. The printed image becomes visible only when specially treated, as with heat, moisture, or a mild acid. (Also called *invisible inks*.)

Thermal curing inks: Inks that dry upon application of heat by cross-linking of two polymers in the presence of an acid. Thermal curing inks cross-link to a hard, permanent, heat-resistant thermosetting film on the substrate. (Also called *heat-reactive inks*.)

Transparent inks: Inks with little hiding or covering power, which thus allow the substrate or previous printing to show through. Intermediate colors may therefore be produced when layers of these inks are overlapped. Transparent inks are used in four-color process work and in most other printing.

Ultraviolet curing inks: Inks containing chemical monomers which polymerize (that is, small molecules join to form large molecules) upon being subjected to high doses of ultraviolet (UV) radiation. The result is instantaneous drying or "curing." The UV source is usually a lamp affixed to, or part of, the press, either at the delivery end or between printing stations. Properly formulated UV curing inks are solventless and therefore do not pollute the environment. The instant-drying feature means that post-press operations, such as folding, die cutting, scoring, or binding, can be performed in-line directly from the press and without the delay for drying required with conventional inks.

Washout inks: The opposite of permanent or indelible inks. Easily removed by laundering or other washing methods, they are used on textiles for such purposes as marking patterns during garment manufacture, when a later process will remove the ink.

Water-based inks: Inks formulated with a vehicle whose binder is water-soluble, water-reducible, or water-dispersible, used for gravure and flexography on absorbent surfaces. Such inks employ reduced amounts of volatile solvents and are thus advantageously used when safety or environmental concerns exist.

Wax-set inks: Inks that set and dry instantly when the printed surface is immersed in a molten wax base. This type of ink is used principally on wax-coated food packaging, such as milk cartons.

PRINTING WITH METALLIC INKS

Walter L. Hecht, ATLANTIC POWDERED METALS, INC.

Gold and silver were used in the graphic arts even before today's printing methods were invented. The use of genuine gold and silver leaf, as found in the early illuminated manuscripts, is hardly practical for mass communication today, but metallic inks offer comparably beautiful design possibilities.

Today, genuine gold and silver have been replaced by pigments consisting of flakes of metals that are less expensive and available in greater quantity. For gold inks, the metallic flake is an alloy of copper and zinc;

for silver inks, aluminum. With these inks, advances in the quality, speed, and efficiency of all the major printing processes can be fully utilized. Metallic-ink printing has a wide variety of applications, including magazines, book covers, advertising pieces, displays, menus, posters, annual reports, and a wide variety of packaging items.

PIGMENT MANUFACTURE
Almost all metallic pigments are now manufactured by the ball-milling technique, in which the metal is broken up into flakes as it is revolved in a large drum containing steel balls. The size of the metal flake can be controlled by sophisticated screening and separating equipment to accommodate a wide variety of printing processes. In general, a coarse flake—that is, one with a relatively large mesh size—produces a brilliant color; a fine flake produces a smoother ink finish and finer reproduction detail but a less brilliant color. The surface treatment of the metallic powder—the amount and type of lubricants added to facilitate ball-milling and the lubricants and chemicals added to retard tarnish—can, like the particle size, be regulated during manufacture. The type of surface treatment is dependent on the printing and end-use requirements and affects the ultimate finish and luster of the printed piece.

TYPES OF PIGMENTS
Metallic pigments are available in a wide range of gold and copper shades, varying silvers, and an assortment of metallic colors produced with the addition of dyes.

Gold pigments, known as *gold bronzes*, are probably the most popular. They are composed of copper alloys; the greater the proportion of zinc to copper in the alloy, the nearer the hue will be to that of real gold. The four basic gold bronze shades are *rich gold* (70% copper and 30% zinc, with a yellow-gold appearance); *rich pale gold* (80% copper, 20% zinc); *pale gold* (90% copper and 10% zinc, with a pink cast); and *copper* (100% copper flake). By making minor changes in the chemical combinations and processing steps of these alloys, manufacturers can provide an almost limitless variety of shades.

Silver metallic pigments are composed of aluminum powders, sometimes with varying amounts of copper alloy. These silver pigments, known as *aluminum bronzes*, are available in approximately the same mesh sizes and surface finishes as the gold bronzes.

Colored metallic pigments, called *patent bronzes*, are aniline-dyed bronze or aluminum powders. They are produced in such colors as bright red, royal blue, and emerald green. Because of their poor lightfastness and lack of solvent resistance, they have a tendency to fade and bleed and are very seldom used in the graphic arts industry. Their main application is in textile printing and in some expendable decorative items.

METALLIC INKS
Metallic powders may be applied dry in certain printing processes, such as bronze dusting, but they are more often used as colorants in wet printing inks.

The formulation or mixing of the various metallic inks, like that of conventional printing inks, consists of dispersing the pigment (metallic flakes) in a vehicle—whether oil-based, solvent-based, or water-based. The vehicle acts both as a carrier to transfer the ink from the fountain onto the substrate and as a means to bind the pigment to the substrate. The mixing process may vary slightly, according to the nature of the vehicle and the printing schedule. Depending on the plant facilities and the requirements of the job, the ink may be mixed at press time by the printer or the printer's ink department or may be purchased press-ready (in liquid or paste form) from an ink company.

An important property of metallic inks which distinguishes them from other inks is *leafing*, the tendency of the flakes to float to the surface of the ink film and to orient themselves in a flat fish-scale pattern. The thin metallic particles settle on or into the paper and meld together to form a smooth and lustrous surface. Considered a measure of quality in metallic inks, leafing requires careful ink formulation.

PRINTING METHODS
Metallic inks are printable by a great variety of processes, each requiring different techniques and producing different effects. The remainder of this article is a discussion of the following applications which are used principally in the graphic arts: (1) bronzing, a dry process in which powder is dusted onto a preprinted adhesive surface; (2) wet printing by the primary processes—letterpress, offset, rotogravure, flexography, and screen printing; (3) specialty printing; and (4) producing metallic coated paper.

Bronzing
Bronzing, or dusting, is still one of the best methods of conveying a "real gold" appearance. The image area to be bronzed is preprinted on a letterpress or offset press with a slow-drying, tacky adhesive known as *gold size*. The sheet then runs through the bronzing machine, where dry powder is dusted over it. A battery of burnishers and cleaning belts rubs the powder into the size, and strong exhaust systems remove loose particles from the paper, leaving ink only on the preprinted image.

Important considerations in bronzing are (1) selecting a coarse flake for a brilliant color; (2) using a powder whose surface coating is grease-free so that it will not stick to the surface of the paper; and (3) selecting the gold size with the paper stock in mind. A smoothly finished paper will bring out the greatest brilliance, and the bronze powder manufacturer will know which grade to suggest for the job at hand. While mostly bronze powders are used in the bronzing process, special grades of aluminum powders can also be used, although this is done very rarely.

The primary printing processes
All of the major printing processes may be used to print metallic inks. Although none of these wet printing processes can match the brilliance of the dry bronzing process, excellent results are possible. While there are many variables involved—such as substrate, printing

facilities, and so forth—the general order of brilliance for the major processes is as follows: screen printing (although it has limited applications), rotogravure, flexography, letterpress, and offset. The selection of printing process is based, of course, on many additional factors.

Offset. Because offset printing allows for only a thin film of ink to be distributed, a very fine powder must be used. Offset printing with metallic inks does not, therefore, produce the high brilliance of color possible with other methods, and quite often two impressions are used to create the desired effect. It does, however, have the advantage of being able to handle many paper stocks and high-speed production. In special instances in which metallic inks are printed on rough-finished and porous papers, it is sometimes advisable to print another color first—usually a buff or yellow—to seal the surface and prevent the metallic ink from disappearing into the fibers of the paper. Control of the fountain solution in offset is very important, and alkaline solutions are usually used to prevent tarnishing of the bronze.

Letterpress. In letterpress printing, a very fine mesh powder is mixed in a ratio of approximately 1:1 with a letterpress varnish. As the ink travels over various rollers in the fountain to the final plate, the ink film is finely distributed and transferred. While letterpress is not generally as fast as offset, it makes possible the application of a fairly heavy film which results in a much brighter metallic image. The plate should just "kiss" the paper, to prevent fuzzy edges.

Both letterpress and offset printing use oil-based inks, which are readily available and are sold in one-pound packages. Even the smallest print shop can turn out good work, especially short-run work for items such as menus, invitations, and the like, by letterpress and offset printing.

During the last decade, however, high-speed methods of printing employing new ink systems have become more popular for many types of packaging and publication printing. Rotogravure and flexography, which use solvent- or alcohol-based ink systems mainly, and in many cases water-based systems as well, have replaced letterpress and offset in many jobs. Generally, gravure and flexography can produce more vibrant metallic finishes than letterpress and offset.

Rotogravure. Because of the high cost of rotogravure cylinders, usually only long production runs are printed by this process. The powder can be somewhat coarser than letterpress or offset powders, since the ink is carried in the engraved wells of the cylinder which can hold a heavier film. Ink vehicles are usually solvent- or alcohol-based and, due to the large quantities used, are frequently mixed in-plant. As solvents evaporate, the press operator should check the viscosity of the ink frequently and clean the doctor blade to remove the sometimes unavoidable slight buildup. Rotogravure printing with metallic inks is used for all types of stocks, from very heavy cardboard to plastic films, and even textiles. For successful printing, the powder must be compatible with the ink vehicle system, the substrate, and the type of copy to be printed—fine line or solid. The engraving of the cylinder should be slightly deeper than for other inks.

Flexography. Because the rubber or synthetic rubber plates used in flexography are less expensive than rotogravure cylinders, this method is recommended for shorter runs. Finer powders must be used, because a thinner film is required than in rotogravure. The result is a less brilliant color than that produced by rotogravure. Flexographic printing has become widely used for high quality multicolor printing and packaging, because it prints well on all stocks, including foil and plastic film. In printing on clear plastic film, it is sometimes advisable to print on a ground color, such as white, to provide better capacity for the metallic film overprinted. Many different flexographic inks are available; water-based ink systems are the newest.

Screen printing. Screen printing is used for many types of short-run printing and often to produce more complicated patterns in such applications as the wallpaper, textile, and greeting card industries; book cover printing; and limited-run art reproductions. Screen printing allows greater flexibility in color changes and color substitutions than the other processes, without much machine adjustment. The inks used are oil- or water-based. Selection of the powder depends, as always, on the substrate and ink to be used; in addition, the mesh size of the powder is dictated by the size of the screen opening. Wallpaper screens and textile screens, for example, have wide openings and allow for coarse powders which yield very vibrant metallic finishes. Fine art work may necessitate small openings, which can tolerate only a powder of very small mesh size.

501

Specialty printing

Thermographic printing is frequently used for greeting cards and invitations. Metallic powder, mixed with a resin, is applied in dry form and cured in a heating tunnel. It produces a very brilliant raised print.

Metallic inks are frequently used in steel-die engraving, a process which uses an engraved steel or copper plate or die to create an embossed impression. Depending upon the image to be printed, the vehicle may be oil- or water-based, and the flakes used may be coarse or fine. This process is used widely for stationery engraving, menus, greeting cards, announcements, and similar short-run items.

Wallpaper printing can be done by various production methods—by a relatively slow-speed letterpress wallpaper machine, by screen printing, or by high-speed rotogravure methods. Most wallpapers use casein binders, and the powders must be specially treated to be compatible with this substrate. Generally, a coarse, brilliant flake is preferred to produce highlights that are easily visible. Today, many wallpaper lines are printed on vinyl or vinyl-coated paper, so vinyl inks have to be used. In this case, treated, nontarnishing powders are recommended to prevent greening.

Metallic coated papers

Metallic coated papers in various shades are used for menus, wine lists, greeting cards, tags, box wraps, booklet covers, and other printed pieces. Metallic coated stock is produced by applying the metallic powder to the paper in a thin casein or pyroxylin film. Roller coating, knife coating, air spray coating, or brush coating may be employed.

The better metallic papers of both types have fine, even brilliant, surfaces and are resistant to rubbing and tarnishing. To give the sheet greater brilliance, the paper may be passed through a heated calendering process after drying, to smooth out the finish and burnish it to a high luster.

SELECTING THE INK

Printing with metals, a continually improving technology evolved from an ancient art, can be an effective tool today in advertising and design. When the printing buyer has specified his or her requirements, the printer will suggest the best printing method from a technical and practical point of view. If necessary, the printer can turn to the ink company or the metallic powder manufacturer for the correct pigment, type of vehicle, and recommended paper stock. The designer would do well to have a file of metallic swatches and metallic coated papers and to keep in mind that many design pieces might be made more effective with the use of a gold-bronze or other metallic shade in place of a routine color.

PRINTING INK MANUFACTURE

This article has been adapted from the Printing Ink Handbook *with permission of the National Association of Printing Ink Manufacturers.*

Depending upon a number of factors—the volume, the properties of the ingredients, the requirements of the final product—ink manufacture may involve any of a number of different types of machines and may consist of from one to several steps. Ink may be prepared in batches, or the ingredients may be fed continuously into and through the processing system. The large majority of all printing inks are made by the batch process; only certain large-volume standardized inks, particularly news inks, employ continuous processes.

Various components are combined to produce the final printing ink. The fluid portion, commonly identified as the vehicle or varnish portion, contains most of the special ingredients that will make up the drying characteristics of the ink, its drying speed, and its special press properties. Into this vehicle portion, the coloring matter, in various degrees of dispersion, and the miscellaneous other ingredients, mostly driers and special compounds, are introduced.

MIXING

Mixing—the introduction of the coloring matter—is a major step in ink manufacture, since the material must be broken down and thoroughly intermingled with the vehicle with the first major input of energy. The nature of the ink vehicle and the pre-dispersion character of the coloring matter introduced at this point will largely determine whether the printing ink can be completely manufactured by the mixing process.

The mixing is done in batch containers with massive mixing blades. The containers may hold from small 5-, 10-, and 20-gallon batches up to 100- and 1000-gallon batches. The selection of the mixing speed, whether a slow stirring of a few revolutions per minute or high-speed intensive mixing of several hundred to thousands of revolutions per minute, depends on the nature of the ink and of the coloring matter being introduced into the vehicle. Many engineering advances and equipment improvements have been achieved in the past 10 years which have increased the range of mixing speeds, blade sizes, blade configurations, and ratio of blade size to tank diameter.

When flushed bases—pigments predispersed in the vehicle—are used, a finished ink can often be made in a mixing operation, without further processing. In such cases, the ink is often filtered after mixing to remove any remaining agglomerates. Filtering has generally been used for low- to medium-viscosity inks. In recent years, higher-viscosity inks have also been made by the mixing and filtering process; however, in this case, filtration is mostly limited to the more fluid web-type inks.

MILLING

Many printing inks cannot be reduced to their final product specifications with simple mixing stages and therefore require more intimate dispersion in other devices during a second stage—*milling* or *grinding*. Among the devices for further dispersion of the coloring matter to preselected dispersion specifications are three-roll mills, ball mills, colloid mills, sand mills, shot mills, turbine devices, and other types of dispersers.

Three-roll mills

The vast majority of three-roll mills are composed of three steel rollers which revolve in opposite directions at three different speeds in the ratio of approximately 1:2:4. (See figure 13.1.)

The ink slurry is fed to the rear roll hopper, either in a continuous fashion from a large batch or, in the case of small batches, by hand. As the slurry moves through the rollers, the pigments are dispersed by grinding and by the shearing force that occurs at the interfaces of the rolls as they revolve in opposite directions under positive pressure applied to front and rear rolls. The ink is removed at the front roll by a knife and allowed to flow down onto an apron.

The speed of the mill, the temperature of the rolls, the pressure between the rolls, and the general care and selection of the mill will determine its grinding efficiency. In the case of some harder pigments, more than one production pass through the mill is usually required.

Figure 13.1: Three-roll mill. *Courtesy of the J. H. Day Company.*

Figure 13.2: Ball mill. *Courtesy of Paul O. Abbé, Inc.*

Ball mills

Ball mills—large, closed drums containing steel balls or similar objects—are generally used for materials such as flexographic and gravure inks which contain volatile solvents that would escape in more open mixing, or for large volumes which may be left unattended for extended grinding. (See figure 13.2.) The ink materials are introduced into the ball mill to a level covering the steel balls or other grinding media. The mill is then sealed and revolved so that the balls cascade and tumble within the mill shell, grinding the ink by the tearing action of their surfaces. The longer the mill rotates, the finer the ink is generally ground. Choice of mill shells and grinding media are determined by the nature of the ink and the need for color integrity.

Sand mills and shot mills

A sand mill or a shot mill has a shaft with revolving disks inside a closed and jacketed vertical steel cylinder. The ink is introduced into the special sand or small metal pellets at the bottom of the mill. The spinning disks on the shaft set up a violent flow pattern, and the ink slurry is forced upward through several sections or chambers of the cylinder and is discharged through a screen at the top.

For hard pigments that can be processed in this system, the shaft speed is slowed to a minimum in order to lengthen the dwell time within the grinding chamber. In such a case, the external steel jacket is filled with circulating cold water to reduce accumulation of heat.

Sand mills and shot mills have enjoyed increasing popularity in the last several years because they capture the advantages of ball mill grinding without the very large investment generally required for ball mill installation and because they may be used in a continuous process, thus being essentially independent of the batch size. The ingredients can be ground to the same degree of dispersion as is possible in a ball mill because the dwell time in the chamber of the shot or sand mill can be regulated.

Colloid mills

Colloid mills have been long used in batch and continuous processes and still have considerable use in the manufacture of printing inks. In a colloid mill, the ink, either fed by gravity or pumped under pressure, is passed between a high-speed rotor and a stator and is forced out of the rotating rotor-stator arrangement at the narrowest edge, where the clearance—which may be adjusted by any of several techniques to meet varying specifications—determines the degree of fineness of grind.

Other devices

There are many other mixers, impellers, turbine mixers, and dispersion devices, such as the dispersion mixer in figure 13.3. In these, generally, a high-speed rotor or turbine moves inside a stator and completes the manufacture of the ink by passing the pigment particles through narrow openings between the moving blades and the chamber or series of chambers. These mixing devices are used primarily in the batch process but are adaptable to continuous process in some cases.

Figure 13.3: Dispersion mixer. *Courtesy of the J. H. Day Company.*

MATCHING EQUIPMENT TO TYPE OF INK

Flexographic inks, gravure inks, and other inks of a thin vehicle system may be prepared in ball mills or by a combination of batch and continuous processing in shot mills and sand mills. They are characterized by the need for closed dispersion systems because of the volatile nature of the solvents used.

For publication and letterpress printing inks, open-style intensive mixing systems may be used, in addition to shot and ball mills, because no solvents or volatile materials are present. Because of the heavier nature of the vehicle system and of the finished product, additional kinds of manufacturing equipment which have slower mixing speeds and heavier horsepower drive systems may be used.

Finally, the heavier inks such as those for lithography require intensive mixers and extremely heavy drive systems in order to intermingle the pigments and achieve any kind of dispersion.

The selection of equipment in the manufacture of printing inks ultimately depends upon the volume to be produced, the pigment hardness, the presence or lack of volatile solvents, the body or viscosity of the finished product, and the method of application.

INK TESTING
Gary G. Winters, INMONT CORPORATION

Because printing inks are critical to successful printing, the inkmaker subjects them to many tests before they are packaged for shipment. Printers also perform a limited number of tests before and during a production run to control production factors. Test methods currently in use have come from several sources, such as printing ink companies, suppliers of ink raw materials, test equipment manufacturers, the American Society of Testing Materials, and the National Printing Ink Research Institute.

Ink is tested for many different characteristics, such as color, gloss, tack, rub resistance, and freedom from grit. The more an inkmaker or printer knows about any special requirements for a particular job, the more precisely and thoroughly he can use his equipment, knowledge, and experience. Communication between inkmaker, printer, designer, and consumer is therefore of great importance.

EQUIPMENT IN COMMON USE

A discussion of some of the properties commonly tested, and the methods used, follows. The equipment is illustrated in figures 13.4 through 13.11. Some tests evaluate physical properties, such as viscosity and rub resistance; others relate to ink color. Additional discussion of color measurement may be found in "The Measurement and Specification of Color," page 21.

Light box

Under different lighting conditions, an ink's hue may appear different. This property is called *metamerism*. It is important that the artist, printer, and inkmaker are all on common ground when selecting, viewing, and matching colors. The light box (or "color viewer") has several types of light sources overhead, and the color swatch or swatches can be viewed under various lights —fluorescent, incandescent, daylight, etc. (See figure 13.4.) When ink must be matched to another color sample under all lighting conditions, it requires the use of exactly the same pigment or dye.

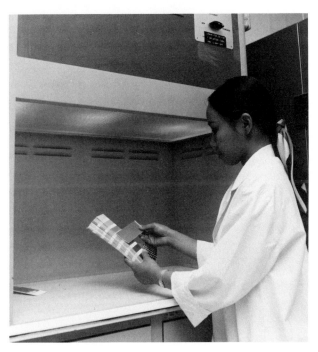

Figure 13.4: Light box.

Reflection densitometer

This piece of equipment is commonly used by printers and inkmakers to measure hue, strength (density or value), and purity (chroma or grayness) of a color sample. It is very useful as a production tool for ink density control during a press run, and is commonly used by printers for that purpose. (See figure 13.5.)

A white light of standard intensity is directed straight down at the sample, and the amount of reflected light (measured in percent) is precisely registered. The measuring head contains four special filters (red, green, blue, and neutral), and the light from the source is projected through one of these filters. Based on all four readings, the exact hue, value, and chroma of a given color can be determined.

The common way to control color strength during a press run is to read the color bars for the process colors (yellow, cyan, magenta, black) through the

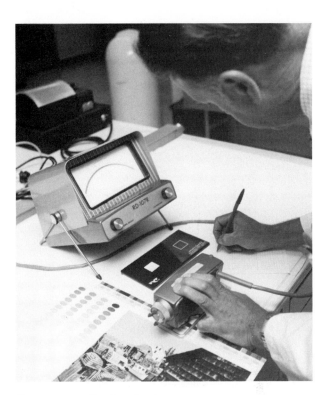

Figure 13.5: Reflection densitometer.

filters of the complementary colors (blue, red, green, neutral). This way, the process colors appear as shades of gray and are easier to measure.

Spectrophotometer

The spectrophotometer measures the reflectance of a color sample under all visible wavelengths of light, thus giving an exact "fingerprint" for the sample. Any other sample with the same curve of reflectance versus wavelength will appear the same under varying lighting conditions. The device is complicated and expensive

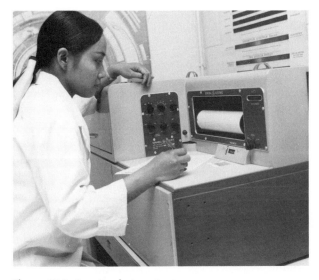

Figure 13.6: Spectrophotometer.

and is used primarily for research and special applications such as precise color matching. (See figure 13.6.)

Gloss tester

Gloss is a function of ink ingredients, substrate, and smoothness of the surface of the ink film. In a gloss tester, a known amount of light is angled onto the ink surface and picked up after reflection. The percent picked up is directly related to what our eyes see as gloss. (See figure 13.7.)

Figure 13.8: Inkometer.

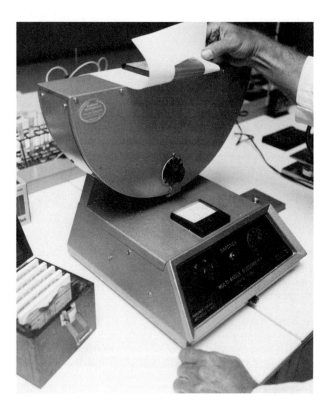

Figure 13.7: Gloss tester.

Inkometer

An inkometer measures the torque produced between two rollers when rotating with ink in between. The measurement relates to the internal cohesiveness (tack) of the ink when subjected to splitting forces. (See figure 13.8.)

Grindometer

An ink is ground to reduce its particle size to develop tinctorial strength and gloss and to avoid printing problems such as hickies and plate wear. In a grindometer, a sample of the ink is drawn between a flat steel bar and a very shallow, sloped depression in a steel plate. Any particles larger than the gap between the bar and the plate cause visible scratches in the ink film. By noting the point in the calibrated slope where the scratches appear (and the number thereof), the sample is assigned a value for quantity and size of particles. (See figure 13.9.)

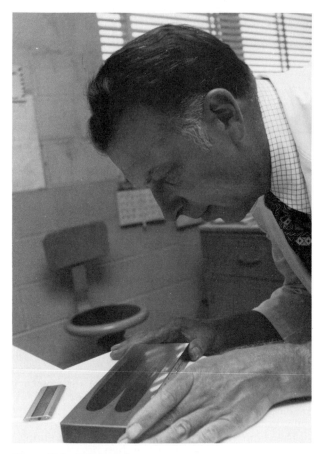

Figure 13.9: Grindometer.

506

Figure 13.10: Rub tester.

Rub tester

The rub tester is used to measure resistance of the printed sample to marring from repeated rubbing of its surface. The tester generally rubs a sample of the unprinted stock against a sample of the printed material for a certain number of cycles and at a predetermined pressure. Visual observation is used to judge the results. (See figure 13.10.)

Viscometer

The viscometer is used by the inkmaker to measure the body (viscosity and yield value) of a lithographic or letterpress ink. (See figure 13.11.) The rate at which a rod falls through a precisely machined hole, when covered with the ink and when subjected to different push forces, is a measure of viscosity (force required to keep it moving at a constant rate) and yield value (force required to cause initial movement).

For low-viscosity flexographic and gravure inks, several methods are used. These generally involve measuring the flow rate of the ink through a precisely calibrated orifice. Because flexo and gravure inks are usually reduced in viscosity by solvent addition before use and because these inks lose solvent and increase in viscosity during use, the printer controls viscosity (and therefore color strength) by careful measurement both before and during a production run.

Draw-down and proof press

The draw-down knife, which is similar to a putty knife, is used by inkmakers and printers to check the general appearance of the ink on the substrate. A draw-down proof, which simulates the final printed result, is made by drawing the bottom edge of the knife across the paper, with a dab of ink trapped ahead of it. The proof press is also used as a means of checking the final appearance of the piece before it is printed. The proof press provides a more controlled sample, since it is basically a rudimentary printing press.

SUMMARY

The following table, summarizing the information above, lists test methods, and indicates why each is used and by whom.

Test equipment	Property tested	Generally used by
Color viewer	Visual hue of ink-paper combination; metamerism; comparison of color swatches	Inkmaker Printer
Reflection densitometer	Hue; color density; grayness	Inkmaker Printer
Spectrophotometer	Color, when precise matching is necessary	Inkmaker
Gloss tester	Gloss of paper and/or ink	Inkmaker
Inkometer	Tack of ink	Inkmaker
Grindometer	Freedom from grit in ink	Inkmaker
Rub tester	Rub-resistance of ink on substrate	Inkmaker
Viscometer	(a) Viscosity of lithographic and letterpress inks	Inkmaker
	(b) Viscosity of flexographic and gravure inks	Inkmaker Printer
Draw-down knife	General appearance of ink on substrate	Inkmaker Printer
Proof press	Same as above, but provides a more controlled sample	Inkmaker

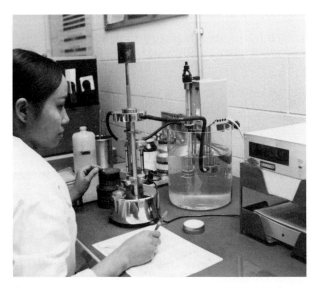

Figure 13.11: Viscometer.

COLOR MATCHING

Color matching is one of the most obvious factors in the ink formulation process, and the one that involves the printing buyer most directly. Any printed job employing colored inks involves precise matching of colors to achieve on paper an appearance which existed first in the designer's mind or on a sample in another medium. Four-color process reproductions, which use standardized matched sets of inks, eliminate the need for special color matches for individual jobs. Non-process color work, however, employs specific colors of inks for individual effects, and here special procedures for matching colors play an important role in the ultimate reproduction quality.

Traditionally, color matching of inks to specified colors has been done on a customized basis, with a unique new ink being prepared each time a job is to be run. More recently developed color matching systems enable a customer to specify desired colors via a predetermined system of standard color swatches and numbers that give the ink matcher a precise formula by which the chosen colors can be duplicated. Such standardized systems have grown rapidly in use, especially with the development of the so-called "universal" systems. Prior to these systems, the predetermined systems in use were proprietary to individual ink companies and could only be used with their inks. The universal systems were established by making standard ink formulas available to all ink manufacturers so that the inks could be obtained from many suppliers in all parts of the country. Another advance in recent years has been the use of the computer to aid in color matching and ink formulation.

CUSTOM COLOR MATCHING

A custom ink color must be matched from a sample or swatch of the color. It must be carefully formulated to counterbalance possible variables between the swatch sample and the finished job, such as the differing visual effects of the materials each is printed on.

In addition to a knowledge of the general principles of color relationships and some experience in the use of color, the color matcher must have a combination of fairly sophisticated skills. These include: (1) an eye for color, since custom matching is essentially performed by visual instinct; (2) a knowledge of what constitutes a "commercial" match, or one that is close enough to a desired color for the purpose intended; and (3) a knowledge of proper formulation which takes into account many complex factors, such as the chemical reactivity, lightfastness, or bleed resistance of certain pigments, and the compatibility of the various ingredients of the ink.

Materials and tools

Custom color matching in ink mixing is accomplished in several steps by using various tools and materials for ink adjustment. The tools include a mixing slab or equivalent on which to work, knives and spatulas for handling and mixing ink on the slab, weighing scales of various sensitivities depending on the batch size, and a file card for keeping a record of the formulation and any subsequent changes for later reference if it is necessary to repeat or continue a job. Usually a press proof or "draw-down" print of the ink in varying thicknesses is also kept on file. Some type of color chart or set of proofs showing base color inks available for combination, in average amounts and on average stock, in solids and screens, and for each of the printing processes, is also used as a beginning point and constant reference in color matching.

The materials used in ink mixing depend to a great extent on the size of the job and the plant facilities. They are widely available in ink manufacturing plants and some large printing plants, and are often supplied to smaller shops through ink mixing and matching services of various ink manufacturers. These materials are of two kinds: a range of colored base inks for combining into the required final color; and a variety of materials for adjusting the final matched ink for consistency on press, proper drying time, surface gloss, and the like. A set of base inks generally includes three or four reds, two yellows, a bright orange, a bright green, three or four blues, a bright purple, three whites (transparent, mixing, and opaque), black, and a neutral gray. Adjusting materials include varnishes, body gum, compounds, and driers.

Matching procedure

In mixing a color-matched ink, the mixer can start in one of two ways. If he has a master color chart from an ink supplier available, he selects the chart color swatch closest to the sample supplied by the customer. The chart color can be reproduced by mixing the ink supplier's base inks in proportion to a formula given on the chart. If the ink mixer does not have such a chart available, he must approximate an ink formula near to the customer color by judging himself just how much of each base color to use. Generally, the chart-selected beginning color is a more accurate method.

In any case, the next step is to make a finger pat-out of the ink on the correct stock, judging what adjustment is needed to make a closer match and then adding the appropriate amount of the required color. This process is repeated until a satisfactory match is achieved. At each stage, however, the mixer must carefully record the exact amounts of each ink added in order to derive a final mixing formula when he is done. Several small trial lots may be needed before a satisfactory match is made.

From this formula, the mixer then makes a larger batch of the ink for use in proofing and testing. Some adjusting of the color match must also be done at this stage, and the formula records must be adjusted also. The final color appraisal is made by running ink from this batch on a proof press with the appropriate stock.

When the color is almost correct, driers and other adjusting substances are added and then the final color balance is made. Non-color ingredients are added just before the final match because they tend to reduce color strength somewhat.

The final stage consists of actually running the ink on the production press at production speeds with samples of the stock to be used in the actual job.

Testing

No mixed ink, whether matched by the custom process or by a predetermined color system, is ready for production runs on press until it undergoes tests for correct color, proper drying, and suitability in running at proper press speed on the appropriate stock. Color can be tested off-press, and sometimes so can drying. But runnability—and sometimes drying—often can be gauged only by performance in an actual test run on the chosen stock on the production machine, although long experience on the part of the ink mixer with certain inks, stocks, and presses can sometimes avoid the cost of such expensive tests.

All tests of inks should be made on the actual paper to be used in the job. "Wet" proofs, on which the ink has not yet dried, usually are slightly different from dry proofs, and most people prefer to make final color comparisons after test proofs have dried. Some expert quality control managers do use wet-proof readings to set specifications because these are most useful to the press operators trying to control high-speed web presses. However, use of such wet-proof methods requires a thorough understanding of high-quality control techniques and complete communication among all parties involved. It should be attempted only if such conditions are possible. Draw-downs are a good test when there is a previous sample of the ink to match. They aid in checking opacity or transparency, undertone, and drying time. (See also "Ink Testing," page 504.)

Properties affecting color matching

Of fundamental importance in ink matching are the concepts of masstone, undertone, and tinting strength. *Masstone* is defined as the hue or color of an ink in a thick mass, such as in the can or press ink fountain, and is determined by the colorants in the ink. *Undertone* is the hue of the same ink in a thin transparent or translucent film such as on the final printed sheet. While the color of ink in the can or fountain is exclusively masstone, the undertone color is determined by the ink colorants as well as the color of light reflected back through the ink film from the paper surface. (See "The Influence of Paper on Color Printing," page 481.) The thickness of the ink film laid on the sheet during printing will affect the final color achieved, depending on the ink's opacity and nature of the undertone effect. A red ink with a bluish undertone when printed on a certain paper, for example, may yield a warm red if run at normal thickness, but produce a cold pink if run spare. No ink is completely free of these effects when printed. *Tinting strength*, on the other hand, is the coloring power or the amount that an ink can be diluted with a white ink to produce a tint of the color. Draw-downs are useful in evaluating tinting strength as well as the effects of masstone and undertone.

Final mixing

Depending on the size and requirements of a particular job, the ink mixing process may be carried out in an ink manufacturing plant, in the ink department of a large printing plant, or in the pressroom of a small shop. Small batches may be prepared by hand by the color matcher; for larger batches, any number of mixing procedures, from mechanical mixers to ball milling operations, may be used. Of course, only inks of the same class are used for mixing. Letterpress and litho shops using standard oil inks must be careful to use ingredients which are compatible. Often when special inks are used, the ink manufacturer or supplier should be consulted on questions of ink compatibility.

PANTONE MATCHING SYSTEM
Lawrence Herbert, PANTONE, INC.

The Pantone Matching System, designed and developed by Pantone, Inc. in 1963, consists of 564 different colors, each of which can be recreated by the printer from 8 standard basic colored inks plus black and white. The 564 colors, each with an identifying number, have been reproduced in a color matching book to be used by art directors and other color specifiers. When a color choice is made, it is communicated to the printer by number. A special formula file supplied by Pantone to the printer or inkmaker gives him the exact ink mixing formula associated with that numbered color, and he uses the formula to prepare the ink. Formulas are given in both fractional parts and metric units.

The mixing formula specifies the quantities of various basic inks that must be mixed to produce the exact color desired. To match the specified color, the printer or ink mixer should use the eight Pantone basic inks. These are available from several thousand ink companies around the world who have obtained licenses from Pantone to produce these inks under carefully controlled conditions. The quality-control conditions for manufacture of these special basic inks (specified as part of the licensing agreement) are vital to the system's success in assuring accurate color matches in a variety of printing plants in many locations.

Upon entering into a licensing agreement with Pantone, the ink manufacturer is supplied with exact specifications for mixing the eight basic colors, including the approved sources of supply for raw materials. With the information, the ink manufacturer can mix the eight basic colors: Pantone Yellow, Pantone Warm Red, Pantone Rubine Red, Pantone Rhodamine Red, Pantone Purple, Pantone Reflex Blue, Pantone Process Blue, and Pantone Green. His ink samples are then tested by Pantone for color accuracy, and if they meet the matching standards, they are approved.

The Pantone Matching System is supported by a line of creative artist's materials, including color markers, papers, and tint acetate overlays. These are numbered with the ink identification codes to allow the designer to do illustrations and mock-ups in the desired colors and then communicate his choice to the printer.

The system is currently being used by organizations requiring duplication of unique colors, such as trademark colors. A corporate color program has been initiated in which special company colors—such as the Exxon blue and red, or the Kodak yellow—are analyzed and a specific Pantone formula developed. This enables regional and international branches to have local printers formulate the company colors for product packages and advertising by using the basic Pantone ink colors.

Another development, the Pantone Color Data System, uses computers to select and print out specifications for individual customized color matches. The computerized system adds speed, flexibility, and accuracy to the customized color matching process. Three basic pieces of equipment are involved: a spectrophotometer, a communications terminal, and either an acoustic coupler for transmission of data via telephone or an interface for direct communication to an in-house computer.

An operator first places a sample of the color in the spectrophotometer, which measures the color and produces the reflectance values in numerical form. Then either the operator dials a local telephone number to connect the terminal to the timeshare computer and places the telephone in the coupler for data transmission or he transmits directly to his in-house computer. The computer processes the data, calculates various alternative color formulations, and transmits the color matches to the terminal. The color matches are typed out as percentages of the basic Pantone inks required to match the original sample.

The chief advantage of the computerized system is its ability to preselect possible combinations of inks to achieve the desired custom color. Previously, the color technician, no matter how adept, had to start with a relatively gross mismatch and go through a number of trial-and-error steps to get to the exact match. The computer greatly reduces the number of steps by providing a starting formulation much closer to the desired end result.

The computer can be quite versatile in dealing with the variables involved in selecting among different colorants. The machine, in searching for possible combinations of materials for a given color match, uses a correction program which alters mixing formulas to compensate for changes in colorant materials which are not exact substitutes for each other. At the same time, the computer can analyze the costs of various combinations of materials which might produce the same result, selecting the lower cost alternatives or identifying ink formulas already in stock.

The computerized system also produces a metamerism index for the requested color. Metamerism is a measure of the variance in appearance of the color under different lighting conditions.

The final printout gives the ink formulator the names of the ink colors to be used, the percentage of color deviation from the sample, and the price per unit for each formulation.

The computerized service is operated through a worldwide teleprocessing network and is now providing information to companies in Western Europe, North America, Japan, and Australia. It is available 24 hours a day, 7 days a week.

METRICOLOR MATCHING SYSTEM
O. Willis Hawrylkiw, METRICOLOR INK SYSTEMS

The Metricolor Ink System, a development of Metricolor United Enterprises, introduced specific features to improve upon existing predetermined color systems.

Thirteen carefully selected base colors, balanced in strength, were selected for their ability to reproduce in combination all colors from the predetermined systems popular today. The same base colors will also reproduce the custom color match when the formula is supplied by a Metricolor inkmaker. This universal feature benefits both printer and specifier.

By introducing screen value controls to the printing of its color selector book, Metricolor has achieved the "reproducible" color system. The four screen values—20, 40, 60, and 80 percent dots with a 133-line screen—provide a valuable guide for the artist, specifier, and press operator. They guarantee that each ink color can be reproduced precisely under actual printing conditions. The fact that the Metricolor Color Book is printed on a 38-inch four-color press in a commercial printing plant, with densitometer controls, further assures that all printers can reproduce this color book.

Metricolor introduced practical metrics with its system. Each formula in the color selector book and in the cross-reference guide to other systems' colors is a simple 100-part formula. Specially designed scales allow the printer to weigh simply and accurately the exact quantity of each color component. Regardless of the weight of the final ink and whether it is measured in pounds, or, in the future, in kilograms, the total numerical value will always be 100. Metricolor designs and maintains small systems suited for instant printers and others so large as to require thousands of pounds of ink. Three basic sizes, however, are the most popular.

Metricolor inks are produced by franchised manufacturers whose agreements call for rigid quality control of all production. The franchised manufacturers, with different technical capabilities, produce the 13 basic Metricolors with a variety of physical properties, in such forms as ultraviolet inks, flexographic inks, and duplicator inks. By expanding on the predetermined systems in its cross-reference guide and extending the physical properties of its 13 basic colors, Metricolor covers the needs of all printed color production.

ACS COMPUTER COLOR CONTROL
Charles Mertz, APPLIED COLOR SYSTEMS, INC.

ACS Color Control Systems are designed to aid companies in controlling and matching colors rapidly and economically through the use of digital computers. While computer color control is widely used in the paint, textile, and plastics industries, its benefits are only starting to be realized in the printing industry, where millions of tons of ink are consumed and, more significantly, wasted.

510

In brief, a computer color control system provides fast, accurate color matching, ink formulation, and batch correction. It also allows the user to work off waste batches and offers a number of quality control functions, including strength and color analysis of incoming ink shipments.

In the ACS system, a digital spectrophotometer optically scans an ink sample in two seconds and transmits color wavelength data to a digital computer. The computer provides a formula from its files to match a target color or correct an off-shade ink. The ink matcher controls the programmed procedure through a video terminal equipped with a typewriter-like keyboard. Communication with the system is in clear, concise English. A printer provides copies of the displayed information for records and reports.

The heart of the system is the set of color control programs provided with it. Precise color analyses based on the science and mathematics of color replace the traditional trial-and-error method of color matching.

The first step in utilizing the color control programs is the preparation of a data file that represents the "fingerprint" of each primary ink used in the operation. Representative primary samples are prepared, and the physical characteristics of each, such as percentage of pigment, are entered into the computer's data file. This file becomes the standard reference for the many control functions provided by the system.

In formulating an ink color, for example, the ink matcher begins by typing the appropriate word on the keyboard that initiates the formulation program. He then presents a target sample of the new ink color, such as a "draw-down," to the spectrophotometer, which measures the color wavelength characteristic of the sample. The computer then reports the optimum color match and the lowest-cost match based on the primary ink colors available in the standard reference file. The appropriate percentage of the primary inks and the actual amount of each required to make the new ink formula are also provided.

In addition to ink formulations, the computer's color control programs offer the ink matchers other production options such as working off surplus or off-color inks into needed ink batches. Virgin ink is added to a waste batch, or various waste batches are first blended together and then adjusted with virgin ink, to obtain the final needed color. In operation, the ink matcher measures the waste batch on the spectrophotometer; measures the needed color, or calls it from the standard file if it is a primary; and then selects the appropriate program function that automatically calculates the additional ink required to match the needed color. The ink matcher also has the option of making additions manually by entering them into the program via the keyboard. This enables the ink matcher to see the effect that certain, inks might have on the batch.

There are many other functions that can be performed by ACS Color Control Systems, including color correction, business data processing, and automated ink color blending and dispensing. Because the system can process large amounts of data, it can handle routines for formula storage, batch ticketing, inventory control, and other functions related to production.

IBM PRINTING INK COLOR PROGRAM

Thomas L. Cordier, IBM INSTRUMENT SYSTEMS, INC.

The IBM Printing Ink Color Program is an interactive program designed for use with the IBM 5110 Computing System and 7409 Scanning Color Sensor. The program provides ink users and manufacturers with a set of functions for color matching, analysis, and control and allows them to evaluate all possible formulations to match a given color using a pre-specified set of colorants. Additionally, adjustments can be made to a calculated formula to compensate for raw material and substrate deviations.

A major advantage of computer-assisted color matching and control is that the computer can evaluate a wide selection of colorants and identify the combination of colorants that provides the best, least metameric, or least expensive match. The computer can do in minutes what could require hours for the colorist. Guided by the alternative formulas and a figure of merit (metamerism, cost, etc.) for each, the colorist can use his experience and judgment to match the required color while balancing customer acceptance criteria and materials costs.

The Printing Ink Color Program utilizes the display on the 5110 to provide a comprehensive set of prompting messages for the operator. This can reduce the time required to learn how to use the system and minimizes operational errors.

The program's functions and capabilities include:

• *Standards program.* The ability to enter and store reflectance curves with associated names for subsequent retrieval.

• *Colorant file program.* The ability to enter reflectance curves which are used to create colorant files (finished ink colorant palettes).

• *Price program.* The ability to enter, change, and list colorant file prices.

• *Match program.* The ability to calculate all possible formulations for a given reflectance curve using a specified colorant file.

• *Correction program.* The ability to calculate adjustments to a calculated formula, compensating for raw materials and substrate deviations.

• *Quality control program.* The ability to calculate color difference through the use of specified color difference equations.

• *Batch add program.* The ability to optimize color properties by adding specified colorants to an existing batch of materials.

• *Formula storage and retrieval program.* The ability to set up a master formula file for storage and subsequent retrieval of finished formulas.

• *Inventory control program.* The ability to set up and maintain an inventory system.

• *Batch ticketing program.* The ability to provide production batch tickets in predefined tickets and adjust the inventory file accordingly.

The 5110 Computing System is a general-purpose computer using the BASIC language, which is easy to learn for use in written programs. In addition to the Printing Ink Color Program, the user can take advantage of a wide range of business applications.

NEW INK TECHNOLOGIES
Gary G. Winters, INMONT CORPORATION

A number of significant changes are taking place today in the types of printing inks being used and in their methods of application. As a result, the ink supplier is becoming a vital part of the overall technological revolution in the printing industry.

INK-RELATED CHANGES

The changes that are happening can be classified into two groups: (1) those which are desired by the printer or printing buyer for the advantages they will yield; and (2) those which are being forced upon printers by external forces or problems. The charts below list some of these changes and the reasons for them.

Desired changes	Advantages
Delivery of completely dry sheets on sheet-fed presses	No setoff; no spray powder required; in-line processing possible
Faster drying inks	Higher press speeds
Elimination of heat on web presses	Elimination of problems in printing on heat-sensitive substrates; better working conditions
Elimination of fountain solution	Simpler press design; easier to run
Variable image (as in ink jet printing)	Ability to make changes in copy without plate changes for on-line printouts for mailing labels, etc.

Forced changes	Reasons for changes
Elimination or reduction of solvents	Air pollution abatement; shortage of solvents (petroleum-derived)
Reduction or elimination of gas for drying of heat-set inks	Natural gas shortage (Supply of gas is forecast to be constant throughout the century.)
Elimination of spray powder on sheet-fed presses	Health (inhalation problem)

Note that there is an overlapping of some of the items from both lists. For instance, delivery of dry sheets on sheet-fed presses would solve the spray inhalation problem and yield several production advantages. Non-solvent inks which would dry without heat on coated paper would save gas, eliminate air pollution, dry faster, and be compatible with heat-sensitive substrates. Thus, even forced changes can bring about improvements, with the proper technology input.

NEW TYPES OF INKS

There are at least 11 types of inks that appeared during the decade of the 1970's. Many of these have become commercial, while a few are still in the developmental or semicommercial stage. They include:

Ultraviolet inks
Low-temperature-drying inks
Heat-reactive inks
Low-solvent inks
Water-based inks
Driographic inks
Infrared inks
Ink plus in-line coating
Electron beam inks
Electrostatic and jet inks
Subliming inks

Ultraviolet inks

Ultraviolet (UV) inks have been tagged the "wave of the future." They are inks which convert (cure or polymerize) under exposure to high-intensity ultraviolet light. This reaction takes place extremely rapidly, so that it is within the current state of the art to cure them at press speeds up to at least 3,000 feet per minute. Ultraviolet inks have the advantage of containing no solvents—yet versions are in the developmental stage for flexography and gravure, which until now have required inks containing large amounts of volatile solvents. The initial acceptance was in lithography and letterpress.

The ultraviolet lamps are powered by electricity, so unavailability of natural gas is no problem.

It is too early to tell if UV inks will attain the widespread use originally projected for them. To a large extent, the future of UV inks will depend upon factors such as the availability of natural gas and the cost and supply of organic solvents (petroleum derived), the success of water-based inks for flexography and gravure, the degree of enforcement of ecology regulations, and the development of low-viscosity UV materials which have a low order of skin sensitization.

One emerging application which appears of commercial interest is the use of a clear UV coating over conventional lithographic inks. The cured UV coating dries immediately and allows the ink underneath to oxidize to a dry state in its normal time. Setoff can be eliminated, and spray powder is not needed. Thus the system yields some of the advantages of an all-UV system at lower cost.

Low-temperature-drying inks

The objective behind the development of these heat-set inks by the manufacturer was the reduction of average web temperatures on heat-set presses from 300°–330° F to 200°–230° F, or about 100° F. The lower temperature offers several advantages, including reduction of up to 40% in natural gas consumption and up to 70% in hydrocarbon solvent emissions, fewer paper problems (reduced yellowing, blistering, bindery cracking, web breaks, etc.), and better ink gloss. Another advantage is the higher productivity these inks yield by virtue of their ability to allow faster press speeds within the confines of fixed dryer capacity. Low-temperature-drying inks are available in both lithographic and letterpress versions.

Heat-reactive (thermal curing) inks

Heat-reactive inks are similar to ultraviolet inks, except that the mechanism for polymerization is thermal (heat) rather than photochemical (light). The primary interest in these inks is that they contain little or no solvent, so a heat-set lithographic or letterpress printer who is subject to severe ecology legislation might use them in existing equipment.

To date, the various versions of heat-reactive inks have been subject to operational problems, mainly related to printability and press-side odor, which have prevented their adoption. These problems will have to be overcome if heat-reactive inks are to become a practical solution to the pollution problem. The technical feasibility still looks promising enough so that active development work is being conducted.

Low-solvent inks

By proper choice of vehicles, it is possible to reduce the solvent content of heat-set lithographic and letterpress inks by 50 percent or more. These inks are intended to reduce visible emissions and/or odor from heat-set dryer stacks. They also reduce hydrocarbon solvent emissions. It is too early, however, to tell if such reductions in smoke, odor, and solvent will provide any more than beneficial interim relief. Significant technical advances will probably be needed to comply with ultimate emissions regulations.

Water-based inks

Flexographic and gravure inks with water as the primary or sole solvent have been available for less critical uses for some time. The desire to reduce or eliminate hydrocarbons and other organic solvents normally found in higher quality flexographic and gravure printing inks has spurred the development of water-based inks suitable for high-quality printing as well.

Drastic formulation changes are required to produce these inks, and in many cases a systems approach taking into consideration every factor—ink, drying method, press facilities, etc.—must be used to achieve success. For example, water can cause many flexographic and gravure papers to pucker, and it requires more heat for evaporation. One approach is to print a thinner film of a stronger ink, so that less water is present. In flexography, changes in the ink distribution system (the arrangement of the rollers) might be needed to give a thinner film. The use of "shallow-etch" cylinders in gravure to lay down less ink than is possible with conventional cylinders is being evaluated. Even with shallow-etch cylinders, however, higher capacity dryers will be required for high-speed printing in some cases.

Based on current and future expected technical advances, water-based flexographic and gravure inks will achieve extensive commercial use, even on non-porous substrates such as plastic film and foil. Recent federal regulations recognize water-based inks (containing up to 25% organic solvent in the volatile portion) as an accepted approach to compliance. This has provided considerable stimulus to the interest in development of water-based inks to replace solvent-based ones.

Driographic inks

The term *driography* was created to describe the process for printing without water from a planographic (smooth) plate which has a special coating in the non-image areas (see "Special Plates," page 395). The driographic ink contains a special additive which makes the adhesive force of the ink to the coating less than the cohesive force within the ink itself. When the dry, smooth plate is inked, the ink will not stick to the non-image area, but it does remain in the bare image area. So far, these inks have not been commercially successful, but development work is still continuing, in this country and overseas.

Infrared inks

Infrared inks are basically conventional sheet-fed inks which contain some solvent. The heat from the infrared unit accelerates the absorption of this solvent into the paper substrate, thus increasing setting speed. In cases where the ink vehicle is largely a resin-solvent mixture, the heat-induced quick setting results in faster drying. Where the drying mechanism is primarily oxidation, the infrared heat has little or no effect on the drying speed.

Now available are infrared emitters that are "color-blind"; that is, they put heat into the light colors at nearly the same speed as the dark colors. This is important in multicolor printing.

A few heat-set web offset presses have been equipped with infrared emitters instead of dryers using natural gas. This provides a way around the unavailability of natural gas. The inks need not be specially formulated, since infrared is simply another way of creating heat to evaporate the solvent.

Ink plus in-line coating

A system using ink plus in-line coating was introduced for sheet-fed presses several years ago to eliminate setoff. It is being discussed currently for heat-set presses, to eliminate air pollution.

The process consists of running sheet-fed inks on the web press, followed by an in-line, overall depositing of a clear coating. A gas dryer is not used, and the inks (being the sheet-fed type) contain no solvent.

The clear coating, which either air-dries immediately or is dried by a low-capacity dryer, protects the wet ink underneath until it has a chance to dry by normal oxidation. The coating does not prevent oxygen from reaching the ink, even when applied on both sides of the paper.

This approach appears to have merit where a coating is to be applied anyway, as on magazine covers. The combined cost of ink and coating (1½ to 2 times conventional heat-set inks alone) probably prohibits the use of this system for producing the inner pages of magazines, at least given current alternatives.

Electron beam inks

These inks are chemically similar to ultraviolet inks, except that no photoinitiator (catalyst) is required. Polymerization is caused by electron bombardment of the monomer rather than by the release of free radicals by exposure of a UV photoinitiator to UV energy. The electron beam method is of considerable interest for the thicker films involved in screen printing and industrial finishes, but it seems unlikely at this time to have much potential for the thin films used in most printing processes. Of the two, UV would seem to be the preferred method.

The electron beam source must be equipped with heavy shielding since X-ray radiation is generated, and nitrogen or inert gas blanketing is required to exclude oxygen, which inhibits the reaction.

Whereas ultraviolet sources emit—and waste—about one-fourth to one-third of input power as heat, electron beam sources emit no heat to the substrate.

Electrostatic and jet inks

Electrostatic toners are a form of ink used to develop electrostatic images. The charge of the pigmented particles is opposite to that of the image; the particles are attracted to and adhere to the image-bearing surface.

These toners may be either dry powder or liquid. In powder form, they are generally mixed with a carrier such as iron powder or glass beads. The carrier imparts the correct charge to the toner by a triboelectric action and carries it to the image-bearing surface. In liquid form, the toner particles are charged and held in a colloidal suspension in a dielectric fluid. This then flows over the image surface, where the toner is deposited. Various electrostatic processes, such as Xerography, use these toners. (See "Reprography," page 429.)

Ink jet systems use an orifice to form a stream of ink droplets. In most systems, the droplets are electrically charged and electrostatically deflected to the image surface. (See "Ink Jet Printing," page 422.)

Inks for these systems are conductive, low in viscosity, and composed of material in a complete solution. The ink consists of a solvent, a resin binder, a dye, and a preservative. Solvents and binders exist in many formulations to permit printing on many different substrates, such as paper, metals, and plastics.

A major advantage of ink jet printing is that no printing plate has to be created. The electric field can be created from magnetic tape, for example, so that on-line printouts from computers or addressing of direct-mail envelopes can be done at high speeds.

Continuing developments in electrostatic and ink jet printing make it likely that these processes will become more widely used, particularly for text work.

Subliming inks

Subliming inks, also called *heat transfer inks* or *disperse dye inks,* are used with the transfer process that is popular for printing textiles. The colorants in the inks—primarily gravure inks—are special dyes, which sublime (convert from solid to gas without going through the liquid state) at a temperature of about 400° F. (See also "Heat Transfer Printing," page 429.)

Although the end use is textile printing, the inks are first printed on a paper carrier sheet on a commercial or publication-type press. The carrier is then rewound for shipment to the textile printer. The fabric and the carrier sheet are fed together over a heated calender drum, at a speed of about 7 to 10 yards per minute. The dye sublimes and transfers to the fabric, where it is "fixed" to the fiber. To date, only dyes substantive to man-made fibers, particularly polyester, are available.

THE ROLE OF INKS

The graphic arts industry continually seeks solutions to its requirements for greater efficiency with higher quality and to the challenges of environmental restrictions and materials shortages. Inks are playing an important role in the printing technologies which are emerging to fill these needs. The new printing inks are formulated to avoid the use of polluting solvents, to save energy, to keep cost and time factors as low as possible while increasing production and providing a functional and attractive end product.

BINDING 14

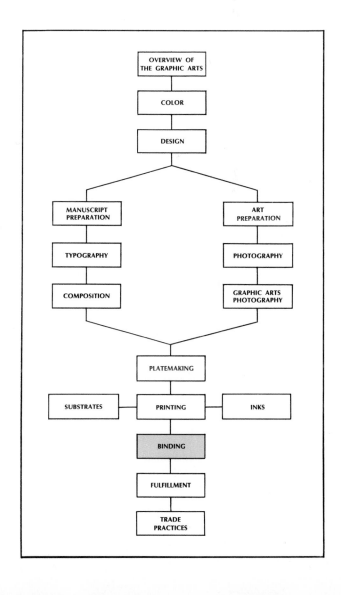

OVERVIEW OF
THE GRAPHIC ARTS

COLOR

DESIGN

MANUSCRIPT
PREPARATION

ART
PREPARATION

TYPOGRAPHY

PHOTOGRAPHY

COMPOSITION

GRAPHIC ARTS
PHOTOGRAPHY

PLATEMAKING

SUBSTRATES

PRINTING

INKS

BINDING

FULFILLMENT

TRADE
PRACTICES

INTRODUCTION TO BINDING

Paul D. Doebler, PUBLISHING MANAGEMENT CONSULTANT

The final phase of graphic arts manufacturing is binding, the process of converting flat printed sheets and raw cover materials into finished books, magazines, catalogs, mailing pieces, brochures, manuals, and a host of other products. Binding is not a single process, but a variety of processes that has been growing more complex in recent years.

The origins of binding could be traced back beyond the first books to the making of boxes or cases to house scrolls and other documents; their modern equivalent is the slip case, a box with one open side used to house fine editions or sets of books. It might even be said that the entire paper box industry, an important part of packaging, derives from the same beginnings. But the main thrust of binding within the traditional graphic arts industries has derived from the construction of books. Since printed sheets of paper first were folded and sewn together and glued into heavy leather covers, many different methods have been developed to hold books and other products together.

In addition to the fastening of pages into printed products, the binding industry includes specialized techniques adapted to the production of finished printed pieces. Various *finishing processes* are used both to add final decoration to bound products and to produce other products such as displays, posters, and labels.

THE BINDING PROCESS

The entire binding process may be broken down into three phases, as shown in the flow chart, figure 14.1. In the first phase, materials are assembled in the correct manner for binding. This process begins with the cutting and folding of large printed sheets, based on the *imposition*, the plan for the final layout of images. The imposition must be planned carefully before the job is printed so that when the sheet is processed later on, all the images will fall in the correct positions. The assembly stage continues with the *gathering* of the folded sheets, or *signatures*, into proper sequence. Sometimes page-size sheets, rather than signatures, are assembled for binding; this process is usually called *collating*.

The second phase is binding proper—fastening the pages or signatures together. A number of methods are used, including sewing with thread, gluing, stitching with wire, and fastening with rings or other mechanisms. There are variations within each of these kinds of binding.

The final processing of the fastened pages may be considered the third phase of the overall binding process. The pages must be trimmed so that their edges are even. Sometimes a cover is applied at this stage, after fastening is completed. Special decoration may be needed as well.

Jobs that are not bound but are finished in other ways share some of the earlier steps with bound products and may be decorated by the same methods, but they usually pass through their own unique processing stages in between.

MAJOR CLASSES OF BOUND PRODUCTS

Bound products can be classified on the basis of several criteria. Terminology for various product groups is sometimes confusing because it refers to more than one classification scheme. Basically, three main characteristics are used to classify bound products: the type of fastening system used to bind the pages together, the type of cover used to house the product, and the use to which the product is finally put.

Types of fastening systems

Four major families of fastening systems are used in binding today—wire stitching, thread sewing, gluing, and mechanical devices.

Wire stitching includes two basic styles, saddle and side. In *saddle-wire stitching*, staple-like wires are put through the backbone fold of a magazine or pamphlet and are crimped inside. In *side-wire stitching*, the wires enter the front cover, go through the booklet, and are crimped in the back.

Sewing includes several types of stitching with thread. In *Smyth sewing*, the folded signatures of a book are held together by stitching through the folded binding edge of the first signature in the book, fastening its pages together, then looping the thread over to the next signature and stitching its pages together in the same way, and so on until all of the signatures are sewn. In *side sewing*, as in side-wire stitching, the book is sewn from front to back. *Saddle sewing* is used to stitch through the backbone fold of single-signature books. In a process called *oversewing*, individual leaves or sheets are sewn into small groups; after each group is sewn it is joined to the next.

The major glue-based fastening system is *adhesive binding*, often referred to by the nickname of *perfect binding*. In this process, the backbone edges of sheets or signatures are ground until they are rough and then are coated with adhesive. A cover is often applied directly to the same film of adhesive that holds the pages together. Other gluing systems are used as well. In one, a thin line of adhesive is applied to each sheet as it is being folded on a folding machine; the glue line sticks to adjacent pages, holding them together.

Mechanical binding systems hold pages together by metal or plastic loops, rings, wires, or other devices passing through holes punched along the binding edge of the pages. There are two general classes of mechanical bindings, looseleaf and permanent or semi-permanent. *Looseleaf* devices, as the name implies,

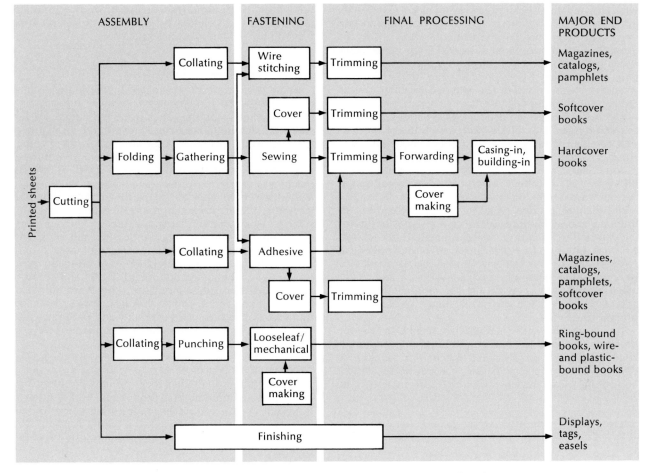

Figure 14.1: General sequence of operations in binding and finishing.

permit the binding mechanism to be opened or closed at any time, while other mechanical bindings generally are intended to be left closed once they are applied to the book.

Types of covers

Every bound product is considered to have a cover even when that cover is simply the outside leaves of the folded, bound, and trimmed sheet on which the rest of the booklet is printed. This kind of product is said to have a *self cover*. Covers of many varieties are available in a wide range of materials.

One broad distinction is made between hard covers and soft covers. *Hard covers*, often called *cases*, are prefabricated with stiff or rigid front and back boards connected at the binding edge by a more flexible area. *Soft covers* are made of a single sheet of heavy paper or another flexible substance, such as plastic.

Covers may be *flush* with the edge of the book's pages or they may *overhang* the pages. Hard covers most often are overhang covers; soft covers typically are flush covers because they are cut to the final page dimension along with the rest of the book at the trimming stage. However, some overhang covers are made of a single sheet of flexible material.

Certain covers are referred to by the material used to make them. Thus, hard covers are often called *cloth covers* because traditionally the boards were covered with cloth (although most hard covers today use other materials). Hardcover books also are often said to be *clothbound* for the same reason. Similarly, books with paper covers are often described as *paperbound* or *paperback* as well as softcover. The terms softcover and paperbound also have been extended to apply to wire-stitched and mechanically bound products using soft cover materials, instead of being limited to the adhesive-bound, paper-covered books sold at newsstands and drugstores. The term paperback, however, still tends to remain limited to this type of product.

Types of products

The third classification system, most familiar to people outside the graphic arts, is based on the types of end products, such as books, booklets, magazines, journals, brochures, pamphlets, folders, and leaflets. Some of these items, such as books and magazines, are well defined, but others enjoy no clear distinction. A folder to one person may be a brochure to another and a leaflet to still another. The differences among a folder, a pamphlet, and a booklet when all are saddle-wire stitched may be unclear. Even more clearly defined products sometimes are hard to differentiate from their neighbors. For the United States Census, for example, a book is defined as having 50 or more pages and a product with 49 or fewer pages is classified as a pamphlet; yet most book industry and binding people would not call a saddle-wire stitched product of less than about 100 pages a book.

A number of general product designations are used in the industry. *Pamphlet binding* refers to the production of small items such as pamphlets, booklets, brochures, folders, and leaflets. The binding of magazines, journals, and other products regularly issued more than once a year is called *periodical binding*—although magazines are often manufactured by the same saddle-wire stitching process used in pamphlet binding. In the area of bookbinding, *edition binding* has traditionally referred to hardcover, sewn volumes. The terminology has blurred, however, because of technological changes. Hardcover adhesive-bound books may also be considered edition bound; similarly, a soft cover may be applied to a sewn book. The more general term *case binding* refers to any book that is bound into a prefabricated case.

While most fastening methods are used primarily for products designed to contain published information, a large amount of looseleaf and mechanical binding is devoted to producing diaries, record books, notebooks, and other volumes in which information is to be written by the user. Most such *blankbooks* are manufactured and marketed by a special group of firms forming the blankbook industry.

OTHER SPECIALIZED PRODUCTS

In addition to products created by the major fastening systems, the binding field produces items which are not actually bound. Such products range all the way from folded posters, brochures, and form letters to advertising displays, tags and labels, and other items with special decorative treatments. Some of these products are made through the use of standard bindery machinery, such as folders and cutters, while some have their own specialized forms of assembly and fastening. Other products require finishing operations, such as die cutting of displays, labels, and folders; display mounting and easeling; embossing, stamping, and laminating; and eyeletting and stringing of tags.

Some highly specialized kinds of production have grown out of the general binding industry and are now actually parts of other industries. Prime examples are folding boxes and manifold business forms; both require specialized forms of assembly and fastening, performed at the plants where the products are made.

TRENDS IN BINDING

Binding traditionally has received less attention than other parts of graphic arts production, but it often is the point at which mistakes made earlier come to light and cause serious problems. If the binder cannot "save the job," such a mistake may require that the job be completely reprinted because it cannot be bound. Binders have long pleaded with others in the graphic arts production chain to be included early in the planning of jobs because requirements for binding help determine how jobs must be handled at earlier stages of production. Yet one of the most common failings of graphic arts planners remains the tendency to give inadequate attention to binding requirements.

Today, because of technological changes in a number of areas, binding is at last receiving more attention. These changes are making some older binding processes more efficient and economical and are opening up new variations in binding methods and materials.

For many years, binding processes remained predominantly labor-intensive; machines used at each step often were hand-fed, and material was moved manually from operation to operation on skids. The most automated process was wire stitching for publication work; signatures were gathered, bound into magazines, and trimmed automatically on continuous equipment lines.

Adhesive binding, the youngest of the major binding processes, also lends itself well to in-line processing. It first achieved significant use for telephone books and thick catalogs and later became the basic process for binding mass-market paperback books. Adhesive binding also took over a good deal of the binding of large magazines from side-wire stitching. Today it is moving into the area of hardcover binding, once the domain of the sewing processes.

With this growth, adhesive binding is encouraging

automated in-line processing throughout the binding field. Not only are adhesive-bound books produced on conveyorized in-line systems, but so are sewn books as far as possible. Looseleaf and mechanical binding have remained relatively untouched by automation so far, but the first in-line spiral binding systems have recently been developed. While the bindery field has been late in moving toward automated operating principles, it is now moving swiftly in this direction and should show major improvement in the future.

IMPOSITION

Abraham Hardis, AE BINDCRAFT, INC.

An imposition is the master plan for the assembly of printed images into a finished piece. It specifies exactly where each image is to be printed on a large press sheet to create the proper sequence and visual effect after the sheet is processed through various binding steps. In addition, the imposition planner must allow for margins for trimming, specify the guide points for machine feeding of the sheets, and take into account paper characteristics such as grain direction and weight of stock. Sometimes considerations outside the bindery also are involved, such as the need to position printed images so that they will run well on press. The imposition must be designed by someone with extensive knowledge of all the equipment involved, and it must be followed carefully by everyone working on the job —from composing room stone hand and lithographic stripper to the platemaker, press operator, and binder. All others in the graphic arts must work to the bindery's imposition requirements—not the other way around. When others do depart from the bindery's imposition requirements, a great deal of trouble inevitably results.

IMAGE LAYOUT

The two binding operations that generally have the greatest influence on imposition requirements are cutting and folding. The layout of the pages or images on the press sheet must lend itself to the cutting and folding operations (see "Cutting and Folding," page 524).

A simple imposition that is commonly used for a 16-page booklet or signature is illustrated in figure 14.2. The diagram shows the page numbers printed on the top side of the sheet within the page areas, while pages printed on the reverse side are indicated by the arrows. The numbers appear jumbled, but they fall into order when the sheet is folded three times. If the three folds are made along the fold lines indicated in figure 14.2, the numbered pages will fall into proper sequence as shown in figure 14.3. This fact can be verified by folding a flat sheet of paper as indicated, numbering the pages at the open corners in sequence, and opening the sheet up again; the sequence of page numbers on the flat sheet will correspond to the numbering scheme in figure 14.2. Imposition planners often make up or verify impositions in just this way, folding sheets

of paper to make certain that the job will assemble properly.

This simple imposition is only one of thousands that can be invented by binders to solve any graphic arts

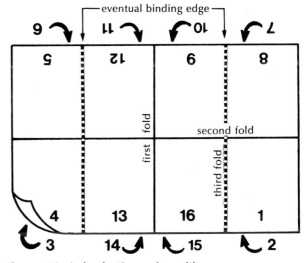

Figure 14.2: A simple 16-page imposition.

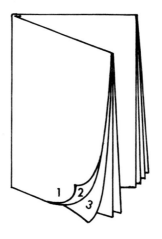

Figure 14.3: The same imposition after folding.

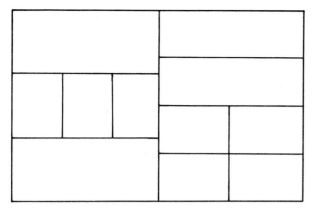

Figure 14.4: Imposition with only one cutting line going across the full sheet. This type of imposition can be cut successfully. Each cut divides the sheet into separate segments, each segment having at least one cutting line running all the way across it.

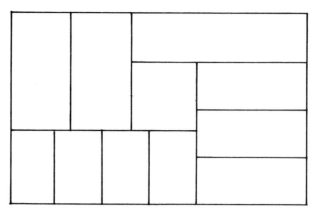

Figure 14.5: Imposition that cannot be cut apart. There is no line running across the entire sheet, so no straight cut can be made.

assembly problem. Thus, while the graphic arts must work within the limitations of binding imposition requirements, the flexibility of binding equipment and the ingenuity of binders in designing impositions allow a broad range of products.

One principle is basic to all impositions: the sheet must be cut or folded from one side to the other in a straight line. In an imposition for a folded signature or booklet, such as that in figure 14.2, every folding line naturally goes straight across the sheet. This imposition could also be cut into individual parts along the fold lines indicated. It is not necessary, however, that all cutting lines run to the edge of the full sheet; only one line on each sheet or segment to be cut must do so. A number of brochures and leaflets of different sizes could be laid out in a single imposition and cut apart successfully. Figure 14.4 is an example of such an imposition. However, it is important to avoid designing an imposition such as that in figure 14.5, which cannot be cut apart on a cutting machine.

It often is difficult to design the most efficient imposition for a job. Most jobs can be produced in a number of ways, often requiring varied amounts of machine running and manual handling. These different ways of running material through the various binding operations will be more or less economical depending on the circumstances of the job, equipment available, and the like. Much of the binder's skill lies in making the best imposition for a given job and set of circumstances.

One factor that affects folding is the grain direction of the paper, that is, the dimension of the sheet along which most of the paper fibers tend to align themselves during manufacture (see "Fundamental Physical Properties of Paper," page 471). Fold lines running in the grain direction are easier to make and tend to be more accurate and uniform because the paper is creased parallel to most of the fibers—not across them, forcing them to bend. A basic rule in making binding impositions is that the first fold should run parallel to the grain; normally, this procedure results in books with the grain running vertically down the pages, mak-

ing them open and stay flat more easily. (Indeed, on some web offset presses, the folding mechanisms require that certain size books, such as 6" x 9" volumes, have the grain running across the pages, and these often do not open well.)

Sometimes factors in the printing process also affect the choice of imposition. Heavy ink coverage on certain parts of the sheet is a prime example. An area of heavy coverage—such as a full-page illustration with a large solid-color background—will draw a great deal of ink from the inking rollers, leaving little ink to cover the images printed immediately behind it on the sheet. Normally, the inking rollers cannot be resupplied fast enough with adequate ink to properly print another heavy solid area immediately following the first, and a faded second image results. Therefore, in making impositions for jobs with heavy ink coverage areas, the images have to be placed far enough apart for the ink supply to be replenished. In some extreme cases, these images have to positioned in alternate rows of pages so that only one heavy-coverage area will draw ink from each section of the ink rollers in each printing cycle. In such cases, extra binding cost may be incurred because the layout required for printing cannot be folded in large signatures but must be cut apart and folded in many smaller units.

A vital bit of information on all impositions—one whose omission can cause great trouble—is an indication of the top or head position of each page or image. Workers imposing forms in the composing room and stripping flats in the stripping department must have this information, as they usually know virtually nothing about the cutting and folding sequences planned for the bindery. Incorrect assumptions made here in the absence of specific instructions on the imposition can lead to upside-down pages, printed forms that cannot be cut and folded at all, extra processing cost, and poor appearance of the finished product. It is particularly important that head margins be specified uniformly on all pages on an imposition to avoid confusion and insure proper page alignment throughout the product.

MARGIN REQUIREMENTS

Many types of jobs require the allowance of extra margins around the basic page or image areas on the printed sheet, to be used in a number of ways during manufacture. The three major uses for these extra margins are trimming, binding, and machine feeding.

Margins for trimming

Margins for trimming are provided by adding a slight bit of extra height and width to each page area as it is laid out on the imposition sheet. Typically, ⅛" is added to the top, front (opening side), and bottom of each page area. After the sheet is folded and the pages are bound together on the binding edge, the top, front, and bottom trim margins will be cut off on a guillotine cutter or an in-line trimming machine to open up the pages and to provide finished, even edges. (See "Cutting and Folding," page 524.) Correct head margins are especially important because pages are aligned in binding machinery by jogging the head edges of folded sheets against machine stops or gauges prior to fastening and trimming.

Trimming margins also are required when printed images such as illustrations are to *bleed* off the edge of the finished page or sheet. Because it is extremely difficult to print an image precisely up to but not beyond the edge of the paper, the bleed illustration is printed well beyond the finished page dimension. And because printing beyond the edge of a sheet creates unacceptable ink buildup and smearing on the press impression cylinder, the paper must be extended beyond the printed area. This extra margin, typically about ⅛", then is trimmed in a cutting machine, cutting right through the printed image to create the bleed off the page. If the bleed illustrations are used in a book with basic page trim margins already provided in the imposition, no additional trim margin usually is required; the illustrations are simply printed out into these trim areas. But on jobs which would normally be printed and cut apart without trim margins, they must be added where bleed illustrations are to be used. Needless to say, the bleed illustrations themselves must be planned with extra area to be cut away, or else some of the image that should be shown on the finished page will be removed.

Margins for binding

In certain processes and circumstances, extra margin in the center of a book is required for binding. Books that are bound so that they open all the way to the center fold—Smyth-sewn and saddle-sewn books and thinner saddle-wire stitched booklets or signatures—need no additional binding margin. In other types of binding, however, some of the inner page margin either is cut off or is bound tightly together; the book does not open all the way to the original page dimension line on the imposition plan unless additional margin is added to the inner, or *gutter*, edge of the pages. The binding processes which require such additional margin allowance in the gutter along the binding edges are adhesive binding, side-wire stitching, side sewing, and saddle-wire stitching of thick books.

The problem in thick saddle-wire stitched booklets is a special one, called *creep*. To visualize this problem, consider a stack of pages ¼" thick, which will be folded at the center binding edge to form a book ½" thick. Imagine that all of these unfolded sheets are exactly the same size. When the stack of sheets is folded, the outside sheets will not extend far enough to completely cover the sheets folded inside; because of the ¼" thickness of the sheets at the fold, the innermost pages will extend ¼" beyond the outermost pages of the book.

However, a booklet is usually manufactured with its front edge squared off. The cover and outermost pages must extend from the outside of the binding edge to the squared-off front edge, while the innermost pages are narrower because they need extend only from the inside binding edge to the front edge. If all of the pages of the book are imposed by using the same dimension from the folded binding edge, the images will be indented from the front edges of the pages more at the beginning and end of the book than in the middle; for our ½" book, the difference will again be ¼", enough to be noticeable and to be considered unsightly in knowledgeable binding circles. Therefore, not only must the imposition for such a booklet allow additional margins for the variation in physical page size, but the printed images must be positioned so that they all will be the same distance from the front edge of the booklet after it is trimmed.

Gripper margins

As press sheets move through printing and binding equipment, they are held by mechanical devices called *grippers*. The third type of margin required is the *gripper margin*, which allows space for the grippers to hold the sheet.

These gripper margins may be required for a number of reasons, both on printing presses and on certain binding machines. On a printing press, a sheet held by gripper devices as it moves through the machine must be held in areas that will not be printed; this principle seems simple enough, but many a letterpress plate has been smashed because someone forgot to allow for gripper margin when laying out the imposition form. Many a pile of paper has had to be discarded after it was cut without allowing the additional non-printing gripper margin area, causing the image to run off the back end of the sheet when it was placed on the press.

In the bindery, special gripper margins, usually called *lips* or *laps*, are often left on one edge of folded signatures. On gathering and sewing machines, these margins, which extend out beyond the rest of the signature, are grasped by automatic feeding equipment to pull individual signatures from hoppers full of stacked signatures.

GUIDE EDGES AND GUIDE POINTS

An imposition must provide for two aspects of machine feeding and handling of paper. One, as just mentioned, is gripping the sheet as it moves through the machine. The second is the provision of proper guide edges or guide points at which the sheet can be positioned in various machines. Every printing and binding operation that involves paper handling requires some form of precise positioning or *registration*, and the positions established by one operation must be retained and used again in succeeding operations.

Positioning of the press sheet

Guide edges for sheets to be used in sheet-fed printing are established at the paper cutter when sheets are cut to press size. Care should be taken when cutting press sheets to provide square edges on the guide sides of the sheets. Even when sheets are purchased from the mill or merchant in the correct press size, they often are trimmed slightly on one or more sides to provide good guide edges.

The guide edges are positioned against guides on the press before the sheet is printed. The gripper edge of the sheet is positioned against the *front guide*, and one side is positioned against the *side guide*.

The number of guide points required on a sheet for registration will vary with the kind of handling the sheet receives during production. For any one registration or positioning operation, at least three points must be provided—two points along the gripper or leading edge and one along one side. With some impositions, all processing in both pressroom and bindery can be completed with just three such points on two edges of the sheet. With other impositions and handling sequences, several more points on a third edge of the sheet may be needed. If more than the three basic registration or guide points are needed, it is generally because of press conditions rather than bindery requirements.

In sheet-fed printing, where the most complex press requirements are encountered, there are four fundamental types of impositions: *sheetwise, work-and-turn, work-and-tumble,* and *work-and-twist.* These names describe techniques for turning the press sheet in order to print more than one impression. Figure 14.6 illustrates how sheets are printed and turned in each of these cases. Also shown are the guide edges and registration points required on the sheets.

In a sheetwise imposition, one image carrier prints the front of the sheet. Then the sheet is turned over lengthwise, so that the gripper edge remains in the same position and the side guide edge moves to the opposite side of the press. A second image carrier then prints the back side of the sheet, so that the two sides have different but complementary copy. The side guide is moved from one side of the press to the other so that the same guide edge may be used for the second impression to insure proper registration.

In a work-and-turn imposition, the images that will finally appear on the front of the sheet and on its backup are first printed side by side on a large press sheet. The paper is turned in the same manner as for a sheetwise imposition. The same image carrier then prints the reverse of both sides of the sheet. The sheet is cut in half, giving two complete signatures from one image carrier.

A work-and-tumble imposition uses one image carrier for both sides of the sheet, like a work-and-turn imposition, but in this case the sheet is turned over so that the gripper edge is moved to the opposite side of the press and the guide edge remains the same. Unlike the side guide, the grippers cannot be moved to the opposite side of the press, so a new edge of the sheet must now be used as the gripper edge. This imposition is not used unless necessary because changing the gripper edge can cause errors in backup registration if the paper has not been cut square.

The work-and-twist imposition is used for one-side printing only. Two components of a single image—the horizontal and vertical rules of ruled forms, for example—are printed next to each other on a sheet. The sheet is then turned 180°, still face up, so that both the gripper and guide edges are reversed. Then the same components are printed so that each is placed over the other to form the complete image twice on the sheet. The paper must be cut square to insure proper register. This imposition is rarely used today. It was used mainly to avoid tedious engraving work (as in the case of crossed rules) or the expense of duplicate plates.

Sheetwise and work-and-turn impositions require the minimum number of guide points, two on the one gripper edge and one on one side of the sheet. These are the most desirable impositions because use of the same three points throughout leaves the least room for error. The work-and-tumble imposition requires two gripper edges and two different registration points on the one guide edge. The work-and-twist imposition, since it is used to print two impressions on the same side of the sheet rather than one on each side, requires registration points on all four sides of the sheet, a particularly sensitive requirement.

Web registration

Web-fed presses generally pose fewer problems. Trimmed sheets with precise registration points are not required because the paper is printed as one continuous web, fed into the folder, and processed while it is still under firm control of the machine. Usually both sides of the web are printed simultaneously in register. Registration is controlled by sensing units which scan the printed image or the edge of the web and signal special tension and angle roller mechanisms to vary the position of the paper in the press. Registration errors can still occur if the web stretches as it is pulled through the press or "wanders" slightly from side to side. However, imposition planning for web registration is greatly simplified: the basic dimensions of the printed sheet are fixed by the web width and by the cylinder circumference, or repeat length; and the registration of the web is handled automatically during printing, cutting, and through to folded signatures.

Registration in the bindery

In the bindery, folded signatures from web presses go directly to gathering and binding equipment. The folded edges of the signatures are used as guides for feeding and jogging to achieve alignment.

However, printed sheets from sheet-fed presses must first be cut and folded. These operations depend for registration on the same guide edges and points used on the printing press. (See also "Cutting and Folding," page 524.)

Figure 14.6: Four types of imposition. For each imposition, first impression is shown at left, second at right. Gripper and guide edges are indicated; X's represent guide points required for registration.

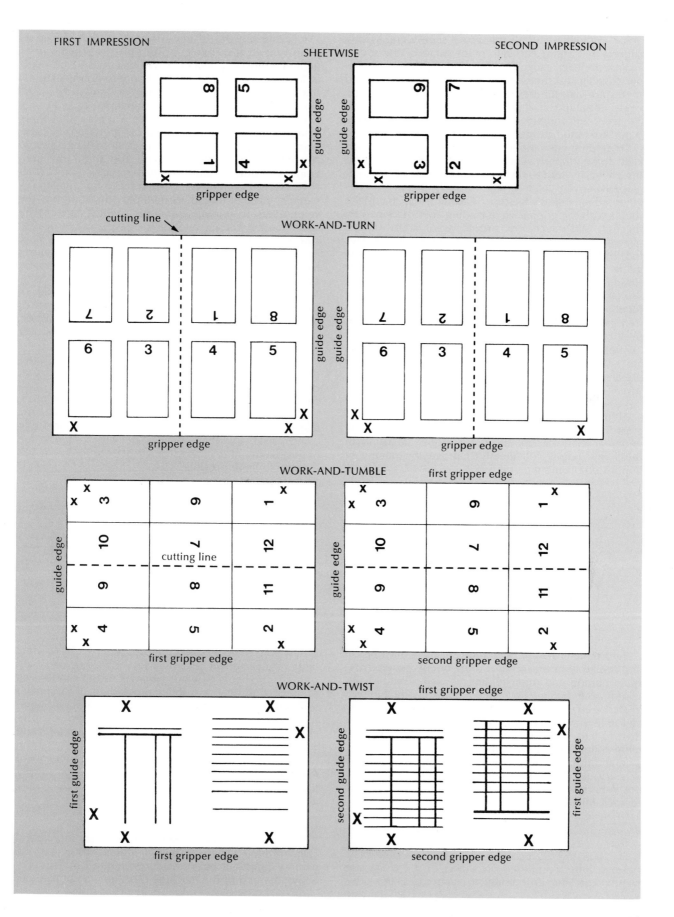

FIRST IMPRESSION

SECOND IMPRESSION

SHEETWISE

guide edge

guide edge

gripper edge

gripper edge

cutting line

WORK-AND-TURN

guide edge

guide edge

gripper edge

gripper edge

WORK-AND-TUMBLE

first gripper edge

guide edge

cutting line

guide edge

first gripper edge

second gripper edge

WORK-AND-TWIST

first gripper edge

first guide edge

first gripper edge

second guide edge

first guide edge

second gripper edge

523

For guillotine cutters the press sheets are usually aligned by jogging the side guide edge of the sheets against the back gauge of the cutter and the press gripper edge against the side frame of the cutter. When the sheets are cut, the new edges are parallel to the side guide edge and at right angles to the gripper edge. For work-and-tumble sheets, of course, the cut edge is parallel to the gripper edge.

On folding equipment a similar technique is used to align folds properly. On a buckle folder the stops on the plates are set to make the sheet buckle at the right place when the leading edge, usually the press side-guide edge, strikes the stops. A knife folder feeds the sheets with the gripper edge leading and is stopped by the first fold gauge. For two kinds of knife folders, quad folders and double-16 folders, the knife makes the fold parallel to the first fold gauge, and the side guide is used to register the sheet for the necessary slitting and perforating for subsequent folds. For jobber-type knife folders the side guide registers the sheet for the first fold, which the knife makes, and the first fold gauge registers the sheet for the perforating and positioning necessary for the second fold.

After folding, signatures printed on sheet-fed presses are processed in the same manner as those from web presses.

COMMON FAILURES IN IMPOSITION PLANNING

Although the complexity of imposition planning creates many possibilities for error, most failures fall under a relatively few headings. Proper attention to these few points will greatly improve the quality of imposition planning.

• Laying out the image positions so that the paper grain runs in the "wrong" direction. As noted earlier, grain should run parallel to the first fold to be made in a sheet. Many graphic arts planners—particularly in the advertising and lithographic printing fields—still violate this established binding principle.

• Planning for right-angle folds when parallel folds, which are more precise, would be preferred. In pamphlet binding, development of the automatic gathering-stitching-trimming machine and the trend in lithographic printing plants to smaller multicolor presses have created a preference in binderies for smaller signatures, parallel-folded in multiples. In addition, developments in folding equipment, which have facilitated parallel folding, and the increasing use of heavier stocks, which are harder to fold at right angles, have reduced the higher cost of parallel-folding signatures to the point where it balances well against the greater control and quality achieved.

• Calling for a "making order," or custom order, of paper in an odd size which will not fit the presses or binding equipment efficiently without special handling.

• Choosing impractical or hard-to-do solutions over easier ones.

The importance of early cooperation between binders and job planners to create the most practical production plan should be self-evident. Binders can, should, and would work with art directors, printers, and others if called upon to be part of the planning team. Their contributions can lead to mechanical efficiency, sizable savings, speedier deliveries, elimination of problems, and even a practical solution to a job thought to be impossible.

CUTTING AND FOLDING

Abraham Hardis, AE BINDCRAFT, INC.

Before materials are bound, they usually must be cut and folded. Jobs that are not to be bound generally require cutting and often folding as well. Traditionally, cutting and folding have been done in the bindery. With the advent of web printing presses, however, special units have come into use at the end of the press line to cut and fold signatures automatically, thus eliminating these operations in the bindery.

In addition to being cut before binding, bound products are usually trimmed after processing in the bindery. A narrow margin is cut from two or more sides to remove folded edges and open up the pages, as well as to make the edges smooth.

CUTTING OF PRESS SHEETS

Some jobs are printed on sheets of the exact size needed for later processing; in such cases, the press sheets are often created before printing by cutting larger sheets down to size. Most jobs, however, are printed on sheets that are larger than the binder will process. Cutting the printed press sheet into smaller sections usually is the first step in the bindery. Sometimes press sheets are also trimmed to provide precisely square edges for alignment to press grippers and side guides on various machines.

Accuracy in cutting is essential for all subsequent operations. Consultation with the binder for proper planning before printing begins will ensure quality and economy.

Guillotine cutters

The machine that is most widely used for cutting large printed sheets is the *guillotine cutter*. As the name suggests, a heavy blade positioned horizontally above the bed of the machine descends to cut through a pile, or *lift,* of paper. A heavy weight called the *clamp* descends automatically just before the knife to hold the pile stationary. Tremendous power is used to drive the knife quickly and cleanly through the lift and to create the pressure needed by the clamp.

Sheets to be cut are placed on the bed of the machine by the operator. Because the sheets are flat, not folded, this type of cutting is known as *flat cutting.* The first requisite for cutting is to have two edges at right angles for precise position. The first cut is usually made across the width of the sheet. The edge of the paper that was the gripper edge on press is usually placed against the side wall of the machine, and the side guide edge aligns against a movable metal bar called the *back gauge.* (This positioning is occasionally reversed.) The back gauge, which is either hand or power operated, is positioned through use of a calibrated scale visible to the operator so that the lift is in precisely the correct position under the knife. After positioning the lift, the operator triggers the knife and the cut is made. The operator then repositions one or both of the cut sections for the next cut if necessary. Depending upon the size of the sheets, two or more piles may be cut at once.

In flat cutting, the knife cuts completely through each pile of sheets in a straight line. This point must always be taken into account in planning the layout of images to be cut. (See "Imposition," page 519.)

The precision and efficiency of the guillotine cutter has been increased through the use of *automatic spacing.* On machines with this feature (nearly all machines today), the back gauge is moved automatically after each cut to precisely the correct point for the next cut. These *running gauges* are controlled electrically on older machines, but many newer cutters, such as the one in figure 14.7, have electronically programmed gauges and magnetic memories that can remember a complete series of settings.

There are also many aids to increase efficiency and to aid the operator. Tables the height of the cutting bed can be installed on the sides of the cutter for keeping piles of paper handy. The bed of the machine and the wings can have air ducts that create a film of air between the heavy pile and the bed to make turning and moving the pile easier. Jogging machines can be used to straighten a badly stacked pile of paper and

then lift it to the height of the bed. Various safety devices are also used to protect the operator against accidents.

Guillotine cutters are made in a wide range of sizes, from small machines to those that can cut sheets over 100" wide. The uses of these machines range from cutting sheets into two or four sections that will be folded into signatures to separating hundreds of printed labels. The guillotine cutter is also used for cutting or trimming unprinted sheets of paper and for trimming folded and bound books and pamphlets; its use as a book trimmer will be discussed later.

Bracket trimmers

A somewhat different cutter, no longer manufactured but still used in many binderies, is the *Bracket trimmer.* This cutter generally handles sheets only up to about 25" wide, so it is used mostly in pamphlet binding rather than bookbinding. It is often used for cutting apart multiple small units, such as labels. The Bracket cutter is similar to the mechanically operated guillotine cutter, but it works faster. The Bracket is fed from behind the knife, so the operator can hold the lift of paper and move it through the machine. After cutting, the sheets can be pushed onto a conveyor, from which they can be removed by a second operator. Trimmed edges are disposed of automatically.

The Bracket trimmer has a series of stops against which the sheets are positioned. The stops can be set to specific points automatically, so a series of cuts can be made without resetting. If a number of parallel cuts are to be made, the operator can push the pile of sheets straight through the machine, repositioning the pile against each stop and making one cut after the next. Because of this feature, the Bracket cutter is particularly useful for cutting apart booklets that have been bound in multiples. Its main use in edition binding is for separating books that have been printed two-up.

FOLDING

In book, periodical, or pamphlet binding, sheets containing a number of pages printed in a specific arrangement (as described in "Imposition," page 519) must be folded into signatures or into complete small booklets. In fact, if a printed piece is to have more than two pages (one on the front and one on the back of a single leaf), it must be folded. In addition, many pieces with only two pages or with printing on only one side—such as leaflets and letters—are folded for mailing or for other purposes.

Types of folds

Folding machines are designed to make two basic types of folds—*right-angle* and *parallel* folds. A right-angle fold is made by folding a sheet at a right angle to a previous fold. A parallel fold is one that is made parallel to a previous fold.

Parallel folding has a number of variations. A *wrap-around fold* consists of a series of parallel folds made in the same direction so that each fold wraps around the previous one. An *accordion fold* is formed by parallel folds made in alternating directions so that they

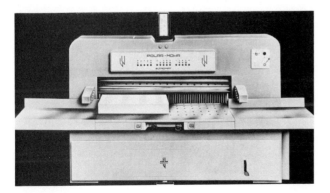

Figure 14.7: Polar electronic guillotine cutter. *Courtesy of Heidelberg Eastern, Inc.*

lie on top of each other and open up like the bellows of an accordion. Another type of fold, the *gatefold*, forms a flap which unfolds to extend beyond the normal page dimension of a book or to enlarge a standard-size brochure or mailing piece.

An amazing number of folding arrangements can be invented to run on various folding machines. The examples in figure 14.8 provide just an idea of the possible variations. So varied is the range of expert knowledge in folding, in fact, that many binders specialize in one type of folding—for example, folding of direct mail or package inserts. Other binders with specialized equipment concentrate on folding large sheets, such as maps or technical diagrams, down to book size. Other specialties include unusual combinations of folds and the folding of unusual stocks.

Folding machines

The two basic methods of folding are the knife method and the buckle method. The knife method is the simpler of the two.

On a knife folder, the sheet is fed by a timed feeder to come to rest under a serrated blunt blade (the "knife"). The knife descends just enough to tuck the sheet between two parallel rollers, creating a fold, as illustrated in figure 14.9. The rollers pull the folded sheet through and deposit it onto moving tapes. The folded sheet is carried to the next knife station, where the same operation is repeated.

On a buckle folder, each folding section has feeding and folding rollers, one or more hollow plates, and an adjustable stop. The sheets are fed continuously from a long feed board into the plate. The forward progress of the sheet is blocked by the adjustable guide, which has been set and tightened at a specific point. As the rollers move the sheet up against the guide, the sheet buckles. The folding rollers catch the sheet, a crease is made, and the sheet is carried forward between the rollers to the next operation, fold first. (See figure 14.10.)

Most buckle folders have several plates, usually four, clustered together in each folding section, so that sev-

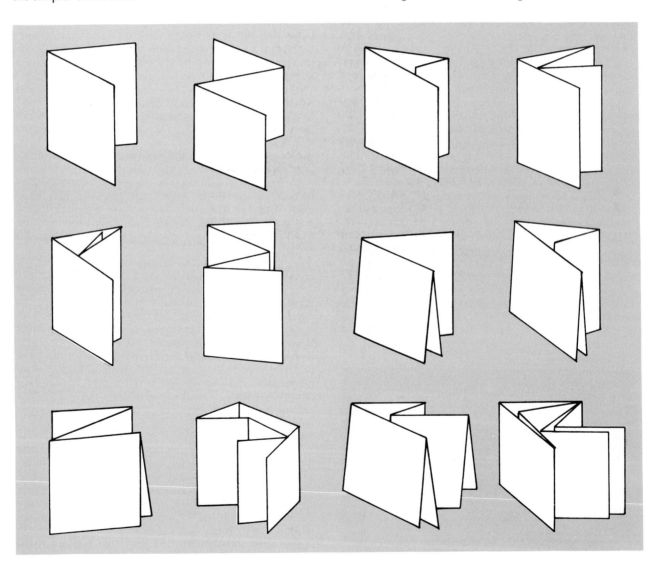

Figure 14.8: Folding arrangements.

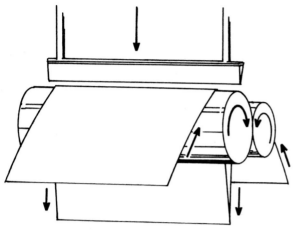

Figure 14.9 (above): Diagram of knife folding.

Figure 14.10 (right): Diagram of buckle folding.

eral parallel folds can be made in succession. The sheet is fed by rollers directly from one plate in the cluster to the next. A number of folding sections can be connected by feeder tables so that many folds can be made in a row. For right-angle folding, the sections are arranged at right angles to each other. Feeder tables called *cross carriers* change the direction of the sheet by 90°. Any number of plates in each section can be used and the others skipped, so parallel and right-angle folds can be made in varied combinations.

Between sections, scorers and perforators can be set up if required for the job. (A buckle folder is shown in figure 14.11.)

There are three main types of knife folders, which were popular in the past but are used decreasingly today: jobber-type knife folders, used in pamphlet binderies; double-16 folders, which produce two 16-page or, with an attachment, two 32-page signatures, for magazine work and paperbacks; and quad folders, used in edition binding, which produce two 32-page

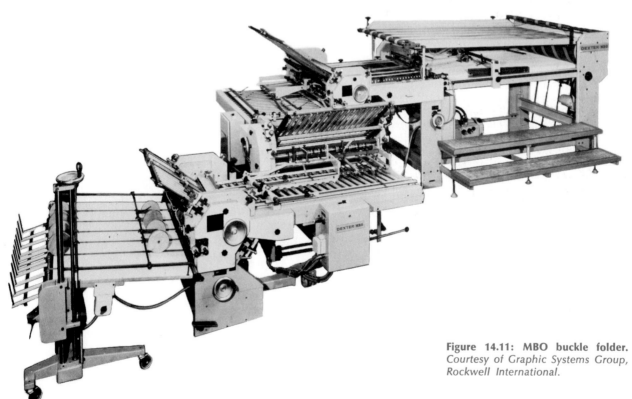

Figure 14.11: MBO buckle folder. *Courtesy of Graphic Systems Group, Rockwell International.*

527

or four 16-page signatures. Some of the largest knife folders can take press sheets of 69" to 70" in length and, in the case of the quad folder, slit them into several sections and deliver up to four signatures at one time.

Knife folders are used mainly for right-angle folding of large sheets into signatures for books and periodicals. Because of the tapes that connect the folding units, knife folders can control the movement of large sheets through the machine better than buckle folders. They can also handle the most difficult types of paper, such as thin Bible stocks, with relative ease.

When the imposition is suitable for the knife folder and the layout can be standardized—for example, for many issues of a magazine—the knife folder is very efficient. However, the choice of combinations of folds on the knife folder is too few to make it a reasonable machine for job work. In addition, because the machine is timed, folding of smaller sheets is very slow.

In job plants, where a great deal of parallel folding as well as right-angle folding is done, buckle folders are quickly replacing knife folders. Buckle folders are better suited than knife folders to handle the smaller sheets used for pamphlets, brochures, and the like. In addition, the movable plates give buckle folders greater flexibility. The operator can extend the number of parallel folds from 4 to 8 or even 12 at any point in the folding scheme, so wraparound and accordion folds are easy to produce. The plates can easily be arranged to produce more combinations of folds than are possible on a knife folder. In addition, changes from one size sheet to another are easier.

SLITTING AND PERFORATING

A common form of cutting, called *slitting*, is not done on a separate cutting machine but is combined with folding on a folding machine. Slitting wheels—small metal wheels with knife-sharp edges—are mounted on shafts between the folding sections. As the paper passes through the folding machine, it is held by rollers against the cutting edges of the wheels. Slitting may be used to cut sheets or to separate folded products that have been printed in multiples.

Perforating may also be done on the folding machine. In this case, a cutting wheel with a number of sharp teeth rather than a continuous cutting edge is used. The wheel produces a series of perforations in the paper.

FOLDING AND SLITTING ON WEB PRESSES

In recent years, more and more folded signatures have been produced directly on folding equipment at the delivery end of web presses. Slitting and perforating are done at the same time.

On simpler presses, the web or webs of paper coming into the folder are first folded lengthwise and then brought between two revolving cylinders, one with a knife and the other with an impression bar for the knife to press against. After cutting, the sheets pass through one or more folding operations to produce finished signatures.

Larger, more complex web presses use the same type of folding mechanisms but may have several folders in one press line. They may also be equipped with a number of slitting stations in front of the folders to cut the full-width web of paper into narrower ribbons. These narrow webs may be run through various rollers and turning bars which place the folds so that the printed images are correctly positioned in the finished signature.

On the largest of these presses, the slitting and turning rollers may extend up a story or more above the press itself. Literally hundreds of special impositions can be run to suit special job requirements. The task of planning the webbing, or the way the ribbons will run through such presses, is very complex. Often the presses slit, interleave, and fold the ribbons into several different signatures simultaneously.

TRIMMING

After books, pamphlets, and other bound products have been folded and bound, they must usually be trimmed on two or more sides. A booklet or signature is assembled by folding large sheets so that the pages fall in proper sequence; thus there are folded edges along the side and top. The trimming operation cuts these folds away, freeing the pages to open. Guillotine and Bracket cutters can both be used for trimming assembled books, but trimming machines with three or more knives are more efficient.

On guillotine cutters, books or booklets can be trimmed just as sheets are cut. The books are piled up, positioned, cut, and turned for the next trim. Trimming is greatly facilitated, however, by the use of back gauges that are split into three parts. Each part can be set individually at the necessary distance from the cutting blade for trimming one of the three unbound edges of the book. Each stack is positioned against the three parts of the gauge in succession.

The Bracket trimmer can also be used for trimming books or booklets. Each side of the pile of books must be positioned and cut in succession. As mentioned earlier, this machine has the advantages of automatic

Figure 14.12: Wohlenberg three-knife trimmer. *Courtesy of Graphic Systems Group, Rockwell International.*

removal of trimmed books and waste paper. However, it is most useful for making a series of parallel cuts.

The most widely used machines for book and booklet trimming are *three-knife trimmers,* as illustrated in figure 14.12. This type of machine cuts three edges of the book in one operation. The book is fed into the cutter, two knives descend together to cut the top and bottom of the book, the book is advanced automatically, and the front is cut by a third knife. The order of the cuts is reversed on some machines, but all three sides are always trimmed automatically. The waste falls into a hopper or onto the floor, and the trimmed book is pushed automatically onto a moving belt.

Some trimmers have more than three knives. They are used to split apart and trim books that have been printed two-up. A four-knife machine can handle books that must simply be cut apart in the center. A five-knife trimmer is used when a portion of paper must be trimmed away between the two books as well.

On multi-knife trimmers, books are fed individually into the machine rather than in stacks as on the single-knife cutting machines. One advantage to single-book trimming is that cutting is cleaner and more precise; the problem of cutting a lift of paper with uneven heights is eliminated. The outstanding feature of single-book trimming, however, is that the machine can be attached in-line to other machines in the binding line. Increasingly, three-knife trimmers are being installed as parts of continuous binding lines, with books being fed and removed by conveyor as they go from one machine to the next automatically.

SEWING AND EDITION BINDING
Kenneth W. James, A. HOROWITZ & SON

Hard covers and the sewing of signatures to hold them together are the features which have traditionally distinguished *edition binding* from other forms of binding. Until recent times books were sewn and bound by hand one at a time or in small batches and covered with leather. The binding of an entire edition of a book was uncommon before the development of binding machinery, which began in the 1820's. At about the same time the process of coloring and treating cloth for use as a covering material was perfected, and machine-made prefabricated cloth cases which could be simply glued onto the book block by machine at high speed came into use. Today various covering materials are turned over boards to make hard covers, and other binding methods, such as adhesive binding, have taken over part of the field from sewing. However, the classic edition-bound book remains the sewn book.

ELEMENTS OF AN EDITION-BOUND BOOK
A number of terms are commonly used to refer to parts of a book (see figure 14.13). The front cover and back cover are connected at the *back* of the book, often called the *backbone* or *spine.* The unbound edge opposite the backbone is called the *front* of the book. The other two edges are the *top,* or *head,* and the *bottom,* also called the *foot* or *tail.*

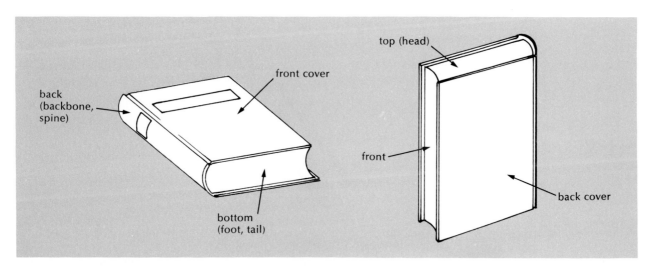

Figure 14.13: Parts of a book.

A sewn edition-bound book is one of the most complex graphic arts products. Its elements are illustrated in figure 14.14. The book consists of two major parts: the *book block*, or set of printed pages; and the cover, often called the *case*.

The book block consists of a number of *signatures*—large printed sheets that have been folded to page size. Usually a signature contains 8, 16, 32, or 64 pages. The signatures are held together at the backbone edge by thread sewn through the paper, variously reinforced by glue, paper, and fabric. *Endpapers* are usually pasted to the outside pages of the first and last signatures of the book; they are used to fasten the case to the book block.

The case is made of two pieces of cover board, plus a thin strip of paper lining material in the backbone area, all glued to the cover material that forms the outside of the case. The cover material is turned smoothly over the edges of the boards to make finished edges. The inside of the case is glued to the endpapers, which in turn hold the case to the book block. The flexible areas where the cover opens and closes, called *hinges* or *joints*, are impressed to provide easier opening. Edition-bound books have overhang covers, which extend beyond the edges of the pages; the area of the cover that overhangs the book block is called the *square*. The cover is usually decorated in some manner.

On better quality books small bits of colored fabric, called *headbands*, are glued to the book block at the top and bottom of the backbone for decoration. (The bands at the bottom of the book may also be called *footbands* or *tailbands*.) Headbands generally are applied by machine automatically during the standard binding process. Other features, however, involve special operations which often must be performed by hand. For example, on very fine books, the top, front and/or bottom edges of the pages may be gilded. The edges of lesser quality books are sometimes dyed or stained instead. In certain types of books, such as Bibles and keepsake editions, a silk ribbon may be bound into the top of the spine so that it folds down between the pages to form a bookmark. Finally, better reference books sometimes are thumb-indexed—that is, circular cut-outs are made in the front edges of the pages at section beginnings to identify them when the book is closed.

SMYTH SEWING AND CASE BINDING

The process of assembling and sewing printed signatures and then applying the hard cover is diagrammed in figure 14.15 and described below. The discussion and the illustration are based on *Smyth sewing*, the most common method for sewing signatures. Other case binding methods, for which some of the processing steps vary, are described after the basic sequence. These alternate methods include three other types of sewing—side sewing, saddle sewing, and oversewing—and adhesive binding, which is increasingly being used for fastening the pages of case-bound books.

Folding

The process begins with folding printed sheets down into page-size signatures with the pages in proper sequence (described in "Imposition," page 519, and "Cutting and Folding," page 524). Several types of folding machines are used in book work, including both knife and buckle folders of various sizes. Smaller machines are used for endpapers, inserts, and small signatures, but larger machines perform most of the folding work for books. One of the most important folders for books is the *quad folder*, which can deliver several signatures from a single press sheet.

As web offset printing has grown in the book industry, an increasing number of signatures have come into the book bindery already folded by equipment built into the delivery end of the printing press. This practice, of course, eliminates the need for a folding operation in the bindery. Both web press folders and the large sheet folders designed for book work produce signatures with *closed heads*—that is, with a folded edge at the top of the pages which permits easy handling on bindery machinery.

Tipping

After folding, the next step is to paste, or *tip*, endpapers to the first and last signatures of the book. Sometimes, in addition to tipping, a reinforcing tape is

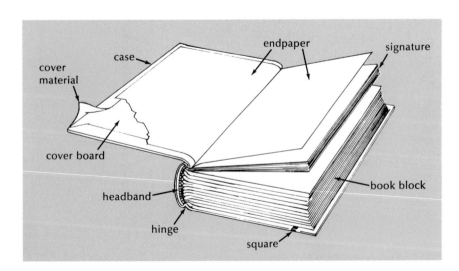

Figure 14.14: Construction of a sewn edition-bound book.

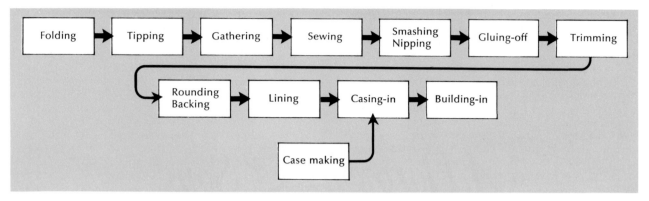

Figure 14.15: Assembly, sewing, and covering process for Smyth-sewn books.

glued around the endpaper and the signature to which it is adhered for extra strength. Each endpaper, sometimes called a lining paper, consists of four pages of stock heavier than the paper used for the main body of the book. Most commonly, endpapers are white, but colored papers are sometimes used to brighten a book's appearance and separate the cover visually from the first and last pages of the body. Endpapers may be printed with a design, map, or picture.

Other tipping operations also are performed at this stage of manufacture. Some books are designed with illustrations printed on separate sheets of stock different from the body stock; these sheets now are tipped onto blank pages left for them when the book was imposed. Such illustrations are usually positioned to fall on pages at the outside ends or at the center of a signature. Tipping can be done easily by machine at either of these locations.

Gathering

The next operation is *gathering,* selecting one copy of each signature in the book and stacking them in the order in which they are to appear in the finished volume. Gathering is done on a long machine (figure 14.16) composed of a series of hoppers and feeding mechanisms which drop copies of the signature one at a time onto a moving belt to form a stack which will become the book block.

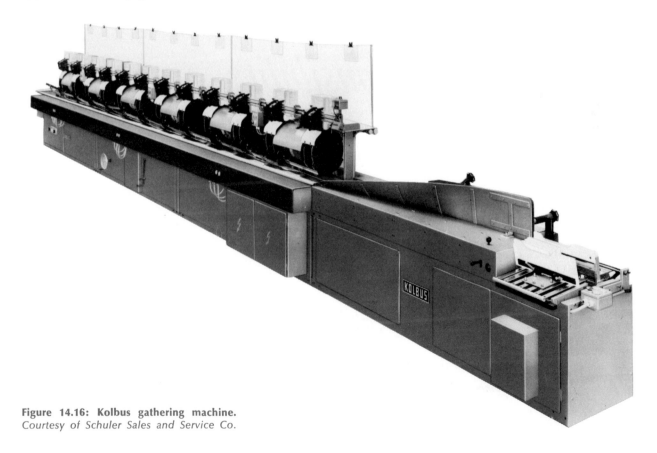

Figure 14.16: Kolbus gathering machine.
Courtesy of Schuler Sales and Service Co.

531

532

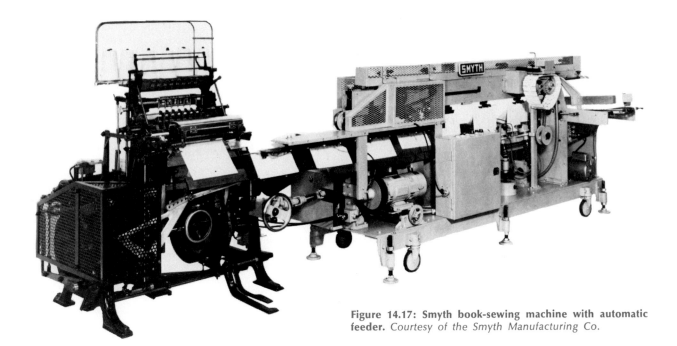

Figure 14.17: Smyth book-sewing machine with automatic feeder. *Courtesy of the Smyth Manufacturing Co.*

Sewing

Gathered signatures move to the sewing operation. In Smyth sewing, the signatures in the book are fed one at a time, in order, into a machine equipped with up to eight spools of cotton or nylon thread and as many sewing heads (see figure 14.17). As a signature is fed into the sewing machine, it is opened at the center and placed over a saddle. A series of holes is punched through the paper along the folded backbone edge. Sewing needles pull the thread through the fold from the outside to the inside of the signature. Then hooks and loopers catch the thread to form a stitch, pulling the thread back out through the fold and on to the next signature. Thus neighboring signatures are attached at their backbone edges. When all of the sig-

natures for the book have been sewn together, the thread is cut and a new book block is begun. Figure 14.18 illustrates the features of a Smyth-sewn book block.

Nipping and smashing

The sewn book blocks are flimsy and uneven in thickness in this raw state, principally because of the swelling effect of the sewing thread within the signatures. Nipping and smashing operations which follow sewing reduce the books to a uniform thickness. *Nipping* applies pressure only to the backbone area of the book block; it is used only on books printed on hard-surfaced papers. *Smashing* applies pressure to the entire surface of the book; it is used for soft and bulky stock.

Gluing-off

The next step is *gluing-off*, applying glue to the backbone area to fill in between the signatures and close any gaps. This operation is extremely critical because the use of too much glue will cause it to squeeze out between the pages of the book and obscure any printing that bleeds into the gutter. Gluing-off helps the book to be held securely during trimming and to retain the rounded shape given the backbone afterward.

Trimming

In trimming, the book block is clamped securely on a trimming machine, and approximately ⅛″ of paper is cut off the head, front, and foot. Occasionally a guillotine cutter is used, but usually trimming is done on a three-knife machine, which cuts all three edges in one operation. (See "Cutting and Folding," page 524.) The previous gluing operation usually feeds in-

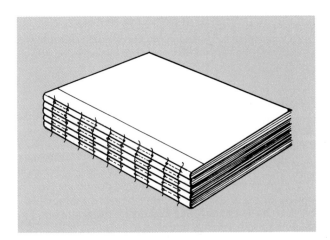

Figure 14.18: Characteristics of a Smyth-sewn book.

line directly to the three-knife trimmer for efficient processing. The trimming operation removes the folded edges of the signatures, freeing the pages of the book to open, and makes the edges smooth.

Rounding and backing

The trimmed book block then moves to *rounding* and *backing,* which shape the block further. Rounding imparts the characteristic concave shape to the front edge of an edition-bound book and the convex shape to the backbone. This shaping is important; later it will keep the pages within the area of the cover or case, protecting them from damage. During the rounding process, a set of rollers and formers "roll" the outside pages away from the backbone toward the front of the book while the center pages are pushed in toward the backbone. Then the entire backbone is hit and rubbed from side to side by a curved *backing iron*. This action causes the sewn edges of the signatures to fan out. These flared areas will act as hinges, or *joints,* when the cover is attached. Books less than one inch thick may not receive this treatment. Figure 14.19 illustrates the effects of rounding and backing.

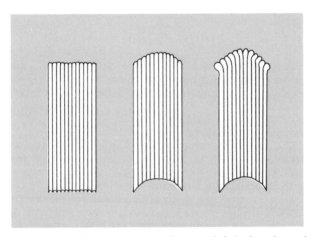

Figure 14.19: Rounding and backing. At left is the trimmed book block before rounding and backing; center, the rounded book block; right, the rounded and backed book block with flared joints.

Lining

The rounded and backed book block is then reinforced, or *lined up,* with a piece of gauze-like fabric, called *crash* or *super,* and a liner made of kraft paper. First, the crash is attached to the backbone with a layer of glue; then the kraft liner is applied with a second layer. The headbands are also glued onto the top and bottom of the liner at this time. The crash extends beyond the backbone area on each side so that it will be glued down to the endpapers and the front and back covers when the case is applied, providing extra strength in the hinge areas where the endpapers must hold the cover to the book block. It is important that glue penetrate through the crash in these areas so that there is good adhesion. For additional strength, an especially heavy crash or two layers of crash may be used.

Casing-in

The book block is now ready to be joined to the case. The process of making the case is discussed later; when the case arrives at the point where it is joined to the book block, it is a finished subassembly requiring no additional treatment or finishing work. The process of affixing the case to the book block is called *casing-in*. Books enter the casing-in machine with their backbones up; they are opened slightly in the center, and a vertical blade is inserted into the book. Then the blade rises, carrying the book block up between two adhesive-covered rollers on each side which coat the outside endpapers with glue. As the book block continues upward, the opened case is positioned above the book block so that their backbones are aligned, and the front and back covers are brought down into contact with the glue-covered endpapers. This operation is executed with precision so that the book block is positioned inside the case with a uniform margin of cover overhang on the top, front, and foot. The book block must be square within the cover; perfect *squaring,* or positioning, is a mark of good bookbinding craftsmanship.

Building-in

If nothing more were done to the book, the cover would be loose-fitting with weak joints or hinge areas. In earlier times, newly cased-in books were stacked on drying racks and pressed tightly together by large clamps for many hours until their glue dried thoroughly. Rack clamping and drying is still used in special circumstances today, but the vast majority of books now are clamped and dried in minutes in a machine process called *building-in*. The building-in machine consists of a series of heated clamps and creasing irons which move in to grip the book tightly for a few moments at a time. Each book moves through a series of grippings or clampings, the number depending on the amount of curing the glue needs. As the main clamps press the covers together against the book block, the creasing irons press inward at the joints to provide a good form to the indented hinge areas and to thoroughly dry the glue. With the completion of building-in, the books are finished and ready for packing and shipping.

In modern binding quite often all the operations from rounding and backing through building-in are tied together through conveyors which carry the books from one machine to the other in one continuous line, as shown in figure 14.20.

ALTERNATE METHODS

Within this sequence of operations, there are alternate methods of sewing; an alternative to rounding and backing; and a substitute for sewing, adhesive binding.

Sewing

Although Smyth sewing is the predominant type of sewing in use today, three other types of thread stitching are used regularly for certain kinds of books: side sewing, saddle sewing, and oversewing.

Side sewing is a process of sewing through the entire

Figure 14.20: Kolbus high-speed bookbinding line. Rounding and backing, lining, casing-in, and building-in are done in a continuous operation. *Courtesy of Schuler Sales and Service Co.*

book block from the front signature to the back, rather than through the center folds. Also called Singer or Mc-Cain sewing after the brand names of the machines used, this procedure begins with the drilling of a hole through the book block. Then the book is moved a fixed distance along the feed table of the machine and a threaded needle thrusts the thread down through the hole; at the same time, another hole is drilled a short distance down the spine of the book block. The book is then moved again the same distance down the feed table and the drilling and stitching are repeated. Side sewing machines stitch books in this manner in a continuous stream, and the blocks are cut apart as they leave the sewing machine. Side sewing makes a

much more rigid binding than Smyth sewing. It is normally used on heavy-duty volumes such as school texts and encyclopedias which will receive extended use. The more flexible Smyth-sewn book opens and lies flat more readily than a side-sewn book. Figure 14.21 illustrates a side-sewn book block.

Saddle sewing resembles Smyth sewing in that the signature is sewn through the center fold. It is used for single-signature books such as juvenile books. Drawn by a straight needle, a continuous thread runs down the length of the backbone, looping around the bobbin thread as it passes through each of a succession of holes. Figure 14.22 illustrates a saddle-sewn signature.

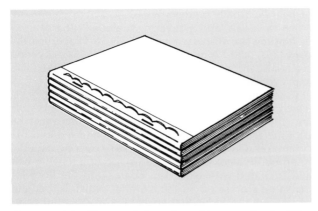

Figure 14.21: Characteristics of a side-sewn book. Wire stitches are placed through the backbone before sewing to hold the signatures. Thread stitches go through the backbone from front to back.

Figure 14.22: Characteristics of a saddle-sewn book. Stitches go through the center fold.

Oversewing is the process of sewing small groups of leaves into a book one after the other. Each group of loose sheets is sewn from the side as in side sewing, except that several parallel stitches are made at one time; then the threads are carried across to the next group of leaves, forming a series of thread links across the back of the book in a manner similar to Smyth sewing. Oversewing is used almost entirely for library binding, a specialized segment of bookbinding which refurbishes and rebinds books for libraries to give them extended life. In such situations, the old cover is removed, the old binding is cut off the book block, the loose sheets are resewn by oversewing, and a new case is applied.

Square-back books

Sometimes edition-bound books are not rounded and backed but are given a *square-back* shape (see figure 14.23). Some volumes are too thin to be rounded and backed in the conventional manner, while others are not given this treatment for reasons of design. In these circumstances, a reinforcing strip is put around the flat backbone, and the case is made with a stiff strip of board down the backbone rather than the thinner lining piece. This gives a hard, square back to the book. A gap is left in the cover between the center strip and the two cover boards; the creasing irons of the building-in machine press into this gap to form the indented joint. Very often this kind of square-back cover is used with side or saddle sewing rather than Smyth sewing.

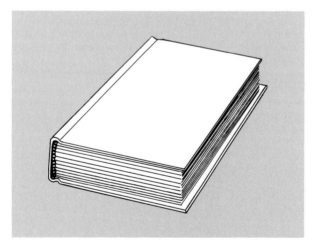

Figure 14.23: Characteristics of a square-back edition-bound book.

Adhesive binding

Increasingly today for many kinds of edition-bound volumes, adhesive binding is being used to replace sewing entirely. The process has been developed in recent years to the point where it can provide comparable strength to Smyth sewing and adequate flexibility for opening and lying flat. The primary reason for

this replacement of Smyth sewing is its inability to fit well into high-speed in-line production systems. All other operations in edition binding can be performed as continuous operations; the machines have been connected into continuous processing lines by conveyors that transport books without human intervention. Smyth sewing machines, however, are generally hand-fed by operators who open the signatures and place them on the infeed saddles of the machines. Several automatic feeding devices have been developed, but even they cannot speed the feeding and sewing of individual signatures enough to match the operating speeds of other machines in the line.

In adhesive binding a single film of glue along the binding edge of the book holds the book block together. Such a binding is formed by first passing the book block over a series of cutting knives which rotate at high speed, cutting off the folded edges of the signatures and leaving the edges of the individual leaves extending downward. These edges then are coated with glue, and various crash and liner materials are applied to this glue film. This process can handle books at a rate of 200 or more per minute, as fast as any other edition binding operation can be performed. (See "Adhesive Binding," page 542.)

Adhesive binding has been used for many years on low-priced hardcover books, and on special editions produced for book clubs. In the last few years, however, improvements in binding quality have brought it into wider use for general trade books, certain college textbooks, and some business and professional books. It is the one binding process that can be used with the Cameron and Wood book production systems, which produce completely printed and gathered books in a single operation (see "Book Production Systems," page 431).

It seems unlikely, however, that adhesive binding will completely replace the classic sewn binding. The sewn book lies flat when opened and is strong enough to withstand long use—characteristics important for fine-quality books.

CASEMAKING

The case of an edition-bound book is an assembly of boards, usually binder's board or pasted chipboard, lining materials, and a covering material. (Boards used in binding are discussed more fully in "Paperboard," page 561, and "Binder's Board," page 564; covering materials are described in "Book Cloth," page 557, and "Nonwoven Cover Materials," page 559.)

Cases are manufactured on casemaking machines, which may be either web-fed or sheet-fed. The boards and the lining strips for the backbone area must be cut to exact size on a cutting machine and fed into the casemaker. On a web-fed casemaker, covering material is fed out in a continuous web on top of a moving belt and is coated with glue. The boards and the liner for the spine are placed on the material, which is then cut to size for the individual cover. On a sheet-fed casemaker (see figure 14.24), individual sheets already cut to size are fed into the machine along with the boards and lining strips. A sheet-fed casemaker is always used for making preprinted covers because the cover ma-

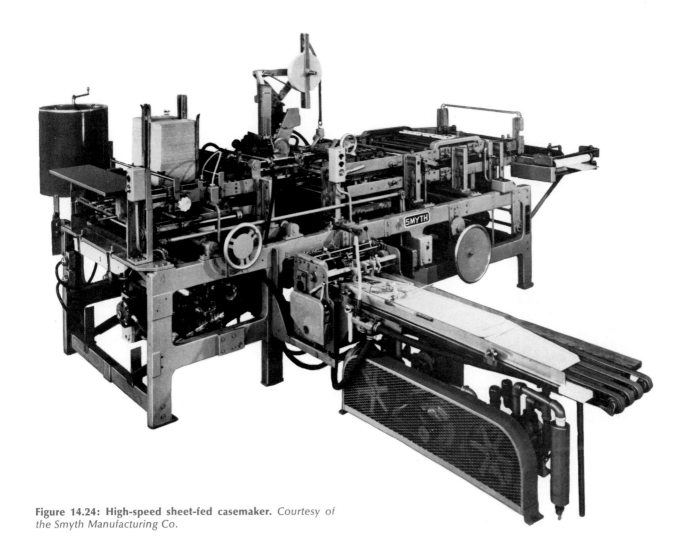

Figure 14.24: High-speed sheet-fed casemaker. *Courtesy of the Smyth Manufacturing Co.*

terial is cut to size before it is printed. On both kinds of machines, the edges of the material are folded over the boards and glued down. Later, when the endpapers are attached, they will overlap the turned-in edges of the cover material to make the inside of the cover neat.

Web-fed casemaking machines can be either *side-feed* or *end-feed* casemakers. On side-feed casemakers, the web width is determined by the height of the book; the case is positioned with the top and bottom of the book parallel to the sides of the web. On end-feed casemakers, the web width is determined by the width of the open book; the case is positioned with the top and bottom running across the web.

Covers having a single piece of material over the boards, as described above, are often referred to as *one-piece covers*. These should not be confused with the cover boards that are prefabricated for the binder in a single piece, also called one-piece covers, or with covers consisting entirely of a single piece of paper or plastic.

Instead of a single piece of covering material, a case may have three separate pieces of material glued to-

gether over the boards, forming a *three-piece cover*. The most common kind of three-piece cover has one type of material on the front and back covers and a stronger material on the spine area, providing extra protection as well as decoration. On another type of three-piece cover, a strip of a different material runs horizontally around the case as decoration. Three-piece covers are produced by feeding three parallel webs of cover material into the casemaking machine.

Cases may be decorated in several ways. Prior to casemaking, certain cover materials may be printed by lithography or screen process. After manufacture, they may be ink or foil stamped, blind stamped, or embossed (see "Finishing Processes," page 551).

Sometimes for fine editions or for books that will be sold as sets, a *slip case* is made to house the volume or group of volumes. A slip case is a protective box with one open side; the volume or volumes are inserted into this open side so that only the spines are exposed. Slip cases normally are made specifically to fit snugly around the book or books they are to house. They are manufactured in a manner similar to cases for

537

hardcover books. Board is cut to size and folded into a slip case of the right dimensions; decorative paper, cloth, or other material is glued to the outer surface and folded around the open edges to form finished, rounded edges as on a case. Usually the material used to cover a slip case is a standard material also used to make book covers, and often the same material is used on both the book and the slip case.

WIRE STITCHING AND PAMPHLET BINDING

Abraham Hardis, AE BINDCRAFT, INC.

As defined in the trade, a pamphlet is a thin bound book with a soft cover. It is usually bound by *saddle-wire stitching*, in which a number of wire staples are driven through the backbone fold to the center of the book, but other fastening methods are sometimes used as well. It almost always has fewer than 100 pages, is rarely larger than 9" x 12", and can be small enough to fit into a package the size of a box of film. The pamphlet format lends itself to a broad variety of applications—from small catalogs and directories to annual reports, bulletins, and small periodicals. This type of binding is inexpensive to produce compared to other methods and has a high production rate. The products are usually lightweight and suitable for mailing.

Pamphlets may consist of a single signature—a folded printed sheet—or a number of signatures. The outside pages of the pamphlet may form the cover, called a *self cover*, or a separate cover of a different stock, usually heavier and stiffer than the text paper, may be used. In addition, some pamphlets may consist of smaller sheets that are fastened together but are not folded or are folded only once.

Other products as well are produced by the pam-

538

phlet binding industry. One is the *flyer,* a single leaf that is neither folded nor bound. Another is the *folder,* a printed sheet that is folded but is not bound. A *broadside* is a type of folder—a very large sheet folded down to practical handling size.

Another type of wire stitching is *side-wire stitching.* This method is not considered a pamphlet binding technique. It is used for generally thicker products—from about one-quarter inch to several inches in thickness. Its two traditional areas of application are magazines and books. In side-wire stitching, the wire staple is inserted through a stack of pages from front to back rather than through the backbone fold.

Saddle-wire and side-wire stitching follow the same basic processing sequence. Large press sheets are first folded. If the product is made up of two or more signatures or small individual sheets, they are placed in the correct order. The term *gathering* usually refers to piling folded signatures one on top of the next in correct order, while *inserting* is the process of nesting one signature inside the next. *Collating* usually refers to piling individual sheets of paper in order. The assembled signatures or sheets are then wire stitched, and the product is usually trimmed. After binding, pamphlets may be folded again for mailing.

SADDLE-WIRE BINDING

Of the two styles of wire stitching, saddle-wire stitching is by far the more common. It is performed on a variety of equipment, most of which includes facilities for other operations, such as inserting and often trimming.

Inserting

If more than one signature is needed to make up the complete product, the signatures are inserted prior to stitching. Inserting may be done by hand for small jobs, but more often today it is done by special *inserting machines* on the binding line.

The inserting machine has a line of hoppers and feeding mechanisms and a continuous moving chain that passes beneath the feeders. Mechanical grippers in the feeding mechanism pull each signature from its hopper, open it at its center, and drop it onto a *saddle,* a metal inverted-V shaped bar located at each feeding station. Each signature has a lip, or extra extension of paper, on one side for the grippers to grasp. Next, small projections on the moving chain catch the signature and slide it off the saddle onto the chain, where the various signatures are collected in their proper order. Inserters often have, in addition, one or more hand-feeding stations where operators can feed extra or special signatures manually. If separate covers are being used, they are inserted on the outside of the signatures.

Stitching

In saddle-wire binding, wire staples are driven through the backbone fold into the center of a pamphlet (see figure 14.25). The stitching head on the machine first unwinds the wire from a spool and straightens it. The wire is fed downward and cut to the correct length. The stitching head then forms the wire

Figure 14.25: Characteristics of saddle-wire stitching.

into a U shape and drives the two ends through the center fold. Clinchers beneath the inside center fold force the two wire prongs flat against the pamphlet to hold the sheets together firmly.

The stitching wire comes in various weights for use with products of different thicknesses. When the book is thinner than the lightest practical wire, the stitches are staggered an inch apart from one book to the next. This process distributes the extra bulk caused by the stitches so that the stitched products can be piled evenly for trimming, without bulges in one place or another.

539

The simplest method of saddle-wire binding is to insert by hand if the booklet is composed of more than a single signature and to stitch the booklet on a simple hand-fed foot-pedal machine, as shown in figure 14.26. The booklets are fed one at a time. The operator opens the booklet manually, drops it onto the saddle, positions it under the stitching head, and activates the machine by pushing the foot pedal. After the first stitch, the operator moves the booklet down the saddle to the next stitching position and triggers the machine again.

Stitching can be done automatically instead on a *gang-stitching* machine. A gang-stitcher has a number of stitching heads instead of only one. The heads operate in unison and place all of the required stitches in the booklet in one machine cycle. On some ma-

chines as many as six or more stitches may be made at one time.

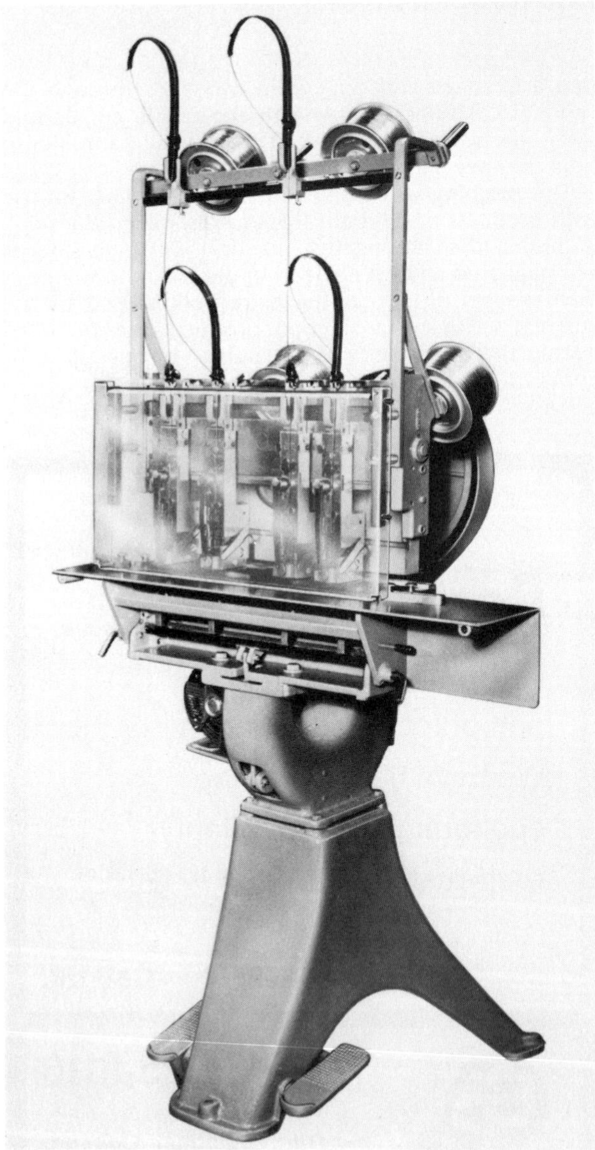

Gang stitchers are integrated with inserting machines to form a continuous processing line. After the signatures have been assembled, the moving chain carries the booklet under the stitching heads. The machines are timed to operate simultaneously to insert and stitch the signatures and deliver the finished booklets onto a canvas stacker.

A variation of the saddle-wire process uses a portable attachment that can be joined with a collator or a folding machine. On the folding machine, all folds but the last are made in the signatures. The attachment then stitches along the line where the final fold is to be made and makes the fold. When used with the collator, the attachment stitches along the center line of a pile of collated flat sheets and then makes a single fold to complete the pamphlet.

Trimming

After binding, folded edges, uneven ends, and all other excess paper must be removed on three sides. The oldest method is to split the back gauge of a guillotine cutter into three parts and to trim three pamphlets at once by placing them at each of the three positions. The Bracket trimmer, another single-knife cutter, may also be used. Three-knife trimmers, which can trim the top, front, and bottom of a lift in one operation, are designed especially for efficient trimming of bound products. (These trimming methods are discussed in "Cutting and Folding," page 524.)

For the most automatic operation, a trimmer, usually the three-knife kind, is often added to the machine line with the inserter and the gang-stitcher. The trimmer is timed to work in synchronization with the other machines to form an integrated *inserter-stitcher-trimmer* line (see figure 14.27). The stitched pamphlet is delivered onto a flat belt, carried into the trimmer, and positioned. Two knives descend to trim the top and bottom of the booklet at one time, and a third knife cuts the front. The booklet is advanced automatically between cuts and is moved onto a belt after trimming. The result is a completely finished product that has been assembled, bound, and trimmed in one continuous operation.

Attachments to the automatic inserter-stitcher-trimmer can score and fold a cover without appreciable loss of production time. Holes can be punched, booklets can be folded after binding, and extra knives can be used so that two books can be trimmed alongside each other at the same time. If the heads of folded signatures are closed, suction cups can be used in place of mechanical grippers to open the signatures, so that the need for a lip is eliminated. Sensing devices can tell if the booklet has the correct number of signatures and can reject those that are improperly assembled. These and other features of the inserter-stitcher-trimmer have helped to improve productivity and reduce costs in pamphlet binding.

Figure 14.26: **Stand-alone saddle-wire stitcher.** *Courtesy of Bostitch Division of Textron Inc.*

SIDE-WIRE BINDING
Unlike saddle-wire stitching, in which the wire is placed through the backbone fold of the pamphlet,

Figure 14.27: Inserter-stitcher-trimmer. *Courtesy of Muller-Martini Corp.*

side-wire binding has stitches that go straight through the book or magazine from front to back (see figure 14.28). The simplest kind of binding is a side stitch or stitches holding together loose sheets that have been collated in proper sequence. Signatures for side-wire stitching are not inserted one into the next but are gathered into a stack. On the gathering machine, they are dropped onto a flat moving belt one on top of the other. The gathered signatures are jogged to align their folded backbone edges and tops; then they are clamped and moved under the stitching head. The stitches are driven from one side of the book to the other, where they are crimped.

The covers of side-wired books and magazines usually are applied after stitching. In most cases, the backbone is coated with glue and the cover is fed from under the book to be positioned automatically on an in-line covering machine. However, on short runs, separate front and back covers may be assembled with the signatures on the gathering machine and stitched to the book. Then a *stripping machine* is used to apply binding tape to the backbone, folding it over the front and back covers far enough to cover the wire stitches and give the book a finished appearance. This process permits the use of very stiff covers, which cannot be folded for application on a standard covering **machine.**

Trimming of side-wired books is done in the same manner as the trimming of saddle-stitched books.

The use of side-wire stitching has dropped considerably in recent years as the use of adhesive binding has grown extensively in the book and magazine fields. Most of the gains made by adhesive binding have been at the expense of side-wire stitching rather than saddle-wire stitching.

One important remaining use of side-wire stitching is as part of the side sewing process (thread sewing) used for edition-bound books. Prior to sewing, the gathered signatures are often side-wire stitched to hold them together during sewing. The wire may be inserted and clinched as described above. In large books, however, the stitches do not go all the way through the book block; they are put into the book from both sides instead of only one.

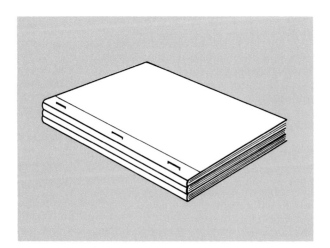

Figure 14.28: Characteristics of side-wire stitching.

OTHER FASTENING METHODS

Although the standard pamphlet binding method is wire stitching, glue can replace wire for fastening. A booklet may be held together by thin glue lines along the backbone edge. Such booklets are manufactured on a folding machine or, increasingly, on the folding section of a web press. Glue-dispensing nozzles are mounted on the folding units so that they lay down a thin line of adhesive along the fold lines before folding. When the sheet is folded, the binding edges of the pages are brought into contact and glued together. This process, however, is limited to booklets with few pages and requires the use of one particular imposition. Other drawbacks are problems of quality and the inability to open flat.

Pamphlets also may be bound by some of the other major binding processes, such as thread sewing or the standard adhesive binding technique. In adhesive binding, the binding edges of the pages are milled away, glue is applied to the edges, and a cover is placed in contact with the glue. Although sewing of pamphlets is not common, Smyth and saddle sewing can be used.

SPECIAL TECHNIQUES

Pamphlets lend themselves to limitless variations. Tip-ins and gate folds are practical to produce. Different papers can easily be used for different sections of a booklet, or sections can be die cut before they are folded. Other decorative techniques, such as embossing and thumb indexing, can be used. Holes can be drilled or punched along the binding edge of a booklet to permit later insertion in looseleaf binders. Folding machines can perforate a flyer for easy removal of a reply card or other piece. Primarily in response to unusual problems presented by customers, binders regularly develop new innovations and new devices to increase the variety of products available in the pamphlet field.

ADHESIVE BINDING

Ralph F. Box, Jr., MULLER-MARTINI CORP.

The area of greatest recent development and growth in the binding field is adhesive binding, which has been steadily replacing thread-sewing and wire-stitching processes. Adhesive binding, also called *perfect binding*, is especially well suited to continuous processing—from gathered signatures to finished bound products—for softcover and hardcover books, thick periodicals, and catalogs.

Adhesive binding converts signatures or sheets into bound products through a series of consecutive machine operations. First the gathered signatures or sheets are fed into clamps which convey them through the main binder. There the folded backbone edge of each tightly clamped book block is removed by rotating blades so that signatures become separate leaves. The edges of the leaves are patterned by roughers to increase their surface for binding, and adhesive is applied to bond the pages together. In magazine and paperback production, paper covers are applied before the adhesive sets, and the covered products are then trimmed and are ready for shipment.

For hardcover books, the cover feeder on the main binder, which applies paper covers for magazines and paperbacks, applies combined end-sheet material instead. This material consists of two end sheets with lining material attached in the center to cover the spine. Then the book block is trimmed and delivered directly to standard case binding equipment (see "Sewing and Edition Binding," page 529). If the books are to have the rounded backbone shape typical of Smyth-sewn books, the book blocks are conveyed to rounding, backing, and lining equipment, and from there to casing-in machines. In square-back book production, rounding and backing is not necessary and the combined end-sheet material applied earlier can serve as the lining material.

DEVELOPMENT

Adhesive binding was born in the early 1900's when the first gathering machines were developed. The first adhesive binding system was essentially a cover application process: the sequence of operations comprised gathering signatures, side-wire stitching, gluing the gathered and stitched signatures, and applying the cover. By 1915, adhesive binding machines had been developed for binding without wire stitching. Mass-produced magazines and telephone directories were the earliest products to be manufactured by adhesive binding, shortly followed by catalogs and then paperback books, whose creation and growth were based on adhesive technology.

To make adhesive bindings comparable or superior to wire-stitched and thread-sewn bindings took long, tedious development. The effectiveness of binding pages by contact with adhesives is not immediately observable or controllable, as is that of wire stitching and thread sewing. The quality of adhesive binding comes out only in extended use or testing. The flow of adhesives around the fibers of a book backbone depends upon natural characteristics of adhesives and paper fibers that slowly came to be understood.

Over the years a variety of methods has been developed for accelerating the aging of adhesive bindings in order to evaluate their long-term strength and flexibility. Cameras have been used to study the dynamics of adhesive application to book backbones. Several generations of adhesives have been developed for the binding of all types of periodicals and books.

Glues

Animal glue has been used in adhesive binding since the early 1900's, and through the 1960's it was still being used for catalogs and telephone directories as well as most paperbacks. Adding emulsion glues to animal glues improved their strength and flexibility. Faster setting adhesives were developed, which aided accurate in-line trimming after backbone gluing.

Emulsion glues also were used for binding hardcover books, but they did not produce books with a strength that could rival thread sewing. The permanency of animal and emulsion glues is limited by the fact that they contain wetting agents which draw the adhesive into the paper fibers of the backbone. As these solvents evaporate over a long period of time, the bindings lose their flexibility. On hardcover books with rounded backbones, the adhesive will ultimately lose its ability to hold the round and the backbone will cave in, forcing the fore edges of the pages outside their protective cover.

Hot melts

In the late 1940's the plastics industry developed *hot-melt adhesives* for bookbinding. These moistureless materials are solid at normal temperatures but melt in the range of 300° to 400° F. Within seconds after the melt is applied, it sets and regains its solid state. There is no evaporation of solvents and so no loss of shape. The *open time* during which another material, such as a paper cover, may be bound to the adhesive-coated backbone is 8 to 16 seconds, depending upon adhesive coating thickness and temperature at application. The fast setting capacity permits immediate trimming with no danger of pages being pushed out of line by the trimming blades. In comparison, emulsion glues require 8 to 12 hours drying time before they can be trimmed.

The growth of hot melts in the magazine and paperback fields was assured by processing speeds of 200 books per minute. Soon book manufacturers sought ways to apply the new speed and efficiency of softcover book manufacture to the relatively slow process of hardcover edition binding, which traditionally involves sewing. To meet the standards for extremely strong bindings set by thread-sewn methods, hot-melt technology had to increase the strength and flexibility of the adhesive, and overcome its resistance to the conventional rounding operation.

The polymer used to add strength to hot melts has high viscosity and good mechanical properties but poor adhesion, tack, and wetting abilities in its molten state. It has a limited flexibility and becomes brittle with age. In order to make hot-melt adhesives useful for binding, a diluent system of wax, flux resins, and plasticizers is added to lower viscosity and increase tack range as well as to add flexibility so that bindings

can withstand atmospheric and handling stresses. The diluent system, however, tends to reduce hot-melt strength as well as heat resistance needed to prevent degradation during application. The development of hot melts has been largely a matter of striking the right proportion of polymers for strength and diluents for applicability.

The difficulty in rounding stems from the fact that thermal-setting plastics have a memory: if a book backbone is coated with adhesive and then rounded after the adhesive sets, the backbone will ultimately return to the flat shape it had when the coating first set.

The two-shot system

The first hot-melt binding system for hardcover editions was called the *two-shot system* since it consisted of an application of an emulsion-glue primer and then an application of hot melt. This method produced a relatively strong book, but its limitations encouraged the development of the *one-shot* system in widespread use today, which uses only hot melt.

The early hot melts used in the two-shot method had high *cold crack* and low *cold flow*. High cold crack means that after storage at 40° to 50° F, quick opening of a book will break its binding to pieces. Low cold flow means that at a temperature of about 90° F, a hot-melt binding will soften and become weak. The two-shot system was also limited by the incompatibility between hot melts and emulsion or animal glues, whose solvents prevent a permanent bond with hot melts. This problem was especially noticeable in the insecure bonding between the hot-melt-coated backbone and the lining material that was attached to it with glue. Further, the problem of hot-melt memory limited the use of the two-shot system to square-back hardcover production. Finally, two-shot binding often produced wrinkled pages, due to absorption of solvents, and also backbone distortions.

The one-shot system

The continued development of hot melts and new methods of preparing backbones for insured adhesion between paper fibers and adhesive led to the development of the one-shot system, which uses only hot melts for binding. Improved hot melts have a cold-crack tolerance of 15° to 35° F and a cold-flow resistance of between 120° and 130° F. Heat disintegration occurs at temperatures in excess of 400° F, and molten adhesive will last up to 90 hours before use. Hot melts are also available with varying open times for use in different manufacturing systems.

The problem of hot-melt memory interfering with the permanency of rounded backbones has been solved in two ways. One solution involves reheating bound and trimmed backbones to a semimolten state, destroying the memory of the first adhesive. Reheating is followed by rounding and backing, after which the adhesive resets in a permanently rounded shape. The reheating process is critical, since too molten a state will interfere with efficient reshaping of the backbone.

The more recent one-shot system uses a "roundable" hot melt that has no memory. Permanent rounding is accomplished by applying force to the backbones. After rounding, the adhesive coating maintains its new shape through plastic stiffness rather than memory. The roundable adhesive is sometimes heated slightly to reduce the adhesive stiffness before rounding, but this operation is not so critical as reheating a hot melt with memory. The roundable hot melt forms a strong binding and has excellent resistance to loss of round.

The process of producing adhesive-bound, rounded books was no sooner successfully developed than predictions of the ultimate phasing out of rounding were being voiced by industry observers with an eye on the needs of automation. They claim that rounding has outlived its realistic value and that square-back books are as useful and permanent as rounded books and offer manufacturing savings. Whether the rounded book is here to stay or not, the continued development of integrated binding systems based on the use of adhesive binding machinery seems to be assured.

Figure 14.29: Sulby hand-fed adhesive binding machine. *Courtesy of Gane Brothers & Lane, Inc.*

MODERN ADHESIVE BINDING SYSTEMS

The simplest form of adhesive binding machine is the hand-fed binder, illustrated in figure 14.29. This inexpensive machine does no more than apply adhesive to the book blocks, which are fed in manually by an operator. It is used to bind reports and other short-run items.

At the other end of the scale is the most complex system, the fully integrated adhesive binding system, which offers high-speed processing of books for edition binding, from gathering through covering, in one continuous operation. Such a machine is shown in figure 14.30.

The first step in the integrated system is the gathering of signatures. The gathering machine's conveyor chain delivers signatures to the binder's infeed chain,

Figure 14.30: Integrated adhesive binding system. *Courtesy of Muller-Martini Corp.*

which in turn moves the signatures into a clamp system. Just before the clamps close, the signatures pass over joggers which level the backbones.

The timing of operations on the main binder is critical; if the binder slows down too much during gathering-machine jams, irregularities in binding quality can result. Binding operations such as backbone roughing, applying adhesive, and applying a paper covering or lining must be performed within a limited time.

Preparing the backbone

After the signatures enter the main binder and are leveled and securely clamped, they pass through rotating blades that cut off the folded backbone edges so that all pages become separate leaves. Usually $\frac{1}{16}''$ to $\frac{1}{8}''$ of the backbone is cut off to remove the folded edge.

The book blocks now pass through the roughing system made up of revolving saws which increase the binding surface and create paths for the adhesive to flow into. After the backbones are roughed, a bristle brush removes all loose particles of paper.

A number of different roughing patterns are used for various effects. For example, *pattern roughing* produces the best adhesion, but books roughed in this way do not open very flat. *Straight roughing* produces a flat-opening book but less than ideal adhesion. Roughing patterns are also related to the type of paper used. Until extensive research in backbone preparation revealed the causes of strong and weak adhesion, coated papers could not be adhesive-bound. Now, however, proper roughing permits their use in adhesive-bound products.

Applying adhesive and trimming

After the roughing operation, the book blocks pass over pots that hold and apply adhesive. Hot melt is stored in a *pre-melter* near the pots, which melts the adhesive, maintains it at a heat range of 300° to 320° F, and feeds the molten adhesive to the pots fast enough to keep up with consumption. The applicator pot usually operates at a thermostatically controlled heat range of 330° to 380° F.

The pot has two wheels that spin through the adhesive and coat the backbones as they pass overhead. Because hot melts have no wetting agents to draw them into the paper fibers, they must be forced into the fibers. The first wheel applies a thin coating of adhesive and forces it around the fibers. The second wheel lays a heavier coat over the first coat. Immediately after the second application, a high-temperature back spinner, which revolves in the direction opposite to book travel, removes the excess adhesive and evens the thickness of the coating.

In magazine and paperback book production, paper covers are applied by a cover feeder before the adhesive sets. Hardcover books usually move from adhesive application to the cover feeder, which is used to apply the combined end-sheet material. Then the book blocks pass directly through a trimmer, which cuts them on three sides. Magazines and paperbacks are now complete; hardcover books require further processing.

A serious setback to the wide use of hot melt has been the contamination of trim waste by hot melt that is on the backbone edge of side trim. Because hot melt is not dispersible at paper mills, the resale value of the trim, a significant source of yearly revenue in larger plants, is lost. Several solutions to this problem have been tried unsuccessfully. One solution utilizes a device called a nibbler, which nips off the portion of the trim that has an adhesive coating. Another method prevents hot melt from being applied to the edges of the backbone and applies cold emulsion instead at a second adhesive application station. Cold emulsion is dispersible and so does not contaminate the trim. These methods have not been developed to the point of being useful; they slow down the process too much and increase the cost of equipment.

Rounding, backing, and lining

If the books are to have square backs, they move after trimming to the casing-in operation; otherwise they are conveyed through rounding, backing, and lining machines. Quartz lamps or other sources of heat may be used to destroy the memory or plastic stiffness of the hot melt prior to rounding. The lining material is usually attached with animal glue. Usually there is no problem with the incompatibility of glues and hot melts because the combined end-sheet material was applied earlier, covering the hot melt. A paper liner with headbands attached may also be applied at this time.

Casing-in

After rounding, backing, and lining—or after trimming, in the case of square-back books—the book blocks are ready to have their covers applied on a casing-in machine. Conveyance from trimming to rounding, backing, and lining and then to casing-in and building-in may be direct or may use storage devices. Increasingly these operations are being integrated into continuous processing lines. There is machinery today that does the rounding and backing, lining, and casing-in and building-in all in one unit without conveyors.

ADHESIVE BINDING AND AUTOMATION

The increasing speed with which new information and educational systems are generated demands that new editions be manufactured more frequently. The permanence of thread sewing is no longer always an asset. By far the more pressing need is for production systems that economically manufacture shorter runs of individual titles and keep pace with sudden demands through fast production.

Even with the most advanced bookbinding equipment, the use of thread sewing creates a break in the work flow. Adhesive binding creates no such breaks and thus permits the full potential of integrated binding systems to be realized.

Increasing automation in book production has introduced new economies into short-run manufacture. Publishers can now more profitably produce shorter runs based on projected sales. They do not have to seek savings through long first runs and incur the risk ot costly warehousing or remaindering in the event of slow sales. Book sales are being more closely monitored so that production and distribution may be based on patterns of demand rather than on prediction.

As an important element in the greater automation of bookbinding, adhesive binding is receiving wide acceptance today. Some of the standard school textbook specifications, originally requiring thread sewing, have been changed to permit the use of adhesive binding. In market tests run to determine the acceptability of adhesive-bound trade and educational titles, users have failed to recognize any change.

As print comes under greater competition from nonprint media, printed products will remain competitive only if manufacturing methods are coordinated with lower costs and timely production. The current trend on the part of book manufacturers toward the purchase of web presses and adhesive binding lines offers a strong indication of how the industry will achieve this goal.

LOOSELEAF AND MECHANICAL BINDING

Matt Sloves, SLOVES PRODUCTS

Looseleaf and mechanical bindings are a family of devices and procedures for securing pages in books by mechanical means, without use of glue, stitching, or sewing. Individual sheets in the book remain loose; they are held in only by wires or rings passing through holes punched in them. In looseleaf bindings, the sheets can be removed and reinserted as desired. Strictly speaking, looseleaf bindings are only one form of mechanical binding; however, in the trade, looseleaf binding is a distinct area requiring different manufacturing procedures and techniques.

These bindings are used on a wide variety of products, from blankbooks such as steno books and notebooks to published manuals, cookbooks, and the like. Both looseleaf and mechanical bindings offer the ability to include different size sheets and different kinds of stock easily in the same book. Many special pages, such as index sheets, section dividers, and pocket pages, are regularly included. Moreover, the pages lie absolutely flat when the book is open; no other type of binding offers this feature.

Both looseleaf and mechanical bindings can be either mass-produced as standard product lines or manufactured in custom runs with special adaptations to meet individual needs. A wide variety of covers and binding devices is available to meet many different application requirements. The basic features of looseleaf and mechanical bindings are illustrated in figure 14.31.

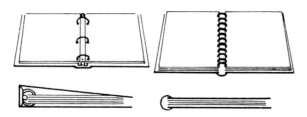

Figure 14.31: Characteristics of looseleaf (left) and mechanical bindings. *Courtesy of* Book Production Industry.

LOOSELEAF BINDINGS

Any looseleaf binder is composed of two main elements—the cover or case, and the binding mechanism which holds the sheets. The mechanism is often referred to as the *metals* because metal is most often used to make its pieces; however, plastic looseleaf mechanisms have gained some usage in recent years. Although the binding mechanism may be glued or otherwise adhered to the case in some kinds of binders, by far the most common method of assembly is riveting the mechanism to the case.

Binding mechanisms

Two main types of binding mechanisms are used—rings and posts. On *ring mechanisms*, several rings of metal or plastic extend up from the base of the mechanism, passing through holes in the sheets inside. The rings can be opened to permit insertion or extraction of sheets; they are held open or closed by a mechanism in the base plate which operates with a snap action.

By far the most common type of ring separates at the top when opened, in a clam-like action. However, other types of rings, often called prongs, open at the side next to the base plate. Rings also come in modified shapes, which are useful in special situations. The D ring, for example, which projects straight up from one side of the base plate before curving over, holds large stacks of sheets in a good square block when the book is closed and still allows the book to be opened easily.

Most people are familiar with the standard three-ring binder, but many photograph and presentation binders are made with multi-ring mechanisms (see figure 14.32). Wire-O Binding Company manufactures the Mult-O mechanism, which uses ½″ centers—that is, it takes sheets with holes whose centers are ½″ apart. It is made in various lengths, and the capacity of the metals—the thickness of the stack of paper they hold—ranges from ⅜″ to 1½″. General Binding Corporation's metals are on ⁹⁄₁₆″ centers and come in

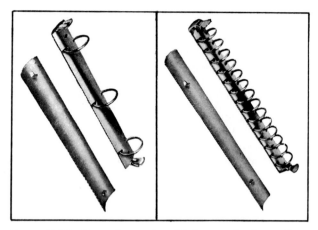

Figure 14.32: Three-ring and multi-ring mechanisms. *Courtesy of* Book Production Industry.

width capacities of up to 2½″. The largest size has 28 rings, taking sheets 17″ long.

A ring binder must have a case with a rigid backbone area wider than the diameter of the rings, in order to permit the case to close around the mechanism. The mechanism normally is mounted on the backbone part of the case, but it sometimes is mounted on the back cover.

Post mechanisms consist of two or more straight rods which extend up through the holes in the sheets and are secured at each end to prevent the sheets from slipping off. Post binders may have cases with fixed backbone areas like ring binders, but they also can be made expandable either with a flexible backbone piece connecting the front and back covers or with separate front and back covers which leave the binding edges of the sheets exposed (see figure 14.33). Because of this variety of formats, post binders employ many different styles of fastening and locking mechanisms to secure the posts to the front and back covers. The posts themselves come in one-piece styles and in multi-unit styles that can be expanded.

Cases

Looseleaf binders employ a broad range of case types, from heavy constructions that will last for many years to covers of lightweight materials intended for short-term use.

One kind is the *assembled case*, made up of boards covered by some type of material. Older styles of assembled cases are made in much the same manner

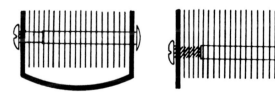

Figure 14.33: Expandable post binders. *Courtesy of* Book Production Industry.

as cases for edition-bound books: the covering material is fed into a casemaking machine and the boards are glued down to the inside surface of the material. Then the edges of the material are turned in and glued to the inside surface of the cover. Cases of this type include mass-produced school notebook covers made with inexpensive paper as the cover material, as well as expensive canvas-covered ledger binders intended to withstand many years of repeated handling.

A newer type of assembled case, which has come into widespread use in the last 20 years, is the vinyl heat-sealed cover. This type of case is made from two sheets of vinyl with boards sandwiched between them. During manufacture, the first piece of vinyl the size of the complete cover is placed on the bed of the sealing machine (figure 14.34), the boards are laid on the vinyl in position, and the second sheet of vinyl is added over the boards. A die in the shape of the cover is brought down and pressed against the vinyl, and radio-frequency energy is applied to the die and vinyl to heat the plastic evenly all the way through. The heated plastic sheets fuse where they are pressed against each other by the die. The cover is fused completely around the edges and also along the two hinge lines, isolating each cover board and the backbone strip within its own pocket. The sealing process takes only a few seconds.

Another type of looseleaf case is simply a piece of stiff paper, creased at the hinges. This kind of cover is very inexpensive and is most often used with low-cost mechanisms such as plastic rings.

The newest style of case is the *one-piece plastic cover*, made of a single sheet of polypropylene or polyethylene. The sheets are stamped with heated dies to form compressed hinge lines, and then the mechanisms are mounted onto the covers. Compressing the plastic gives the hinge areas the strength and flexibility

Figure 14.34: Heat sealing machine. *Courtesy of Cosmos Electronic Machine Corp.*

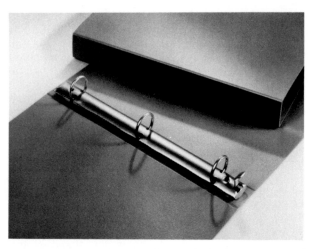

Figure 14.35: One-piece plastic looseleaf cover. *Courtesy of National Blank Book Co.*

to withstand many openings and closings. These covers offer low cost coupled with good durability and are used in many applications today. (See figure 14.35.)

In addition to the basic book-style looseleaf binder, many kinds of special cases are manufactured. One popular style for presentations is the easel binder, which has a rear leg built into it that can be pulled out to support the rings and pages in an upright position. Other special cases are built within box-like structures which close up like briefcases. Some of these special binders are manufactured for sale through commercial stores, but many are produced on a customized basis for companies that want distinguished sales kits and specialized presentations.

All of these looseleaf cases can be decorated by a number of printing or foil stamping processes. However, inks and foils must often be adapted specially to work with particular substrates. In addition, the vinyl case can be decorated by another unique process —sealing other colors of vinyl onto the cover sheet by the same heat sealing process used to make the case itself. Elaborate multicolored designs and trademarks can be built up this way, with all of the wear characteristics of the cover itself.

Other looseleaf features

Cases and mechanisms which form the basic looseleaf binder are not the only features of this type of binding. A number of supplementary elements typically used in looseleaf books are considered an important part of the looseleaf field.

Sheet holders or *protectors* are rigid pieces of board or plastic with holes to match the rings in ring binders. These devices are as long as the sheets they are to protect and about one-third to one-half as wide. They are inserted at the front and back of a binder to hold the sheets away from the point where the rings bend under and enter the base piece, where they might get caught and tear.

Index pages and *dividers* are looseleaf pages made of heavier paper. Most often they have die-cut tabs extending beyond the width of the regular sheets in the binder. They are used to mark section beginnings in a looseleaf book.

Guides, *tabs*, and *signals* are used to mark sections and other special pages when the pages themselves do not have projecting tabs. There are a wide variety of guides, tabs, and signals, but all clip or glue onto the edges of pages and most provide some sort of writing area for labels or notations.

Reinforcements consist of small pieces of fabric or plastic with a hole punched in the center and glue on the back. They are glued to the areas around the holes in looseleaf sheets to provide extra tear resistance. Some reinforcements are continuous strips which line the entire binding edge of the page rather than simply the immediate areas around the holes.

Classifications of binders

Most looseleaf binders sold through commercial retail and wholesale outlets can be grouped into standard classifications used in the trade, including the following types.

Ring binders: Books with rings that can take stacks of sheets ½″ to 3″ in thickness.

Memo books: Ring binders that will handle stacks of sheets ¼″ to 1″ in thickness. Memo books generally are smaller in height and width than regular ring binders, often designed to fit into pockets or brief cases.

Visible record binders: Books with ½″ to 2″ ring metals or 2″ or 3″ prong metals, with ¾″ spacing between the rings or prongs, for storing sheets in a partially overlapping, "shingled" manner.

Post binders: Books with expandable posts, for storing business records.

Ledger binders: Highest quality post binders with limited expansion capacity controlled by a crank mechanism.

Storage binders: Relatively inexpensive post binders with either fixed or sectional posts, for storing records which do not require frequent access.

Prong binders: Binders with prongs that take stacks of sheets 1″ to 4″ in thickness, designed for heavy use.

Catalog binders: Expandable binders with telescoping posts that can extend the binders' capacity up to 75 percent.

Magazine, pamphlet, and *directory binders:* The only binders which differ in construction from the standard ring or post construction. These binders have one or more short posts at the top and bottom, with long metal bars running the length of the backbone between the posts. The bars are passed between the center pages of the magazines or books and secured to the posts to hold the publications in the case.

MECHANICAL BINDINGS

Mechanical bindings are formed by the use of a single binding element which both secures the pages and forms whatever backbone the book has. Unlike looseleaf bindings, mechanical bindings do not involve the use of special cases. Mechanical binding elements are of two kinds, those made out of a continuous length of metal or plastic wire, and those cut and formed into plastic combs. All of these bindings hold sheets in the book by passing wire or comb prongs through holes punched in the pages; often these holes are specially shaped to work with the binding element.

Ordinarily, mechanical bindings are permanent; that is, they are not meant to be opened after the book is bound for removal and insertion of sheets. However, on some semipermanent forms, sheets may be removed or inserted by reopening the comb. If the sheets are punched with T-slots, they may be added or removed without opening the comb.

There is no limitation on the types of cover materials used on mechanically bound books because the covers are treated just like other pages in the book. They are drilled or punched with the same kinds of holes and held into the book in the same manner as the inside pages. Usually, separate sheets of cover stock are prepared for front and back covers, but some report binders are manufactured with single-piece covers which wrap around the backbone, with the wire or prongs of the binding element passing through the backbone area of the cover. This semiconcealed backbone is produced for aesthetic reasons; it does not add strength to the binding.

Binding elements

Several types of mechanical binding elements are available from commercial suppliers, some of which are proprietary designs. Figure 14.36 illustrates some binding elements and the types of holes that are punched into sheets that work with them.

Plastic comb binding is a continuous strip of plastic with individual teeth to hold the pages. The combs can be manufactured with a wide round back, a narrow back, or an oval back. They hold stacks of pages ranging from ³⁄₁₆" to 2" in thickness and usually take sheets up to 20" long. Books longer than 20" can be bound by using more than one piece of comb.

A number of companies make plastic comb bindings. Plastic Binding Corporation manufactures their *Plastico* binders using both ½" centers, or 22 holes on an 11" sheet, and ⁹⁄₁₆" centers, or 19 holes on an 11" sheet. The combs are available in clear, red, white, blue, green, black, brown, ivory, orange, gold, and silver. Spiral Binding Company also makes a plastic comb binding with ⁹⁄₁₆" and ½" centers in black, white, green, red, blue, and brown. General Binding Corporation's *Cerlox* plastic combs are on ⁹⁄₁₆" centers and have thickness capacities of ³⁄₁₆" to 1⅛". They come in red, white, blue, green, black, brown, and orange. In addition, for 1¼" to 2" capacities, General Binding offers the *Sure Lox* binding, a plastic comb with locking hooks.

All wide-backed plastic comb binding can be foil stamped or screen printed in one or more colors, but these processes are economical only for production-run quantities in commercial binderies.

General Binding Corporation also manufactures a binding element called *Slide Ring*. This element is a continuous piece of plastic with a removable backbone; sheets can be changed by sliding the backbone off. Slide Rings come in ⅜" and ½" thickness capacities. They are manufactured with clear rings and red, white, blue, green, or black backs.

Wire-O is double-looped wire that can be manu-

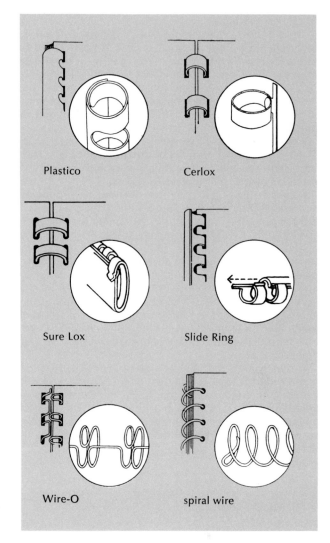

Figure 14.36: Mechanical binding elements. *Courtesy of Book Production Industry.*

factured in any length, depending on the size of the punching dies available. Its thickness capacity ranges from ³⁄₁₆" to ¾". Wire-O is made in nickel, blue, gold, green, yellow, black, white, red, and brown.

Double-O wire, manufactured by Spiral Binding Company, is similar to Wire-O, but it comes in ¼" to ⅞" paper capacities. Its colors are generally limited to nickel, black, and white.

Spiral wire is a continuous coil binding which ranges from ¼" to 2" in diameter. It can be manufactured in any length, depending on the number of punching dies the binder has available. Ordinarily, spiral wire is not put on books larger than 24". If the book is over 2" thick, an inserting rod can connect two, three, or more loops of spiral wire to make a book of any thickness. Spiral wire is available in nickel, copper, black, white, or, in sufficient quantities, any special color.

Spiralastic is similar to spiral wire, but it is made out of continuous loop plastic; it comes in black, white, red, blue, and green, or, with a large enough order, in any other color.

Binding systems

Unlike most other graphic arts processes, a number of mechanical binding processes can be performed in the individual end user's office, or by printers and other graphic arts suppliers not specially trained in bindery technology. General Binding Corporation has led this movement; in addition to mechanical binding elements, the company offers a complete range of machinery for producing its bindings.

One such device is the sheet collator shown in figure 14.37. This type of equipment provides office duplicating departments with economical means of assembling products made up of individual sheets.

Several office-type machines for use in producing comb-style bindings are shown here. Figure 14.38 is a typical punching unit for placing holes in sheets. A comb binder is shown in figure 14.39. To use it, the operator places a plastic comb in the unit, presses down the operating lever to open the comb prongs, places the sheets in position, and raises the lever to allow the comb to close through the holes in the sheets. Figure 14.40 is a more advanced binding machine, which holds a supply of combs on a roll and feeds them into binding position automatically. Commercial mechanical binding plants often utilize similar equipment.

Other styles of mechanical binding, particularly spiral wire, require heavier automatic equipment and are generally limited to use on larger production runs. Spiral bindings are used mostly for blankbooks, although some long-run commercially published books, such as typing instruction manuals, have been spiral-bound.

Figure 14.38: Automatic punch machine. *Courtesy of General Binding Corp.*

Recently in-line spiral binding systems have been developed. Bielomatic manufactures an automatic mechanical binding machine with high-speed capability, which punches sheets and binds them with steel or plastic wire. It may be teamed with a press and suitable collating equipment to form a complete in-line printing and binding system.

Figure 14.37: Collator. *Courtesy of General Binding Corp.*

Figure 14.39: Comb binder. *Courtesy of General Binding Corp.*

Figure 14.40: Automatic comb binder. *Courtesy of General Binding Corp.*

One book manufacturer has set up a complete in-line system for printing and binding spiral-bound books. The system, similar in concept to the Cameron and Wood book production systems (see page 431), is the proprietary property of Spindex Corp., of Long Island City, New York. It is composed of a web offset press which prints and feeds the web of paper into a patented slitting, collating, thumb-indexing, punching, and wire inserting unit. Plastic wire is used in this system. The process is completely in-line: blank paper is fed into one end of the system, and bound books are delivered at the other end, ready for shipping.

FINISHING PROCESSES
William B. Freedman, FREEDMAN CUT-OUTS, INC.

As the uses of printing have expanded, creating a wide variety of printed products, mechanical operations have been developed to transform printed matter into final product form. These operations, called *finishing processes*, constitute the same importance for myriad products as binding does in the completion of books and periodicals. In addition, some of these processes are used to enhance bound products.

DISPLAY MOUNTING
Mounting is the term used to describe the finishing operation in the manufacture of advertising displays. Since most printing cannot be done directly on heavy rigid cardboard, the copy is usually printed on 70- to 80-pound paper and then glued onto cardboard of suitable thickness, usually between .040″ and .100″ or slightly less than 1/16″ to 1/8″ in thickness.

The mounting machine applies a fine coating of glue and combines the paper and board at a series of pressing stations. The combined sheet is then placed in a hydraulic press and given tremendous pressure to assure a firm bond and the elimination of wrinkles. It is then put under weight and given ample time to cure and dry thoroughly before further handling.

TIN EDGING
Tin edging is a low-cost method of combining sheets and at the same time stiffening a display piece and preparing it for hanging. Tin edging is particularly useful for calendars and is also used for wall charts made of a single sheet of paper. The tin edging and a hook for hanging can be attached to the top of a chart or calendar in one operation. A wall chart can be tin edged at the top and bottom for further rigidity.

The tin edging comes in various colors. The proper length is cut and formed on one machine from full sheets of metal. Then it is clinched with the calendar or chart on another machine that attaches a hanger at the same time. No more than 12 to 15 sheets of 80-pound stock should be combined.

EASELING

Easeling is the process of gluing or stitching an easel onto a display. Easels for advertising displays, counter cards, and merchandise cards are made of cardboard and applied to the backs of displays to prop them up. The more common types are single wing, double wing, lock top folding, straight lock, chair, and box easels. These are illustrated in figure 14.41. Special types of easels may be designed and custom-made for unique purposes. Most die cutters keep in stock standard single and double wing easels in graduated sizes from 3″ to 40″ ready to be affixed to the back of a display card.

The easel is usually two-thirds the height of the display and is cut with a slanted bottom so that the card leans back slightly. Easels are creased for folding and are equipped with locking devices. They can be stacked flat for shipping and assembled easily.

DIE CUTTING

The manufacture of printed products cut and formed into unique shapes is referred to as *die cutting. Cutouts* usually include advertising displays, folding boxes, trick folders, pop-ups, labels, pocket folders, coin cards, slide charts, paper dials, easels, washers, and numerous industrial items.

Most of these products are made with *steel-rule dies* mounted on presses. Steel-rule dies can also be used for scoring and creasing. The dies are custom-made for each job. The principles of their manufacture are simple, but only a skilled craftsman can produce an ac-

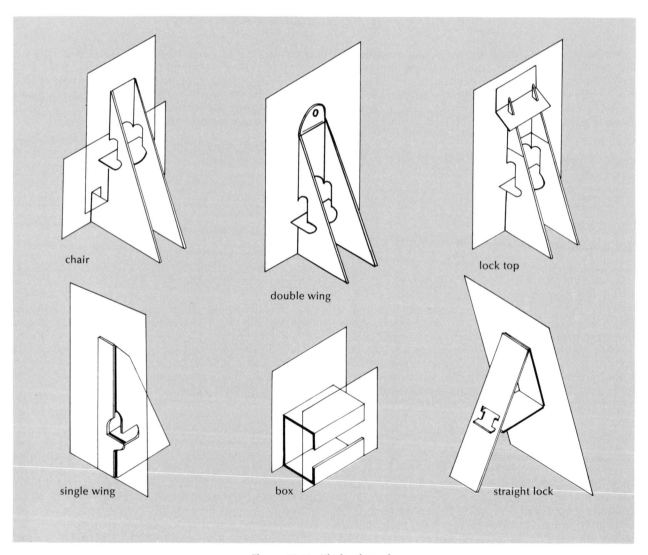

Figure 14.41: Kinds of easels.

553

curate die. The outline to be cut is first traced onto the *die board,* a block of plywood about ¾" thick. The outline is then jigsawed to make a track ¹/₃₂" wide. Small gaps are left unsawed so that the die board remains intact. A strip of steel rule with a sharp cutting edge, or with a blunt edge for creasing, is then bent on a special machine and inserted into the jigsawed gaps in the die board. The steel rule is about 1" high and projects ¼" above the wood base. The rule is notched to fit the unsawed areas on the die board. Small squares of sponge rubber are glued to the wood on each side of the blade to act as springs that eject the cut-out unit from the die.

Die cutting presses cut one piece at a time or very small lift quantities. Makeready procedures insure that cuts or creases will be made evenly and cleanly and in proper register with any printing. The sheets are fed into the corner of the press, using the same edge of the sheet that the printer uses for register. Dies will stand up for well over 100,000 impressions without getting dull if the makeready is carefully done.

Several types of presses may be used, depending on the nature and size of the job. The platen cutting and creasing press is usually used for very thick board or for small-quantity work. High-speed flat-bed cylinder presses are used for stock that is flexible and usually under .030" thick. Reciprocal action presses are effective on stock between .004" and .065" thick, especially if there are many internal openings to be removed automatically. Rotary die cutting, the latest process, is effective on very long runs at the highest speeds. It can be done as an additional in-line operation on web printing presses, with excellent results for specialized products. Rotary die cutting is diagrammed in figure 14.42.

High, or *hollow,* dies are used particularly for cutting jobs such as paper labels, which do not require internal cut-outs, scores, perforations, or punches. The use of high dies is more practical and economical than steel-rule die cutting for this type of work, especially

on thin paper. The dies are made from tooled steel that is forged and welded into desired shapes.

EYELETTING AND STRINGING

Eyeletting and *stringing* of tags is done on a high-speed tag machine. In a continuous operation, the machine punches the hole, applies the metal or paper eyelet reinforcement when required, and inserts and ties the string for hanging. Other machines attach wire instead of string.

Besides serving to reinforce holes, metal eyelets are also used to fasten cards together to form circular dials and slide charts.

EMBOSSING

Some of the most beautiful effects are obtained by *embossing,* or creating relief images or designs on paper or cover stock either after the stock has been printed or on blank paper. There are two kinds of embossing: *roller embossing,* usually called *pebbling* or *roughing;* and *plate,* or *spot, embossing.* In pebbling, die-cast steel rollers produce a pattern over the entire surface of the stock. In plate embossing, individual images or patterns are created by dies mounted on heavy-duty embossing presses. Plate embossing may be of two types: *blind embossing,* done on a blank area; and *register embossing,* which creates relief images in register with printing.

The effectiveness of embossing derives from the contrast in finish between the raised embossed area and the surrounding area, created by polishing or smoothing the texture of the paper. In the case of coated stocks, the contrast is heightened by the reflection of light from the beveled edge of the embossing. When printing and embossing are done together, precise register is important: if the bevel falls on the edge of the printing, the printing is in a shadow and the sense of depth is lost.

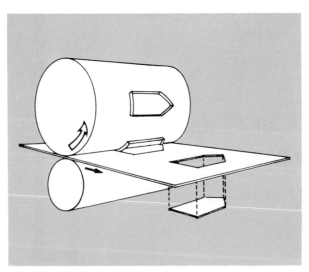

Figure 14.42: Diagram of rotary die-cutting.

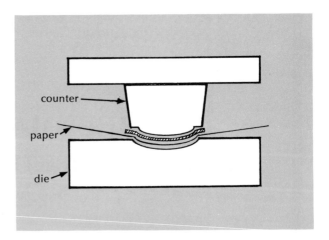

Figure 14.43: Principle of embossing. Pressure is applied to the counter to force the paper into the engraved areas of the die and, in register embossing, to transfer the ink in the cavities to the paper.

554

Plate embossing

The intaglio dies used in plate embossing are made of brass, copper, or magnesium, depending on the subject and result desired. Dies may be etched by hand, by machines such as pantographs, or photomechanically. If a die is etched from a photographic image, it is hand tooled afterward. On a single-level die, special bevels are hand tooled; multilevel, sculptured dies are hand tooled in full detail to form an image that creates great depth. Duplicates are readily made in plastic for multiple setups on large runs.

The dies are positioned on a honeycomb base and carefully mounted on the head of an embossing press to be in exact position for impression. A relief, or male, *counter die* is made by pressing the female intaglio die into a special soft-surfaced makeready plate mounted on the bottom of the press. The makeready plate hardens to form a relief image corresponding to the female die's pattern. When the paper is forced into the recesses of the intaglio die by the raised areas of the counter, embossing is achieved. Embossing presses exert great pressure and often use heat. Figure 14.43 is a diagram of the embossing process.

Pebbling

Pebbling or roughing is produced by feeding paper stock between two rollers. The upper impressing roller is steel, engraved with the male impression. The lower, female roller consists of a soft paper surface on a steel core. The design is transferred to the female roller by running in the male impression under heavy pressure, causing the lower roller to form a perfect reverse of the male impression.

Pebbling gives an antique or roughened surface to otherwise smooth stocks. Fine halftones can be printed in full color on high gloss stock and then pebbled to attain an antique linen, moiré, or eggshell finish as well as other designs. Other uses of pebbling are breaking fibers on label stock for improved adhesion of labels on bottles, breaking fibers for better folding quality, and imitating cloth and leather finishes.

STAMPING

Stamping dies are usually made of metal ¼″ thick —steel, brass, copper, or magnesium, depending on the length of run.

Blind stamping

Blind stamping, or debossing, uses a heavy impression but no ink, to give a depressed effect. Very heavy duty vertical presses as well as platen presses are used for this process. Smoothing or calendering an area of textured stock makes a debossed panel. A counter or matrix on the platen will accentuate debossing and raise the reverse side of the stock. Special brass dies are sometimes tooled to produce a combination of embossing and debossing.

Ink stamping

Ink stamping is essentially a letterpress printing process used to decorate book covers and other materials. Certain platen presses are used for ink stamping in binderies, but high-speed production is achieved

on special heavy-duty rotary presses designed specifically for this type of work. Ink stamping requires a heavier impression than ordinary letterpress printing, often creating a debossed effect in the stamped area.

Hot leaf stamping

Hot leaf stamping, also called *gold stamping, roll-leaf stamping,* or *hot foil stamping,* produces decorative images by pressing a die that is covered with colored metallic foil against an area of stock. Heat is used to release the coloring material from the foil and bind it to the stock. Hot leaf stamping is used extensively for the decoration of book covers, as well as for decorating other printed products.

Stamping dies are made in a variety of ways and with different materials depending on the number of impressions and the intricacy of the work to be produced. Steel and brass dies, as well as chromium-plated brass dies, are preferred for long run, quality production. If stamping is to be embossed, instead of flat, a combination brass die must be hand tooled. The stamping presses used for such work have a critical makeready since all areas must be stamped but not filled in. Stamping presses are capable of exerting tremendous pressures and are adjusted for the right amount of heat and pressure for each job.

The stamping press has a roll-leaf attachment that automatically pulls the leaf into position over the die. The foil is stamped and then is advanced for the next impression.

DECKLING

Deckling is the process of giving paper an irregular feather edge similar to that found on hand-made paper. Deckled edges are produced at paper mills by the use of a stream of water. In commercial plants, the finished printed paper can be deckled by running the sheets between a special circular blade and a steel roller. The blade has triangular points along its edge. The final product has an irregular edge closely resembling the edge produced in papermaking.

COATING AND LAMINATING

Coating and laminating give a sparkling effect to printed products and protect their surfaces from scuffing and scratching. Book and catalog covers, labels, menus, and packages are among the products that may be coated or laminated. In these processes, a clear liquid or film is applied to the base material.

Film laminating

The *film laminating* process bonds a thin film of plastic material to a sheet by the use of adhesives or heat and pressure. Commonly used film laminations include cellulose acetate, polypropylene, vinyl, and Mylar. They are more expensive than liquid coatings but give high gloss and good protection. A laminating machine is illustrated in figure 14.44.

Liquid coatings

Coatings include varnishes, lacquer, vinyl, and polyesters. Most coatings are applied by roller on coating machines or are sprayed on, but varnishes may also be applied on printing presses. Lacquer, polyester, and vinyl require the application of heat to drive off the solvents they contain.

Press varnishes are coatings that are applied on a printing press, either after printing or by one of the printing units of a multicolor press during a run. These coatings are often called *spot varnishes* because they can be deposited in isolated and uniquely shaped areas by the plate used in their application. Press varnishing is fast and economical but produces a relatively low sheen and has poor scuff resistance. It requires the use of nonabsorbent, high-grade coated papers. This type of varnish tends to yellow. Varnishes may also be applied by screen printing when added thickness, and therefore added gloss, is desired.

Lacquers are distinguished by their high luster, good heat resistance and scuff resistance, and light color. Lacquer finishes will accept subsequent printing but have a poor resistance to alcohol and react to light by yellowing.

The term *liquid lamination* is used to refer to coating with plastics in liquid form. Vinyls produce a finish that will accept printing and that has good chemical resistance and scuff resistance, a light color, and good luster. They have a yellowing reaction to heat and light. Polyesters are applied with heat and a catalyst

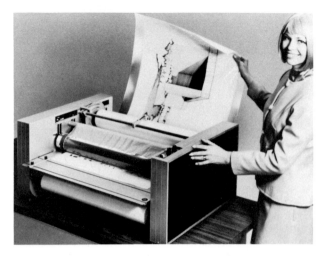

Figure 14.44: Laminator. *Courtesy of General Binding Corp.*

that causes them to polymerize or harden. The finish is a thick film that has a very high luster, chemical resistance, and scuff resistance.

In any type of coating, it is necessary to check with the finisher regarding gripper margin requirements and nonspray surfaces. If there is a subsequent operation such as spot-mounting a label or gluing a pocket, dry areas must be left for applying the glue.

BRONZING

Bronzing is a method of decorating products with gold-colored metallic powder, called *gold bronze*. On a printing press, an adhesive called *gold size* is applied to the areas to be decorated; then the powder is dusted on and rubbed into the adhesive. (See also "Printing with Metallic Inks," page 499.)

FLOCKING

Flocking is a finishing process that involves applying an adhesive to a surface, scattering finely cut cloth fibers (flock) over it, and removing the excess fibers. The fibers can be made of cotton or silk or, more often today, synthetic materials such as rayon, nylon, and dacron. Flocking produces a textured surface that simulates suede, felt, or velvet. It is often used on wallpaper, greeting cards, record jackets, and other novelty items.

Screen printing is usually used to apply the adhesive size to the areas to be flocked. A wide variety of substrates can be used, including three-dimensional objects. The flock can be blown onto the adhesive-coated surface by a spray gun or air jets, or it can be drawn into the adhesive by a static charge or an electrostatic force.

BOOK CLOTH

John Klein, PHILIPS OFFSET COMPANY, INC.

Book cloth is a woven cotton material, called greige or "gray goods" in its unbleached and unfinished state. To be converted into finished book cloth, the greige must first be bleached to remove dirt and other impurities. The cloth may be left white or may be dyed; then it is coated with one of several materials.

The quality of the cloth can be expressed by thread count (the number of threads per square inch), weight, strength, and other characteristics. Book cloth is categorized into grades A to F, according to specifications of the National Association of State Textbook Administrators (NASTA) and the Library Binding Institute. Grade F indicates the highest quality. In addition, there are nonspecification cloths, which do not fulfill the criteria for grading. Care should be taken to check the requirements that a book must meet before selecting a cloth.

COATING

Book cloth can be coated by various methods to produce different characteristics and satisfy different requirements. Materials used for coating include starch, pyroxylin, and acrylic.

Starch-filled book cloth is made by sizing the cloth with a slurry consisting of water, starch, clay, a coloring pigment, and a softener. The cloth is knife-coated or roller-coated with the mixture to fill the interstices between the threads and bind the pigment to the threads. Often two or more coats are used; each coat is dried before the next is applied. The cloth is then calendered to give it a relatively smooth finish.

Although starch-filled cloth is the most economical to produce, it will not stand up well to moisture because starch is a water-soluble material. Schoolbooks, cookbooks, and other books that are likely to encounter moisture, as well as cloth that will be decorated by lithography (which involves the use of water), should not be cased in starch-filled cloth.

Book cloth may also be impregnated with pyroxylin or acrylic or a combination of the two. The coating is applied in basically the same manner as for starch-filled cloth.

The pyroxylin consists of nitrocellulose dissolved in a volatile spirit solvent, to which coloring pigments mixed in oil or plasticizer are added. Because of the resistance to moisture and the greater flexibility derived from the plasticizer, pyroxylin-impregnated cloth, unlike starch-filled cloth, is suited for books that will be exposed to moisture or spills. It is used primarily for offset lithography.

Acrylics are water soluble, so no solvent is needed; this characteristic gives acrylics an ecological advantage over pyroxylin. Once dry, acrylics are no longer water soluble, so they can be used for the same purposes as pyroxylin. Acrylics are more flexible than pyroxylin and add opacity and weight to the cloth.

Book cloth may also be coated, rather than impregnated, with pyroxylin or acrylic or both. Instead of being forced between the fibers of the cloth, the coating is laid on top of the cloth. Up to six coats are often applied in this manner. This type of coating originally was designed to simulate leather; the thick coating covers the threads of the cloth. It is used principally for cloth that is to be decorated by hot stamping; the thickness of the coating provides a good surface for stamping and protects the cotton fibers from breaking under the pressure of the stamp.

FINISHES

Book cloth is also divided into three classifications which describe its appearance: vellum, linen, and natural. A *vellum* finish is obtained by dyeing the cloth before it is coated, so that the fibers blend in with the pigmented coating. A *linen* finish is created by applying a pigmented coating to undyed cloth and then scraping the coating so that some of the white threads of the cloth show through. If a *natural* finish is desired, the cloth is coated on one side only; the uncoated and dyed side goes face up on the book.

Book cloths come in a variety of textures, from smooth to rough, and can be embossed in patterns such as leather and canvas (see "Finishing Processes," page 551). The texture should be compatible with the printing process to be used. In general, smoother finishes yield better halftone resolution. Color depends upon the reflection of light, so the appearance of a colored cloth will vary with the embossing pattern.

DECORATION

Hot foil stamping (see "Finishing Processes," page 551) is the predominant method of decorating book cloth, but many other processes can be used; the choice depends on cost considerations as well as the effect desired. Excellent halftones and high color saturation can be achieved with lithography when printing is done on white cloth. Slower and more expensive, screen printing offers an alternative that produces excellent color hold-out on dyed cloth, particularly cloth with deep color. For long runs, gravure can be used.

HOW A WISE OLD COMPANY CALLED JOANNA WESTERN STAYS MODERN IN THE EVER-CHANGING BOOK COVER INDUSTRY.

Joanna's Book Cover expertise begins in the lab.

Joanna's twenty-one chemists and technicians make sure the problems and challenges facing the book cover industry are not only solved but improved upon.

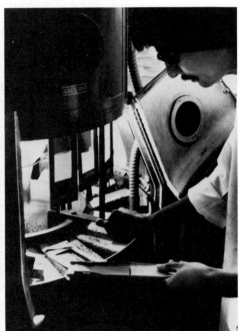

New Product Development   Color Fastness Control

Of course the Joanna Western labs are involved with basic research, new product development and trouble shooting, too. You know how rapidly the book cover industry is changing. Joanna's large research laboratory keeps up with these changes to keep up with your needs.

Joanna offers you Jet Service. Just call 800-621-2715 for instant information regarding stock, prices, samples and very speedy shipping of 305 stock colors in 14 grades of starch filled and impregnated book cloth and coated papers.

Book Cover Materials
2141 South Jefferson Street
Chicago, Illinois 60616

558

NONWOVEN COVER MATERIALS
Ralph S. Heilman, RIS PAPER COMPANY

The term *nonwoven cover materials* encompasses a broad variety of materials that go around books, pamphlets, magazines, or brochures. Nonwovens include, in effect, any flexible covering material except book cloth.

TYPES OF NONWOVENS

The National Association of State Textbook Administrators, in its textbook specifications developed in consultation with the Association of American Publishers and the Book Manufacturers' Institute, defines a nonwoven material as:

A fibrous web, produced by bonding and/or interlocking of fibers, accomplished by mechanical, chemical, thermal, or solvent means, or by a combination thereof. Nonwovens include, but are not limited to:

Type I—Paper: Natural cellulose fiber webs.
Type II—Reinforced Paper: Polymer or resin reinforced cellulose fiber webs.
Type III—Synthetic-Fiber Structure: Strands of interconnected fibers.

These nonwoven materials may be white or colored, coated or printed, embossed or smooth. They may be coated with clays, pyroxylin, acrylics, latex, vinyls, or whatever is functional for the end use.

Nonwovens were essentially developed as a replacement for cloth in hard cases, but the technology has been extended to softcover books as well. Hardcover materials generally are thinner; like book cloth, they are intended to be turned over boards to form cases. The softcover materials have enough strength and stiffness to stand alone as the entire cover—although, of course, they remain flexible.

HARDCOVER MATERIALS

Covering hardbound books with something other than cloth is by no means new. Paper, if it could be pasted and turned in and was suitably attractive, printable, and low in cost, was substituted for cloth as much as 40 years ago. What is new is the proliferation of materials of both natural and synthetic origins, of all ranges of cost and quality.

Development

The impetus to develop nonwovens came after World War II, when the shortages and the rising cost of cotton fiber encouraged Europeans to put cloth on their backs instead of on their books. This transition has continued slowly, until today a large percentage of European books are covered by nonwovens.

The need for strength and durability in relation to end use induced manufacturers to improve upon plain paper (Type I) by producing Type II nonwovens. These solid-color, resin-impregnated, embossed "papers" were first used for the side panels of three-piece bindings, with a stronger material for the spine, but their increased strength, foldability, and resistance to scuffing proved adequate for many one-piece cases. For example, ordinary postwar paper might have resisted a hundred double folds, while the impregnated paper withstood a thousand folds or more. Since then, resins, latexes, acrylics, and other polymers have improved the physical properties of Type II hardcover materials even further. With additional coatings, some Type II materials have proven sufficiently durable to be approved for textbook use.

Coatings for the early Type I nonwovens were either white for lithographic preprinting or colored to simulate cloth or leather. The base stocks were either white or compatibly colored papers. Because the early coatings were not very durable, an obvious disadvantage of using colored coatings on white paper was the show-through when the books were subjected to even normal wear.

Modern-day coated nonwovens are available in a wide variety of colors and may be embossed in cloth-like finishes and leather grains. Show-through is less of a problem now because the coatings are more durable and base materials are more commonly dyed to closely match the coating. A further development is an additional top coating applied after the book covering is printed. The base coating holds the top coating on the surface, providing further protection and esthetic appeal. Even with these improvements, nonwovens remain less expensive than cloth for hardcover use.

The most recent development has been Type III nonwovens, made of strands of interconnected synthetic fibers and often identified as *spun bonded*. When these materials were first introduced, they were not much less expensive than cloth and new techniques had to be discovered to print, top-coat, and bind them. The potential for better printing, coupled with the fact that world demand for cotton was increasing the cost of medium-grade cotton book cloth, accelerated the use of Type III products. Volume production tended to lower the cost substantially.

However, in spite of the improvements in coated and synthetic nonwovens, there is increasing return to plain, old-fashioned, colored paper (Type I), usually with some texture, for the sides of books on three-piece covers. This trend has been hastened not only by the continuing rise in cloth prices but also by more recent increases in the cost of some of its Type II and Type III replacements. The use of paper has been further encouraged by the availability of strong, attractive colors. Several distributors of these plain paper products stock them in rolls, making three-piece cases on end-feed casemakers economically feasible.

Selection

For some purposes, there may be no substitute for cloth. Nevertheless, the selection of book covering materials should be considered in the context of fiber and paper shortages and the increasing costs of manufacture. Nonwovens often satisfy the needs of a job while reducing the cost of covering.

Trade books probably offer the greatest opportunities for variety in selecting nonwovens. Inexpensive uncoated Type I's for three-piece covers and the less expensive of the coated Type I's and II's are available in hundreds of colors and many finishes. For a book that will be purchased with a dust jacket, read by a few people, and then left on a bookshelf, these materials may be adequate.

The book's size, price, and method of distribution all influence selection of covering. Buyers may expect a better covering material on a "coffee table" book than on a novel distributed by a book club.

The same basic considerations apply to hardcover juvenile books. Because juvenile books involve the greatest variety in design, the expanded choice of materials offered by nonwovens may prove more useful here than anywhere else.

Textbooks were the bastion of cloth covering until recent years. "El-hi" (elementary and high school) books are generally preprinted by offset and require a material that meets the rigorous strength specifications which have been approved by the National Association of State Textbook Administrators (NASTA). Modern technology has developed Type III nonwovens which, when coated, have produced a satisfactory alternative to cloth on the basis of cost, quality, and availability. Over 90 percent of today's textbooks are covered by such nonwovens. In addition, certain saturated base stock Type II nonwovens, after several years of testing, were approved in 1976 by NASTA, thus providing another readily available nonwoven to replace cloth.

Teacher's editions of those same textbooks, not required to meet the specifications for pupils' books, were frequently covered in a less expensive grade of cloth. Today, a Type I nonwoven might be used at one-third the cost.

Even books intended at least in part for library distribution, where cloth is traditionally required, are being covered with Type III nonwovens. In many instances, this trend has eliminated the practice of doing two bindings, one for library editions and one for trade distribution.

College textbooks, while not having to meet specifications, pose still another problem. They should last, because the student probably will want to resell them, but they should not be too expensive in the first place. A $30 medical or law book might still command buckram cloth. A $10 math book could use a Type I or certainly a Type II material.

Reference books have a wide range of acceptable product quality. One only has to compare a "supermarket" encyclopedia to Webster's unabridged dictionary to see how far the gamut can run.

SOFTCOVER MATERIALS

The original softcover materials were merely a heavier basis weight of the stock used for the text. These covers would have been classified as Type I materials. Some specialized materials were developed years ago—for example, cloth-lined papers, perhaps best recognized as traditional savings bank passbook covers—but their volume was not significant.

For paper covers, the end use dictates the weight, strength, and surface. For example, a 70- or 80-pound book paper (basic size 25" x 38") might be sufficient to cover a magazine, but a paper twice as heavy would be used for an annual report.

Conventional cover papers (basic size 20" x 26") range from 50-pound to as high as 130-pound in basis weight. Coated grades range in thickness from .006" to .012". Uncoated stocks are somewhat bulkier, weight for weight, as the degree of smoothness influences the caliper. For extra strength, two or more layers of paper are often bonded together. (For additional information on cover paper, caliper, and basis weight, see Section 12, *Substrates*.)

Type II materials are not often used as replacements for traditional plain-paper soft covers. While the Type II's used for hard covers are less expensive than the cloth they are replacing, softcover Type II's are more expensive than ordinary paper.

The use of Type II softcover materials has increased substantially, however, to cover books that heretofore were given hard covers. Flush-cut educational books require more strength than the conventional Type I's can provide. Here the economy is not in the material but in the binding process; the expense of the Type II material is offset by the lower cost of attaching a soft cover. Like Type II's used for hardcover books, softcover Type II's may be white or colored, smooth or textured, and of several weights.

While Type III materials theoretically may be extended to softcover use, a practical Type III has not been marketed because less expensive materials will usually meet the needs of softcover books.

A criterion in the selection of softcover nonwovens, after the necessary protective qualities are considered, is the surface. It will influence the printability, the look, the feel, and the choice of finishing processes such as varnishing, laminating, or embossing. Uncoated papers generally have more character and a softer feel, and printing on them is easier. Rough and textured papers do not varnish or laminate well, but rich effects may be obtained with them by using such techniques as blind embossing (see "Finishing Processes," page 551). Coated stocks run from matte to high-gloss finishes. The principal reason for the selection of finish is the quality and the effect of the printing desired. Ink hold-out is usually a prime consideration, and if protection is required, the hold-out of varnish or another top coating must be taken into account.

PAPERBOARD

Fred G. von Zuben, BOOK COVERS, INC.

Materials made of wood pulp or recycled paper stock and generally over .010″ in thickness are referred to as paperboard. All heavyweight paper may therefore be referred to as paperboard; but paperboard, with its own characteristics and end uses, is considered a separate industry.

Trade terms describe various types of board in terms of manufacturing method, composition, or end use. *Boxboard,* for example, is board mainly intended for use in folding boxes and cartons but having a wide range of other uses, including book covers. Most boxboard is made on a cylinder machine, which combines several layers of stock; this board is called *combination boxboard.* The machine has multiple cylinders. Each cylinder picks up stock from a vat and forms a web of material; while still wet, the webs are joined together to form a multi-ply sheet.

The outer layers of combination board are often of a different stock or color from the inner layers. When the liner is applied on the cylinder machine, the board is said to be *vat-lined.* A liner may also be applied after the board is made; such board is said to be *sheet-lined.*

Several layers of board may also be pasted together after manufacture, to form *pasted board.* The individual layers are often of uniform thickness and color, and the board is usually thicker than lined board.

Boards manufactured as multi-ply sheets on cylinder machines are made from recycled fibers and are often referred to as *recycled paperboard.* Two boards of this kind are *chipboard,* made from waste stock such as box cuttings, and *newsboard,* made from old newspapers. They sometimes are lined with another type of stock or are pasted in layers.

Boards may also be coated for added color and a better printing surface. *Clay-coated board* is newsboard or other board that is coated with clay to give it a high-quality white surface for printing.

Board that is made with a single uniform layer of fibers is called *solid board.* Such board is usually made on a Fourdrinier machine (see "How Paper Is Made," page 457). One kind of solid board is *kraft* board, made from unbleached sulfate pulp. Bleached pulp, as used in papermaking, may also be used to make paperboard. With growing public pressure for ecological measures, there is also increasing use of recycled fibers on Fourdrinier machines. Another type of solid board is *binder's board,* made specifically for book covers. It is made on a *wet machine,* a single-cylinder machine which forms a thick, dense board from a single web of stock. This board is described separately in "Binder's Board," page 564.

BOARD CHARACTERISTICS

Within the broad categories described above, paperboard can be more specifically identified by grade.

Common grades are listed in table 14.1. These grades are actually general in nature and may be used for a variety of products. The grades most commonly used for making cases for books are plain chipboard, pasted chipboard, and *specification cover board,* which includes both high-quality pasted chipboard and binder's board. These grades provide the bulk and strength needed for the cover and are used in combination with some type of covering material.

Each grade of board has certain general characteristics, such as a thickness range, a standard color (or colors, if lined on one side), general printability properties, and bending quality. The board may be further engineered to suit a particular end-use requirement, according to the specifications of the printer or converter.

Descriptions of some important characteristics of paperboard follow. Some of these are listed for the common grades in table 14.1.

Caliper. The thickness of a board is measured in thousandths of an inch and is commonly referred to as the board *caliper.* Each thousandth of an inch is called a *point of caliper* or just a *point* (so a board .050″ thick is a 50-point board).

Density. Density is simply the weight per unit of volume. However, the papermaker will manufacture to a weight per 1,000 square feet given a particular board caliper. The denser boards are generally smoother and stronger, as a result of machine processing. The *yield*— the total printing area for a given amount of board by weight—is inversely related to the density.

Points of finish. Points of finish is an old industry measurement still used, but to a decreasing degree, in the book and rigid box industries. As indicated in table 14.1, points of finish is the product of caliper and *regular number* (R.N.). Regular number is the number of pieces 25″ x 40″ (1,000 square inches) that weighs 50 pounds. Thus, points of finish is a measure of the thickness or height of a 50-pound pile of boards 25″ x 40″ in size. Because points of finish is a measurement combining caliper, surface area, and weight, it is useful for comparing relative densities and yields of various grades. A higher value for points of finish indicates higher yield, lower density, and rougher surface.

Printability. The printing quality of a board surface is a function of many properties, including smoothness, whiteness, uniformity, and the ability to hold the ink on the surface (see "Printability and Runnability," page 475). In table 14.1, "excellent" means suitable for high-quality offset or gravure printing. The "fair" rating applies to grades which are perhaps letterpress printed and do not require fine color separation or exceptional smoothness. Other grades are not used for printing, so printability is not applicable.

Color. The standard colors for each grade are listed in the table. Nonstandard colors are available from the

Grade	Caliper (in inches)	Points of finish (caliper x R.N.)	Print-ability	Standard color (Top/Bottom)	Bending quality	Major use
Solid bleached sulphate (S.B.S.)	.010–.026	1600–1750	Excellent	White/White	Excellent	Folding cartons
Machine clay-coated news	.016–.040	1700–1850	Excellent	White/News	Excellent	Folding cartons
Fourdrinier kraft	Sold by lb/1000 sq. ft.	N/A*	Fair	Kraft	N/A	Corrugated containers
Cylinder kraft	.014–.040	1750–2000	Fair	Kraft	Good	Tubes; cores; cartons
White lined news; patent-coated; bleached manila	.016–.040	1700–2100	Good	White/News	Good	Folding cartons
Bending chip	.016–.040	1900–2100	Fair	Brown	Good	Folding cartons
Plain chip	.020–.060	1900–2200	N/A	News	Poor	Rigid boxes
Mounting chip	.020–.060	1800–2000	N/A	News	Poor	Mounting board
White vat-lined news	.020–.060	1900–2200	N/A	White/News	Poor	Rigid boxes
Pasted chipboard	.065–.240	1900–2100	N/A	News	N/A	Books; games; looseleaf binders; albums
Specification cover board	.060–.120	1450–1750	N/A	News	N/A	Books

* N/A represents "not applicable."

paperboard manufacturer for almost every grade. Such specialty colors are not practical on a small-volume basis.

Bending quality. The ability of a board to accept a creasing score without fracturing of the top liner is a function of fiber quality, board thickness, fiber formation, and the bending angle. An excellent "bender" will fold 180° when scored properly, with no fracturing of the top liner, leaving the surface without obvious defects.

Stiffness. Stiffness is a measure of the resistance of a standard-size sample to a force bending it from a vertical position. This property restricts bulging and is particularly important in folding cartons. It varies directly with the caliper. The stiffness of a given board is greater in the grain direction than in the across-the-grain direction (grain direction is discussed in "Fundamental Physical Properties of Paper," page 471).

Tear. Tear is a numerical specification of the ability of a board to resist a tearing force. It is a function of fiber quality and board thickness. Tear is greater in the across-the-grain direction.

Mullen. Mullen is a measure of the force required to puncture a given area of board and is used extensively in the shipping container industry. It is a function of fiber quality and density.

Surface treatment. Standard printing grades are all clay-coated and are suitable for most printing jobs. Additional surface treatments are available for unusual effects or to enhance the printing quality of a lower grade. Uncoated white-lined news can be treated to give adequate ink hold-out, although below that of a clay-coated sheet. Lower grades can also be treated to increase ink hold-out. Very high gloss surfaces can be achieved by polishing the coating to a waxlike finish.

Water resistance can also be specified. Although no single application will provide a total barrier to water or water vapor, the rate of transfer of moisture from air or the rate of water absorption can be reduced or retarded with surface treatments. These treatments will not affect the edges unless the individual sheets are immersed, so allowance must be made for edge penetration, or wicking. Total surface barriers are best attained with the use of waterproof liners. Tests are available to specify the level of moisture absorption.

ORDERING PAPERBOARD

An order for paperboard, whether in sheets or rolls, should state the grade, caliper, density, and any specifications for appearance, strength, printability, or special end-use requirement. The nearest applicable grade should be used regardless of additional specifications. Caliper is specified in thousandths of an inch but may vary according to industry standards by ±5%.

To insure uniformity of density and therefore of yield, two methods are commonly used in writing specifications. One is to specify *basis weight*, the weight in pounds of 1,000 square feet of a given board. (Note that basis weight is defined differently in the paper industry; see "Paper Names and Classifications," page 447.) This method is the simplest form of measurement and is used in the folding carton and shipping container industry. Lists giving basis weights for particular grades, calipers, and finishes are readily available.

The second method of specifying density is in terms of regular number or count. The regular number—the quantity of sheets 25″ x 40″ (1,000 square inches) required to make a bundle weighing 50 pounds—can be calculated from the following formula:

$$\text{R.N.} = \frac{7200}{\text{basis weight}}$$

The *count* is the number of odd-sized, or "ordered" size, sheets that are required to make a bundle of 50 pounds, given the basis weight and caliper. The count is determined as follows:

$$\text{Count} = \frac{\text{R.N.} \times 1,000}{\text{area of sheet}}$$

When sheets are ordered, size is stated in terms of width, length, and overall skid or pallet size for ease of handling in the plant. The width will be cut to ±⅛″. Size requirements below these tolerances usually entail slitting or trimming charges. *Slitting*, the process of rotary cutting in both directions, is usual in the processing of small panels of 100 square inches or less. *Trimming*, the use of an overcutter or vertical knife, is generally used for processing larger sheets. Rotary-slit pieces are more accurate and can be cut to a tolerance of ±1/32″. In both methods a good right-angle corner will be achieved for accurate feeding on high-speed equipment. Quantity may be specified in tons, number of sheets, or number of 50-pound bundles all of a given size.

Unless otherwise specified, the width of the sheet, or first dimension given, will be in the across-the-grain direction. On a 20″ x 30″ sheet, for example, the grain runs in the 30″ direction and is said to be *grain long*. A 30″ x 20″ sheet has the grain in the 20″ direction and is said to be *grain short*. Awareness of grain is needed to design or lay out paperboard products because characteristics such as stiffness and tear vary with the grain direction.

When board is ordered in rolls, size is specified by stating the width, the maximum outside diameter of the roll, the core opening, and whether the top liner is to be wound in or out. The outside diameter and core opening will be determined by the feed mechanism of the equipment to be used in later processing. Top liner position is especially important because on most recycled paperboard the top and bottom have different characteristics. Quantities can be given in tons, number of rolls, or area in square feet.

BOARD FOR BOOKS AND LOOSELEAF BINDERS

The basic mill grades used for manufacturing hard covers for books and looseleaf binders are plain chipboard; pasted chipboard, in which two or more plies of plain chip are laminated; and binder's board (discussed separately on page 564). Plain chip is supplied directly from the paper machine in sheets or rolls. Pasted chip, which requires an additional step for lamination, is not available in roll form. In addition to standard sheet stock, the mill or supplier can furnish pasted chipboard in a semiconverted form, such as

panels for case bindings. These semiconverted components can be sent directly to the casemaker or dielectric heat sealer with or without a number of "built-in" features, such as extra-strength hinge material or prepunched rivet holes.

Hardcover books

Paperboard is used to provide bulk and rigidity for the cover panels of both round-back and square-back hardcover books. The panels, or *cover boards*, are either various types of pasted chipboard or specification board. Specification board is the name given to board which meets the physical specifications for elementary and high school textbooks set up by the National Association of State Textbook Administrators. Cover boards which meet the NASTA specifications can be made of either binder's board or high-density pasted chipboard, as the papermaking process is not specified.

If there are no NASTA specifications to meet, the major considerations are caliper and finish. The caliper will determine the bulk and to a great extent the rigidity of the cover board. The board must be relatively smooth and free from surface imperfections. Most mills furnish three basic densities or finishes of board—medium, smooth, and extra-smooth—under separate trade names. Greater density increases strength and smoothness but also increases the cost because of the resulting lower yield. For all but the very demanding cover materials, a medium- or smooth-finish board is sufficient for hardcover books.

Sheet stock can be purchased from the mill and cut into panels by the converter, or the paperboard can be ordered in semiconverted form.

The mill will supply *rotary-slit panels* cut to the exact size required for cover boards for a particular publication. The size tolerance on these panels is generally accepted to be ±1/32″ in either dimension, with the standard paperboard tolerances for density and thickness.

One-piece covers—single units composed of two panels and a spine—can be ordered as a grooved blank or joined cover. The *grooved blank* is a single piece of board with the "plowed" space on each side of the spine. The grooved blank is used only for square-back books, which require the heavy material in the spine area. A *joined* cover is made of two or more separate pieces joined with a flexible hinge material, for use on rounded books. The hinge can be paper, cloth, or a variety of materials to add strength or to enhance the appearance of the finished cover. Joined covers can improve production rates because of easier feeding and better spine alignment. This advantage holds particularly for juvenile books which have large panels and narrow spines. (These one-piece cover boards should not be confused with other materials also called one-piece covers. See page 537.)

Covers can be padded for extra depth or a cushion effect. Either cotton wadding or plastic foam is used in combination with paperboard. Cotton wadding can be bought separately and is generally applied or inserted by the book manufacturer. Foam is available already laminated to paperboard; because of its uniform characteristics and appearance it is more widely used, particularly on high-speed equipment. Foam-padded covers can be purchased as sheet stock, in cut-to-size panels, or in a joined cover. Foam is available in a number of thicknesses and can be supplied with a paper lining sheet to give a better gluing surface.

Looseleaf binders

Cover boards for looseleaf binders can be rigid or flexible. The flexible cover boards can be any one of a number of strong, low-caliper materials including a high-density kraft-filled paperboard. A rigid binder is covered on either ordinary casemaking equipment or a dielectric heat sealer. The board considerations for a case-made looseleaf binder are identical to those for hardcover books.

The vinyl heat-sealed binder creates additional demands on the cover boards, given the high-speed equipment being developed and the nature of vinyl. Clean-cut, non-fuzzy edges are needed for uniform edge sealing. Dimensional stability of the cover boards must be held to a close tolerance to avoid edge penetration into the sealing area. Vinyl is soft, and surface imperfections are easily transferred through it from the cover boards. A high-quality vinyl binder has a smooth surface, a tight fit of board to vinyl at the edges, and a uniform seal on the edges. For these reasons, a board with a smooth- or extra-smooth finish should be used, and the method of cutting panels should be watched closely.

The board is available as sheet stock or in semi-converted form. For looseleaf binders, rotary-slit panels and spines can be cut to exact size $\pm \frac{1}{32}''$ and then round-cornered in a separate operation. Dimensional stability is good, and if care is taken the edge quality is acceptable. This method is the least expensive and it assures a reasonable level of quality.

Die-cut panels are also available, providing excellent edge quality and reasonable dimensional stability. Extra care must be taken to avoid variations in size from different die positions. This method is less efficient than rotary slitting and therefore more costly. The dies add to the cost, and there is less flexibility for size changes.

One-piece covers for looseleaf binders have the panels and spines joined with a heat-sealable hinge material. The edge quality is similar to that of rotary-slit panels and dimensional stability is good. The unit cost of these covers is high, but only a single feed is required on the heat sealer for each cover. Top efficiency is possible, however, only with large quantities of binders of uniform size. This method offers particular opportunities for high efficiency when used for binders with multiple spines and more than two panels.

One-piece covers offer an added advantage: they may be supplied with a number of built-in features that save costly converting steps for the manufacturer. Steel or styrene plies can be built into the spines. Rivet holes can be punched out for the exposed-rivet binder. Strip gluing on the panels can provide an opening for die-cut inserts. Similarly, the spine can be strip-glued to allow for concealed-rivet construction.

BINDER'S BOARD

Alfred Brooks, THE DAVEY COMPANY

Long before the first printing presses, bookbinding was an established craft. It began with the protection and preservation of priceless manuscripts. One of the basic elements of these fine bindings was a strong, dense, resilient board.

Today bookbinding is a high production industry, but the need for a quality binder's board is still a primary requisite for a lasting binding. Although the board is not visible in the finished book, its importance is nonetheless vital. The cover material, end leaves, and reinforcement are all adhered to the board. Consequently, the life of a binding depends largely on the strength, toughness, and durability of the board.

Binder's board is the only board developed specifically for bookbinding. The production of this board is a specialized industry demanding a knowledge of binding processes and problems acquired in years of experience. Binder's board is a high-quality paper fiber board manufactured to full thickness in one operation and is not a chip, news, or pasted board. (These are discussed in "Paperboard," page 561).

METHOD OF MANUFACTURE

There are distinct differences between binder's board and these other types of board. The primary difference is in the manufacturing process, which makes binder's board the strongest and densest board for book covers.

Binder's board is made on a wet machine. A screened cylinder revolves in a vat of stock, picking up a web of pulp approximately .005" thick. The web is transferred onto a continuous moving felt or blanket and is carried to the press rolls, where it is transferred to the upper press roll. The cylinder continues to pick up stock and transfer it to the press roll until a homogeneous sheet of the desired thickness is formed. A finished sheet of binder's board may run from .050" to .300" in thickness.

The wet sheet is then discharged from the press roller and moved through a hydraulic press where up to 6,000 tons of pressure may be applied. This process removes the greater part of the water, compresses the board to half its original thickness, and mats the fibers

HIGH DENSITY
BUILDS
HIGHER PROFITS

The .9 density of Davey Board gives book-binders a profitable plus in their investment, operation and reputation.

Davey Board's high density provides greater book protection than any other board. It results in truer, smoother, cleaner cuts and fewer rejects. .9 density gives Davey Board outstanding stability, uniformity, dependability and strength.

Trouble-free in production, Davey Board surpasses all industry and government specifications. It is made 100% of reclaimed fibers and is acclaimed everywhere as the number one binders board.

These qualities have been building profitable businesses for bookbinders since 1842. Today more than ever—on a per reader basis—Davey Red Label binders board is your most economical buy.

THE **DAVEY** COMPANY

Distributors in all principal cities.

SOLID BOARD
EST. **DAVEY** 1842
RED LABEL

164 LAIDLAW AVENUE, JERSEY CITY, NEW JERSEY 07308
MILLS AT: AURORA, ILL. • DOWNINGTOWN, PA. • JERSEY CITY, N. J.

more closely. It constitutes the second important manufacturing difference between this board and lesser grades of board. The exceptional density of binder's board is due in large part to the use of this extreme pressure while the sheet is still wet.

The third important difference is in the method of drying. Single sheets of board are dried slowly in ovens where speeds, temperatures, and air are regulated depending on the thickness of the board. The drying sheet is free to contract in all directions as the moisture evaporates, giving the board its strength and toughness.

After the boards are dried they contain no moisture. They are then sprinkled with water to reintroduce moisture to a predetermined extent, depending upon thickness and weather conditions, and then left for a time to allow the moisture to spread evenly throughout the sheet.

In the final manufacturing operation the boards are calendered between steel rolls, compressing them at least another 25 percent, increasing their density, and producing the smooth, hard-rolled finish characteristic of binder's board. Immediately after this calendering, each sheet is visually inspected for defects prior to packaging.

SPECIFICATIONS AND STANDARDS

Specifications for binder's board are set down by the United States Department of Commerce in Commercial Standard C.S. 50-34, in which binder's board is described as "a single ply, solid board made on a wet machine from a base stock of mixed papers, kiln or plate dried." Although binder's board may run from .050" to .300" (50 to 300 points) in thickness, the most common calipers are between .070" and .098", ranging to .120" for high-quality books such as "coffee-table" books, to .150" or .160" for yearbooks, and up to .225" for some ledgers.

Other general requirements are that binder's board be reasonably smooth and flat and be free from surface lumps and indentations. Binder's board must also conform to standards for thickness, bursting strength, and flexural properties. The natural pulp color, without addition of color, is regarded as standard. The average minimum density of any shipment of binder's board must not be less than .9 grams per cubic centimeter. The grain is always understood to run parallel to the direction of the second dimension of a given size unless otherwise specified by the purchaser.

The board is sold by weight, the size and thickness being specified. The size specified is exclusive of trim and is expressed in inches. Thickness is expressed in points, a point being one-thousandth part of an inch. Binder's board is usually divided into bundles of 50 pounds each. A tolerance of three pounds over or under the standard weight of the bundle is allowed.

Today a large portion of binder's board is sold cut to the exact size needed for casemaking and ready for use. However on full sheets an overage on size of not less than ½" nor more than 1" in both dimensions is allowed.

The number of blank pieces per ton can be calculated by multiplying the width times the length of the board times the caliper. Dividing this cubic dimension into 58,240 (the cubic inches per ton) yields the number of blanks per ton. This final figure divided by 40 tells the number of blanks per bundle.

Bookbinders and publishers have come to know binder's board as a uniform, stable, dependable product that assures good protection for case-bound books.

WELDED BINDINGS
Bernard T. Sendor, SENDOR BINDERY, INC.

Welded Binding is a totally new binding technology using specially treated weldable paper in the manufacture of books, pamphlets, periodicals, and other bound products.

Developed and patented by Mortimer S. Sendor and Bernard T. Sendor of Sendor Bindery, Inc., the binding process uses high-energy sources to bond weldable paper, eliminating the need for other materials such as glue, thread, and wire to hold pages together. It produces bindings stronger than those of other processes because every piece of paper is individually held along the welded edge. The area of the weld can be controlled precisely so that the book opens easily and stays flat when open.

Heat to form the weld can be applied with a number of high-energy sources, including direct heat, infrared, high-frequency waves, and ultrasonics.

In the binding of a paperback or case-bound book, the gathered book block is gripped at the spine. A high-energy source is applied to the binding edge, penetrating through all of the sheets, causing the resin on each sheet to flow and combine with the resin on adjacent sheets. When the energy source is removed, the resin returns to its original solid state. The radiated area becomes, in effect, a single piece of plastic, with the leaves of the book embedded in it. Saddle-welded books, composed of one section, can be welded directly on the folding machine by the addition of specially built welding attachments.

The weldable paper used in the binding process is

made with a thermoplastic resin embedded in its surface. Discrete thermoplastic resin particles are present over the entire paper surface. It is manufactured on conventional papermaking equipment. Any part of the sheet can become a binding edge, so any folding imposition can be used. Available in matte coated stock, weldable paper prints well and has the added advantage of being recyclable after binding. Weldable paper is currently being made by P. H. Glatfelter Company and marketed under the name "Self-Binding Paper."

The Welded Binding process is now being used commercially in the manufacture of paperbacks, casebound welded books, and saddle-welded pamphlets. Applications to many other paper products are presently in the developmental stage.

WEB PRINTING AND BINDING SYSTEM

J. V. Bellanca, J. F. Cosgrove, and W. B. McCain, McCAIN MANUFACTURING CORP.

This article has been reprinted from TAGA Proceedings, *with the permission of TAGA.*

Historically, the output of a web-fed printing press, when used in production of a magazine, catalog, brochure or other such printed product, has been signatures—cut, folded, and paginated paper sections bearing printed images. Signatures are removed from the delivery of a printing press, manually or by semi-automatic equipment, and are skid piled or bundled for storage and transfer to the binding operation.

When delivered to the bindery, the skids or bundles are placed behind the gathering feeders and the signatures are manually loaded into their hoppers. Some automation of this loading process has been accomplished in recent years. After the signatures are gathered in page order, they are bound into a finished product. The two major binding processes generally in use today for catalogs, brochures, and magazines are saddle-wire binding and adhesive binding.

The McCain Web Binding System is a printing and binding system in which paper is unwound from a roll, printed, scanned for print-quality imperfections, punched for register, slit into multiple webs, and rewound into rolls. When unwound later, the paginated webs become input material for a comprehensive bindery machine, which produces booklets, catalogs, or other printed products. This system is designed to provide an increase in productivity for certain types of printed matter.

NEW TECHNOLOGY

Fundamental to the basic health of the graphic arts industry is the requirement that there be available practical methods of increasing productivity per man-hour in the future, in order that printed and bound products be competitive with other forms of communication.

The present methods of production of printed and bound products have yielded, through the years, substantial increases in productivity. Further increases are, however, becoming quite difficult to obtain because of the structure of the present methods and the mechanical limitations they impose.

In general, at least two approaches to this productivity challenge can be delineated. The first is to integrate the binding system with the printing process to achieve one large production unit whose input is a roll of paper and whose output is a bound book (see "Book Production Systems," page 431). While a fine technological advance in book manufacture, the integrated unit is restricted by its inability to put variations in the end product as well as by the speed limitation that the binding process imposes on the press. Moreover, the trend in magazines is toward more variation and customization, rather than toward uniformity. This flexibility is difficult to achieve on an integrated printing and binding production line.

The second approach, taken by the McCain Web Binding System, is to remove the present binding operations of cutting and folding from the end of the press, and place them in the bindery on a comprehensive binding machine. This method maximizes press productivity without a loss of bindery and product flexibility. The printing couple and the dryer determine the limits of press speed, rather than the press folders.

With this system, rolls of printed paper are the end product of the press. These rolls are input material for the bindery operation, which produces the signatures. The bindery-produced signature is then combined with other such signatures, a card, a separately produced cover, or all of these elements, to form a gathered and bound printed product in continuous automatic operation. Bindery-produced signatures may also be combined with other signatures fed on a variable basis from feed-on-command hoppers activated by a computer information source, yielding a final product with variations in the text matter and number of pages, to be directed to particular subscribers.

PREPARING WEBS ON THE PRESS

To keep the gathered webs in proper juxtaposition during the binding operation, holes must be punched along the sides of the web so that the repeat length is uniformly and properly divided into an even number of increments, each having its punched hole. If the web is split into smaller webs, holes can be punched on both sides of the smaller webs, allowing suitable register and control in gathering. This means that the repeat lengths of the gathered webs will be precisely in alignment with each other in the bindery and held there by the pins protruding through the holes punched in the sides of the webs. No web slippage or drift can occur with the holes properly utilized.

As the web emerges from the dryer, it passes through an optical scanning device which allows each side of the web to be viewed by a series of mirrors which move precisely at web speed; the image on the web is optically "stopped" for visual inspection of the print image quality, and by use of magnification the critical portions of the printed image may be carefully monitored.

As long as the web quality is satisfactory, the webs are rewound onto roll-stand spindles after the punching process. Rolls may be spliced and parts removed, without stopping the press, by automatic equipment similar to web splicing units in wide use today. If the web quality should deteriorate, as observed through the optical scanning device, the unsatisfactory web section may be redirected to a reject roll without contaminating the roll of good product being rewound.

The partial roll of good quality product must then be removed while adjustments are being made to the printed image, and replaced by an empty spindle which will rewind the good quality product when it is again available. These rewinding operations can be accomplished without stopping the printing press, and they assure that good rolls are available to the bindery for finishing. Rewinding also allows a careful accounting for waste by balancing the total of the good rolls and reject rolls against the input rolls.

The output of the press is rolls of properly printed and paginated repeat lengths of paper, having holes punched along the web edges for alignment purposes in the bindery operation. The finished rolls are marked with the number of impressions contained, wrapped in the original mill covering, and stored again as a roll of paper would be stored, probably in tall, vertical stacks, occupying substantially less space than an equivalent amount of skidded or bundled folded signatures.

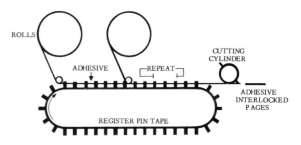

Figure 14.45: Unwinding, collating, and cutting of webs in the McCain system.

GATHERING WEBS IN THE BINDERY

As shown in figure 14.45, when the rolls are brought to the bindery they are placed on the spindles of a *web collator*. A web collating machine is one in which rolls of paper are loaded onto spindles which allow the rolls to unwind. As they unwind, the webs are laid down onto a raceway, and holes in the sides of the web are engaged by register pin tapes moving in the raceway at web speed. The center-to-center distance of the pins, on the register pin tapes, must equal the center-to-center distance of the holes punched in the sides of the webs. These pins help move the webs through the raceway and assure that the repeat lengths of the webs, laid one on top of another, move in proper alignment to the cutting cylinders.

Between the webs, a glue bead is placed along the line of eventual fold, or binding edge, so that an adhesive interlock exists to bind the paper leaves together and reinforce the eventual binding process.

The pile of printed, paginated, aligned, registered, and adhesively interlocked webs is fed through a set of cutting cylinders which sever the pile of webs at the repeat length and equal fractions thereof, according to the particular imposition.

These cut piles of paper are transferred automatically to a folding mechanism which creates the signature by action of a knife and counter-rotating rollers and delivers it to a gathering feeder for subsequent handling and binding into a finished product. The bindery-produced signatures may be used alone or combined with conventional signatures to produce a saddle-stitched or adhesive-bound book.

FUTURE TRENDS IN CASE BINDING

Peter de Florez, THE DE FLOREZ COMPANY, INC.

Changes in case binding will be relatively slow in developing and evolutionary in nature, as they have been in the past. Case binding is a rather complex operation and too small an industry to attract large capital investment in new technology and machine de-velopment. Nevertheless, changes will occur. While the binding of the future may closely resemble the binding of today, the bindery of the future will incorporate many innovations.

Binding is essentially a packaging operation. A binding must fulfill the same functions as any other package: it must provide protection for the product, convenience for the user, adequate shelf life, and eye appeal. Overriding all of these considerations is the factor of cost. All future changes will be motivated by efforts to provide the best compromise between good packaging qualities and low cost.

There are basically three areas in which changes can be made in pursuit of this objective: the physical configuration of the book itself, the binding materials, and the machinery of the bindery.

THE SHAPE OF THE BOOK

The basic configuration of the book has remained virtually unchanged for hundreds of years and is likely to continue so for a great many more, so the opportunities for development in this area are limited.

One important trend already in evidence is greater standardization of trim sizes. Without detracting from the appearance or function of the book, standardization increases the efficiency of the bindery by reducing the amount of lost time associated with changeover and makeready between different editions. Standardization of trim sizes has been encouraged by the growth of web offset printing, and the resulting binding economies will further promote its acceptance.

Another trend in the area of book configuration is the growth and acceptance of the square-back book. Rounding and backing produces an esthetically pleasing binding, but today its visual impact is often negligible. It is doubtful that the average buyer or reader notices whether or not a book has been rounded and backed. The original structural purpose of this operation no longer has much validity, and the advent of paperbacks has certainly conditioned the public to square backs.

From the binder's point of view, a square back eliminates the complex and relatively costly rounding and backing process and simplifies the subsequent casing-in operation because a dimensionally stable and more predictable page block is being processed.

NEW MATERIALS

The areas where new materials will play the greatest roles are in binding and casemaking. The increasing use of adhesive binding and its acceptance by publishers have been largely the result of developments in adhesives; improvements in and use of adhesives will continue. No other binding method can match the efficiency of adhesive binding, which lends itself to straight-line automated production, and its further growth is assured.

The use of plastics in casemaking has for the most part been limited to coatings and finishes on paper and cloth substrates; however, the all-plastic case is a strong possibility for the future. These cases may be made by casting, injection molding, or extrusion. They promise the advantages of light weight, excellent wear, no waste, unlimited decorating possibilities, and dimensional accuracy.

The development of one-piece plastic cases offers the possibility of forming, decorating, die cutting, and adhesive treating the case in a single operation. The combination of a perfect case and a dimensionally accurate square-back page block, attached without wet adhesive, would greatly simplify casing-in and building-in.

PRODUCTION MACHINERY

Change will continue to occur in the technology and machinery of the bindery. In recent years, most emphasis has been placed on developing higher speed units and providing automatic transfer devices between individual machines to reduce handling. Studies have indicated that, because of the short-run nature of much edition binding, machine speeds may have reached at least a temporary practical plateau. Means other than further increasing machine speeds must be found for increasing net productivity. The most promising course lies in the reduction of downtime, particularly during changeover and makeready. The next phase of machine development will be the simplification and mechanization of critical setup and running adjustments. The ultimate goal is fully automated setup based on an input of digital information describing the job to be run, with a system of feedback which will maintain quality by making running adjustments as required.

A key element in this coming automation is the computer. Programmed with a model of the bindery, it will continuously schedule operations along the most efficient path, using a continuous input of information including new orders and those on hand, availability of materials, promised delivery dates, availability of machines, and a myriad of other data. Computers will also be used in such areas as machine setup and maintenance scheduling.

Adhesive binding systems lend themselves most readily to this concept. Progress has already been made in automated setup and running adjustments. End-sheet tipping and trimming also can be made fully automatic fairly easily. Finally, as pointed out earlier, the elimination of rounding and backing, along with improved adhesives and new casemaking technology, will make possible the design of new and simplified casing-in and building-in machines.

THE IMPLICATIONS OF CHANGE

To sum up, we are entering a new phase of automation, in which computers teamed up with more sophisticated machinery will make possible markedly increased productivity and bindery efficiency. Automation will reduce the direct labor required in manufacturing but will require much greater capital investment.

This mechanization and automation will require a new level of sophistication in management science and greater training and discipline among operating personnel. Downtime due to poor maintenance, poor planning, or operational errors will no longer be tolerable.

Long-term contracting for book manufacturing services will be increasingly important for stabilizing production flow and justifying the high capital investment that will be needed. The future for the case bindery is technologically interesting and will be rewarding for those with the imagination and the means to grasp it.

COMPUTER CONTROL IN THE BINDERY

William A. Whitescarver, BINDERY SYSTEMS DIVISION, HARRIS CORPORATION

Binding has lagged behind other areas of the graphic arts in the development of new, efficient techniques and products. The need for more efficient typesetting, bigger and faster presses, better inks and faster drying, and more creative use of quality color have left their impact on the industry. Yet the bindery has been an area of great inefficiency. Most manufacturers have required the lowest priced, most flexible machinery and little else.

In recent years there has been a move to improve bindery efficiency and reduce production costs. An important factor has been the trend to shorter runs of books and split-run production of magazines, which necessitated the modification of traditional binding techniques. Computer control is making it possible for binderies to meet these new requirements with more efficient operation of bindery equipment. The CABCON (Computer-Assisted Bindery Control) gatherer-binder, developed in 1976 by the Bindery Systems Division of Harris Corporation, uses a computer to improve the efficiency and flexibility of the traditional binding line.

COMPUTER-ASSISTED GATHERER

The most difficult machine on a bindery line to set up and keep running is the gatherer. Its operation involves the coordination of a number of feeding stations, each consisting of a hopper, usually called a *pocket* or *box*, and a feeding mechanism. Each hopper holds a stack of copies of one signature; these must be fed into the machine one at a time to coordinate with the rest of the signatures in the book.

The CABCON system can activate or deactivate the gatherer or any single signature pocket automatically in response both to feeding faults and to programmed delivery sequences for each pocket. The ability to automatically control pockets has resulted in a vast improvement in the process of start-up and fault correction during a run.

Misfeeds and jams that occur during a gatherer run on a traditional binding line result in downtime for readjustment and for clearing improperly collated or jammed books from the gathering chain. A misfeed also results in considerable spoilage because a fault at one box is compounded as long as other boxes continue to feed signatures onto the improperly collated book. These problems are particularly severe in periodical production, in which insert cards, gatefolds, and other special items must be collated in addition to ordinary signatures.

The CABCON gatherer has made a considerable advance in this process with its computer-directed inhibit-and-reject operation. When a misfeed occurs, the computer senses the fault and permits only one more signature to be fed. As the gathering chain space containing the faulty product continues down the race-

way, all infeed heads are temporarily deactivated so that the faulty space does not receive additional signatures. All other chain spaces containing good product are fed properly. The gatherer continues to run, and the improperly collated book is automatically discarded at a reject gate. Slight running adjustments can be made on the infeed heads during machine operation.

More often, the operator uses the system's fault-limit feature. In this case, he can select the number of faults he will tolerate in the heads. If a head malfunctions the prescribed number of times, the computer will shut the gatherer down and direct the operator to the faulty head by means of lights at the control console and at the faulty head.

The CABCON gatherer also reduces downtime for a gathering jam. When a jam occurs, the gatherer will still automatically shut down, as do older machines, but the operator has only to remove the jammed signatures and then start the machine again. The signatures around this chain space are then tracked and rejected by the computer.

CABCON CONTROL CONSOLE

Besides improving the functioning of the gatherer, the CABCON computer compiles data on many operating functions of the bindery line. This information, which includes the number of faults for each hopper, is displayed on a 32-character alphanumeric

Figure 14.46: CABCON control console.

terminal. A matrix of indicator lights tells every time an input or output circuit is activated. The lights are used for displaying normal control sequence status and for maintenance purposes in the event of problems. (See figure 14.46.)

COST CONTROL

Faster makeready and start-up, less downtime, and accurate performance data are keys to the efficiency of the CABCON system. The information from the CABCON computer facilitates maintenance and improvement of the system. Now that a gathering line can operate longer without interruption, production variables such as manning systems, edition scheduling, and the use of special insert items that must be bound into the publication can be evaluated in terms of their effect on system productivity.

Productivity of the system improves in direct relation to the number of pockets used in the gatherer and the gatherer cycling rate. Preliminary estimates place the improvement at about 8 percent for a 10-pocket gathering line cycling at 200 cycles per minute. A 40-pocket gathering line cycling at 200 to 300 c.p.m. has a potential productivity increase of 30 to 40 percent over conventional equipment.

TRENDS IN BINDERY AUTOMATION

Thomas B. Cosden, FREE-LANCE EDITOR

During the last decade, automation engineering has significantly reshaped the capabilities and horizons of the bindery. New approaches to the automatic manufacture of books and periodicals have been developing along two fronts. One is an extension of traditional efforts to boost machine output rates and place more diverse operations in-line. The other is the attempt to increase the productivity of individual bindery machines and of fully in-line systems by reducing downtime for makeready and operating malfunction.

EXPANSION OF IN-LINE PROCESSING

The first steps in the automation of binding machine operation beginning in the 1940's concentrated on connecting machines with conveyors to form fully in-line processing systems. Individual machines were also developed to perform more and better coordinated functions at higher speeds. These advances resulted in block-long systems that were fully automatic once set up and that had output rates which surpassed the productivity of older systems. Examples of such in-line systems are adhesive binding lines that produce thicker periodicals and softcover and hardcover books, from gathering through covering; the production of thread-sewn hardcover books from smashing through covering; and gathering, stitching, and trimming lines for periodical manufacture.

Lately the automated binding of books has seen expansion through the development of the Cameron Belt Press system. In this case, expansion has taken place *upstream* through the connection of printing and binding. The Cameron system prints a complete book on a continuous web of paper in one pass of the web through the press. The printed web is then slit, folded, and collated through a unique book assembly process, and then delivered directly to an adhesive binding line. This development centers on press design, however, and is described in detail in "Book Production Systems," page 431.

In addition, recent developments have expanded the capabilities of in-line systems beyond the conventional collating, binding, and covering operations in the *downstream* direction, especially in the area of processing of finished products for mailing or storage. Before operations such as address labeling or wrapping were automated for in-line processing, the output potential of binding lines was shortchanged by the downstream break in the work flow. However, several types of downstream operations have been developed for integration with binding lines. These include labeling and mailing, strapping and tying, and shrink-wrapping.

Labeling and mailing

Equipment that can automatically prepare periodicals for mailing immediately after they are trimmed is available in a variety of designs each of which features different capabilities. Some equipment first sleeve-wraps periodicals and then applies mailing labels. Another type of unit does not sleeve-wrap but applies labels directly to magazine covers. The Harris BC500 system, for example, is composed of a high-speed trimmer, label applicator, divert section, counter-stacker, and town sort unit. The entire system operates at a speed of 15,000 books per hour.

The town sort control automatically senses marks indicating the end of a particular zip code area. The counter-stacker is programmed to divide each zip code order so that no stacks contain less than 5 magazines. If, for example, the present upper limit for a stack is 20 magazines, a zip code area having 22 orders will automatically be divided into stacks of 17 and 5. The counter-stacker diverts groups of less than 5, and if a zip code area has, say, 3 orders, that stack will be automatically diverted for separate handling.

(For information about labeling and mailing equipment, see "Fulfillment of Mass Mailings," page 576.)

Strapping and tying

Another downstream process that has been under development for its integration with binding lines is strapping and tying of books for shipping or storage. A wide range of equipment is available for such operations as plastic-strapping loads of a few books or horizontally strapping large pallets containing several hundred books. Systems are also made for wire tying. Much strapping and tying equipment can be interfaced with counter-stackers at the end of binding lines. Some units now have totally in-line connections and do not require manning.

Shrink-wrapping

A downstream operation that has grown steadily because of the diversity of its applications is shrink-wrapping. In this process, an object is loosely enclosed in a plastic envelope and conveyed through a heating oven, which shrinks the plastic tightly around the object. Various films and processing systems are used for such purposes as unitizing large pallets of books, individually wrapping and protecting books or periodicals, and providing product identification for packages of books. Because of improved addressing capabilities, strapping and palletizing systems are being increasingly interfaced with counter-stackers for the strapping and mailing of individual magazines. On-line shrink-wrapping is becoming popular for bulk shipments to newsstands and other distribution points.

AUTOMATION TO REDUCE DOWNTIME

Makeready for in-line bindery systems is lengthy, and downtime after start-up can be frequent since a fault on one unit can shut down the whole line. The high processing speeds of these systems render each minute of makeready time clearly expensive in terms of lost production. For example, a hardcover edition binding line may be operated at a rate of 100 books per minute and may require one hour for setup. If the average run for this line is 10,000 and net production is 5,000 books per hour, excluding makeready, the line will produce 50,000 books and require five setups in a two-shift 15-hour day. If one minute of setup time were eliminated, five minutes would be added to system production each day and 415 more books would be produced.

The high output potential of these in-line systems has been geared to long-run production, where the percentage of operating time is not too seriously reduced because of downtime for makeready and fault correction. Today, however, book runs are growing smaller in response to the fast information turnover and the need to reduce investment risks. Run lengths of hardcover trade books are falling to the 4,000 level and below, and those of trade novels and college texts may be heading for the 2,000 level. In this type of production scheme, setup rather than speed is clearly the limiting factor in equipment productivity. In the above example, more time would be spent in setting up the equipment than in running it.

Short edition runs can be produced on fully in-line systems if they are grouped in a production schedule with other titles having similar makeready requirements. Such grouping of titles reduces and can even eliminate makeready between editions. Although standardization will continue to grow, it will not lessen the need for improving makeready and downtime requirements.

Automation of setup

An early effort to reduce downtime that had particularly dramatic results was the redesign of some setup adjustments. For example, the setup of an adhesive binder requires that the clamps which carry books through the binding machine be adjusted for book thickness. On older binders an operator had to use a wrench to adjust each clamp. On a 40- to 50-clamp binder this could take an hour or two for one man depending on the extent of the adjustment. On today's binders, clamp settings have been fully mechanized. As the clamps pick up books, they automatically compensate for any difference in book thickness. No physical adjustment is necessary, so setup time is eliminated.

Some mechanized adjustments can now be made while a machine is running. An operator can reset an adjustment that has drifted during an operation or can do fine tuning without stopping the binder. This procedure eliminates not only downtime for readjustment but also the spoilage that formerly occurred before the defect was noticed.

One example of a running adjustment is on the cover applier and cover breaker on adhesive binders manufactured by the Bindery Systems Division of Harris Corporation. On an adhesive binding line, the cover is applied to the adhesive-treated backbone of a soft-cover book or magazine, and the cover breaker creases the cover and folds it around the book block. Improper adjustment of the equipment results in poor alignment of signatures and covers. The Harris system permits on-the-fly adjustments to correct improper cover register or faulty cover breaker operation.

Mechanized setup adjustments have far-reaching applications in further bindery system automation. A casing-in machine, for example, may have a dozen bulk settings such as those for infeed guides, escapement, case forming, and others. When these are mechanized, they may also be connected electrically so that all adjustments may be made for a run simultaneously. A further degree of sophistication would entail the integration of bulk settings for all machines on a line. The same principle could be applied in varying degrees for trim and case dimensions. And beyond push-button control lies the use of computer signals based on programs with the basic specifications for a production run.

There are some adjustments on a binding line that do not lend themselves to mechanization, and there will probably always be a need for some manual as well as automatic controls. During gathering, calipers that detect paper thickness require fine adjustment from lot to lot of the same paper stock. Vacuum suckers that pick up sheets in feeder devices must also be adjusted for a wide variety of paper characteristics.

Another obstacle to automation of setup is the use of interchangeable parts that must be replaced by hand during the makeready process. Changing of parts has been simplified on modern gatherers and binders, which now have hand knob and/or hand wheel adjustments with built-in scales or dial indicators, eliminating the need for wrenches. The problem might also be solved by the development of adjustable parts.

Central control consoles

To reduce downtime it is also necessary to control the speeds of all the machines in a bindery line. This type of control has been achieved through the development of central control consoles.

Each machine in a line must operate slightly faster than the unit which precedes it so that there are no pile-ups. Once the speeds of machines are properly spaced, an override control on a central console may be activated so that the speed of the entire line may be changed without losing the difference in speeds between the units. When the override control is de-activated, the speeds of individual machines may be adjusted independently of each other. In some cases, consoles do not contain speed controls for each machine. When they do, the controls are usually "trim" controls which can vary machine rates by 10 percent for purposes of spacing. Otherwise the speed controls are located at each machine.

When a line is changed for a new job, the override control is used for the limiting factor of a new run. For instance, a stock that is difficult to cut may require a slower speed at the trimming unit. Or an adhesive may require longer drying time than was required in the previous job. When the override switch is used to set the proper speed for such a factor, all other machines are adjusted accordingly for automatic system synchronization.

Central consoles also have run-stop-jog controls for the line as a whole and for individual units. A switch enables an operator to control all machines simultaneously from one set of buttons, or to disengage the master control so that each unit can be manipulated independently during setup. In this way, a unit can be adjusted while other units are operating. Some consoles have start-stop controls for auxiliary functions such as air compressors and vacuum systems, although these motors are usually kept running during machine stops. All consoles have an emergency stop button that shuts down everything.

Bindery consoles also have a panel of indicator lights which perform a variety of functions. Some lights are connected to jam switches on the machines so that they can monitor the place on a line where a fault has occurred. Other lights are used in conjunction with push-button controls to test whether certain electrical circuits are operating. On-off conditions of various devices from complete machines to auxiliary devices such as glue-pot motors and drying units are also monitored by lights. Still other lights are used to show the *safe-on* condition of all units in a line. This means that a *safe switch*, which keeps the machine from running, has been left on. Often an operator will forget to turn off a safe switch after makeready. Before the development of indicator lights, considerable time had to be spent searching the line for the switch that was left on.

While central consoles offer some control over an entire system and point out some areas where faults have occurred, they provide no real control over the effect of a fault. In the future, running adjustments may be made on consoles, but today control over the effect of operating faults is developing on the line.

Gatherer fault response

In adhesive binding systems, the relationship between gatherer and binder can be critical. If the binder is repeatedly slowed or stopped for gathering down cycles, the quality of books will be affected adversely, and the binder may go out of adjustment and require resetting—a delicate and troublesome operation. An adhesive binder performs a series of functions in timed sequence, and there is a limited margin for alteration in, for example, the effective speed of saws which increase the binding surface of book backbones or the timing between the moment when a book receives an application of adhesive and when it receives its cover. In order to prevent a gatherer down cycle from reducing the efficiency of the binder, the binder today automatically declutches and continues to run at a slower speed, completing the books within the binder at acceptable quality. When the gatherer fault is corrected and the gatherer is restarted, the system is re-engaged automatically and goes back up to its preset run speed.

Storage systems

The coordination of machines on the binding line is also facilitated by devices that temporarily hold or store unfinished books. Accumulating systems are used between binders and trimmers, for example, to hold piles of books so that all machines on the line do not have to stop if one stops. Machines upstream of the trimmer can continue to run during momentary stops on the trimmer or other downstream equipment, such as wrappers and mailers; and the trimmer can continue to run if upstream equipment stops.

Storage devices of different types are used as buffers between many other binding machines. In periodical production, inserter-stitcher-trimmers are connected by storage units to mailing machines so that a mailer shutdown does not stop the whole line. Also, on hardcover book lines, machines for preparing books for covering are connected to casing-in units by storage devices because of the frequency of casing-in machine malfunction.

Computer control

Another line of attack on the problem of coordinating the gatherer and the binder has been the use of the computer to make the operation of the gatherer more efficient. In the Harris Corporation's CABCON system, the gatherer responds automatically to faults on the line. Improperly collated signatures are rejected, and the machine continues to operate normally. This feature greatly reduces downtime. (See "Computer Control in the Bindery," page 570.)

The computer assisted gatherer also makes possible the efficient production of split-run editions of magazines. Split editions are sub-editions of a basic product, each of which has unique content segments that are tailored for special groups in the overall market for the product. The principal use of split editions today is in the periodical field where large-volume magazines are broken down into sub-editions that offer advertisers direct access to special groups of subscribers.

There are currently two basic types of split editions available for the advertiser: geographic and demographic editions. The geographic type is offered by many magazines in a variety of area sizes ranging from multi-state regions, individual states, and major metropolitan areas to zip code areas of high average family income. Demographic editions are made up of subscribers in a specific occupational or age class, for example, college students, doctors, and top management officers.

Split edition production places a strain on the bindery because of the need for manual changeover from edition to edition on conventional gathering machines. For example, in geographic editions ad pages going only to an edition for one metropolitan area must be run in the edition for its state. Ad pages for that state must be run in its multi-state region. If two metro editions are run in the same state, one metro is produced, the gathering line is stopped for changeover, and then the next metro is run. The same holds true for each state in a multi-state region.

The complexity of demographic edition production is even greater. Subscribers to a demographic edition are listed on address label reels made up for each region. Regional edition binding is stopped when an area of demographic circulation is reached. The demographic reel is then placed in operation on the mailing unit, and the demographic ad pages are added to the gatherer. After the list is completed, regional binding is resumed, and interrupted again for the demographic subscribers in the next region. It is even more complicated to do two demographics (for example, students and doctors) in one region.

Two methods are used for manually changing a line over from one edition to another. One method is to supply the pockets of a gathering line with signatures for one demographic or sub-regional run only. When that edition is completed, pockets containing signatures for the special edition are manually emptied and refilled with signatures for the next edition. The other method is to fill pockets for more than one run. The appropriate pockets are activated for one edition, and when the edition is completed, pockets with its signatures are deactivated, and pockets for the next edition are turned on.

Manual start and stop procedures are time-consuming and highly inefficient. Setting up a new run means that gathering pocket delivery heads must be tuned for proper delivery of signatures to the gathering chain. Infeed calipers require fine adjustment even for differences between different lots of the same stock.

In a bindery system of the future, however, a computer could be used to control the delivery sequence of each pocket in order to produce demographic and regional editions. Zip code areas have a delivery sequence that could control which pockets feed signatures to the gathering chain in a given unit of time. If, for example, a zip location contained a number of student subscribers, the arrival of that location on the computer tape would signal the gatherer. Gatherer pockets holding signatures for students would deliver them as signatures for the surrounding region as required. Since all residents of the region would not receive the students' edition, the pockets for students would deliver an appropriate number of times, stop, and deliver again for the next zip code area according to its number of students.

It should also be possible to produce more than one demographic edition for each zip code area. Pockets for one edition could be signaled to deliver a set number of times for students, and then pockets for another edition could deliver signatures for doctors. This would also hold true for a mixture of demographic and metro editions within the same region. Each edition's pockets could be controlled so that they would not deliver when the pockets for a different edition were cycling. This would prevent ads for doctors and ads for students, for example, from being collated in the same issue.

The use of the computer to control gatherer activity in the CABCON system has already increased bindery efficiency in high-speed, large-volume periodical manufacture. This increase in productivity might be curtailed by the slower speeds and shorter runs characteristic of book production. However, the speeds of adhesive-bound book production lines are closing in on periodical manufacturing speeds. As setup and operating control are progressively automated, the balance between the productivity and the cost of computerized equipment could change in favor of computer control in the book bindery.

It has been predicted that the mechanization of running adjustments may also be computerized for *closed loop* systemization. This means that the computer will sense deteriorating functions or operating faults and signal running adjustments. This kind of electronic fault prevention and fault correction would make storage units and other on-line devices that compensate for faults unnecessary. However, substantial gains in the productivity of the binding line will have to be realized in order to justify the expense of such sophisticated technology.

FULFILLMENT

15

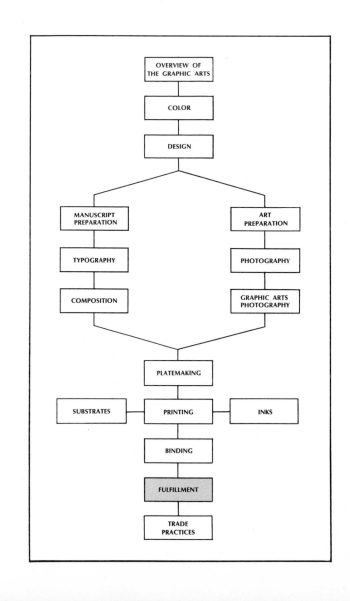

FULFILLMENT OF MASS MAILINGS

Stanley J. Fenvessy, PRESIDENT, FENVESSY ASSOCIATES, INC.

The graphic arts industry, like every other manufacturing industry, must ship its finished products to its customers. Sometimes the products are simply packed and shipped in bulk to the customer's warehouse or some other delivery or end-use point. These products travel via distribution channels used for other manufactured goods and require no special handling or expertise on the part of the carriers. However, a large portion of the graphic arts industry's output goes directly to the individual reader-consumer through the distribution system traditionally associated with the written word—the United States Postal Service. Special classes of mail have long been established in the postal system for printed products.

As the use of printed communications has grown over the years, a unique specialized industry segment has emerged in the graphic arts to handle mailing operations. Mailing, or *fulfillment*, as it is referred to in the trade, encompasses a number of operations, such as list maintenance, addressing, inserting, and preparing material for delivery to the post office. Firms which specialize in these operations have become known as mailing or fulfillment houses.

These specialized fulfillment houses have by no means captured the market. Everyone in business, from the Fortune 500 giants to the corner drugstore, employs the mails as a channel of communication or as a tool to increase sales. Mail has become a major vehicle for information; in many instances, it is the very lifeblood of a business.

Mass mailings require specialized production techniques and equipment. The fulfillment of mass mailings is an important and expensive operation for any firm; it deserves the same careful and thorough engineering and cost control attention that is applied to the main production activity of a business.

TYPES OF MASS MAILINGS

Broadly speaking, mass mailings are used in three ways: for the distribution of company communications, for direct marketing, and for the distribution of publications.

Company communications. Sales bulletins, standard-practice instructions, personnel policies, announcements, and all types of reports frequently are printed centrally and distributed to field offices, plants, substations, subsidiaries, and stockholders. In large organizations the distribution involves hundreds of offices worldwide, thousands of stockholders, and thousands of copies of each dispatch or publication.

Direct marketing. Catalogs, brochures, samples, announcements, solicitations, and questionnaires frequently are mailed directly to businesses or individuals to obtain orders, sales leads, or information—or just to advertise a product or service. This type of mailing is classified as direct mail marketing. Sales attributable

to direct mail marketing are estimated to exceed $50 billion annually. A majority of the largest corporations are involved in direct marketing activities, including the "Generals"—General Motors, General Foods, General Mills, and General Electric.

Distribution of publications. Newspapers, consumer magazines, business trade publications, newsletters, and technical journals are mailed to subscribers on a regularly scheduled basis. Subscriptions to these publications are either sold or offered without charge (referred to as *controlled circulation*). It is reported that there are over 40,000 subscription publications. The fulfillment of book club orders is also included in this category. The book industry includes several hundred book clubs which mail selections to their members regularly in a manner similar to that of subscription periodicals.

The execution of the foregoing types of mass mailing involves two essential production elements: (1) the employment of a mailing list, and (2) the preparation of the media for delivery to the post office—including the functions of addressing, folding, inserting, labeling, weighing, metering, sorting, tying, and placing in sacks or trays. Equipment, practices, services, and helpful suggestions pertaining to each of these steps are discussed in this article.

THE MAILING LIST

Accurate and up-to-date mailing lists are needed to solicit orders, to send out sales materials, to distribute company communications, and to circulate publications. The establishment and maintenance of the names and addresses of customers, sales prospects, employees, subscribers, members, field locations, stockholders, public relations media, and so forth, are among the most important operating functions of a mass mailing operation.

Once a decision has been made to compile a mailing list, the precise information to be captured and the format for retaining the data must be determined.

Components of name and address

Most commercial list-maintenance and label printing and unduplication programs are designed to handle four-line addresses. Whenever possible, the following format should be used:

Line 1   Full first name, middle initial, last name
Line 2   Company or organization
Line 3   Street number and name, building or apartment number
Line 4   City, state, and ZIP code

Where possible, the number of characters on each line should be restricted to a maximum of 23. This format facilitates the most efficient computer processing.

Anyone planning a system for a new mailing list should provide space for the additional four digits that are soon to be added to the ZIP code. This will require a total of ten print spaces on the label because a dash will separate the old five numbers from the new four. The space will be blank for the present but will be available when necessary.

Not all parts of the name and address are equally important. Personnel preparing names should concentrate especially on these key elements: first initial, first five letters of the last name, all digits of the street number, first four letters of the street name, and all digits of the ZIP code. These elements affect deliverability and also are the basis for computerized unduplication (elimination of duplicate names) of lists.

The way a list will be used does much to determine the amount of detail to be included in addition to the basic name and address. Specific decisions must be made as to whether the following elements should be incorporated:

· Terms of address such as Mr., Ms., Dr., Col., Hon.
· Full first names instead of first initials
· Titles such as President or Manager
· Department names

Additional information assists in mail delivery and increases personalization. On the other hand, a recent survey shows that 56 percent of business executives change jobs or titles annually. Naturally, outdated information can have a reverse effect.

The match code

Unique alphanumeric codes for individual names on a mailing list are helpful in sorting, in identification, and in the elimination of duplicate listings. Such designations, called *match codes* in the trade, permit computer manipulation of names and addresses on the basis of a fixed number of characters which can be computer-generated. Various versions of match codes are used to control magazine subscription lists and other major mailing lists. The match code numbers appear on the address label.

A match code provides a technique for identifying individuals by using selected data from their own name and address. The degree of match code complexity is related to the size of the list and the amount of control required. Here is an example of a sophisticated match code that was constructed for the following name and address:

```
04263     ALE D     PNE 015

MR   DAVID C ALLEN
15 PINEWOOD WAY
NORTH LEEDS  MAINE     04263
```

In the match code (first line in the example above), *04263* is the ZIP code; *ALE D* is derived from the first, third, and fourth letters of the last name and the first initial; and *PNE 015* is derived from the first, third, and fourth letters of the street name and the last three digits of the address number.

Use of a match code requires consistency of abbreviations and address formats. The Direct Mail/Marketing Association has prepared a booklet, *Standards For Computerized Mailing Lists,* available at a cost of $10. It is advisable to consult this reference before undertaking the construction of any mailing list.

Information record

In addition to name, address, and match code, provision is frequently made in the mailing list format for recording essential data concerning the addressee but not related to mail delivery. This information record might include such information as:

Original source of name
Telephone number
Subscription expiration date
Number of shares and type of stock owned
Size and type of company
Purchase history (total number and value of orders, date of orders, and products purchased)
Demographic information pertaining to individual or residential area
Psychographic or attitudinal data

Maintaining the list

After a list is created, the information on it must be kept current if the usefulness is to be preserved. Between 15 and 25 percent of names and addresses on a typical mailing list change each year, depending on the type of list. Therefore, lists should be updated at least twice a year, and preferably four times. To receive new addresses for customers, subscribers, stockholders, prospects, and others, the sender can take the following steps:

· Include change of address forms in all publications and mailings.
· Print "Address Correction Requested" periodically on mailings going third class. The post office will notify the sender of new addresses or undeliverable names for that mailing. The service now costs 25 cents for each notice returned, so it should be used carefully on first-hand lists and seldom on lists obtained from others.
· Check the list with the post office. Names and addresses typed or printed on cards will be checked for accuracy by the post office servicing the area. For 10 cents each (with a minimum charge of $1), the post office will check each card, update the address, and return the cards to the sender.

Mailing lists which are created as a by-product of normal company operations (such as accounts receivable, stockholder records, and customer sales histories) require relatively little incremental cost to create or maintain. On the other hand, considerable extra cost is involved in organizing and maintaining mailing lists which are specially created from source media such as warranty cards, coupons, sales inquiries, rosters, and directories. List-processing costs increase when source documents are handwritten, when the same names appear repeatedly, or when the flow of names over a period of time is irregular.

Security provisions

The value of a mailing list used for direct mail marketing increases with the potential revenue from its use. Many direct marketing lists have a value of $1 per name. The names on some lists are worth $40 to $50 or more in future revenue. If company policy permits, lists can be rented to other concerns at rates ranging from $20 to $40 per thousand names. This practice has been a good source of additional revenue for some companies. There are over 30,000 mailing lists available for rental; each has its own special characteristics and worth to a mailer.

The value and importance of mailing lists dictates that they should be protected by a number of security provisions. Here are a few:

Seeding of list. Every list owner should place a number of decoy names in the list. Names of individuals available for such a mail-monitoring service can be obtained from commercial monitoring services. For its members, the Direct Mail/Marketing Association will supply names for seeding. Names should have varying spellings and should be distributed geographically or otherwise throughout the list. Each address should be valid and the name similar enough to that of the person located at the address to assure deliverability. Individuals whose names have been seeded forward all mail they receive under the decoy name to the company executive responsible for controlling the list. Unauthorized use thus can be discovered easily.

Limited access to records. Admittance to areas where mailing lists are created or maintained should be restricted to personnel specifically authorized. Computer tapes or trays of address masters should be retained in a locked room and logged out when removed from that area. Original source documents used for the creation of a list should be stored in a secure area and destroyed after they are no longer required.

Controlled delivery of computer tapes. With the growing use of list merge-and-purge techniques, the shipping of duplicate computer tapes is becoming widespread. Tapes should be sent only to service bureaus or firms whose reputation and procedures are highly regarded. Tape reels should be labeled clearly, using code designations. A signed guarantee should be obtained, stating that the list will not be duplicated or used in any unauthorized fashion.

Creation of a security duplicate. Duplicate computer tapes or galley prints of mailing lists maintained on other systems should be stored for safekeeping at a secure off-premises location. If accounts receivable or other current records are used to generate the list, the tape record or printout from the previous month should be stored at a second location. Many banks and specialized security storage companies have special arrangements to pick up and protect lists against catastrophes.

Maintenance of accurate counts. Counts of names broken down into important segments, as well as counts of names on the total list, should be maintained on a current basis for purposes of control and marketing. At a minimum, summary statistics should be maintained by state, first three digits of ZIP code, class or source of name, recency of action, and monetary value of transactions or account balance.

ESTABLISHING ADDRESSING REQUIREMENTS

Mailing lists can be maintained on materials ranging from typewritten sheets of gummed labels to computer tapes or discs. Determining the addressing require-

ments is the first step in the selection of an addressing system and/or machine. These are some of the factors to consider:

Names
Number of names expected to be accumulated
Additional information to be kept about each name
Need for selection coding according to specific data or criteria

Mailings
Type of mailings and frequency
Class of mail to be used
Range and kind of material to be addressed
Speed with which addressing must be performed
Visual quality of the label or imprint

The size of the list is a very important element. Certain systems are best for small lists and infrequent mailings; other systems, such as those using computers, can handle almost an unlimited number of names and mailings. Converting a large mailing list from one system to another in the future might involve considerable expense.

The type of mailing—the mailing pieces themselves as well as the number—must also be considered. Will the system be used to address envelopes, for example, or catalogs, or publications? Will it be handling window envelopes or self-mailers? Will it be used to create labels? (On small mailings of uniform size, the ability to address directly on the piece may be an advantage because the additional step of affixing a label is eliminated.)

Once the requirements and alternatives have been examined and determined, the selection of an appropriate addressing system or machine can proceed.

LIST-MAINTENANCE AND ADDRESSING SYSTEMS

There are five major addressing systems in general use today: hand-held systems, embossed metal or plastic plates, typewritten stencils and plates, typewritten chemical transfer cards, and electronic data processing.

In general, the noncomputerized systems (the first four above) should be considered only under these conditions:

- List size under 25,000
- Limited selection criteria
- Only small amount of information needed, in addition to name and address
- No requirement to match and eliminate duplications with lists that may be borrowed or rented
- Addresses always prepared in same sequence

A brief description of the principal list-maintenance and addressing systems follows.

Hand-held systems

A hand-held system is the simplest and least expensive of all addressing methods. Although it can be used to address any type of mailing, it is only as fast as the user and therefore presents limitations for larger lists.

One type of hand addresser is manufactured by Heyer, Inc. of Chicago. It features a spirit master roll of typed names and addresses that loads like a roll of old-time camera film. Each roll holds up to 250 addresses, each of which produces up to 100 impressions. Fluid is applied and the address is printed with a sweep of the hand.

The Instant Printer by Master Addresser Company of Minneapolis uses paper plates that have been typed with a reverse carbon image on the back for spirit reproduction. The Instant Printer is rolled across the surface of the area to be addressed to moisten it. The paper plate is placed on the moistened section and the printer is rolled over the paper plate, leaving the impression of the address.

Embossed metal or plastic plates

Many sizes and kinds of metal or plastic plates, known among manufacturers as *data carriers,* are used for mailing lists. They are embossed by special machines. The resulting raised image is printed directly on mailing pieces or labels by a machine which stamps the plate against an inked ribbon. Each plate, which contains a single name and address, costs from 3 to 10 cents, plus the labor cost for embossing. Despite their small size, plates can contain a surprising amount of information—up to 460 characters in up to 10 lines. Selection coding can be indicated by metal tabs, holes, or notches.

There is no limit to the number of impressions from a metal or plastic plate. Metal plates can also make sharp, uniform impressions on several carbons. Plastic plates can be embossed with a special OCR typeface for data entry into a computer. Portions of the information on a plate can be printed or omitted as desired.

Plastic data carriers also come as *stress-white* (self-tipping) cards. One advantage of a stress-white card is that it is easier to read. When the card is embossed, the letters appear white against the colored surface.

Plate addressing machines, known as *addresser-printers,* are available in various sizes from small, fully manual desk-top models to complicated electronic machines that perform many functions. One of the larger machines is AM Addressograph's Model 4000. Its rated speed is 125 addresses per minute. At a minimum, an embossed plate addressing system requires an embossing machine (unless that task is contracted out), an addressing machine to imprint, and plate storage equipment. Rebuilt equipment can be obtained at substantial savings.

In most large cities there are firms which prepare metal or plastic plates at a relatively low cost, eliminating the need to purchase a plate embosser while the list is small. Some firms will take on the entire task of maintaining plates and addressing mailings.

Metal and plastic plate systems are in widespread use. Before the advent of computers, such systems were used to address magazines. The principal manufacturers of this equipment are AM Addressograph/A Division of AM International, Pitney-Bowes, and Speed-O-Print Corp.

Typewritten stencils and plates

A cardboard rimmed *fiber stencil* (usually 4½" x 2"), prepared on a typewriter, serves as another recording medium. A master costs about 5 cents plus time of typing. The master prints directly onto the mail pieces using a special machine which forces ink through the positioned stencil, as in mimeographing. Selection coding is indicated by specially placed holes punched in the rim of the stencil. The stencils can also be color-coded. The life of a stencil is rated at more than 10,000 impressions.

This system was employed by some of the large Chicago mail order companies before the introduction of the computer. A large stencil card was used and the amount and date of the customer's order were recorded in ink on the cardboard rim. Package labels were produced from the stencil using an inked roller; catalog wrappers were addressed by an automatic machine.

The most popular of the stencil equipment is Dymo Business Systems' Elliott Model 6725 desk-top, automatic selective addresser which prints up to 5000 pieces an hour. Rebuilt equipment is also available.

Most office electric typewriters can also be used to create a *foil plate.* The foil is light, tough, and inexpensive. It costs about 3 cents for the foil and 3 cents for a carrier for each name and address. The foil provides a clear, legible impression; unlike a fiber stencil, it can make a carbon copy. Because many businesses need small, fast-changing mailings, foil plates have become increasingly popular in recent years.

Foil is available in two ways: in strip form for inserting in metal carriers, and in cards which are similar to punched cards with the addition of a foil insert. The strip system holds up to 328 characters; permanently mounted 3¼" x 7⁵⁄₁₆" data cards can hold up to 500 characters. Both manual and automatic addressing equipment for foil plates are manufactured by Pitney-Bowes.

Typewritten cards

Specially prepared cards can also be used as the recording medium. Two systems are available: one, using chemical transfer cards, applies the address directly onto the mailing piece; the other transfers the address by Xerography onto labels.

In the first system, address masters are typed by standard typewriters at a specified position on the card. The cards are inexpensive—just a few cents each. An easily read typed address is produced on the front of the master, while a backing sheet produces a reverse image on the back. A special imprinting machine directly transfers a small amount of fast-drying solvent onto the material to be addressed. With proper handling of masters, about 500 address transfers can be made from a master before the image loses a significant amount of clarity. Although the quality of reproduction may not be as good as with metal plates, this system is used when a large turnover is expected in the list and low addressing cost is needed.

The best-known source of supplies and equipment is Scriptomatic, Inc., of Philadelphia, which manufactures different addressing systems for mailings ranging from 50 to 500,000 names. The Model 29 series of addressing machines offers selectivity using mark sensing technology. Desired categories are marked on the addressing master with a pen, and the machine automatically picks up the markings. A standard feature is an audible automatic ZIP code stop, which saves a considerable amount of time and money in bulk rate and first class presort mailings. The Model 80 series accepts a wide variety of mailing copy and will address up to 7,000 pieces per hour.

In the Xerographic system, standard typewriters prepare addresses on tabulating cards. The cards are inserted into a machine (manufactured by Cheshire/A Xerox Company) that transfers the typed images onto a continuous label strip. The system consists of the 730 Address Card Lister, which Xerographically prepares the address label, and the Mod IV which automatically applies it. The label is a glossy finished print. Up to 10,000 address labels can be printed, counted, and stacked in an hour. Since the process is by photocopy, there are no plates to wear out.

In this system, coding can be entered into the typed card with a standard IBM keypunch. Using punched-card sorting and collating machines, the card masters are filed or selected as needed. Another model, the 730S, adds a selectivity feature which utilizes electronic scanning to select desired lists, eliminating the need for sorting and punching cards.

Electronic data processing

The computer, a new force in most facets of business today, has also invaded the mailroom. The maintenance of mailing lists on computers is increasing in groundswell proportions. The increase can be attributed to the constant reduction in the cost of computerizing mailing lists, the high degree of speed and flexibility available, and the growth of numerous computer service organizations specializing in mailing list maintenance.

Magnetic tape is the commonly used recording medium for mail lists. A computer can print over 1,000 addresses per minute, much faster than any plate or stencil system. The addresses are printed out in label form in four or five columns on continuous, marginally punched, fanfold printout paper, 11" x 14$\frac{7}{8}$" in size. Special labeling machines can be used to apply the labels directly to mail, documents, or publications.

For very large volumes and unusual requirements, special label addressing equipment can be used in conjunction with name files on a computer. The equipment is expensive and has been employed principally by large consumer magazine publishers and governmental agencies. An early machine was A. B. Dick's Videograph label printer which, although still in use, is no longer manufactured. This off-line magnetic-tape-activated electrostatic address printer produces rolls of ZIP-code-sequenced address labels at speeds as high as 38 five-line labels per second.

More recently, machines have been developed which use the ink jet printing process in which small droplets of ink are propelled across a short air gap. (See "Ink Jet Printing," page 422.) These units can print directly onto the mailing piece and eliminate the need for label stock.

One of these machines is A. B. Dick's Videojet Printer, which is used with Muller-Martini Corporation's electronic equipment to address newspapers at press speed or to address publications on-line with binding machines. Addresses are stored on magnetic tape, and the data is fed into the ink jet system. The Videojet Printer is also used by other companies with their own electronic equipment to address catalogs, brochures, and direct mail pieces. A. B. Dick is cur-

rently offering a new system, using the 9400 series Videojet Printer. Known as the Videojet Mailer, the system is designed to upgrade existing mailing bases, such as those offered by Cheshire, allowing the operator to print directly on the mail piece. Data input is via magnetic tape, and the system is capable of producing six lines of information on plain or coated stock with a variety of inks at operating speeds of all conventional mailing equipment. It can be adapted for on-line addressing and numbering in binding systems.

Mead Digital System's 2700 series is a self-contained ink jet printer which produces up to 80,000 lines of digital information per minute. Fonts can be changed from line to line and within a line; light and bold characters can also be printed within a line. Mead is also offering a new ink jet addressing system, known as AD/MARK, which is a self-contained mobile unit to be used with existing base feeders, such as Cheshire's. The system uses black ink and has a wide array of available fonts. Magnetic tape is the source of address data. The system supports speeds in excess of 30,000 pieces per hour.

Another ink jet addressing system is Bell & Howell's I/J System 96. The rate at which it addresses mailings ranges from 7,200 to 18,000 mailing pieces per hour, depending on the size of the pieces. The system provides a variety of options: a ZIP-sort attachment, a ZIP-break indication, a bar-code read or imprint, and a capability for adding message lines. Names and addresses can come from magnetic tape or floppy disc. Character height may be increased or decreased on any line or lines of the imprint. A companion device is the L/M System 96, a mini-computer system programmed specifically for mailing-list maintenance. The system has all devices necessary for creating, updating, and addressing mailing lists and can provide a computerized list facility for an organization without the need to acquire a full-size data processing installation.

There is no "rule of thumb" to determine at what size a mailing list should be computerized. It depends on many factors besides size, such as usage, amount of information required, desire to rent out lists (computerized lists are more easily rented), and the availability of the computer service either in-house or externally.

When a mailing list exceeds 25,000 names and is used frequently, a company should discuss its requirements with a computer service bureau that specializes in mailing lists and has the computer software for sophisticated list maintenance. Because equipment and personnel are shared, the use of outside computer contractors, in some instances, is surprisingly low in cost for the type of service rendered.

LABELING EQUIPMENT

The noncomputerized addressing equipment previously discussed all utilizes addressing plates or other data carriers. There are other machines, however, whose purpose is to apply already prepared labels. There are four principal label application processes:

Paste. Individual labels are glued onto the mailing piece.

Heat sensitive. Individual labels are bonded to the mailing pieces by a heat process.

Heat transfer. Carbon images of the address are transferred from the printout to the mailing pieces.

Pressure sensitive. Self-sticking labels are applied either for permanent bond or easy removal.

Labeling machines can be classified as *semi-automatic* or *automatic.* Label dispensers, to aid in manual affixing of labels, are also available from vendors who specialize in manufacturing labels and mailing equipment. A pressure-sensitive label dispenser, for example, can be very helpful.

Automatic labelers for use in volume mailing operations are manufactured by Pitney-Bowes, Cheshire/A Xerox Company, Phillipsburg Division of Bell & Howell, Avery Label/An Avery International Company, and Kimball Systems/A Division of Litton Industries.

Several high-volume machines are available which can apply labels to envelopes, cards, magazines, catalogs, and self-mailers. Cheshire has models that address up to 30,000 pieces per hour. They apply computer-printed continuous address forms to mailing pieces and, with the ZIP separator attachment, can divide mail into geographic groupings. Magnacraft by Bell & Howell has the same capabilities. It can be adapted to an in-line operation, addressing as the product comes off the binding or inserting equipment.

For smaller volume operations, Kimball Systems has an automatic labeler capable of applying 8,000 pressure-sensitive, pin-feed, or spot labels per hour. It takes either rolls or flat folded sheets of labels and applies them to magazines, catalogs, folded cartons, book covers or documents. Avery Label manufactures two tabletop units, the Tab-O-Matic and the Tab Mailer II. They apply self-adhesive labels at speeds up to 10,000 per hour.

INSERTING MACHINES

To achieve volume cost-effectiveness and expeditious handling, the automation of collating, folding, and inserting is next in importance to a good addressing system. It is vital to consider these functions when the printed piece is originally designed.

Inserting machines vary in utility, speed, and price in accordance with these characteristics:

Feed (suction or friction)
Number of stations
Sizes and thickness of material handled (envelopes, inserts)
Special features (folding, counting, sealing, stacking, error detection, etc.)

The spectrum of inserting machines is extremely broad, with over a half dozen manufacturers and a wide selection of equipment, capacities, and features. Inserters are manufactured by Phillipsburg Division of Bell & Howell, Pitney-Bowes, AM Addressograph/A Division of AM International, and Cheshire/A Xerox Company.

Several inserters are offered by Bell & Howell. Typical is the EI System 10,000. It features a 10,000 piece-per-hour insertion capability and an electronic vacuum envelope feed. Maximum envelope size is 10" x 6½" with maximum size of 9" x 6" for inserts. It processes light, heavy, or multifolded inserts and turns out completed and sealed envelopes.

Pitney-Bowes has six inserter models. Its Model 3144 Insertamax, for example, is available in one to six stations; signal light-detectors ensure a complete set of enclosures in each envelope, and cycle speed can be adjusted for any job or any operator.

Cheshire's Model 790 folds, inserts, and seals up to 4,200 pieces per hour. It can make two cross folds and two parallel folds and can handle both window and non-window envelopes in one pass.

EQUIPMENT FOR FINAL HANDLING

At the end of the outgoing mass-mailing fulfillment cycle are the physical handling functions required to prepare the mail for delivery to the post office. Four separate steps are involved in the final processing of high-volume mail: (1) weighing, (2) metering, (3) presorting, and (4) traying or tying and sacking. Equipment available for use in each operation is discussed below.

Weighing

Scales are available in all sizes for all kinds of jobs. Basically, there are three types of mail scales: pendulum, beam, and spring. Pendulum scales are the most commonly used; beam scales are used mainly when the mail falls within a slim weight range; spring scales are used when mail volume is light and when the bulk of the weight does not exceed 20 ounces. Some spring scales, however, handle weights up to 70 pounds.

General purpose mail scales are manufactured and/or distributed by Pitney-Bowes, Pennsylvania Scale Co., ADS-Postalia, Inc., Triner Scale and Manufacturing Co., Pelouze Scale Co., Hansen Scale Co., and Fairbanks Weighing Division of Colt Industries.

Within recent years, electronic scales have become more popular because of their speed, accuracy, ease of calibration, and versatility. They can be used for weights from a fraction of an ounce to 70 pounds.

These new versatile electronic scales are being marketed by a number of manufacturers. Several can be interfaced with a postage meter. They can automatically compute and dispense postage for first class and third class mail, parcel post, and United Parcel Service; they can also be programmed to meet special requirements such as book rate, library rate, and Express Mail. International rates are structured into most systems. The digital displays show both weight and dollars, and allow comparative analysis of postage rates instantaneously. Some units produce daily or weekly summaries of accumulated costs for each of the services. Electronic scales are manufactured and/or distributed by Friden Mailing Equipment, Pitney-Bowes, Orbitron Co., Inc., and Better Packages, Inc.

For high-volume weighing, Bell & Howell's Electronic Mailweigh machine, using a gravimetrical principle, automatically weighs and sorts envelopes at speeds up to 3,600 pieces per hour. It sorts mail into six postage weight categories and can weigh envelopes to within one-fortieth of an ounce.

Metering

Among metering machines, Pitney-Bowes is perhaps the best known. It offers a wide range of equipment, including its Model 4385 Mailomatic which is designed for volume mailers. The unit can apply metered postage, postmark, precancel, seal and power-stack envelopes, and keep track of the postage at the rate of

200 pieces per minute. It handles envelopes up to 15¼" x 13½" in size. Mailomatic's principal competition is Friden Model 9150, an electronic mailing machine which performs similar functions at the rate of 185 envelopes per minute. Friden also has other models in its line. Also in the field is the Postalia Meter, a lightweight postage meter manufactured by ADS-Postalia, Inc.

When stamps are desired instead of a meter imprint, the Postmatic stamp applicator can be employed. It provides a quick changeover for Pitney-Bowes mailing machines, replacing the postage meter head on metering machines without adjustments. The unit applies one, two, or three stamps per envelope at the same speed as the regular meter head.

For high-volume parcel weighing and metering, Pitney-Bowes has a computerized system called Parcelmatic II. After the parcel is placed on the scale console and the appropriate zone button is pushed, a moistened tape (postage or United Parcel Service) is delivered, and a printed record of the shipping charges is made on an invoice or other document positioned by the operator. The new model, Parcelmatic III, adds an electronic scale as an integral unit and includes all rate structures: domestic, international, and UPS.

Presorting

To obtain the low third class bulk rates, the mailer must presort mail to reduce post office handling. Postal regulations specify the methods for tying, marking, and filling mail bags. These steps can be accomplished more easily if the material is addressed or labelled in ZIP code sequence.

As mentioned previously, attachments for some machines cause a separation between mailing pieces when there is a change in ZIP code, facilitating presorting. For example, Cheshire makes a ZIP separator (Model 592) which electronically separates mail by ZIP code, town, state, or zone in combination with high-speed labeling or addressing. The machine separates mail at labeling and addressing speeds up to 24,000 pieces per hour. Cheshire also makes a small office system (MOD VII) which handles up to 7,500 pieces per hour. The Scriptomatic Model 100-10S addressing system also has a ZIP code separator.

In addition to the mandatory presorting for third class, mailers can get a reduction in the postage fee by sorting mailings to the actual carrier route. This is attractive when mailings are very large or when there is a heavy concentration in certain areas. For most mailers, this can be best accomplished by sending the computer tape of names to a service organization that will put them in the correct carrier route sequence. The fee for this service is generally much less than the postal savings. (This carrier routing is *not* the same as the nine-digit ZIP code that is planned.)

First class mail need not be presorted, but the Postal Service is now offering a small reduction in postage for high-volume mailers (500 or more pieces) who make up their first class mail in a manner similar to that required for third class bulk. The savings of two cents per piece for letter size and one cent for postcards on qualifying mailings is not a strong inducement for most businesses, but the potential for faster delivery may provide an additional incentive.

Traying, tying, and sacking

First class mail that is thrown loosely into a bag must be culled (separated) and faced (in one direction) at the post office before it can be processed. Traying such mail makes it easier for the sender to handle and eliminates these two steps for the post office. The Postal Service supplies large stackable trays without charge to qualified mailers. The local postmaster decides on eligibility; in some areas, postal representatives consider 10,000 pieces per day the minimum to make traying practical.

If trays are not practical, large rubber bands are available from the post office without charge for customers who presort mail. Twine tyers such as those manufactured by B. H. Bunn Co., which has been making mail-tying equipment since 1907, are fast and economical ways to bundle mail. Saxmayer Corp. manufactures a portable table-model tyer and also provides a system that cross-ties mail with two ties at right angles, offering greater security and reducing the possibility of pilferage. It can pack mail in bundles up to 14" x 14" x 18" at the rate of 1,500 bundles per hour. These bundle tyers are also used in printing plants for packaging brochures, labels, and so forth.

HELPFUL SUGGESTIONS

The following suggestions should help senders obtain faster and more economical mail handling and fulfillment service.

ZIP code all mail. ZIP codes are basic to the activities of the new Postal Service. If the ZIP code is omitted, mail takes a much more time-consuming route.

Deposit mail early. Mail deposited before 4:00 P. M. reaches the post office before its peak period. It is handled promptly; frequently a whole day is picked up in service time.

Coordinate time of mailing with post office schedules. Mailings that are synchronized with the departure times of trains, planes, and the new Highway Post Office vehicle service save a day in delivery time.

Presort mail. Presorting mail saves sorting time in the post office. At least stamped mail, metered mail, airmail, local mail, and out-of-town mail should be separated. Presorting by the first three digits of the ZIP code gets mail directly to the sectional distribution center. Labels or tags should be affixed to show the sorts.

Be sure addresses are clear and legible. Addresses must be properly prepared for the Postal Service's optical character reader. The city, state, and ZIP code must be on the last line.

Sack mail going to one destination. If a large quantity of mail is going to one address—a branch office, for example—it should be put in a single sack. It will be delivered without any post office sorting.

Pool and case parcels. When a number of parcels are going to the same post office (not necessarily to the same address), they can all be placed in a large carton and addressed to the post office. The parcels will travel more safely.

Inquire about plant loading. High-volume mailers may qualify to have Postal Service trucks pick up mail at the office or plant.

Check mailing scales. Inaccurate scales can result in sizable overpayments or the risk of underpayment with postage due at the other end.

Tag timely mailings. If timing is an essential element of a high-volume mailing, the sender should discuss it with the postmaster well in advance of the proposed mailing date. It also helps to staple a sample of the mailing to the bag tag, indicating the desired delivery date.

Monitor the mail service. Periodic samplings will indicate how effective and consistent the mail service really is. Problems uncovered by such sampling should be discussed with the customer service representative of the local post office.

Make the postmaster a partner in business. The United States Postal Service has an enlightened customer service attitude. In most major cities postal customer councils meet periodically to discuss mailing practices and problems. The Postal Service also offers free training and orientation sessions for fulfillment personnel.

Subscribe to "Memo to Mailers." There is no charge for this monthly Postal Service newsletter that provides interesting and valuable information concerning rate and rule changes and offers money-saving ideas. To subscribe, write to *Memo to Mailers*, P.O. Box 1, Linwood, N.J. 07221.

Consider a consultant. An outsider looking at a company's fulfillment operations can often spot trouble areas and come up with viable solutions. There are management consulting firms that specialize in helping companies improve their overall fulfillment services and reduce costs at the same time. Consultants can help organize the function, streamline manual operations, introduce computer and production equipment where appropriate, set up production scheduling and standards, and train personnel and supervisors.

There are no shortcuts or pat formulas to reducing mail handling costs and improving fulfillment service. A good fulfillment operation is a combination of well-motivated people, appropriate equipment, proper schedules, and dozens of specialized techniques.

ENVELOPE STYLES AND SIZES

The envelope, which creates the first impression for its contents, is too often thought about last. The size, shape, type of paper, and printing of the envelope all contribute their functional importance to the package. Proper prior planning is the ingredient that pulls them all together at the least cost. The following illustrations, lists, and other data describe standard styles and qualities of envelopes and should help the designer and production person select the proper envelope efficiently and economically.

ENVELOPE SIZE
The formula for determining the proper envelope size for an enclosure is:

Length of envelope = length of enclosure + ½"
+ thickness of enclosure

Width of envelope = width of enclosure + ¼"
+ thickness of enclosure

ENVELOPE TERMINOLOGY
Figure 15.1 identifies the parts of two styles of envelope: the *diagonal-seam* and *side-seam*, or *booklet*, styles. Envelopes with the flap on their long dimension, as shown, are *open-side*; those with the flap on their short dimension are *open-end*.

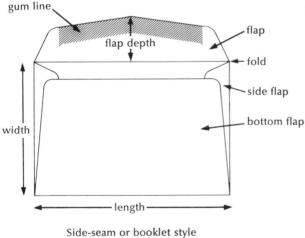

Side-seam or booklet style

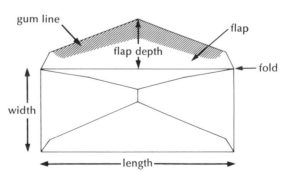

Diagonal-seam style

Figure 15.1: Envelope terminology.

583

COMMERCIAL AND OFFICIAL ENVELOPES

Commercial and official envelopes are general-purpose business correspondence envelopes. All are commonly available in white wove and in bond, including rag-content bonds. Sizes are standard regardless of the style.

	Size number	Dimensions (in inches)
Commercial sizes	5	3¹/₁₆ x 5½
	6¼	3½ x 6
	"data card"	3½ x 7⅝
	6¾	3⅝ x 6½
Official sizes	7¾	3⅞ x 7½
	8⅝	3⅝ x 8⅝
	9	3⅞ x 8⅞
	10	4⅛ x 9½
	10½	4½ x 9½
	11	4½ x 10⅜
	12	4¾ x 11
	14	5 x 11½
	16	6 x 12

Round-flap or die-cut style. (See figure 15.2) Available in all standard sizes.

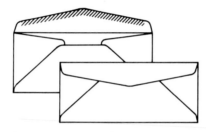

Figure 15.2: Round-flap or die-cut style.

Pointed-flap or web-cut style. (See figure 15.3) Common sizes:

6¼	9
6¾	10
"data card"	

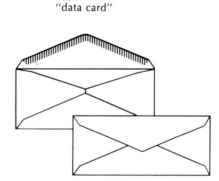

Figure 15.3: Pointed-flap or web-cut style.

Wallet-flap style. (See figure 15.4.) The large flap and wide gumming are designed for extra security. Available in side-seam and diagonal-seam styles. Available in kraft papers as well as white wove and bond.

Common sizes:

6¼	9	12
6¾	10	14
7¾	11	16

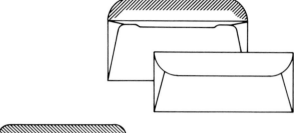

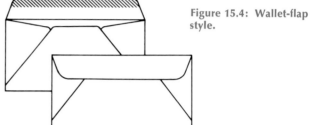

Figure 15.4: Wallet-flap style.

Square-flap style. (See figure 15.5.) Available in side-seam and diagonal-seam styles. Sizes:

6¼	9	11
6¾	10	12
7¾	10½	14

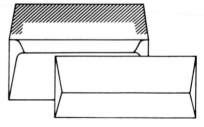

Figure 15.5: Square-flap style.

Windows. Commercial and official envelopes are available with windows of various styles and sizes. The two standard window shapes are round-end and square-end. Windows may be open-face, consisting of a plain, uncovered opening, or may be covered with cellophane or glassine, clear or tinted. The standard style of window envelope has a single window positioned as in figure 15.6; other styles are also available with the window in a different position or with two or more windows. For use in inserting machines, window envelopes are available with the window patch affixed with gummed strips both inside and outside to prevent snagging.

In addition to commercial and official envelopes, many larger mailers and special-purpose types are available with windows.

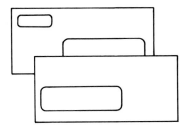

Figure 15.6: Window envelopes.

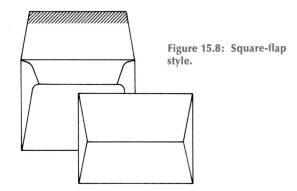

Figure 15.8: Square-flap
style.

ANNOUNCEMENT ENVELOPES

Announcement envelopes are commonly used for both business and social announcement purposes. While the standard paper is white vellum, many sizes also are available in colored and textured papers.

Low-cut, pointed-flap style. (See figure 15.9.) Same sizes as Baronial.

Pointed-flap style or Baronial. (See figure 15.7.) Standard sizes:

Size number	Dimensions (in inches)
2	$3\frac{3}{16} \times 4\frac{5}{16}$
3	$3\frac{1}{4} \times 4\frac{1}{8}$
4	$3\frac{5}{8} \times 4\frac{11}{16}$
5	$4\frac{1}{8} \times 5\frac{1}{8}$
5½	$4\frac{3}{8} \times 5\frac{5}{8}$
5¾	$4\frac{1}{4} \times 5\frac{3}{4}$
6	5×6

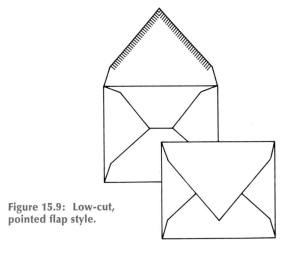

Figure 15.9: Low-cut,
pointed flap style.

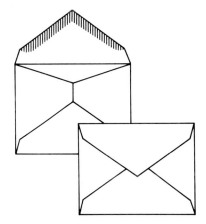

Figure 15.7: Pointed-flap style or Baronial.

Wedding and school announcement style. (See figure 15.10.) The longer top flap makes these envelopes more formal than Baronials. They are usually sold in sets, with one outside envelope and a slightly smaller inside envelope identical in style but ungummed. Sizes range from $3\frac{3}{8} \times 5\frac{3}{8}$ to $5\frac{1}{2} \times 6\frac{7}{8}$.

Square-flap style. (See figure 15.8.) Standard sizes:

Size number	Dimensions (in inches)
A-2	$4\frac{3}{8} \times 5\frac{5}{8}$
A-6	$4\frac{3}{4} \times 6\frac{1}{2}$
A-7	$5\frac{1}{4} \times 7\frac{1}{4}$
A-8	$5\frac{1}{2} \times 8\frac{1}{8}$
A-10	$6\frac{1}{4} \times 9\frac{5}{8}$
A-Long	$3\frac{7}{8} \times 8\frac{7}{8}$

Similar in construction to this style are wallet-flap announcement and latex-seal announcement styles.

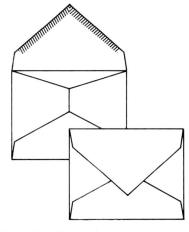

Figure 15.10: Wedding and school announcement style.

LARGER AND HEAVY-DUTY MAILERS

Booklet style. (See figure 15.11.) These are open-side envelopes with side-seam styling, which leaves large areas for printing. Available in white wove, vellum, and kraft papers. Available with or without windows. Sizes:

Size number	Dimensions (in inches)
2½	4½ x 5⅞
3	4¾ x 6½
5	5½ x 8⅛
6	5¾ x 8⅞
6½	6 x 9
6¾	6½ x 9½
7	6¼ x 9⅝
7¼	7 x 10
9	8¾ x 11½
9½	9 x 12
10	9½ x 12⅝

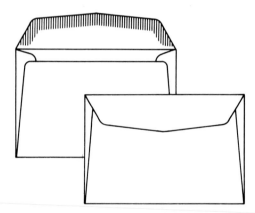

Figure 15.11: Booklet style.

Flat mailer, pointed-flap style. (See figure 15.12.) Papers: kraft, white wove. Common sizes:

6 x 9	9 x 12	10 x 13
6½ x 9½	9½ x 12	10 x 15
7½ x 10½	9½ x 12½	12 x 16

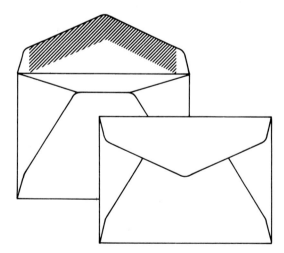

Figure 15.12: Flat mailer, pointed-flap style.

Flat mailer, wallet-flap style. (See figure 15.13.) Paper: brown kraft. Common sizes:

With diagonal seams	With semi-diagonal seams
9 x 12	6½ x 9½
10 x 13	9½ x 12½

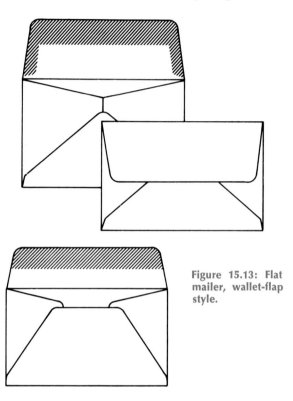

Figure 15.13: Flat mailer, wallet-flap style.

Center-seam mailer, square-flap style. (See figure 15.14.) Papers: kraft. Available with latex seal. Common sizes:

5 x 11½	10 x 13
9½ x 12½	10½ x 15

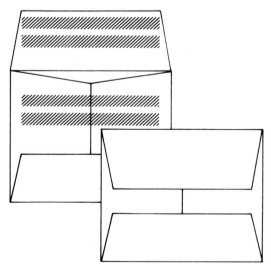

Figure 15.14: Center-seam mailer, square-flap style.

Center-seam mailer, pointed-flap style. (See figure 15.15.) Papers: kraft, white vellum. Usual size: 9 x 12.

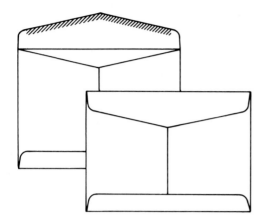

Figure 15.15: Center-seam mailer, pointed-flap style.

Open-end style. (See figure 15.16.) Types include glove, policy, scarf, and catalog. Available with a variety of closures, including gum, latex seal, button and string, and metal clasp. Papers: white and brown kraft, manila, white wove. Common sizes:

	Size number	Dimensions (in inches)
Glove	7	4 x 6⅜
	8	3⅞ x 7½
Policy	10	4⅛ x 9½
	11	4½ x 10⅜
	12	4¾ x 11
Scarf	1	4⅝ x 6¾
	3	5 x 7½
	4½	5½ x 7½
	6	5½ x 8¼
Catalog	1	6 x 9
	1¾	6½ x 9½
	3	7 x 10
	6	7½ x 10½
	8	8¼ x 11¼
	9¾	8¾ x 11¼
	10½	9 x 12
	12½	9½ x 12½
	13½	10 x 13
	14½	11½ x 14½

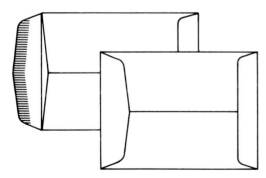

Figure 15.16: Open-end style.

Expansion mailer. (See figure 15.17.) Available in open-end and open-side styles. Open-end sizes, including expansion, range from 5 x 11 x 2 to 11 x 15 x 2; open-side sizes range from 9 x 12 x 2 to 11 x 17 x 2. Paper: brown kraft.

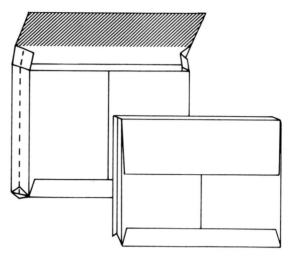

Figure 15.17: Expansion mailer.

Letter and legal. (See figure 15.18.) Papers: brown kraft, manila. Most sizes available in ungummed, gummed, or button-and-string closure styles. Common sizes:

8¾ x 11¾	9⅜ x 15
8¾ x 15	10 x 15
9½ x 11¾	13 x 17
9½ x 12	

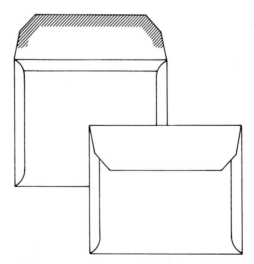

Figure 15.18: Letter and legal size mailers.

SPECIAL-PURPOSE ENVELOPES

Besides the selected special-purpose envelopes discussed and illustrated below, envelopes are available either in stock or made-to-order for every purpose. These include payroll and coin envelopes; packing list envelopes with the back gummed for affixing to packages; long, open-end policy jackets with or without windows; air mailers in lightweight papers, printed with a red and blue border; cushioned mailers; X ray and negative envelopes; and a wide variety of transparent envelopes in glassine and other materials.

Drug-pay-theater. (See figure 15.19.) Papers: white wove; pay envelopes also available in manila. Sizes:

	Size number	Dimensions (in inches)
Drug	1	$1\frac{3}{4}$ x $2\frac{7}{8}$
	2	$2\frac{1}{16}$ x $3\frac{1}{2}$
	3	$2\frac{5}{16}$ x $3\frac{5}{8}$
Pay	2	$2\frac{1}{2}$ x $4\frac{1}{4}$
Theater	3	$1\frac{15}{16}$ x $4\frac{7}{16}$
	4	$2\frac{1}{8}$ x $4\frac{3}{4}$

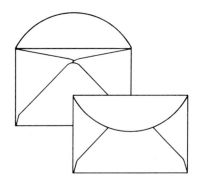

Figure 15.19: Drug-pay-theater envelopes.

No-bend mailer. (See figure 5.20.) Designed for mailing photographs and other materials that must not be folded. Sizes range from $6\frac{3}{4}$ x $8\frac{3}{4}$ to $11\frac{3}{4}$ x $14\frac{3}{4}$. Paper: strong, white board.

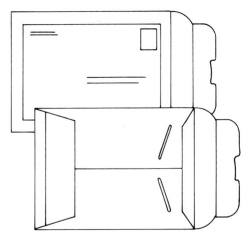

Figure 15.20: No-bend mailer.

Interoffice or messenger service. (See figure 5.21.) Paper: brown kraft. Available with metal clasp, button-and-string, and snap closures. Sizes:

$9\frac{1}{2}$ x $12\frac{1}{2}$
10 x 13

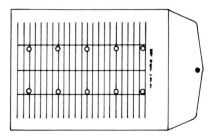

Figure 15.21: Interoffice or messenger service envelope.

Banker's flap. (See figure 5.22.) Designed for mailing important documents such as bank statements and checks. The deep flap and extra-wide gumming give the contents extra protection. Paper: brown kraft. Available with or without windows. Sizes:

Size number	Dimensions (in inches)
$7\frac{3}{4}$	$3\frac{7}{8}$ x $7\frac{1}{2}$
9	$3\frac{7}{8}$ x $8\frac{7}{8}$
10	$4\frac{1}{8}$ x $9\frac{1}{2}$
$10\frac{1}{2}$	$4\frac{1}{2}$ x $9\frac{1}{2}$
11	$4\frac{1}{2}$ x $10\frac{3}{8}$
12	$4\frac{3}{4}$ x 11
14	5 x $11\frac{1}{2}$
16	6 x 12

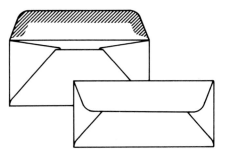

Figure 15.22: Banker's flap style.

Safety-fold. (See figure 15.23.) At both top and bottom, part of the body of the envelope is folded over to form part of the flap, so that the envelope is completely sealed at all corners. Paper: brown kraft. Common sizes:

5 x 11	6 x 12	10 x 15
5 x $11\frac{1}{2}$	9 x 12	$11\frac{1}{2}$ x 16
$5\frac{1}{2}$ x $11\frac{1}{2}$	10 x 13	12 x 18

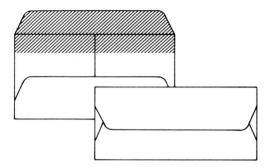

Figure 15.23: Safety-fold envelope.

Two-compartment. (See figure 15.24.) Using this type of envelope, available in two styles, assures that third-class materials and a first-class covering letter will arrive together. Available with or without window on first-class envelopes. Sizes:

7½ x 10½	10 x 13
9 x 12	11½ x 14½
9½ x 12½	

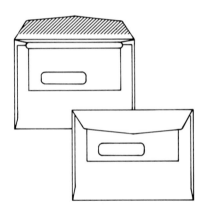

Figure 15.24: Two-compartment envelopes.

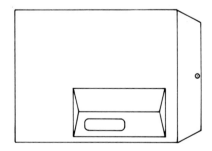

Send-and-return. (See figure 15.25.) This type of envelope serves the purpose of two. The style in 15.25A, shown before use at the left, is first sent with the wide flap tucked in (center). On the return trip, the flap, which is printed with the return address, is sealed over the front of the envelope, as shown at the right. In another style, 15.25B, the wide flap, shown open at left, is sealed by a gummed tab on the first trip (center). For the return trip, the flap is detached along a scored line, exposing the return address (right). This leaves a narrow, gummed flap, which is sealed. Common sizes:

Size number	Dimensions (in inches)
6	3⅜ x 5¹³⁄₁₆
6¼	3½ x 6
6½	3½ x 6½
6¾	3⅝ x 6½

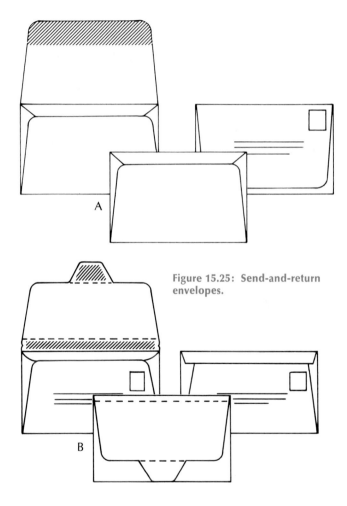

Figure 15.25: Send-and-return envelopes.

TRADE PRACTICES

16

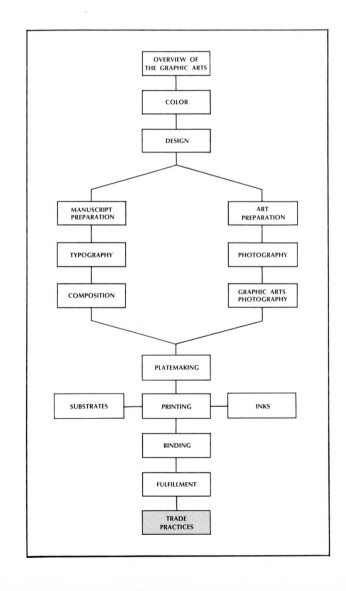

PLANNING AND BUYING A PRINTING JOB

Jay Wieder, RETIRED, SUDLER & HENNESSEY, INC.

Every production manager is familiar with the phrase, "I need an estimate for this job—and I need it tomorrow." All too often this demand is made with the slight change of "today" for "tomorrow."

Although a very simple job (such as a four-page black-and-white or two-color folder) can be estimated rapidly, a more complex job requires time for thinking and planning. If the printer is called in before the job is planned and before specifications are drawn up, it may be necessary to re-estimate the job at a later date, causing complications, delay, and embarrassment to all concerned.

PRELIMINARY STEPS

Many decisions must be made before a job can be sent out for an estimate. The art director or designer, production manager, and editor or writer should discuss the layout of the job to clarify all questions and avoid impracticalities. The discussion should cover such basic questions as:

• How many and what size pages?

• How many four-color illustrations in the piece?

• What will be the form of the art—will it be transparency or reflective art? If transparency, 35mm—or larger? How many units can be shot in the same focus?

• What stock—coated, dull-coated, or antique, for example—will be used? What weight of stock? (Consideration should be given to the folding quality and opacity of the stock.)

• What type of cover? Will it be a self-cover, or printed separately of a different or heavier stock? Should the cover be varnished or laminated?

• What type of binding? Possibilities might be adhesive, sewn, mechanical, and so on.

When the basic format is set, the next step should

SUDLER & HENNESSEY INCORPORATED / 130 E. 59 ST. **S&H** NEW YORK, NEW YORK 10022 / PHONE: (212) 751-1250

JOB SPECIFICATION SHEET

CLIENT: Lawrence & Landon Laboratories   DATE: 4/18/79

PRODUCT: Antibiotic Monograph No. 4   JOB NO.: 5154

DESCRIPTION: Full Color Brochure

QUANTITY: 60,000

FLAT SIZE:

TRIM SIZE: 16 pages plus cover - 8" x 8" plus bleed

STOCK: COVER: 80 lb. Mead B&W Coated Cover
       TEXT: 80 lb. Mead B&W Coated Text Weight

PRINTING: 4 color process throughout - see layout

FINISHING: Score cover - fold and bind with 2 saddle stitches

BLUES & COLOR PROOFS: 3 sets of blues and color proofs for OK

SPECIAL INSTRUCTIONS: Paper band in lots of 50

SAMPLES: 75 Samples to Sudler & Hennessey, Inc.

DELIVERY: Pack in cartons. Delivery F.O.B. Clifton, N.J.

Figure 16.1: Sample job specification sheet.

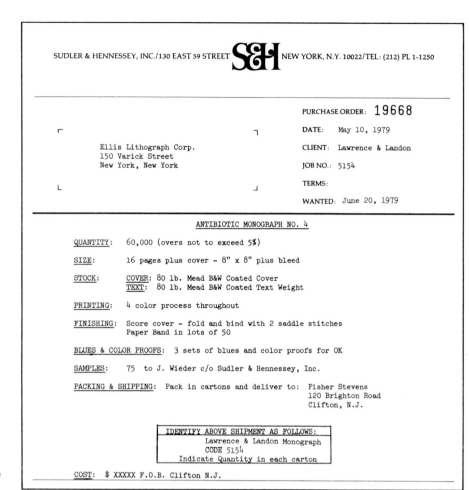

SUDLER & HENNESSEY, INC./130 EAST 59 STREET   S&H   NEW YORK, N.Y. 10022/TEL: (212) PL 1-1250

PURCHASE ORDER: 19668

DATE: May 10, 1979

Ellis Lithograph Corp.
150 Varick Street
New York, New York

CLIENT: Lawrence & Landon

JOB NO.:   5154

TERMS:

WANTED: June 20, 1979

ANTIBIOTIC MONOGRAPH NO. 4

QUANTITY: 60,000 (overs not to exceed 5%)

SIZE: 16 pages plus cover - 8" x 8" plus bleed

STOCK: COVER: 80 lb. Mead B&W Coated Cover
         TEXT: 80 lb. Mead B&W Coated Text Weight

PRINTING: 4 color process throughout

FINISHING: Score cover - fold and bind with 2 saddle stitches
             Paper Band in lots of 50

BLUES & COLOR PROOFS: 3 sets of blues and color proofs for OK

SAMPLES: 75 to J. Wieder c/o Sudler & Hennessey, Inc.

PACKING & SHIPPING: Pack in cartons and deliver to: Fisher Stevens
                                                        120 Brighton Road
                                                        Clifton, N.J.

IDENTIFY ABOVE SHIPMENT AS FOLLOWS:
Lawrence & Landon Monograph
CODE 5154
Indicate Quantity in each carton

COST: $ XXXXX F.O.B. Clifton N.J.

Figure 16.2: Sample purchase order.

be the preparation of a dummy—particularly when a job is being prepared for a client's approval. If, during the earlier discussions, there were questions as to stock weight, or binding, or type of cover, it would be wise to have alternate versions of the dummy made. The dummy shows how the booklet or brochure or pamphlet will look and feel, and acts as a vehicle to be shown to the client. It determines the final form of the stock, the binding, and the physical appearance of the job.

CHOOSING A PRINTER

When the basic information for estimating the job is complete, it should be prepared for prospective printers. An efficient and expeditious method is to use a job specification sheet like the one shown in figure 16.1.

It is wise to obtain at least three competitive estimates. Several factors determine the selection of printers to be called in. They should be equipped for the required printing process—web or sheet-fed, for example. They should be big enough, but not too big, to handle the quantity to be printed. They should have a reputation for integrity and reliability and inspire confidence. Finally, they should be able to meet the proposed schedules.

As the estimates come in, suggestions made by the printers should be considered: they may expedite the job, improve upon it, or economize. A slight change in trim size, for example, can make a big difference in cost. The estimates must be checked to see that they reflect packing, shipping, and delivery costs. For a big job these costs can be substantial.

When all the estimates are in, a determination must be made as to which printer should receive the order. Price is an important factor—but not necessarily the deciding one. Personal experience and judgment enter into the decision. When the job is finally authorized and the estimate approved, the selected printer is duly informed.

ORDERING THE STOCK

The first important business is to place an order for stock, to assure delivery prior to the scheduled press date. Stock often takes several weeks for delivery, and a late delivery can ruin the schedule for the job.

Once the stock has been ordered, the production manager must be informed immediately if there should be any change from the original specifications. Certain changes can be made within a reasonable amount of time, but a late change in size or number of pages can be disastrous. It is therefore incumbent on all concerned with the job to remain in close communication throughout its preparation.

PREPARING THE PURCHASE ORDER

The importance of the purchase order cannot be overestimated. Not only does it summarize all the specifications and requirements of the job, but it also acts as the printer's guide throughout all the departments in his plant, assuring proper fulfillment of the order.

It should be issued to the printer as promptly as possible to avoid any misunderstandings. It should be thorough and complete, leaving nothing to chance or imagination. In addition to the basic specifications, it should include the number of blueprints to be submitted, the number of sets of press proofs to be sent for approval, special banding (if applicable), any special packing instructions, and the cost of the job. Shipping instructions may be included, or they may be communicated at a later date. Figure 16.2 is a sample purchase order, based on the specifications illustrated in figure 16.1.

CONCLUSION

This article has attempted to describe the basic ingredients for the planning and purchasing of a printing job. However, no recipe for this procedure is ever really complete without the careful and thorough supervision by the chef. There is no substitute for thoroughness, conscientiousness, good judgment, and experience. Foresight and experience go hand in hand, and each problem requires its own solutions.

PRINTER-CUSTOMER RELATIONS

Paul D. Doebler, PUBLISHING MANAGEMENT CONSULTANT

Relationships between printing buyers and the companies that supply them have probably never been as unsettled as they have been during the past decade. The shortages of the early 1970's and rapidly rising prices in recent years have upset operations and budgets. This situation has created uncertainties in the graphic arts marketplace and may bring some new twists in long-term trends.

The fundamental dilemma facing printers and printing buyers lies in how to handle the unpredictably of the market. Prices are so unstable that comprehensive planning of budgets and writing of contracts has become hazardous at best, and in some cases is almost impossible.

For many years throughout the printing industries, long-term contract buying has been spreading gradually at the expense of the traditional single-job bidding system of obtaining individual items as needed. Printing of periodicals has been done under long-term contract arrangements for as long as anyone can remember, and large buyers of standard items such as stationery and business forms have for many years purchased under such agreements. Other companies have set up contractual arrangements for the production of their thousands of informational bulletins and technical literature, material which was not yet conceived or written when the contract was negotiated but which would be produced in standardized formats when the time came. In the last few years, such traditional job buyers as book publishers, who typically treat each book as an individual project, have begun applying this principle to their purchase of paper and manufacturing services.

Such contracts have enabled the printing industry to advance technologically well beyond what would have been possible under the single-job buying concept. Printers with long-term contracts have been able to arrange financing of expensive new presses, binding lines, typesetting systems, and other machinery because they had firm commitments for business to pay for the investments. Their customers, of course, have benefited immeasurably from the rapid introduction of web offset, photocomposition, adhesive binding, and other new techniques which have improved quality and lowered production costs while handling ever larger volumes of work.

Recently, however, shortages and inflation have tended to undermine the basis on which such contracts are written—the ability to predict some distance into the future what costs of printed materials will be when they are manufactured. This uncertainty has led many graphic arts companies to rethink their basic business strategy for the years ahead. For example, book manufacturers, who have pleaded for years with their publisher customers to move toward standardization and contract purchasing, have become aware of the need to change their thinking for a time and to consider short-term adaptation to evolving conditions, rather than long-range planning. Some paper companies, during recent years, have asked customers to order paper farther in advance but to accept delivery at the prevailing price at the time of delivery, a level which could not be predicted at the time of order.

Pressures remain in the graphic arts industry for a better system than single-job bidding. One is the inherent high cost of handling involved in single-job bidding. Each job must be treated as a unique project even though it may be utterly routine; this duplication costs a great deal in executive and clerical time and paperwork throughout the supplier network as well as the buyer's office.

Another is the pronounced specialization prevalent among printers today. In area after area, highly specialized producers who concentrate on producing a limited range of products have gained control of large volumes of the available work. Over the last 30 years, many types of printing have become concentrated in specialist plants—books, magazines, catalogs, directories, greeting cards, business forms, black-and-white correspondence and office communications, and various specialties such as playing cards and calendars. Such plants operate best when huge amounts of similar work are manufactured in a continual stream, a requirement which does not fit well with customized job-bid purchasing by customers.

A third force is the gradual standardization of many printed products, a trend which has been fostered in large part by the specialization movement with its highly productive special-purpose equipment. Business forms are a prime example of this standardization. Years ago every company had its own set of forms which were produced individually by a local printer. Then new techniques of forms manufacturing enabled a few national suppliers to produce standard forms usable in all kinds of companies. For special needs, the forms manufacturers developed standardized procedures for adjusting the forms to individual needs while retaining the basic economies of mass manufacture. Today business forms are sold both to companies directly and through retail stationery stores as standard product lines, making it sometimes possible for small businesses to operate without having to print anything other than stationery.

This last trend may afford an alternative to contract purchasing in other areas as well. If standardization of printed products were to develop far enough to fill the needs of most users, then printers could offer product lines which could be priced in the open market through published price lists.

An example of a relatively new development in the book industry is instructive here. One book manufacturer has developed a series of "standard book plans" which are offered to publishers on a price-list basis. Each plan sets forth standardized specifications for a particular kind and format of book—a fixed trim size, binding, cover construction, and so on. Certain choices are given the customers: they may choose from several standard papers and cover materials, for instance. For books manufactured under these plans, the customer can calculate the cost of manufacture from the price list.

Such principles could be applied to many kinds of relatively routine products. If the structure of such products were stabilized, prices could be isolated and treated separately as an independent variable. This system would permit the purchase of many printed materials on a basis similar to that used for other business and industrial commodities in open markets, where prices fluctuate without affecting other conditions of the buying-selling relationship.

If, as some believe, we are leaving an era of consumption for a new era of conservation of economic resources, then basic changes such as these are likely in the relationships of printing buyers and sellers.

METRICATION AND THE GRAPHIC ARTS INDUSTRY
Clive A. Cameron, PRINTING INDUSTRIES RESEARCH ASSOCIATION

The earliest civilizations, in addition to their native tongues, needed another language, a numeric language, in order to trade and barter and count the head of cattle. As people became more settled they needed to build permanent homes. The straw, logs, or stones of the most primitive shelter had to be measured if it was to stand firmly and look habitable. Thus, from the earliest times, weights and measures developed and increased in importance concomitantly with the growth of civilization.

The first linear measurements, based on the various parts and proportions of the body, have passed through the ages virtually unchanged. The digit, hand, foot, and the fathom—the distance between a man's outstretched arms—are just a few examples.

Although measurement of weight and volume was a much later development, the use of weights and scales has a long history. One of the earliest units of weight was the seed, such as the grain from wheat or some specified seed native to a particular region—for example, the carob seed, from which the "carat" was derived. But the majority of trading and commercial exchange was done by counting and measuring by volume, while accurate weighing was restricted to gold and silver and other precious metals.

Gradually, from these earlier civilizations and empires, Sumerian, Egyptian, and Roman, there evolved a conglomeration of measurements based on decimal, duodecimal, and sexagesimal units, the same system of measurements which, with only minor modifications, is used extensively in most of the English-speaking countries to the present day.

ESTABLISHMENT OF THE METRIC SYSTEM

Unlike other systems of measurement which gradually evolved through use and favor, the metric system was developed and planned.

The seventeenth and eighteenth centuries were times of extraordinary advance in scientific thinking and methods. However, the scientists were handicapped in communicating their discoveries by the lack of an international standard of measurement. A measurement system that could be used for all purposes and all groups, scientific, technical, engineering, educational, and commercial, was obviously desirable.

In 1790, the National Assembly in France appointed a committee to develop a system of weights and measures. After considering several proposals, they decided to use the quadrant of the meridian circle as an initial base. The distance between Dunkirk and Barcelona was accurately surveyed and measured; then the distance from the North Pole to the equator was projected by calculation to determine the length of the meridian quadrant. This length was divided into 10 million parts. The name given to this new unit of linear measurement was the "meter" (from the Greek word *metron*, meaning "measure").

When the metric system was first established it was confined to the basic requirements of length, volume, and weight. However, the rapid growth of science and industry brought about the need for the measurement of other physical quantities. In 1900, the metric system was based on the meter, kilogram, and second units (MKS). Soon after, the ampere was added (MKSA); and by 1954 the kelvin and the candela were also added. In 1960 at the International Weights and Measures Conference (CGPM) this system was formalized under the title "Le Système International d'Unités," commonly referred to as Standard International (SI).

There are now three classes of SI units: base units, derived units, and supplementary units. The *base units* of the metric system are: *meter* (m), unit of length; *kilogram* (kg), unit of mass; *second* (s), unit of time; *ampere* (A), unit of electric current; *kelvin* (K), unit of thermodynamic temperature, although degrees Celsius (°C) is commonly used; *candela* (cd), unit of luminous intensity; and *mole* (mol), which in physical chemistry and molecular physics is the unit of amount of substance. Prefixes are attached to the name of the base unit to describe larger or smaller values; thus, one kilometer (km) is 1,000 meters; one millimeter (mm) is one-thousandth (0.001) of a meter. The base units may be combined to create *derived units*, for example: *square meter* (m^2) for area; *meter per second* (m/s) for velocity. The *supplementary units* are purely geometrical units: *radian*, unit of plane angle; and *steradian*, unit of solid angle.

THE METRIC SYSTEM IN THE UNITED STATES

The Continental Congress introduced decimal coinage in 1785, but when the French tried to impose their revolutionary new metric measurements on their ally in the New World, they ran into firm opposition. Congress was caught between a decimal system based on the inch and foot, proposed by Thomas Jefferson, and the French importation. Congress made no decision and, in the absence of legislation, there was no change from the traditional English system.

In his message to Congress in 1816, President Madison said in part that "no adequate provision has yet been made for the uniformity of weights and measures contemplated by the Constitution." Congress immediately referred the matter to the Secretary of State, John Quincy Adams, who began a thorough analysis of the problem. A House committee studied the problem at the same time and submitted a report advising the adoption of Jefferson's plan. Again Congress took no action. Two years later Adams, although personally convinced of the virtues of the metric system, advised Congress not to adopt it "because it would be hazardous to deviate from the practice of Great Britain." Congress readily accepted his recommendations.

The only important metric legislation to be approved by Congress in the nineteenth century was a bill in 1866 which made the use of the metric system legally permissible. It is interesting to quote the committee report on this bill for its lucid prophesy: ". . . while the United States was the first to move in the direction of a decimal system [for currency], the effect of the delay of this Government has been to render it possible that the United States will be among the last in the columns of nations to take this great step in civilization." Which, of course, proved correct. In 1875, however, the United States was a signatory to the Treaty of the Metre, signed in Paris by 17 nations, which set up machinery for the standardization of metric weights and measures.

In recent years the United States has moved closer to metrication. In 1968, the Metric Systems Study Act was signed into law by President Johnson. It provided for a three-year study to determine the effect of extending the use of metric units of measurement in the United States. Following the report of the study committee in 1971, Secretary of Commerce Stans recommended a gradual changeover to the metric system over a ten-year period, resulting in considerable planning activity on the part of industry, commerce, and educational authorities. An education bill passed by Congress in 1974, acknowledging that the use of the metric system is increasing worldwide and will become the dominant system in the United States, provided funds to encourage schools and agencies to prepare students to use the system more readily.

In December of 1975, President Ford signed into law the Metric Conversion Act. The law indicates that the United States is adopting the metric-SI system in order to harmonize its system of measurement with the rest of the world and that it will do so on a voluntary basis. A 17-member United States Metric Board was established to coordinate voluntary conversion.

With the signing of the Metric Conversion Act of 1975, the United States was officially on its way toward metrication, but progress has been slow. The government's role is still being debated, and there is much public resistance to the change. However, because of the interdependence of American and foreign industry, it seems likely that the metric system will ultimately be adopted. A discussion of some of the problems facing the graphic arts industry follows.

PAPER STANDARDS

The most common or standard paper size in North America is 8½″ x 11″. The majority of business stationery, magazines, school notebooks, publicity folders, business forms, etc., falls into this category. This size, or multiples thereof, consequently dictates the sizes of printing presses, plates, folders, and, to some extent, other ancillary equipment.

But why a size of 8½″ x 11″? In the latter part of 1921 a committee on the simplification of paper sizes was appointed to work with the Bureau of Standards as part of President Hoover's program for the elimination of waste in industry. This committee, which was largely made up of representatives from the printing paper and related industries, was to concern itself with the standardization of sizes and types of paper used in books, magazines, forms, newspapers, etc., as well as in bond paper and letterheads. The committee recommended the following basic sizes for bond and writing papers for general printing and lithography: 17″ x 22″, 17″ x 28″, 19″ x 24″, 22″ x 34″, 28″ x 34″, and 24″ x 36″. It does not appear, even in the selection of 8½″ x 11″ paper (a subdivision of 17″ x 22″), that any analysis was made to prove this size optimal for commercial letterheads. The selection was made merely to reduce paper inventories: this size would cut from a basic size of stock with no trimming waste.

At about the same time the Permanent Conference on Printing established the 8½″ x 10″ standard letter size for all agencies of the United States Government. Again no records show the basis upon which this standard was developed. This 50-year-old standard was officially discarded a few years ago.

In Germany, standards for industry were established in 1922. The work of a technical subcommittee resulted, after much careful thought, in the establishment of paper sizes on a thoroughly systematic basis. These standards for paper, known as DIN (Deutsche Industrie Normen) sizes, were based on the metric system. Eventually it was proposed that these standard sizes should receive international acceptance by being incorporated into those adopted by the International Organization for Standardization (ISO).

Metric sizes of paper

The ISO standards are based on a unique property of a rectangle whose sides are in the ratio of one to the square root of two (1 : 1.414). Regardless of how many times such a rectangular sheet is folded (halving the longer sides), the subdivisions always remain in the same constant proportion. Use of the ISO series considerably eases the resizing of art work, drawings, and photographs, since the proportions are maintained.

The basic standard sheet, designated A0 (A-zero), measures 841 x 1,189 mm (33.1″ x 46.8″), an area of one square meter. Each numeral after the series initial A indicates a halving of the previous area. Thus A1 (594 x 841 mm) is one-half, A2 (420 x 594 mm) is one-quarter, and A3 (297 x 420 mm) is one-eighth of A0. A4, which measures 210 x 297 mm (8.27″ x 11.69″), is the common European and British letterhead and publication size. For sheet sizes larger than A0, the numeral is *prefixed* to the letter; thus 2A is twice as large as A0 (that is, 1,189 x 1,682 mm).

All the preceding A sizes are trimmed sizes. Those prefixed R are untrimmed stock sizes from which the A series is obtained; another series, prefixed SR, is suitable for work requiring extra bleed or extra trim. Thus, A0 (841 x 1,189 mm) is trimmed, RA0 (860 x 1,200 mm) is with normal trim, and SRA0 (900 x 1,280 mm) is with extra trim.

The ISO series includes other letter designations, namely B, C, and (rarely) D. The B series is normally used for posters and other printed items such as wall charts where the difference in size of the larger sheets in the A series represents too large a jump. The basic B size B0 is 1,000 x 1,414 mm. The C series is used for folders, postcards, and most conveniently for envelopes. The A, B, and C sheets retain the same geometrical relationship. The C series of envelope sizes is suitable for insertion of A series sheets either flat or folded; for example, a C6 envelope will take an A6 sheet flat, an A5 sheet folded once, or an A4 sheet folded twice, and so on.

The Universal Postal Union has agreed on some specifications to aid the international handling of mail. To meet these requirements envelopes should be:

• At least 90 x 140 mm and not larger than 120 x 235 mm.

• Oblong in shape with the longer side at least 1.414 times the shorter.

• Made from paper weighing at least 63 g/m².

Metric weights of paper

What is meant by "paper weighing at least 63 g/m²"? Manufacturers and users of paper must define its substance, or weight, as well as its size.

Let us think for a moment about the customary method of selecting paper in the United States. Although our familiarity allows us to handle it quite easily, it is practically without logic or reason. At present, papermakers and their customers describe, sell, and purchase paper by pound weight per ream. For example, "70-pound book" indicates that 500 sheets of book paper, basic size 25″ x 38″, weighs 70 pounds; or 1,000 sheets weigh 140 pounds, abbreviated 140M. However 1,000 sheets of this same paper in a basic size of 23″ x 35″ would weigh 119 pounds. The confusion here arises from the fact that printing papers have different basic sizes and correspondingly different basis weights. For example, a 24-pound bond (basic size 17″ x 22″) is equivalent to a 60-pound book (basic size 25″ x 38″).

A change to metrication and the introduction of ISO paper sizes offers an improved system for measuring paper size and basis weight because there is a logical connection between them. The metric method of expressing the weight of paper is in grams per square meter (g/m²). The basis weight, or *grammage*, of paper is the same, whatever the size and number of sheets. It is derived from the weight of a single sheet the area of which is one square meter (A0). For example, an onionskin will be 28 g/m², or grammage 28; newsprint, grammage 52; the Postal Union requires paper weighing at least grammage 63 (answering the question posed above); writing bond is grammage 75; a coated book, grammage 140; and cover stock, grammage 280. In the example above, both

24-pound bond and 60-pound book would be grammage 90; both weigh 90 grams per square meter.

One further point: In setting up a standard series of basis weights, geometric progressions known as the R20 and R40 series are used. Each basis weight in the R20 series is obtained by multiplying the previous one by the 20th root of 10, or 1.12; the R40 factor is the 40th root of 10. The R20 series yields, for example, the following weights: 20, 22.4, 25, 28, 31.5, 40 g/m², and so on. The R40 series offers twice the number of intermediary sizes to allow for special requirements. Unlike an arithmetic series, a geometric series offers a greater choice at the lower or lighter end of its scale.

TYPOGRAPHY

The typographical measurements currently used are so well established, ingrained, and widely understood in the English-speaking world that it would be a bold prophet who would predict their demise even if we were to fully embrace most other aspects of the metric system.

The pica-point system was formulated by a Frenchman, Fournier, in the early eighteenth century and refined in the United States in 1886. By 1892 the newly formed American Type Founders' Company had taken over 23 foundries whose output, based on the new system, then amounted to 85 percent of the total for the United States. It has been used since that time without change.

A great deal has been written but very little achieved in the area of metric standardization of typographic measurements. In 1811 Napoleon commissioned Firmin Didot, a typefounder and typographer, to engrave a series of types based on the metric system, but they were never widely used.

Even though opponents of metrication of composition argue that metric typography for metal typesetting machines is technically and financially impossible, metrication has, in fact, been accomplished in these areas of composition. In the 1950's the MeterKonKordanz, a system in which 48 points are exactly equal to 18 mm, was introduced by Letouzey in his firm at Bourg-la-Reine in France. In 1954 Heinrich Schoenig was in charge of the changeover to a metric system at his firm in West Germany. Two years later, the GEG-Druckerei, Hamburg, followed Schoenig's example. In both cases Linotype and Monotype equipment was involved, the adjustments required for the composing equipment were comparatively simple, and the equipment manufacturers gave their full cooperation. It would be only fair to add that GEG-Druckerei, after 13 years, decided to abandon metrics and return to the point system.

The above systems and all others proposed were based on a conversion of the Didot point to a metric equivalent; for instance, one Didot point equals 0.375 mm, 12 equal 4.5 mm, and so on.

The now well-established techniques of phototypesetting and computer-assisted composition have removed the special restrictions imposed by customary typographical measurements. The full advantages of such developments can be realized only if a new approach is used, relating typographical measurements directly to visual appearance.

THE EFFECT ON CAPITAL EQUIPMENT

The great majority of printed material in the United States is based on the "quarto" (8½" x 11") standard. If it were to be replaced by the nearest ISO metric equivalent, the A4 size (210 x 297 mm or 8¼" x 11⅝"), the apparently modest difference between the two standards would be quite significant.

Graphic arts machinery, office equipment, and furniture, such as copying machines, duplicators, and filing cabinets, are designed to give an optimum fit to the customary 8½" x 11" standard. The sizes of sheet-fed presses also are designed as a multiple of this standard. The same principle applies to the width and, more significantly, to the nonadjustable cut-off length of reel-fed rotary presses. If the A4 size replaced the 8½" x 11" standard it would inevitably mean phasing out much capital equipment.

The replacing of manufacturing machinery in the printing industry would obviously take a long time. It would not be a serious problem with equipment that is infinitely variable up to its maximum size on machines such as sheet-fed presses, camera copy boards, and guillotines. Although perhaps not operating at maximum efficiency during the period of transition, gauges and scales could be changed to metric quite easily.

A changeover requires considerable planning. Almost certainly, during the transition, customary and metric equipment would be in use at the same time and spare parts would require extra storage and dual inventories. During World War I, the French were grateful when the Americans supplied them with ammunition, but not very happy when they found they had been supplied with 6-inch (152-mm) shells for their 150-mm guns!

CHANGING TO THE METRIC SYSTEM

The impact of metric change has so far been modest in the United States. In the printing and allied industries it has been insignificant. It is of little persuasion to the American printer to learn that ISO metric paper sizes have been in common usage in Europe for more than 50 years and in the United Kingdom for more than 15. We can hardly expect American press manufacturers to build presses for metric specifications when there is no demand for them, or graphic art designers to create material in metric formats when there is no equipment on which it can be produced conveniently. But the purpose of change is not just for change. A quick glance at one of the major offset plate manufacturer's catalogs shows over 200 sizes. This is a ludicrous situation that applies to other printing materials. It indicates the urgent need for national standards which logically should be based on the metric system of measurements.

The Metric Conversion Act of 1975 gave impetus to what some believed was a long-overdue step in the United States. Even before its passage, companies such as General Motors, Caterpillar Tractor, Ford, Timken Roller Bearing, and the optical, photographic, and pharmaceutical industries had converted or were in the process of converting. In the graphic arts and related industries, companies such as Xerox and IBM, Honeywell, Rockwell, and Weyerhauser were also in the process of converting. Many smaller companies which do not trade overseas, however, have been reluctant to proceed. Distrust of conversion apparently lingers and, despite the endorsement of the changeover by the government, there are still calls for further consideration of the issue.

The total changeover, of course, requires a tremendous overall planning effort. It is necessary to review and assess, on an industry-sector basis, every existing standard to determine what is to be done to conform to a metric-SI system. With the cooperation of industry and appropriate trade associations for each sector, it is the role of the United States Metric Board to coordinate this effort.

The advantages in using the metric standard may not seem obvious at first, but they should soon assert and prove themselves. The increased efficiency through technical innovations, the opportunity for improvement in design, the eventual reduction in inventory, and a common standard for industry and commerce on an international scale are but a few of the advantages to be considered.

COPYRIGHTS, PATENTS, TRADEMARKS, AND TRADE SECRETS

Robert R. Strack, EISENMAN, ALLSOPP & STRACK

Copyrights, patents, trademarks, and trade secrets often support rags-to-riches dreams that are far more illusory than is commonly appreciated. The exclusive right to copy a poorly painted picture, to prevent others from making or selling a poorly designed machine, to use an unintelligible logo, or to keep secret the composition of an ineffective drug is of little value. The true value of any item necessarily lies in the quality of the item itself; the various forms of protection available under the law will not necessarily enhance its value. However, the various forms of protection will establish clear limits defining the extent of the owner's interest, offer the commercial advantage of exclusivity, and often serve to render the property more marketable or better subject to commercial exploitation.

Each of these areas—copyrights, patents, trademarks, and trade secrets—is designed to yield a specific type of limited protection from unauthorized competitors. Secrets have been used to retain exclusive knowledge since people first began to communicate. Trademarks, as a tool of commerce, must have been adopted by the earliest traders. Common law copyright, protecting creative efforts in artistic works and writings, has a heritage long recognized by the courts. In contrast, patents and statutory copyright have been developed by governments through legislation, in order to encourage and protect individuals, companies, and organizations, enabling them to justify public exposure of the fruits of their efforts and allowing society to benefit from the creative efforts of its gifted members.

A considerable body of law has developed over the years in all these fields. Attorneys now specialize in copyright, patent, and trademark law. The Patent Offices of the United States and most foreign countries require testing and registration of qualified individuals before permitting them to represent others. In addition, inventors, authors, and trademark owners are entitled to represent themselves before the appropriate government body. As with all complex fields, it is advisable to seek expert advice if problems arise. On the other hand, it is worthwhile for authors, inventors, managers, and general counsel to have sufficient background to initially evaluate a situation and know if and when aid should be sought.

Copyrights generally protect authors, artists, composers, and other creators, from the unauthorized publication of their works. Broadly, copyrights cover works of art and published or printed material. *Patents* prevent the unauthorized manufacture, use, or sale of an invention, and embrace unique processes, machines, articles of manufacture, compositions of matter, designs, and special varieties of plants. Anything that falls outside these specific categories is not appropriate subject matter for a patent. *Trademarks* differ in that they do not protect particular objects or unique characteristics; rather, they identify the origin of goods or services. They may be affixed to goods in order to notify consumers regarding the source of the goods. The essential characteristic of a trademark is that it not be confusingly similar to marks used by competitors. Finally, *trade secrets* require confidential retention of specified knowledge. This knowledge may exist within an almost unlimited area including not only technical subjects, but commercial information, customer lists, pricing information, and so on. The scope of material protectible by trade secrets is far broader than the statutorily limited areas protectible by copyrights and patents.

A discussion of the basic features of these forms of protection, the steps involved in using them, and details regarding their cost and complexity follows.

COPYRIGHTS

A copyright gives the owner the exclusive right to print, reprint, publish, copy, sell, translate, convert, arrange, adapt, deliver, or perform the copyrighted work.

In 1976 the United States Congress passed a general revision of the federal copyright law. This revision, among other things, provides for limited unauthorized photocopying for "face-to-face" classroom teaching, and for the single copying of scholarly articles for private study. Sweeping changes were also made in the duration of copyright protection. Under the old law, each copyright had a term of 28 years and was renewable for an additional 28 years. Since January 1, 1978, under the revised law, the copyright period has been extended for the lifetime of the author plus 50 years. Any copyright that was in its first term on January 1, 1978, can now be renewed upon expiration for a further term of 47 years. Copyrights in their second term, for which renewal was requested between December 31, 1976, and December 31, 1977, could have been extended to a total term of 75 years, measured from the date of first procurement.

Specific areas of protection have been classified and subdivided for handling in the Copyright Office as follows:

Non-dramatic Literary Work (TX). This broad category includes all types of works written in words (or other verbal or numerical symbols) such as fiction, nonfiction, poetry, periodicals, directories, catalogs, and advertising copy.

Work of the Visual Arts (VA). This category consists of pictorial, graphic, or sculptural works, including photographs, prints and art reproductions, maps, globes, charts, technical drawings, diagrams, and models.

Work of the Performing Arts (PA). This category includes works prepared for the purpose of being performed before an audience or indirectly by means of any device or process. Examples are: musical works including lyrics, dramatic works including music, pantomimes and choreographic works, and motion pictures and other audiovisual works.

Sound Recording (SR). This category covers works resulting from the fixation of a series of musical, spoken, or other sounds, except for the audio portions of audiovisual works.

Publication

The procedure for creating a copyright is deceptively simple. You need merely publish the work with the proper form of notice. Upon publication, the work is automatically protected. The notice should include the appropriately placed word "Copyright," the abbreviation "Copr.," or the symbol © accompanied by the name of the proprietor, and if the work is a printed literary, musical, or dramatic work, the year of first publication. A preferred form is: "Copyright, 19___, by John Doe."

The Universal Copyright Convention, in effect in the United States, enables citizens of the signatory countries to receive reciprocal rights. The notice prescribed by the Universal Copyright Convention comprises ©, the year date, and the copyright proprietor. Care must be taken that the notice appears in the proper location and is sufficiently large to be read by the naked eye. The proper owner should be identified and traceable, and pseudonyms should be avoided, if possible.

A distinction is made between common law copy-

right and the statutory copyright existing as a result of federal law. Common law copyright was recognized, both in this country and abroad, long before the statutory scheme came into being. In general, as long as a work is not published, it is protected under common law without regard to the time or other limitations of the federal statutes, and the courts will prevent the copying, publication, or use of the unpublished work, without the author's consent. In the event that an unauthorized publication takes place, the author is entitled to seek damages in court. The federal copyright law provides that certain types of work may be copyrighted prior to publication; however, an author should carefully weigh whether or not such pre-publication protection is advantageous.

Publication is the essence of copyright protection under the federal statutes. Publication takes place with the earliest date of unrestricted sale or distribution of copies of the first authorized edition. Commencing with this publication, the statutory copyright now extends, as previously noted, for the life of the author plus 50 years. The first publication must include the required copyright notice. In the absence of this copyright notice, the publication may place the work within the public domain and may prevent the subsequent obtaining of the statutory copyright. Furthermore, a publication without appropriate notice might revoke any privileges that the author may previously have had under the common law copyright.

It can be seen that on the one hand a party loses the right to copyright protection if he or she publishes without proper statutory notice, and on the other hand, he or she is not entitled to obtain copyright protection until publication with the statutory notice. In an attempt to ameliorate the possible damage done by accidental publication, a double standard has been applied by the courts, but the area is a nebulous one. The courts tend to require a general publication rather than a limited publication in order to impose the penalty of non-registerability. In contrast, it has been held that a single sale of one copy bearing the appropriate statutory notice would be sufficient to support exercise of the copyright laws.

Once a work is copyrighted, all its subsequent published forms must bear the copyright notice and include the original publication date. New editions of a previously published work should bear the original publication date, and when they contain new matter, should also bear further copyright notices which include the subsequent year dates of publication. The original copyright will protect the originally published material commencing on the date of first publication, and the subsequent copyright notices will protect all new copyrightable material commencing with the year date of this new publication. Where a copyright notice appears on a cyclopedic or other composite work, it is construed to cover all copyrightable material contained in the work.

Registration

Following publication, before action may be taken against an infringer, the work must be registered with the Register of Copyrights at the Library of Congress on one of the printed forms available there. Individual forms correspond to the four categories listed above, and each form includes clear instructions for its completion. The Register of Copyrights is extremely cooperative and will assist a registrant if requested. The appropriate forms for any of the classes may be obtained by writing to the Register of Copyrights, Library of Congress, Washington, D.C. 20559. The statutory fee for registering a copyright is $10. One copy of works not reproduced for sale must be furnished with the registration form and two copies of published works must be furnished. Certain three-dimensional works may be registered by the mere submission of photographs; other provisions are made for segmented registration of motion pictures and the like.

In rare recognition of the government's gain through participation in the registration of copyrighted works, individuals are entitled to the free mailing of copy deposits to the Register of Copyrights.

Copyrightable subject matter

In "legal" language the law states that:

Copyright protection subsists . . . in original works of authorship fixed in any tangible medium of expression, now known or later developed, from which they can be perceived, reproduced, or otherwise communicated, either directly or with the aid of a machine or device. . . . In no case does copyright protection for an original work of authorship extend to any idea, procedure, process, system, method of operation, concept, principle or discovery, regardless of the form in which it is described, explained, illustrated, or embodied in such work. (17 USCS §102)

This language may be translated broadly to mean that any original work of an author, in almost any form, is suitable subject matter for a copyright, but the protection against unauthorized copying will not extend to prohibiting use of the ideas embodied in the copyrighted material. The Copyright Office has summarized the requirements regarding what is copyrightable by indicating that a work must contain at least a certain minimum amount of authorship in the form of original literary, artistic, or musical expression. A large variety of things have been determined to be lacking in this "minimum amount of authorship."

Copyright cannot be secured for names, titles, slogans, advertising phrases, mottos, column headings, simple checklists, and the like. The format, arrangement, or typography of a blank form or similar work is not copyrightable. It is also not possible to copyright works consisting entirely of information that is common property or that contains no original authorship, such as standard calendars, height and weight charts, or tape measures.

It is important to realize that it is only the particular manner of expression an author or artist uses that is protected by copyright. The ideas, plans, methods, or systems that are described or embodied in the work are not copyrightable and consequently may be used and expanded upon with impunity by others.

As an illustration, a photographer may take a photograph of the Empire State Building from a particular angle and under particular light conditions. Another photographer may make an independent photograph from the same location at a similar angle and under similar light conditions, with the result of a substantially identical picture. Each photographer is entitled to obtain a copyright, because each has created a work of art. Both photographers have a cause of action against any third party who knowingly sets out to imitate their work, setting up a camera in the same place, angle, and light, to produce a substantially similar photograph. A requirement of copyrightability is that the treatment of the subject matter originate with the artist. In this example, neither original photographer copied from the other; they each created their own product. The third photographer was a copier.

Use and enforcement

The copyright owner has the exclusive right to reproduce the copyrighted work in copies or phonorecords, to prepare derivative works, to distribute copies or phonorecords, and to perform and/or display appropriate works publicly. The derivative works protected include translations, musical arrangements, dramatizations, fictionalizations, motion picture versions, sound recordings, art reproductions, abridgements, condensations, or any other form in which a work may be recast.

Some limitations are placed upon these broad areas of exclusivity. "Fair use" may be made for purposes of criticism, comment, news reporting, teaching, scholarship, or research. The determination of whether a use is a fair use includes consideration of: the purpose and character of the use, the nature of the copyrighted work, the amount of the work used, and the commercial effect of the use of the work. Since subjective rather than objective considerations are involved in evaluating infringement charges, it is advisable to obtain the author's consent to any questionable use.

Copyrights may be sold and assigned in whole or in part. In order to be binding against subsequent *bona fide* assignees, every assignment should be recorded in the Copyright Office. The Copyright Office has records of all copyrighted material and will provide searches of its records for a minimum of $5 per hour. Such searches might include searches for assignments, for certificates of registration, and for titles of books or songs. All material is open to public inspection at the Library of Congress and searches may be conducted personally by interested individuals.

The owner of a copyright is entitled to seek injunction restraining infringement, damages and profits, impoundment of the infringing article, and destruction of infringing copies and plates. Although they are rarely invoked, the Copyright Act also provides criminal penalties in the case of willful infringement or fraudulent copyright notice. The copyright law also provides for the recovery of full costs and attorney's fees by successful parties.

Generally, infringement is established by a side-by-side comparison of the copyrighted article and the alleged infringing article. It is a subjective determination if a sufficient degree of similarity exists to establish infringement. The particular factual situation is important; if similarities can be attributed to something other than copying, the presumption of infringement is greatly weakened. Thus, an essential element in proving infringement is that the infringer had actual access to the work copied. A defendant who is able to prove lack of access will prevail.

A common technique for establishing an infringement case lies in the inclusion of errors present in the original work. The reappearance of such errors in the alleged infringing work is obviously persuasive evidence that copying took place.

As with other types of proprietary protection, statutory copyright law is effective within the jurisdiction of the country which promulgates the law. Registration under the United States copyright law yields protection in this country. To obtain protection within other countries, one must comply with the rules of each country. Whereas registration in the United States is carried out easily by an applicant utilizing the forms discussed above, it is generally necessary to obtain assistance in order to be sure that rights are properly protected abroad. The Universal Copyright Convention is adhered to by most major countries and if publication is properly conducted, it ensures protection throughout much of the world. When publication abroad is contemplated, it should be coordinated carefully with the United States publication to be sure that neither publication adversely affects the protection available.

PATENTS

Unlike copyright protection, which provides an owner with a positive right to exclusive performance of certain acts regarding a work, a patent gives the owner the negative right to prevent others from the unauthorized manufacture, use, or sale of an invention. This is an important distinction. It is quite possible that a patent owner will be barred from using his own invention because it incorporates the prior invention, or inventions, of others.

Approximately 1,500 patents are granted each week in the United States alone. Each of these patents circumscribes a portion of an industrial art and prevents the unauthorized use of the defined subject matter. In many instances, as improvements appear, patent coverage overlaps and a number of patents dominate the use of certain devices and processes. This gives rise to the practice of licensing and cross-licensing.

Patent applications are filed at the Patent Office; correspondence is carried on with the Commissioner of Patents and Trademarks, Washington, D.C. 20231. Information regarding the requirements for patent applications, the attorneys registered to practice before the Patent Office, and other pertinent data are available in booklet form at modest cost. Such booklets include: "Patent Office Rules of Practice," the "United States Patent Law," "Guide for Patent Draftsmen," "Patents & Inventions, An Information Aid for Inventors," and a roster of "Attorneys and Agents Registered to Practice Before the United States Patent Office."

Types of patents

There are three types of patents: utility patents, design patents, and plant patents.

Basic utility patents cover new and useful processes, machines, articles of manufacture, compositions of matter, or new and useful improvements thereof. These patents are granted for an unextendable period of 17 years from the date of issuance. A government filing fee of $65 is required upon filing the application, and upon allowance there is a minimum base issue fee of approximately $110. When patent attorneys are retained for preparation and prosecution of an application, one may anticipate minimum legal fees for filing in the neighborhood of $750, and additional charges during pendency.

Design patents cover the new, original, and ornamental design of articles of manufacture. The inventor is entitled to select a term of 3 years and 6 months, 7 years, or 14 years. The government fee for filing a design patent application is $20. The issuance fees are $10 for a 3½-year term, $20 for a 7-year term, and $30 for a 14-year term. Attorney's fees for filing this type of application range upward from $200. Since design patents protect the ephemeral ornamental nature of the invention as opposed to the structural aspects which lend it functionality, they tend to overlap some of the three-dimensional materials that are suitable for copyright. Accordingly, the designer should consider the relative merits of each form of protection.

Plant patents cover new varieties of asexually reproduced plants, including cultivated sports, mutants, hybrids, and newly found seedlings, other than a tuber-propagated plant or a plant found in an uncultivated state. These patents are granted for a term of 17 years and require the same filing fees as the basic utility patents.

The patent application

Since utility patents make up the vast majority of patents issued, the discussion that follows will deal principally with the features of these patents.

In the United States, only the inventor has the right to file a patent application. This right may be, and frequently is, assigned; however, the inventor is always identified on the issued patent. If the inventor is deceased or otherwise unavailable, specified representatives may, upon presenting sufficient proof of the fact, file on his or her behalf.

The application is an original legal document combining a complete technical disclosure of the invention and a definition setting forth the desired scope of protection. The disclosure preferably comprises a discussion of the relevant prior art. It must include a sufficient description to enable those skilled in the art to practice (make use of) the invention without further guidance. A drawing or set of drawings is required whenever possible. The definition of the invention takes the form of one or more carefully worded "claims" which appear as numbered paragraphs at the end of the specification. These claims serve as the metes and bounds upon which hinge the validity of the patent in view of prior knowledge and whether an alleged infringer is actually practicing the invention. Many patentees have been unable to enforce the rights to their inventions because of defects in the critical language of the claims.

The patent application is presented to the Patent Office as a draft of the Letters Patent Document that the applicant wishes the Patent Office to grant. When it is filed, a filing receipt is issued which shows the filing date and the serial number. Serial numbers are assigned sequentially up through 999,999 and are then repeated. When the patent is finally granted, it receives a new sequentially issued patent number. By the end of the bicentennial year of 1976, more than 4,000,000 patents had been issued.

When the application is filed, it assumes the status of "patent pending." The application is kept in secret by the Patent Office and is available only to the applicant and his or her authorized representative. The Patent Office assigns each application to a group of Examiners skilled in the particular art involved. These Examiners handle each case in order of filing; frequently there is a backlog up to one year in length. The Examiner reviews the application and issues an "Office Action" citing prior art which is believed to anticipate the invention. Within three months, the applicant must file an "Amendment" refuting the Examiner's position and/or modifying the application to place it in better condition for acceptance. This procedure may be repeated until a "Final Office Action" is issued. An applicant whose position is not accepted may appeal to the Board of Appeals or Court of Customs and Patent Appeals.

Requirements for patentability

As explained above, patentable subject matter is limited by law to machines, articles of manufacture, compositions of matter, processes, designs, and certain plants. Mere ideas are not patentable; they must be given substance by incorporation into a structure or process. The inventor does not have to actually build the structure or carry out the process, but must be able to describe it in sufficient completeness to enable others skilled in the art to do so. When the invention is not physically "reduced to practice" (that is, in a complete working embodiment), the filing of the application with its complete disclosure serves as a constructive "reduction to practice."

In addition to falling within the statutory categories, an invention must satisfy criteria of novelty and unobviousness. It is too late to file a patent application if someone else is the first inventor; if the invention was known or used by others in this country; if it was patented or described in a printed publication in this or a foreign country before the invention thereof by the applicant; or if it was in public use or on sale in this country more than one year prior to the date of application.

Where there is conflict between parties who have filed patent applications for the same invention, priority of invention is based upon the respective dates of conception and reduction to practice of the invention. If the one who was first to conceive was last to reduce to practice, but was reasonably diligent in working on and improving the invention, he or she has priority in obtaining a patent—even if another inventor finished earlier but started later.

Although patentability does not depend upon the manner in which the invention is arrived at (a "flash of genius" is not necessary), the subject matter sought to be patented must be sufficiently different from the prior art that it would not be obvious to a person having ordinary skill in the art. It is presumed that an inventor has access to all existing publications and if a combination of the disclosures of these publications obviously yields the invention, it is not patentable.

A useful test to evaluate patentability is to compare the structure, operation, and results of the alleged invention with the prior art. An important difference in any one of these criteria suggests patentability. If there are important distinctions in all three, the possibility of patenting is very good. Furthermore, if one achieves a synergistic effect—if the combined effect of several components is greater than the individual components would suggest—this is good evidence of patentability.

Before filing a patent application, it is advisable to conduct a preliminary novelty search through the issued patents and available literature in order to determine the state of the prior art and evaluate the patentability of a likely invention. All issued patents are classified and filed according to subject matter in the Patent Office Library. They are available to the public for personal study, or professional searchers will perform novelty searches for fees ranging upward from $75. Unless the applicant is familiar with the patent law it is advisable to have a registered patent attorney evaluate the pertinence of any prior art uncovered. Although there are companies that offer service in exploiting and commercializing unpatented inventions, the highly specialized nature of patent law usually requires legal assistance. Before engaging such a company, check it with your local Better Business Bureau or similar agency.

Use and enforcement

Prosecution of a patent application in the Patent Office may require from one to three years. At present, several years may elapse before the grant of a patent. During this time, all details of the application are maintained in secret and the public is unable to determine the scope of the protection being sought. If the applicant has marked the product "Patent Pending," potential competitors are warned that a patent may issue at any time, but they cannot be sure of its strength or the degree of protection that it will provide. The applicant cannot take action against an infringer until the patent is granted; nevertheless, financially sound competitors may be loath to expand or develop an inventory that might be in direct infringement of any patent that will issue in the future, or to take any action that may subject them to patent infringement lawsuits.

When a patent has issued, it is appropriate to mark all further items embodying the invention. This marking need only include the number of the patent, and might take the form: "Patent 3,462,347." The use of patent marking is important because in the event of litigation, damages may be limited to run from the date on which an infringer actually had notice of the patent.

A patent owner may do several things with the patent: hold the invention off the market and sue any infringers that appear; selectively license others to manufacture, sell, or use the invention; or assemble the necessary capital to manufacture and sell the invention. The law has no preference for the manner in which the owner acts, except that the action must not run afoul of the antitrust laws by improperly expanding upon the patent rights with tie-in sales, restrictive covenants, or the like.

Patent licenses are essentially a contract between the patent owner and the licensee. The specific terms vary according to the desires and bargaining position of the parties. Typically, in return for royalties, the patent owner extends either exclusive or nonexclusive rights to the licensee, by authorizing the manufacture, use, or sale of the invention.

Royalty may be based upon a single payment, or periodic payments. Where the commercial value of the invention is uncertain, periodic payments may be based upon a percentage of net sales. Because of the wide variety of inventions, there is no rule of thumb regarding a fair royalty rate. A rate of a fractional percent may be excellent in some instances involving large volumes, while 25 percent or more is reasonable where only a few high-priced items are involved. Royalties between 3 percent and 5 percent are most commonly encountered.

A patent licensor should require periodic reports, the right to verify a licensee's accounts, use of the patent marking where appropriate, prompt payment of royalties, penalties for breach of terms, a minimum annual royalty to sustain the license, and licensee diligence in exploitation of the invention. On the other hand, a patent licensee should seek to obtain assurance that the patent owner will sue infringers, a warranty that practicing the invention will not result in infringing other patents, agreement that royalties will terminate if the patent is subsequently ruled invalid by any court, rights under any improvement patents, and the right to assign their position to others in the event of a sale of the business.

A basic licensing consideration at the present time involves the tax effects of the license. An inventor is entitled to capital gains treatment in the event of a complete sale or in the event of issuance of an exclusive license. Capital gains treatment is also available where the inventor has transferred ownership rights to a company in which he or she has only a specified minority interest. Where large proceeds are anticipated, a patent owner should carefully consider the tax results of any agreement.

Where agreement on a license is not possible, or where the patent owner has insisted without avail that an alleged infringer cease and desist from infringing acts, the remedy lies in the federal courts. Both plaintiff and defendant should approach patent litigation with caution; it is a field requiring specialized technical and legal skills. Litigation costs for either party rank second only to costs in antitrust suits. The plaintiff patent owner places the validity of the patent in jeopardy and the defendant infringer runs the risk of being enjoined from further use of the alleged invention. A successful patentee is entitled to injunction relief, damages, lost profits, and attorney's fees.

Each patent suit involves two basic issues: whether or not the patent is valid, and whether or not the defendant's acts come within the terms or scope of the patent. The burden of establishing invalidity is upon the defendant inasmuch as the patent is *prima facie* valid. In contrast, the burden of establishing the defendant's infringing acts falls upon the plaintiff.

Statistics indicate that almost 50 percent of all patent litigation results in invalidity of the patent or failure to establish proof of infringement.

Employer-employee agreements

A great deal of inventing takes place while employees are performing the work for which they have been hired. The law holds that when an invention is produced by an employee using the equipment of the employer, the time of the employer, and the employer's support, the employer is entitled to "shop rights." Thus, the employer is able to utilize the invention in these circumstances, even without a license agreement, but employment contracts do generally stipulate that the employer directly owns any inventions that are developed and also provide for the manner in which the employee will be compensated for these inventions. This compensation may range from simply the anticipated salary to bonuses or participation in discernible profits which result from exploitation of the invention. Most employment agreements also include confidential relationship provisions under which an employee agrees not to divulge confidential material. Clearly, such agreements cover inventions developed while employed and remain operative after the employment has terminated.

Confidential disclosures

An inventor soliciting interest in an invention will often present the invention, or attempt to present it, to potentially interested parties. In the vast majority of the cases, these parties refuse to examine the disclosure until the inventor submits to a nonconfidential disclosure agreement.

This situation arises because the law of confidential disclosures is extremely broad. One who receives information in confidence, even though not patented or patentable, and later uses this material, may become subject to huge damages. To protect themselves against this threat, recipients of disclosures purporting to be of value should as a matter of prudence require that the disclosure not be in confidence. The inventor's protection in such a situation must reside in having sought all available protection through the patent or copyright laws.

As a practical matter, these nonconfidential disclosure forms often must be signed in order to expedite consideration of the invention. On the other hand, some forms are so extremely limiting and are of such severity that they deprive the submitter of substantial rights. It is advisable that the opinion of counsel be obtained whenever possible.

Foreign patenting

A patent is effective only within the jurisdiction of the country that grants it. On June 1, 1978, the European Patent Office began operation in furtherance of the European Patent Convention. While it is now possible to obtain a "European patent," this patent is effective only in countries designated by the applicant at the time he files his application. Each participating country has continued its national patent system, and the applicant may find it desirable, and more economical in some instances, to file separate national applications rather than participate in the multinational system. The types of patents and protection available differ from country to country. Most countries require payment of annual taxes to maintain a patent in force. In addition, some countries insist that the invention be either manufactured or licensed within their boundaries in order to continue the patent in effect.

The major nations of the world are members of the International Union for the Protection of Industrial Property (Paris Convention). Under the terms of this treaty, each country agrees to treat the citizens of member countries under the same rules which govern its own citizens. It is agreed that if an applicant files patent applications in member countries within one year of the filing date of his or her first patent application, the later filings will be accorded the same effective filing date as the first application. This "priority right" is important because it often makes it possible to overcome bars to obtaining a patent because of intervening sales or publication of the invention.

TRADEMARKS

A trademark is a distinctive mark, symbol, word, or words, used to distinguish the goods of a particular manufacturer. The trademark is applied to the goods manufactured and sold by the owner in order to identify their origin and thereby differentiate them from similar goods manufactured and sold by others. Trademarks are registered with the United States Patent Office for a term of 20 years and are renewable for additional 20-year terms, as long as the mark is continuously in use.

Trademarks are frequently an integral part of establishing unfair competition and proving that a competitor has "reaped where he did not sow" by palming off products and misrepresenting their origin. The individual states have unfair competition laws and a number have statutes creating state trademarks. The federal government enacted the Lanham Act of 1946, under which the vast majority of trademark activity occurs.

The Lanham Act defines four varieties of marks entitled to registration. *Trademarks* include any word, name, symbol, or device adopted and used by a manufacturer or merchant to identify goods and distinguish them from those manufactured or sold by others. *Service marks* are used in the sale or advertising of services to identify the services of one person and distinguish them from the services of others. *Certification marks* are used upon or in connection with the products or services of one or more persons other than the owner of the mark to certify regional or other origin, material, mode of manufacture, union participation in manufacture, quality, accuracy, or other characteristics of such goods or services. *Collective marks* are trademarks or service marks used by the members of a cooperative, a union, an association, or other collective group or organization to indicate membership therein.

Selection of a mark

In selecting a trademark a conflict arises between its function as a sales tool and its function in establishing the legal distinctiveness of the owner. The salesman often tends to prefer a mark that is immediately suggestive of the product or its qualities. On the other hand, the best and most effectively maintained marks from a legal standpoint are those which are coined, arbitrary, or completely fanciful. Although salesmen encourage the public to adopt their name for a product as the generic name, trademark lawyers view with alarm any indication that the public is adopting the trademark as a generic name for the product.

A new trademark must not be identical to, nor of such near resemblance to, existing marks as to be likely when applied to the goods to cause confusion, mistake, or deception. If a proposed mark is confusingly similar to existing marks because of shape, sound, or meaning, it is not registerable. However, the issue of confusion also relates to the similarity of goods. Thus, identical marks used on totally disparate goods, sold to different markets, would not be held to be confusing.

Other unacceptable marks include: those comprising immoral, deceptive, or scandalous matter, or matter which may disparage or falsely suggest a connection with persons, living or dead, institutions, beliefs, or national symbols, or bring them into contempt or disrepute; those comprising the flag or coat of arms of the United States; those comprising the name, portrait, or signature of a nonconsenting living individual; those merely descriptive of the goods involved; and those which are merely geographically descriptive. Still further, it is not possible to register a trade name, as distinguished from a trademark. While a company name is not registerable as such, if it is also used as a trademark and treated properly, it may be permissible.

When a mark has been selected, it is advisable to conduct a search of prior federal and state registrations, trade directories, and company names to evaluate its distinctiveness. Several agencies are available to attorneys and the public for such searching. Typical searches cost about $50. Federal registrations can be searched directly in the Patent and Trademark Office Library. The library contains files of registered marks and pending marks arranged in alphabetical order and according to the type of symbol. These searches are considerably easier than those carried out prior to filing patent applications.

Registration

The Lanham Act provides for registration of marks on either the Principal Register or the Supplemental Register. Where there are impediments to registration on the Principal Register, but the mark is capable of distinguishing goods and services, it may be placed on the Supplemental Register. Though lacking many advantages of registration on the Principal Register, supplemental registration will provide a basis for foreign registration of the mark, prevention of its possible registration by another, a vehicle for assignment, and support for suit in the federal courts.

Application

The form of a trademark application is prescribed in detail by the Patent and Trademark Office. Sample forms are included in a booklet entitled "Trademark Rules of Practice of the Patent Office with Forms and

Statutes," available from the Superintendent of Documents, U.S. Government Printing Office, Washington D.C. 20402. An application comprises the appropriate completed form, a formal drawing of the mark, five specimens, and a filing fee of $35. In connection with registration, trademark owners may be represented by themselves, by attorneys admitted to practice before the highest court of their state, or by registered attorneys specializing in patent and trademark law.

The goods and services covered by trademarks are categorized in schedules established by the Patent and Trademark Office. Each application must indicate the particular goods and services to which the mark is related. The law limits the exclusivity of each mark to the goods or services specified in the certificate finally issued. If the goods or services span more than one classification, separate registrations are required.

To qualify for registration, a mark first must be used in either international or interstate commerce. Such use requires that the mark was placed on or affixed to the goods, their containers, or the displays accompanying them, and that they were actually sold. The use must be a valid trademark use; mere appearance of the mark in advertisements or correspondence is inadequate. A single sale is sufficient, but it should be valid and not one solely for the purpose of establishing a date for the trademark application. The sale need not have been by the applicant if made by a "related company" which was under the applicant's control regarding the nature and quality of goods.

Opposition proceedings

The Patent Office acts upon trademark applications in the order in which they are received. An Examiner considers each application and either confirms registerability or indicates why the application or mark is believed to be unacceptable. The applicant is given the opportunity to traverse the Examiner's position and/or amend the application. When the mark is found entitled to registration, it is published in the weekly Official Gazette of the United States Patent Office. Any person who believes that he or she would be damaged by the registration of a mark may file an opposition within 30 days of this publication.

Opposition proceedings involve the presentation of legal arguments to establish the respective rights of the applicant and the opposer. The opposer may seek to prevent registration or simply to restrict use of the mark in selected areas. These proceedings are in many ways similar to court actions, carried out in accordance with the Trademark Rules. Since an opposer is directly concerned with the competitive effect of a proposed trademark, these proceedings often require far more time and effort than the initial proceedings before the Trademark Examiner. Attorney's fees for registration run upwards from $200, while a full opposition is much more expensive.

Cancellation proceedings

Having gone through the hurdles of registration, registrants are not free from further dealing with the Trademark Office. They may be faced by a cancellation proceeding, and they must file certain affidavits to keep the registration in effect.

Any person who believes he or she is or will be damaged by registration of a mark on the Principal Register may petition for cancellation within five years of the registration. In addition cancellation can be requested at any time if a mark becomes the common name for an article, if it has been abandoned, fraudulently obtained, or is being used by the registrant to misrepresent the source of goods or services. A certification mark may be subject to cancellation at any time if the registrant does not exercise control over its use, engages in the production or marketing of goods to which the mark is applied, permits its use for other than certification, or discriminately refuses to certify goods of persons who maintain the standards which the mark certifies.

To avoid some possibilities of a cancellation action, a registrant may file an affidavit showing five consecutive years of continuous use subsequent to registration and that the mark is still in use.

During the fifth year following registration, the registrant must file in the Patent Office an affidavit showing that the mark is still in use or that its nonuse is not due to any intention to abandon the mark. In the absence of this affidavit, the mark will be cancelled at the end of six years.

Finally, within the six months preceding expiration of each 20-year term, the registrant may renew by paying $25 and filing a verified application setting forth the details of use and a specimen of the current use of the mark.

Use and enforcement

Upon issuance of the certificate of registration, the owner should give notice of registration by displaying with the mark the words "Registered in U.S. Patent Office," "Reg. U.S. Pat. Off.," or preferably ®. In the absence of such notice, in any suit, no damages or profits will be recovered unless the defendant had actual notice. It is improper to use the symbol ® in connection with an unregistered mark.

Correct trademark use requires continual care and policing to assure that the mark does not acquire a generic meaning and is not weakened by the proliferation of similar marks. Whenever a mark is used it should be capitalized or placed within quotation marks. It should never be used without inclusion of the generic name for the product, because this may lead to its adoption by the public.

The trademark may be used directly by its owner or by a related company which controls or is controlled by the registrant as to the goods or services with which the mark is used. It may be assigned with the goodwill or that part of the goodwill of the business connected with the use of the mark. Such assignments should be recorded in the Patent Office.

A trademark owner is entitled to bring civil suit to recover profits or damages, enjoin further acts, and/or have infringing labels and the like destroyed. These remedies are available against anyone who uses in commerce any reproduction, counterfeit, copy, or colorable imitation of a registered mark in connection with the sale, offering for sale, distribution, or advertising of any goods or services, which is likely to cause confusion, mistake, or deception. Trademark protection enables the owner to bring action in either federal or state courts.

Another valuable right of the trademark owner is to ban importation of goods which copy or simulate the mark. Once again it is to be noted that trademark laws, like patent laws, bind the actions of parties within the jurisdiction of the registering country. Registration and protection of trademarks throughout the world requires submission to the appropriate agency in each country. The United States is an adherent to the International Convention for the Protection of Industrial Property. Under this treaty and others, persons are entitled to trademark benefits equivalent to those granted to the citizens of the participating countries.

TRADE SECRETS

The methods of protection discussed above stem from statutes and are limited in duration. In contrast, the law of trade secrets is an accumulation of court decisions construing the common law. Essentially, these decisions seek to promote commercial honesty and prevent unjust enrichment. As long as a trade secret is kept confidential, even if for one thousand years, it will be protected by the courts. However, once it is legitimately discovered, it becomes public property and can be used by anyone.

There is no specific limitation on the subject matter that is subject to trade secret protection. It encompasses any information not generally known in the trade. The secret need not be of patentable stature. Customer lists, credit ratings, delivery schedules, chemical formulas, blueprints, design criteria, machine features, and manufacturing techniques are only a few of the areas that have been recognized as containing material suitable for trade secret protection.

A substantial amount of secrecy must exist so that, except by the use of improper means, there would be difficulty in acquiring the information. Matters of general knowledge in an industry cannot be appropriated as a secret, nor can one allege secrecy regarding matters that are completely disclosed by examination of one's goods.

There is no need to register or publicly identify the subject matter of a trade secret. In fact, the opposite is essential. One must take precaution to assure that the public is excluded from knowledge. The advantages include unlimited duration and exclusive knowledge. The disadvantages include possible complete loss of exclusivity at any time due to legitimate discovery by others, and restrictions on plant and employees to prevent discovery and dissemination.

To keep secret or to patent?

An invention can sometimes be treated either as a secret or as subject matter for a patent. In these situations, the owner must make a choice; if a patent issues, the public disclosure automatically terminates the trade secret position.

Obviously, if the sale of products embodying the invention will reveal the secret, patenting is indicated. It is also wise to patent if the secret is likely to be dis-

covered by a diligent competitor. If it is believed that the invention can be exploited best through licensing, then preparing and policing patent licenses will be more desirable than maintaining trade secrets.

On the other hand, if the life expectancy of the market for an invention is short, one may prefer to keep trade secrets. Timing may suggest retention of trade secrets; for example, in the toy and fashion industries, the several year delay in patent issuance exceeds the marketable life of most inventions and designs. If the invention is marginal and can be designed around, but its discovery requires considerable time or expense, teaching competitors through a full patent disclosure may be undesirable. Also, some production machinery and processes may be used privately in the owner's plant with little likelihood of detection by competitors. In this case, there is no advantage in disclosing the details in a patent. It should also be appreciated that the initial cost of maintaining a secret is negligible compared with that of filing a patent application.

The advantages of patent protection include a definite 17-year period of protection, assured access to the federal courts, freedom of disclosure, and ease of licensing. The advantages of maintaining a trade secret are unlimited life during secrecy, immediate applicability, coverage of marginally unique and unpatentable materials, nondisclosure to competitors, and minimum cost. These advantages in combination with the sometimes concomitant disadvantages must be weighed in determining the course to follow.

Maintaining the secret

Since the essence of a trade secret is the fact that it is not well known or readily ascertainable, the owner must be active in maintaining its status.

Employees must be made aware of the secrecy of the matter and preferably bound in writing to preserve confidentiality. This provision should be an element of the employment contract and should be reviewed with any departing employees. If the secret can be written down, the record should be kept under lock and key, with access limited to necessary persons only. All disclosures of related material should be reviewed and censored, if necessary. Related company documents should be marked "Confidential." Areas in the plant should be restricted or closed to visitors, if the secret would be detectable by mere observation.

CONCLUSION

The owner of a secret, invention, creative work, or proprietary symbol has a number of avenues of protection available; some are exclusive, others are coextensive. There is a wide variance in the degree of protection, the cost of procurement, the assurance of procurement, and the future effects and responsibilities. Many details have, necessarily, been merely suggested here. The information, however, should enable the owner to identify the areas of possible interest and to decide whether to seek professional assistance or to proceed alone.

TRADE CUSTOMS AND THE LAW

Irving E. Field, ATTORNEY AND PUBLISHER

A custom does not become established overnight; it requires the passage of time for general acceptance. A custom is a practice or usage common to many, either general in application or limited to a particular place, class, or trade. In the business world, a trade custom is an established practice of a particular trade, considered an unwritten law. In time, trade customs may become established in any type of business.

In the graphic arts industry there are, generally speaking, six major areas in which trade customs have gained acceptance: printing, typography, paper, envelopes, business forms, and binding. Each of these segments has its own customs. Printing and typographic trade customs have been in use in the printing industry in the United States for more than 50 years; other segments of the graphic arts industry have established trade customs in more recent years. (Trade customs current in four major areas are reprinted in the four articles that follow.)

CONDITIONS FOR LEGAL ACCEPTANCE

Every contract, to avoid dispute, should specify the trade customs which will bind the parties. If it does not do so, certain preliminary conditions must be met before a trade custom can be used as a legal precedent in a case, or have the force of legal proof. These preconditions are:

• The existence and scope of the trade custom (also sometimes called *trade usage*) must be proved.

• The trade custom or usage must be regularly observed and well settled.

• The trade custom or usage must be reasonable. (General acceptance by regular observance establishes *prima facie* that it is reasonable.)

• It cannot contradict or alter the express terms of an unambiguous contract between the parties.

• It must not be in opposition to fixed rules of law.

• It cannot validate a legally void contract.

• It cannot be used for the purpose of accomplishing an unfair or immoral interpretation of the contract.

• It cannot alter or vary statutory enactments.

• It cannot create a contract if there has been no agreement by the parties and none is implied by law.

IMPORTANCE OF THE CONTRACT

Trade customs by themselves are not enough to establish an agreement. Before they can come into play, there must be a contract or agreement between the parties; then the usage may give particular meaning to an agreement or may supplement or qualify it.

In the graphic arts industry many contracts are in writing. Each segment of the industry has its own contract—for example, a contract between a printer and his customer, between a typesetter and customer, or between a paper buyer and the mill or paper merchant. There may even be a complete production contract between publisher and book manufacturer.

It must be remembered that trade customs are not unconditionally accepted in every part of the United States. Nevertheless, although there is some opinion to the contrary, where parties specifically incorporate a usage into their contract by reference, such usage generally will be honored by the courts in the interpretation of the contract. If the trade customs are spelled out explicitly in the contract between the parties, the chances of nonacceptance are reduced even further, and they would most likely be honored by the courts, wherever they may be.

To be safe, trade customs should not be printed in small type on the back of the printed form. To ensure that both parties will be bound by the trade custom, it should be printed in the same size type as the body of the contract, in the body of the contract—then there can be no doubt. All the particulars of the custom should be set forth clearly. In addition, it is wise to have an attorney periodically check and review the contract in use.

UNIFORM COMMERCIAL CODE

Trade customs have become the subject of a uniform law which has been adopted by many of the states. This law, called the Uniform Commercial Code, at the time of this printing had been adopted by some 30 states. Among these are New York, New Jersey, Pennsylvania, Illinois, and California, states which house a great portion of the graphic arts industry. The adoption of the code is of fairly recent vintage—the earliest enactment (Massachusetts) was on October 1, 1958. Below is a list of states which have adopted the Uniform Commercial Code.

Alaska	Maryland	Ohio
Arkansas	Massachusetts	Oklahoma
California	Michigan	Oregon
Connecticut	Missouri	Pennsylvania
Dist. of Columbia	Montana	Rhode Island
Georgia	Nebraska	Tennessee
Illinois	New Hampshire	Virginia
Indiana	New Jersey	West Virginia
Kentucky	New Mexico	Wisconsin
Maine	New York	Wyoming

One major purpose of the Uniform Commercial Code is "to permit the continued expansion of commercial practices through custom, usage and agreement of the parties." The Uniform Code defines a *usage of trade* as:

. . . any practice or method of dealing having such regularity of observance, in place, location or trade as to justify an expectation that it will be observed with respect to the transaction.

In everyday English, this means that a trade custom regularly used in a certain place is a trade custom of that place. The code requires that custom or usage be considered wherever reasonably consistent with the express agreement of the parties. However, as stated before, where the agreement is inconsistent with the trade custom, the express terms of the written agreement will govern.

TYPOGRAPHIC INDUSTRY TRADE CUSTOMS

The following trade customs, issued jointly by the International Typographic Composition Association (ITCA) and the Advertising Typographers Association of America (ATA), are reprinted with permission. Typographic trade customs were originally adopted in 1920 and were restated in 1921, 1922, 1940, 1947, 1960, and 1973.

1. ALTERATIONS (*any addition, change, or modification of work in progress made by the customer in copy, style, or specifications originally submitted to the typographer*). Alterations will be charged for at prevailing rates at the time of alteration. When type selection and style are left to the best judgment of the typographer, charges will be made for the customer's alterations.

2. CHANCE ORDERS (*work produced without charge in speculation of an order*). No work will be produced on the chance an order may be placed.

3. CHARGES FOR WORK (*the basis upon which work will be performed*). Charges for work may be at either the hourly rate, on a piecework basis or total job price, as determined by the typographer at his discretion at either the time of making a quotation or invoicing the work.

4. COMPUTER PROGRAMS AND UNDERLYING MATERIALS (*a computer program is a system, consisting of a series of instructions or statements in a form acceptable to a computer, prepared in order to achieve a certain result; underlying materials are those production tools necessary to the development of the computer program*). Computer programs, systems analyses and underlying materials developed by the typographer in order to produce work for a customer with the use of data processing machines or computers are the property of the typographer. No use shall be made of, or ideas taken from, such programs, analyses or materials without the express permission, and only upon payment of just compensation to the typographer.

5. CORRECTIONS (*changes in composition and other work performed by the typographer due to errors by the typographer*). Corrections of errors will be made by the typographer without charge, but no financial liability is assumed for errors beyond making the corrections.

6. CUSTOMER'S PROPERTY (*all property, materials, and/or supplies belonging to the customer which are delivered to the typographer for use in the production work*). Customer's property delivered to the typographer for use in producing work is received by the typographer without any liability for loss or damage from causes beyond his control, such as acts of God, fire, water, theft, or strikes. All such property, materials, and/or supplies used in producing the work will be considered dead six months after completion of the related work and disposed of, unless prior written instructions are given by the customer.

7. DELIVERY (*conveyance of work to points or receivers designated by the customer*). Delivery is complete upon conveyance of the work to points, receivers (such as common carriers) designated by the customer, or upon deposit in the National Postal Service. The typographer assumes no responsibility after delivery.

8. ESTIMATE (*a preliminary projection of cost which is not intended to be binding*). Estimates are based upon prevailing wages, the anticipated hours of work, and cost of materials and supplies necessary to produce work in accordance with preliminary copy, style, and specifications, and are not binding upon the typographer.

9. EXPERIMENTAL WORK (*innovative attempts to create unique production tools, samples, or style pages*). Experimental work performed at the request of customers will be charged for on the basis of prevailing rates.

10. HANDLING AND SHIPPING (*the preparation of work for transportation and the conveyance or mailing of the work*). Handling and shipping charges must be paid by the customer.

11. INPUT DATA STORAGE (*information which has been prepared in specialized form for utilization by data processing machines or computers*). Punch cards, magnetic and paper tapes, disc packs, programs, or other documents, materials, or property relating to work either in progress or completed may be stored for 12 months by the typographer at the client's risk. Input data will be destroyed after such time, unless there is a specific written agreement.

12. LAYOUTS, STYLE PAGES, DUMMIES, AND PASTE-UPS (*preliminary representations of work created as production tools or prototypes for the production of the work*). Layouts, style pages, dummies, paste-ups, or other specially-created production tools made or developed by a typographer at the order of a customer shall be charged for on the basis of prevailing

rates. No use shall be made of, or ideas taken from such production tools or prototypes without the express permission and only upon payment of just compensation to the typographer.

13. LIEN (*a right to hold the property of another pending the satisfaction of an outstanding obligation*). All materials or property belonging to the customer, as well as work performed, may be retained by the typographer as security until all just claims against the customer have been satisfied.

14. METAL (*alloys composed of lead, tin, and antimony which are commonly used in the manufacture of printers' types, rules and spacing materials*). All metal delivered to customers in the form of composition, made-up pages, or forms shall remain the property of the typographer until the customer either returns or pays for the metal in accordance with the prevailing local customs. Made-up jobs must be returned intact to receive maximum credit. Linotype and Monotype metal, except when returned intact in made-up jobs, must be separated when returned to receive maximum credit. All mixed metal not in made-up form will only be credited at the scrap metal price. Metal which contains any brass, copper, zinc, or harmful chemicals will be classed as "junk" metal and will be credited as such.

15. ORDERS (*verbal or written requests for specific goods and/or services*). Orders accepted by a typographer can only be cancelled on terms that provide for just compensation for work commenced and necessary work-related obligations entered into pursuant to the order. Verbal orders and instructions must be confirmed in writing prior to commencement of the work to be binding on the typographer. All orders are accepted subject to contingencies such as strikes, fires, vandalism, acts of God, and other causes beyond the control of the typographer.

16. OUTSIDE PURCHASES (*any materials purchased by the typographer as necessary to produce work in accordance with a customer's order*). All outside purchases will be charged for on the basis of cost.

17. OVERTIME (*work performed by employees in excess of the prevailing regular daily and/or weekly schedule of hours, or as provided by law*). Overtime may be charged at the typographer's prevailing rates.

18. PRELIMINARY PROOFS (*reproductions of composition, illustrations, or other graphic representations*). Preliminary proofs (also referred to as rough, customer, or galley proofs) submitted to a customer for approval must be marked "OK" or "OK with Corrections or Alterations" (with such alterations and/or corrections indicated with standard proofreaders' marks) and signed or initialed by the customer.

19. QUOTATIONS (*statements of price for which specified work will be performed*). Quotations are based on the number of man hours at the prevailing scale of wages, and the cost of materials, supplies, and services necessary to do the work. Quotations are based on copy, style, and other specifications and information originally submitted, and *any* change therein, including delivery requirements, automatically voids the quotation. Quotations are only valid for 30 days or as otherwise specified and must be in writing.

20. STANDING TYPE AND ELECTROTYPE FORMS, MECHANICAL ART, AND FILM OR PAPER MAKEUP (*metal, film, or paper assembled for reproduction into final plates, proofs, negatives, or other graphic products*). All metal, film, or paper assembled for reproduction is considered to be dead 7 days after reproduction and may be destroyed without notice unless written instructions are provided prior to the date of destruction. All such materials will be subject to storage or rental charges after 60 days.

21. TERMS (*conditions of sale*). Work may be billed either on the basis of work completed, or upon completion of the order at the discretion of the typographer. C.O.D. jobs must be paid for upon delivery of first proofs. The value of all metal furnished as type, borders, ornaments, and other materials shipped will be included in the C.O.D. charge.

22. TYPE (*letters, figures, symbols, and ornaments individually cast from lead alloy*). The value of type used for direct printing and for molding (except less than five wax molds) will be charged to the customer in addition to composition charges.

23. WORKING NEGATIVES AND POSITIVES (*original or intermediate images, on film or paper, of type composition, illustrations, or other graphic representations used in the production of work*). Working negatives or positives, made by or developed for the typographer for the production work, remain the property of the typographer.

PRINTING INDUSTRY TRADE CUSTOMS

Printing trade customs were originally promulgated at the annual convention of the United Typothetae of America in 1922; they were revised, updated, and repromulgated at the annual conventions of the Printing Industries of America (PIA) in 1945 and 1974. Trade customs were also adopted by the National Association of Photo-Lithographers at their annual convention in 1937 and amended and reaffirmed in 1950, in 1957, and again at the annual conventions of the National Association of Printers and Lithographers (NAPL) in 1975 and 1980.

The most recently revised trade customs of the

printing and lithographic industries, issued jointly and approved by both PIA and NAPL, are reprinted here with permission.

1. QUOTATION. A quotation not accepted within thirty (30) days is subject to review.

2. ORDERS. Orders regularly entered, verbal or written, cannot be cancelled except upon terms that will compensate printer against loss.

3. EXPERIMENTAL WORK. Experimental work performed at customer's request, such as sketches, drawings, composition, plates, presswork, and materials will be charged for at current rates and may not be used without consent of the printer.

4. PREPARATORY WORK. Sketches, copy, dummies, and all preparatory work created or furnished by the printer shall remain his exclusive property and no use of same shall be made, nor any ideas obtained therefrom be used, except upon compensation to be determined by the printer.

5. CONDITION OF COPY. Estimates for typesetting are based on the receipt of original copy or manuscript clearly typed, double-spaced on 8½" x 11" uncoated stock, one side only. Condition of copy which deviates from this standard is subject to reestimating and pricing review by printer at time of submission of copy, unless otherwise specified in estimate.

6. PREPARATORY MATERIALS. Artwork, type, plates, negatives, positives, and other items when supplied by the printer shall remain his exclusive property unless otherwise agreed in writing.

7. ALTERATIONS. Alterations represent work performed in addition to the original specifications. Such additional work shall be charged at current rates and be supported with documentation upon request.

8. PROOFS. Proofs shall be submitted with original copy. Corrections are to be made on "master set," returned marked "OK" or "OK with corrections," and signed by customer. If revised proofs are desired, request must be made when proofs are returned. Printer regrets any errors that may occur through production undetected, but cannot be held responsible for errors if the work is printed per customer's OK or if changes are communicated verbally. Printer shall not be responsible for errors if the customer has not ordered or has refused to accept proofs or has failed to return proofs with indication of changes or has instructed printer to proceed without submission of proofs.

9. PRESS PROOFS. Unless specifically provided in printer's quotation, press proofs will be charged for at current rates. An inspection sheet of any form can be submitted for customer approval, at no charge, provided customer is available at the press during the time of makeready. Any changes, corrections, or lost press time due to customer's change of mind or delay will be charged for at current rates.

10. COLOR PROOFING. Because of differences in equipment, paper, inks, and other conditions between color proofing and production pressroom operations, a reasonable variation in color between color proofs and the completed job shall constitute acceptable delivery. Special inks and proofing stocks will be forwarded to customer's suppliers upon request at current rates.

11. OVERRUNS OR UNDERRUNS. Overruns or underruns not to exceed 10% on quantities ordered up to 10,000 copies and/or the percentage agreed upon over or under quantities ordered above 10,000 copies shall constitute acceptable delivery. Printer will bill for actual quantity delivered within this tolerance. If customer requires guaranteed "no less than" delivery, percentage tolerance of overage must be doubled.

12. CUSTOMER'S PROPERTY. The printer will maintain fire, extended coverage, vandalism, malicious mischief, and sprinkler leakage insurance on all property belonging to the customer, while such property is in the printer's possession; printer's liability for such property shall not exceed the amount recoverable from such insurance.

13. DELIVERY. Unless otherwise specified, the price quoted is for a single shipment, without storage, F.O.B. local customer's place of business or F.O.B. printer's platform for out-of-town customers. Proposals are based on continuous and uninterrupted delivery of complete order, unless specifications distinctly state otherwise. Charges related to delivery from customer to printer, or from customer's supplier to printer, are not included in any quotations unless specified. Special priority pickup or delivery service will be provided at current rates upon customer's request. Materials delivered from customer or his suppliers are verified with delivery ticket as to cartons, packages, or items shown only. The accuracy of quantities indicated on such tickets cannot be verified and printer cannot accept liability for shortage based on supplier's tickets. Title for finished work shall pass to the customer upon delivery, to carrier at shipping point, or upon mailing of invoices for finished work, whichever occurs first.

14. PRODUCTION SCHEDULES. Production schedules will be established and adhered to by customer and printer, provided that neither shall incur any liability or penalty for delays due to state of war, riot, civil disorder, fire, strikes, accidents, action of government or civil authority, and acts of God or other causes beyond the control of customer or printer.

15. CUSTOMER FURNISHED MATERIALS. Paper stock, camera copy, film, color separations, and other customer furnished materials shall be manufactured, packed, and delivered to printer's specifications. Additional cost due to delays or impaired production caused by specification deficiencies shall be charged to the customer.

16. TERMS. Payment shall be net cash thirty (30) days from date of invoice unless otherwise provided in writing. Claims for defects, damages, or shortages must be made by the customer in writing within a period of thirty (30) days after delivery. Failure to make such claim within the stated period shall constitute irrevocable acceptance and an admission that they fully comply with terms, conditions, and specifications. Printer's liability shall be limited to stated selling price of any defective goods, and shall in no event include special or consequential damages, including profits (or profits lost). As security for payment of any sum due or to become due under terms of any agreement, printer shall have the right, if necessary, to retain possession of and shall have a lien on all customer property in printer's possession including work in

process and finished work. The extension of credit or the acceptance of notes, trade acceptances, or guarantee of payment shall not affect such security interest and lien.

17. INDEMNIFICATION. The customer shall indemnify and hold harmless the printer from any and all loss, cost, expense, and damages on account of any and all manner of claims, demands, actions, and proceedings that may be instituted against the printer on grounds alleging that the said printing violates any copyright or any proprietary right of any person, or that it contains any matter that is libelous or scandalous, or invades any person's right to privacy or other personal rights, except to the extent that the printer has contributed to the matter. The customer agrees to, at the customer's own expense, promptly defend and continue the defense of any such claim, demand, action, or proceeding that may be brought against the printer, provided that the printer shall promptly notify the customer with respect thereto, and provided further that the printer shall give to the customer such reasonable time as the exigencies of the situation may permit in which to undertake and continue the defense thereof.

BUSINESS FORMS TRADE CUSTOMS

These trade customs report the results of a survey taken in 1973 by the Trade Customs Committee of the International Business Forms Industries (IBFI), a section of Printing Industries of America (PIA). The committee ruled that no trade custom would be included that was not subscribed to by at least 75 percent of the respondents. The material is reprinted with permission.

1. ORDERS. Orders regularly entered, with a bona fide purchase order, cannot be cancelled except upon the terms that will compensate the manufacturers against loss. All work done to the date of cancellation is billable to the customer with a normal profit. The work done to the date, and/or materials, if billed to the customer and paid by the customer, remain the customer's property and the manufacturer has the right to immediately ship all material to any point designated F.O.B. his door. If the material is the property of the manufacturer and at the selection of the manufacturer, he may use said materials on other production and advise the customer of his decision.

2. EXPERIMENTAL WORK. Experimental work performed under the direction of a customer's request and against a bona fide purchase order, or in lieu of this, a proper letter of direction from an authorized person shall be charged to the customer on a "cost plus profit" basis.

3. LAYOUTS AND DUMMIES. All layouts and dummies that are created by the manufacturer remain the property of the manufacturer and may not be used by the customer. Conversely, all layouts or dummies supplied by the customer to the manufacturer remain the property of the customer and may not be retained as the property of the manufacturer without the written consent of the customer.

4. ART WORK, NEGATIVES, PLATES, AND TEMPLATES. All of these items are the property of the person who supplies them. If the manufacturer supplies them, they remain his property and cannot be transferred to the customer without full payment, plus profit, for the work involved. Conversely, if they are supplied by the customer, they remain his property, but they now become his liability. The forms manufacturer is no longer required to do any more than faithfully reproduce his product from the materials supplied to him. His liability goes no further.

5. ALTERATIONS. On each proof, alterations must be clearly spelled out and signed by the customer and by the sales representative of the manufacturer, indicating item by item whether it is a customer's alteration and must be charged for, with a proper profit to the manufacturer, or whether it is a manufacturer's alteration or error and is in no way chargeable to the customer.

6. PLATES AND NEGATIVES. Refer to 4; ownership depends entirely upon who has supplied them; if the manufacturer supplied them, they remain his property; if the customer supplied them, they remain his property. However, the manufacturer will not be required to store these items beyond the time of delivery of the product, unless he so chooses. If the storage is agreed upon, the agreement must clearly spell out whether the manufacturer remains liable for the item, in the event of loss or damage.

7. PROOFS. At least one proof of each plate and each part is submitted along with the original customer copy. The proof, and the original copy, are to be returned to the manufacturer as his manufacturing guides. If additional proofs are required, they are charged for.

8. POSITIVE OVERLAYS AND TEMPLATES. Where a positive overlay, that is color-separated, is required and/or a template is required, the manufacturer will establish with the customer whether, at an additional cost, either the color-separated positive and/or template is to be returned for manufacturing and remain the property of the manufacturer.

9. STATEMENT OF PROOF STABILITY AND SIZE. It is the responsibility of the manufacturer to state clearly

whether or not his proof is completely representative of the exact spacing, color, etc. of the final job.

10. DEVIATIONS IN QUANTITY. All orders are subject to plus or minus 10% of the original quantity. This is necessary so as to conserve vital materials and avoid waste. Any deviation from this practice will be clearly spelled out by the customer and accepted by the manufacturer. If at the completion of the job, the plus or minus 10% has been exceeded, the manufacturer will have the right to go to the customer and request that the overrun or underrun be accepted. It will be the final decision of the customer whether such an overrun or underrun is accepted. In the case of an overrun that is not acceptable, the customer, at the option of the manufacturer, must return or destroy the overrun. In orders involving special materials which are often shipped short, the manufacturer will not be liable to make up deviations below 10%.

11. NUMBERING. Clearly spelled out on the quotation request by the customer, and confirmed by the manufacturer on his bid, will be the statement of the type, location, and style of numbering. It is understood that there is no responsibility for the makeup of missing numbers, unless clearly stated in the quotation, accepted by the customer, and placed in the manufacturer's bid and clearly stated in the purchase order. Crash numbers are recommended to the customer wherever possible to minimize missing numbers except for MICR and OCRA.

12. DELIVERY. Unless otherwise specified, the price quoted is for a single shipment, without storage, and is F.O.B. the manufacturer's loading dock. All proposals, based upon a series of shipments at one time, or a series of shipments throughout a given period of time, requiring or not requiring storage, shall be specifically stated in the quotation request confirmed in the bid and stipulated in the purchase order. In the event that storage takes place, under no circumstances will storage be required for more than six months. Liability for damage to forms in storage will be assumed by an insurance policy covering the items stored. At the end of the six-month period, as a portion of the terms and conditions on the back of the manufacturers quotation forms will be the statement that all forms are to be shipped and, if not paid for, to be paid for at that time. If storage is to continue from that time forward, as the property of the customer, it will be done on the basis of a cost plus profit to the manufacturer of yielding a monthly storage charge. Taxes incurred as a result of storage will be paid by the manufacturer but will be a part of the cost of the forms to the customer.

13. DELAYS IN DELIVERY. All items produced by the manufacturer are made contingent upon his inability to deliver due to shortages of material, carrier delays, wars, strikes, fires, floods, accidents, government decree (foreign or domestic), or other contingencies beyond the manufacturer's control, such as acts of God. The manufacturer shall not be responsible in such contingencies.

14. REPAIRS AND CHANGES. Repairs and changes are recognized as a gray area unless the product is not exactly as specified in the order and copy submitted and/or does not run as required on the machines that were clearly specified on the purchase order. All changes must be covered in writing.

15. CLAIMS. All claims of defective merchandise should be made to the manufacturer in writing within a reasonable time from the receipt of delivery. The manufacturer shall not be held liable for any costs for customer down time, programming time, processing time, or other consequential damages, including profits (or profits lost). The manufacturer's liability is limited to cost or replacement of the product and normal freight charges only.

16. PAPER STOCK FURNISHED BY THE CUSTOMER. If the customer desires to furnish paper stock or any other material, it must be, first of all, completely satisfactory to the manufacturer and he must be fully aware of this at the time of bid. The manufacturer must be informed of the manufacture of the material, the method of delivery, and the dates of delivery. Material supplied must be of a quality that the manufacturer considers completely acceptable. In addition to this, any costs due to delays because of production problems on press, collator, or bindery, etc., attributable to materials supplied will be chargeable on a cost plus basis to the customer with the addition of profit in that particular area. The manufacturer will not be responsible for waste incurred in the use of stock furnished by the customer.

17. SPLICES AND BREAKS. The manufacturer is not responsible for any splicing or for manufacturing forms with less than one break in every three carbons, unless clearly spelled out on the bid, on the quotation, and on the final purchase order from the customer. Splicing of all parts and carbons must be acceptable to the manufacturer.

18. THE RIGHT TO REJECT AN ORDER. The manufacturer reserves the right to reject an order that is not acceptable to him and/or if material as quoted is not available at the estimated price and delivery time, when the order is placed. The order must be a duplicate of the quotation and must be entered within a period of 10 days of the date of quotation.

19. SPECIALIZED INK COLORS, SUCH AS "OCR INKS". All OCR read and drop-out colors, along with the paper that is supplied by the manufacturer, will be tested by the manufacturer and guaranteed to be acceptable on the stated scanner(s).

20. PERFORMANCE OF THE PRODUCT. The customer shall not expect or hold responsible the manufacturer for the running qualities of forms such as a continuous form, on a high-speed printer, scanner, decollator, etc., unless the following factors have been met:

(a) The machine that is using the form has been clearly spelled out in the quotation request, the bid, and the purchase order.

(b) The machine that the form is running on is in top condition and not in need of repair that would make the product malfunction.

(c) The customer, in the event of a dispute, will have the C.E. (Customer Engineer) present for the various companies that are involved and to the satisfaction of the manufacturer will demonstrate that the equipment being used is in proper running order and "A-1" condition.

BINDERY TRADE CUSTOMS

The following bindery trade customs, used by the Binding Industries of America (BIA), are reprinted here with permission.

1. MATERIAL. Following the acceptance of binder's quotation but before commencement of actual production by customer, customer shall request from binder dummy showing the correct imposition of forms.

2. CUTTING. Jobs requiring any register shall be furnished with stock squared prior to printing, together with cutting layout or workable dummy. Failure to do so relieves binder of responsibility for errors.

3. DELIVERY OF GOODS TO BINDER. All jobs shall be furnished to binder jogged, securely wrapped or skidded, and dry, or otherwise protected from damage. Guide and gripper sides shall be marked.

4. CASES AND SKIDS. All cases, skids, boxes, and so on, furnished by customer to binder in connection with his work become the property of binder, unless agreement made otherwise with appropriate charge for their return.

5. CUSTOMER'S PROPERTY. The binder shall charge the customer, at current rates, for handling and storing customer's property held for more than 30 days. All customer's property whether in storage or in production is at customer's risk. The binder is not liable for any loss or damage thereto caused by fire, water leakage, theft, negligence, insects, rodents, or any cause beyond the binder's control.

6. TERMS. Terms are net cash 30 days. All jobs are figured on work being produced as a unit. For pre-liminary deliveries and setups requiring additional expense or if ordered to cease operations or delayed beyond binder's control by the customer, binder reserves the right to bill customer for all additional cost incurred.

7. ACCEPTANCE. Unless otherwise stated in estimate, quotation is subject to acceptance within 10 days and work to start within 30 days thereafter unless otherwise agreed upon.

8. QUANTITIES. Quotation covers only specified quantity stated to be bound or completed as an initial order. Should, however, customer in initial order call for a part or lot less than entire job, it is understood that binder on such parts or lots may add any increase in the cost of labor or material to the quoted price. Overruns or underruns, not to exceed 10% of the bound or printed sheets furnished, shall constitute an acceptable delivery and any excess or deficiency shall be charged or credited to the customer proportionately. Loads and customer's order to be plainly marked in the event excess is not to be processed.

9. COUNTS. The binder makes no hand count on receipt of sheets or other material unless separate and distinct agreement is made, carrying extra charges. The basis of count shall be folded and gathered record made as soon after receipt of sheets as convenient.

10. OVERTIME. All quotations based on work being performed on a straight time basis. Any deliveries requiring overtime because of customer's delay in furnishing material or short delivery required shall be billed at overtime rates.

NOTES ON THE CONTRIBUTORS

Charles Aaron, currently managing director of Cameron Graphic Arts, holds an M.M.E. degree from the City College School of Technology and is a licensed professional engineer in New York State. In 1966, as director of research and development for Cameron Machine Co., he undertook the development of the Cameron Book Production System. He became manager of Cameron Graphic Arts in 1968, after the successful start-up of the first Cameron Belt Press, and for a time was director of market and product development for the Cameron-Waldron Division of Midland-Ross Corp., the parent company of Cameron Machine Co.

Howard Aber, presently a sales vice-president with Wood Industries, has been associated with various aspects of the printing industry in both sales and engineering capacities. Prior to his involvement with the Wood Industries Book-O-Matic, he was closely associated with the Huck Book System and with the Cameron Book Production System. For the future, Mr. Aber envisions the application of the Book-O-Matic in non-book areas where printing and subsequent sequential collating are required.

Andrew J. Alagna is a lithographic platemaker with over 30 years of experience. He was an instructor for five years and director of platemaking for six years at the Lithographic Technical Institute in New York City. The Institute, dedicated to the training of lithographic craftsmen, is jointly administered by the Metropolitan Lithographers Association and Local One, Amalgamated Lithographers of America. Mr. Alagna has also written articles for trade journals.

G. H. Anthony is currently a graphic arts consultant. He began his career in the graphic arts in 1930 with his contribution to the development of photographic silk screens capable of process-color halftone printing. For 34 years he was associated with Chase Bag Company where, as manager of the Central Art & Ink Division, his responsibilities included design, finished art, process photography, platemaking, printing, inks, purchasing, inventory, and quality control. A former member of the board of directors of the Flexographic Technical Association, he has frequently served as moderator and panel member for various seminars and forums of FTA and other trade associations. He attended the University of Dayton, Dayton Art Institute, and Chicago Art Institute; and he is a recipient of the Elmer G. Voigt Award. Mr. Anthony is the author of *Flexography and the Graphic Arts* and associate author and editor of *Flexography—Principles and Practices,* second edition (both books published by FTA). He has written numerous articles for various publications, and currently authors a monthly column, "Printing in Focus" for *Paper, Film & Foil Converter* magazine.

Samuel N. Antupit was graduated from Yale College with a degree in English in 1954 and from Yale School of Art and Architecture with a degree in graphic design in 1956. He was assistant art director of *Harper's Bazaar* and of *Show* magazine, assistant corporate art director at Condé Nast Publications, and a designer at Push Pin Studios. From 1964 to 1968 and, briefly, in 1977, he was art director of *Esquire.* He is proprietor of Cycling Frog Press (founded in 1961) and has been an instructor at the Harvard Publishing Procedures Course since 1965. He is presently executive art director of the Book-of-the-Month Club. His firm, Antupit & Others, designs magazines, books, annual reports, educational materials, and record albums. He is a member of Alliance Graphique Internationale and has received awards, medals, and certificates from the Art Directors Clubs of New York and Boston, the Society of Illustrators, the Type Directors Club, the Society of Publication Designers, the American Institute of Graphic Arts, and *CA* magazine. He was awarded an Emmy for "Free to Be . . . ," best children's TV special.

Edmund C. Arnold is an internationally known newspaper designer. As consultant to scores of leading papers in North America, Europe, and New Zealand, he is credited with popularizing downstyle headlines and was an early proponent of six-column format. Author of 17 books and over 2,000 articles, he won the George Polk Award. Long with Syracuse University, he is now on the faculty of Virginia Commonwealth University. In 1978 he was named the Outstanding Teacher in Journalism by Sigma Delta Chi/Society of Professional Journalists.

John R. Battiloro, Jr., is the executive vice-president of Robert Crandall Associates, which he joined in founding in 1952. He has developed techniques and processes used there as well as in other studios, and has served as consultant to separation and printing companies for duplication and retouching problems. He attended the New York School of Art and Design and several PIMNY schools. A member of The Navigators since 1964, he served as president in 1971–72.

Joseph V. Bellanca is an inventor and consultant in graphic arts and is owner and president of Web Binding Systems. He is a graduate of Rochester Institute of Technology and has experience in printing-plant management as well as in the graphic arts machinery field.

Ralph F. Box, Jr., is executive vice-president, sales, of Muller-Martini Corp., a subsidiary of Muller-Martini A. G., Switzerland, manufacturers of bindery equipment. Before joining Muller-Martini nine years ago, he spent over ten years with the Smyth Manufacturing Company. Mr. Box is a director of the Book Manufacturers' Institute and a member of the executive committee of the Research & Engineering Council of the Graphic Arts Industry. He has written articles for *Book Production Industry* magazine and has been a speaker at the Research & Engineering Council binding seminars and at other trade bindery association and litho club meetings.

Alfred Brooks, a graduate of New York University, has been associated with the bookbinding industry for 18 years. He is a manufacturer's representative for The Davey Company of Jersey City, N.J., and previously worked for Chas. H. Bohn Co. of New York as scheduling and production manager. He is a past president of the Book Binders Guild of New York.

Michael H. Bruno is recognized worldwide as an eminent consultant and research scientist. His professional career in graphic arts spans over 42 years of research, research management, consulting, trouble shooting, lecturing, writing, and teaching. He has a degree in chemistry from Yale University, has worked as a research engineer in collotype and lithographic plants, and was a research officer at the Army Map Service during World War II. He joined the Lithographic Technical Foundation (now GATF) in 1945, where he served for 22 years as research manager, research director, and technical director. In 1967, he joined International Paper Company as manager of graphic arts research in its corporate research and development division, and from 1970 to 1976 was corporate consultant, graphic arts. After retiring from International Paper in 1976, he joined the University of Missouri at Columbia as an associate professor in graphic communications engineering. In 1977, he returned to industry as a consultant. Mr. Bruno has made over 700 appearances and speeches in 14 countries, has written over 100 articles for the trade press, is the author of sections of a number of graphic arts books, is the editor of the IP *Pocket Pal*, and publishes his own graphic arts newsletter. He is a Fellow of the Institute of Printing (England). He was a founder of TAGA (in 1948) and its first president, and is an active member of TAPPI, GATF, the Research & Engineering Council of the Graphic Arts, the Society of Photographic Scientists and Engineers, and the New York and Chicago Litho Clubs. He is the recipient of many honors in the graphic arts, including Craftsman of the Year (NAPL, 1953), Man of the Year (Lithographers Guild of New York, 1968), Elmer G. Voigt Award (1970), Golden Keys Awards (1970, 1971, 1974), Gold Key of Gamma Epsilon Tau (1974), Robert F. Reed Technology Medal (GATF, 1974), Man of the Year (Navigators, 1976), Coating and Graphic Arts Division Medal (TAPPI, 1976). He is a consulting editor of *American Printer and Lithographer, New England Printer and Publisher, Penrose* (England), and the *Graphic Arts Manual*.

Steve Byers is a typographer at Mergenthaler Linotype Company, Melville, N.Y. He holds a B.F.A. in graphic design from Carnegie-Mellon University (1968) and an M.F.A. in graphic design from Yale University (1973).

Clive A. Cameron is presently working at Pira, the British Printing Industries Research Association in Leatherhead, England, as a composition and printing processes consultant. Before joining Pira he worked at the Graphic Arts Research Center in Rochester, N.Y., and prior to that as a production manager in San Francisco. He was apprenticed as a compositor in London and studied for three years at the London College of Printing. He received his B.S. degree from Rochester Institute of Technology. Mr. Cameron is author of *Going Metric with the U.S. Printing Industry*, a book published by the Graphic Arts Research Center at R.I.T. in 1972.

Thomas J. Cavallaro was area resident manager, customer services, for Mead Paper in New York City until his recent death. Before joining Mead, he was with Oxford Paper Co. for five years and, prior to that, was the technical director and manager of quality control at Arkay Packaging Co. A former member of the research committee of GATF and a past officer of the New York Litho Club, he received a B.S. in E.E. degree from Clarkson College of Technology and degrees in chemistry from N.Y.U. and Pratt Institute.

Frank E. ("Al") Church was a founding member of the AAAA/MPA joint committee on magazine advertising reproduction and served as chairman of the MPA production committee on two occasions. He was co-chairman of the GATF committee on letterpress proofing and still serves as secretary of the ANSI PH.2 subcommittee on standard lighting for the graphic arts. In 1960 he received the Gold Key of Gamma Epsilon Tau, the graphic arts honorary society, and in 1972 was elected to GATF's Society of Fellows. In 1961, following 30 years at Time Inc., he joined the *Reader's Digest*. For 18 years he represented the *Digest* as a member of various industry association committees. In the Manhattan and Pleasantville *Digest* offices he assisted the production director with the coordination of art, editorial, and production staff operations. Now semi-retired, he continues to serve the industry as a consultant to magazine publishers.

Jim Cokeley, now a free-lancer in Swarthmore, Pa., wrote direct mail copy for a wide variety of clients at Ayer Direct, New York, N.Y., for more than eight years. His copy has won Mailbox Awards from the Direct Mail/Marketing Asso-

ciation and the Philadelphia Direct Marketing Club. He has also served as editor of the *Philadelphia Direct Marketing Club News*. Prior to his direct mail experience, he wrote copy for all media at Ayer. His background includes public relations for Procter & Gamble and experience as advertising manager at NuTone, Inc., Cincinnati, Ohio.

Thomas L. Cordier, a marketing representative for IBM Instrument Systems, Inc., received his B.S. degree from Marist College in Poughkeepsie, N.Y. He has spent the last five years in the development and marketing of the IBM Color Analyzers, which are used in a variety of applications for color matching and color analysis.

Michael P. Corey is product manager for business and converting papers at Champion Papers, Division of Champion International. Previously, as manager of merchandising services, he developed collateral advertising and sales promotion projects for Champion Papers and edited *The Printing Salesman's Herald*. He has administered marketing programs for other divisions of Champion International, including Federal Office Products, Nationwide Papers, Champion Packages Co., and Trend Carpets. He holds a B.A., *cum laude*, from Fairleigh Dickinson University and an M.A. from the Graduate Faculty of Political and Social Science of the New School for Social Research. He is a member of the Direct Mail/Marketing Association and AIGA, and is on the advisory council of the In-Plant Printing Management Association.

Thomas B. Cosden has devoted most of his editorial career to the graphic arts field. He was assistant editor of *The Paper Trade Journal* and was with *Book Production Industry* from 1968 to 1971, where he served in several editorial positions including managing editor. He received a Golden Keys Award from the Association of Printing House Craftsmen for best in-depth reporting in the graphic arts and, in 1970, received the Jesse H. Neal Editorial Achievement Award.

James F. Cosgrove is vice-president of engineering of Mc-Cain Manufacturing Corp. and attended the College of Engineering, University of Illinois. He holds a number of patents and has been active in the design of graphic arts machinery for 25 years.

Daniel M. Costigan is a systems analyst with Bell Telephone Laboratories where he helps develop electronic and micrographic information systems. He has a vocational background in electronics (from the former RCA Institutes) and a B.S. degree in business administration from New York University. He chairs a committee on microfilm-facsimile standards for the National Micrographics Association and is the author of the only current comprehensive book on facsimile communication, *Electronic Delivery of Documents & Graphics* (Van Nostrand Reinhold, 1978). Two other books he has authored are *FAX* (Chilton Books, 1971) and *Micrographic Systems* (National Micrographics Association, 1975).

Robert S. Crandall is president of Robert Crandall Associates, Inc., in New York City, a leading transparency color preparation firm. He studied chemistry and chemical engineering at the University of Rochester and photographic technology at Rochester Institute of Technology. He began his career as a commercial and legal photographer and later worked for Eastman Kodak Research Laboratories as a color development engineer on Kodachrome, Kodacolor, and Ektachrome film. In 1951 he founded Robert Crandall Associates, Inc., where he continued research and development of highly specialized color techniques to help advance the field of color reproduction. He has been active as a consultant to the electronic scanning field, from its initial concept to the present time. In addition to being an authority on color reproduction, Mr. Crandall is a recognized photographer, with many *Fortune* and *Time* magazine cover and editorial credits.

618

Peter de Florez is president of The de Florez Company, Inc., designers and manufacturers of special bookbinding machinery. He is also a consultant, specializing in techno-economic studies of book manufacturing processes, automation, and equipment development. He was formerly president of MGD Research & Development Corp., designers and builders of high-speed bookbinding machines and other graphic arts equipment. He holds a B.S. degree in engineering and business administration from Massachusetts Institute of Technology, 1938. He is the author of "The Impact of Technology on Graphic Communications 1976–1981" for the binding and finishing section of GATF, and of technical articles published in *Book Production Industry*.

Paul D. Doebler is a publishing, information, and printing management consultant. His broad and diversified experience in graphic arts includes special emphasis on organizational and operations analysis, market research and evaluation, systems design, and the application of new electronic editing and composition technology to all kinds of publishing operations, including books, data bases, periodicals, newspapers, and in-house corporate publishing departments. He is a regular speaker at various industry meetings and seminars and has many years of editorial, publishing, and management experience. He is currently a contributing editor to *Publishers Weekly* and writes occasionally for other industry publications. He was editor of *Book Production Industry* from 1964 to 1971, during which time the publication's staff won many awards. While editor of the magazine, he also directed its marketing research program and future planning. He has also contributed to the *Annual Review of Information Science*, published by the American Society of Information Science, and has worked closely with the Information Industry Association on special projects. Mr. Doebler is a member of Associated Information Managers, has been a member of the SIC review committee of the American Marketing Association, and has been active in other industry trade associations. Earlier in his career he was a production manager of a trade composition firm, a planning engineer for Mergenthaler Linotype Co., and a newspaper reporter. He holds B.S. degrees in journalism from Northwestern University and in printing management from Carnegie Institute of Technology; he also attended the Graduate School of Business at New York University. He is a consulting editor of the *Graphic Arts Manual*.

Warren R. Erickson has been in the decal business for more than 25 years and has a broad background of experience in production. He is currently marketing services manager of The Meyercord Co., designers and manufacturers of quality decalcomania and transfer marking systems. He has been with the company at its corporate headquarters in Illinois for the past 16 years and has been involved in market research, sales analysis, advertising, and promotion. Previously he was employed at the Kalasign of America Division of Meyercord in Kalamazoo, Mich.

Eugene M. Ettenberg, editor and book designer, is a graphics consultant for the U.S. Department of Interior and a federal graphics judge for the National Endowment of the Arts. He holds a B.F.A. degree from Pratt Institute and an M.A. and an Ed.D. in fine arts from Columbia University. During his long career in the graphic arts he has been editor-in-chief of *Advertising and Publishing Production Yearbook* (1936–1941), manager of the Gallery Press (1945–1961), art faculty member at Pratt Institute (1947–1952) and at Columbia University (1953–1968), author of *Type for Books and Advertising* (1947), contributing editor to *American Artist* (1947–1970), and typographic editor of *Inland Printer* (1955–1975). He was a director and vice-president of AIGA, president of the Typophiles and of the Type Directors Club, and a recipient of the Carey Thomas Award and the Golden Keys Award of the Association of Printing House Craftsmen. He has had

exhibitions of his graphics and books at Pierpont Morgan Library, the Architectural League, and Columbia University Library. Currently he is director of the Waterbury Arts Council, arts editor of the newspaper *Voices,* and president of the Pomperaug Valley Art League.

Philip C. Evanoff has been with the Mead Corporation since 1933. He started in the laboratory at the Dill & Collins Division in Philadelphia and in 1946 became technical director. In 1949 he moved to the sales service department of Mead in Chillicothe, Ohio, becoming associate director of the department in 1957 and later, in 1964, the director of the customer services department. He is presently manager, graphic arts technology, for Mead Paper in Chillicothe. He attended the University of Pennsylvania and Temple University.

Murray A. Falick, a graduate of Parsons School of Design (1949), also studied fine arts (oils) under Farnsworth at Cape Cod and sculpture at the New School for Social Research. He was president of Robert Sullivan Associates, Inc., an advertising agency, and president of Paste-Ups Unlimited, Inc., a creative design and photo studio for advertising. He has held executive positions in several lithography plants and is currently president of Fali-Co Art Studios, Inc., an advertising art and production firm.

Bernard Fein, a former art major who changed direction to photography, is a graduate of the School of Modern Photography, 1947. He worked in several areas of photography before entering the graphic arts field in 1949. He founded Scott Screen Prints in New York City in 1955 as a velox house. The services of the firm have since been diversified to include photocopies, combination offset negatives, photography, photo-art techniques, rotogravure assemblies, photolettering, retouching, and mechanicals. He has designed several unique screen patterns that are used exclusively by his firm.

Stanley J. Fenvessy is a certified management consultant and an attorney. He is president of Fenvessy Associates, Inc., a management consultant firm specializing in all phases of mail handling, fulfillment, and direct marketing, with offices in New York and Chicago. Formerly an executive in the mail-order business, Mr. Fenvessy has been a consultant for over 20 years and is the holder of U.S. patents on addressing equipment. He is a graduate of the Wharton School of Finance and Commerce of the University of Pennsylvania and of Georgetown University School of Law. His articles have been published in over a dozen magazines and he is the author of the book *Keep Your Customers and Keep Them Happy!* (Dow Jones–Irwin, Inc., 1976). He has spoken before groups both here and abroad.

Irving E. Field has been a practicing attorney for 38 years in the New York State and U.S. courts and is a consultant in publishing and international finance. He holds a B.B.A. degree in finance and LL.B. and J.D. degrees. He is the former publisher of *The Musician's Guide,* has written articles for publication, and is the co-author of *Not For Illegal Aliens Only,* a book on labor certification and immigration procedures. He is the executive editor of the *Graphic Arts Manual.*

William Field is a graduate of Harvard University (1957) with a B.S. in anthropology. He was with Polaroid Corp. for approximately 19 years, holding various positions, including production manager, art director, and, for ten years, director of design. He recently resigned and founded a free-lance design firm in Sante Fe, N. Mex. His work over the years has received many awards, including gold and silver medals from the Boston and New York Art Directors Clubs. He has been the subject of special recognition by AIGA and by *Graphis, Publicity, Print,* and *CA* magazines; in 1971 he was named Art Director of the Year for New England.

William B. Freedman is president of Freedman Cut-Outs Inc., which was founded in 1918 and has grown under his leadership into a widely known firm engaged in die cutting, display finishing, embossing, and gold stamping. An innovator and inventor, he holds numerous patents in this field and has designed several jigs and machines for die-cutting automation. He has written many articles and has conducted classes, lectures, and plant tours on all phases of his firm's intricate, exacting work; and he has frequently addressed graphic arts groups in the metropolitan New York area. A founding member of the Young Printing Executives Club, he was chosen in 1975 for the Man of the Year Award.

Ronald C. Gibson is product manager, LogEflo Products, for LogEtronics, Inc., Springfield, Va., a major manufacturer of graphic arts film processors and associated equipment. He holds a B.F.A. degree in graphic arts from Columbia University (1958). He began his career in the graphic arts as a process-color photographer at Pioneer Moss Engraving Company in New York. For eight years, as an employee of HCM Corp. and RCA Graphic Systems, he was associated with sales and technical sales support of color scanning and phototypesetting systems manufactured by Dr. Hell.

Wayne M. Gilgore, director of research at New Venture Technologies in Nashua, N.H., is known for his many contributions in graphic arts research and copying equipment development. He developed the first high-speed graphic arts quality electrostatic printing system, which images on plain paper, wood, glass, plastic, and even corrugated board without pressure. He also developed "Color Copy Paper" which, when used in any black-and-white electrofax copier, will make color copies using only black toner. He has written many articles and has given more than 50 seminars for the graphic arts and copying industries through such organizations as TAGA, TAPPI, the Institute for Graphic Communication, the Society of Photographic Scientists and Engineers, Rochester Institute of Technology, and the Graphic Arts International Union.

Jack Golden is president of Designers 3, Inc., a design organization founded in 1946 and specializing in the production of total-concept design programs. After graduating from Cooper Union in 1936, Mr. Golden began his professional career as an advertising photographer. Through the years, in addition to a multiplicity of design projects for his clients, he created unique greeting cards, which led to the formation of The Golden Archives and the marketing of a complete line of greeting cards nationally. He served a three-year term as president of the Society of Publication Designers and is at present its treasurer. He is also vice-president, publications, of the American Printing History Association and is on the board of the American Historical Print Collectors Society. He has lectured extensively before many graphic arts and allied groups on his collection of printed ephemera comprising many unique examples of the printing arts produced in this country and Europe during the eighteenth, nineteenth, and early twentieth centuries.

Edward M. Gottschall is director of information and marketing services, International Typeface Corporation; vice-president of Design Processing International; and editor of *Typographic i* magazine. He was formerly executive director of the American Institute of Graphic Arts, editor and co-publisher of *Art Direction* magazine, managing editor of the *Production Yearbook,* editor of the four *Advertising Directions* books, and co-author of *Commercial Art as a Business.* Active in the graphic arts since 1938, he has judged many art and design shows and addressed numerous design and production conferences. For 14 years he taught printing production and a course on business problems for the commercial artist at Pratt Institute and a production course at New York University. A past president of the Type Directors Club, he was the first recipient of a TDC medal and the founder of the annual TDC exhibition. He is a consulting editor of the *Graphic Arts Manual.*

Ellen Greene began her career in 1966 with Doubleday & Company, Inc., where she worked almost exclusively on illustrated books involving all phases of color and pre-separated art reproduction. She is currently with Watson-Guptill Publications, specializing in high-quality large-format art, graphics, and photography books.

Mark Harberman is a graduate of Syracuse University. For the past 20 years he has been with Finley Photographics, Inc., where he is a principal of the company. He is a member of Reproduction Artists of America and has lectured on graphic arts photography at various colleges.

Abraham Hardis, presently with AE Bindcraft, Inc., has been in the binding business for 50 years. He started with H & H Bookbinding Co. in New York City, a family business. After deactivating H & H in 1975, he joined Garber Pollack Co. as sales manager of the binding division and was subsequently with Charlton Tag and Label Co. as a vice-president in charge of sales. He has been active in PIMNY affairs, serving on the executive committee and the labor negotiation committee for over 12 years and on the publicity and education committee for many years. He taught pamphlet binding at PIMNY night school (1970–1972) and has been treasurer, vice-president, and president of the Binders Group (now the Metropolitan Binders Association) of PIMNY.

O. Willis Hawrylkiw is technical director of Metricolor Ink Systems and a member of the board of directors. Formerly with Fred H. Levey Ink Co. and with Borden Chemical/Cilco Ink Division in Canada, he has had over 20 years experience in all phases of printing ink manufacturing and marketing.

Walter L. Hecht, vice-president of Atlantic Powdered Metals, Inc., was born and educated in Nuremberg, Germany. He served in the United States Naval Air Corps during World War II. He has spent 30 years with Atlantic Powdered Metals, a family business for more than three generations. His experience ranges from the basic manufacturing of metallic pigments to technical sales and service.

Ralph S. Heilman is vice-president of the book publishing division of Ris Paper Company in New York City. He has been involved in supplying paper and cover materials to the publishing industry for over 30 years. Many of these years were spent with the Canfield Paper Company, where he was instrumental in developing distinctive nonwoven book-covering materials and endleafs, and where he established a department to market them. He has also participated in the work of the Book Manufacturers' Institute, particularly in the area of nonwoven cover materials.

Lawrence Herbert, president of Pantone, Inc., began his association with the company in 1956. Working as a color chemist, he developed and implemented a specially engineered and equipped system of split-fountain printing, which allows Pantone to run up to as many as 48 colors simultaneously. This was the key tool in his later development of the Pantone Matching System. He became president of Pantone in 1962 and recently introduced Pantone's Color Data System, a computerized color matching system utilized worldwide. An alumnus of Hofstra University and New York University, he is a frequent lecturer at graphic arts, printing, and trade association meetings throughout the world.

Thomas E. Hess, advertising and sales promotion manager for The Beckett Paper Company in Hamilton, Ohio, has had wide experience in both text and cover papers and coated printing papers during his 17 years in the paper industry.

He began his current position early in 1974 following extensive experience with Consolidated Papers, Inc., manufacturer of coated enamel printing papers, where he served in the promotion, advertising, and marketing areas. He is a graduate of Grinnell College, Grinnell, Iowa, where he majored in English and journalism.

Richard S. Hunter received his B.A. degree from George Washington University. He did research work at the Bureau of Standards from 1927 to 1946 and was chief engineer of the H. A. Gardner Laboratory, Bethesda, Md., from 1946 to 1952. He is currently president of Hunter Associates Laboratory in Fairfax, Va., which he formed in 1952. Mr. Hunter developed the technique of photoelectric tristimulus colorimetry and, using this technique, designed the Multi-Purpose Reflectometer and Color Difference Meter. He has written many articles on color measurement, and his book *The Measurement of Appearance* was published by Wiley in 1975. Among his honors are: ASTM Award of Merit, Armin J. Bruning Award, TAPPI Testing Division Award, OSA David Richardson Medal, and ISCC Macbeth Award. He is a former president of the Inter-Society Color Council and now chairs ASTM Committee E-12 on the appearance of materials.

Kenneth W. James has been in edition bookbinding for over 33 years. He is vice-president and general manager of A. Horowitz & Son of Fairfield, N.J., a post he has held since joining the firm in 1962. Prior to that he was president of Publishers Book Bindery.

John Klein has been employed by Philips Offset Company, Inc., Mamaroneck, N.Y., since entering the graphic communications industry. He is currently vice-president, with full responsibility for manufacturing. He was previously a teacher in the New York State public school system. He holds a B.S. degree in graphic arts management from Carnegie Mellon University and an M.B.A. from New York University. His work has been published by, and he has spoken before, the Graphic Arts Technical Foundation.

Fred Klinger is president of Lehigh Press Lithographers, nationally recognized as one of the leading multicolor bookcover and commercial printers. He has been associated with the Lehigh organization in various executive capacities for over 42 years and since 1969 has served on the board of directors of The Lehigh Press, Inc. He is also very active in the Book Manufacturers' Institute and has conducted many seminars on cover printing throughout the industry.

Hans Kung, born in Villmergen, Switzerland, studied at the Kunstgewerbeschule in Zurich with Hansjoerg Mattmuller and Rudi Bircher. He worked as a graphic designer for *Annabelle* (a fashion magazine) and Globus department stores in Zurich, and as a free-lance designer for major companies in Germany and Switzerland. In 1969 he moved to New York, where he worked for Corchia, de Harak Inc. He has taught at several schools, including Parsons School of Design. In 1973 he opened his own studio in New York City.

Harvey Langlois is plant superintendent of Lehman Brothers, New Haven, Conn., manufacturers of engraved stationery, where he has been employed for 30 years. He is an active member of the Engraved Stationery Manufacturers Association and is on its new products and techniques committee and its technical committee. He is also a member of the Manufacturers' Research Institute.

Kenneth B. Latimer, presently a graphic arts consultant, holds a B.A. in chemistry from the University of Western Ontario and an M.Sc. in pharmaceutical chemistry from the University of Michigan. After seven years in the pharmaceutical field, he joined Time Inc. in research and development. His work at Time Inc. (1945–1970) involved all phases of graphic arts,

including development work on laminated plates, photopolymer plates, letterpress and offset presses, binders, pigments, coatings, and twin-wire paper machines. From 1957 until his retirement, as associate and then assistant technical director of Time Inc.'s Springdale Laboratories, he was in direct charge of the lightweight paper program, including both coating and twin-wire machine development.

Alexander S. Lawson was the Melbert B. Cary, Jr., professor of graphic arts at Rochester Institute of Technology, where he taught typography for 30 years until his retirement in 1977. For a period of 12 years he was composing room editor of *Inland Printer/American Lithographer*, and since 1966 he has directed the "Typographically Speaking" department of *Printing Impressions*. He has also published *A Printer's Almanac* (1966) and *Printing Types: An Introduction* (1973).

Leo Lehrer has been associated with the photographic and graphic arts industries for approximately 35 years. He has worked as a technical film salesman and has owned and operated his own photolab, printing plant, and color separation trade shop. He has also been quality control and research director for one of the country's largest graphic arts firms. A speaker, writer, and teacher, mainly of graphic arts prepress processing techniques, Mr. Lehrer has traveled widely in America and abroad in the course of his business interests. He is president of Graphic Arts and Sciences Co., Inc., of Cherry Hill, N.J., manufacturers of quality control instrumentation for the graphic arts. The firm also does consulting for the graphic arts industry under the name of Leo Lehrer Associates.

Joel A. Levirne, president of Joel A. Levirne/Graphic Images Ltd. in New York City, specializes in all phases of line conversion techniques—tone line, mezzotint, straight line, and other processes which provide for the rendering of pure line print work without the need for a halftone dot effect. His line conversions are presently being used on many corporate accounts. He studied at Pratt Institute, New York University, and the School of Art and Design.

Stanley E. Loeb has been for many years an editor of language arts materials for grades K–12. He is co-author of English texts published by Macmillan and by Science Research Associates and is a long-time member of the National Council of Teachers of English. As an undergraduate at Brown University, he was elected to Phi Beta Kappa and was graduated *magna cum laude*. He took advanced degrees in literature at Johns Hopkins where, for three years, he taught composition and literature. His publishing career in educational books has included acquiring and editing materials as well as presenting them to sales representatives, educators, supervisors, and teachers.

Robert Loekle entered the lithographic industry in 1951 after receiving his B.A. degree from Columbia College. He has worked in the industry as craftsman, foreman, and plant superintendent, and in 1969 was appointed director of graphic arts photography and color reproduction at the Lithographic Technical Institute in New York City. He is a member of the research committee of GATF and the graphic arts technical committee of the American Society for Quality Control, and is chairman of the TAGA color committee and of the TAGA delegation to the Inter-Society Color Council. Mr. Loekle is now an industry consultant in the areas of process-color reproduction and quality-control methods for printing, and is at work on the text of *A Quality Control Manual for Printing*. He is a consulting editor of the *Graphic Arts Manual*.

Jon Lopez holds a B.F.A. degree from Pratt Institute and an M.A. from Columbia University. Before opening his own design firm, Jon Lopez Design, Inc., he worked as a graphic designer for George Lois and for the Museum of Modern Art in New York City. He has received awards from the Art Directors Club of New York, the American Institute of Graphic Arts, and *CA, Graphis,* and *Photographis* magazines.

Kenneth D. Love, over the past 18 years, has participated as a designer and design director in many corporate identity/visual communications programs. Born and educated in the Chicago area, he initially was associated with Peter Muller-Munk Associates in Pittsburgh. He was a design director and associate partner with Chermayeff & Geismar Associates and is currently design director and principal with Anspach Grossman Portugal Inc., where he directs corporate identity, architectural graphics, and environmental design programs.

Theodore Lustig is manager, communications services, for Sun Chemical Corporation, a Fortune 500 company which develops, manufactures, and markets products and equipment principally for the graphic arts industries. An accredited member of the Public Relations Society of America and the International Association of Business Communicators, he has held managerial public relations positions with technically oriented companies for the past 18 years. Interested in printing and typography since his early teens, he has owned and operated a private press for over 20 years and is an active member of the American Printing History Association.

William B. McCain is the third generation of the McCain family to be involved in the design and manufacture of machinery for the graphic arts industry. A mechanical engineering graduate of Illinois Institute of Technology, he is president and chief executive officer of McCain Manufacturing Corp., located in Chicago, and holds many U.S. and foreign patents in the bindery machinery field.

C. S. McCamy received the B.Ch.E. degree and the M.S. degree in physics from the University of Minnesota and taught mathematics at the University of Minnesota and physics at Clemson University. He joined the National Bureau of Standards in 1952 and was chief of the image optics and photography section. In 1970, he joined the Macbeth Division of Kollmorgen Corp. in Newburgh, N.Y., where he is now vice-president, science and technology. Mr. McCamy has participated in developing numerous national and international standards for photography and has published over 70 scientific papers and articles on photography, color, and other aspects of chemistry and physics.

Timothy B. McSweeney is a graduate of the University of Arkansas with a major in printmaking. He has been active in the screen printing industry since 1970, holding production management positions in decal, outdoor sign, textile, and heat-transfer screen printing operations. He currently directs technical services for the Screen Printing Association International.

Charles Mertz attended Pennsylvania State University, where he majored in mechanical engineering. In 1956 he joined Ford Motor Company in the paint and vinyl operation, where he developed methods for the utilization of color-control equipment for both laboratory and production applications. Mr. Mertz joined Applied Color Systems in 1972 and is currently vice-president of their technical applications area.

Max Michalski was assistant vice-president of engineering at Berkey Technical Co., a division of Berkey Photo, Inc., at the time of his death a few years ago. Mr. Michalski received a B.S.E.E. degree from the University of Glasgow, Scotland, and continued his education at the City University of New York. In 1953 he joined Ascor (now a part of Berkey Technical) as project engineer and worked on design and applications of electronic flash equipment. This pioneering work

led to the development, under his direction, of the first pulsed xenon lighting equipment, introduced as Ascorlux in 1958; the first automated Berkey Direct Screen Color Separation System in 1966; and the first metal halide lamp equipment for platemaking and proofing, introduced as Addalux in 1967. He was issued 18 U.S. and 42 foreign patents, with others pending. A well-known and respected authority in his field, he presented many technical papers and published numerous articles in the fields of graphic arts lighting, UV curing, environment and safety.

Ralph W. Mirkin, manager of marketing for Allied Paper Incorporated, holds a B.S. degree in geology and a master's degree in marketing with emphasis in the graphic arts. He has been in the graphic arts field since 1956, in both the printing and paper industries, and was involved in the dramatic growth of lightweight printing paper usage during the 1960's and 1970's. He has contributed to various industry publications as an author and expert on lightweight paper.

Richard D. Murray is director of conferences for the Institute for Graphic Communication in Boston, Mass. He has had 20 years of broad reprographic technical and market research experience acquired at Itek, Cue, and EG&E, and in his present position at IGC. He has developed several novel imaging processes in the fields of thermography, diazo, and electrographic recording. Since 1968 he has organized over 350 conferences in graphic and visual communications.

Edward R. Novota, a graphic arts consultant, was formerly with Printing Developments Inc., Chicago, Ill., as midwestern regional manager, U.S. Scanner Division, and manager of the Chicago Color Center (now a division of Collins, Miller & Hutchings—Division of Beatrice Foods). He was a member of the scanner development group at Time Inc.'s Springdale Laboratories when, in 1956, he became affiliated with Printing Developments Inc., Time's subsidiary. He attended Morton Junior College and Illinois Institute of Technology, where he majored in chemistry and electronics. He entered the graphic arts field when he joined R. R. Donnelley & Sons in 1938. During World War II he served with the Air Force as a radar engineer. He is chairman of the densitometer committee of the Gravure Technical Association and a member of the Technical Association of the Graphic Arts, the Society of Photographic Scientists and Engineers, and the Inter-Society Color Council.

Ann Novotny is a free-lance picture researcher and writer. In 1965, after five years of editorial experience at Time-Life Books, Grolier, and other New York City publishers, she founded Research Reports & Pictures, an editorial consulting service for clients in publishing and communications. She and her partner, Rosemary Eakins, now act as photo consultants for books and magazines, films and educational filmstrips, exhibitions, posters, advertisements, and political campaigns; they edited the *Picture Sources 3* directory for the Special Libraries Association. She is the author of *Alice's World* (1976), *Strangers at the Door* (1972), and other nonfiction books, as well as articles on pictures in *Publishers Weekly* and *Special Libraries.* She is a former president of the American Society of Picture Professionals and has taught picture research at the Harvard Summer School Publishing Procedures Course and at The International Center of Photography. She received an M.A. in English from McGill University, Montreal, in 1960.

Frank Preucil is a graphic arts consultant with a wide production and research background in photoengraving, lithography, rotogravure, and silk screen. His writing, research, and teaching have been instrumental in effecting improvements in color printing in the past decade. He has conducted or been consultant for color seminars in 15 countries and 130 cities. He is the originator of the Preucil Systems of color analysis using graphic arts primaries in color circles and subtractive color triangles with gray as a new fourth dimension of colors in printing processes. His former business connections include: graphic arts consultant, RCA; supervisor of color printing reproduction studies, GATF; research director, Chicago Rotoprint Co.; and director of photography, Gerlach Barklow Co. A Fellow of GATF and of the Society of Photographic Scientists and Engineers, he has received honorary awards from TAGA, NAPL, and the Education Council of the Graphic Arts Industry. He was a chemistry major at Joliet College and the University of Illinois.

Archibald D. Provan is an associate professor at Rochester Institute of Technology, where he has been teaching typographic composition since 1964. He is also counselor for the courses in printing in the College of Continuing Education at R.I.T. and for the past six years has been staff chairman of the design-composition section of the School of Printing. He is the author of a number of articles on typography which have appeared in several trade periodicals.

Bently Raak, a recognized international expert on type, was at the time of his death in 1978 a full-time typographic consultant. Mr. Raak received his B.S. degree in printing at South Dakota State University in 1926. After coming to New York, he studied type design under Frederic W. Goudy. He was assistant art director for *McCall's* magazine for six years, was art director in an ad agency for four years, and taught at Syracuse University in the School of Journalism for three years. From 1940 through 1974 he designed typefaces and was director of typography for AM Varityper, a division of AM International, Inc.

Steve J. Reiter is an account executive with The Chartmakers, Inc., New York City, one of the largest firms designing and producing charts, sales presentations, training programs, multimedia programs, corporate literature, and manuals. With the firm for 12 years, he spent five years as production manager prior to assuming his present duties as an account executive, responsible for customer service and consultation.

William A. Rocap, Jr., has been with the Printing Group of Meredith Corp., Des Moines, Iowa, for the past 14 years as director of research and development and training. He is also a part-time instructor in graphic arts at Des Moines Area Community College and has published a number of papers on printing and photography. He was previously director of research at Curtis Publishing Co. for 20 years. Mr. Rocap is a member of the American Management Association, the Gravure Technical Association, GATF, and TAPPI. He served as a board member and vice-president of PERI (now the International Association of Photoplatemakers) and is a former president of TAGA. He holds a B.A. degree in chemistry from the University of Pennsylvania and was awarded the Elmer G. Voigt Award for graphic arts education in 1979.

Frank J. Romano, Graphic Arts Marketing Associates, Salem, N.H., is an independent consultant in the development, marketing, and application of photocomposition systems. He is the author of five books in the field of automated composition, including *Automated Typesetting* and *Photocomposition and You.* He serves as photocomposition editor for *American Printer* magazine and writes and lectures extensively. He has held positions with Mergenthaler and Compugraphic and has handled special marketing and development projects for other graphic arts manufacturers. He holds bachelor's and master's degrees from the City University of New York.

Bob Salpeter studied at the School of Visual Arts. From 1954 to 1957, he was a designer and illustrator with Ben Lorenz Associates. After three years of free-lance work, he joined IBM World Corporation as art director, responsible for cor-

porate design, exhibits, and advertising design. In 1971, he joined Dick Lopez to form the design firm of Lopez Salpeter, Inc. He has lectured at design seminars in the United States, Europe, and Japan, and was an instructor at Pratt Institute for seven years. He has received more than a hundred awards from type and art directors' clubs, Mead Library of Ideas, and the American Institute of Graphic Arts.

Bernard T. Sendor is president of Sendor Bindery, Inc., of New York City, one of the largest and oldest trade binderies on the East Coast. The firm, now in its seventy-ninth year, produces virtually all varieties of binding, including pamphlet, paperback, hardcover edition, plastic, and mechanical. Operations are geared to large mass-produced jobs as well as intricate and unusual specialty work. Mr. Sendor, well-known in the industry for his leadership and activity in trade organizations, served as vice-president of AIGA and is currently on the boards of directors of AIGA and the Metropolitan Binders Association of PIMNY. He is recognized as an authority and speaker on bindery technology and management and has written many articles for trade publications. Together, he and his brother, Mortimer S. Sendor, hold patents for several bookbinding processes and are responsible for many innovations in binding styles and techniques. The latest patent is a paper-welding process and machinery to bind books by welding the sheets together without using thread, adhesives, or wire.

Harold Sigler is vice-president of Printing Techniques International, Inc., a company that specializes in importing European graphic arts equipment into the American market. Previously, he was director of international sales for the eastern hemisphere for Berkey Technical Co. He has, for over 20 years, been involved in the design and marketing of graphic arts products, including step-and-repeat machines, presses, finishing equipment, graphic arts lighting equipment, enlargers, photoelectric engraving machines, photopolymer processing equipment, phototypesetting equipment, and color scanners. Mr. Sigler holds an M.E. degree and an M.S. degree in chemical engineering. He has presented several TAGA papers and addressed various craftsman and litho clubs on graphic arts lighting, color scanners, and pin register systems.

Matt Sloves is president of Sloves Products, a design and packaging company in Albuquerque, N. Mex. He is a recent winner of the first-prize award for sales-promotion package design from the New Mexico Advertising Federation. He was formerly affiliated with Dataco, Inc., a direct mail and commercial printing company in Albuquerque, and with Sloves Mechanical Binding Co., Inc., in New York City. He is a graduate of Brandeis University and a member of the New Mexico Advertising Federation.

George Sohn has been with Photo-Lettering, Inc., in New York City for the past 26 years and is currently its president and general manager. He initially studied lettering at Pratt Institute and also attended St. Johns University. He has written articles for trade magazines and has lectured at the New York Art Directors Club.

Dan X. Solo is an advertising typographer. His firm, Solotype Typographers, specializes in the use of antique, ornamental, and exotic types. His lifelong interest in the technology of types and its influence on their design has aided him in originating several unique display types. He serves as typographic adviser to a number of corporations and is a frequent lecturer on the subject. He has edited six collections of alphabets published by Dover Publications, Inc.

Victor Spindler attended Pratt Institute, majoring in advertising design. Upon graduation, he joined CBS Television Graphic Arts as an art director. During his Army service he was the head of the art department, Army Signal Corps Television Division, Fort Gordon, Ga. In 1967 he joined Aaron Burns & Co. (which later merged with Rapid Typographers to form TypoGraphics Communications, Inc.) and as studio manager started the company's slide department. In 1970 he formed The Slide House, Inc., which became the first independent slide maker to have a complete phototypesetting service. In 1976 he opened his own company, Spindler Slides, Inc., with complete services including art, type, and a professional audio and programming facility.

Liz Stalcup, a graduate of Adelphi University, *magna cum laude*, with honors in English and philosophy, is a professional proofreader and copy editor, with more than 30 years of experience. She has worked in trade composition plants, on newspapers, and with book publishers, either as an employee, including supervisory positions, or as a free-lancer. She has taught the course on proofreading and copy editing at the School of the Printing Industries of Metropolitan New York (PIMNY) for 20 years. She is currently a free-lancer.

J. James Stone is manager of research and engineering in the information products division of A. B. Dick Company, Elk Grove Village, Ill. He holds a B.S. in E.E. from Virginia Polytechnic Institute (1948) and an M.S. from Harvard University (1949). Since 1959, he has been responsible at A. B. Dick for the development of high-speed digital printing and display equipment, including the Videograph process, the ink jet process, and word-processing equipment. He was previously involved in developing digital and analog computer systems and simulators at Oak Ridge National Laboratory and at Batelle Memorial Institute.

Robert R. Strack is a lawyer and electrical engineer. As a registered patent attorney in the United States, Canada, and the Philippines, he has prosecuted patents throughout the world for the last 20 years and for several years has taught postgraduate courses in patents, trademarks, and copyrights. Initially employed as an engineer and patent attorney with Bell Telephone Laboratories and General Electric, Mr. Strack is now a partner in the law firm of Eisenman, Allsopp & Strack and also serves as the managing officer of a metal products manufacturing company.

Walter L. Strong has spent over 25 years in various positions in the printing industry. Most recently he was manager of customer service for the Masters Division of Mead Paper; earlier he was in Mead's graphic arts technology and sales services departments. He was a member of the board of directors of TAGA, has been active in the TAPPI graphic arts section, and served for over six years on the GATF research steering committee.

William R. Thompson is executive vice-president, sales, Bergstrom Paper Company, Neenah, Wis. He joined the company in 1950 as a salesman, became manager of the Chicago sales office in 1960, and was sales manager from 1967 to 1970. He holds a B.S. degree from Lawrence University, Appleton, Wis. He has been vice-president of the Sales Association of the Paper Industry, chairman of the paper committee of the Book Manufacturers Institute, and chairman of the printing and writing division of the American Paper Institute. He is also a member of the Chicago Book Clinic and serves on the administration finance committee of the Book Manufacturers Institute.

Fred G. von Zuben is vice-president of operations for Book Covers, Inc., the largest manufacturer of paperboard components for the book, looseleaf, album, and game industries. Book Covers, Inc., is a wholly owned subsidiary of The Newark Group, Inc., Newark, N.J., the leading manufacturer and merchant of recycled paperboard in the United States. Mr. von Zuben previously held various marketing positions with Container Corporation of America's mill division in Philadelphia, New York City, and Chicago. In his present position, he has been working with various segments of the graphic arts industry in product development and distribution. He holds a B.A. degree from Colgate University and an M.B.A. degree from Columbia University.

James Wageman is a free-lance graphic designer with extensive background in book design. He has worked as a designer at the Museum of Modern Art, New York, and on the design staffs of both trade and university press publishers. His work has been exhibited in *Graphis Annual*; in the annual shows of the American Institute of Graphic Arts, the New York Type Directors Club, the Society of Publication Designers, and the Association of American University Presses; and in other book shows across the country. A graduate of Park College, he has an M.A. degree from the University of Hawaii.

Dave A. Ware, manager of engineering for General Electric's computed image systems and services operation, was one of the originators of the Genigraphics system. He holds technical degrees from Brown and Syracuse universities and studied computer and systems science at Cornell University. Prior to becoming manager of engineering, he was project leader responsible for developing the Genigraphics interactive console.

William A. Whitescarver is vice-president, sales, for the Bindery Systems Division of Harris Corp., where he is responsible for the sale and marketing of Bindery Systems products worldwide. He was, for more than 20 years, with the Schriber Division of Harris Corp., most recently as vice-president, sales. Before joining Harris, he worked for the Frigidaire Division of General Motors. He holds a degree in mechanical engineering from the University of Cincinnati.

Jay Wieder, recently retired, was formerly manager of print production for Sudler & Hennessey, Inc. (an affiliate of Young & Rubicam), the leading pharmaceutical agency in the United States. During the 18 years he was with the agency, his printing purchases ran into the millions of dollars. Previously, he was with Doyle, Dane, Bernbach for five years as production manager. He is a graduate of Columbia University and the Mechanics Institute of New York. Several of his articles have appeared in the trade press and he has participated as a judge for printing awards. He is a past president of the Advertising Production Club of New York.

Gary G. Winters is director of marketing of Inmont Corporation's Printing Ink Group in Clifton, N.J. He has had extensive experience in marketing, sales, and new product areas since joining Inmont in 1967. Prior to that time, from 1954 to 1967, he was with Union Carbide Corporation in a variety of sales, product management, and market management positions related to organic chemicals. A graduate of West Virginia University with a B.S. in mechanical engineering (*cum laude*), he served as a captain in the United States Air Force from 1955 to 1957. He is a member of the GATF ad hoc heatset advisory committee and of the heatset committee of the Environmental Conservation Board of the Graphic Arts.

Ernest Wuchner, a fine arts photographer, is director of Arthur Jaffé Heliochrome Company, collotype printers. They specialize in color reproductions of the world's finest art works.

ASSOCIATIONS

Listed below are major associations active in the graphic arts industry. Many of these organizations offer information (through publications, reports, seminars, annual meetings) concerning their specific spheres of interest. An alphabetical cross listing by acronym follows the main list.

Advertising Typographers Assn of America (ATA)
461 Eighth Ave.
New York, N.Y., 10001
(212) 760-1704

American Assn of Advertising Agencies (AAAA)
200 Park Ave.
New York, N.Y. 10017
(212) 682-2500

American Business Press (ABP)
205 East 42nd St.
New York, N.Y. 10017
(212) 661-6360

American Institute of Graphic Arts (AIGA)
1059 Third Ave.
New York, N.Y. 10021
(212) 752-0813

American National Standards Institute (ANSI)
1430 Broadway
New York, N.Y. 10018
(212) 354-3300

American Newspaper Publishers Assn (ANPA)
11600 Sunrise Valley Drive
Reston, Va. 22070
(703) 620-9500

American Newspaper Publishers Assn Research Institute (ANPA/RI)
PO Box 598
Easton, Pa. 18042
(215) 253-6155

American Paper Institute (API)
260 Madison Ave.
New York, N.Y. 10016
(212) 340-0600

American Photoplatemakers Assn (APA)
See: International Assn of Photoplatemakers (IAP)

American Society for Testing and Materials (ASTM)
1916 Race St.
Philadelphia, Pa. 19103
(215) 299-5400

American Society of Magazine Photographers (ASMP)
205 Lexington Ave.
New York, N.Y. 10016
(212) 889-9144

American Society of Picture Professionals (ASPP)
PO Box 5283, Grand Central Station
New York, N.Y. 10017
(212) 663-4463

Association of American Publishers (AAP)
One Park Ave.
New York, N.Y. 10016
(212) 689-8920

Binding Industries of America (BIA)
200 East Ontario St.
Chicago, Ill. 60611
(312) 751-0452

Book Manufacturers' Institute (BMI)
111 Prospect St.
Stamford, Conn. 06901
(203) 324-9670

Direct Mail/Marketing Assn (DMMA)
6 East 43rd St.
New York, N.Y. 10017
(212) 689-4977

Flexographic Technical Assn (FTA)
95 West 19th St.
Huntington Station, N.Y. 11746
(516) 271-4224

Gold Bronze Powder Council (GBPC)
PO Box 2054
Princeton, N.J. 08540
(609) 799-3300

Graphic Arts Technical Foundation (GATF)
4615 Forbes Ave.
Pittsburgh, Pa. 15213
(412) 621-6941

Gravure Research Institute (GRI)
22 Manhasset Ave.
Port Washington, N.Y. 11050
(516) 883-6670

Gravure Technical Assn (GTA)
60 East 42nd St.
New York, N.Y. 10017
(212) 661-8936

Institute of Paper Chemistry (IPC)
PO Box 1039
Appleton, Wis. 54912
(414) 734-9251

Inter-Society Color Council (ISCC)
Dept. of Chemistry, Rensselaer Polytechnic Institute
Troy, N.Y. 12181
(518) 270-6000

International Assn of Photoplatemakers (IAP)
(Formed by merger of PERI and APA)
552 West 167th St.
South Holland, Ill. 60473
(312) 596-5110

International Typographic Composition Assn (ITCA)
22621 Hall Place NW
Washington, D.C. 20007
(202) 965-3400

Library Binding Institute (LBI)
50 Congress St.
Boston, Mass. 02109
(617) 227-7450

Magazine Publishers Assn (MPA)
575 Lexington Ave.
New York, N.Y. 10022
(212) 752-0055

National Assn of Printers and Lithographers (NAPL)
780 Palisade Ave.
Teaneck, N.J. 07666
(201) 342-0700

National Assn of Printing Ink Manufacturers (NAPIM)
550 Mamaroneck Ave.
Harrison, N.Y. 10528
(914) 698-1004

National Assn of State Textbook Administrators (NASTA)
c/o Technical Director, Advisory Commission on
   Textbook Specifications (ACTS)
PO Box 237
New London, N.H. 03257
(603) 526-4744

National Paper Trade Assn (NPTA)
420 Lexington Ave.
New York, N.Y. 10017
(212) 682-2570

National Printing Ink Research Institute (NPIRI)
Sinclair Memorial Laboratory
Lehigh University
Bethlehem, Pa. 18015
(215) 861-3580

Optical Society of America (OSA)
1816 Jefferson Place NW
Washington, D.C. 20036
(202) 223-8130

Paper Stock Institute of America (PSI)
A Division of the Natl Assn of Recycling Industries
330 Madison Ave.
New York, N.Y. 10017
(212) 867-7330

Platemakers Educational and Research Institute (PERI)
See: International Assn of Photoplatemakers (IAP)

Printing Industries of America (PIA)
1730 North Lynn St.
Arlington, Va. 22209
(703) 841-8100

Printing Industries of Metropolitan New York (PIMNY)
461 Eighth Ave.
New York, N.Y. 10001
(212) 760-1700

Research & Engineering Council of the Graphic Arts Industry (R&EC)
1340 Old Chain Bridge Rd.
McLean, Va. 22101
(703) 821-6777

Screen Printing Assn International (SPA)
307-F Maple Ave. West
Vienna, Va. 22180
(703) 281-1800

Society of Photographic Scientists and Engineers (SPSE)
1330 Massachusetts Ave. NW
Washington, D.C. 20005
(202) 347-1140

Technical Assn of the Graphic Arts (TAGA)
PO Box 3064, Federal Station
Rochester, N.Y. 14614
(716) 475-6662

Technical Assn of the Pulp and Paper Industry (TAPPI)
One Dunwoody Park
Atlanta, Ga. 30338
(404) 394-6130

CROSS LISTING BY ACRONYM

AAAA	American Assn of Advertising Agencies
AAP	Association of American Publishers
ABP	American Business Press
AIGA	American Institute of Graphic Arts
ANPA	American Newspaper Publishers Assn
ANSI	American National Standards Institute
APA	American Photoplatemakers Assn
API	American Paper Institute
ASMP	American Society of Magazine Publishers
ASPP	American Society of Picture Professionals
ASTM	American Society for Testing and Materials
ATA	Advertising Typographers Assn of America
BIA	Binding Industries of America
BMI	Book Manufacturers' Institute
DMMA	Direct Mail/Marketing Assn
FTA	Flexographic Technical Assn
GATF	Graphic Arts Technical Foundation
GBPC	Gold Bronze Powder Council
GRI	Gravure Research Institute
GTA	Gravure Technical Assn
IAP	International Assn of Photoplatemakers
IPC	Institute of Paper Chemistry
ISCC	Inter-Society Color Council
ITCA	International Typographic Composition Assn
LBI	Library Binding Institute
MPA	Magazine Publishers Assn
NAPIM	National Assn of Printing Ink Manufacturers
NAPL	National Assn of Printers and Lithographers
NASTA	National Assn of State Textbook Administrators
NPIRI	National Printing Ink Research Institute
NPTA	National Paper Trade Assn
OSA	Optical Society of America
PERI	Platemakers Educational and Research Institute
PIA	Printing Industries of America
PIMNY	Printing Industries of Metropolitan New York
PSI	Paper Stock Institute of America
R&EC	Research & Engineering Council
SPA	Screen Printing Assn International
SPSE	Society of Photographic Scientists and Engineers
TAGA	Technical Assn of the Graphic Arts
TAPPI	Technical Assn of the Pulp and Paper Industry

ADVERTISERS

INDEX

saddle sewing, 516, 535
saddle-wire stitching, 516, 538, 539-540
safelight, 325
safe-on condition, bindery central control console, 573
safe switch, bindery central control console, 573
safety base, film, 326
safety-fold envelope, 588, 589
safety inks, 499
safety paper, 456
St. Anns Board Mill, 468
St. Louis Post-Dispatch, 73, 240
sand mill, ink, 503
Sandoz Pharmaceuticals, Mellaril brochure, 89
sans serif typeface group, 116
Sarnoff, Robert W., on graphic symbols, 78
satellite, and fax, 240
satellite press, 407
   see also common impression cylinder press
saturation, color, 22, 368
   and ink colorant, 492
   in pictorial reproduction, 303-304
   and undercolor removal, 355
Saxmayer Corp., 582
scale compression, in conventional photoengraving, 382
scaling
   art, 257-258
   in design, 37-38, 56, 57
scanning
   in character generation, 217
   color, 353, 358-361
   fax, 237
   OCR, 226-227, 228-230
   see also color scanner
scanning head, 359
scanning platemaker, vs. fax system, 238
Sci-Tex Response 300 system, 364
Scotchprint, 205
Scotch Roman typeface, 116, 163
scratch board, 252, 253
screen(s)
   halftone, 318-319, 322-323, 342, 343
   image carrier, 378
   for line conversion, 292-293
   for screen printing, 388, 416
screen angles, 256, 320, 344, 347-350
screen distance, 342
screened print, 290, 291, 344
screenless lithography, 396, 421
screen printing, 5, 401, 416-418
   advantages, 418
   copy preparation, 418
   and decals, 428
   flat-screen press, 417
   and flocking, 417, 556
   on foils and films, 486
   inks, 417, 499
   and metallic inks, 501
   and paper performance, 476-477
   rotary-screen press, 389, 417-418
   screens for, 388, 416
   stencils, 388-389, 401
   see also printing
Screen Printing Association International (SPA), 626

screen process, *see* screen printing
screen ruling, 319, 322
Scriptomatic, Inc.
   Model 29 series, 579
   Model 80 series, 579-580
   Model 100-10S, 582
script typeface group, 116
scrolling, VDT, 235
scuff-resistant inks, 499
scumming, 438
searching, VDT, 235
second (metric measurement), 596
second-stage proofs, 97
secrets, trade, 607
security provisions, mailing list, 577-578
seeding, mailing list, 578
Selectric Typewriter "golf ball" typing element, 207
Self-Binding Paper, 567
self cover, 517, 538
self-mailer, 92
semilogarithmic scale, chartmaking, 266
send-and-return envelope, 589
Sendor, Bernard T., 566
Sendor, Mortimer S., 566
Sendor Bindery, 566
Sensitivity Guide, GATF, 317, 440, 441
Sentry Insurance, graphic symbol, 78
series, type, 115
serif, 110
   and legibility, 118
Serif Gothic typeface, 162, 163
service mark, 605
setoff, 406, 439
set width, type, 110
sewing, book, 6, 516, 529-536
Shaar, Edwin, 117
shading sheets, patterned, 253
shadow dot, 320
shadow series, 30
sharpened images (skinnies), 324
Shearson, Hammill & Co., annual report, 85
sheet collator, 550
sheet-fed casemaker, 536-537
sheet-fed gravure, 385, 386, 412-413
sheet-fed lithography, 405, 410
sheet-fed press, 10, 403, 407
   and paper performance, 476
sheet-lined board, 561
sheetwise imposition, 372, 522
shift code, 221-222
shipping printed products, *see* fulfillment
shot mill, ink, 503
shrink-wrapping, 572
shutter speed, 274, 316
SIC, *see* Standard Industrial Classification
side-feed casemakers, 537
side guide, 522
side-seam envelope, 583
side sewing, 516, 534-535
side-wire stitching, 516, 539, 540-541
signals, looseleaf, 548
signature(s), 10, 516, 530
   fastening, 516
   folding, 519-520, 527-528, 530
   gathering, 516, 531, 539, 541, 544-545

signature(s) (*cont.*)
   inserting, 539
   sewing, 516, 533, 535
silhouette halftone, 319
silhouetting, for contrast, 56
silk screen, 388, 416
   see also screen printing
silver emulsion plates, 396-397
silver inks, 499-500
silver pigments, ink, 493, 499-500
silverprint, 365
Singer sewing, 535
single-color press, 403
SI system, 596
size (adhesive), gold, 500, 556
size (dimensions)
   annual report, 84
   book, 45
   envelope, 583, 584-589
   magazine, 60-61
   newspaper, 71-72
   paper, 450; metric, 597
   type, 114, 118; metric, 598
sizing (dimension), art, 258
sizing, pulp, 458
sketch, 252
skinnies, 324
slack-sized paper, 458
Slide Ring, 549
slip case, 537
slit-light system, 338
slitting
   on folding machine, 528
   paperboard, 563
   on web press, 528
slug, 199
slur, 438
slur gauge, 440, 441
smart typewriter, 431
smashing, sewn book block, 533
smoothness, and printability, paper, 475
Smyth sewing, 516, 530-534
   vs. adhesive binding, 536
snowflaky solids, 438
Society of Photographic Scientists and Engineers (SPSE), 626
soft cover, 517, 538, 542, 560
soft display, keyboard, 224
solarization, 294, 296
solid board, 561
solvents, ink, 493-494
   emission, and pollution, 356, 494, 512
sonic tablet, VDT, 232
Sonne KPM 2000 plate, 384
sorts, 100, 203
sources, for picture researcher, 309-313
South Carolina National Bank, graphic symbol, 78
Souvenir typeface, 163
SPA, *see* Screen Printing Association International
spaceband, Linotype, 202
spaces, in metal type, 199, 201
spacing
   automatic, guillotine cutter, 525
   type, 112-113; and legibility, 118
spacing material, in metal composition, 195
special-purpose envelopes, 588-589